COLLEGIATE
DICTIONARY
OF
BOTANY

DELBERT SWARTZ

UNIVERSITY OF ARKANSAS

THE RONALD PRESS COMPANY • NEW YORK

PREFACE

The field of botany contains a vast number of technical terms and proper names, many of which are not included in the best standard reference works. The student or even the trained botanist will sometimes find it difficult to locate definitions for such terms as "greffe des charlatans" or "Hoogeveld." At the same time, depending on the references used, several definitions could be found for such words as "cognole" or "meroplankton." Problems of this nature are a constant source of confusion and frustration to the botanist.

Many botanists have long felt the need for a modern dictionary of botanical terms, a single volume to which the student of botany could turn—thus avoiding frequent and time-consuming searches in several sources. My husband, the late Delbert Swartz, recognized this need more than 30 years ago when, with the intention of compiling a dictionary, he established a card file of terms which gradually grew into an extensive collection. In 1963 Dr. Swartz began the task of transforming the file into a dictionary. He had almost completed the first draft of the manuscript at the time of his death in 1966. Fortunately, my own background in botany and my familiarity with the project and with Dr. Swartz's aims and methods have enabled me to complete his work.

The dictionary contains nearly 24,000 entries, compiled from more than 170 sources. In many instances different sources offer varying definitions of a single term. For some terms it was appropriate to include several definitions; for others, a choice was made which I believe will prove acceptable to most botanists. Samuel Johnson expressed the problem well: "Every other author may aspire to praise; the lexicographer can only hope to escape reproach."

Botanical terms in general use which can be found in the average abridged dictionary have not been included. American usage, rather than British, has been employed in terminology and spelling. Few Latin names are included in the dictionary; however, a brief outline of the Plant Kingdom appears at the back of the book.

The scope of the book has limited the inclusion of biochemical terms to those most commonly used in the field of botany. In accord with modern usage diacritic marks have been eliminated from English words.

I wish to acknowledge the assistance of the many students and staff members of the Department of Botany at the University of Arkansas, without whom the entries for the dictionary could not have been assembled. To these helpers, Dr. Swartz was always grateful for their interest and dedication. To his colleagues at the University of Arkansas my thanks for their counsel and understanding. Special credit is due Mrs. La Verne Peterson, whose patient and careful typing of the manuscript was an invaluable aid.

Finally, I would like to express particular appreciation to Dr. E. Leighton Rudolph of the English Department of the University of Arkansas for his help and encouragement, without which I could not have completed the dictionary.

Sylvia G. Swartz

Fayetteville, Arkansas
September, 1971

COLLEGIATE
DICTIONARY
OF
BOTANY

A

a-. A prefix meaning without, not.

A. Used to signify flowers with freely exposed honey.

A-layer or A- horizon. The upper layer of soil composed of varying decomposing organic materials, as leaf litter, raw humus, and decomposed humus resting on residual soil.

A-spore. Alpha-spore.

ab-. A prefix meaning from.

AB. Used to signify flowers with partially concealed honey.

A, B, C, etc. Symbols used to represent genes or their corresponding characters: AA represents a dominant homozygous pair of genes or characters, aa represents a recessive homozygous pair of genes or characters, Aa represents a heterozygous pair of genes or heterozygous characters.

abapical. Situated at the lower pole or related to it.

abaxial. Situated facing away from the axis of the plant, e.g., the undersurface of a leaf; situated off axis; applied to embryos which are out of the axes of seeds because of the one-sided thickness of the albumen or to an embryo whose axis does not have the same direction as the axis of the seed; see EX-CENTRIC.

abbreviated. Curtailed, shorter than an adjoining part, shortened abruptly.

aberrant. Differing more or less widely from the accepted type; deviating from the normal range of variation within the species or genus; abnormal.

aberration. 1. Any structure, or part of a structure, not true to type and not hereditary. 2. Irregular and unusual distribution of chromosomes during mitosis or meiosis.

abertos. Liliaceous trees resembling yuccas forming savannahs.

abhymenial. Occurring on the opposite side of the gill from the hymenium, as of the hairs on gills of *Schizophyllum*.

abietic. Resembling the genus *Abies*; pertaining to coniferous products, not necessarily derived exclusively from *Abies*, the fir tree.

abietic acid. An acid isolated from resin obtained from coniferous trees, an ingredient of frankincense.

abietic anhydride. The resin ordinarily found in turpentine.

abietiform. Shaped like a fir tree.

abietin. A resin derived from *Abies pectinata*.

abietine. 1. Of or growing upon firs. 2. A volatile oil distilled from the resin or balsam of gray pine, almost pure normal heptaine.

abietinous. Growing upon or resembling fir trees.

abietite. A sugar derived from the leaves of *Abies*.

abiocoen. The nonbiotic habitat.

abiogenesis. Spontaneous generation, the assumed origin of living matter from nonliving.

abiology. The study of nonliving things.

abjection. 1. The throwing of spores from a sporophore with force. 2. The ejection of seeds.

abjoint. To delimit by a septum or joint, to separate at a joint.

abjunction. Delimitation by septa of portions of growing hyphae, separation; see AB-STRICTION.

ablactation. The arching inward.

ablaqueation. The loosening of soil around trees.

ablast. The complete suppression of an organ, as distinct from abortion.

ablastic. Applied to parts of flowers or other organs which have not developed.

ablastous. Lacking germ or bud.

abnodation. The removal of knots from trees, ordinarily by cutting.

aboospore. A parthenogenetically developed oosphere.

abortive. Imperfectly formed, defective, barren, undeveloped.

abranchiate. Without gills.

abruptly acuminate. Having a point which arises from a broad extremity.

abruptly bulbous (of bulb of a stipe). Not rounded above.

abruptly pinnate. As a pinnate leaf ended by a pair of leaflets, pinnate but lacking a terminal odd leaflet.

abscise. To cut off or detach by separation at the zone of connection.

absciss. Fall, as of leaves.

absciss layer. 1. A layer of cells along which the leaf or fertile organ breaks away in autumn. 2. A structure or layer of cork which separates the leaf petiole from the stem to cause separation but also serves as a protective layer which seals the tissue to prevent drying.

absciss mechanism. The absciss layer.

abciss-phelloid. A crust of unsuberised cells which develop where parts of a plant (as leaves, twigs, etc.) are shed.

abscissile layer. See ABSCISS LAYER.

abscission. 1. The natural detachment of membranes from another part by means of a layer of separation. 2. The separation of parts. 3. Of spores, detachment from the sporophore by disorganization or disappearance of a connecting zone. 4. Of leaves, the fall due to the formation of the absciss layer.

abscission layer. See ABSCISS LAYER.

absinthic. Referring to *Artemisia ahsinthium*.

absinthin. The bitter ingredient of *Artemisia absinthium*.

absolute growth rate. The growing rate of a plant, or part of one, under controlled conditions of time, light, moisture, nutrients, etc.

absolute transpiration. The rate of loss of water from a plant as determined by experiments.

absorbing hair. A hair which absorbs water, a root hair.

absorption. 1. The passage of materials, usually nutritive, into or through living cells. 2. The process by which substances are admitted into a cell through the cell wall. 3. Osmosis of nutrient or other materials. 4. The process of absorbing.

absorption bands. Dark bands visible at definite places in the spectrum when a ray of white light has been passed through coloring matter or through a prism.

absorption ratio. The comparative amount of a specific ion absorbed into plant tissue in relation to that still remaining in a controlled nutrient expressed *i/e* (internal/external).

abstergent. A substance having cleansing qualities, a substance used in cleaning.

abstriction. The separation of a spore from its stalk or hypha by abjunction or abscission.

abterminal. From the end inward.

abysmal. In the greatest depths of the ocean, abyssal, immeasurable.

abyssal associations. Associations of organisms living in the depths of the ocean.

acajou. 1. The cashew tree and its fruits. 2. The mahogany tree or any one of several related trees.

acalycalis. 1. Without a calyx. 2. Having no adhesion to the calyx.

acanaceous. Having thorns or prickles, said of such prickly plants as thistles.

acantha. Acanthon, a spine, prickle, or thorn; a spiny process.

acanthaceous. 1. Belonging to or resembling the *Acanthaceae* family. 2. Bearing prickles, thorns, or spines.

acanthifolious. With leaves like *Acanthus*, the type genus of the *Acanthaceae* family.

acantho-. A prefix meaning thorny or like a thorn.

acanthocarpous. Having spiny fruit or fruit covered with prickles or spines.

acanthocephalous. Having a hooked beak, as in mosses.

acanthocladous. Having spiny branches.

acanthocomous. Spiny haired or crowned.

acanthophorous. Bearing spines, prickles, or thorns.

acanthophysis. A thick, sterile hair with short-pointed outgrowths on the surface.

acanthosicyos. Deep rooted.

acanthospheres. Ciliated bodies formed in the cells of *Nitella, Stachelhügeln*.

acanthus. Representative leaf decoration used on the capitals of Corinthian columns.

acapnia. Diminution of or need for CO_2.

acarodomatia. Formations on some plants in which mites are sheltered.

acarophily. Acarophytism, symbiotic association between plants and mites (*Acarina*).

acarophyta. Plants which harbor mites.

acarpotropic. Said of plants which do not throw off their fruits.

acarpous. Fruitless, producing no fruits, having no fruits.

acaudal. Having no tail, acaudate.

acaulescence. A state in which stems are abnormally suppressed.

acaulescent. Apparently without stem, that is, with the main stem underground and only basal leaves and slender leafless flowering stems appearing above the ground level.

acauline. Stemless or nearly so, acaulose.

acaulosia. A condition in which there is an abnormal deficiency of stem.

acayallagic. See CARYALLAGIC.

accelerator. Material which improves the efficiency of an enzyme; an activator.

acceptor. The body or substance receiving or uniting with another introduced substance.

accessorial. 1. A term applied to those branches of *Pithophora* which arise near the base of the mother cell. 2. Other than essential, additional.

accessory. Helping, assisting, supernumerary (as of buds), sometimes applied to the border of the apothecium in lichens when substances or color differ from that of the disk.

accessory branches. Branches which arise from accessory buds; supernumerary branches in the same axil.

accessory buds. Buds in addition to the axillary or normal buds which frequently assume the function of the latter; additional axillary buds; secondary or supernumerary buds.

accessory cell. 1. A subsidiary cell. 2. A cell associated with the guard cells of a stoma but differing from it in structure and differing from the epidermal cells.

accessory character. A nonessential character of a species sometimes used to distinguish one race from another.

accessory chromosome. The sex-determining or "x" chromosome.

accessory food factors. Vitamins, hormones, etc.

accessory fructification. In lower plants a reproductive structure which is not sexual or concerned with sexuality.

accessory fruit. A fruit whose formation involves other floral parts in addition to the ovary, as in the apple, pear, strawberry, etc.

accessory gonidia. Gonidia in certain *Mucorales* in addition to those typical of the group.

accessory indusium. That indusium formed in ferns where the margin of the frond is inflexed over the sorus.

accessory multiplication. Asexual reproduction.

accessory organs. Parts of flowers formed in addition to those which form the perianth.

accessory pigment. Any pigment found in a plant cell other than the four (chlorophyll a, chlorophyll b, carotin, and xanthophyll) which are collectively called chlorophyll. It may occur either in solution in the cell sap or in plastids called chromatophores.

accessory reproduction. Any reproductive process which is not sexual.

accessory spore. 1. A spore of nonsexual origin. 2. A conidium of a type different from that usual in the species.

accidental. Sometimes used for adventitious, occasional, irregular, extraordinary.

accissus. An end possessing an acute sinus between two rounded angles.

acclimation. The natural process of becoming inured to climate which was harmful at first, climatic adaptation, the process of becoming acclimated.

acclimatization. Preferred to ACCLIMATION when referring to human action in adapting plants to a strange climate.

accolus. A neighbor.

accommodation. The ability of a plant to adapt to gradual changes in its environment.

accrescent. Increasing in size with age; continuing to grow after the normal period of growth after the formation of the flower, especially any increase in size of the calyx; enlarged and persistent; growing after the flowering period has passed.

accrete. To agglutinate, to grow together in any manner, to be naturally grafted onto a contiguous body.

accretion. An increase in size due to the addition of particles to the outside; growth caused by the external addition of new material.

acculeate. With narrow spines.

accumbent. Lying mutually one against the other; lying in contact; lying upon.

accumbent cotyledons. Cotyledons whose edges lie against the main axis of the embryo or the radicle; cotyledons lying against something else; see INCUMBENT.

accument. Accumbent.

-aceae. A suffix used in naming plant families.

acelerate. Somewhat acerose.

acenium. See ACHENE.

acentric. Lacking a center or centromere, as in a piece of a chromosome or a chromatid.

acentronic. Without a geometric or definite axis.

-aceous. A suffix meaning pertaining to, belonging to, or in the nature of.

acephalous. 1. Having no head. 2. Headless (used to designate ovaries which are not terminated by stigmas). 3. Also used when the style is attached to some part other than the summit.

acer. 1. Used by some authors in place of *acris*, meaning sharp or pointed or acrid, as in *Ranunculus acris*. 2. The generic name for maple trees. See ACRID.

aceraceous. Of or pertaining to the large genus *Acer* (the maples) or its allies.

acerate. Having the shape of a needle; pointed at the end, as of spicules.

acerb. Harsh or sour to the taste; astringent, as unripe fruit.

aceric. Of or pertaining to the genus *Acer* (the maples).

Acerosae. The *Coniferae*.

acerose. Acerous, needle-shaped (as the leaves of pines), narrow and slender with a sharp point, intermediate between acicular and subulate.

acervate. Occurring in tufts, heaps, clusters, or cushions.

acervulatus. Heaped, massed.

acervuline. Irregularly heaped or grouped together.

acervulus. 1. A small cluster, as a tuft of mycelium-bearing spores. 2. A small cluster, used in describing fungi on bark or leaves.

acervus. A heap, a multitude.

acescent. Sour, tart, acid.

acetabuliform. 1. Shaped like a shallow saucer (used to describe fructifications of some lichens). 2. Having a broad concave bottom with nearly upright sides; see COTYLIFORM.

acetabulum. The receptable of some fungi.

acetaldehyde. An intermediate substance in the production of acetic acid, an important step in the synthesis of organic compounds. It retards or inhibits germination and the growth of some fungi.

acetarious. Of or pertaining to herbs or plants used for salads.

acetary. Salad.

acetic acid. An acid formed during vinegar making (CH_3COOH), the acid in vinegar formed by the action of certain bacteria on alcohol.

acetic fermentation. Oxidation of alcoholic liquids, the formation of vinegar.

acetose, acetous. Sour, acid, producing acidity, like vinegar, acetosus.

acetylation. The production of an acetyl radical from pyruvate during photosynthesis. The enzyme concerned is co-enzyme A.

-aceus. -aceous, a suffix meaning "like."

achaenium. See ACHENE.

achaenocarp. Achaenocarpium; see ACHENOCARP.

achascophytum. Any plant with an indehiscent fruit.

acheilary. 1. Without a lip (as in some orchids). 2. Having an underdeveloped labellum. 3. Without labellum.

achene. A dry, one-seeded fruit with a firm, close-fitting pericarp which does not split open along regular lines, i.e., indehiscent. The seed lies free in the ovary except for its attachment by the funiculus, an akene.

achene beak. The persistent and hardened style of an achene.

achenium. See ACHENE.

achenocarp. Any dry indehiscent fruit.

achenodium. A double achene, as the cremocarp of *Umbelliferae*.

achillary. Having no lip, as some orchids.

achilleafolious. With leaves like those of *Achillea*, a large genus of aster-like plants.

Achlamydeae. Flowers which lack perianths.

achlamydeous. Having no perianth, without calyx or corolla, without sepals or petals.

Achlamydosporeae. A series of *Monochlamydeae*.

achlorophyllaceous. Having no chlorophyll.

achondroplasia. Dwarfism where the individual is normal but has stunted limbs.

Achorion. A genus or subgenus of fungi parasitic upon the skin of man and other animals, sometimes included in the genus *Oidium*.

Achras. A genus of tropical American trees, usually called *Sapodilla*, of the *Sapotaceae* family.

achromasie. The emission of chromatin from the nucleus; see CHROMASIE.

achromatic figure. The double set of delicate strands seen in the preparations of dividing nuclei and in the asters in dividing cells.

achromatic spindle. In cell division, a system of apparent fibers joining the poles of the nucleus unstained by basic dyes and diverging towards the equator.

achromatin. That part of the nucleus which does not stain with basic dyes, generally comprising the nuclear sap or ground-substance; nuclein.

achromatophile. Any structure which does not take a stain.

achromin. The unstainable part of the nucleus.

achromous. Achromus, achrous, achroos, colorless, hyaline, not readily stainable.

achroocyst. A cell of the terminal meristem which has clear contents; see CYANOCYST.

achroodextrin. One of the dextrins which cannot be colored by iodine; see ERYTHRODEXTRIN and AMYLODEXTRIN.

achrous. Colorless; see ACHROMOUS.

achyranthes. Tropical amaranthaceous herbs properly belonging to the genus *Iresine*, ornamental-leaved bedding plants.

achryophytum. A plant having glumaceous flowers, as in the grasses.

acicula. 1. The bristle-like continuations of the rhacilla of grasses, needle-shaped spines, prickles or other similar bodies. 2. The tooth-like processes in the hymenia of certain *Hymenomycetae*.

acicular. Having projections which are needle-like.

acicular fibers. Fibers or raphidines which are formed in the *Acanthaceae*.

aciculate. Finely grooved as if scratched with a pin with the markings not necessarily parallel; acicular or acerose. Distinguished from striate by being marked more finely.

aciculisilvae. Forests of needle-leaved trees or coniferous woods.

acid. A substance characterized by an excess of free hydrogen ions.

acid humus. Humus which is acid in reaction (with pH of less than 7), probably due to the absence of alkaline residual soil. Tor f.

acid plant. 1. A plant which grows in acid soil, as many members of the Heath family. 2. A plant containing organic acids in its sap, as wood sorrel.

acidic. 1. Having stains whose color determinant plays the part of an acid when acting on protoplasm. 2. Acid in reaction.

acidophiles. Plant cells which are stained by acid stains.

acidotous. Pointed or ending in a spine or hard point, as branches or organs.

acies. The angles or edges of some stems.

acimarious. With globose vesicles, as certain algae.

acinaceous. 1. Full of kernels or pips. 2. Scimitar- or saber-shaped.

acinacifolious. Having a scimitar-shaped fleshy leaf.

acinaciform. Scimitar-shaped, acinasiform.

acinarious. Having stems covered with vesicles like grape seeds.

acine, acinus. 1. A single member or drupelet of such fruits as raspberry, blackberry or grape. 2. A grape or berry. 3. A small seed or stone of a grape or berry.

acini. The small stones or seeds in grapes, strawberries, etc.

acinodendrus. A plant with fruits in bunches.

acinose, acinosous. Grape-like, having a granular structure resembling bunches of grapes.

aciphylla glacialis. Alpine or snow plants with linear pointed leaves.

aciphyllus. A linear pointed leaf.

acladium. A peduncle of the terminal flower head in *Hieracium*.

aclythrophytum. A plant with seeds which have no pericarps.

acme. The peak of development and vigor of an individual, race, or species.

acolytes. Varieties.

acondylose. Without nodes or joints.

aconitifolious. Aconite-leaved, palmately cleft or dissected like *Aconitum*.

aconitin. An alkaloid derived from monkshood, *Aconitum Napellus*.

aconitrase. An enzyme involved in the citric acid cycle (Kreb's Cycle).

acorin. A glucoside used in perfumery derived from *Acorus Calamus*.

acorn. The leathery fruit of the oak tree, a single large seed enclosed basally in a cup formed from bracts.

acospore. A plant having seeds with awns, as in grasses.

acotyledon. A plant lacking cotyledons or seed lobes.

acotyledones. An old term used for nonflowering plants.

acotyledonous. Lacking cotyledons where they are normally found, as in seeds.

acquired. Used to denote characters which arise during the lifetime of an organism in distinction to hereditary characters; refers to modifications of bodily structure, function, or habit which are impressed on an organism in the course of individual life.

acquired variation. A structural irregularity which develops as the plant grows.

acramphibrya. Dicotyledons and gymnosperms.

acramphibryous. Denoting plants which produce lateral and terminal buds, and which grow laterally as well as at the apex; see ACROGENOUS.

acrandry. The condition in which antheridia are at the apex of the stem, as in bryophytes.

acranthi. Terminal inflorescences in mosses.

acranthous. Applied to a sympodium with a main axis of annual portions of successive axes, each beginning with scale leaves and ending in an inflorescence.

acraspedote. Lacking a velum.

acrid. Sharp, bitter, peppery.

acris. Acrid; see ACER.

acro-. A prefix denoting apex.

acroblast. A body in a spermatid which gives rise to an acrosome.

acroblastesis. The germ tube of lichens when it proceeds from the end of a spore.

acroblastic. Pertaining to the branch of an inflorescence which arises from a terminal bud.

acrobrya. Plants which grow only at the apex, as all acrogens which have a distinct axis.

acrocarpi. Mosses having fruits borne terminally on the main stem.

acrocarpous. With terminal fruit, having a terminal sporophyte on a stem or ordinary branch, having the archegonia borne at the extremity of a primary leafy axis the growth of which is thereby arrested.

acrocecidium. A deformity of the terminal bud due to the activity of gall insects.

acrochlamydeae. Haplostemonous *Gamopetalae* exclusive of *Cucurbitaceae* but including the *Umbelliferae*, a group which is considered by some at the head of the dicotyledons.

acroclinium. Any plant of certain species of *Helipterum* formerly included in the genus *Acroclinium*.

acroconidium. One of those conidia which mature successively and break away from the apex of the conidiophore.

acrodomatia. Structures on plants adapted to shelter mites of supposed service to the host or hosts.

acrodrome. A leaf with nerves converging at its tip.

acrodromous. Having veins parallel with the leaf-edge and united at the apex, as in *Plantago*.

acrofugal. Basipetal.

Acrogamae. Porogamae; see CHALAZOGAMAE.

acrogamous. Denoting those plants in which the egg apparatus is produced at the summit of the embryo sac, as in most angiosperms.

acrogamy. The condition of having the egg apparatus produced at the summit of the embryo sac. Double acrogamy has both egg apparatus and pollen tube at the summit of the sac; see BASIGAMIC.

acrogen. A plant in which the growth is said to be acrogenous, a plant in which the growth takes place at the apex from a terminal bud or by the apical cell only (as in ferns and mosses).

acrogenesis. Formation of terminal fructification.

acrogenous. Growing from the apex (as the stems of ferns and mosses), borne at the tips of hyphae.

acrogenous plants. Plants which grow or develop only from the apex or summit of the stem.

acrogens. 1. Ferns, a general term applied to the cryptogamous plants. 2. Fungus spores produced at the apex or end of a filament.

acrogonel. A concentration of parts making a monocentric axis.

acrogonidium. A gonidium formed at the summit of a gonidiophore.

acrogynous. Having stems terminated by female organs, denoting those forms in which the growth of a shoot is terminated by the appearance of archegonia which are formed near the apical cell or from the apical cell itself.

acrogyratous. Having an elastic ring at the point, as in *Schizaea*.

acronus. An ovary without a basal disk.

acronychious. Curved like the claw of an animal.

acropetal. In the direction of the summit, produced successfully toward the apex, developing from the base upward, developing leaves and flowers from an axis so that the youngest arise at the apex.

acropetal succession. The development of lateral members or parts in such order that the youngest is nearest the tip of the axis.

acropetalous inflorescence. A raceme.

acrophilous. Living in an alpine region.

acrophytes. Alpine plants.

acrophytia. Alpine plant formations.

acropleurogenous. Having spores borne at the tips and on the sides of hyphae.

acrosarc. The pulpy berry resulting from the

union of the ovary and an adnate calyx, as in the currant.

acroscopic. Looking toward the summit, on the side toward the summit, facing the summit, the reverse of basiscopic.

acrose. Fructose.

acrosome. The apical body at the tip of a spermatozoon (also called perferatorium from the supposed function of penetrating actively into the egg); see ACROBLAST.

acrosperms. Those angiosperms presumed to have begun with a simple porogamous mode of impregnation.

acrospire. The first of a germinating seed, the extruded radicle, the first shoot, the plumule.

acrospired. Germinated, as in malting.

acrospore. A spore formed at the summit of a filament or sporophore.

acrostichoid. Resembling *Acrostichum*, a genus of ferns with fused sori.

acrothecal. Applied to virescent anthers when the polleniferous portion is confined to the apex with the lower portion becoming leaf-like.

acrotonic. Applied to the *Orchidaceae* when the apex of the anther loculi is next to the rostellum.

acrotonous. Denoting the prolongation of the pollen sac to the upper end of the anther, as in certain orchids.

acrotriche. Hairy-lipped.

acrotropism. The direction of a root as long as its apex is not injured.

actad. A plant of rocky shores.

actinenchyma. Cellular tissue which is star-shaped, as seen in cross section of *Juncus*, the rushes.

actiniform. Having rays, having a radial shape.

actinism. The chemical action of the sun.

actino. A star-shaped spicule.

actinoblast. The mother cell from which a spicule is formed.

actinocarp. A fruit which has carpels or placentae radiating like the spokes of a wheel.

actinodromous. Palmately veined or with veins radially arranged.

actinogonidial. Having radially arranged genital organs.

actinometer. A light-measuring instrument for measuring actinic rays.

actinomorphic. Having flowers of a regular star-shaped pattern which are capable of bisection in two or more planes into similar halves, radially symmetrical or symmetrical along any plane passing through the center, regular and polysymmetrical.

actinomycosis. A chronic disease of animals caused by the ray fungi *Actinomyces sp.* characterized by the formation of tumors which contain sulfur-yellow, sand-like bodies which are usually found on the tongue, jaws, or in the stomach (as lumpy jaw in cattle).

actinophryds. Globes with radically arranged pseudopodia in *Pseudospora*, a parasite on *Vaucheria*.

actinostele. 1. The stele of most roots and certain stems which consist primarily of alternating or radial groups of xylem and phloem without a pericycle. 2. A prostele with vascular tissue arranged in radiating arms interspersed with parenchyma.

actinostomous. Denoting certain radiate structures around the ostioles of some lichens and other cryptogams.

actium. A plant formation characteristic of rocky sea shores.

activation by light. The effect of light in photosynthesis which results in chemical changes in a plant.

activator. A substance which must be present during enzymatic activity, a substance which activates, a co-ferment, an enzyme which stimulates as opposed to a paralyzer.

active transport. The movement of nutrient in a plant to replace that used to manufacture stored food or that used to produce energy.

actophilous. Applied to those plants growing on a rocky seashore.

actophyte. A plant growing on a seashore.

aculeate. Prickly, thorny, armed with spines or aculei.

aculeolate. Beset with diminutive prickles, having few or small prickles.

aculeus. A sharp epidermal emergence such as a prickle or thorn, a rigid hair-like projection growing from the epidermis.

acuminate. Having a long, slender, sharp point; tapering gradually toward the apex; drawn out to a long point; tapering at the end.

acuminiferous. With pointed tubercles.

acuminifolious. Having acuminate leaves.

acuminose. Approaching acuminate, having a sharp or tapering point, with an acuminate point.

acuminulate. Having a small terminal point, with a very sharply tapering point, with an acuminate point.

acus. Needle, referring to the needle-like leaf of such conifers as pines.

acutangular. Having sharp angles.

acutate. Slightly sharpened, as at the apex.

acute. Pointed, less than a right angle, sharp edged, not prolonged.

acute disease. A disease which quickly reaches a crisis.

acutifidous. Acutely or sharply cut.

acutiflorous. Denoting a perianth with acute segments.

acutifolious. With an acute leaf.

acutilobous. Having acute lobes.

acutipetalous. With petals acute or sharply pointed.

acyanophoric. Not producing cyanogen.

acyclic. With floral leaves arranged in a spiral; with all floral organs in a continuous spiral, not in whorls.

acystidiate. Without cystidia.

ad-. A prefix meaning to.

-ad. A suffix meaning of or related to (used in some names of plants such as cycad); a suffix indicating an ecad.

adaptable. Capable of becoming adapted, having the ability to originate ecads.

adaptation. The change or changes by which an organism adapts itself to a new environment, an adjustment to changed conditions of life, the modification of a plant to fit itself into its environment, the modification of an organ for a particular function.

adapted race. A physiological race.

adaptive director. An advantageous change by a reaction to a stimulus.

adaptive enzyme. An enzyme, not normally present, which develops in response to the presence of an unusual nutrient in the substrate of a bacterial culture.

adaptive modifications. See ADAPTATION.

adaptive parasites. Saprophytic fungi which may or which have become parasites.

adaptive races. Races or species which are identical morphologically but differ physiologically. Compare BIOLOGICAL RACES.

adaptor compound. A carrier compound, e.g., RNA, responsible for the transfer of a substance to the site of reaction.

adaxial. Next to the axis, ventral, turned toward the axis; facing the stem.

adaxial surface. That surface of a leaf that faces the stem during development, i.e., the upper side of the leaf.

adcrustation. The deposition of material on a cell wall in contrast to encrustation where the materials are deposited between existing molecules.

adder's-mouth. Any orchid of the genus *Achroanthes*.

adder's-tongue. A fern of the genus *Ophioglossum*.

addition stage. The gain of a factor in heredity.

additive fixative. A reagent which unites chemically with the protein of the material being studied.

adducentia vasa. The spirals in tracheids which were formerly thought to be vessels.

adductores. Archegonia.

adeciduate. Not falling or coming away, applied to evergreens.

adelogamicae. Fungi and lichens.

adelome. Alburnum.

adelomorphic. Indefinite in form.

adelosiphonic. Denoting a dictyostele when it is complex and becoming less tubular.

adelphia. A collection of stamens united by their filaments into one bundle.

adelphogamy. Fertilization between neighboring plants of the same species; union of a vegetative mother cell and one of its daughter cells.

adelphophagy. The union of two gametes of the same sex.

adelphotaxy. Mutual attraction between spores of *Achlya* and *Pedastreae* after extrusion.

adelphous. Having brotherhoods of stamens, having stamens united by their filaments; see MONODELPHOUS, DIADELPHOUS, POLYDELPHOUS.

aden-. A prefix meaning a gland or tubercle.

adenine. A substance which occurs in RNA, DNA, ATP, ADP, AMP. Found in beet juice and tea leaves, it stimulates bacterial growth.

adenocalyx. A calyx studded with glandular spots.

adenocyst. The membrane of the cell or cells surrounding a gland.

adenoid organ. A ligule of the fossil tree *Lepidodendron*.

adenopetaly. The transformation of nectaries into petals or similar structures.

adenophore. A stalk supporting a gland, a stalk of the nectar gland.

adenophyllous. Having glands on the leaves.

adenopodous. Having glands or gland-like tubercles on the petiole or peduncle.

adenose. Glandular, gland-like, bearing glands.

adenosine. One of the nucleic acids.

adenosine diphosphate (ADP). The diphosphate of adenosine which is involved in the transfer of energy during respiration.

adenosine monophosphate. Adenylic acid.

adenosine triphosphate (ATP). The triphosphate ester of adenosine closely related to ADP. Most frequently found in mitochondria.

adenostemon. A stamen with glands.

adenylic acid. Adenosine monophosphate. A constituent of DPN.

adermin. A vitamin necessary for the growth of lactic acid bacteria, certain yeasts, and fungi.

adesmy. An abnormal condition in a flower when parts that are normally united are separate.

adfluxion. The attraction by which sap is drawn toward leaves.

adglutinate. Grown together, accrete, glued together; see AGGLUTINATE.

adherence. The state of union of some parts, sometimes referring only to dissimilar parts; adhesion; see COHERENCE.

adherent. Adnate, denoting union of parts, naturally united to, attached, grown fast to a structure of a different kind (as a stamen grown fast to a petal).

adherent vernation. Vernation in which the bases of fern fronds are continuous with the caudex.

adhesion. The growing together of organs or parts which are normally separate, the union of dissimilar parts, adherence.

adiabatic. Not transferable, as a substance which cannot be transferred from one tissue to another.

adiantoid. Resembling the genus *Adiantum*, the maidenhair fern.

adichogamy. The development of both sexes at the same time.

adipocelluloses. Celluloses containing a large amount of suberin as in cork tissue, bodies

or groups of bodies which make up the cuticular tissues of leaves and fruits.

adipos celluloses. A cellulose.

adiscalis. Without a disk.

adjustment. The processes of changing in response to stimuli, functional responses to stimuli.

adligant. Holding fast or binding (as in the aerial holdfasts in ivy); see ALLIGANT.

adminiculum. A fulcrum.

admotivus. Said of the albumen remaining attached to the sheath of the cotyledon during germination.

adnascent. Growing to or upon something else, e.g., moss on a tree trunk.

adnate. Designating the condition of being congenitally united or grown together; designating the union of unlike parts such as gills attached to stems, scales to stems, anthers attached along their entire length.

adnate anther. An anther attached for the entire length to the inner or outer face of the filament.

adnation. 1. The fusion with or attachment to another plant structure by its whole length from the beginning of growth. 2. The union of vascular bundles. 3. Adhesion.

adnexa. Structures or parts closely related to an organ.

adnexed. Reaching only to the stem but not adnate to it (as the lamellae of certain agarics), slightly attached to the stipe by the upper corner only.

ADP. See ADENOSINE DIPHOSPHATE.

adpressed. Appressed.

adscendent. Ascendent, ascending.

adsere. The portion of a sere which precedes its convergence into any other at any time before the climax stage.

adsociatus. Clustered.

adsorption. Adhesion of the molecules of a gas, liquid, or dissolved substance to a surface; adhesion of molecules to solid bodies.

adspectus. Sight, appearance.

adspersed. Scattered or widely distributed.

adsurgent. Assurgent, ascending, rising to an erect position.

adult cells. Cells which show the highest degree of differentiation which is characteristic of them.

aduncate. Crooked, twisted, hooked, bent.

adustous. Fuliginous, soot-colored, swarthy, burned, blackened.

adventitious. Accidental; out of usual place; foreign, as a plant introduced but not established; developing in an abnormal position, e.g., roots developing from stems.

adventitious bud. A bud arising in a location where such a bud would not be expected (as a bud arising not from a node but from a leaf, shoot, or wound).

adventitious embryo. An embryo formed without fertilization.

adventitious meristem. Meristematic tissue which arises from permanent cells.

adventitious roots. Roots which arise from the surface of stems or leaves, or out of order or from an unusual position, i.e., from other than the radicle or its subdivisions.

adventitious shoot. A shoot arising from a root or leaf, or from a place other than normal.

adventitious vacuoles. Small vacuoles in those cells which also contain one or more sap cavities.

adventive. Of plants becoming naturalized, adventitious, recently or incompletely naturalized, temporarily established.

advenus. Newly arrived, adventive.

adverse. Opposite, facing the main axis.

adversifoliate. Having opposite leaves, adversifolious.

adynamandry. Self-sterility, as in a flower which does not set seed from its own pollen.

adynamogyny. The loss of function by the female organs of a flower.

aecial. Resembling or related to the type genus *Aecidium* or referring to an aecium formation.

aecialform. Referring to a stage of development of a fungus in which an aecium is formed, cup-shaped.

aecial lesion. A diseased area bearing one to many aecia.

aecidiolium. In the *Uredinaceae*, a small form, usually a later development, of the aecium stage; a spermogonium.

aecidiospore. See AECIOSPORE.

aecidiostage. See AECIOSTAGE.

aecidium. See AECIUM.

aeciospore. A spore formed in an aecium, a yellow one-celled binucleate spore of the rust fungus formed in a special cluster or cup-like structure called an aecium.

aeciostage. That stage in the development of a rust fungus which has hyphae with binucleate cells and from which the binucleate single-celled aeciospores develop.

aecioteliospore. A spore having the aspect of an aeciospore but the nature of a teliospore.

aecium. A cup-like structure produced on certain plants by rust fungi in which binucleate single-celled spores are borne.

aecology. See ECOLOGY.

aegagropilae. The marine algae which are more or less spherical and which are freely driven about in the sea.

aegilops. The wild oats or any other grass growing as a weed in a grain field.

aelophilous. Scattered by the wind.

aeneous. The color of brass, copper-colored, bronze-colored, verdigris.

aeolian. Liable to rapid erosion by wind.

aequaliflorous. Denoting heads or clusters of flowers in which all members are alike in form and character.

aequi-, equi-. A prefix denoting equal.

aequichromosomal. With the exchange of chromosomes or of their quality.

aequihymeniiferous. With equal development of the hymenium all over the surface of the gill.

aequilateral. Equilateral, having equal sides, opposed to oblique (in floral organs).

aequimagnus. Of equal magnitude or size.

aequinoctial. Of or pertaining to the equinox (used to describe plants having flowers which open or close at stated intervals).

aequipetalous. Equal-petaled.

aequipotential. Of equal power (applied in the theory of phyllotaxis).

aequitrilobous. Having three equal lobes.

aequivalvis. With valves of flowers or fruits of equal size.

aequivenius. Having all veins equally distinct.

aerating roots. Roots which arise from mud or other soil and which have loose corky tissue (aerenchyma) with conspicuous intercellular spaces whose function is aeration.

aerating tissue. Loosely constructed tissue with large intercellular spaces through which air can circulate through a plant.

aeration. The entrance of air, the mixing with air.

aerenchyma. Respiratory tissue formed by the phellogen, special tissue for aeration regarded by some as simply floating tissue, cortical tissue containing air spaces within the parenchyma.

aereola. See AEROLA.

aereous. Copper-colored, bronzed.

aerial. Living above the surface of the ground or water.

aerial plants. Plants not rooted in soil, such epiphytic plants as *Tillandsia* and tropical orchids.

aerial roots. Roots growing from adventitious buds into the air. Some are parasitic, others contain chlorophyll.

aerial water. Rain or dew as distinguished from the water of the ground.

aeriobiotic. Thriving only in the presence of air.

aerobe. An organism usually requiring free oxygen for its life processes, an aerobiont or an aerobium; see ANAEROBE.

aerobic energesis. The disruptive process by which energy is released.

aerobic respiration. A form of respiration which requires the presence of elementary oxygen which produces energy and releases carbon dioxide and water.

aerobiont. A plant depending upon free oxygen for its respiration.

aerobiosis. Life which requires oxygen, existence in the presence of free oxygen.

aerobious. Growing in the air.

aerocarpy. Production of fruit above the ground.

aerocyst. An air bladder found in certain algae.

aerogams. Phanerogams, the seed plants.

aerogen. A microorganism which forms gas during its metabolism.

aeroidotropism. See AEROTROPISM.

aerola. Wall markings or cracks in the *Bacillariophyceae* (crustaceous lichens) consisting of thin areas bounded by ridges of siliceous material and having an aggregation of many fine pores which aid in aeration.

aeromorphosis. Certain changes in the manner of growth of water plants caused by exposure to air or wind.

aeropermeable. Permeable to the passage of gases.

aerophilae. Algae which live exposed to the air and not on the ground.

aerophilous. Pertaining to organisms which are essentially aerobic, a term pertaining to renovation buds which are produced above the ground.

aerophilous shoot. The shoot which arises from the so-called renovation buds produced above the ground.

aerophyte. A plant growing attached to an aerial portion of another plant, an air plant, an epiphyte.

aeroplankton. Microorganisms floating in the air.

aeropyle. The pore found at the base of the pods in certain legumes.

aeroscope. An apparatus used to collect spores, dust, bacteria, etc., in the air.

aerotaxis. Movement of microorganisms toward or away from oxygen, positive stimulation of zoospores by oxygen.

aerotropic. Curving (of a plant or plant parts) toward a greater concentration of oxygen.

aerotropism. The adjustment to the stimulus of gases.

aeroxyl. A term which is applied to trees and woody plants with a visible bole and branches above the ground.

aeruginius. Verdigris-green.

aeruginose. Clear, light, bluish green (the rust color of brass).

aeschynomenous. Sensitive, as the leaves of certain plants, e.g., the sensitive plant.

aesculin. An alkaloid derived from *Aesculus*, the horse chestnut or buckeye.

aestatifruticeta. Deciduous bush formations, summer coppices.

aestatisilvae. Deciduous forests.

aesthesia. The capacity of an organ to respond to definite physical stimuli, sensibility.

aestilignosa. Trophophytic woodland of temperate regions. Subdivided as aestisilvae, temperate deciduous forest; and aestifruticeta, deciduous bush communities.

aestivaria. The summer quarters of plants in botanical gardens.

aestivation. 1. The passing of the summer in an inactive state. 2. The typical unfolding of floral parts from a hitherto dormant bud. 3. The manner in which floral parts are folded before expansion. 4. Prefloration.

aestuarium. A flat shore which is flooded with sea water at spring tide.

aeterio. See ETAERIO.

aethalium. A sessile, rounded, or pillow-shaped fructification formed by a massing of all or part of the plasmodium in the *Myxomycetes*.

aetheos-. A prefix meaning unusual.

aetheogamic. Cryptogamic, without seeds.

aetheogamous. Cryptogamous.

aethereus. Aerial.

aethiopicus. Ethiopian, African.

aetiogenia. External causes.

aetiology. A branch of biology concerned with cause of disease, etiology, aitiology.

aeturus. External.

affinis. Related to another species.

affinity. Similarity as regards important organs, the closeness of relation between plants as shown by similarity of important organs.

affixed. Fixed upon, inserted upon, attached.

afforestation. The act of conversion into a forest or woodland.

aflagellar. Without flagella.

afoliate. Leafless, having no leaves, aphyllous.

aftermath. The second growth of grasses in the same season after they have been cut off.

afternoon-lady. The four o'clock flower which blooms in the afternoon or evening.

after-ripening. 1. The period of dormancy in many seeds and spores before germination. 2. The chemical and physical changes which take place before germination can take place.

agad. A beach plant.

Agamae. *Cryptogamae*, the plants without flowers and true seeds.

agamandroecism. A condition in which both male and neuter flowers occur in the same individual or inflorescence.

agametes. Those reproductive bodies which are capable of growth without syngamy.

agametospore. Agamospore.

agamic. Destitute of sex, reproducing without male gametes, asexual.

agamobium. A term used for the asexual generation in organisms showing alternation of generations, the sporophyte.

agamocytogony. Asexual reproduction.

agamogenesis. Parthenogenesis, asexual reproduction of any kind (i.e., by buds, gemmae, etc.) without formation of functional gametes.

agamogony. Schizogamy, asexual reproduction.

agamogynaecism. A condition in which female and neuter flowers appear in the same inflorescence.

agamogynomonoecism. The appearance of perfect, female, and neuter flowers in the same inflorescence.

agamohermaphroditic. With hermaphroditic and neuter flowers in the same plant.

agamohypnospore. A large resting spore.

agamonoecia. Those plants with hermaphroditic and barren flowers in the same inflorescence.

agamophyta. Protophytes.

agamospecies. An apomict population the constituents of which, for morphological, cytological, or other reasons, are to be considered as having common origin. See APOMIXIS.

agamospermy. Asexual formation of an embryo and the subsequent development of a seed.

agamospore. A spore formed without fertilization.

agamotropic. Denoting flowers which remain open, said of flowers which do not close after having once opened.

agar (agar-agar). A gelatinous product derived from certain sea weeds, a higher carbohydrate much used in laboratory media also called Ceylon moss and Bengal Isinglass.

agar hanging-block. A hanging drop (microscopic mount) made with a small block of nutrient agar.

agaric. A mushroom or fungus belonging to the *Agaricaceae* family or the genus *Agaricus*, a mushroom with gills.

agaric acid. An acid found in *Polyporus officinalis*.

agaricole. A parasite on mushrooms.

agaricolous. Living or parasitic on mushrooms, agaricicolous.

Agave. An important economic plant having stiff spines with long succulent leaves usually borne basally or in rosettes (*Amaryllidaceae*).

age and area. A theory that the longer a species has been in a region, the greater the area it covers.

agchylolaimic. With a crooked neck.

agenius. Neuter.

agents. Organic or inorganic means effecting seed dispersal (such as wind, water and animals), also agents of pollination (such as wind, insects, etc.).

agenus. Denoting cellular cryptogams which are enlarged by the addition of new parts.

ageotropism. The condition of not reacting to gravity.

ageratifolious. Having leaves like *Ageratum*, a common decorative plant grown for its decorative flowers.

aggedula. The sporangium of mosses and of *Puccinia*.

agger arenae. Sand bar, silt, mud, sand, and gravel brought down by torrents and rivers.

aggeres. Banks or rock works in botanic gardens.

agglomerate, agglomerated. Clustered (as a head of flowers), crowded together but not cohering.

agglomerate soil. Soil containing angular rock fragments loosely embedded.

agglutinate. Accrete, to be glued together as masses of pollen in *Asclepias* and orchids, to be clumped, to be brought together.

agglutination. The act of bringing together, the formation of certain clumps of floccules by some bacteria, a specific test in bacteriology leading to the clumping of some bacteria.

agglutinin. A substance formed in the blood of animals which agglutinates an antigen, an immune body, an antibody, a substance causing agglutination.

agglutinogen. A substance producing agglutinin which has the property of clumping and precipitating blood corpuscles or bacteria.

aggregatae. A cohort of *Sympetalae* or *Gamopetalae*.

aggregate. Clustered or massed together, crowded close together, formed into a cluster (usually applied to an inflorescence).

aggregate flowers. Flowers gathered into a head but not capitulate, flowers with several florets in the same head (as in clover).

aggregate fruit. Fruit composed of several ripened ovaries from a single flower and joined together by a common receptacle; the product of a polycarpellary apocarpous gynaecium; a fruit formed by the coherence of the ovaries which were distinct in the flower; a fruit in which distinct carpels of a single flower are crowded on the receptacle into one mass as in raspberry and magnolia.

aggregate plasmodium. In *Acrarieae*, a pseudoplasmodium resulting from the aggrega-

tion of myxamoebae for fructification, not for vegetative purposes.

aggregate ray. A group of small xylem rays.

aggregate species. A group of closely related species denoted by a single name.

aggregation. The condensation of cell contents under some stimulus; the movement of protoplasm in tenacle or tendril cells of sensitive plants which causes the tenacle or tendril to bend toward the point stimulated; the coming together of plants into groups.

aggressin. Toxic substances produced by pathogenic organisms which inhibit the defensive reaction of the host.

aggressiveness. The capacity of a parasite to attack its host, aggressivity.

agium. An association made up of beach plants, a beach formation.

agouti. The brownish color produced by hairs which are banded alternately with light and dark pigment.

agrad. A cultivated plant.

agrestal. Growing in arable ground or fields; rural, growing in cultivated land but not itself cultivated (as weeds).

agrestic. Growing in fields.

agricultural botany. The branch of botany dealing with the plants of agriculture, economic botany of farm plants.

agricultural regions. Regions fitted for the production of agricultural plants.

agricultural species. Constant forms or varieties of cultivated plants.

agrium. A culture formation or grain field.

agroceric acid. A constituent of humus.

agrology. The science of soils and their support of special vegetation.

agronomy. The study of field crops and their cultivation.

agrophilous. Growing in grain fields or cultivated areas.

agrophyta. Cultivated plants.

agropyretum. A formation composed of wheat grasses, *Agropyron*.

agrostemma. Conducting tissue of the style.

agrosterol. A constituent of humus.

agrostidetum. An association of *Agrostis*, bentgrass.

agrostography. The description of grasses.

agrostology. That branch of botany dealing with the study of grasses.

agrumi. Name given by Italians to any kind of citrus fruit.

agynarius. Denoting stamens which are free from the ovary, without pistils.

agynous. Denoting monstrous flowers which lack pistils, without pistils.

aheliotropic. Neutral to the light stimulus (i.e., neither attracted nor repelled by light), apheliotropic.

aianthous. 1. Constantly flowering. 2. Having everlasting flowers (as in helichrysum).

aigialium. A formation of beach plants.

aigialophyta. Plants growing on the beach or strand.

aigicolous. Inhabiting a stony beach or strand.

aigret. Any feathery crown or tuft attached to the seed (as the pappus of a thistle), egret.

aima- haema-. A prefix meaning blood-colored or related to blood.

aiophyllous. Evergreen-leaved.

aiphyllium. An evergreen forest, a broad-leafed evergreen forest.

aiphyllophilous. Growing in a broad-leaf evergreen forest.

aiphyllophyta. Broad-leafed evergreen plants forming a forest.

aiphytium. An ultimate or fixed plant formation, a stable community.

air-bags. Bags or cavities filled with air, follicles.

air-bladders. Organs filled with air which keep the plants floating in water (as in sea weeds).

air cavity. See AIR CELL.

air cell. 1. A large intercellular space in a leaf or stem into which a stoma opens. 2. A cavity in the upper surface of some liverworts opening externally by an air pore and containing chains of photosynthetic cells. 3. A large intercellular space in which air is stored in some water plants.

air chamber. See AIR CELL.

air passage. An extended opening between cells containing air (as in the stems of many water plants).

air pits. Well-developed pits in thick-celled walls for aeration.

air plants. Epiphytes, plants growing in the air detached from the soil (as certain orchids, etc.); see AEROPHYTES.

air pores. Stomata, pneumathodes of hepatics, breathing pores.

air roots. Pneumatophores, roots growing in the air.

air sacs. Cavities containing air (as in the pollen grains of *Pinus*).

air spaces. 1. Intercellular spaces. 2. Spaces enclosed in folded leaves. 3. Carinal cavities in the fibrovascular strands of *Equisetum*; see CARINAL CANAL.

air vesicle. A greatly inflated air space often occurring in aquatic plants which serves as an aid in floating.

air vessels. A term formerly applied to empty tracheids.

aithalium. A formation of an evergreen thicket.

aithalophilous. Denoting plants which evidently grow better in evergreen thickets.

aitiogenic. Aitigenous, due to external causes.

aitiomorphosis. Change in shape caused by external factors.

aitionastic. Bent from an external cause (said of a curvature by a plant in response to a diffuse stimulus).

aitionomic. Due to external stimuli (as in the case in some growth curvatures).

aitiotropism. Any movement or curvature which depends on external stimuli.

aizoid. Like an aizoon.

aizoon. An evergreen or tenacious plant.

akaryote. 1. A chromidial condition after the close of the vegetative stage in certain *Plasmodiophoraceae* when the nucleus is lacking. 2. A cell in which the nucleoplasm has not aggregated to form a nucleus. 3. A cell without a nucleus.

akaryote stage. A stage in the life history of some lower plants during which the nuclei are very difficult to stain or have been extruded into the cytoplasm.

akene. See ACHENE.

akenium. See ACHENE.

akinesis. Increase which takes place without karyokinesis.

akinetes. 1. Single cells of the thallus of certain green algae whose original walls thicken and which separate from the thallus and become resting spores before germination (like the chlamydospores in fungi). 2. Nonmotile reproductive cells formed without true cell formation or rejuvenescence. 3. Resting spores.

akladium. See ACLADIUM.

ala. 1. A wing. 2. One of the side petals of a papilionaceous flower (as in the pea and its relatives). 3. A membranous outgrowth of a fruit which serves in wind dispersal (as in a maple seed). 4. A narrow leafy growth down a stem from a decurrent leaf. 5. The basal lobe in the leaves of mosses. 6. A continuation of a structure (as the lacerated and shaggy extensions of the reticulations of some types of *Boletus*). 7. An obsolete term for the axil.

alabastrum. An old term for flower bud.

alakescent. Having the properties or the effects of an alkali.

alanine. An amino acid found in proteins.

alar cells. 1. Cells at the basal angles of a moss scale or leaf which differ from cells of the main part of the leaf in size, shape, or color. 2. Cells in the forks or axils of a stem.

alate. Winged (as certain seeds or stems), having wing-like extensions.

alate pinnate. Pinnate with a winged petiole.

alatepinnatus. The condition in which the petiole of a pinnately compound leaf has marginal wings.

albatus. White, whitened.

albefaction. Blanching, whitening, bleaching.

albescent. Becoming white, whitish, hoary.

albicant. Tending toward whiteness.

albication. Becoming blanched or variegated with white.

albicaulis. White-stemmed.

albifrons. White-fronded, white-herbaged.

albinism. 1. A diseased condition resulting from the absence of normal coloring producing an albino. 2. The absence of pigmentation in which condition the chromatophores are colorless.

albino. A plant having colorless chromatophores due to the lack of chlorophyll in chloroplasts; see ALBINISM.

albinotic cells. Cells lacking chlorophyll.

albispermous. White-seeded.

albispinous. White-spined.

albocinctous. White-girdled or white-crowned.

albofarctous. White-stuffed.

albolutescens. Whitish yellow.

albopelliculatous. Having a layer of colorless cells below the epidermis, with a green core.

albopictous. White-painted.

albopilosus. White-shaggy.

albospicous. White-spiked.

albotunicatous. With a white tunic-like covering, albopelliculatous.

albumen. Nutritive material stored within the seed usually surrounding the embryo but not within the embryo, the nutritive matter in the seed used by the young plant until it develops roots and leaves; see ENDOSPERM.

albumen cells. Groups of cells with granular contents and large nuclei on outer flanks of the phloem of each bundle in the stems of gymnosperms.

albumen crystals. Protein bodies in the form of crystals.

albumin. The proteids which readily coagulate from their aqueous solutions by the action of heat or acids.

albuminates. Nitrogenous substances not soluble in water but soluble in certain dilute acids or alkalis (as the gluten of wheat), enzymes formed with albumen.

albuminoids. Organic substances containing nitrogen in their composition (e.g., protoplasm), proteids.

albuminous cells. 1. Cells rich in contents. 2. Parenchyma cells in gymnosperm phloem morphologically and physiologically associated with sieve cells but not derived from the same source.

albuminous seed. A seed having endosperm.

albumoses. Similar to albuminates but soluble in water, common constituents of aleuron.

alburnitas. A disease of trees in which there is a tendency to remain soft like the recent wood.

alburnous. Relating to the sapwood, pertaining to alburnum.

alburnum. The outermost and youngest portion of the wood which is still permeable to fluids, the sapwood or the outer rings of wood in dicotyledonous trees, newly formed wood.

albus. Dead-white, white without luster.

alcaliotropism. A chemotropism caused by alkalies.

alchemilletum. An assemblage or association of *Alchemilla* plants (rosaceous herbs).

alcicornous. Elk-horned.

alcohol. A colorless, volatile, pungent, organic liquid compound often obtained from the sugars stored in plants or obtained by fermentation.

alcoholase. 1. An alcoholic solution. 2. Used in the past for zymase.

alcoholic fermentation. See FERMENTATION.

alder-willow association. A woods usually showing a dominance of alder with a mixture of willows and sometimes containing ashes and oaks.

-ale. A suffix meaning colony.

alectorioid. Filamentous like the thallus of the genus *Alectoria* from which the word is formed.

alembic. A vessel used in distilling.

alepidote. Having no scales or scurf.

aleppicus. Of Aleppo, Syria.

aleppo. A cultivated form of *Andropogon* (or *Holcus*) *halepensis* (a sorghum).

aleppo galls. Nut galls which contain gallic and gallitannic acids. They are excrescences of various oaks which are used in tanning leather.

-ales. A suffix indicating taxonomic orders of plants.

aletophyte. A wayside plant.

aleuriospore. A conidium formed laterally on a hypha by certain fungi (characteristic of many which cause skin diseases).

aleurone. Protein granules (proteids) of globulins and peptones found in ripe seeds, crystalloid proteids in seeds, the outermost layer of the endosperm in cereals when it is rich in gluten.

aleurone grains. Grains of nitrogenous food material stored in reserve tissues of seeds; see ALEURONE LAYER.

aleurone layer. A layer of aleurone grains found in the periphery of most seeds.

aleurospore. A simple lateral conidium of dermatophytes.

alexandrinus. Of Alexandria, Egypt.

alexine. A hypothetical substance assumed to be formed by some plants for protection against bacteria.

alexipharmic. Antidotal, able to counteract a poison.

alexiteric. Having the power to counteract poisons.

alga. A chlorophyll-bearing thallophyte which reproduces by unicellular structures which lack sterile cells or rarely reproduces by multicellular structures in which each cell forms a gamete.

algal layer. A layer of green algal cells lying inside the thallus of a heteromerous lichen, also called the gonidial layer or algal zone.

algal zone. See ALGAL LAYER.

alganin. Algin.

algarroba. 1. An evergreen tree bearing large, edible, fleshy pods; the carob. 2. Its beans or pods (also called St. John's bread). 3. The common or honey mesquite. 4. Its edible pods.

algerine. Of or pertaining to Algeria, Algerian.

algicide. An agent or substance which destroys algae.

algicole. Living on algae.

algidus. Cold.

algin. A gelatinous substance obtained from certain algae commercially marketed.

alginous. Resembling filamentous algae.

algist. Algologist, a student of algae.

algo-lichens. Certain plants which are interpreted as transitional between the algae and the lichens.

algonkian. The late Proterozoic Era.

algs. Algae.

alien. An introduced plant which has become naturalized.

aliferous. Winged, having wings.

aliform parenchyma. Vasicentric parenchyma which has wing-like extensions.

aligerous. See ALIFEROUS.

aligular. A term used for that leaf-face in *Selaginella* which is turned away from the ligule and stem.

alimonia. Ascending sap.

alinit. A commercial culture of bacteria sold at one time in Germany which was supposedly capable of fixing atmospheric nitrogen.

aliquote. The constant temperature for a certain event in the life cycle of an organism.

-alis. A suffix meaning belonging to.

alismaceous. Belonging to *Alisma*, the water plantains.

alizarine. The coloring matter found in the roots of madder.

alkachlorophyll. A hypothetical constituent of chlorophyll which is produced by an alkali.

alkalescent. Of the nature of an alkali, slightly alkaline, having the properties or effects of alkali.

alkali. Any basic substance or hydroxide that is soluble in water and can neutralize acids. Alkalis turn litmus paper from red to blue.

alkalitropic. Chemotropism produced by an alkali.

alkaloids. Compounds C H N with or without O_2 of alkaline reaction, the organic base in many plants markedly medicinal or poisonous.

alkanet. The common name of plants whose roots are used to prepare a red dye used for food coloring. Originally *Alkanna tinctoria* was used, but now several additional plants of the genus *Anchusa* are used.

allagophyllous. Having alternate leaves.

allagostemonous. Having stamens attached alternately to the petals and torus.

allantodioid. Applied to ferns resembling the genus *Allantodia* in habit and fructification.

allantoid. Sausage-shaped, botuliform, narrowly oblong, cylindrical with somewhat hemispherical terminations.

allantoin. The nitrogenous portion of allantoic fluid.

allantosporae. Having cylindrical spores, lunately curved.

allassotonic. Said of movements induced by a stimulus, auxotonic, pertaining to movements caused by increase or decrease of turgidity of mature organs.

allassotonic movements. The movements of mature organs (as the sleep of plants), movements of variation.

allautogamia. 1. The ability of plants to pollinate by two methods, one usual, the other facultative. 2. Unusual methods of pollination.

allegogamy. See ALLOGAMY.

alleles. Unlike genes that occur at the same locus on homologous chromosomes; see ALLELOMORPH.

allelomorph. In Mendelian inheritance one of a pair of alternative contrasting characters of which one is dominant and the other is recessive, each determined by a gene occupying the same locus in a pair of homologous chromosomes; one of a pair of genes controlling an alternative contrasting character, either the dominant expression or recessive condition.

allelomorphism. A relation between two characters in which the determiners of both do not enter the same gamete but in which they are separated into sister gametes.

allelositism. A peculiar antagonistic relationship existing between some lichens (as in the *Morialiaceae*), syntrophism.

allelotaxis. The mutual depressing effect of one cell upon another; see CYTOTROPISM.

allergen. A substance which induces allergy.

allergy. The reaction shown by an organism against a substance for which it has been sensitized, changed reaction on second or subsequent inoculations, exaggerated susceptibility.

allesis. The ability of an organ to show interference.

alliaceous. Having a garlic or onion odor; onion-like in shape, odor, or taste.

alliance. A group of allied families or orders, a natural group of orders within a class, a cohort.

alliariafolious. Alliaria-leaved.

alliarius. See ALLIACEOUS.

alligant. Adligant.

alligator. An appendage of a leaf (as a prickle or stipule).

allocarpy. Fruiting from cross-fertilized flowers.

allochlorophyll. A second green substance accompanying chlorophyll.

allochoric. An ecological term pertaining to species which inhabit two or more closely related formations in the same or adjoining forests or grasslands.

allochronic speciation. The gradual development of a new species over a long period of time in which the gradual changes can be followed from one species to the next.

allochrous. Changing from one color to another.

allochthonous. Exotic or foreign, applied to peat accumulated from drifted material deposited in still water.

allogamous. Requiring two individuals to accomplish sexual reproduction; habitually cross-fertilized although capable of self-fertilization.

allogamy. Cross-fertilization; see GEITONOGAMY and KENOGAMY; the opposite of AUTOGAMY.

allogene. The recessive element in a couplet or pair of allelomorphs.

alloiogenesis. The alternation of a sexual and a nonsexual generation.

allometron. A quantitative change, the genesis of new proportions in an existing character.

alloolysis. The mode in which natural diastase acts on the endosperm of the date and the resulting change.

allopatric species. Species which have developed through long isolation due to geographic physical barriers, as oceans, mountains, etc.

alloplasm. The differentiated portion of the cell substance which performs special functions but does not contribute to the formation of independent organs.

alloplasmatic. Concerning the differentiated portion of cell protoplasm, alloplasmic.

alloplasmic. Alloplasmatic.

alloplast. A morphological cell unit of more than one kind of tissue.

alloploid. Polyploid resulting from an interspecific cross (thus containing two different genomes).

allopolyploid. Having more than two sets of chromosomes in the somatic cells, the additional set or sets having been derived from a different species by hybridization.

allosome. A sex chromosome as opposed to an autosome.

allosperm. An embryo arising through allogamy.

allospore. A spore from which a gamete ultimately arises.

allosyndesis. The pairing in a polyploid of chromosomes derived from different parental species.

allotetraploid. Having two diploid sets of chromosomes each derived from a different parental species, an allopolyploid.

allotrophy. The condition in flowers which have a low adaptation to insect visitors, the condition during which plants are not able to assimilate CO_2.

allotropism. Appearance in an unusual form.

allotropous. Denoting plants which have stores of honey open to all insect visitors.

allotropous flowers. Flowers in which the nectar is readily accessible to all kinds of insect visitors.

allotropic lakes. Lakes which receive drainage containing organic matter which adds to that produced internally.

allotypic division. Atypic mitosis, heterotypic followed by homotypic nuclear division.

allozygote. A homozygote which shows only recessive characters.

alluring glands of Nepenthes. Glands in the pitchers which tempt insects to go down the tubes.

alluvial association. The community of plants characteristically found on alluvial deposits which are subject to inundation.

alluvium. Soil, usually rich, deposited by water, a flood plain; see MELANGEOPHYTIA.

alnetum. An association of plants of the genus *Alnus* (alders).

Aloe. A genus of succulent plants, chiefly South African, with basal, long, thick, fleshy leaves (the century plant).

aloifolious. Aloe-leaved.

alomeristic. In groups which differ meristically from the majority of related groups.

alopecurus. Foxtail, also the generic name of foxtail grasses.

alpester. Alpestrine.

alpestrine. Applied to those plants growing above the limits of forest growth but below the alpine region, subalpine.

alpestris. Subalpine, alpine, alpestrine.

alpha spore. The fertile spore formed in the imperfect stages in genera of *Diaporthaceae*; see BETA SPORE.

alphitomorphous. Like barley meal (said of some fungi).

alpigene. Alpine.

alpine. Properly descriptive of the plants of the Alps but frequently used in a broader sense for plants which grow above the timberline, an ecological life zone.

alpine alpine. Restricted to actual alpine plants.

alpine, basal. Hygrophilous and warmth-loving, as plants of the foothills.

alpine, montane. Similar to basal alpine but able to endure cooler temperatures.

alpine region. A region supporting alpine plants.

alpino-arctic community. A community of frequently similar species which grow in both alpine and arctic regions in patches of soil deposited by melting ice and snow.

alsad. A grove plant.

alsinaceous. 1. Referring to plants with polypetalous corolla with intervals between petals. 2. Used of petals with a short, distinct claw. 3. Belonging to or resembling that group of plants to which Alsine belongs, in the genus *Arenaria*.

alsium. A grove formation with trees and grass.

alsocola. Dwelling in groves.

alsodes. Growing in woods.

alsophilous. Growing in groves, resembling the genus *Alsophila* (the tree ferns).

alsophytes. Grove plants.

altaicus. Of the Altai Mountains in Siberia.

alternariose. Descriptive of a fungus disease caused by a species of *Alternaria*.

alternate. Said of plant parts which are neither opposite nor in whorls but placed singly on the parent axis, descriptive of a zigzag arrangement of various plant parts as single leaves or branches that occur on opposite sides of the stem at successive nodes, or petals that grow between the sepals, or stamens that grow between the petals.

alternate host. One of the two hosts of an heteroecious rust (usually the host of lesser economic importance). Alternative host.

alternately pinnate. Having pinnate leaves with the pinnae alternating on opposite sides of the midrib.

alternate pitting. A type of pitting in which the pits are in diagonal rows.

alternation. Interchange by turns, the heterogeneous arrangement of plant groups and formations, mixed succession.

alternation of generations. 1. The growth of reproductive bodies into structures which differ from those from which they are reproduced. 2. The occurrence in one life cycle of two or more modes of reproduction which are differently produced and which differ morphologically. Usually the sexual forms (gametophytes) and the asexual forms (sporophytes) alternate, the sporophytes containing double the number of chromosomes found in the gametophytic generation.

alternation of parts. The general rule that leaves of different whorls alternate with each other (as sepals with petals and stamens with petals).

alternative. The condition in aestivation when the perianth segments are in two rows, the inner so covered by the outer that each exterior member overlaps the half of two interior members.

alternative host. The alternate host.

alternative inheritance. A distribution of ancestral characters among descendents so that the individuals show one or the other characters in question. Combinations or blends of the characters are absent or exceptional.

alternes. Sudden changes in plant communities in response to changes of soil, water, shade, or other environmental conditions which lead to alteration of communities within the same spatial area; alternation of plant dominance in the same spatial area due to changes in edaphic conditions.

alternifoliate. Being alternately leaved.

alternipetalous. Denoting the condition in which the stamens alternate with the petal.

alternipinnate. See ALTERNATELY PINNATE.

alternisepalous. Denoting petals which alternate with the sepals.

altheine. A product derived from the marshmallow *Althaea* (the hollyhock).

altherbosa. Communities made up of tall herbs such as occur after forests are destroyed by fire.

altifrons. Tall fronded, tall herbaged.

altitude. The height of a vegetational formation above sea level.

altoherbiprata. A division of terriprata characterized by a dominance of tall-growing herbs.

alumina bodies. Substances found in the mesophyll and cortex of *Symplocos* (the sweetwood or yellowwood).

alumnus. Well-nourished, flourishing, strong.

alum root. A North American herb of the *Saxifragaceae* with a root having astringent properties.

alutaceous, alutaceus. Light leather-colored, isabelline, pale tan, leathery in texture, coriaceous.

alvar. A type of peculiar dwarfed growth (such as the steppe vegetation in Öland, Sweden, etc.).

alveola. A cavity or pit on the surface, a honeycombed pattern, a surface cavity, the pore in the *Polyporaceae*.

alveolar plasma. Trophoplasm, granular protoplasm.

alveolar spheres. Certain bodies in the microsporangium of *Cupressus* which do not take stain.

alveolar theory. A theory of protoplasm as a foam-like substance.

alveolation theory. The theory that chromosomes become honeycombed with numerous vacuoles in the telophase of nuclear division.

alveoles. Vacuoles which split chromosomes into a network of chromatin.

alveolization. The process during which a granular or honeycombed appearance becomes evident, a honeycombed condition.

alveus. A sand draw, a sand community.

amadou. The substance found in certain fungi which is used as tinder. It may also be used as a styptic when derived from *Melanostoma hirta* (a phanerogam). German tinder.

amaebula. A swarm spore which creeps like an amoeba.

amalthea. An aggregation of dry fruits formed within a calyx which does not become fleshy.

amanitia. The two poisonous substances in *Amanita phalloides*.

amanitin. The red pigment of the fly agaric, the poisonous alkaloid derived from *Aminita* (a genus of white-spored mushrooms which includes the deadly fly agaric and the death angel).

amanthicolous. Growing in sandy places.

amanthium. A sand hill or plain community.

amanthophilous. Dwelling in sandy plains or on sand hills.

amaranth. 1. The common name for widely known flowers which have long-lasting showy clusters of flowers and highly colored leaves (including celosia, love-lies-bleeding, cockscomb, etc.). 2. An intense dark purplish red.

amaranticolor. Amaranth-colored, intense reddish purple.

amaricans. Bitter, irritating.

amaricaulis. Bitter-stemmed.

amarus. Bitter.

amathad. A plant living on sand hills.

amathium. A formation of sand hill plants or plants of sandy plains.

amathocola. Plants dwelling on sand hills.

amathophilous. Dwelling on sandy hills or in sandy plains.

amazonicus. From the region of the Amazon River.

ambient. Relating to the environment.

amber. The British name for succunite, a fossil resin (one of the St. John's-worts), sweet gum.

amber forest. A fossil forest whose trees yield the resin that fossilized into amber.

ambigenous. Denoting those perianths in which the outer surface resembles a calyx and the inner surface a corolla.

ambiguiflorous. Of flowers of an indeterminate form.

ambiguous. 1. Said of organs whose origins are uncertain. 2. Said of plants when their

places in the scheme of classification is doubtful. 3. Doubtful.

ambilateral segregation. Unrestricted to either sex, not limited by sex.

ambilinearity. The ability of an organism to pass on cytoplasmic particles (plastogenes or plasmogenes) from either the female or male parent.

ambiparous. Producing two kinds (as a bud which contains both flowers and leaves).

ambisexual. Said of a character common to both sexes.

ambisporangiate. Producing hermaphroditic flowers (i.e., producing both micro- and megaspores), plants with sporophylls which produce both ovules and pollen sacs.

ambitus. The outline of a figure (as of a leaf), the periphery.

amblecarpous. Denoting those flowers in which most of the ovules abort and in which only a few form perfect seeds.

amblydon. Having blunt teeth (as some fungi).

amblystegietum. An association formed by the moss *Amblystegium*.

ambrosia. The mycelial or oidial stage of a fungus which is found in the burrows made by beetles in fruit trees and which is believed to be used as food.

ambulacrum. A walk laid out in a botanic garden.

ameiosic. With one division of the nucleus at meiosis (instead of two), so that the chromosome number of the mother cell is not reduced.

amelia. The absence of limbs.

ameliorating plants. The bacteria which form nodules on the roots of the *Leguminosae*.

ament. A slender, usually flexible spike of unisexual flowers; a catkin or scaly spike, usually bracteate; an amentum.

amentaceous. Bearing catkins, amentiferous.

amentifloreae. Wind-pollinated, catkin-bearing plants.

amentula. The so-called catkins of the male "inflorescence" in sphagnum.

ameristic. Said of those fern thalli which lack adequate meristematic tissue and fail to produce archegonia because of the underdevelopment of cambium tissue which failure is believed to be due to the lack of adequate nourishment.

amerospore. A one-celled spore.

Amerosporeae. Multicellular spores including the *Allantosporeae*, *Hyalosporeae*, and the *Phaeosporeae*.

amerosporous. Having one-celled spores.

ametabolic. Not metabolic, developing without metabolism.

ametabolous. Denoting those species of *Equisetum* whose fertile shoots die away after spore dispersal showing little change in development from young to adult.

amethysteous. Amethyst-violet.

amethystine. Violet-colored, amethysteus, amethystinus.

amethystoglossus. Amethyst-tongued.

ametoecious. Denoting parasites which do not change hosts, confined to a single host (the opposite of metoecious).

amicrobic. 1. Free of microbes. 2. Not caused by bacteria.

amicron. An element so small that it can be seen only with the ultramicroscope.

amidase. An enzyme occurring in the mycelium of *Asperigillus* which catalyses the hydrolysis of urea (a final product of protein metabolism).

amide plant. A plant which forms asparagine or glutamine from amino acids; an acid plant.

amides. Certain substances found in plants which are soluble in water, diffusible, crystallizable, and which do not coagulate on boiling (such as asparagin, leucin, tyrosin, etc.).

amidoplast. A starch former; see AMYLOPLAST.

amidulin. Soluble starch which is present in small quantities in ordinary grains of starch.

amiglin. The product of the action of diastase on starch.

amine. A derivative of ammonia by hydrogen replacement.

amino acids. 1. A group of fatty acids in which a hydrogen atom is the hydrocarbon radical which is exchanged for the amino group, one of the building stones of protein. 2. An important product from the decomposition of proteids.

aminoid. Scents which have an amine for their foundation.

amitosis. Nuclear division without karyokinesis, cell division without the formation of spireme or chromosomes so that the chromosomes may not be equally distributed or the cell contains two or more nuclei.

amixis. Reproduction by undifferentiated cells lacking fertilization (as in some bacteria and some fungi), agomogony.

amme-. See TROPHO-.

ammochthad. A plant living on a sand bank; an ammodyte.

ammochthium. A formation of plants living on a sand bank; an ammochthadium.

ammochthophyte. A plant growing on sand banks.

ammocolous. Denoting species inhabiting dry sand.

ammodytes. Plants living in sandy places.

ammonia plant. A plant which forms ammonia and organic acids from amino acids.

ammonification. The production of ammonia by certain bacteria.

ammonifying bacteria. Bacteria which are able to decompose nitrogenous substances of animal or vegetable origin with the formation of nitrogen and ammonia.

ammonisation. The conversion of complex organic compounds (i.e., albuminoids) into ammonium salts by the action of bacteria as the first stage in nitrification in the soil.

ammonobacteria. Bacteria which produce ammonia from compounds containing nitrogen.

ammophiletum. An association of dune grass (*Ammophila*).

ammophilous. Growing in sandy places.

amnicolous. Growing on sandy banks of rivers.

amnion, amnios. A seldom used term denoting the viscous fluid which surrounds certain ovules in very early stages, the contents of the embryo sac before the formation of the embryo.

amnis. A brook, a creek.

amniotic sac. The embryo sac.

amoebiform. Shaped like or resembling an amoeba.

amoebocyte. Any cell having the properties or the shape of an amoeba.

amoeboid. Like an amoeba, without a cell wall, with a small amount of protoplasm showing a creeping movement by putting out the retracting pseudopodia (applied to the gelatinous plasmodium in the myxogasters and their swarm cells and the zoospores of some phycomycetes).

Amoeboideae. The lowest forms of plant life which lack chlorophyll.

amoeboid movement. Movement with constant changes of shape.

amoebule. 1. A pseudopodiospore or swarm spore. 2. A body formed by the separation of the plasm around the nuclei in *Sorosphaera*.

amorphous. Without definite form, structure, or position.

amorphous cortex. Cortex formed of thickened hyphae with indistinct walls (said of lichens).

amorphophyte. A plant having anomalous flowers.

ampelid. A climbing plant.

ampelographist. A writer on vines.

amphanthium. The dilated receptacle of an inflorescence (as in the *Compositae*).

amphiaster. The achromatic figure formed in the prophase of mitosis consisting of the two asters and the spindle between them.

amphiastral. Said of a type of mitosis in which true asters are present at the spindle poles.

amphibious. Denoting adaptable plants which grow either on land or in water.

amphibious alternation. The adaptation of organisms which are originally aquatic to subaerial habitats.

amphibrya. Monocotyledons.

amphibryous. Growing by increase over the entire surface.

amphicarpic. Producing two kinds of fruits which differ either in form or period of ripening, amphicarpous.

amphicarpium. An archegonium which persists as a fruit envelope after fertilization has taken place.

amphicarpogenous. Producing fruit above ground which later develops beneath ground; see HYPOCARPOGENOUS.

amphichromatism. The production of two or more differently colored flowers on the same stalk due to the changes of seasons.

amphichrome. Used for plants which abnormally produce flowers of two different colors on the same stalk; see POLYCHROME, HETEROCHROME, METACHROME.

amphichromy. A display of two distinct colors when in flower.

amphiclinous hybrids. Those hybrids in the F₁ generation some of which resemble one parent and the remainder the other parent.

amphiclinous progeny. A family resulting from a cross in which some of the hybrids resemble one parent and some resemble the other parent.

amphicoelous. Being concave on both sides.

amphicotyledons. Cotyledons which are united to form a cup.

amphicotyly. See AMPHISYNCOTYLY.

amphicribral. Having a bundle with the phloem completely surrounding the xylem.

amphicribral vascular bundle. A concentric bundle in which the phloem is on the outside of the central strand of xylem.

amphicryptophytes. Helophytes having their vegetative organs amphibious.

amphidiploid. Pertaining to a hybrid between parents or species of different chromosome number the chromosome number of which is the sum of the numbers of the parents. Such forms occasionally arise in normal self-sterile hybrids and are themselves self-fertile.

amphigaeus. Said of plants which are native to both the Old and the New Worlds or of flowers which arise from the root stock.

amphigamae. Plants whose fructification is unknown, possibly of both sexes.

amphigameous. Denoting plants which lack sex organs or with sex organs as yet undiscovered.

amphigaster. Peculiar leaves (of *Hepaticae*) imitating stipules, ventral rudimentary leaves of foliose liverworts, the ventral row of the leaves of a leafy liverwort, a peculiar stipule-like leaf of liverworts.

amphigeal. Applied to those plants having dimorphic flowers (the upper flowers from the stem and the lower from the root or root stock).

amphigen. A thallogen or thallophyte.

amphigenesis. Sexual reproduction, the union of gametes to form a zygote.

amphigenetic generation. A generation which forms zygotes.

amphigenous. Growing all around a plant part or any object and not restricted to any particular surface, growing on both sides of a leaf, growing over an entire surface.

amphigenous castration. The action of *Ustilago antherarum* when it mingles the characters of both sexes by developing in each some of the characters of the other.

amphigonel. A reproductive apparatus having polycentric axes.

amphigonium. The archegonium.

amphigony. Sexual reproduction, reproduction involving two individuals (one male and one female).

amphigynous. Denoting the oogonium of *Phytophthora* when it projects from the top of the antheridium and the male surrounds the female element.

amphikaryon. A normal diploid nucleus which contains two haploid groups of chromosomes or their descendants.

amphilepsis. The ordinary result of fertilization when the influence of both parents is shown in hybrids; see MONOLEPSIS.

amphimixis. Sexual reproduction, the union of parental characters in the embryo, the mingling of hereditary units of two parents in sexual reproduction.

amphinereids. Amphibious plants.

amphinucleolus. A double nucleolus consisting typically of basophilic and oxyphilic components in close association.

amphinucleus. 1. A nucleus which has both generative and somatic functions. 2. A new nucleus formed by the union of two nuclei each of which had but half the normal number of chromosomes.

amphiont. A zygote formed by the coming together of two individuals.

amphiphloic. Applied to the central cylinder of stems when there is phloem on both sides of the xylem.

amphiphloic haplostele. A stele in which the solid central xylem is traversed by a continuous internal strand of phloem connecting with the external phloem at the nodes.

amphiphloic phyllosiphony. The condition when the tubular central cylinder has foliar gaps without external phloem.

amphiphloic prostele. See AMPHIPHLOIC HAPLOSTELE.

amphiphloic siphonostele. A cylinder of xylem which has phloem on both the inside and the outside of the cylinder.

amphiphloic solenostele. See AMPHIPHLOIC SIPHONOSTELE.

amphiphylous. Referring to pollination affected by both wind and insects or to the flowers pollinated by these agencies.

amphiphyte. A plant on the boundary zone of wet land amphibious in life and hydrophytic in adaptation.

amphipyrenin. 1. The substance of which the nuclear membrane is composed. 2. The membrane of the pyrenin, the body of the nucleus.

amphisarca. 1. A multilocular indehiscent fruit which is dry without and pulpy within (as a melon). 2. A berry with a hard rind or a succulent fruit surrounded by a woody or crustaceous layer (as a gourd).

amphisorus. A group or collection of amphispores.

amphispermium. A one-seeded pericarp which is conformed to the seed, an akene.

amphispermous. Denoting a structure which is closely investing the seed so that it has the same form (as the ovary in *Gramineae*).

amphisporal. Relating to an amphispore or sometimes a mesospore.

amphisporangiatae. Plants possessing stamens and pistils or microspores and megospores.

amphisporangiate. Ambisporangiate, denoting plants of the amphisporangiatae.

amphispore. 1. A thick-walled uredospore which by morphological adaptation functions as a resting spore. 2. A reproductive spore in certain algae which may function as a resting spore.

amphistomatic. Denoting leaves having stomata on both surfaces.

amphisyncotyly. A condition in which the cotyledons have become coalescent to form a funnel or trumpet (usually shortened to amphicotyly).

amphitactism. Mutual attraction of several hyphae for each other; see ZYGOTACTISM.

amphitene. The early stage in synapsis, the synaptic stage of meiosis in which the nucleus contains thin spireme threads (leptotene) uniting two by two to form thick threads (pachytene), that stage of meiosis in which spireme threads unite in pairs.

amphithecium. 1. The outer layer of a moss sporangium, the outer layer of cells surrounding the early developing endothecium of the capsule of a moss. 2. The outer layer of algal cells and medulla that continues upward from the hypothecium and nearly surrounds the hymenium in the apothecium of lichens.

amphitoky. Parthenogenetic reproduction of both males and females.

amphitrichous. Having flagella at both poles of a bacterial cell.

amphitrisyncotyl. A tricotyledonary seedling with a special development.

amphitropal. See AMPHITROPOUS.

amphitrophy. Growth when it is greatest in the lateral shoots and buds.

amphitropous. Said of an ovule or seed which is curved so that both ends are near each other placing the hilum or point of attachment in the middle or in a lateral position intermediate between the micropyle and the chalaza, a term applied to a partly inverted ovule, semiantropous.

amphivasal. Having a leptocentric bundle, having a concentric bundle in which the xylem surrounds the phloem.

amphivasal vascular bundle. A concentric bundle with the xylem on the outside of a strand of phloem.

amphora. The lower division of a pyxis, a pitcher or pitcher-shaped organ.

amphoteric. Having both acidic and basic properties.

amphoterospynhesmia. See SYNHESMIA.

amplectans. Amplectant, amplectivus, embracing, clasping or winding tightly around some support (as tendrils).

amplexicaulis. Said of a stem which is surrounded or clasped by an enlarged petiole, leaf, or stipule.

amplexifolious. Leaf-clasping.

amplexus. In vernation when one leaf overlaps both sides of the one above it.

ampliate. Enlarged, dilated.

ampliatiflorous. Denoting those *Compositae* which have enlarged ray florets, as in the corn flower.

amplification. Changes which lead to increased formal or structural complexity of the plant.

ampulla. 1. A bladder. 2. A flask-shaped organ. 3. A kind of hollow leaf, as in *Utrichularia.*

ampullaceous. Swollen, flask-shaped, swollen like a bottle or bladder, ampulliform, ampullaceal.

amurensis. Of or pertaining to the Amur River region in Siberia.

amycelicus. Without mycelium.

amygdale. The almond.

amygdalaceous. Of or pertaining to the *Amygdalaceae*, a family of trees and shrubs of the rose family now included in *Prunus.*

amygdalin. A glucoside found in many fruits of the *Rosaceae* with characteristic almond flavor.

amygdaline. 1. Pertaining to or resembling the almond. 2. Having an odor and taste like that of peach or cherry stones.

amylaceous. Starchy, having the properties of starch, resembling or composed of starch or amylum.

amylase. Diastase, an enzyme capable of converting starch to sugar.

amyliferous. Bearing or producing starch.

amylin. A product of the action of diastase on starch.

amylites. Skeletons of starch grains which are made up of amylodextrin.

amylobacteria. Bacteria which ferment starch.

amylocellulose. A supposed constituent of the starch granule.

amyloclastic. Enzymatic breaking down of starch.

amylodextrin. An intermediate in conversion of starch into dextrin; see ACHROODEXTRIN.

amyloerythrin. A carbohydrate similar to starch which occurs in rice and millet.

amylogenesis. The formation of starch in the plant cell.

amylogenic bodies. Leucoplastids.

amylohydrolist. An enzyme which transforms starch by hydrolysis.

amyloid. A starch-like cellulose substance found in plants which reacts differently from starch to some dyes (Melzer's reagent); a substance resembling boiled starch found in many sea weeds, seeds of beans, almonds, etc.

amyloid substances. Cell-wall substances which are colored blue with a dilute solution of iodine.

amyloleucites. Plastids which produce starch granules.

amylolysis. The transformation of starch into other substances such as sugar.

amylolytic enzyme. A ferment which changes starch into dextrin and sugar, a starch-digesting enzyme.

Amylome. Starch-containing xylem parenchyma.

amylon. Amylum, starch.

amylopectin. A mucilaginous constituent of starch.

amylophylly. The production of starch leaves.

amyloplast. A leucoplastid, a colorless granule of protoplasm that forms a starch grain.

amyloplastid. A plastid which stores reserve starch.

amylose. The substance forming starch.

amylostatoliths. Simple or compound starch grains.

amylosynthesis. The formation of starch.

amylum. Starch.

amylum bodies. Rounded bodies in a chlorophyll band or plate which are the centers of starch formation, chlorophyll vesicles.

amylum centers. See PYRENOIDS.

amylum grains. Starch grains, the laminated bodies which are formed by leucoplasts of starch as reserve materials in plant cells.

amylum star. A tuber-like organ in *Chara stelligera* which is packed with starch. It consists of an underground node.

anabaena. A small, widely distributed blue-green alga which causes an unpleasant taste and odor in drinking water.

anabasetum. An association of *Anabasis aphylla*, a leafless undershrub.

anabiont. A perennial which flowers and fruits many times.

anabiosis. The condition of latent life which may be overcome by the return of favorable physical conditions, as the revival of a plant after its apparent death by the addition of water.

anabix. 1. A series of ascending metabolistic changes in protoplasm by which food is assimilated. 2. The vegetative portion of cryptogams which withers below but vegetates above, as in *Lycopodium*, lichens, and hepatics.

anabolic. Referring to the constructive metabolic processes which result in the development of the living body.

anabolism. Metabolism which results in greater or more progressive complexity of organization, the constructive process which builds up or repairs tissues, the constructive function of living cells. The reverse of catabolism.

anabolite. Any product of constructive metabolism in plants; see CATABOLITE.

anacampyla. Lacerations of the epidermal layer, as in certain agarics.

anacanthous. Without spines or thorns.

anacardiaceous. Resembling *Anacardium*, the cashew nut tree, as to shape or arrangement of fruit.

anachromasis. The sum total of the prophasic changes of the nucleus by which the spireme threads and chromosomes arise.

anachoresis. The retrograde metamorphosis of an organ or whorl.

anaclinotropism. Positive clinotropism, i.e., having a horizontal or oblique direction of growth.

anacrogynae. Liverworts in which the archegonia are borne in regions other than at the tip of the stem. The stem usually continues to grow after the archegonia are formed.

anacrogynous. In *Hepaticae*, with gametangia borne in a lateral position (thus the sporophyte is borne laterally); see ACROGYNOUS.

anadromous. Denoting the type of venation in which the first set of nerves in each fern frond is given off on the upper side of the midrib towards the apex (as in *Aspidium*, *Asplenium*, etc.) to form a helix.

anaereticus. Having an abnormal arrangement of leaves in single rows on the axis.

anaerobe. An organism ordinarily living in the absence of free oxygen.

anaerobe, facultative. An organism which is able to live in the absence of free (uncombined) oxygen although it usually lives only where it is present.

anaerobe, obligate. An organism which can exist or thrive only in the absence of free (uncombined) oxygen.

anaerobic decomposition. The incomplete breakdown of organic material by bacteria in the absence of free oxygen.

anaerobic energesis. The release of energy without air.

anaerobic respiration. The production and release of energy in plant respiration in the absence of oxygen. Facultative anaerobes can use free oxygen, obligate anaerobes do not. See FERMENTATION.

anaerobiosis. The state of living in a situation destitute of uncombined oxygen.

anaerobium. An organism which is unable to thrive in the presence of free oxygen.

anaerophyte. A plant which does not need a direct supply of air.

anaerophytobionts. The anaerobic organisms living in the soil.

anagenesis. The regeneration of tissues, progressive evolution.

anagyroid. Like the genus *Anagyris*, trifoliate leguminose shrubs of the Mediterranean region.

anakinetic. Leading to the restoration of energy and the construction of reactive, energy-rich materials.

anakinetomeres. Reactive energy-rich molecules.

analine. An amino acid, possibly formed from pyruvic acid during respiration.

analogous. Resembling but not homologous; denoting those organs which agree in appearance or function but not in descent, mode of origin, or position; see HOMOLOGOUS.

analogues. Organs of different plants or animals which have like functions but different origins.

analysis. The process of classifying and finding the names of plants, the systematic examination of a plant preliminary to the determination of its position in the system of classification.

analytic. Separating into parts. The destructive function in metabolism is analytic.

anametadromous. Said of the venation of ferns when the weaker pinnules are anadromous and the stronger are catadromous.

anamorphosis. A gradual change in form traced in a group of plants the members of which have succeeded each other during geological time.

anandrous. Having the floral envelope and pistils but lacking stamens, having no stamens.

anantherous. Without anthers (also applied to filaments destitute of anthers).

anantherum. An altered, abortive, and sterile stamen.

ananthous. Without flowers.

anaphase. The phase in mitosis or meiosis during which the daughter chromosomes move apart, the period following the metaphase during which the daughter chromosomes are passing toward the poles of the spindle.

anaphylaxis. Hypersusceptibility to a foreign protein, a sensitive condition which sometimes results from the use of antitoxin serum.

anaphysis. A tiny pedicel in the fructification of the lichen *Ephebia*.

anaphyte. A potentially independent branch or shoot.

anaplast. Leucoplastid.

anaporetic. Having botanic skill in the laboratory rather than in the field.

anarhizophyte. A plant able to root in the soil which bears its parents.

anarthrodactylous. Concerning a joint with ultimate rays of a single cell in the *Characeae*.

anarthrous. Having no distinct joints or nodes.

anasarca. Dropsy in plants.

anaschistic. Splitting longitudinally, applied to bivalents or tetrads which have two longitudinal divisions in meiosis and are typically split longitudinally in the anaphases of the heterotypic division of chromosomes.

anasorium. The building up of nutritive material in the protoplasm but not as an integral part of it.

anastates. The various materials which arise as products of anabolic or ascending conversion of food material into protoplasm.

anastatic. Denoting those plants which can revive after desiccation.

anastomose. 1. Joined or united like the parts of a network. 2. Inosculated or run into each other. 3. Confluent, united, intertwined. 4. Fused, as vascular bundles at nodes.

anastral. Denoting the type of mitosis without aster formation.

anataximorphosis. Teratologic changes which are in agreement with the normal order.

anatolicus. Of Anatolia, in Asia Minor.

anatomy. The study of the intimate structure and form of plants, the study of the formation and arrangement of the parts of plants, the study of minute structures, histology.

anatropal. Anatropous.

anatropistic. Anatropous.

anatropous. Applied to ovules or seeds which grow in an inverted position; having an ovule bent over in growth so that the micropyle is near the base of the funicle, with the body of the ovule united to the funicle.

anaxial. Having no distinct axis, asymmetrical.

anbury. A disease of crucifers in which the root becomes clubbed caused by *Plasmodiophora Brassicae*, amberry.

ancad. A canyon plant.

anceps. See ANCIPITAL.

ancestry. Those members of past generations which are related to any given species by descent.

anchor. A plant holdfast.

anchoraeform. Anchor-shaped.

anchor hairs. Hairs having recurved barbs.

anchoring disk. A growth from the rhizoids of *Lejeunia*.

anchoring organs. The ends of tendrils with flattened disks for clinging.

anchoring roots. Holdfasts which support but do not obtain nourishment.

anchusin. The coloring matter found in *Anchusa azurea*, clear blue coloring.

ancipital. Two-edged, flattened, or compressed (said of leaves). Ancipitous.

ancistrous. Barbed.

ancium. A canyon forest formation.

ancocolous. Living in canyons.

ancophyte. A plant found in canyons.

andean. Of the Andes Mountains, alpine.

ander-, andra-, andro-, andrum-. A prefix meaning male.

andian. See ANDEAN.

andine. See ANDEAN.

andrase. The enzyme or hormone which is sometimes called the male determining factor.

andrecium. The entire set of stamens in a flower; see ANDROECIUM.

androchores. Plants which are spread by humans.

androclinium. The part of the column of orchids which contains the anther.

androconidium. A spermatium of assumed male function.

androcyte. A cell which eventually develops into an antherozoid, a sperm mother cell or spermatid.

androdioecious. Said of a species in which some plants bear staminate flowers and others are hermaphroditic; having perfect and staminate flowers on different plants.

androdynamous. Denoting those dicotyledons in which the stamens are highly developed.

androecium. The male reproductive organs of a plant, the collective name for the stamens or antheridia.

androecy. The occurrence of purely male individuals in a given species.

androgametangium. An antheridium, the organ producing the male gamete.

androgametes. The male sex cells, sperms, zoosperms.

androgametophore. The plant bearing male gametes, as in *Equisetum*, etc.

androgametophyte. A gametophyte within the wall of the pollen grain which produces the androgametes.

androgamy. The impregnation of a male gamete by a female gamete (either cytoplasmic or nuclear).

androgenesis. The development of an individual from a male cell, the development of an egg with only chromosomes and nuclei from the paternal parent; see GYNOGENESIS and PARTHENOGENESIS.

androgenous. Bearing males.

androgenous castration. The action of the fungus *Ustilago antherarum* when stimulating the production of male organs.

androgone. Any antheridial cell other than the androcyte or the androcyte mother cell, the earlier cell generation from which arise the androcytes and sperm cells of plants; see ANDROGONIUM.

androgonial cells. Four primary cells in a developing antheridium of some bryophytes and pteridophytes, which divide many times to form androcyte mother cells. Androcytes are produced by the diagonal division of the mother cells.

androgonidia. 1. The cells which usually give rise to the spermatozoids in *Volvox*. 2. Small male plants known as dwarf males.

androgonium. An early stage of the formation of sperm cells in plants.

androgynal. Hermaphroditic, i.e., having both male and female flowers in the same inflorescence; see ANDROGYNOUS.

androgynaris. Said of double flowers in which stamens and pistils have become petaloid.

androgynary. Having flowers with both stamens and pistils which develop into petals.

androgynicus. Of or pertaining to hermaphroditic flowers.

androgyniflorous. The appearance of hermaphroditic flowers in the head of a composite.

androgynism. The condition of bearing both stamens and pistils, hermaphroditism.

androgynocladogonidium. An hermaphroditic merid.

androgynophore. The stalk bearing both androecium and gynoecium.

androgynous. Having both staminate and pistillate flowers in one cluster, hermaphroditic, having both male and female organs on the same branch or thallus.

androgyny. Hermaphroditism, the monoecious or androgynal condition.

andromedotoxin. A glucoside which occurs in *Andromeda* and certain other *Ericaceae*.

andromonoecious. With perfect and male flowers but lacking female flowers on the same plant, bearing staminate and bisexual flowers on the same plant.

andromorphosis. Certain changes caused by the stimulation of the pollen tube.

andropetalous. Denoting those double flowers in which the stamens have become petaloid and the pistils have remained unchanged.

andropetalarius. See ANDROPETALOUS.

androphile. A plant which is partial to the neighborhood of man, a nitrophile.

androphore. 1. An elongation of the receptacle of the flower which supports a column of stamens, as in *Malvaceae*. 2. A stalk supporting an androecium or antheridium.

androphyll. The modified leaf bearing microspores, the stamen, a microsporophyll.

androphyte. The male plant in the gametophytic generation.

androplasm. The active protoplasm in the male gametes.

androplasmic. Denoting ability to produce sperms.

andropleogamy. The condition in which one individual has staminate, perfect, and andromonoecious flowers.

androsaceous. Like *Androsace*, the rock jasmine (small tufted alpine plants).

androsacile. An association of *Androsace*.

androsaemifolious. With leaves like *Androsaemum* (Hypericum).

androsporangium. The sporangium in which androspores are produced.

androspore. 1. A male spore which on germination produces a body which gives rise to the male sex organ. 2. An asexual spore which gives rise to a dwarf male plant in *Oedogonium*. 3. The swarm spore which gives rise to small short-lived plants which produce spermatozoids.

androsporophyll. In seed plants an appendage that bears the androsporangium.

androstrobilus. A strobilus bearing microsporangia or pollen sacs.

androtermone. A male-determining substance.

-androus. An adjectival termination denoting the presence of stamens, referring to the number of stamens (as 6-androus).

androzoogonidia. The male filaments derived from the zoogonidia in *Oedogonium*.

anectaria. Flowers which lack spurs.

anelectrotonus. The diminished response of plants to a constant current of electricity from the anode.

anemad. A blow-out plant, a plant on wind-blown soil.

anemium. A plant formation in a blow-out.

anemo-. A prefix signifying wind.

anemochore. Any plant distributed by wind.

anemochory. The dependence on wind for dissemenation.

anemodium. The plants of blow-outs in the sand dunes.

anemodophilous. Said of those plants which live in blow-outs.

anemoentomophily. The adaptation for either wind or insect fertilization in a polymorphic species.

anemogamae. Plants which are wind-pollinated.

anemoneflorous. Anemone-flowered.

anemonefolious. Having leaves like *Anemone*, the wind flower.

anemonin. An acrid substance which is obtained from several species of *Anemone*.

anemophile. A plant growing in a breezy or windy habitat, an anemophilous plant.

anemophilous. Denoting flowers which are wind-pollinated, having the pollen carried by the wind, disseminated by wind, dwelling in sand draws.

anemophily. Pollination by wind.

anemophobe. A plant which suffers greatly upon exposure to wind.

anemophyte. A plant in which wind-fertilization (pollination) takes place.

anemoplankton. Small organisms which are passively transported through the air by the wind.

anemosis. Wind-shake (a disease of timber trees).

anemosporeae. Plants which are disseminated by the wind.

anemotaxis. A taxic orientation of an organism to wind and air currents.

anemotropism. A change in position of a plant in response to a wind current, tropic responses of organisms to wind and air currents.

anethifolious. With leaves like *Anethum*, the dill plant.

aneuploid. Having a chromosome number other than the basic or neuploid number (a cell that is deficient is monosomic, a cell that is in excess is trisomic), an unbalanced polyploid.

aneurin. A vitamin thought to stimulate root-growth and growth of some fungi and bacteria. Vitamin B_1, thiamin.

aneurus. Nerveless.

anfractuose. Wavy, full of turnings and winding passages, sinuous, twisted.

anfractuosus. Twisted, abruptly bent hither and thither (as in the case of the stamens of *Cucurbita*), spirally twisted.

ange-, -ange. A prefix or suffix meaning a closed structure, cavity, or locule.

angeosere. The climax of the angiosperms in the Cenozoic period.

angiantheous. Similar or related to *Angianthus*, a genus of *Compositae*.

angienchyma. Vascular tissue of any kind.

angio-. A prefix meaning a closed structure, cavity, or locule.

angiocarp. A fruit or fruitbody which is encased with a covering (as an acorn in its cup, as a lichen having the apothecium embedded into the thallus, or as a fungus having the hymenium develop within the sporophore and protected by a covering).

angiocarpous. With the fruit embedded in or invested by a calyx, receptacle, or some other covering; with enclosed fruit; with spores enclosed in a receptacle of some kind.

angiocycads. The fossil cycads which have hermaphroditic flowers.

angiogamae. A group proposed for *Angiospermae* and *Gymnospermae*.

angiolum. A spore case of certain fungi.

angiomonospermous. Denoting those plants with only one seed in a carpel.

angiosperm. Any plant of the *Angiospermae*; a plant bearing seeds enclosed in an ovary or seed case; a plant with seeds in a pericarp; a plant bearing ovules in a closed carpel (a macrosporophyll); an anthophyte.

angiospermae. One of the two great divisions of seed plants distinguished by having true flowers and seeds which are enclosed in a carpel. They constitute the dominant vegetation today.

angiospermal stomata. Those stomata characterized by the development of the inner and outer borders of the cuticle with the outer border usually much thickened.

angiospermia. An artificial order suggested and used by Linnaeus.

angiosporeae. Those plants (cryptogams) which produce spores in a closed receptacle, plants having spores contained in a theca or spore capsule.

-angium. See -ANGE and ANGIO-.

angle. 1. A term used in botany to denote the meeting of two planes to form an edge as in angular stems. 2. The angle formed where the leaf is attached to the stem.

angle cells. The cells on the leaves of some gymnosperms which form small teeth.

angle, ideal. A theoretical angle for a "central station of rest" in phyllotaxis.

angle of deviation. The angle which a leaf, root, or branch makes with the axis on which it is borne.

angle of divergence. The degree of difference in the position of two adjacent leaves or organs on the same or different planes.

anglicus. English.

angonekton. Short-lived organisms which live in water pools in or on earth, rocks, tree stumps, leaf axils, etc.

anguilluliform. Worm-like or eel-like in shape.

anguinus. Snake-like, serpentine.

angular. A term used when an organ shows a determinate number of angles, as the stems of *Labiatae*; having angles; sharp cornered; composed of or furnished with angles; of spores which are not regular in outline; of scales or pileus when showing cracking of cuticle, etc.

angular cells. See ALAR CELLS.

angular divergence. See ANGLE OF DIVERGENCE.

angulate. More or less angular, having angles or corners usually of a determinate number.

angulinerved. Denoting the condition of angle formation by veins where they join the midrib.

angulo-dentate. With angular teeth, angular and toothed.

angustate. Narrow.

angustifoliate. Having narrow leaves.

angustiseptae. Plants which have a narrow-partitioned fruit.

anhalonine. A poisonous alkaloid resembling strychnine which is derived from *Anhalonium*.

anilophyll. A product derived from chlorophyll by treating it with aniline.

anime. A transparent resin, copal.

anisatus. Having the scent of anise (*Pimpinella Anisum*), a herbaceous plant grown for its carminative and aromatic seeds.

aniso-. A prefix meaning unequal.

anisobrious. Said of endogens possessing greater development force on one side than on the other resulting in only one cotyledon.

anisocarpic. Having fewer carpels than the number of parts in the other floral sets.

anisocotyledonous. Having unequally developed cotyledons.

anisodorus. With the odor of anise.

anisodynamous. See ANISOBRIOUS.

anisogametangous. Capable of copulation when gametes are diverse sexually, as in the case of antheridia and oogonia.

anisogametes. Sexual cells differentiated into males and females.

anisogamy. The union of two similar motile gametes differing chiefly in size, with the smaller being the male and the larger female; see HETEROGAMY.

anisogenomatic. Said of a chromosome complement made up of unlike sets of chromosomes.

anisogeny. A variety in offspring.

anisogonous. Of or pertaining to hybrids which do not equally combine the parental characters; see ISOGONOUS.

anisogynous. Having fewer carpels than sepals.

anisohologamy. The union of gametes which differ somewhat in size but with slight sexual difference.

anisokont. With two unequal flagella.

anisomerogamy. Oogamy, the union of macrogametes and microgametes or eggs and spermatozoa (as in many algae and fungi).

anisomerous. With floral parts unequal in number in the different whorls, unsymmetrical.

anisomery. The condition of a flower in which the successive whorls do not all contain the same number of members.

anisomorphy. A change in form of an organ which is caused by its position in relation to the horizon of the mother-axis.

anisopetalous. Having petals of unequal size.

anisophyllous. Exhibiting anisophylly, denoting inequality in the two leaves of a pair as to shape or size.

anisophylly. The condition of having leaves of two or more sizes on the sides of a horizontal or oblique shoot. Heterophylly.

anisophanogametes. Flagellate gametes of various sizes.

anisophytes. A former name for *Muscineae*.

anisopleural. Bilaterally asymmetrical.

anisopterous. Unequally winged (of seeds).

anisos. Unequal.

anisoschists. Denoting unequal gametes some of which are degraded or aborted.

anisosepalous. Having unequal sepals.

anisospores. Spores which are dimorphic (with the male and female spores of different sizes).

anisospory. The condition in which the younger spores remain hyaline and do not have the germination slit which is found in the first-formed spores.

anisostamenous. 1. With stamens of different sizes. 2. With a different number of stamens than petals.

anisostichous. With unequal rows in the stem cortex, of *Chara*.

anisostyly. The occurrence of short and long styles in the same species but with no difference in sexual properties.

anisotropic. Crystalline.

anisotropism. The tendency of a plant or a plant organ to respond in different ways to external stimuli, as stems which respond positively to light and roots which shun light.

ankylosis. See ANCHYLOSIS.

anlage. The embryonic basis of any developed part, a rudiment, a primordium, a fundament.

annectent. The intermediate species of genera.

annexed. See ADNATE.

annexus. See ADNATE.

annotinous. Denoting distinct yearly growths; applied to leaves, etc., which are annual and renewed every year; sometimes applied to branches of last year's growth; applied to the ring upon a stem which marks the close of a season's growth.

annotto. See ARNATTO.

annua. Annual.

annual. Yearly, living only one year, with a life cycle of one year's duration.

annual habit. Those plants which go from germination to seed production in one year have the *annual* habit.

annual, monocarpic. A plant which fruits only once.

annual ring. The layer of wood produced each year by the cambium ring in a dicot stem.

annual shoot. The shoot produced each year in the spring by a plant with a perennial root system when the above-ground part dies at the end of the growing season.

annual, winter. A plant with seeds which germinate in the fall. The plant lives over winter, produces seeds in the spring, then dies.

annular. In the form of a ring; marked transversely by rings; forming a ring or circle; applied to certain vessels in xylem owing to ring-like thickenings in their interior.

annular cells. Cells with ring-like markings; see ANNULAR VESSEL.

annular duct. A vessel with ring-like secondary thickening.

annular fiber. A fiber with ring-like thickening of the walls.

annular rhytidoma. See RINGED RHYTIDOMA.

annular ring. The thickened ring in the walls of vessels.

annular vessels. Trachea with ring-like thickening, xylem cells with annular wall thickenings.

annularis. Ring-like; see ANNULAR.

annulate. Marked with rings, ring-shaped.

annulate vessel. A tracheid or vessel of protoxylem bearing rings of thickening materials on its walls.

annulatiform. Ring-like.

annulations. Rings, belts, or circles.

annuliform. Like a ring.

annulus. 1. A ring-like structure. 2. In some ferns the thick-walled cells extending from the stalk over the sporangium which are involved in the bursting of the sporangium cover. 3. In mushrooms, the ring or collar found around the stipe which is formed by the remains of the veil after the expansion of the cap. 4. In mosses, the line of cells found between the mouth of the capsule and the operculum which is the line of separation when the operculum is detached. 5. In *Equisetaceae*, the imperfectly developed foliar sheath below the fruit-spike. 6. In *diatoms*, the compressed rim of silica within the frustule of some genera. 7. The fleshing rim of the corolla in some *asclepiads*.

annulus inferus. In *Hymenomycetes*, a collar attached to the stipe below the apex formed by the rupture of the marginal veil around the margin of the pileus.

annulus mobilus. In *Hymenomycetes*, the portion of ruptured marginal veil which remains as a movable annulus around the stipe after the pileus has expanded.

annulus superus. The armilla in *Hymenomycetes*.

annuosus. Aged, old.

annuus. Annual, living but one year.

anocladous. Denoting those branches which curve outward.

anodal. In the upward direction on the genetic spiral; turned toward, said only of that half of a leaf which is turned toward the course of the genetic spiral.

anodermous. Without a covering membrane or cuticle, having no skin.

anodic half of leaf. The half turned in the direction in which the genetic spiral winds.

anomaloecious. See POLYGAMOUS.

anomodromy. Any venation which cannot be assigned to any special order.

anomophyllous. 1. Having leaves abnormal for the genus. 2. Having leaves irregularly placed.

anomospermous. Having seeds which are produced but are not normal for the genus.

anopetalous. With erect petals.

Anophytes. The *Muscineae* or *Bryophytae*, the mosses and liverworts.

anosmatic. Having no sense of smell.

ansae. The partial leaf stalks of a compound leaf.

anestemonous. Said of an androecium in which the stamens are not equal in number to the petals and to the sepals.

ansulate. Coiled at the apex and then bent over in a loop, as in the growing tip of the *Cucurbitaceae*.

antagonism. Antibiosis or opposition; the interaction of microorganisms upon each other, as checking the growth of parasites in plants.

antagonistic symbiosis. The condition in which the symbionts are not mutually helpful or neutral but harmful, at least on the part of one; the struggle between organisms; harmful parasitism of one lichen on another.

antapical. A term for posterior in dinoflagellates.

antapical plate. The part of the hypovalve (the posterior extremity of the cell) of *Peridinales* which is not postcingular.

antarcticus. Of or pertaining to the Antarctic regions.

antarctogaea. The Australian region exclusive of New Zealand and Polynesia.

antecedent genome. That part of a chromosome which plays the dominant part in determining inheritance.

antechamber. The space just below the guard cells of a stoma, the upper angle or space between the guard cells of a stoma.

antedimorphism. The condition of a species before it becomes dimorphic.

anteform. An original form which has disappeared but has left modified offspring.

antemarginal. Descriptive of those sori which lie within the margin of a frond.

antemedius. Opposite, standing before the middle of another body or structure.

antennae. Two slender horn-like appendages of the rostellum in the orchid *Catasetum*.

antennaeformis. Describing those fruits in which the two styles suggest the antennae of insects.

antepetalous. See ANTIPETALOUS.

ante-phyllome. The theoretic leaf; see POST-PHYLLOME.

ant-epiphytes. Plants cultivated by ants.

anteplacental. In front of the placentae; see INTERPLACENTAL.

anteposition. 1. The location of parts oppositely instead of alternately. 2. The superposition of whorls in a flower which are typically alternate.

anterior. 1. In front or away from the axis. 2. Of a flower, next to or facing the bract, i.e., away from the axis of the inflorescence. 3. In an agaric, at the end of the gill at the margin of the pileus. Opposite of POSTERIOR.

anterior side. That part of a flower which faces the bract.

antero-posterior. Median.

antero-posterior plane. A vertical plane which bisects an organ into right and left halves.

antesepalous. Inserted opposite the sepals, antisepalous.

ante-sporophyll. The rudimentary structure of the modified leaf bearing spores.

ante-trophophyll. The ancestral form of a leaf.

ante-trophosporophyll. The ancestral leaf-like organ possessing the functions of the leaf and the sporophyll.

ant-guards. 1. Ants attracted by nectaries on involucral bracts. 2. Some *Compositae* which guard the flowers from predatory beetles.

anthacriny. Decomposition into humus.

anthecological. Referring to one flower and its surroundings, such as insect visitors, etc.

anthecology. The study of insect relationships with flowers.

anthela. A cymose inflorescence in which the lateral axes exceed the main axis in length creating a concave cluster, as in some rushes (*Juncus* sp.); a paniculate cyme.

Anthelietum. An Arctic alpine association in which *Anthelia* is a constituent; see SNOW-FLUSH.

anthelmintic. Capable of killing worms.

anthemia. A flower cluster of any kind, anthemy.

anthemideous. Pertaining to *Anthemis*, a large genus of Old World herbs. Many are weeds.

anther. 1. The upper part of the stamen in which pollen is produced, the pollen sacs or groups of pollen sacs. 2. The microsporangium. 3. In *Hymenomycetes* anther was formerly used for cystidium or antheridium.

anther cap. In orchids, the outer deciduous case or bag surrounding the pollinia, the anther case.

anther dust. Pollen.

anther-like. In the form of a stag's horn.

anther lobes. Those cells which contain pollen.

anther tube. A tube formed by coalescent anthers, as in the sunflower family.

anther wings. Name applied to the horny lateral expansions from the lobes of the anther in *Asclepiadeae*.

anthera. 1. An old term for the antheridium in fungi. 2. Used by Linnaeus for the seta and capsule of mosses.

antherangium. The sporocarp, which contains both mega- and microspores in the genus *Dioon*, a cycad.

antherid. See ANTHERIDIUM.

antheridangia. The microspores of *Marsilia*, etc.

antheridial cell. The cell which results from the prothallial cell when it divides and develops into the stalk cell and the generative cell (antheridium).

antheridial mother cell. The cell inside the pollen grain of flowering plants which divides to form the male gamete.

antheridiophore. The structure upon which an antheridium is borne, an antheridial receptacle.

antheridium. A male organ of reproduction in the cryptogams, a spermary, a male gametangium, the analogue of anther in the phanerogams. It is a single cell in fungi and algae, many cells in bryophytes and vascular plants. An antherid.

antherine. Like an anther.

antherizoa. Spermatozoids, male cells produced in antheridia.

antheroblast. See ANDROCYTE.

antherocyst. An antheridium, a unicellular structure producing antherozoids.

antherogenous. Applied to double flowers which result from the transformation of anthers.

antheromania. An inordinate development of the anther.

antherophore. The cylindrical or flattened axis in *Ephedra* which bears the anther.

antherophylly. The virescence and the phyllomorphy of anthers.

antherosporangium. A microsporangium.

antherostigma. An anther resulting from a transformed stigma.

antherozoa. One of the motile fertilizing bodies which is produced in an antheridium, a spermatozoid.

antherozoid. 1. A male cell developed in an antheridium (usually motile). 2. The motile male cell in the cryptogams. 3. The pollen grain in phanerogams. See SPERM, SPERMATOZOID.

antherozoidium. See ANTHEROZOID.

anthesis. The period of flowering, the time of the expansion of a flower, the period of pollination.

anthesomolysis. The metamorphosis of inflorescence.

anthesmotaxis. The arrangement of the different parts of the flower.

anthesmus. An inflorescence.

anthine. Of or pertaining to a flower, obtained from or having the flavor of a flower.

anthobiology. The life history of the flower.

anthocarp. A utricular fruit surrounded by the persistent base of the perianth.

anthocarpium. The fruit formed by the union of the floral organs, or part of them, with the fruit itself.

anthocarpous. Having a body of combined flowers and fruits which are united in a single mass, as in pineapple and mulberry; having fruits with parts other than the ovary, as multiple or accessory fruits.

anthocerotoid. Of or pertaining to *Anthoceros*; resembling *Anthoceros*, a liverwort.

anthochlorin. The yellow coloring in some flowers, xanthein.

anthoclinium. The receptacle of an inflorescence, such as the *Compositae*.

anthocrene. A flower-fountain.

anthocyanin. The pigment in flowers and fruits which varies from pink to blue according to the acidity of the cell sap; a collective name for pigments, mostly blue or greenish in an alkaline and reddish in an acid cell sap. It is generally a water-soluble glucoside but sometimes is in a crystalline or amorphous form.

anthodium. The capitulum or flower head in *Compositae*.

anthoecium. The spikelet of such grasses as *Panicum*.

anthoecologist. One who studies plant life in its environment, an ecologist.

anthogamae. The *Bryophyta* (liverworts, hornworts, and mosses) and the *Charophyceae* (stoneworts).

anthogenel. With a developed corolla.

anthoid. Resembling a flower; flower-like, as the sporophytes of cryptogams.

antholeucin. The so-called coloring matter of white flowers.

antholite. A fossil plant having the appearance of a flower.

anthological. Pertaining to flowers or flower gathering.

antholysis. The retrograde metamorphosis of a flower in which the parts become more or less foliaceous.

anthophaein. The brown coloring matter found in some flowers, the color of the black spots on the corolla of *Vicia faba*.

anthophilous. Fond of flowers, feeding on flowers, denoting plants which have visit-insects which aid in cross-fertilization.

anthophilus. A florist or one who cultivates garden flowers.

anthophore. An elongation of the floral receptacle or thalamus between the calyx and corolla supporting the interior organs, as in *Silene*.

anthophorous. Bearing flowers, floriferous.

anthophytes. The angiosperms or seed-bearing plants which develop seeds in a carpel with endosperm.

anthoplankton. Water bloom, algae which produce the "breaking of the meres."

anthoptosis. The falling of leaves.

anthorcarpologic. Concerning the relation between flower and fruit.

anthos-. A prefix meaning flower.

anthosperm. A colored concretion which is scattered in the tissue of some fucoid plants.

anthospermae. A division of plants intermediate between the *Gymnospermae* and the *Angiospermae.*

anthostrobiloid. The adjective denoting the primitive type of an angiospermous flower, as the fructification or flower of certain cycads; anthostrobilous.

anthotaxis. The arrangement of flowers on an axis.

anthotaxy. The study of the arrangement of flowers on the stem.

anthotropic. Relating to any curvature of the peduncle during flowering.

anthotropism. Any movement of the flower or its parts.

anthoxanthin. The yellow pigment of flowers and fruits, carotin.

anthoxanthum. A little flower, also a small genus of European grasses.

anthozymase. An enzyme in the petals of flowers.

anthracine. Coal black.

anthraciny. The breakdown of organic material by fungi and the further transformation by passing through the alimentary canals of insects and worms producing a dark-colored soil.

anthracnose. A common type of plant disease caused by several species of melanconiaceous fungi, as the "birds' eye rot" of grape vines.

anthrageny. The formation of peat by decomposition.

anthrax. A disease in man and certain animals caused by *Bacillus anthracis.*

anthrochore. See ANTHROPOCHORE.

anthropeic. Indicating human influence upon the mutual conditions of a plant community.

anthrophile. A plant which usually follows cultivation or follows civilization.

anthropochore. A plant distributed by man or involuntarily introduced.

anthropogenic climax. A climax of vegetation produced under the influence of human activity.

anthropophile. A plant which follows the migration of man.

anthropophyte. A plant which is incidentally introduced by cultivation; see HEMEROPHYTE.

anthropozoic characters. The relationships and modifications brought about by man or animals upon plants or plant communities; see CULTURE COMMUNITY.

anthurus. A flower cluster at the end of a long stalk.

-anthus. A suffix meaning flower.

anthyllidifolious. With leaves like the genus *Anthyllis*, one of the *Fabaceae.*

antiarine. The active poisonous ingredient of the upas tree, *Antiaris toxicaria*, the juice of which is used on poisonous arrows.

antibacterial. Protective against bacteria.

antibionts. Antipathetic organisms, plants which do not graft easily.

antibiosis. A harmful association of one or more organisms, the effect of an antibiotic on a susceptible organism.

antibiotic. A substance capable of antibiosis, i.e., a substance derived from a living organism which is capable of killing or incapacitating another organism.

antiblastic. Denoting immunity which is due to forces which prevent the growth of invading organisms.

antibody. An agent in the blood of animals which reacts with (destroys in some cases) other substances called antigens; a substance produced in a body to counteract some foreign substances or organisms (usually bacteria).

antical. Fore, front, anterior, on the anterior side, remote or turned away from the axis, introrse (said rarely of anthers), the upper surface.

antice. In front.

anticentral. Said of plants whose distribution tends toward the coasts and away from the center of an island.

antichemism. The protoplasm-producing energy as an antagonizing chemical force.

anticipatory inheritance. A condition now called precocity.

anticlinal. Perpendicular to the surface.

anticlinal cells. Parent cells which persist in their primitive state without producing antipodal cells or vesicles.

anticlinal planes. Planes which cut the surface or the periclinal cell walls at right angles.

anticlinal walls. A cell wall perpendicular to the surface of a growing point; see ANTICLINAL PLANES.

anticlinanthous. Denoting those inferior scaly parts of some composite flowers.

anticlines. See ANTICLINAL PLANES.

anticonsimilitude. The condition when the plane of a diatom divides the frustule into two similar parts which are doubly inverted.

anticous. Facing toward the axis of a flower, facing anteriorly.

anticryptic coloration. Coloration for aggressive resemblance, protective coloration which facilitates attack.

anticryptogamic. Denoting mixtures which are used to destroy fungi.

antidimorphism. The condition of an individual plant in which similar organs vary in shape (not applied to the variations in two distinct plants).

antidromal. Being twisted or coiled in an opposite direction to that with which it is compared.

antidromal torsion. A twist against the direction of twining.

antidromy. The condition in which the course of a spiral is reversed from the usual direction.

antienzyme. A substance or body which counteracts the action of an enzyme.

antiferment. Antienzyme.

antigen. A substance which stimulates the formation of antibodies in blood when it is injected into a living body.

antiheterophylly. See ANTIDIMORPHISM.

antikinase. See ANTIENZYME.

antillaris. Of the Antilles, West Indies.

antilysin. Any substance which prevents catalytic action.

antimorphic. Having an effect opposite to that of the normal, nonmutant allelomorph.

antimycotic. Fungicidal, destructive to fungi.

antipathetic. Denoting those plants which do not unite readily when grafted.

antipeduncular. Situated opposite a peduncle.

antipetalous. Denoting stamens which are situated in front of petals, inserted opposite to a petal, antepetalous.

antiphyte. That generation in the alternation of generations which produces reproductive cells asexually, the antithetic generation.

antipleion. A lean year or cycle of scarcity.

antipleon. Areas of deficiency in cycles of 2.5 years; see PLEON.

antipodal. Against the foot; applied to cells at the base or foot of the embryo sac, the farthest from the micropyle in the seed.

antipodal cells. Three primordial cells at the chalaza end of the seed embryo sac of angiosperms.

antipodal cone. The cone of astral rays opposite the spindle.

antirrhiniflorous. Flowered like *Antirrhinum*, snapdragons.

antiscrophulous. Antiscorbutic, efficaceous against scurvy.

antisepalous. Opposite to or upon a sepal and not alternate with it, oppositisepalous.

antiseptic. Applied to those substances which may be used to destroy bacteria with little or no harmful effect on the living body; a substance which prevents putrefaction; a substance which represses the development of microorganisms.

antiserum. A preparation from the blood of animals (usually blood serum) which contains specific immune bodies.

antispermy. The coalescence of fertile divisions of the phyllome into a single fertile body opposed and superposed to the sterile division in phanerogams.

antisporangism. Antispermy in pteridophytes.

antisymmetric. Having a part turned upside down, inverted, or distorted; see ANTICONSIMILITUDE.

antithetic. Applied to alternation of generations when the different generations (gametophyte and sporophyte) are structurally and fundamentally unlike; the opposite of homologous alternation.

antithetic alternation of generations. The explanation of alternation of generations which states that the two are distinct: the gametophyte represents the primitive aquatic phase, while the sporophyte is secondary, having arisen from the germinating zygote in relation to the migration from an aquatic to a terrestrial habitat.

antitoxin. An antibody which counteracts the effects of a toxin, a substance secreted by a plant to protect itself against harmful bacteria.

antitropal. Orthotropal as applied to ovules, applied to embryos with a radicle directed away from the hilum, inverted.

antitrophy. A condition in which secondary roots arise from the main axis in a regular outward manner.

antitropic. Turning against the sun.

antitropous. Less properly antitropal; denoting those embryos which have the radicle directed away from the hilum, as in the case of orthotropous seeds.

antitropy. See ANTITROPHY.

antizymotic. Of or pertaining to those substances which prevent or check fermentation, antizymic.

ant-plants. Plants utilized by ants for habitation, myrmecophytes.

antrorse. Directed upward or forward, opposite to retrorse; see ANTICOUS.

anucleate. Without a nucleus.

-anum. A suffix meaning layer.

anygdalin. Amygdalin.

ap-, apo-. A prefix of negation or meaning from.

apaerotaxis. The negative stimulus by oxygen in anaerobic organisms.

apagynous. See MONOCARPIC.

apalogamic. Denoting cells each of which contains two unfused nuclei; see DICARYOTIC.

apandrous. Denoting those *Oomycetes* with oospores formed in the absence of antheridia.

apandry. 1. The loss of function of the male organ. 2. The fusion of the antheridium with the oogonium.

aparaphysate. Having no paraphyses, with sterile filaments in the hymenium of fructifications of fungi.

apenninus. Of or pertaining to the Apennines (Italy).

aperispermic. Denoting seeds without nutritive tissue; see EXALBUMINOUS.

apertiflorous. See CHASMOGAMIC.

apertura. 1. Formerly used to denote the dehiscence of anthers. 2. The ostiole in the fruiting structures of certain fungi.

apetalae. A division of dicotyledonous plants characterized by an absence of petals.

apetalous. Being without petals or with petals reduced to inconspicuous scales, apetalose.

apetaly. The condition of being without petals.

apex. 1. Tip, the extreme end, the summit, the growing point of a stem or root. 2. An old name for anther and for the ostiole in certain fungi.

apex, floral. The apex bearing flowers.

apex, time. The time between the latent period and the recovery when a leaf moves after a shock or touch stimulus.

aphaneri. Those organisms which to be visible must be treated by a reagent.

aphanimere. Amitosis.

aphanisis. The suppression of parts.

Aphanocyclae. Plants in which the whorls are not very easily seen, as in *Nymphacaceae*.

aphaptotropism. The condition of not reacting to contact stimuli, as not being influenced by touching stems or other surfaces; see THIGMOTROPISM and TROPISM.

apheliotropic. Negatively heliotropic, turning away from the sun.

aphercotropism. The turning away from an obstruction.

aphlebia. Anomalous pinnae on the rachis of certain fossil ferns.

aphlebia traces. Pinnae traces in *Diplolabis*, a fossil fern.

aphleboids. Pinnules which serve as bud protectors in fronds of *Gleichenia*.

aphotic. See APHOTISTIC.

aphotic zone. The portion of a body of water which is not penetrated by light (below 3000 feet).

aphotistes. A plant growing in the dark or in very little light, as truffles, fungi, etc.

aphotometric. Denoting those leaves or certain other structures not affected by light, as phototactic zoospores which turn the same end away from light.

aphototaxis. The condition of organisms which are unaffected by the light stimulus.

aphototropic. Bending or turning away from a source of light.

aphrostase. Cellular tissue.

aphthae. The small, round, white ulcerous vesicles of the lips, gums, and intestinal wall in the disease called thrush or moniliasis, caused by the yeasts *Candida* (usually *C. albicans*).

aphthaphytes. The fungi causing the disease known as thrush.

aphthous. Resembling something covered with little ulcers.

aphydrotaxis. Repulsion from water.

aphyllae. Plants which have no leaves or rudimentary ones, a term sometimes applied to *Thallophytae*.

aphyllopodous. Said of the stem of some plants when a basal rosette of leaves is lacking.

aphyllous. Leafless, without foliage leaves.

aphyllous forest. A forest formed of *Casuarina* found in Java and Sund.

aphylly. The suppression or absence of leaves.

apical. At the tip or apex, at the summit, belonging to the apex or point.

apical axis. In diatoms, referring to a line through the center of the pervalvar axis in the direction of the rapha at equal distances from homologous points on the girdle band surfaces and through apices.

apical caps. Rings on the side walls of the tips of the filaments of some of the green algae (*Oedogoniales*).

apical cell. The meristematic cell at the tip of a filament or organ which divides repeatedly to form new tissues for the plant or organ. It is found in filamentous lower plants, the thallus of mosses, and at the root and shoot tips of the higher plants.

apical cell theory. A discarded theory that tissue of higher plants develops from a single cell.

apical cone. The growing point, the extremity of a stem or other central point where the cells are in the process of division and growth; see PUNCTUM VEGETATIONIS.

apical growth. An extension in the length of the axis at the apex only.

apical meristem. The meristematic cells at the tip of a stem or root from which all the tissues of the mature axis are ultimately formed.

apical placentation. The condition in which the ovule or ovules are inserted at the top of the ovary.

apical plane. In diatoms, the plane at right angles to the valvar plane which passes through the pervalvar and apical axes; see PERVALVULAR and TRANSAPICAL.

apical pores. Special hydathodes in monocotyledons.

apicicircinatus. Terminating circinately, coiled.

apicifixed. Attached by the apex, as a suspended anther.

apicillary. Inserted upon or pertaining to the summit, as in the dehiscence of the capsule of *Cerastium*.

apicle. A small tooth or point at the apex.

apicula. 1. A sharp and short point, which is not stiff, in which a leaf or lobe may end. 2. A point formed by the prolongation of a vein.

apicule. 1. The short, often sharp papilla at one end of the spore by which it was attached to the sterigma. 2. A small acute projection.

apiculiform. Like a little point.

apifera. Bee-bearing.

apigenin. A glucoside found in many *Umbelliferae*, especially in *Apium*, celery.

apiifolius. Apium-leaved, with leaves like celery.

apilary. With the upper lip wanting or suppressed in the corolla.

apileate. Without a pileus; see RESUPINATE.

aplanetism. The absence of motile spores (zoospores) and having therefore thick-walled sporangiospores (usually in *Saprolegniaceae*).

aplanogametangium. The organ in which aplanogametes are formed.

aplanogametes. A nonmotile, nonciliated gamete which may or may not be set free.

aplanoplastids. Nonflagellated cells.

aplanosporangia. Organs giving rise to aplanospores.

aplanospores. 1. Nonmotile resting spores of algae. 2. Nonmotile nonciliated reproductive cells of some green algae. 3. Nonmotile cells formed asexually by true cell formation and rejuvenescence which are detached for propagation.

aplasmodiophorous. Denoting those *Myxogasters* which do not produce plasmodia.

aplastic. Said of substances not capable of being organized or converted into animal or vegetable tissue.

aplerotic. Of oospores of fungi which do not fill the oogonium.

aplolepideous. See HAPLOLEPIDEOUS.

aploperistomatous. See HAPLOLEPIDEOUS.

aploperistomic. Having a single row of teeth (or none) in the peristome.

aplostemonous. With a single row of stamens.

apo-. A prefix meaning from.

apobasidimycetes. A term for the *Gasteromycetes* on the basis of the apobasidium type of basidium.

apobasidium. The symmetrically arranged terminal spores of a basidium.

apobatic. Repulsive; see STROPHIC.

apoblast. A barren shoot, as from pollard willows.

apocarp. A fruit with separate carpels in the gynoecium.

apocarpous. Term applied to the carpels when they are separate and unfused; see SYNCARPOUS.

apochemotaxis. Negative attraction, repulsion due to chemical influence.

apocynaceous. Relating to or resembling the

genus *Apocynum*, dog-bane or Indian hemp or allies.

apocyte. A multinucleate cell or a plurinucleate mass of protoplasm.

apocyty. A term for certain noncellular tissue in fungi and algae in which the cells are reduced to several nuclei within the cell wall.

apodial. Without a foot-stalk or podium.

apodogynous. Denoting a disk which is not adherent to the ovary.

apoembryony. The condition in which the embryo stage is suppressed, and the oosphere gives rise immediately to the vascular members.

apogalvanotaxis. Negative galvanotropism, curvature shown when subjected to galvanic current toward the negative electrode.

apogamous. Showing apogamy, developed without fertilization, applied to perpetuation of the plant by vegetative means only.

apogamy. 1. Development of an embryo without the fusion of gametes. 2. The loss of sexual function without the suppression of the normal product of reproduction. 3. Vegetative reproduction where sexual reproduction usually occurs. 4. Asexual reproduction, apomixis.

apogamy, diploid. See EUAPOGAMY.

apogamy, generative. See MEIOTIC APOGAMY.

apogamy, haploid. See MEIOTIC APOGAMY.

apogamy, meiotic. Apogamy after meiosis occurring when the sporophyte originates from the oosphere or from gametophytic tissue.

apogamy, obligate. 1. Abnormal budding and production of a bion by a prothallus without the intervention of sex. 2. The fusion of the nuclei of vegetative cells; see PARTHENAPOGAMY.

apogamy, somatic. See EUAPOGAMY.

apogeny. The loss of power to reproduce sexually with the functions of both male and female organs being destroyed.

apogeosthetic. Denoting the upward bending of the young hypocotyl.

apogeotaxis. Negative geotaxis, negative response by plants to gravity.

apogeotropic. Growing away from the earth, as in many ordinary stems; negatively geotropic.

apogeotropism. The tendency to react contrarily to the force of gravity, negative geotropism.

apogestation. The gestation of the germ of one plant in the tissue of a wholly different plant from the generating system.

apogyny. The loss of the reproductive function by the female organ.

apolar. Without tracheae (referring to the indeterminate fibrovascular mosses).

apomictic population. A population resulting from parthenogenesis.

apomixis. Loss of sexuality; abnormal budding and reproduction in reproductive organs without sexual intervention; the condition in which sex cells develop vegetatively in the absence of fertilization.

apopetalous. Having free petals, polypetalous, having the petals of the corolla unattached to each other, eleutheropetalous, choripetalous.

apopetaly. That condition in which petals are separate and distinct.

apophototaxis. The action of light which causes no definite arrangements of organisms or of chlorophyll granules.

apophyllous. Applied to the parts of a single perianth whorl when the petals are free.

apophysate. Having an apophysis.

apophysis. 1. An enlargement of the seta below the theca in certain mosses. 2. A thickening on the scales of the cones of certain pines. 3. Any irregular swelling. See HYPOPHYSIS.

apophytes. 1. Lichens. 2. Autochthonous plants which follow cultivation.

apoplasmodial. Said of the *Acrasieae* in distinguishing them from the myxogasters in the nonfusion of the cytoplasmic elements.

apoplastogamous. See APOPLASMODIAL.

aporachial. Denoting structures directed away from the rachis.

aporogamy. The condition when the pollen tube does not pass through the micropyle.

aposchist. A gamete in which cell division does not occur, but the cell itself directly assumes the behavior of a gamete.

aposematic. Said of warning colors which give notice to enemies of supposedly distasteful or injurious quality, colors which frighten enemies.

aposepalous. With free sepals, having the sepals of the calyx unattached to each other.

aposmotaxis. The repulsive influence of certain solubles on organisms.

aposperms. Plants integrated separately from the placenta.

aposporogony. 1. The absence or suppression of spore formation. 2. The production of a gametophyte from a sporophyte by a vegetative process, as budding, without spore formation or meiosis.

apospory. The production of a gametophyte from a sporophyte by a vegetative process without spore formation or meiosis, suppression of spore formation with the prothallus developing directly from the sporophyte.

apospory, direct. Normal but somewhat prolonged apospory.

apospory, induced. The condition of apospory where the prothalli produce the buds forthwith.

apostasis. The separation of organs by an unusual or abnormal extension of the internodes.

apostaxis. An abnormal loss of nutritive or secreted fluids by bleeding, gumming, etc.

apostrophe. The arrangement of the row of chloroplasts parallel to the rays of light; the position assumed by chloroplasts during intense light along the side of cell walls instead of the outer surface.

apostrophe, negative. Apostrophe caused by weak light.

apostrophe, positive. Apostrophe caused by strong light.

apostrophic interval. The space on the photrum which is capable of apostrophizing chlorophyll granules, sometimes called apostrophion.

apostrophization. The act in which the chlorophyll granules take up the position of apostrophe.

apotaximorphosis. A term used to denote any teratologic change which seems antagonistic to the normal laws governing the organism.

apothecium. A disk-like, cup- or bowl-shaped fruit-body borne on lichens and discomycetous fungi. The spores are borne on the inner surface and are exposed while the ascospores are maturing.

apothermotaxis. The condition of being insensible to the influence of temperature.

apothigmotaxis. That irritability which is induced by contact with a solid body.

apotropic. Denoting the ascending axis.

apotropism. See APOGEOTROPISM.

apotropous. Used of an anatropous ovule

which has a ventral raphe, said of an anatropous ovule which has an averse raphe when it is pendulous.

apotype. A supplementary type which aids in the completion of descriptions; see HYPOTYPE.

apotypic. An anomalous departure from the general law of development.

apotypose. Denoting abnormality in development.

apparent noon. The time when the sun crosses the meridian, i.e., sun noon as distinguished from noon standard time.

appendage. An attached subsidiary or secondary part, as a projecting part, a hanging part, or supplement; a part added to another; any super-added or subordinate part as hairs, prickles, leaves, etc., of a stem; a sucker, limb, or branch attached to a tree trunk.

appendent. Said of the hilum when it is directed toward the upper part of the seed which is sessile or nearly so on the placenta, as in stone fruit.

appendicula. 1. Small appendages. 2. Branching hair-like processes at the summit of the sporocarp.

appendicular. 1. Pertaining to the limbs or appendages. 2. Applied to ovules which are derived from foliar organs.

appendicular ridges. Ridges on guard cells which divide the front cavity into two compartments.

appendiculate. 1. Having appendages. 2. In agarics, when the veil hangs in small fragments from the margin of the pileus or when the veil is cob-webby. 3. Having winged petioles or spurred corollas.

appendiculate cilia. Cilia with small transverse spurs attached at intervals along the margin.

appendix. 1. That which is attached. 2. The specialized upper part of an inflorescence axis not bearing flowers (characteristic of the *Araceae*).

appense. Like a hat on a peg, an approach to pendulose.

applanate. 1. Of pilei, flattened out or horizontally expanded. 2. Flattened or expanded, as thallus of liverworts and lichens.

apple. One of the pome fruits; technically a fleshy, inferior, plurilocular, multiseeded fruit.

applicative. Folded together forward and

lengthwise in any manner, complicate; see CONDUPLICATE.

applicatus. Joined, attached, applied face to face without folding.

apposifoliar. See OPPOSITIFOLIAR.

apposite. Said of similar parts when they are placed close to each other or side by side.

apposition. 1. The condition of being side by side or close together. 2. The theory that the growth of a cell wall is due to repeated placing of layers of substance on the internal surface of the original cell wall.

appressed. Lying close and flat, pressed against closely and flatly along the entire length of an organ or part.

appressor. The organ of attachment of germinating filaments of a parasite to the host.

appressoria. In parasitic fungi the tuft-like tips of hyphal branches which serve as organs of attachment, not to be confused with haustoria or absorbing organs.

approximate. 1. Close together but not united. 2. Of gills, free from but approaching the stem.

approximation. See ASSOCIATION.

apricarium. 1. The place in botanic gardens where plants are grown for exposure to sun and air. 2. The summer location of plants in a garden.

apricot. A stone fruit closely related to the peach and nectarine.

apricus. Growing wild in open, dry, sunny places.

apterous. Wingless; having no membranous margins which may be called wings, used of petioles, seeds, etc.

apthaphytes. Fungi causing the disease known as thrush, as *Candida albicans*.

apus. Stalkless.

apyrenous. Having fruits which are seedless, as certain cultivated oranges, grapes, pineapple, etc.

aquatic. Living in water, growing naturally in water or under water.

aquatic community. A community of plants growing under aquatic conditions.

aquatilis. Aquatic.

aquatosere. A sere beginning in a wet, bare area and developing to an aquatic climax.

aqueous. 1. Denoting some colorless structure or hyaline tissue. 2. Having much water in the tissue, watery; see HYALINE.

aqueous tissue. Tissue lacking interspaces and chloroplastids made up of one or more

layers of parenchyma cells which contain much watery sap and act as reservoirs.

aquiferous tissue. See AQUEOUS TISSUE.

aquiherbosa. The herbaceous communities living in swamps and ponds.

aquilegifolious. Leaved like the genus *Aquilegia*, the columbines.

aquilinus. Eagle-like.

aquilonary period. See XEROTHERM.

aquilonian region. An ecological region including Europe, Asia north of the Himalayas, Africa south of the tropics, and America north of about 45°.

aquiprata. Plant communities composed of herbs, grasses, and bryophytes where influenced by ground water; damp meadows.

aquosus. Watery.

arabans. The gums, pectins, mucilages, etc., derived from arabinose.

arabicus. Arabian.

arabin. A substance derived from gum arabic which deflects the polarized beam to the left.

arabinose. A glucose obtained from arabin and from cherry gum; a pentose sugar; an aldose.

arabiloxylan. A hemicellulose found in the bran of wheat and rye.

araceous. Relating to the family *Araceae*, which includes Jack-in-the-pulpit, water-arum, etc.

arachniferous. Having cobwebby-like hairs similar to the web-covered flowers in *Poa arachnifera*.

arachnoid. 1. Covered with long and loosely entangled hairs longer and fewer than in tomentose, cobwebby, like a spider web. 2. Of the partial veil when it is like a cobweb.

araliaefolious. Leaved like *Aralia*, the type genus of the family *Araliaceae*, which includes gingseng, English ivy, etc.

araliaceous. Resembling the genus *Aralia*.

araneose. See ARACHNOID.

araroba. A powdery excretion in the cavities of the Brazilian tree *Andira Araroba*.

araucarian. Resembling *Araucaria*, a genus of tall pinaceous South American trees.

araucarietum. An association of *Araucariae*.

arbor. 1. A tree, a woody perennial plant with the branches growing from a bole. 2. A place shaded by trees or vines on a latticework, a bower.

arboreal. 1. Pertaining to trees or forests. 2. Growing on or in trees.

arboreous. 1. Tree-like, in distinction to frutescent or shrubby. 2. Of or pertaining to a tree.

arborescent. 1. Approaching the size or height of a tree. 2. Tree-like. 3. Becoming small trees. 4. Branched like a tree. 5. Woody.

arboret. A small tree or shrub.

aboretum. A collection of growing trees; a place assigned to the culture of trees and woody plants, usually in a systematic order.

arboricoline. Living on trees, as some fungi and epiphytes.

aboriculture. The cultivation and growing of trees.

arboroid. Tree-like; in the form and shape of a tree, as the structure of a protozoan colony.

arbor vitae. A tree of the genus *Thuja*, the tree of life.

arbuscle. 1. A low shrub with the form of a tree. 2. Tufts of hyphae within cells in endotrophic mycorrhiza.

arbusculariform. Shrub-like.

arbustive. Coppiced, like a grove of small trees regularly cut.

arbustum. 1. A shrub, a branched woody perennial plant lacking a distinct bole, a sylva. 2. An account of the woody plants of a country.

arbutifolious. With leaves like *Arbutus*, a genus of ericaceous shrubs and trees.

arbutin. A glucoside derived from many plants, especially *Ericaceae*.

arcesthidia. A closed, fleshy cone resembling a berry, as found in the juniper.

-arch. A suffix meaning sere.

archaic. Denoting a vegetative type of a former age, as *Casuarina*.

archebiosis. The origin of life, the beginning of other development of life; see SPONTANEOUS GENERATION.

archegone. See ARCHEGONIUM.

archegonial. 1. Of or pertaining to the archegonium. 2. Applied to stomata which have the outer guard walls thickened, inner walls a thin lamella, and the guard cells separated in their central part but not at the poles, as in gymnosperms.

archegonial chamber. A small depression at the tip of the female gametophyte in the seeds of cycads.

archegoniates. Plants belonging to one of the main divisions of the plant kingdom, the

bryophytes and pteridophytes, characterized by the presence of the archegonium as the female organ and by the regular alternation of generations of gametophyte and sporophyte in the life cycle.

archegoniophore. The archegonial receptacle; the branch which bears the archegonia in mosses, ferns, and liverworts.

archegonium. The flask-shaped organ in the higher cryptogams which corresponds to the pistil in the flowering plants; the flask-shaped female reproductive organ in bryophytes, pteridophytes, and some gymnosperms composed of a narrow upper portion (the neck) pierced by a canal enclosing one or more necks (neck-canal cells) which lead to a basal dilated portion (the venter) containing one oospore (the ovum) with a smaller cell at the entrance of the neck canal (the ventral canal-cell). After fertilization the embryo is developed in the venter.

archenema. The gametophytic structures of the *Thallophyta*.

archenteron. A sac in *Volvox* which communicates with the outside by a blastopore.

archeocytes. Cells which arise from undifferentiated blastomeres and ultimately give rise to germ cells and gametes.

archeophytes. Weeds which were introduced into cultivated ground in prehistoric times.

archeozoic. Of the earliest geological era and the age of unicellular life.

archephyta. The earliest vegetal organs.

archesperm. 1. The fertilized contents of an archegonium. 2. A plant with obligatory and archespermic seeds with monomorphous embryos.

archesphere. The archesperm before fertilization.

archespores. The cells which give rise to the spore mother cells; in lichens, the daughter-gonidia; see ARCHISPORIUM.

archesporial pad. A mass of cells which develop beneath the sporogenous tissue of some pteridophytes.

archesporium. The cell or group of cells which give rise to spore mother cells or the layer of cells which forms the pollen sac.

archetype. An original primitive type restricted to a series of forms from the simplest to very complicated with a common type of structure and phylogenetic connections.

archiamphiaster. The amphiaster forming a

first or second polar body in the maturation of the cell.

archiangiosperms. Primitive angiosperms.

archianthemum. A well developed flower at the apex of a botryoid inflorescence where it is normally absent.

archiblast. The protoplasm of the egg.

archiblastic. Having total and equal segmentation.

archicarp. 1. The female reproductive organ or cell in *Ascomycetes* which gives rise to the spore sac (ascus) after fertilization. 2. The single primary coiled hypha in the *Pyrenomycetes* which develops into the fruit body or a part of it (as the perithecium).

Archichlamydeae. A term including the *Polypetalae* and *Incompletae* of the phanerogams; dicotyledons which lack a perianth or have a calyx only or have a corolla of many distinct petals.

Archichlamydeae, Age of. The Middle Tertiary Period, during which the *Archichlamydeae* flourished.

archicleistogamy. The condition of having permanently closed flowers whose organs are considerably smaller than those of normal flowers.

archidium. The structure in the higher plants which bears the sporangia.

archigonic. Arising by spontaneous generation.

archigoniophore. A gametophore in cryptogams borne on a specialized branch with a terminal receptacle having female organs.

archigony. The spontaneous generation of life at the beginning of organic history.

archigymnosperms. The ferns and lower gymnosperms, those in which fertilization is accomplished by antherozoids.

archil. A purple dye obtained from lichens.

archilichens. Lichens in which the gonidia are bright green.

archimycetes. Unicellular fungi which are parasitic on diatoms.

archiplasm. The deeply staining protoplasm which surrounds the centrosome. It is the source of the material which makes up the spindle fibers and astral rays during cell division. It consists of hyaloplasm from the cell body and achromatin from the nucleus. It is modified cytoplasm associated with the Golgi apparatus. Archoplasm, arcoplasm, idioplasm, kinoplasm.

archiplast. The protoplasmic unit of the *Cyanophyceae*.

archiproctum. An exit that is formed early for spent materials in the genus *Volvox*; see ARCHENTERON.

archisperms. 1. Another name for gymnosperms because of their presumed antiquity. 2. Structures formed before fertilization or at an early stage in the macrospore.

archisphere. The contents of an archegonium prior to fertilization.

archistoma. 1. A primitive formation. 2. A primitive oral opening in *Volvox*.

archistreptes. The principal spirals that are formed in phyllotaxis.

architomy. Asexual reproduction in which no zone of division is evident before the division actually begins.

archocleistogamy. The condition of flowers that remain closed at the time the sexual organs ripen.

archoplasm. See ARCHIPLASM.

archoplasmic sphere. An achromatic spindle.

arciform. Shaped like an arc or bow.

arctalpine. Referring to alpine plants in the arctic zone or to those plants of the boreal life zone beyond the limit of tree growth because of altitude or latitude.

arctic. A term applied to a climatic region comprising three zones named superarctic, midarctic, and inferarctic; relating to plants growing above the limits of cultivation.

arctogaea. A region composed of the Palaearctis, Nearctis, Oriental, and Ethiopian regions. These include Europe, Asia, Africa, and North America as far south as Mexico.

arctostaphyletum. An association of *Arctostaphylus adans*, a genus of ericaceous plants which includes the manzanita.

arcuate. Of gills or margins of a pileus, curved like a bow; bent like a bow; arched.

arcuate-decurrent. Of gills, extending down the stem; curved and extending down the stem.

arcuato-areolatus. Divided into areas by curves.

arcuato-contortus. Forming a somewhat depressed spiral, as in some legumes.

-ard. A suffix for terms which deal with water content of soils.

ardella. Small, seemingly dusty apothecia of certain lichens, as *Arthonia*.

ardion. Ardium.

ardium. A succession or formation of plants due to irrigation.

ardosiaceous. Slate gray or full grayish blue, Saccardo's slate.

-are. A suffix denoting a community.

area. 1. A space; ground occupied by a plant formation or association; a rather large space bounded by cracks, lines, veins, or parts differing in color or texture. 2. In diatoms, the surface of a valve when circular or lacking a stauros. 3. The receptacle of certain fungi. 4. The space around the sporangium in *Isoetes*.

areal. Of or pertaining to the areas enclosed by the reticulate vessels of leaves.

arecoid. Like *Areca*, pinnately leaved palms of tropical Asia.

areg. A sand desert, dunes in Algeria.

arenaceous. Denoting plants which grow in sandy places, having the properties of plants which grow in sand.

arenarietum. An association of plants in which the dominant or exclusive plants are of the genus *Arenaria*, a silenaceous plant, the sandworts.

arenarium. Sandy soil.

areola. 1. A small space on the surface of a plant organ which differs in texture, structure, or color from the surrounding area, as a space marked by anastomosing reticulate veinlets in the tessellated areas on leaves or on the thallus of some lichens. 2. A small cavity within a cell or a cavity bounded by cells of an organ, like the lumen in the sporangium of *Achlya* or cavities in the cell walls in leaves, in particular in the leaves of mosses.

areolated dots. Markings made by woodcells or tracheids in cross sections of coniferous wood which are so regular in pattern as to be a determining factor in the recognition of some genera; also called bordered pits and discoid markings.

areolation. 1. The cellular mesh or network of the leaf. 2. The spacing between leaf veins. 3. In moss scale, the network formed.

areole. 1. Small spine-bearing areas in the *Cactaceae*. 2. A pit in the surface of a plant organ. See AREOLA.

arescent. Drying.

argan oil. An oil extracted from the seeds of the Moroccan tree *Argania*, the fruits of which are used as cattle feed and the oil used like olive oil.

argentate. With a silvery tint or luster, shining white with a tinge of gray.

argenteo-guttatus. Silver spotted.

argenterum. Silvery.

argentine. Silvery.

argillaceous. 1. Clay-colored, drab, resembling ochraceous-cinnamon-brown. 2. Resembling or containing a large amount of clay.

argillicole. Living on clay.

arginin. A proteid peculiar to the *Coniferae* occurring in the seeds or etiolated seedlings.

arginine. A simple protein produced by plants.

argodromile. Of slow-flowing streams.

argophyllous. Silver-leaved, white-leaved.

argos. Pure white.

argotaxis. The passive movement due to surface tension.

argute. Sharp, very sharply toothed, acutely dentate.

argyraeus. Silvery.

argyrocomous. Silver-haired.

argyroneurus. Silver-nerved.

argyrophyllous. Silver-leaved.

arhizal. Without roots.

aricine. An alkaloid from cinchona bark from Arica, Chile.

arid. Dry, as destitute of sap; with little rainfall; of gills, dry, somewhat like parchment.

arietinous. Like a ram's head.

aril. 1. A fleshy and often colored outer covering of a seed. 2. A fleshy organ around the hilum or base of the ovule. 3. An expansion of the funiculus which arises from the placenta and envelops the seed. 4. Any outgrowth of the funiculus or the coat of a seed. 5. The exterior coat of some seeds, as the mace of the nutmeg (more often found in tropical plants).

arilliform. Shaped like an aril, bag-shaped.

arillode. A false aril which covers the seed but not arising from the placenta; an aril-like structure which frequently arises near the micropyle.

-arinus. A suffix used in enumerating stamens instead of Linnaeus' suffix *-androus*.

arista. A bristle-like appendage like those on the glumes of many grasses, a beard, a short bristly awn.

aristolochiaceous. Of or pertaining to the

genus *Aristolochia*, climbing and erect perennials, including the pipe-vine.

aristostylous. Denoting a flower which has an exserted style which is bent toward the left.

aristulate. Having a short awn.

arizonicus. Of or pertaining to Arizona.

arizophytes. A term sometimes used to include the bryophytes and thallophytes.

arkansanus. Of or pertaining to Arkansas.

arm. In horticulture, a large branch of a vine which is trained horizontally.

armature. Any kind of defense mechanism, as prickles or thorns.

armed. Having thorns, thorny, with spines or prickles.

armeniaceous. 1. Having the color of an apricot, apricot buff, dull orange. 2. Of or pertaining to Armenia.

armilla. In *Hymenomycetes*, the frill of the stipes of agarics which is left attached on the expansion of the pileus which forms a covering of the hymenium; a bracelet-like frill.

armillaris. Having a bracelet or collar.

armillate. Made up of rings or circles, fringed, frilled.

armor. A covering of old leaf-bases on the stems of *Cycads* and some ferns.

armpalisade cells. Those cells which have protrusions which amalgamate with each other in the palisade tissue.

armpalisade portion. Two-armed hairs.

armpalisade tissue. Tissue developed by armed-cells which form the letter H.

arn. The alder tree.

arnatto, arnotto, annotto. The red coloring matter which is derived from the pulp of the fruit of *Bixa orellana*.

arnica. 1. A drug. 2. A large genus of asteraceous herbs.

Arnold. A type of steam sterilizer used for sterilization with steam not under pressure.

aroideology. A study of aroids (the members of the *Araceae* family, the arums, calla lily, etc.).

arrect. Stiffly erect, directed upward from an inclined base.

arrhenatherum. 1. The awned staminate floret of grasses. 2. A generic name of a grass.

arrhenokaryon. A nucleus having two separate sets of haploid chromosomes.

arrhenoplasm. Male protoplasm.

arrhenotoky. The parthenogenetical production of eggs which produce males exclusively.

arrhizal. Rootless.

arrhizoblastus. An embryo which does not have a radicle.

arrow. The uppermost joint of the culm of the sugar cane, the inflorescence.

arrow root. A pure starch obtained from some plants.

arroyo. A dry water course, a wed.

artemisietum. An association of plants belonging to *Artemisia*, a large genus of asteraceous plants.

artemisiifolious. Having leaves like *Artemisia*, wormwood or sage brush.

arthonoid. Resembling the apothecium of the lichen *Arthonia*.

arthrodactylous. Joined like a finger, as the ultimate rays of the alga *Nitella*.

arthrodesmoid. Resembling the form of the genus *Arthrodesmus*.

arthrogenous. Describing the separation of portions of cells and their gradual development into distinct individuals.

arthrogenous spores. Spores formed from portions of some bacterial cells, these portions having become separate from the cells; see ARTHROSPORES.

arthrophytes. The *Equisetales*. See SPHENOPSIDA.

arthrospores. 1. Spores formed by segmentation. 2. Thick-walled vegetative spores produced by certain algae. Opposed to ENDOSPORES.

arthrosporic. Applied to those *Schizomycetes* which have no endogenous spore formation; arthrosporous.

arthrosterigma. A jointed sterigma found in some lichens which is composed of cells from which spores are abstricted.

article. A joint of a stem or fruit body.

articular membrane. A membrane consisting of the thin enlarged base of the petiole on which the leaf scar occurs.

articular tegment. Articular membrane.

articulate. 1. Jointed. 2. Having joints or nodes where natural separation may take place. 3. Of teeth of peristome, marked by cross bars.

articulation. 1. A joint, a node. 2. A septum. 3. A segment which is marked or separated by a joint. 4. The basal portion of the sensitive bristle in *Dionaea*.

articuli. The segments of coralline algae, usually incrusted with lime.

artifact. A substance or structure which does not naturally exist but which results from laboratory treatment.

artificial. Term applied to any scheme of classification which is based on one or a few characters as opposed to a natural scheme which takes all characteristics into account; not natural, synthetic.

artificial community. A plant community kept in existence by artificial means, e.g., a garden.

artificial parthenogenesis. The artificial initiation of the development in an egg without fertilization.

artificial system. A system of classification based on one or a few features and not intended to show true relationships.

artioploid. Applied to even multiples of the gametophytic number.

artiphyllous. Applied to nodes which bear manifest buds.

artocarpous. Of or pertaining to the breadfruit or to the genus *Artocarpus*.

artolin. The proteid in the gluten of wheat.

aruncoid. Having the characteristics of *Spiraea aruncus*.

arundinaceous. Reed-like, having a stem like tall grasses.

arundineous. Reedy or abounding in reeds, like a reed or cane, like the genera *Arundinaria* or *Arundo*.

arvensis. Growing in cultivated fields or ground, pertaining to cultivated fields.

arvum. A grain field.

-as. A patronymic suffix, being derived from.

asafoetida. A gum resin having a persistent alliaceous odor and taste, obtained from *Ferula* and related forms.

asarifolious. *Asarum*-leaved.

asarin. A bitter derivative of *Asarum*.

asarine. A crystallized substance resembling camphor.

ascalonicus. Of Ascalon, Syria.

ascan. Pertaining to or produced in an ascus.

ascellus. The diminutive of ascus (used to denote the spores of certain fungi).

ascendant. Rising upward, as the ascending axis which is oblique at first and then becomes erect; as a flower which stands above the horizontal position; as stems which are directed upward.

ascending. 1. Rising gradually upward; rising obliquely or curving upward from near the base; in an upward direction but not truly erect, opposed to descending. 2. Said of gills in the case of a conical or an expanded pileus.

ascending aestivation. Aestivation in which each petal overlaps the edge of the petal posterior to it.

ascending axis. The stem.

ascending metamorphosis. See PROGRESSIVE METAMORPHOSIS.

ascending ovule. An ovule that is attached above the base of the ovary and directed upward.

-ascens. A suffix meaning becoming, e.g., cinerascens, becoming ash-colored.

ascidiform. Ascidium-shaped, pitcher-shaped.

ascidium. 1. A pitcher-shaped or flask-shaped organ or appendage, as the leaves of *Sarracenia*, *Nepenthes*, etc. 2. Sometimes used to denote the asci of certain fungi.

ascigerous centrum. The specialized tissue arising from the archicarp inside the perithecial wall which gives rise to asci and paraphyses.

asciiform. Hatchet-shaped, in the form of an ascia; see DOLABRIFORM.

asclepiadeous. Having a structure similar to *Asclepias*, the milkweed, or its allies.

asclepiadology. The science concerned with the *Asclepiadeae*.

ascocarp. In ascomycetes, the sporocarp producing asci and ascospores. There are three kinds: the apothecium or discocarp, the perithecium or pyrenocarp, and the cleistothecium or cleistocarp.

ascoconidiophore. An ascus-like conidiophore.

ascoconidium. A conidium in an ascoconidiophore.

ascocyst. A large, empty, hyaline cell having a thick wall which occurs in *Myrionema* and certain other genera; a paraphysis.

ascogenous. 1. Producing asci. 2. Denoting those hyphae of *Ascomycetae* which develop from the ascogonium and give rise to the asci.

ascogonium. The carpogonium or female organ in ascomycetes before fertilization; the cell or group of cells which receives the nuclei from the antheridium and from which ascogenous hyphae arise; an ascogone, an archicarp.

ascolichens. Those lichens in which asci are produced.

ascolocular. Of or pertaining to, or having the characteristics of the subdivision *Ascoloculares.*

ascoma. 1. The receptacle and hymenium of the larger fungi. 2. A disk-like ascocarp found in the *Pezizales* and related orders.

ascomycete. A fungus of the class *Ascomycetae* in which spores are borne in sac-like cells called asci; molds, yeasts, mildews, etc.

ascophore. 1. A structure bearing, producing, or containing asci. 2. An ascus-bearing hypha. 3. An apothecium. 4. The pileus of *Helvellaceae*, etc.

ascophyses. The hyphae which comprise the ascogenous cushion in *Chaetomium.*

ascoplasm. The protoplasm of the ascus.

ascospore. A spore formed in an ascus and characteristic of ascomycetes.

ascostome. The pore in the tip of many asci, an ascospore.

ascostroma. A simple type of fructification in ascomycetes which consists of an undifferentiated mass of tissue or stroma on or in which asci are formed.

ascus. 1. In ascomycetes a large sac-like cell, usually the swollen tip on a hyphal branch in the ascocarp within which ascospores (typically eight) are developed. 2. The theca of *Pezizales*, the cup fungi.

ascus apparatus. The portion of the sporocarp in ascomycetes which consists of asci together with the ascogenous cells.

ascuspore. A pore in the tip of an ascus.

ascus suffultorius. The basidium.

ascyphous. Without scyphi.

asepalous. Without sepals or calyx.

asepsis. The absence of microorganisms or septic material.

aseptate. Having no cross walls, partitions, or septa.

asexual. Neuter, not sexual, without male or female sex organs, having a reproductive process in which no sexual fusions or gametes are involved, sexless, without functioning sex organs, propagating by shoots rather than by seeds.

asexual generation. In alternation of generations, that generation which produces spores asexually but is itself the product of

the sexual act. In ferns, the full-grown leafy plant is the asexual form or sporophyte, and the prothallus is the sexual form or gametophyte.

asexual reproduction. Reproduction without the union of sex cells.

asexual spore. Any spore formed by an asexual reproductive process.

ash-oakwood association. A woodland having a quantity of ash trees with oaks as co-dominants.

ashwood association. An association in which ash trees (*Fraxinus*) are predominant.

asiaticus. Asian.

asincronogonism. Dichogamy.

asiphonogam. A cryptogam fertilized by antherozoids.

asiphonogamic. Without a pollen tube and having the spermatozoids discharged from the antheridium.

asomatic. Denoting those organisms which have only embryonal parts.

asomatophyte. Any plant without permanent tissues but which retains its power of growth and multiplication.

asparagi. The name for turiones on any scaly shoots from an underground root-stock, as asparagus.

asparagin. A common amide which was first obtained from *Asparagus officinalis*. It occurs in other plants. Asparagine.

aspect. A term denoting the seasonal impress of a plant formation, i.e., spring aspect, etc.

aspect society. A plant community dominated at a given season by a species or a group of species.

aspection. The periodic changes in the appearance of the constituent species, such as foliation, flowering, etc., which are reflected in the general physiognomy of any situation or habitat.

aspen. One of the poplar trees, as the quaking aspen, genus *Populus.*

asper. Rough, furnished with harsh hairs, rough with hairs or points.

aspergilliform. 1. Resembling or having the shape of *Aspergillus*, the genus of some common molds. 2. Brush-like or brush-shaped, as the stigmas of some grasses.

aspergillin. A pigment found in the spores of *Aspergillus niger*, the common bread mold.

aspergillosis. An infection in which some species of *Aspergillus* is the causative agent.

aspericaulis. Rough-stemmed.

aspermous. Seedless.

asperous. Scabrous, asperate, rough, harsh.

aspersed. Scattered.

asperulous. Slightly roughened by small points.

asphodeloid. Like *Asphodelus*, a genus of liliaceous plants.

asphyxia. A condition of insensibility in plants which is brought on by the suspension of respiration due to the absence of oxygen.

aspidetum. A bog-marsh plant association of *Carex* and *Aspidium* or *Dryopteris*.

aspidiaria. 1. Lepidodendroid stems when the cortex has been stripped off. 2. Formerly a genus of fossils.

aspidospermotype. A wind-dispersed seed resembling the seed of aspidosperma, which is circular in shape with the weight of the seed in the center.

asplenifolious. Having leaves like the fern genus *Asplenium*.

A-spore. See ALPHA-SPORE.

asporogenic. Not forming spores.

asporogenous yeast. A yeast which reproduces asexually by budding and does not produce ascospores.

asporomycetes. *Fungi Imperfecti.*

assembly. The smallest community units, as plants found on fallen logs or on a dead animal, etc.

asser. A branch, beam, or post.

assimilata. The first-formed products.

assimilates. Plant foods converted into living protoplasm through plant activities.

assimilation. The actual incorporation of nonliving matter into living protoplasm; the conversion of foreign material into the substance of the plant; the vegetative and nonreproductive production of living matter.

assimilation number. The calculation of the amount of photosynthesis taking place in a leaf in a given time with a specific amount of chlorophyll present.

assimilation quotient. The relation of the volume of carbon dioxide absorbed to that of oxygen set free in a given time.

assimilative. Conducive to assimilation.

assimilative filaments. Those filaments which grow intermixed with the sporangia of certain algae, as *Ectocarpus*.

assiminum. See SYNCARPIUM.

association. 1. A plant community of definite floristic composition presenting an essentially uniform physiognomy and growing in uniform habitat conditions; a climax community having two or more dominants. 2. An ecological unit which is smaller than a plant formation, which is sometimes made of associations. 3. The pairing of two threads or half-univalent spiremes to form a univalent chromosome.

association, chief. A stable association.

association, closed. An association in which the ground is fully covered by plants.

association complex. The associations in any unit area taken collectively; a union of associations to form a phytogeographical unit.

association fragments. Aspects of an association which vary from the normal or optimal.

association, intermediate. An association in which the ground is more or less covered.

association, mixed. An association in which several species are competing for dominance.

association, open. An association partly covered with vegetation.

association passage. A plant avenue leading from one association to another.

association, progressive. An association which is open and intermediate and tending toward stability.

association, pure. An association in which a single species is dominant.

association, retrogressive. A stable association which is decaying.

association, stable. An association which is in a state of equilibrium.

association, subordinate. A progressive or retrogressive association.

association, substitute. A secondary formation.

association, transitional. An association in the course of development.

association type. 1. All associations which resemble one another in physiognomy and ecological structure. 2. Associations which are formed from the series of associations which inhabit them.

association, unstable. An association leading to an intermediate association.

associes. Transitory units; the developmental units of consocies; a nonpermanent community to be replaced by another in the process of development or association.

associon. A stable synusium which is composed of one or more consocions and which is dominated by a definite group of species.

associule. A microcommunity of associes-rank in a serule.

assoziations-individuum. A concrete example or strand (relict after man) of a given association.

assumenta. The valves of a silique.

assurgentiflorous. Bearing ascending flowers.

astathe. A substance which was supposed to be located between the outer and inner lining of a cell; a secondary membrane.

astaxanthin. A pigment found in some algae, as the *Euglenophyta*.

astely. The condition of lacking a stele or the axial cylinder of tissue.

aster. 1. A stage in nuclear division in which the chromatin forms rods over a great part of the nucleus with its poles being occupied by fine achromatic filaments. 2. The radiating star-shaped figure which surrounds the centrosome in a cell during mitosis. 3. The type genus of the family *Asteraceae*.

astericetum. An association of asters.

asteridia. Spinous or stellate bodies which occur in the cells of the *Conjugatae*, possibly as some parasitic form.

asterigmate. Not borne on sterigmata.

asterile. A society of asters.

asterineous. Star-like, radiate.

asteroid. Stellate, radiate, of or pertaining to the genus *Aster* or the family *Asteraceae*; see ACTINIFORM.

asteroma-like. With a radiating subicle.

asterophysis. A star-shaped sterile stalk characteristic of the spore-bearing surface of some fungi.

asterosphaeria. See ASTERIDIA.

asthenic. Tall and slender, leptosome.

astichous. Not arranged in rows.

astigmatae. The archegoniatae.

astigmaticae. Wind-pollinated plants which do not have stigmas, as gymnosperms.

astilic. Astelic.

astipulate. Exstipulate.

astomatous. Without pores in the epidermis, not having a stoma, lacking breathing pores.

astomous. Bursting or opening irregularly, as moss sporangia which lack a regularly dehiscent operculum or lid.

astragaloid. Dice-shaped, of or pertaining to the genus *Astragalus*.

astral. Of or pertaining to the aster in cytology.

astral ray. One of the fibrils in the cytoplasm which seem to play a part in the delimitation of ascospores.

astrocenter. The central body; the bodies which are variously known as attraction spheres, directive spheres, etc.; centrosomes.

astromatoid. Without stroma.

astrophe. See APOSTROPHE.

astrophiolate. Having no strophiole.

astrosclereids. Certain thick-walled, star-shaped cells occurring in some leaves, bark, and surrounding parenchyma cells.

astrosphere. The central mass of the aster exclusive of the rays, an aster exclusive of a centrosome, an astrocenter.

asturicus. Of Asturias, Spain.

asymblasty. The various periods of germination of the seeds of the same plants.

asymmetrical. Not isobilateral, zygomorphic, irregular in outline or shape.

asymmetricous. Irregular in outline or shape, indivisible into two symmetrical halves in any vertical plane, having two sides unlike.

asymptotic populations. Those populations which have attained a size beyond which they will not increase no matter how long they are allowed to reproduce provided that the environment remains constant.

asyngamy. The condition in which two species or individuals cannot be cross-pollinated because the flowers develop at different times.

asynthetic gonidia. The free lichen gonidia which are found on the outside of the thallus.

atactodesmic. Having the scattered vascular bundles characteristic of the monocotyledons.

atactosteles. 1. The monosteles of monocotyledons which have scattered vascular bundles embedded in conjunctive ground-tissue. 2. Meristeles of dicotyledons which are not arranged in a single circle.

atavism. The appearance of grandparental characters in an individual, contrasted with reversion, which is the appearance of more distant ancestral characters; the resemblance to some remote ancestors or the reappearance of a character after a lapse of one or more generations; the reversion to a primitive type.

atavism, false. Vicinism, variation due to uncontrolled pollination causing reversion to undesirable types or primitive types, a throwback.

atavist. A plant showing atavistic tendencies.

ataxinomic. Used for teratologic abnormal structures which are not seen when the plants are in a normal condition, as fasciation, chloranthy, etc.

ataxonomic. Referring to those parts of botanical science which are not concerned with systematic work.

ategminous. Having naked ovules.

ateleosis. Dwarfism in which the proportions are normal but the parts are of reduced size.

atelomitic. Denoting those chromosomes which have intercalary spindle attachments instead of terminal attachments.

ater. Pure lusterless black, coal black.

athalamous. Said of lichens which do not have apothecia on their thalli.

athera. An arista or awn, a stiff bristle.

athiorhodaceous. Of or pertaining to a group of purple sulfur bacteria.

athyroid. Resembling *Athyrium*, a small genus of polypodiacious ferns.

atlantic type of distribution. The distribution of plants which occur most frequently along the coast of the Atlantic Ocean.

atmobios. Organisms which live in the air.

atmograph. An instrument used for recording the amount of water which is evaporated.

atmometer. An instrument used in measuring evaporation.

atoll. 1. A ring-shaped coral island nearly or quite enclosing a lagoon. 2. A term for circular zones of *Sphagnum* due to a season of regression of the water of a pond which is followed by a year of increase in area and level.

atomarius. Speckled.

atomate. Said of the pileus or stem when it is covered with minute, shining, point-like particles.

atomogynia. The angiosperms of Linnaeus.

Atracheata. The bryophytes.

atractenchyma. Prosenchyma, a tissue made up of fusiform cells.

atramentarious. See ATROUS.

atrial. See ATRIUM.

atrichous. Without flagella or cilia.

atricolor. Inky black; see ATROUS.

atriplicetum. An association of species of *Atriplex* with *Suaeda* and similar plants.

atrium. A pore or canal through which air and infection can enter.

atro-. A prefix meaning black.

atrocarpous. Dark-fruited.

atrocyaneous. A dull dark blue.

atro-fuscus. Dark.

atro-nitidus. Black and shining.

atropal. Atropous, orthotropous.

atrophic. Aplastic, undergoing or having undergone atrophy, not eating or digesting food.

atrophy. The abortion or degeneration of organs or parts, a stopping of growth or development, a dwarfed or stunted condition.

atrophytes. Those fungi which cause atrophy of various organs of the host plant.

atropiceous. Black as pitch.

atropine. A poisonous alkaloid which is obtained from *Atropa Belladonna*.

atropous. Not turned or inverted, e.g., an ovule which is borne on a line with the funiculus; see ORTHOTROPOUS.

atropurpureous. Dark purple.

atrorubens. Dark red.

atrosanguineous. Dark blood-red; see ATROPURPUREOUS.

atrous. Dark gray to dead black.

atroviolaceous. Dark violet.

atrovirent. Dark, dull yellow green.

atrovirid. Deep dark green.

atrygia. Self-sterility.

attachment. A union, a joint, a fusion, the permanent fusion of any two parts.

attachment area. The place of junction on the anterior schizont in the *Peridinales*.

attachment constriction. A constriction in a chromosome to which the spindle fiber is attached.

attachment disc. A holdfast of an alga.

attachment organ. 1. A disc-like or branched outgrowth from the base of the thallus attaching an alga to a solid object. 2. A hooked barb or similar structure which serves to attach a fruit to an animal, thereby assisting dispersal.

attenuate. Tapering slenderly, becoming narrower, drawn to a point, devitalized, weakened, with pathogenicity lessened.

atterminal. Toward a terminal.

atticus. Of or pertaining to Attica or Athens, Greece.

attire. An obsolete term once used for stamens and pistils.

attolens. Raising.

attraction glands. Glands found in some plants, as *Nepenthes.* which lure insects further down into the tube of the flower.

attraction sphere. A small body situated on or near the nucleus in the cells of some lower plants consisting of two centrospheres containing centrosomes. It exercises an important function in mitosis.

attraction spindle. The pole of the spindle toward which the divided chromosomes are drawn during cell division.

attrita terra. Bad lands.

-atus. A suffix used to denote the presence of some organ or part.

atypic. 1. Not typical, departing from type. 2. In mytosis, having indirect nuclear division which does not proceed normally. See ALLOTYPIC MITOSIS.

aubretioid. Like the genus *Aubretia*, purple rock cress, a crucifer.

auctus. Augmented, enlarged by an addition, enlarged after flowering, accrescent.

aucuparious. Attracting birds, used in bird snaring and baiting.

Aufnahme. An analytic study of the flora of a region; see SOCIOLOGICAL RELEVE.

augment cells. The modification of an auxospore in diatoms. When it becomes transformed into daughter cells by division, the daughter cells become the starting points of new generations.

augmentation. The increase beyond the normal number of parts, especially applied to the production of additional floral whorls.

aulacanthous. Said of the stem-cortex of *Characeae* in which the secondary grooves are more prominent than the primary and have spine cells in the furrow.

aulacocarpous. Having a furrowed fruit, sulcate.

aulaeum. The corolla.

aulax-galls. Galls frequently produced on certain plants by gall wasps of the genus *Aulax*. These galls frequently resemble stone fruits in general external appearance.

aulogamae. The *Muscineae*, the mosses.

aulophyte. A plant living in another plant for shelter only and not parasitic upon it, as some *Protococcaceae*.

auranthiaceous. Of an orange color darker than aureus.

aurantiacous. Orange or golden colored.

aurantifolious. Having golden leaves.

aurantium. A succulent superior fruit which has a rough rind, as the orange (*Citrus aurantium*).

auratus. Metallic yellow, golden yellow, yellow with golden luster.

aurea. A plant lacking or deficient in chlorophyll.

aureous. Golden yellow, golden, glowing yellow but not metallic.

auricle. 1. A small lobe or ear-shaped appendage frequently found at the base of leaves. 2. Any ear-shaped structure. 3. A small patch of cells at the basal angle of the leaves in mosses. 4. The minor lobes of *Hepaticae*.

auricomous. Golden-haired.

auricula. The specific name of a yellow-flowered European primrose (*Primula auricula*); see AURICLE.

aurigo. A disease of leaves in which they have a yellow color due to intumescence.

aurofusarin. An orange-yellow pigment found in *Fusarium colmorum*.

auroglaucin. A golden-orange pigment from *Aspergillus* spp.

auroral. 1. From the first appearance of dawn until midmorning. 2. Of, pertaining to, or resembling the aurora. 3. Rosy or golden.

australiensis. Of or pertaining to Australia.

australis. 1. Southern. 2. Sometimes applied to plants native to warmer countries even if they are not from the Southern Hemisphere.

austriacus. Austrian.

austrinus. Southern.

autacoid. An internal solution such as a hormone, etc.; a substance produced in one part of a plant which is transported to another part where it produces its effect; autocoid.

autaesthesia. Sensitivity to some internal stimulus.

autallogamia. Normal pollination.

autallogamy. Homodichogamy, the existence of homogamous and dichogamous individuals in the same species.

autamphinereids. Autotrophic amphibious plants.

autatrygia. Self-sterility, the need of a stigma for pollen from another flower or plant to achieve fertility.

autecology. Autoecology, the relations of individual plants to their habitats, the relations and adaptation of individual species to their environments; see SYNECOLOGY.

autembryosperm. The parthenosperm in which the endosperm is the result of fertilization by pollen from the same flower.

autendosperm. A plant in which the embryo is the result of fertilization by the pollen from the flower which produces the seed.

auten-form. Applied to rusts which are autoecious and have all spore stages.

autephaptomenon. The autotrophic type of plants in which are included those which are half-parasitic.

auteuform. An autoecious rust having all spore stages, an eu-form.

autoallogamy. That condition of a species when some individuals are adapted for self-fertilization and others for cross-pollination.

autobasidiomycetes. A group of basidiomycetes composed of the subordinate groups, hymenomycetes and gasteromycetes, which usually have four basidiospores.

autobasidium. An individual basidium in which nuclear division is not followed by septation.

autobiology. Autecology.

autoblasts. Bacteria and other minute organisms which are called independent bioblasts.

autobolites. The product derived from division of the living protoplasm.

autocarp. A fruit resulting from self-fertilization.

autocarpous. 1. Developed from a self-fertilized flower. 2. Consisting of the pericarp alone and having no adnate parts. 3. Developed from a superior ovary which was not adherent to the calyx.

autocarpotropic. Having fruit naturally separated into segments.

autocarpy. The fruiting of a self-fertilized flower, the product of autogamy.

autocatalysis. 1. Self-fermentation. 2. The dissolution or reaction of a cell or substance due to the influence or secretion from the cell itself.

autochore. Motile plants or plants having motile spores.

autochoric. Of or pertaining to plants which are distributed by their own movements.

autochorologic. Denoting the self-distribution of plants as systematic units such as species, genus, or family; isogenotypic.

autochronologic. Self-timed, as of fossils.

autochthon. An indigenous plant, an aboriginal form.

autochthonous. 1. Autochthonal. 2. Of characteristics, those which are inherited or hereditary. 3. Of the autochthonal theory, which states that each species originated where it is now found. 4. Native.

autoclave. 1. A sterilizing instrument utilizing steam under pressure. 2. To sterilize with pressurized steam.

autocoid. See AUTACOID.

autocolony. 1. The product of a mother cell in coenobic algae. 2. Plants living beyond their usual range.

autodeliquescent. Becoming liquid by a process of autodigestion, as in the mushroom of the genus *Coprinus*.

autodepletion. Self-digestion of endosperm as in the case of certain grasses and palms.

autodifferentiation. The inherent power of some organisms to vary.

autodigestion. Self-digestion of reserve food material.

autoecious. Said of a parasitic fungus which inhabits the same host plant through all of its stages of growth; autoxenous.

autoecism. The condition in which a parasite runs its entire course on a single host of a particular species.

autoecology. See AUTECOLOGY.

autoeuforms. Those species of *Puccinia* which produce every kind of spore on the same host.

autofecundation. Self-fertilization.

autogamous. Requiring only one individual to accomplish self-fertilization.

autogamy. 1. Self-fertilization, the fertilization of a flower by its own pollen. 2. The fusion of nuclei in pairs within a single cell of the female organ but not accompanied by cell fusion.

autogenesis. Self-production, spontaneous generation, autogeny.

autogenetic. Self-derived.

autogenetic-fertilization. Self-pollination.

autogenetics. Changes of floras which result from the condition of the district and the plants themselves.

autogenotypic. See ISOGENOTYPIC.

autogenous. Self-originating, applied to diseases which have their origin or cause within the affected organism; a vaccine made from a patient's bacteria rather than from stock cultures of bacteria.

autogenus. Monogenus, a term suggested in place of monotypic to indicate that the genus contains only a single species.

autogeny. See AUTOGENOUS.

autogony. See AUTOGENESIS.

autohybridization. Natural crossing.

autoicous. Said of those mosses which have both archegonia and antheridia on the same plant but in separate clusters.

auto-infection. Self-infection, reinfection of a host by an organism already parasitic on it.

auto-intoxication. Poisoning of self by poison produced within the body, reabsorption of a toxic substance produced by the body.

auto-irrigation. The automatic addition of water to a culture.

auto-irrigator. Apparatus used in auto-irrigation.

autolysis. The breakdown of the contents of a cell or an organ by the action of enzymes produced in the cells themselves; self-digestion.

autolytic. Denoting those structures produced by a cell for its own destruction.

automatic. Referring to the spontaneous movement of certain parts, as in the case of the leaflets of *Desmodium gyrans*.

automatism. Involuntary action, the state of being automatic.

automixis. Self-fertilization which follows the copulation of two closely related sex cells or sex nuclei.

automorphosis. See MUTATION.

autonarcosis. The state of being poisoned, rendered dormant, or arrested in growth owing to the self-production of carbon dioxide.

autonastism. The curvature of an organism which is not caused by any outside force.

autonereids. Autotrophic water-plants.

autonomic. Denoting those plants which are perfect or complete in themselves and which are not simply phases of other forms as a stage or cycle in the life history or development of an organism.

autonomic movements. Those movements which result from inner impulses.

autonomous. Existing independently of other plants, said of autotrophic land plants which possess chlorophyll and are independent of other plants.

autonomous movements. Spontaneous movements, movements originating from inherent tendencies.

autonyctitrophic. Denoting those plants which spontaneously assume the position usual during the night; see PHOTOPERIODISM.

autonyctonastic. See AUTONYCTITROPHIC.

autoorthotropism. The tendency of an organ to grow forward in a straight line.

autoparasite. A parasite growing upon another parasite, secondary parasitism.

autoparthenogenesis. The development from unfertilized eggs which are activated by chemical or physical stimuli.

autopelagic. Denoting plankton which live on the surface all of the time.

autophagy. 1. Complete fusion of gametes. 2. Self-devouring, eating one's own tissue.

autophagy, reciprocal. See SEXUAL AUTOPHAGY.

autophagy, sexual. The sexuality in primitive forms of algae further differentiated into protogamy, hologamy, and merogamy.

autophilous. Self-pollinated, autogamous.

autophyllogeny. The growth of one leaf upon or out of another.

autophyte. A plant capable of manufacturing its own food; the opposite of saprophyte or parasite.

autoplast. A plastid, a chlorophyll granule.

autoploid. A polyploid resulting from the duplication of a single genom.

autopolyploid. A polyploid having similar sets of chromosomes, an organism with more than two haploid sets of chromosomes which have come from the same parent species.

autopotamic. Denoting algae which have become adapted to living in streams or algae which are adapted to inland waters, modified tychopotamic plankton.

autopsia. The careful inspection of a plant or phenomenon.

autopta. An observer who makes an autopsy or autopsia.

autoscoliotropous. Having the tendency to grow in a curved line.

autosome. A typical chromosome other than the sex chromosome.

autosperm. A plant whose embryo arises through autogamy.

autospore. 1. A spore-like body arising from the division of the protoplast which usually assumes the character of mother cells before being liberated. 2. In lichens, the daughter gonidia.

autosymbiontic. Denoting those cephalodia which have similar commensals.

autosyndesis. The pairing in a polyploid of chromosomes which are derived from the same parent.

autosynthetic. Able to reproduce itself.

autotemnous. Capable of spontaneous division, as ordinary growing cells.

autotetraploid. A tetraploid with four identical sets of chromosomes.

autotoxin. A toxin or poison originating with the body.

autotroph. A plant that requires only inorganic substances and light as an energy source for growth and development.

autotrophic. Capable of procuring food independently; applied to those bacteria which act directly on mineral matter, i.e., which are able to utilize carbon dioxide in assimilation.

autotrophic lakes. Lakes which are dependent upon internal forces for their supply of organic matter; see AUTONOMOUS and AUTEPHAPTOMENON.

autotrophic nutrition. Complete self-nutrition.

autotropism. The tendency of any organism to grow in a straight line.

autoxenous. See AUTOECIOUS.

autoxidation. The slow oxidation of certain substances due to exposure to air or a second substance, auto-oxidation.

autoxidators. 1. The olefine-oxygen compounds which act as carriers or intermediate agents during oxidation during the autoxidation process. 2. Cell substances which can, by absorption of molecular oxygen, be oxidized by decomposing water.

autumnal wood. The wood formed at the end of the growing season notable for its smaller cells.

autumnal xanthophyll. The yellow coloring matter in leaves.

auxablast. Any shoot which can serve for vegetative reproduction.

auxanagrammes. Bacterial fields of increase which are marked by greater development within the diffusion area of a nutrient substance.

auxanometer. The apparatus used in measurement of the increase of growth in plants.

auxesis. 1. The increase or dilation in the valves of diatoms. 2. The new formation of organs. 3. The predominance of leaves, hairs, etc., on a particular side.

auxetics. Chemical agents which cause cell divisions.

auxiliaries. Synergids.

auxiliary cells. The cells with which the carpogonial filament fuses after fertilization in the red algae.

auxiliary vesicles. Synergids, the nuclei which constitute the egg-apparatus.

auximone. See AUXIN.

auxin. An accessory growth-promoting substance in the food of plants, a hormone produced in the tips of plants which travels through the plant from cell to cell. Auxin veers away from light and causes the plant to grow faster on one side and curve toward light.

auxocyte. The spermatocyte, oocyte, or sporocyte during the growth period.

auxosis. A change in the general growth period of an organ.

auxospireme. A spireme formed after syndesis, vaguely applied to the spireme of auxocytes.

auxospore. A rejuvenating spore found in the diatoms. It forms as a result of shedding the cell wall, enlargement, and formation of a new cell wall.

auxotonic. Denoting those movements incident to an increase in size of growing organs.

auxotonic movements. Those made by growing organs such as twining stems, etc.

available water. The total amount of water available in the soil at a given time which can be used by plants.

avellaneous. Drab, hazel, hazelnut brown.

avenaceous. Like oats, the genus *Avena*.

avenine. A substance obtained from oats.

avenius. Veinless or apparently so.

average deviation. A mathematical expression measuring variability obtained by averaging the deviation of all individuals from the mean of the race or population.

average distance. A computation which

equals the square root of the area divided by density computed for each species.

averruncation. Pruning, uprooting, clearing.

averse. Turned back, turned or facing away from the central axis or other object.

avicennia. 1. The bark of the mangrove tree used for tanning. 2. The generic name of the mangrove trees and shrubs which grow in swampy land in the tropics.

avicennietum. A mangrove community.

avicularis. Pertaining to birds.

avitaminosis. A disease caused by vitamin deficiency.

avocado. The large pear-shaped, oblong, or nearly globular fruit of *Persea americana*.

avoform. The still-existing stem-form of *Ramiform* and *Praeform*.

avulsus. Torn off, separate.

awl-shaped. Narrow and tapering to a point, subulate, sharp-pointed from a broader base.

awn. 1. A slender bristle-like organ or beard of a grass. 2. In *Chaetoceras*, a diatom, prolongations of the frustules which resemble the beards of certain grasses.

axenic. Germ-free, gnotobiotic.

axeny. 1. Passive resistance by a plant to disease organisms. 2. Freedom from pathogenic or foreign materials. 3. Inhospitality to outside influences.

ax-form. Having the form of an axe or hatchet; see DOLABRIFORM.

axial. 1. Of or pertaining to an axis. 2. The upper angle between a leaf and the stem on which it is borne. 3. The smooth surface between the margins of diatoms.

axial area. The hyaline area which sometimes occurs on the diatom valves on each side of the raphe.

axial cell. A primary cell in the development of the cover cell and the lower central cell in the beginning growth of the archegonium of bryophytes and pteridophytes.

axial filament. The central filament of certain sperm flagella.

axial gradient. A quantitative gradient in specific protoplasm representing a physiological axis and direction of order and a pattern of development.

axial plant body. A plant body which has a stem as an axis.

axial row. The two or more first-formed cells in the embryo sac.

axial shoot. 1. A cylindrical appendage in the axil between stem and leaf in *Zygopteris*. 2. A prolongation of the axial strand, itself the stele of the main stem.

axial wood. The normal central xylem cylinder.

axiate pattern. The arrangement of parts with reference to a definite axis.

axicolous. Growing on the axis.

axiferous. Having an axis but without leaves or other appendages.

axil. 1. The angle between a leaf petiole and the stem on the upper side, usually an acute angle. 2. The angle between an organ and its axis.

axile. 1. In the axis of any structure, situated in or belonging to an axis. 2. Central in position, as in some algae, where the chloroplast is centrally located.

axile placentation. Placentation in which the ovules are borne on a central axis in separate chambers in the fruit.

axile strand. 1. A vascular system with conducting elements in the center of the plant axis giving off strands to the leaves. 2. An equivalent of a prostele but includes the strands present in the larger mosses.

axillant. Subtending an angle.

axillary bud. A lateral bud borne in the axil of a leaf.

axillary ovary. An ovary in which the ovules are attached to a central column in a compound ovary.

axillary placentation. See AXILE PLACENTATION.

axillary shoot or strand. A bundle in *Zygopteris* with a five-lobed vascular cylinder in the main stem.

axis. 1. The line running lengthwise through the center of an organ. 2. The stem or root itself. 3. An imaginary line around which organs develop.

axis, accessory. An axis of secondary rank.

axis, apical. See APICAL AXIS.

axis, appendages of the. Organs, including leaves, flowers, etc.

axis, ascending. The stem.

axis of cell. An imaginary line passing through the nucleus and centrosome of a cell.

axis, descending. The root.

axis of embryo. An imaginary line drawn

through the uncleaved egg in the position of the future anterior-posterior direction.

axis of inflorescence. The part of the stem or branch upon which the flowers are borne.

axis, pervalvar. The main or longitudinal axis in diatoms.

axis, transapical. The axis passing at right angles to the apical axis of diatoms and through the center of the pervalvar axis.

axis, transversal. The axis lying in the transverse plane of diatoms which cuts the pervalvar axis.

axogamy. The condition in which plants bear sexual organs on a leafy stem.

axophyte. A plant having stems and roots, a plant with an axis.

axospermous. Denoting those plants which have axile placentation of ovules.

azaleoid. Like *Azalea*, a large genus of ericaceous shrubs closely related to *Rhododendron*.

azoic. Without life, pertaining to the early lifeless period of the earth.

azonal. Denoting those communities which lack any resemblance to radial symmetry.

azonate. Azonous, without zones, without circular bands of different colors.

azoosporia. Motionless reproductive cells found in certain species of freshwater algae.

azoricus. Of the Azores.

azote. Nitrogen.

azotification. The process of nitrifying.

azotised. Made or compounded with nitrogen.

azotobacteria. Bacteria which are able to change elemental nitrogen into fixed nitrogen.

azureus. Sky-blue.

azygosperm. See AZYGOSPORE.

azygospores. Spores developed from a gamete without conjugation, structures resembling zygospores morphologically but not resulting from previous sexual unions of gametes or of gametangia.

azygote. The offspring of a haploid individual without fertilization, an asexually produced individual.

azygous. Unpaired; without a corresponding part, as a leaflet which does not have another leaflet on the opposite side of the rachis.

azymous. Without fermenting agents, unleavened.

B

B. Used to signify flowers with fully concealed honey.

B¹. A class of flowers similar to B but having the flowers in heads.

B horizon. The lower or second zone or layer of a soil profile upon which humus rests.

B-spore. See BETA SPORE.

babata. Barbate, bearded.

babylonicus. Babylonian.

bacca. A berry or a succulent fruit with seeds embedded in the pulp, as a gooseberry; a berry formed from an inferior ovary.

bacca corticata. A berry with a rind (as melons and oranges), a term usually applied to the ovary.

bacca sicca. Berries which are succulent when unripe but dry when mature, as almonds.

bacca spuria. Any fleshy fruit, as raspberry or strawberry, which is not a true berry.

baccate. Berry-like, pulpy, fleshy.

baccated. Covered with berries or bodies which look like berries.

baccatus. Berried, baccans, having a fleshy or pulpy texture.

baccaularis. A carcerule; a dry indehiscent, many-celled superior fruit.

baccausus. An etaerio, an aggregate fruit composed of achenes or drupes.

baccetum. A syncarp; an aggregation of berries in one flower, as in the mulberry or magnolia.

bacciferous. Producing or having berries.

bacciform. Having the form or shape of a berry; see BACCATE.

bacillar. Rod-shaped, club-shaped, bacilliform.

bacillariophyta. A group of unicellular algae distinguished by the heavily silicified cell with yellow or brown coloring, called diatoms.

bacillicide. An agent which destroys bacilli.

bacilliform. Having the shape of a bacillus, bacillus-like, rod-shaped.

bacillosis. The state of having bacilli present.

bacillus. 1. A rod-shaped bacterium. 2. A genus of the schizomycetes.

back cavity. The inner cavity of a stoma.

back chamber. The part of the porus in a stoma which is above the lower projecting ridges.

back-cross. The cross of a hybrid with one of the parental races, a mating between a heterozygote and a homozygote.

backshore. The part of a shore which is covered by water only during exceptional storms.

bacteremia. The presence of bacteria in the blood stream.

bacteriad. Any bacterium.

bacterial flora. The species of bacteria characteristic of the soil or any other natural media.

bactericidal. Germicidal, killing bacteria.

bactericidin. A substance which kills bacteria without lysis.

bacteriform. Bacterium-like, shaped like bacteria.

bacterin. A bacterial vaccine; a suspension of dead bacterial cells in oil, saline solution, etc.

bacterioblast. A gelatinous body, homogenous at first, then becoming successively finely and coarsely granular, and at last becoming detached bacteria.

bacteriochlorophyll. Chlorophyll found in bacteria.

bacterioids. 1. Bacterial organisms which resemble bacteria in shape, found in the tubercles on the roots of leguminous plants. 2. Degenerate forms occurring in some bacterial situations. 3. Protoplasmic bodies which show Brownian movements and resemble bacteria. See DIPHTHEROIDS.

bacteriology. The science which deals with the form, structure, function, and activities of bacteria.

bacteriolysin. A substance which neutralizes the toxin of bacteria or destroys bacteria, a substance which breaks down bacterial cells.

bacteriophage. A destroyer of bacteria, a bacteriolytic agent.

bacteriophilous. Bacteria-loving.

bacteriopurpurin. A purplish coloring matter which is characteristic of some bacteria.

bacteriorrhiza. A symbiotic relationship between a root and bacteria.

bacteriosis. Any bacterial disease.

bacteriostatic. Having growth-inhibiting substances which prevent multiplication of bacteria but do not destroy them.

bacteriotoxin. 1. Any substance which is poisonous or harmful to bacteria. 2. A toxin produced by bacteria.

bacteriotropin. 1. An ingredient found in blood serum which renders bacteria more readily acted upon by phagocytes. 2. A relatively thermostable substance in immune serum resembling opsonin in its action.

bacterium. A unicellular schizomycetous fungus, the rod-shaped type of the *Bacteria*.

bacteroid tissue. The root tubercles of various plants.

bactrosporous. Having rod-shaped spores.

baculiferous. Having canes or reeds.

baculiform. Stick-shaped, rod-like, like the ascospores of certain lichens.

badious. Bay red, dark reddish, chestnut brown.

badlands. Areas which are severely eroded, the gullies being relatively close together in contrast to a ravined area where the gullies are relatively more widely separated; see ATRITA, TERRA, etc.

baeomycetoid. Like the genus *Baeomyces*, lichens.

bahada (bajada). Alluvial aprons with long straight profiles at the bases of mountains, applied to the slopes in Central America and the southwestern United States; see TALUS.

balance. The condition in which the genes are adjusted in proportions which give satisfactory and normal development of the organism.

balance hair. A stalk bearing a cross beam.

balance, secondary. A new balance derived by change in the proportion of genes, as in a secondary polyploid, from an old balance and capable of competing with it.

balanced solution. A solution of two or more salts in such proportions that the toxic effects of the individual salts are mutually eliminated. Sea water is a balanced solution.

balanophorin. A waxy substance found in quantity in the stems of *Landsdorffia*, a genus of the *Balanophoraceae*, a family of tropical root parasites.

balata. The coagulated latex of the bullet or

sapodilla tree (*Achras Sapota*). It has properties similar to gutta-percha but is softer and more ductile and is used extensively in golf balls and for impregnation of duck belting; the chicle is used in chewing gum.

balausta. Any fruit which is many-seeded, many-celled, and indehiscent and has a tough pericarp, as the pomegranate and similar fruits.

bald. Without pubescence or downy appendages, without a beard or awn.

bald achenes. Achenes which are naked at the summit or without a pappus or crown.

balds. Treeless areas in the Great Smoky Mountains which are dominated by woody ericaceous or herbaceous species and grasses.

bale. The outer glume of grasses.

balearicus. Of or pertaining to the Balearic Islands.

ball. The round central flower of *Stapelia*.

balling. 1. The fusion of nuclei into one nucleus. 2. A method of wrapping to protect plant roots for shipping and replanting.

ballistic fruit. A fruit which discharges its seeds by means of some elastic propulsion, catapult fruit.

ballistospore. A fungus spore which is forcibly ejected from its asymmetrical attachment to the sterigma.

balm (balsam). A thick, usually resinous exudate which is said to have some medical use.

balsa wood. The wood of *Ochroma Lagopus*, corkwood from the West Indies which is highly porous and is valued for its extreme lightness.

balsam. A mixture of resins with volatile oils, the resins being produced from the oils by oxidation so that a balsam may be regarded as an intermediate product between a volatile oil and a perfect resin; a fragrant gum.

balsam of Peru. A tree of medicinal value, *Myroxylon Pereirae*.

balticus. Of or pertaining to the Baltic Sea.

balustra. See BALAUSTA.

bamboo. The stems of certain grasses, especially species of the genus *Bambusa*, one of the largest grass-like plants of the bamboo family.

bambusetum. A tropical bamboo forest association.

bañados. The shallow swamps in Paraguay.

banana. A tropical fruit grown extensively for local use and for export to temperate regions, the elongated thick-skinned yellow berry produced by the tree of the same name.

banaticus. Of or pertaining to Banat in southern Hungary.

Bancroft's law. The proposition that organisms and communities tend to reach a state of equilibrium with their environments.

band. The space between two ridges in the fruit of umbellifers, any stripe between elevated lines or ribs, a broad transverse marking, a vitta.

band-shaped. Linear-shaped, as of long linear leaves.

bands of protoplasm. Strands of protoplasm which cross the vacuole.

bank. The rising ground which borders a lake or river; the margin of a water course.

banner. The standard of a papilionaceous flower, the large erect petal of the leguminosae; see VEXILLUM, STANDARD.

bar. A subaqueous ridge which may completely span a bay, a spit that has one free end, a structure which has risen above the surface of the water and has become a beach.

bar-like thickenings. Ingrowths, especially of the cell wall, which may or may not be branched which protrude into the cell cavity.

bar of Sanio. A horizontal rod or band of thickening consisting of pectic materials or of cellulose occurring between pits in the walls of tracheids and vessels.

barb. A hooked hair which is doubly forked; a sharp reflexed point on an awn or other process; a hair or other process which has such reflexed points or with a reflexed tip; a hooked, hair-like bristle; a straight process armed with one or more teeth which point backward.

barbadensis. Of the Barbados Islands.

barbate. Bearded; with long, weak hairs.

barbellae. 1. The stiff, short, straight hairs formed on the pappus of the *Compositae*. 2. Very small barbs or bristles.

barbellate. Having minute barbs.

barberry. The alternate host of the fungus *Puccinia graminis* which causes black stem rust of the cereal grains. The aecial stage and the pycnial stage occur on this host.

barbigerous. Bearing barbs or beards.

barbinervis. Having bearded or barbed nerves.

barbinoda. Bearded nodes on stems.

barbula. The row of teeth in the peristome of mosses.

barbulate. Finely bearded.

barbule. 1. A small barb. 2. The inner row of teeth in the peristome of such mosses as *Tortula*.

bared. Stripped of bark.

barilla. 1. The crude soda obtained from *Salsola* and allied genera. 2. A term for either species of *Salsola* or saltwort, which yield soda ash when burned.

bark. The outer covering of a trunk or branch, all tissues found outside the cambium, the cortical covering of a stem.

bark-bound. Having the bark tight and impeding growth.

bark-galled. With injured bark.

bark grafting. Grafting in which the scions are inserted between the bark and wood of a stub, erroneously called crown grafting.

bark inhabitants. See ENDOPHLOIC.

bark parenchyma. The cortex parenchyma.

barm. The floating yeast in bread making, the yeast formed in brewing liquors.

barmy. Yeasty, containing yeast, full of barm or froth, in a ferment.

barotaxis. The reaction to a mechanical stimulus, the reaction to the pressure stimulus or barometric stimulus.

barotropism. The tropic response of organisms to a change in barometric pressure.

barrage. The phenomenon of natural repulsion between haploid isolates of *Hymenomycetes* which results in a zone between them barren of mycelium of the two paired haplophytes.

barren flower. The staminate flower, a flower without a gynoecium.

barrier. Any physical or biological force or obstacle that hinders migration, dispersion, or excesis of plants.

bars. The persistent portions in a scalariform perforation.

bartiseaefolious. Leaved like the genus *Bartisia*, herbaceous plants of the arctic-alpine regions.

barymorphosis. A change in an organism as a result of the gravity stimulus.

basal area. The area of the cross-section of a tree expressed in square feet, usually referring to section at breast height (4 1/2 feet).

The sum of the basal area of trees in a forest is the basal area of the stand.

basal body. A granule in the cell from the substance of which a flagellum or cilium grows.

basal cell. 1. A cell at the base or a sister cell below the antheridial mother cell. 2. A cell at the base or insertion of a leaf or scale. 3. The first cell of an angiospermous embryo which becomes attached to the wall of the embryo.

basal cover. The ground surface actually covered by plants.

basal leaf. A leaf produced near the base of a stem.

basal meristem. A full meristem at the base of the part produced by it.

basal-nerved. With nerves radiating from the base of a leaf.

basal placentation. The condition in which the placenta is at the base of the ovary.

basal sheath. The covering which encircles the base of pine leaves.

basal wall. The primary wall in the *Archegoniatae* dividing the oospore into an anterior and a posterior half.

basal walls. The walls which separate the hypobasal and epibasal halves of a fern embryo when it consists of eight cells.

base. 1. The extremity of any organ by which it is attached to its support. 2. The part nearest the stipe of a gill. 3. The extremity opposite the apex.

base leveling. See PENEPLAIN.

base pair. One of the pairs of bases forming the cross-links in the DNA molecule. They are always paired as follows: Adenine and Thymine, Guanine and Cytosine or 5-methyl Cytosine.

baselloid. Like the genus *Basella*, climbing herbaceous plants native to tropical Asia and Africa.

basic. 1. Fundamental. 2. Denoting those stains that act in general on the nuclear contents of a cell. 3. Of dyes, a term applied primarily to the coal tar colors in which the color-determining radical plays the part of a base, e.g., safranin, methyl green, or Bismarck brown. Basic dyes are in general nuclear as distinguished from plasma staining agents.

basic number. The number of chromosomes found in the gametes of a diploid ancestor of a polyploid.

basichromatin. Chromatin, that portion of

the nuclear network stained by basic tar-colors; see BASIC.

basidiocarp. The basidia-producing fructification of the *Basidiomycetes*.

basidiogenetic. Borne or produced on a basidium.

basidiogonidium. The basidiospore.

basidiolichens. The group of lichens embracing the few genera in which the fungus is a basidiomycete.

basidiomycete. Any fungus which produces its spores on basidia.

Basidiomycetes. The large class of the higher fungi having septate mycelia and bearing their spores upon basidia.

basidiophore. A sporophore bearing a basidium.

Basidiorhizae. *Basidiomycetes*.

basidiospore. An asexual spore which is acrogenously abjointed upon a basidium, the spore which is characteristic of *Basidiomycetes*.

basidium. The club-shaped structure characteristic of certain fungi (*Basidiomycetes*) at the tip of which spores (usually four) are produced on short, slender stalks (the sterigmata).

basifixed. Attached by the base or lower end, as an anther is attached to the filament.

basifugal. Developing from the base upward, proceeding away from the base, acropetal, centripetal when applied to the order of inflorescence.

basigamic. Denoting the condition in which the normal position of the egg apparatus and the antipodals is reversed, with the oosphere and the synergids at the lower end of the mother cell of the embryo sac (the endosperm).

basigynium. The stalk of an ovary above the stamens and petals, the stalk of a pistil which elevates it above the receptacle, a carpophore or a thecaphore.

basilar cells. Cells at the base or insertion of the leaf often differing in shape and color from those of the main part of the leaf.

basilatus. Arising from a broad base, as certain hairs, thorns, etc.

basin. 1. The depression at the apex of an apple. 2. The connection between the pouch of certain secretory cells and the cell wall, as in the *Magnoliaceae* and a few other families.

basinerved. With the veins of a leaf or petal starting from the base.

basipetal. With growth in the direction of the base; developing from the apex toward the base; developing downward, as in certain inflorescences.

basipetal sorus. See GRADATE SORUS.

basiphil. Having a strong affinity for basic stains.

basiplast. A leaf whose permanent tissue first appears at the apex while the lower portion continues at meristem for a longer time.

basiramous. Branching from the base.

basiscopic. Looking toward the base, i.e., on the side toward the base; facing the base; the opposite of ACROSCOPIC

basisolutus. Used of such leaves as those of *Sedum*, which are prolonged downward beyond their true origin.

basithecal. Having virescent anthers in which the upper portion is leafy with the pollen-bearing portion extending toward the base.

basitonic. Having the base of the anther against the rostellum.

basitonous. Having the tissue of the pollen sac prolonged to the lower end of the anther.

basophil. A cell that readily takes stains from basic substances, a plant cell whose granules stain only with basic dyes.

bass. See BAST.

bassora gum. A mixture of Indian bassorin gums.

bassorin. A kind of gum of uncertain origin supposed by some to be the product of peach or almond trees or the East Indian tree *Sterulia*; a polysaccharide which is the chief ingredient of bassora gum, tragacanth, and the gum of the stone fruits. Bassorin swells in water but does not dissolve to form a mucilagenous liquid; it is used as an adulterant in tragacanth.

bassorin layer. The layer of tissue in which bassorin is produced.

bast. The inner bark; the inner layer of the fibrous bark; the phloem, the outer part of a fibrovascular bundle that contains the sieve tubes and usually the bast fibers; the long, tapering, thick-walled phloem cells characteristic of such bark.

bast cell. One of the long and tough flexible cells of which bast is composed, the essential component of bast.

bast collenchyma. Tissue composed of cells with side walls thickened on all sides.

bast cylinder. See STEREOME CYLINDER.

bast fibers. The plant fibers of commerce (liber or phloem fibers). They are long, slender, thick-walled cells (sclerenchyma) with tapering ends.

bast group. The phloem tissues and the individual vascular bundles.

bast, hard. Liber fibers, the fibrous part of the phloem.

bast islands. See PHLOEM ISLANDS.

bastnerves. Libriform cells which are found in the leaves of *Naja graminea*.

bast parenchyma cells. Tissues of the parenchymatic class, sometimes sclerenchymatous; those cells which arise from one and the same cambial fiber forming a bast parenchyma fiber.

bast rays. See MEDULLARY RAYS.

bast sheath. The layer of thin-walled cells surrounding the fibrovascular cylinder next within the cortex; see PHLOEM SHEATH, PERIPHLOEM.

bast, soft. The portion of the phloem which is composed of sieve tubes, the thin-walled tissue of phloem which is not lignified.

bast tissue. See PHLOEM.

bast vessel. See SIEVE-TUBE.

bast wedges. Groups of phloem which in section are wider toward the outward edge.

bastard embryosperm. A plant which has a parthenogenetic embryo with the effective pollen derived from another individual or variety.

bastard endosperm. Any plant which has a parthenogenetic endosperm with the effective pollen derived from another individual or variety.

bastardocarpy. The production of fruits by hybrids.

Batesian mimicry. The external resemblance for protective purposes of a palatable species to a distasteful one.

bat flower. A flower pollinated by bats.

bathile. Of or pertaining to lake bottoms of deep waters, below 25 meters.

bathmism. The force or energy of growth.

bathybic. Of or pertaining to organisms living in the deepest parts of the sea.

bathylimnetic. Denoting those plants occurring in deep water, either floating or rooted.

bathymetry. The distribution of plants on the sea bottom and the depths at which they grow.

bathypelagic. Inhabiting the deep sea, used to denote masses of plankton which daily descend from the surface.

bathyphilous. Dwelling in lowlands.

bathyphytium. A lowland plant formation.

bathysmal. In the deepest depths of the sea.

batology. The study of brambles and forms of *Rubus*.

batrachietum. An association of any water crowfoot or any form of the *Batrachium* section of the *Ranunculaceae*.

bavaricus. Of or pertaining to Bavaria.

bay. Reddish brown or chestnut color, dun color, badious.

bays. The recesses or undulations of cell walls.

beach. The shore of a sea or of a lake that is washed by waves, the strand.

beaded. 1. Of gills, with a row of droplets exuded from the edge. 2. In stab or streak bacterial cultures, with disjointed or semi-confluent colonies along the line of inoculations. 3. Having tufts of long hairs or awns.

beak. 1. A pointed projection, a narrow prolonged tip, a long process resembling the beak of a bird. 2. The long point at the tip of the operculum of mosses.

bean. Common name applied to the plant, fruit, or seed of certain species of *Phaseolus*.

beard. An awn, barbed or bristly hair-like outgrowth on grains, long or stiff hair of any kind.

beardletted. Having minute barbs or awns.

bearers. Carriers, flower buds.

bebeerin. An alkaloid obtained from the greenheart, *Nectandria Rodiaei*. The native name is *bebeeru*.

bedding. The growing of plants in garden beds.

bedeguar. A mossy red gall on the common wild rose once supposed to have medicinal value.

bee bread. A yellowish-brown, bitter substance consisting of pollen stored in the honeycomb used mixed with honey as food by bees.

bee bread flowers. Flowers which afford honey to an insect having a proboscis 7 mm (.275 in.) long.

beech. The common name applied to species of the genus *Fagus*.

beechwood association. A natural association of beech trees.

beggiatoetum. An association of *Beggiatoa*, a genus of motile filamentous bacteria some of which are able to reduce sulphur compounds.

Begleiter. Companion species.

behavior. The sum total of the reactions of a plant or animal to its environment.

behind. Of gills, toward the stipe.

belemnoid. Dart-shaped.

belisand. Heath sand which is very poor in soil nutrients since the humus-formed acids in the soil have been removed by the percolation of water.

bell nucleus. A solid mass of cells derived from the ectoderm lying between the ordinary ectoderm and the mesogloea at the apex of the medusoid bud.

bell-shaped. Campanulate, expanding from a short rounded base to a spreading border.

bellwort. Any campanulaceous plant or any liliaceous plant of the genus *Uvularia* having bell-shaped flowers.

bellying. Swelling out on one side, as the tube of the corolla in many species of *Labiatae.*

belts. Zones of vegetation in mountain altitudes and those created by edaphic conditions on the borders of lakes, streams, etc., usually more or less concentric; see ZONATION.

belt transect. A strip of a few inches, feet, or yards in width with the constituent plants recorded.

Beltian bodies. See BELT'S CORPUSCLES.

Belt's corpuscles. The food bodies found in certain species of *Acacia* eaten by ants.

Benedict's solution. A solution used in sugar tests.

benghalensis. Of or pertaining to Bengal in eastern India.

bennettitean. Of or pertaining to the fossil genus *Bennettites*, a fossil gymnosperm.

benthic. Of or pertaining to benthos or benthon, living and generally attached to the bottom of aquatic habitats.

benthon, benthos. The attached aquatic plant or animal organisms as distinct from the free-floating forms as plankton, etc.

benthon, nectonic. Organisms which float freely.

benthon, sessile. Aquatic plants which remain attached.

benthon, vagil. Wandering organisms.

benthophyte. A plant whose habitat is at the bottom of a sea, lake, or stream.

benthopotamous. Living on the bottom of a river or stream.

benzoin. A fragrant resinous exudation from *Styrax Benzoin*, a small genus of aromatic shrubs or trees native to eastern North America and eastern Asia.

benzoloid. Having a fragrance derived from an aromatic body such as eugenol (oil of cloves), flowers of heliotrope, lilac, etc.

berberine. A yellow bitter substance derived from the root of *Berberis vulgaris.*

bergamot. 1. A variety of citrus fruit whose rind is the source of an essential oil much used in perfumery. 2. Any of several species of the mints. 3. A variety of pears.

Bergeria. A lepidodendron stem from which the epidermis has been stripped, a fossil tree.

berolinensis. Of or pertaining to Berlin.

berry. A fleshy fruit without a stone usually containing many seeds embedded in the pulp. It is called a bacca when formed from an inferior ovary, a uva when formed from a superior ovary.

berry cone. The ripened cone or strobilus of certain coniferous plants in which the scales are fleshy and fused together, as in *Juniperus.*

besimen. A spore.

besom. The broom, the heath.

Bestand. A durable form, a unit area, an association.

beta. The beet.

beta spore. A usually sterile spore in the imperfect stage of the genera of *Diaporthaceae*. It is usually hyaline, one-celled, filiform, and allantoid or curved and develops after the first (alpha) spore; see ALPHA SPORE.

betaceous. Beet-like.

betain. An amide-like substance derived from *Beta*, the beet.

betonicaefolious, betonicifolious. Leaved like *Betonica*, a European mint.

betulaefolious. Having leaves like *Betula*, the birches.

betulase. An enzyme, the same as gaultherase, which is obtained from the bark of *Betula lenta.*

betulase hylocomiosa. An association of birch and *Hylocomium.*

betuleta cladonosa. An association of birch with the lichen *Cladonia.*

betuletum. An association of birch trees.

betulicole. Growing on birches.

betulin. A substance which is derived from the outer bark of birch.

betuline. Birchen, of or pertaining to birch.

between races. A classification for an intermediate variety, one which differs superficially from the species from which it originated.

bi. bi-. A prefix meaning twice, two, or having two.

biachaenium. A schizocarp which has two carpels, as in *Galium.*

biacuminate. Having two tapering points.

biaiometamorphosis. A disadvantageous change in response to a stimulus.

biaiomorphose. The form produced by biaiometamorphosis or biaiomorphosis.

Bianconi's plate. A plate of sclerenchymatous fibers near the vascular bundles toward the concave or sensitive face of tendrils.

biangulate. With two angles or corners.

biarticulate. Double-jointed.

biastrepsis. Torsion, the condition of transition from decussate to spiral phyllotaxis.

biatorine. Resembling the lichen genus *Biatora* with soft, waxy, often highly colored apothecia.

biatoroid. With apothecia similar to those of the *Biatora* section of species of *Lecidea.*

biauriculate. With two ear-like appendages.

biaurite. See BIAURICULATE.

biaxial. Denoting spores which germinate at both ends.

bibacca. A double berry as produced by some species of *Lonicera*, the honeysuckle.

bibracteate. Having two bracts.

bibracteolate. With two bracteoles.

bibulous. Capable of absorbing moisture.

bicalcarate. Having two spurs.

bicallose. Having two small hard spots or protuberances, having two callosities.

bicapsular. Having two capsules or a bilocular capsule.

bicarinate. Having two keels, as the upper palea of grasses.

bicarpals. A series of phanerogams which are gamopetalous and have two carpels.

bicarpellary. Having two carpels or pistils; see DICARPELLARY.

bicarpellate. With a two-celled fruit, with two carpels.

bicaudate. Having two tail-like processes.

bicellular. Composed of two cells.

bicephalous. Having two heads.

bichronic. Applied to an equation in which the mutations multiplied by the intervals of time equal the biologic time.

biciliate. Having two cilia.

bicipital. With two stalks or two supports, two-headed, dividing into two parts at one extremity.

biclavuligerate. Bearing two club-shaped branches.

bicollateral. 1. Having two sides alike. 2. Applied to vascular bundles which have two groups of phloem lying on opposite sides of the xylem, having phloem on the outer or inner faces of the xylem.

bicompound. Twice compounded.

biconcentric. Applied to the fibro-vascular bundles in *Eriocauleae*, having the axial hadrome bundle enclosed in a layer of leptome which in turn is enclosed in a second hadrome layer.

biconic. Being conical at each end.

biconjugate. Twice-paired, as when a petiole forks twice and each of the secondary petioles bears a pair of leaflets.

biconjugate-pinnatus. Similar to biconjugate but each petiole is pinnate.

biconvex. Convex on both sides, lens-shaped.

bicornes. The heaths because of their two-horned anthers.

bicorticus. Having two barks.

bicostate. With a double costa or rib; having two principal ribs running longitudinally, as in some leaves.

bicotyledonary. With two seed lobes, dicotyledonous.

bicrenate. Doubly crenate; with two crenatures or rounded teeth, as leaves with notch-toothed margins.

bicrural. With two legs or supports; with two appendages or elongations, as the pollen masses of asclepiads; bicruris.

bicuspid. Having two sharp stiff points or cusps, ending in two points, bicuspidate.

bicyclic. Having two cycles or whorls.

biddulphioid. Resembling *Biddulphis*, a genus of diatoms.

bidental. With two teeth or tooth-like processes.

bidentate. With two teeth; being doubly toothed, as some leaf margins.

bidenticulate. Having two small teeth or tooth-like processes; diminutive of bidentate, as of some scales.

bidenton. A term sometimes used for the genus *Bidens.*

bidigitate. With two finger-like divisions.

biduous, biduos. Lasting only two days.

biennial. A plant which completes its life history (cycle) in two growing seasons, usually fruiting during the second season.

bieremus. A two-celled fruit whose cells are so far apart that they seem separate.

bifacial. Having two faces, as the distinct upper and lower surfaces of a leaf.

bifariam imbricatus. Imbricated in two rows.

bifarious. In two rows, one on each side of an axis; distichous.

biferous. Double bearing, producing two crops in one season.

bifid. Two-parted, two-cleft, forked, divided into two lobes, split into two segments.

bifistular. Having two tubular openings.

biflagellatae. A group of the phycomycetes with spores having two flagella.

biflagellate. Having two flagella.

biflex. Twice-curved.

biflorate. Having two flowers.

biflorous. Flowering in autumn as well as in the spring; see BIFLORATE.

bifoliate. 1. Having or producing two leaves. 2. In a compound leaf, having two leaflets.

bifollicular. Having a double follicle, as in *Asclepias*.

biforate. Having two perforations; with two openings, pores, or apertures, as the anthers of *Rhododendron*.

biforin, biforine. An oblong cell opening at each end containing raphides found in arums and other plants which become turgid when placed in water and discharge their contents from both ends.

biform. Of two forms.

bifrons. Having two faces or aspects, two-fronded; see AMPHIGENOUS.

bifurcate. Divided or forked into two branches, having two prongs.

big tree. The big trees of California, *Sequoia gigantea*.

biggatulatus. With two globules or vacuoles.

bigeminate. Doubly paired; twin forked; bearing four together, as in a compound leaf with a pair of leaflets having a forked petiole with a pair of leaflets at the end of each division; see BICONJUGATE.

bigeminous. In two pairs, as in the placentae of many plants.

bigener. A plant arising from a cross between two genera, the result of a bigeneric cross; see GENUS HYBRID.

bigeneric. Hybridized from two distinct genera.

bigeneric half-breed. The product of a cross between varieties of species of different genera.

bigibbous. With two swellings, projections, or pouches, usually at the base.

biglandular. Having two glands or gland-like bodies.

biglumis. Two-glumed.

bignoniaceous. Of or pertaining to the genus *Bignonia* or its family, which includes the trumpet vine, cross vine, catalpa, etc.

biguttulate. Having two globules or vacuoles.

bihilatous. Having two scars, as in some pollen grains.

bi-indusiate. With a double indusium.

bijugate. 1. Having only two pairs of leaflets. 2. Having pinnate leaves with evenly divided leaflets, i.e., the same number on each side of the rachis.

bijugus. Yoked together, joined.

bilabellulate. Two-lipped.

bilabiate. Two-lipped, as in the corolla of the *Labiatae*, the mints, or the *Scrophulariaceae*, the figworts.

bilabiate dehiscence. The opening by a transverse split across the top.

bilamellar. Formed of two plates, having two lamellae, having two flat lobes or divisions.

bilaminar. With two plate-like layers; see DIPLOBLASTIC.

bilateral. Having two sides which are equal, two-sided, arranged on two sides.

bilateral cleavage. The type of cleavage in which the egg substances are distributed symmetrically with respect to the median plane.

bilateral flower. An irregular flower which is symmetrical in one plane only.

bilateral symmetry. The condition when an organism is divisible into similar halves in one plane only; see ZYGOMORPHISM.

bilobate. Having two lobes.

bilobular. Having two lobules.

bilocellate. Divided into two locelli or compartments, having two secondary compartments.

bilocular. With two cavities, having two chambers or locules, two-celled.

bilomentum. A bicarpellate pod which develops constrictions as it matures and breaks into sections divided by a membranous partition with a seed on each side of the membrane, as found in *Raphanus*, a radish; see SILIQUE.

bimaculate. With two spots or stains.

bimestris. Lasting two months.

bimodal. Characterizing a two-peaked frequency curve.

bimucronate. Tipped with two sharp and rigid points.

bimus. Lasting for two years.

binae. Pine trees whose leaves grow in twos in the same basal sheath; see GEMINATE.

binary. Double, made up of two members.

binary fission. The division of a cell into two daughter cells by the apparent simple division of the nucleus and cytoplasm.

binary nomenclature. The system of double names given to plants; see BINOMIAL NOMENCLATURE.

binate. 1. In twos or pairs, as of a simple leaf nearly divided into two parts. 2. Applied to a leaf composed of two leaflets at the end of a common petiole.

binato-pinnatus. Bipinnate.

binatus. Twin, double, two and two.

binding species. Species which bind an association or community together.

bine. A twining or climbing stem, rarely used except in combinations such as woodbine, etc.

binervate. Having two nerves or veins, or two which are especially prominent.

binervulatus. With two vascular strands.

bini. Twins, two together.

binodal. Consisting of or having two nodes.

binomial. Consisting of two names, the generic and specific names which comprise the botanical name; see BINOMIAL NOMENCLATURE.

binomial nomenclature. The system of applying two Latin names, a generic name and a specific name.

binuclear. With two nuclei, binucleate.

binucleolate. Having two nucleoli, with two oil drops.

bio-. A prefix meaning life.

bioblast. A hypothetical ultimate vital unit; a biophore; the unit of life, visible or invisible, having the power of growth and division.

biocatalyst. An enzyme.

biocellate. Having two ocelli or two eyespots.

biocharacters. Characters which are found separable as units in heredity, evolution, or individual development.

biochemistry. The branch of chemistry concerned with living organisms.

biochore. A climatic plant boundary, a climatic boundary in biological plant geography based upon the statistics of life forms.

biochronic. Of the period during which mutations have been possible.

bioclimatic zonation. See AREAS OF NORMAL, OCCASIONAL, and POSSIBLE ABUNDANCE.

biocoenology. The quantitative and qualitative analysis of plant and animal successions of communities.

biocoenose. Comprising both the vegetative and animal population of a habitat.

biocoenosis. The relationship of plants and animals toward each other, symbiosis.

biocoenotic connection. The definite, although sometimes indirect, relationships that bind together a community (large or small) of organisms, as for example, those of a plant species with phytophagous insects and their parasites; see COACTION.

biocolloid. A mixture of a base and an inert carbohydrate, as agar and albumen.

bio-community. A community of living organisms, such as may be studied in ecology.

biodynamics. The study of vital powers and forces, that branch of physiology that deals with the vital life processes of plants and animals.

biogen. A hypothetical protein molecule of unstable nature which is assumed to be primarily responsible for the phenomena of life, a hypothetical ultimate unit of which life is built.

biogenesis. The theory that all life arises from pre-existing life forms.

biogenetic law. The hypothesis that each individual during its development (ontogeny) repeats in an abbreviated form the history of the development of the race (phylogeny).

biogenous. Growing on living organisms, not necessarily as a parasite.

biogeography. Biology which deals with the geographical distribution of plants and animals.

biologic species. See BIOLOGICAL RACES.

biological barrier. Any obstacle to the activities of organisms which prevents the occupation of an area by plants. Plant communities already established may act as a biological barrier; town-building by man is an extreme example.

biological factors. The influences of plants upon each other or upon animals and the influences of animals on plants and other animals, e.g., shading by trees, grazing, etc.

biological form. A race of a parasitic fungus

quite normal in morphology but restricted for some physiological reason to one species of host plant or to a strain of that host plant which then is also a biological form of its species, biological specialization.

biological races or species. Those races or species which differ only in their physiological behavior but are morphologically alike.

biological spectrum. A list of the categories of life forms with the number of species of each category in the constitution of the population.

biological type. See LIFE FORM.

biology. The science of living organisms, the science of life.

bioluminescence. The light produced by some groups of animals, bacteria, and fungi.

biolysis. Decomposition by living beings.

biolytic. Injurious to or destructive of life.

biomass. The quantity of plankton substance in weight.

biomes. 1. Biotic communities; communities of the rank of formations which are similar in climate, soil, and life forms, such as deciduous forests, prairies, tundras, rain forests, etc. 2. Evidences of past human communities or past climates.

biometer. An organism or group of organisms which may be used as indicators of the conditions or suitability of a climate or location.

biometrics. The statistical study of living organisms and their variations; see BIOMETRY.

biometry. The study of biological problems by means of statistical methods.

biomolecule. A living molecule.

biomonad. A symbiotic system of biomores which when very complex constitutes a cell.

biomoneron. A unit of life.

biomore. An aggregation of living particles.

bion. An individual which is morphologically and physiologically independent, an independent living organism.

bionergy. Vital force.

bionomics. The study of organisms in relation to their environment; see PHYTOBIOLOGY, ECOLOGY.

bionomy. The science of the relation of living things to each other and to their environment.

biont. A living thing.

biophagism. The absorption and the digestion of living organisms.

biophagous. Feeding on living organisms, parasitic.

biophilous. Parasitic on leaves and stems of living plants.

biophore. The smallest conceivable unit of living matter, the vital unit of life, the ultimate unit of life, a hypothetical unit of life.

biophoric. Having vital and heritable properties.

biophysics. Biodynamics, the physics of living matter.

biophytes. Plants which obtain food from living organisms; see BIOPHAGOUS.

bioplasm. Any living fluid or protoplasm in a living, forming, or germinal state.

bioplason. Bioplasm.

bioplast. A minute quantity of living protoplasm capable of reproducing itself, nearly equivalent to a cell.

biorgan. An organ in the physiological sense not necessarily a morphological unit.

bios. The bios factor. 1. An accessory substance obtained from the environment believed to be essential for plant and animal growth, especially important for yeasts. It includes many of the vitamins essential for development. 2. Organic life (plant and animal).

bioseries. In evolution, a historical sequence formed by the changes in any one single heritable character.

biosis. The state of vital activity, life.

biosis factors. The ecological relationships of plants to each other.

biosis succession. The sequence of living forms.

biosociology. The study of the life of organisms in communities; see SYNECOLOGY.

biosphere. The part of the atmosphere and geosphere where life exists, that part of the land and air that influences vegetative growth and is affected by it.

biospheric. Pertaining to the influence of vegetation upon the migration of man.

biostatics. The branch of physiology dealing with structure in relation to function.

biota. The flora and fauna of a region.

biotic adaptation. Morphological or physiological changes in organisms brought about by competition.

biotic climax. A climax community maintained in a stable condition by some biotic factor, e.g., grassland which is prevented by grazing from passing into woodland.

biotic factors. The relation of organisms to each other from an ecological viewpoint.

biotic potential. The inherent quality of an organism to survive, i.e., increase in numbers; the potential power that an organism has to reproduce and survive in its environment.

biotic succession. A sequence of living forms.

biotin. Vitamin H. An essential growth substance for yeasts.

biotonus. The ratio between assimilation and dissimilation of biogens.

biotope. The life area of the smallest space, a microhabitat within the phytocoenosis.

biotype. A group of individuals all of which have the same genotype or pure line.

biovarial. Derived from the ovaries of the same plant.

bipaleolate. Having two paleae or small scales in grasses, with two lodicules, bilodiculate.

bipalmate. Twice palmate, palmately compound, palmate with secondary palmate petioles.

biparental. Having two parents.

biparietal. Having two parietal eminences.

biparous. Bearing two, as a leaf with two leaflets.

biparous cyme. A normal dichotomous cyme-type inflorescence.

bipartible. Divisible or separable into two parts.

bipartite. Divided nearly to the base into two parts, two-parted, bifid.

bipartition. The act of dividing into two equal parts.

bipectinate. Toothed like a comb on two sides.

bipeltate. Having two shield-shaped parts.

bipenniform. Feather-shaped.

bipentaphyllous. With two to five leaflets.

biperennial. A plant part that lives two years although the plant reproduces itself indefinitely.

bipes. See BICRURAL.

bipetalous. Having two petals.

bipinnate. Twice pinnately compound; doubly pinnate, used of leaves growing on paired stems.

bipinnatifid. Twice pinnatified, with the divi-

sions of a pinnatifid leaf themselves pinnatifid.

bipinnatiparted. See BIPINNATIFID.

bipinnatipartite. Bipinnatifid but with the divisions extending nearly to the midrib.

bipinnatisect. Twice pinnately divided, with divisions extending to the midrib but with the segments sessile.

biplicate. Twice or doubly folded, having two folds.

bipolar. Having two poles.

bipolar expansion. Growth at both ends, as of the root and shoot.

bipolar germination. The germination of a spore by the formation of two germ tubes, one from each end.

bipolarity. 1. The condition of having two poles or polar processes. 2. In plant distribution, the occurrence of the same species toward the North and South Poles but not in intermediate regions.

bipolymorious. Having two or more parts.

biporose. Having two pores, opening by two pores as the anthers in *Erica*.

biprophyllatous. Having two prophylla.

bipunctate. Having two dots or spots, with two vacuoles.

biradial. Disymmetrical, symmetrical both radially and bilaterally.

biradiate. Having two rays.

biramose. Divided into two branches.

birchwood association. An association of birch above the limit of the oaks in highland valleys.

bird-attracting. See AUCUPARIOUS, ORNITHO-.

bird-footed. Pedate; resembling a bird's foot, as the bird's-foot violet.

bird's-eye grain. The appearance when worked timber shows large numbers of small circular areas dotted about the wood. The rings are due to almost dormant buds which give rise to thin cylindrical strands of soft tissue lying almost horizontally in the trunk appearing circular when cut across.

birimose. Having two clefts, slits, or narrow openings.

birostrate. Having two beaks or beak-like processes.

bisaccate. Having two little sacs, bags, or pouches.

biscoctiform. Biscuit-shaped.

biscuit-shaped. Oblong and slightly constricted in the middle.

biscutate. Resembling two bucklers placed side by side.

bisect. A vertical section of a quadrat to show the layers of soil and roots in normal position to reveal the influence of water and nutrients on plant growth; a layer transect.

biseptate. Having two partitions or septa.

biserial. 1. In two rows or series. 2. Applied to flowers which have both gynoecium and an androecium but no perianth. 3. Achlamydeous flowers having only two whorls or series.

biseriate hairs. Hairs which consist of more than one row of cells.

biserrate. Twice serrate, with the serratures serrate, doubly serrate; see BIDENTATE.

bisetose. Having two seta or bristles, bisetous.

bisexual. Having both sexes on the same plant body, hermaphroditic, having both stamens and pistils in the same flower or inflorescence.

bisexual heredity. The transmission of the qualities of both parents.

bispathellulate. Consisting of two glumes.

bispinose. Having two spines.

bispirous. With elaters having two spirals; see DISPIROUS.

bisporangiate. Having both microsporangia and megasporangia, having both stamens and carpels.

bispore. 1. A two-spored tetraspore. 2. An ascus which has two cells instead of the normal eight.

bissy nuts. Cola (kola, korra, or gorra) nuts, tropical nuts used in medicines and drinks, and as stimulants; *Cola acuminata.*

bistelic. Having two steles.

bistipulate. Having two stipules.

bistortus. Twice-twisted.

bistrate. With an indumentum of two layers, the outer one falling off to disclose the inner.

bistratose. With two layers of cells.

bistriate. With two parallel lines or striae.

bisubtripinnate. Nearly twice pinnate.

bisulcate. Two-grooved, having two furrows.

bisymmetric. Bilaterally symmetric, with each side alike.

bisymmetrical. Divisible into two similar halves by either of two longitudinal planes passing through the axis at right angles to each other.

bitegminatae. Phanerogam seeds with double integuments.

bitegminy. The condition of having double integuments, as of ovules.

biternate. With three main divisions each with three leaflets.

bitricrenate. Crenate two or three times.

bitripinnate. Twice tripinnate.

bi-tri-ternate. Growing in threes twice or three times.

bitten. Abruptly ended, praemorse; see EROSE.

bitter orange spots. A disease on leaves and fruits caused by *Colletotrichum gloeosporoides.*

bitter pit. An abnormal spotting of the fruit of the apple.

bituminous. Coal black.

bitunicate. Having two walls.

bitypic. Said of those genera which have two widely separated species.

biuncinate. Two-hooked.

biuret test. A test applied for the presence of protein which produces a pinkish-mauve color in the presence of a strong alkaline solution (biuret) and copper sulphate.

bivalent. Having two homologous chromosomes united at the first division of meiosis.

bivalent, asymmetrical. With paired chromosomes of different shape by reason of their kinetochores being located at different positions.

bivalent, unequal. With paired chromosomes of different size due to one of them having a deficiency or a duplication.

bivalve. Having two valves, bivalvular.

bivascular. Having two vessels.

biventricose. Having two bellied or distended portions.

biverted. Having an inverted diagonal symmetry, as in diatoms.

biverticillate. Branching at two levels.

bivittate. Having two vittae or oil tubes, with two partitions which appear as bands or fillets.

bixin. The coloring matter characteristic of *Bixa orellana.*

bizzaria. A fruit which is a hybrid between the orange and the citron.

blackberry. The common aggregate of drupelets by that name.

black blight. A disease of citrus leaves caused by *Capnodium citricolum*.

black earth. A type of earth rich in mineral salts found in the Asiatic steppes and in North America.

blackjack. A common oak of the eastern and central United States which often forms dense thickets in poor soils.

black knot. A disease of plum and cherry caused by *Plowrightia morbosa*.

blackleg. A bacterial disease of potatoes caused by *Bacillus phytophthorus*.

black root rot. A common rot caused by *Thielavia basicola*.

black rot. Any of several diseases of cultivated plants which are caused by species of fungi and bacteria which result in discoloration and decay.

black rust. A very widespread rust which attacks cereal grains caused by *Puccinia graminis*.

black scab. A disease of potatoes caused by *Synchytrium*.

Blackman reactions. Reactions in the photosynthetic process which take place in the absence of light (dark reactions). Named after the discoverer.

bladder. 1. A small sac filled with air. 2. An inflated pericarp, as in *Physalis*. 3. An appendage on roots that traps insects in *Utricularia*. See AIR BLADDER.

bladder plums. An abortion of the fruit of plums in which the stone is lacking and the rest of the fruit is represented by a thin bladder.

blade. The lamina or flat expanded portion of the leaf which is usually green in color.

blanched. Whitish by absence of light, etiolated, the whitened appearance of a stem or leaf artificially produced by the exclusion of light so that the chlorophyll is not formed due to iron deficiency.

blanching. 1. Losing color. 2. The whitening or discoloring of the usual green parts of plants. 3. A preliminary step in food preparation, heating in water to stop further development.

blast. A blighted bud or blossom.

blastea. The spherical covering which surrounds a colony of green algal cells as in the genus *Volvox*.

blastea chlorophytes. Green algae which are surrounded by a gelatinous matrix such as the *Volvocineae*.

blastelasma. Any germ layer formed after formation of the epiblast and hypoblast.

blastema. 1. The lichen thallus. 2. The axis of an embryo (the radicle and plumule) excluding the cotyledons. 3. Any point of growth or budding.

blastemal. Rudimentary, asexual.

blastematicus. Thalloid.

blasteniospore. A two-celled spore of lichens with a thick median wall traversed by a connecting tube, a polarilocular spore.

blastesis. The reproduction of the thallus of lichens by gonidia.

blastic action. A catalytic action exerted by light on a plant stimulating division and enlargement of cells.

blastidia. The secondary cells formed in the anterior of another cell, daughter cells.

blastidules. The reproductive bodies which are not spores but are produced asexually, such as gemmae, propagula, etc.

blastocarpous. With the seed germinating within the pericarp, as frequently occurs in the mangrove.

blastochore. A plant distributed by offshoots.

blastocoele. The segmentation cavity or the cavity of the blastula.

blastocoelion. The central cavity of *Volvox*.

blastocolla. The gummy substance on many buds usually produced by the glandular hairs.

blastocyst. The germinal vesicle.

blastogenesis. 1. Reproduction by budding. 2. Any method of asexual reproduction. 3. The theory of the transmission of inherited characters by germ plasm.

blastogenic. Originating in the germ plasm.

blastography. The study of buds.

blastomania. The production of an abnormal number of leaf shoots.

blastomycetes. The yeasts, the *Saccharamycetes*, fungi that reproduce by budding.

blastoparenchymatous. Having several filaments so closely joined that they appear as one filament.

blastophore. The sac around the viscous fluid in a thickened scale which forms a case in which the embryo lies.

blastophthoria. The deterioration of the germ as the result of disease or other disturbing agents.

blastophylls. Germ layers.

blastopore. The pore opening into a gastrula.

blastosphere. The blastula, a hollow ball of cells.

blastospore. A spore which arises by the process of budding, the sprout cell.

blastotomy. The separation of the cleavage cells or portions of them in the early stages of development.

blastula. An embryonic stage in the shape of a hollow sphere, one cell thick, formed by repeated cleavages, as in the mother cell of *Volvox*.

blastus. The plumule.

blaze currents. An electric response in a definite direction in plants.

blea. The inner bark, sapwood.

bleb. A pith cell.

blechnoid. Of or pertaining to the greenhouse-fern, genus *Blechnum*.

bleeding. The exudation of sap because of injury, as seen frequently in spring during the expansion of the leaves.

bleeding heart. The common name for plants of the genus *Dicentra*.

bleeding pressure. Exudation pressure, the internal force necessary to cause such abnormal flow.

blema. Covering.

blematogen. The thick-walled layer of hyphae forming an undifferentiated membrane covering the button stage of an agaric, the universal veil, blemmatogen.

blend. A hybrid which shows characters intermediate between parents.

blending. Forming a hybrid by the crossing of races.

blending inheritance. An inheritance in which the characters of the parents seem to blend in the offspring.

blendling. A hybrid arising from the crossing of races; a hybrid between races, not between species.

blepharae. The teeth of the peristome of a moss, blipharae.

blephariglottis. Fringed-tongued.

blepharoplast. 1. A basal body in relation to a motor cell organ, as the flagella in the flagellates. 2. The specialized protoplasm which gives rise to the motile cilia of antherozoids, as in *Zamia* and *Cycas*.

blepharoplastoids. The two bodies which appear between the two- and four-celled stage at each pole of the two spindles in nuclear division and disappear into the cytoplasm before the appearance of the blepharoplasts themselves.

blet. A soft spot on fruit.

bletting. The change in consistency of certain fruits without putrefaction.

blight. A vague term signifying a number of types of diseases in plants caused by the attack of insects or of parasitic fungi.

blind. 1. Aborted, as when a flower bud is said to go blind, i.e., does not develop. 2. Producing leaves rather than flowers or fruits as a malformation.

blind pit. A pit without a complement, a common form opposite an intercellular space.

blipharae. See BLEPHARAE.

blister. A subcutaneous bubble or bladder filled with fluid, a plant disease, a resin pocket.

blister blight. A disease of the tea plant caused by *Exobasidium vexans*.

blister rust. A plant disease due to *Peridermium* or *Cronartium*.

bloom. The white powdery layer on some plants, a delicate down that may be removed by rubbing, a blossom.

blossom. The flower, the corolla.

blossom bud. See FLOWER BUD.

blotched. With distinct irregular spots of color, with color irregularly disposed in patches.

blow. 1. To cause to blossom, to put forth blossoms. 2. A bloom, a state of blossoming, a mass of blossoms.

blow-off layer. An epidermal layer which forms the outermost investment of the testa of Palaeozoic seeds.

blowout. An excavation in sandy ground produced by the action of the wind.

blueberry. 1. The common name for certain North American *Vaccinia*. 2. The fruit of such plants.

blue-green algae. The *Myxophyceae* or *Cyanophyceae*. Closely related to the bacteria but with chlorophyll and numerous other pigments, they vary greatly in color according to the pigments present and the pH concentration of their habitats. Usually lacking well developed nuclei and asexually reproduced, they are often surrounded by a gelatinous sheath.

blue timber. A wood disease produced by fungi causing a bluish discoloration.

bob. A popular name for the inflorescence (thyrse) of sumac.

Bodenschicht. Ground stratum; see STRA-TIFICATION.

bodies, suspensory. Pseudovacuoles.

body cell. 1. The cell in certain conifers which divide to form the male cells. 2. A somatic cell as distinguished from a germ cell.

body, central. An incipient nucleus.

bog. A quagmire filled with moss and other vegetable matter; wet spongy ground; a poorly drained depression filled with peat, sphagnum, or bogmoss.

bogmoss association. Moorland vegetation with sphagnum dominant.

bogmoss xerophytes. Plants presenting the appearance of xerophytes although growing in water.

bog plants. Those plants living in bogs rather than in the water of lakes or ponds.

bolarious. Dark red, brick red, bolaris.

bole. The trunk of a tree, particularly a large tree with a distinct trunk.

bolete. One of the *Boletaceae*, fleshy agaric-like fungi with tubular hymenophores.

boleti. The term used by Pliny the Elder (A.D. 77) for all fungi which developed from an envelope called a volva. All other types were called fungi by the Romans.

boletiform. Descriptive of spores of some *Boletaceae* rather than the inaccurate term *subfusiform*.

boletinoid. Having the characteristics of the genus *Boletinus* with the tubes hardly separable, with tubes more or less radially arranged, and with more or less prominent veins.

boletoid. Like the genus *Boletus*, with pores more or less regular, not elongated or radially arranged, and not separated by veins.

boletus. Originally the common name for *Aminita caesarea* but now used as the generic name for tubular hymenomycetes (*Boleti* and polypores).

boletol. A blue coloring matter found in some fungi, chiefly in the *Boletaceae*.

boliviensis. Of Bolivia, South America.

boll. A globular pericarp, as in cotton.

bolling. See POLLARD.

bolochore. A plant which is distributed by propulsion.

bolt. To produce seed prematurely, as in carrots when they produce seed the first year.

bombardus. Cannon-like.

bombycine. Silky; feeling as smooth as silk like the silk-cotton trees of the tropics, *Bombaceae*.

boot. A popular name for the sheath of grains and other grasses.

booted. Sheathed by the volva or universal veil, peronate.

boragineous. Of or pertaining to the *Boragineae*, the borage family.

boragoid. Of or pertaining to the genus *Borago*, a small genus of perennial herbs.

borbonicus. Of Bourbonne, France.

border. 1. A narrow planting along a boundary or division line or against a wall or building. 2. The expanded portion of a gamopetalous corolla consisting of the united limbs. 3. The brim or spreading part of a corolla. SEE LIMB, BORDERED PIT.

border parenchyma. A sheath of one or more layers of parenchymatous cells surrounding a vascular bundle.

bordered pit. A thin spot with a thick edge in the wall between two vessels or tracheids through which liquid passes.

bordered pore. In sphagnum, an opening surrounded by a distinct flattened ring; see BORDERED PIT.

boreal. Of or pertaining to Boreas, northern.

boreal life zone. The zone of living organisms in the northern part of the world, one of three major life zones in North America.

borer. Any of the various animals which burrow into wood or other substances during the larval stage.

borragoid. See BORAGOID.

Boschveld. The parkland of northern Transvaal, Africa.

bosselated. Covered with knobs, set or covered with bosses or small protuberances.

bostrychoid cyme. A sympodial branch-system in which the right or left branch is always the more vigorous; see HELICOID CYME.

bostrychoid dichotomy. The repeated forking of an inflorescence of a bostrychoid cyme.

bostrychoidal. In the form of a ringlet or bostryx.

bostryx. A cymose inflorescence with blossoms on one side only of the rachis causing it to curl, a uniparous helicoid cyme.

botanical garden. A garden which is especially devoted to the culture of plants for scientific ends; a collection of plants systematically arranged for study, often with libraries, herbaria, laboratories, and museums.

botanical geography. The study of plants in relation to their geographic distribution.

botanical nomenclature. The names of plants and the laws for their application.

botanical terminology. The scientific vocabulary used in plant study.

botanize. To look for plants in their various habitats and to study their nature and habits; to collect plants or to study them in the field.

botany. The science of plants, the branch of biology dealing with plant life.

bothrenchyma. Plant tissue which is composed of dotted or pitted ducts or cells.

bothrium. A sucker, a sucking groove.

botrus. A grape-like cluster, a botrys.

botrycymose. Of racemes or any botryose clusters cymosely aggregated, botryose.

botryoid. Having the form of a bunch of grapes, botryoidal, botryose.

botryopterid. Allied to the fern *Botryopteris* or *Botrychium.*

botryose. Racemose, botryoid.

botrys. A raceme, a cluster.

bottle ore. The common rockweeds of the Atlantic sea coast.

bottle-shaped. Shaped like a Florence flask; see LAGENIFORM.

bottom-heat. The heat which affects the roots of plants if they are exposed to a higher temperature than that of the air in which the aerial parts are growing.

bottom-yeast. Low yeast, the yeast which forms at the bottom of vats.

botuliform. Sausage-shaped, allantoid.

botulism. A disease caused by *Clostridium botulinum*, a spore-forming anaerobic bacterium.

bouillon. An infusion of beef which is frequently used in the cultivation of bacteria; meat broth.

bound. 1. With the bark so tight that growth is impeded. 2. The external limiting line of some object or space.

bound water. Water held in organic substances by absorptive or other physical forces.

boundary cell. A heterocyst.

bouquet. 1. The polarized stage of synapsis in which the spireme-threads, commonly loop-shaped, are polarized towards one pole of the nucleus near which the central

bodies lie. 2. A nosegay. 3. A bunch of herbs for flavoring.

bourgeon. To bud or sprout; burgeon.

bracheid. A brachysclereid, a stone cell.

brachiate. With spreading branches (especially opposite and decussate), widely diverging, with pairs of opposite branches spreading at right angles.

brachidodromous. Used of nerves in leaves when they form loops within the blade, as in *Aristolochia, Olea,* etc.; loop-veined.

brachy-. A prefix meaning short.

brachyandrous. Short-stamened.

brachyanthous. Short-flowered.

brachybiostemonous. Having nonpersistent stamens.

brachybiostigmatic. With stigmas which are short-lived and wither before their proper anthers ripen, protogynous.

brachyblast. A short branch or spur, a brachyoblast.

brachybotrys. Short-clustered.

brachycarpous. Short-fruited.

brachycephalic. Short-headed or broad-headed.

brachychimous. Exposed to short winters.

brachycladous. Having short branches.

brachycomous. Short-haired.

brachydactylous. Short-fingered.

brachydodromous. Brachidodromous.

brachyelytrum. A short husk.

brachyforms. The species of rust fungi in which the aecidia are omitted from the life history or are replaced by primary uredosori (rusts which lack aecidia but have spermagonia, uredospores, and teleutospores on the same host).

brachymeiosis. A simplified form of meiosis completed in one division, the second reduction in the chromosome number which takes place in the second or third division in the ascus, the second meiosis.

brachynema. An aspect of meiosis which is derived from strepsinema, the twisted threads in the nucleus.

brachyoblast. See BRACHYBLAST.

brachypetalous. With short petals.

brachyphyllous. Short-leaved.

brachypodous. Short-stalked.

brachysclereids. Stone cells, the sclereids of barks and fruits.

brachysomes. Tetrads.

brachysteles. The upper small, short branches in the *Characeae.*

brachystylous. Microstylous, short-styled.

brachytherous. Exposed to short summers.

brachytheroxerochimous. Denoting organisms adapted to short summers and dry winters.

brachytmema. A disk-shaped cell which by its rupture frees a gemma in certain species of bryophytes.

brachytrichous. Short-haired.

brachytylous. Short-knobbed.

brachyxerochimous. Inured to dry and short winters.

bracken. *Pteridium aquilinus*, the bracken fern.

bracket cells. The secretory cells in *Lonchocarpus* (a tropical leguminose shrub or vine) with papillose epithelia.

bracket epithelium. A leaf epithelium which shows finger-like differentiations of the component cells.

bracket fungus. One of a number of species of basidiomycetes occurring on tree trunks and projecting in the form of a rounded bracket.

bracket hairs. Hairs which are hooked or bent at the apex.

bracket-shaped. Curved like a parenthesis.

brackish. Somewhat salty.

bract. 1. A relatively small leaf just below an inflorescence, flower, or flower part. 2. A leaf or scale in whose axis an inflorescence, flower, or floral organ is produced. 3. A small rudimentary or imperfectly developed leaf. 4. A leaf subtending a flower.

bract cell. A cell on the branchlets of *Chara*.

bract scale. In coniferous plants, the scale immediately below the seed-bearing scale.

bracteal leaf. A bract or bracteole.

bracteody. The change of foliar organs into bracts.

bracteola. A small bract; see BRACTLET.

bracteole succulents. Plants which lose their leaves by drying, but the bracteoles around the flowers enlarge and become succulent.

bracteomania. Excessive development of bracts.

bracteose. Having conspicuous or numerous bracts.

bractlet. A secondary bract, particularly as borne on the pedicels; a smaller bract borne on a pedicel or secondary branch.

bracts, involucral. The bracts surrounding a flower head.

brady-. A prefix meaning slow.

bradycarpic. Fruiting after winter in the second season after flowering; see ASPECTION.

bradyschist. A broad mother-cell in which successive nuclear divisions are completed before cell division.

bradyspore. A plant which disperses its seeds slowly; see ANEMOCHORY.

braird. To germinate.

brak soil. An alkaline soil usually formed by extreme changes of temperature. Found in South America.

bran. 1. The coat of the caryopsis which consists of the pericarp and seed coat united. 2. The husks or outer coats of ground corn which are separated from the flour by bolting.

bran-like. Scurfy in appearance, like bran in nature.

branch. A shoot or secondary stem which grows from the main stem, a division of a stem or other elongated organ.

branch abscission. The shedding of branches by means of an organized separation layer.

branch gap. An interruption in the vascular cylinder at the point of origin of the branch (a characteristic of stems containing pith).

branch leaf. A highly developed leaf from the middle or lower part of a sterile spreading branch.

branch leaf gaps. In a fern stele, those openings in the central cylinder where a branch is given off.

branch spine. A twig spine.

branch tendril. A tendril formed from a modified branch.

branch trace. A primary vascular supply to a lateral branch.

branchery. The ramifications in the pulp of fruits.

branches, intercalary. The branches which arise below the apical cell, as in some *Hepaticae*.

branching, terminal. Branching in which the branches arise from a division of the apical cell.

branchlet. A small branch or subdivision of a branch, a twig, an ultimate branch or subdivision of an axis.

brand. A plant disease on leaves caused by fungi, as *Ustilago*; the smuts.

brand fungi. See USTILAGINALES.

brand spore. The spore of the smut fungi, *Ustilaginales*; a thick-walled resting spore of the brand fungi.

brasiliensis. Of or pertaining to Brazil.

brasilin. The coloring matter of brazil wood, *Caesalpinia brasiliensis*.

brassicaceous. Resembling or belonging to *Brassica*, a genus of herbs including cabbage, mustard, cress, etc.

Braun's series. See FIBONACCI SERIES.

Brazil nut tree. A very tall tree of tropical America with three-sided edible nuts widely exported, genus *Bertholletia*.

breadfruit. The fruit of *Artocarpus communis*, native to the Malayan archipelago, whose seeds are used as food.

break. 1. To put out new leaves or buds. 2. To depart widely from type and produce a new variety, to sport, to show variation.

break-back. A reversion to an earlier type.

break stain. The smallest border per unit of a transverse unit of a strand which will cause rupture.

breaking. 1. The beginning of growth of buds. 2. A popular expression for a sudden profusion of algal life in some lakes or meres. 3. The development of striping in the flowers of tulips.

breaking of the meres. See WATER BLOOM.

breast height. Four and one-half feet above the average ground surface or root collar, the height at which the diameter of standing trees is usually measured.

breastwood. Branches which project outward from a wall or espalier.

breathing pores. Stomata.

breathing root. A root produced by mangroves and other large plants growing in mud. It projects above the mud and water and provides a means by which air is conveyed into the roots below.

breech fertilization. See CHALAZOGAMY.

breed. A race or variety, artificial or natural, that perpetuates itself from seed.

breeding. Improving animals and plants or the experimental investigation of genetics by testing, hybridization, and selection.

brevi-. A prefix meaning short.

brevibarbis. Short-haired.

brevicaudatus. Short-tailed.

brevicaulis. Short-stemmed.

brevicidal dehiscence. Having the annulus of a fern sporangium interrupted by the stalk.

brevicollate. Short-necked.

brevifoliate. Having short leaves.

brevifrons. Short-fronded, short-leaved.

brevifurcatous. With short-forked branches.

breviligulatous. Short-liguled.

brevilobous. Short-lobed.

brevipaniculatous. Short-panicled.

brevipedunculatous. Short-peduncled.

brevipes. Short-footed, with a short pedicel or petiole.

breviramose. Short-branched.

brevirostris. Short-beaked.

breviscapous. Short-scaped.

brevischistostyle. A floral type with a short style folded some distance down and a badly formed stigma.

brevisetous. Short-bristled.

brevispathous. Short-spathed.

brevistylous. Short-styled.

brick-like. Resembling brick work, as a tissue of rectangular cells; muriform.

bridal wreath. *Spiraea prunifolia* and *Spiraea trichocarpa*, cultivated shrubs.

bridge. A narrow band of tissue which connects larger masses of the same kind of tissue; see DISJUNCTOR.

bridging. Breaking down immunity to a disease as in certain species of *Bromus* which act as an intermediate host of fungi and thus break down immunity.

bridging host. A temporary host of a parasitic fungus by means of which it may pass from one species to another, a bridging species.

bridging hypha. A special branch hypha forming a bridge between two other hyphae.

bridles. 1. Strings or strands of protoplasm which often connect the nucleus with the layer of protoplasm next to the cell wall. 2. Strands of cells connecting other tissues.

brigalow scrub. A scrub community composed chiefly of *Acacia harpophylla*.

bristle. 1. A rigid hair, a stiffish elastic hair, which may be straight or hooked. 2. A long, hollow outgrowth of the cell wall in some algae.

bristle-pointed. Terminating in a short, stiff hair.

bristle trichomes. Rigid hairs.

brizaeform. Nodding like the genus *Briza*, quaking grass.

broad ray. A vascular ray many cells in width consisting of cells which are rounded in transverse section.

broccoli. The common vegetable, *Brassica oleracea italica*.

brochidodromous. See BRACHIDODROMOUS.

brochonema. 1. The stage of nuclear division in which the number of loops in the spireme equals the number of the chromosome pairs. 2. The looped spireme threads found during nuclear division.

broken mother skein. A figure in nuclear division after the spireme has broken into individual chromosomes.

bromare. A community of *Bromus*.

bromatium. A swelling on a fungus tended by ants and serving as a source of food for them.

brome grass. Any grass of the genus *Bromus*.

bromelin. A proteolytic enzyme which is abundantly present in the juice of the pineapple.

brometum. An association of *Bromus*.

bromus. Food, the brome grasses.

bronchonema. A spireme thread that becomes looped in cell division.

brontesis. An injury to plants caused by an electric shock.

bronzing. 1. Turning bronze or becoming copper-colored. 2. A form of sun scorch in plants caused by atmospheric heat and the lack of root moisture.

brood. A bulbil, a soredium, a gonidium; see GEMMA.

brood bodies. Gemmae on leaves of mosses which become detached and grow into protonemal filaments.

brood bud. 1. In lichens, a soredium. 2. A vegetative reproductive bud or structure. 3. In *Bryophytae*, a bulbil.

brood cell. A propagative cell which is naked or with a membrane produced asexually and which may separate from the parent and develop into a new plant.

brood gemmae. Multicellular propagative bodies which are not differentiated, are produced asexually, and which may separate from the parent and develop directly into new plants. Gemmae are intermediate between bulbils and brood cells.

broom bush. *Parthenium*, a composite.

broom, butcher's. *Ruscus aculeatus*, a lily.

broom corn. *Sorghum vulgare*, a kind of sorghum which has a jointed stem with a stiff panicle which is used in making brooms.

broom-rape. Any of the various root-parasitic plants of the genus *Orobanche*.

broom root. A Mexican grass which is used in making brushes and whisk brooms.

broom tree. The genus *Baccharis*.

broth. A liquid in which meat (and sometimes other substances such as barley or rice) has been boiled, a thin or simple soup frequently used in bacteriological laboratories.

brotiocolous. Inhabiting man's house; see CULTURE COMMUNITY.

brotium, brotion. A succession of plants due to the action of man.

brotochores. Plants distributed by man.

brown algae. The *Phaeophyceae*, large conspicuous sea weeds, as *Fucus*, *Sargassum*, etc.

brown rot. A serious disease of orchard fruits. The fungus causing brown rot is *Sclerotinia*.

Brownian movements. The movements of minute particles when suspended in a liquid, oscillations of particles that are not translocations in space.

brucine. A poisonous alkaloid from *Strychnos Nux-vomica*.

bruguieretum. An association of *Bruguiera*, a mangrove formation.

brumalis. Pertaining to the winter solstice, flourishing in midwinter.

brunissure. An injury caused to grape vines by *Plasmodiophora vitis*, a disease of grape vines produced by the development of an excessive amount of oxidase due to defective nutrition. It causes discoloration and loss of foliage.

brunneous. Brown, brownish.

brush. 1. The young fruit of the hop when the stigmas are protruding. 2. Forest scrub. 3. An asteraceous plant of the western United States resembling the cone flower but having a greatly elongated brush-like disk.

brush form. Denoting the stigmas of some papilionaceous flowers as in *Phaseolus*, *Vicia*, *Lathyrus*, etc.

brush-shaped. Aspergilliform, divided at apex into numerous hairs and filaments.

Brussels sprouts. *Brassica oleracea gemmifera*, a biennial vegetable whose sprouts are produced the first year and seeds the second.

bryo-. A prefix meaning moss.

bryogams. Bryophytes.

bryology. The division of botany dealing with mosses and liverworts.

bryoma. The vegetative parts of mosses.

bryonine. A poisonous substance extracted from the roots of the plant *Bryonia alba*.

bryophytes. Liverworts, hornworts, and mosses.

bryozoon. A polyzoon so named because of its moss-like appearance.

buccae. The lateral sepals or wings of the flower of aconite.

bucephalous. Ox-headed.

buckler-shaped. Resembling a buckler with a raised rim; see SCUTATE, SCUTIFORM, PELTATE.

buck-mast. The fruit of the beech trees.

bud. The undeveloped state of a branch or flower cluster with or without scales, an undeveloped shoot or stem, the rudimentary or resting end or branch of a stem, an embryonic shoot, a growing point or undeveloped axis covered with the rudiments of leaves.

bud, accessory. An extra bud in an axil.

bud, adventitious. A bud occurring where buds are not usually found.

bud, axillary. A bud produced in a leaf axil.

bud cones. Arrested or abortive inflorescences of the carob.

bud-corm. The root system of some herbaceous plants.

bud, dormant. A branch bud which does not develop at once, a leaf bud in winter condition.

bud, extra-axillary. The altered leaf which protects the bud when it is dormant.

bud-gall. A leafless or leafy gall which involves several or all of the members of a shoot.

bud glue. See BLASTOCOLLA.

bud, growth. A determinate growth-bud which bears all the structures that will develop the following growing season. An indeterminate bud contains only the growing point with the leaves and flowers developing and continuing to grow indefinitely during the entire growing season.

bud, lateral. A bud on the side of a stem.

bud mutation. A germinal change which occurs in the very early history of a bud so that the branch produced from it differs germinally from the remainder of the plant.

bud protection. The protection of a bud from external influences by stipules.

bud rot. Any rot affecting the bud, as *Pythium*, which attacks palms.

bud, rudimentary. The cell in *Chara* which is cut off from a proembryonic branch as the primordium of the young plant, the primordium of a shoot or branch.

bud scale. One of the modified leaves or stipules forming a part of a covering which protects the contents from dessication and other injuries.

bud scar. The scar remaining on a stem after a bud has been removed.

bud sport. An abnormal branch, inflorescence, or flower produced from a bud as a result of mutation; a somatic variation in a bud; a variation in color or form of a bud.

bud, terminal. A bud at the apex of a stem.

bud variation. See BUD SPORT.

bud variety. A variety resulting from bud variation, a bud sport.

bud, ventitious. See BUD ADVENTITIOUS.

bud, yeast. An asexual reproductive body in yeasts; see BUDDING.

buddage. Propagation by buds.

budding. 1. The formation of buds. 2. A form of asexual reproduction in which a small secondary part is produced from the parent organism and gradually grows to become independent, as in yeasts and certain other fungi. 3. A means of artificial propagation in which a bud taken from one plant is inserted under the bark of another from which a shoot subsequently develops.

buddleifolious. With leaves like *Buddleia* (*Buddleja*), a large genus of shrubs or trees, mostly tropical.

budlet. A small bud attached to a larger one.

buffalo wallow. A small, more or less temporary body of standing water in a prairie which has been enlarged and packed by the wading and wallowing of bison or cattle.

buffer. 1. A region surrounding a nature sanctuary to protect it from outside influences. 2. A chemical able to neutralize strong acids with a small change in free hydrogen ions.

bufonius. Of or pertaining to the toad.

bugle-shaped. With the shape of a bugle head varying from oblong to obovoid.

bulb. A large bud of various shapes, usually subterranean, made up of a short, thick stem with roots at the base and having a number of membranous or fleshy overlapping scale-like leaves; a subterranean leaf-bud with fleshy scales or coats; a fleshy bud.

bulb-geophyte. A plant that grows underground and lives from year to year by means of a bulb.

bulb-like. Resembling a bulb in outer appearance but differing structurally from a bulb; see CORM.

bulb, naked. A bulb having scaly modifications of the leaves, as in the lily.

bulb plumule. A bulb produced directly from a seed.

bulb runner. A bulb arising from a stolon.

bulb scale. The thickened scale-like leaves of a bulb, the modified leaves of bulbs.

bulb, solid. 1. A corm. 2. The swollen base of the stipe of the sporophore of some hymenomycetes.

bulb, tunicated. A bulb with broad thin scales which form successive overlapping coats, as in the onion.

bulbate. Appearing bulbed, blistery, or bladdery.

bulbel. A bulblet, a bulb arising from a mother bulb, a small or secondary bulb about as large as the mother bulb.

bulbiceps. A stem bulbous at the base.

bulbiferous. Bearing bulbs, producing bulbs, bulb bearing as when bulbils are among the florets of an inflorescence or in the axes of leaves.

bulbil. 1. A deciduous bud usually formed on an aerial part of a plant in the axils of leaves, as in many lilies. 2. A little bulb, a bulblet, a brood bud. 3. In certain fungi, a small pluricellular body incapable of germination in *Ascomycetes*. 4. A deciduous leaf bud capable of developing directly into a new plant in bryophytes and ferns. See GEMMA.

bulbillate. Of stipes, provided with a small or obscure bulb.

bulbilles. The young fern plants growing on a parent frond.

bulblet. 1. A small bulb. 2. An aerial bulb, a bulb borne above ground in the axils of leaves and ferns. 3. A bud found in the inflorescence of grasses, as *Poa bulbosa* and others. See GEMMA.

bulbo-gemmae. See BULBIL.

bulbo-tuber. A corm, an upright tuber seldom produced on an elongated subterranean stem.

bulbodium. A corm, a solid bulb.

bulbopodium. A marginate depressed bulb characteristic of certain fungi as *Cortinarius*, a bulbopod.

bulbosine. A poisonous alkaloid of certain mushrooms. As the alkaloid was never isolated, the name is no longer used.

bulbous. Bulbose, swollen like a bulb, enlarged at base, having a bulb at the base of the stem.

bulbous hair. A hair with a swollen base.

bulbs. A class of plants in horticultural terminology arising from bulbs, corms, tubers, or thickened root stocks that may be cured, dried, and stored over winter.

bulbule. Bulblet, as in lilies and ferns.

bulbus. An enlargement at the base of the stipe of an agaric.

bulgaricus. Of Bulgaria.

bulgarine. The orange yellow pigment produced by the fungus *Bulgaria polymorpha*.

bulkheads. The transverse divisions and air chambers in the stems of *Scirpus*.

bulk ratio. The ratio of the diameter of an axis to that of the primordium arising from it.

bulla. A bubble.

bullate. 1. With a blistered or puckered surface, bubble-like, having one or more hemispherical outgrowths. 2. Of pilei, having a rounded knob.

bullate leaf. A leaf with inflated convexities on the upper surface and corresponding cavities below often seen in corn.

Buller phenomenon. In basidiomycetes and ascomycetes, when a bisexual mycelium makes a unisexual mycelium or fruit-body rudiment diploid.

bullescentia. The condition of being bullate or blistered.

bullhead. An abnormal flower in which the foliage leaves partly or completely replace the elements of the corolla.

bulliform cells. Cells in leaves of grasses (e.g., corn leaves) that have a bladder-like appearance.

bullions. Coal-balls.

bullose. Swollen, blistered.

bullula. A small swelling.

bundle. A strand of specialized tissue, the vascular or fibrovascular bundle, a sheathed fascicle of conducting tissue consisting of xylem and phloem traversing the body of a plant.

bundle, bicollateral. A bundle in which a second baststrand exists on the inner medullary side of the wood of the bundle.

bundle, cauline. A bundle confined to the stem.

bundle, closed. A bundle in which there is no

cambium, as in many monocotyledonous plants.

bundle, collateral. A bundle in which the wood and the bast lie side by side.

bundle, common. A fascicle of conducting tissue which extends from the stem into the leaf from which, upon separation, a leaf-scar or leaf-trace remains on the stem.

bundle, concentric. A bundle in which the wood surrounds the bast system or vice versa.

bundle, conjoint. A system consisting of both wood and bast.

bundle, cortical. A bundle of the cortical region.

bundle, end. The termination of a small vascular bundle in the mesophyll of a leaf or in the peripheral regions of stems.

bundle flanges. The connections between the unbranched leaf bundles of gymnosperms and the tissues which surround them.

bundle, medullary. A vascular bundle occurring in pith where there is a well defined exterior ring.

bundle, open. A bundle having cambium.

bundle, phloem. The bast portion of the bundle.

bundle, radial. A bundle in which the strands of xylem and phloem alternate, as in roots.

bundle scar. A trace within a leaf scar which is produced by a vascular bundle, a mark on the surface of a leaf scar denoting former attachment of the bundles of a leaf to those on a stem.

bundle sheath. A sheath of parenchymatous or sclerenchymatous cells surrounding a vascular bundle, the parenchyma tissue surrounding a bundle.

bundle traces. The points on a leaf scar where the bundle passed from the stem into the leaf. The patterns made by the traces are used to identify trees and shrubs in winter condition.

bundle trunks. Bundles which pass through the stem, root, leaf-stalk, and thick nerves of the leaf.

bundle, vascular. The entire strand of conducting tissue consisting chiefly of xylem and phloem, the fibro-vascular bundle.

bundle, xylem. The xylem or wood portion of the bundle.

bunt. The smut disease of wheat caused by *Tilletia tritici* and *T. levis*, the stinking smut, the fungi which destroy the wheat grain by converting it into an ill-smelling brownish-black powdery mass; puffballs.

bupleurifolious. Bupleurialeaved; having leaves like *Bupleurum*, a round-leaved umbelliferous plant.

bur. A fruit, seed, or head bearing hooked or barbed appendages which serve as a means of attachment to various animals, thus aiding dissemination.

burd (o). A graft hybrid believed to have arisen from the union of vegetative nuclei derived from the stock and the scion.

burgundy pitch. A resin obtained from species of *Abies*.

burl. 1. A knot or woody growth of very irregular grain, usually formed due to the continued activity of many slowly developing buds or branch rudiments; an overgrown knot or an excrescence on a tree. 2. The veneer made from woods containing knots.

burr. A hooked fruit, a woody outgrowth from the bark of certain trees; see BUR, BURL.

bursa. A sac-like cavity, the antheridium of *Chara*.

bursicle. A little pouch-like or purse-like receptacle.

bursiculate, bursiform. Shaped like a bag, pouch-like.

bursicule. 1. A small sac or pouch. 2. The pouch-like expansion of the stigma into which the caudicle of some orchids is inserted.

bush. A low shrub branching from the ground lacking a trunk, a scrub.

bush land. Shrubs and small trees constituting a formation.

bushland, arctic. A bushland having *Betula nana* as an important component.

bushland, subalpine. An area heavily covered with *Rhododendron, Vaccinium*, etc.

bushswamp. A swampy area composed of woody plants such as alder and willow with marsh plants as undergrowth.

bushwood. Brushwood, undergrowth, a woodland in which shrubs or small trees predominate.

butterfly flowers. Flowers pollinated by butterflies whose long proboscis can reach the stored honey, lepidopterid flowers.

button. 1. The young fruit of an agaric before the pileus has expanded and exposed the hymenium. 2. A bud. 3. The rounded receptacle of a rose. 4. A small rounded fruit that is stunted. 5. To form small buds, as in cauliflower.

button bush. An American rubiaceous shrub, *Cephalanthas*, so called because of its globular head of flowers.

buttress. The knee-like growth of trunk or roots in certain trees, a plank-like growth at the base of certain trees.

buttress root. An aerial root, often adventitious, which aids in keeping the stem of a plant in an upright position.

butyric ferment. A fermentation produced by *Bacillus amylobacter*.

butyrous. Of butter-like consistency.

buxeous. Having the color of box-wood; of or pertaining to the box tree, *Buxus*.

buxetum. An association of *Buxus*, the box-wood tree or shrub, an ornamental tree grown for its handsome evergreen foliage.

buxine. An alkaloid from *Buxus sempervirens*.

by-fruit. An unusual form of a fruit.

bynedestin. A globulin present in barley malt.

bynin. A protein soluble in alcohol contained in barley malt.

byssaceous. Consisting of a mass of fine threads and resembling cotton in appearance, having a delicate filamentous structure.

byssine. Cottony, of silken or flaxen material.

byssisede. With cottony subicle, the felty hyphae from which fungus fruit bodies arise; byssisedous.

byssoid. See BYSSACEOUS.

byssus. 1. The stipe of certain fungi. 2. The filamentous mycelium of certain fungi. 3. A filamentous plant belonging to the cryptogams.

byzantinus. Byzantine.

C

C horizon. The material from which a soil is derived.

C.O.V. See CROSSOVER VALUE.

caa-gapu. A palm forest; see REBALSA.

caa-guazu. A forest of the low Amazon plains; see SELVA.

caa-puera. The underbrush in a selva.

caatinga. A Brazilian forest which is deciduous during the hot, dry seasons; see SERTAO.

cable type. A consolidated filamentous soma.

cacainus. Chocolate brown, from the name of *Theobrome cacao*.

cacaliaefolious. With leaves like Indian plantain, *Cacalia*, a composite.

cachemiricus. Of Cashmere.

cachrys. The cone of a pine tree.

cacogenic. Dysgenic, racially degenerative, not able to hybridize, kakogenic.

cactal. Cactus-like or pertaining to the *Cactaceae*.

cactiform. Applied to succulent stems like those of cacti or *Euphorbia* species.

cacumen. The apex of an organ.

cadavericolous. Living on dead bodies.

cadens. Describing the funiculus which passes over the top of the seed, as in *Plumbagineae*.

cadmicous. Metallic, like tin.

caducous. Deciduous, lasting for a short time, soon falling from the plant, applied to the calyx of a flower when it falls off before the flower expands, not persistent, caducus.

caecum. An outgrowth from the embryo sac into the endosperm in some plants, a prolongation of the embryo sac.

caen-, caeno-. See CEN-.

caenobio. Coenobio; see CARCERULE.

caenodynamism. The replacement of complex functions by simpler ones.

caenogenesis. See CENOGENESIS.

caenomorphism. The development of a more simple modification from a complex one in living organisms.

caeoma. A form of aecidium of the *Uredinales* in which the spores are surrounded by a few sterile hyphae, not by a well-formed peridium, so-called from the genus *Caeoma*, which has spores in chains and lacks a peridium.

caeomoid. Like a caeoma, without a peridium.

caeomospores. Spores formed in a caeoma in *Uredineae*.

caeruleous. Sky blue.

caesalpinaceous. Of or pertaining to the genus *Caesalpinia*, tropical leguminose trees, including the poinciana.

caesian. Resembling the dewberry, *Rubus caesius*.

caesious. Bearing a bluish-gray waxy covering or bloom, lavender-colored.

caespes. Tufts.

caespitellose. Somewhat tufted.

caespitose, caespitous. See CESPITOSE.

caespitulose. Somewhat crowded in tuft-like patches.

caetonium. Coetonium.

caffeine. An alkaloid derived from coffee berries, *Coffea arabica*.

caffer. Caffra or kaffir.

caigin clearings. Clearings for agriculture achieved by cutting out the tropical vegetation.

cajanifolious. *Cajanus*-leaved, resembling the genus *Cajanus*, the pigeon pea.

cakletum. An association of *Cakile maritima*, the sea-rocket, a weed along the shore.

calabricus. Of Calabria in southern Italy.

calamagrostidetum. An association of *Calamagrostis*, reed-bent grass; a calamagrostetum.

calamariae. 1. A term of vague application which has been used for plants resembling grasses, chiefly sedges, but even including *Isoetes*. 2. Sometimes restricted to fossil plants, as the *Equisetineae*.

calamarian. Sedge-like or calamitean.

calamiferous. Bearing or having a hollow stem.

calamifolious. Having hollow reed-like stems, producing reeds.

calamite. A fossil plant resembling a gigantic *Equisetum*.

calamogrostiditum. See CALAMOGROSTIDETUM.

calamoid. Having long slender elastic stems as in the genus *Calamus*, having a fistular stem without an articulation, like the quill of a feather.

calathide. 1. The involucre of a flower head. 2. The capitulum itself.

calathidimorphic. Having the form of a calathide.

calathidium. The head of flowers in *Compositae* or sometimes the involucre only.

calathiflorous. Having a calathidium or capitulum.

calathiform. Bowl-shaped, basket-shaped, cup-shaped, or having a hemispherical outline.

calathidiphorum. The stalk of a capitulum.

calathinous. Basket-like.

calathis. A calathide.

calathocladium. In *Hieracium* and its allies, the upper part of the stem bearing flower heads as distinct from the unbranched part or cladophore.

calcanthemy. An abnormal condition in which the calyx becomes colored, resembling the corolla.

calcar. A hollow tube or spur at the base of a petal or sepal, usually nectariferous.

calcarate. Bearing one or more spurs.

calcareous. 1. Coated with or containing lime. 2. Chalky white in color. 3. Growing in chalky or limestone places. 4. Having the substance of chalk, as the chalk glands of certain saxifrages.

calcareous pan. A hard layer of limy material more or less impermeable to water formed below the surface of the soil and affecting the water supply of the plants growing above it.

calcariform. Shaped like a calcar or spur.

calcarion. A plant formation on calcareous soils.

calceiform. Calceolate.

calceolate. Slipper-like or slipper-shaped like the one petal of the lady's slipper orchid, calceiform.

calcicole. A plant dwelling on chalky soil, a plant thriving in soils rich in calcium carbonate, a gypsophyte, a calcipete, a plant loving the neutral soil of limestone or shell-marl.

calcicolous. Living on chalky soils.

calciferae. Monocotyledons with a distinct calyx and corolla.

calciferous. Bearing lime.

calcification. 1. The deposition and/or the accumulation of calcium salts on or in cell walls. 2. The conversion into a rigid or more or less stony substance. 3. Petrification.

calcifugal. Shunning chalk, like heather and other ericaceous plants which grow in acid soils; calcifobous.

calcifuge. A plant which is intolerant of limy soil.

calcipete. A plant thriving on chalky soil.

calcipetrile. Of basic rock communities.

calciphile. A plant which occurs more or less exclusively in limy soil.

calciphobe. A calcifuge.

calcivorous. Consuming or living on limestone, as lichens which live on limestone and gradually etch into it.

calcosaxicoles. Plants living on rocky limestone.

calculary. Gritty or sclerogenous.

caldarium. An intermediate or warm greenhouse.

calendarium. An arrangement of plants according to their period of flowering.

calendulaceus. Calendula-like.

calendulin. A gummy or mucilaginous tasteless substance obtained from the pot marigold, bassorin.

calicalis. Calycalis.

caliche. A crust-like layer of red soil which is produced on grassland by extreme heat. The calcium carbonate layer becomes thickened and hardened by the heat.

Caliciflorae. A subdivision of the flowering plants in which the stamens and petals are borne on the calyx, calyx-flowers.

calicinarius. Calycinarius.

calicle. A calycle or epicalyx.

calico. See MOSAIC DISEASE.

calicular. Cup-shaped.

calidarium. A hothouse.

California bees. See GINGER-BEER PLANT.

californicus. Of California.

calina. The fine dust occurring on the plains of Spain.

caline. A plant hormone which promotes root growth (rhizocaline) and stem growth (caulocaline).

caliology. The juvenescence or dynamics of the young cell.

calix. Calyx.

calli. Hard or thickened spots or roughened protuberances.

callicarpous. Beautifully fruited.

callistachyous. Beautifully spiked.

callistegoid. Like *Calystegia* of the genus *Convolvulus*, bindweed.

callolyte. A ferment which dissolves callus from sieve-plates.

callose. A component of a plant cell which produces hardened spots or protuberances, a carbohydrate insoluble in cupra-ammonia but soluble in the cold in 1% solutions of caustic alkalies. It occurs in the callus pads which form over sieve plates and in calcified cell walls.

callosity. 1. A deposit of material inside the wall of a cell around the entering germ tube of a parasitic fungus which may prevent the establishment of a parasite in the cell. 2. The leathery or hard-thickening part of an organ; see CALLUS.

callososerratous. Having hardened or thickened serrations.

callous metaplasia. The condition resulting from metaplastic change of the cells affected.

callunetum. A plant association of heather, *Calluna vulgaris*.

callus. 1. A mass of parenchymatous cells formed by plants over or around a wound. 2. A hard protuberance or prominence in a cutting or on a severed or injured part. 3. An extension of the inner scale of a grass spikelet. 4. An abnormally thickened part as the base of a cutting from which roots develop. 5. A verruca.

callus cushions. The hemispherical pads covering the pits on the sides of sieve tubes.

callus hairs. The hairs at the base of the floret of *Calamogrostis* and some other genera.

callus heteroplasis. The formation of heteroplastic tissue.

callus homoplasia. A callus formed from wound stimuli.

callus hypertrophy. An abnormal growth with voluminous vesicles.

callus pads. Pads of callus deposited in the sieve-plates of algae.

callus plate. A pad of callose formed over a sieve-plate either as winter approaches or as the sieve tube ages and degenerates, a covering on one side of the partition wall in sieve tubes.

callus heteroplasy. The cell structures or tissues which arise as the result of a wound.

callus homoplasy. An increase of normal tissue due to an injury.

callus metaplasy. A change in the cell contents but not in the cell wall caused by injury to an organ.

callus rods. Thread-like rods which cross through apertures in the walls of sieve tubes.

calocepalous. Beautiful-headed, with beautiful hairs.

calophyllous. With beautiful leaves.

calopodium. A spathe.

caloritropic. Thermotropic.

caloritropism. Curvature caused by conducted heat.

calpa. The capsule of the moss *Fontinalis*.

calvescent. Becoming bare, calvous.

calvitium. A bald spot.

calvous. Naked, as an achene without a pappus; bald.

calybio. A hard, one-celled, inferior dry fruit, such as the acorn or hazel nut; a calybium.

calyc. A cup or cluster; see ANTHEMY.

calycalis. Of a calyx.

calycals. The *Calyciflorae*.

calycanthemous. 1. Having the calyx resemble the corolla in color and development. 2. Having the sepals wholly or partially converted into petals.

calycanthemy. An abnormal condition in which the sepals become petalloid.

calycatous. Having a calyx.

calycia. A stipitate and boat-shaped apothecium.

calycicolous. Living on the calyx.

Calycifloreae. 1. Plants having their petals and stamens adnate to the calyx. 2. A series of *Polypetalae*, the cup flowers.

calyciflorous. With the stamens and petals adnate to the calyx.

calyciform. Cup-shaped; calyx-shaped, as when the indusium of ferns is attached all around the margin of the receptacle.

calycin. A bitter yellow substance which may be crystallized and is obtained from *Calicium chrysocephalum*.

calycinal. Pertaining to or resembling a calyx, calycine.

calycinaris. Polyphylly of the calyx, an increase in the number of sepals in the calyx.

calycinarious. Formed from the calyx.

calycine flower. A flower with a calyx of unusual size.

calycinianus. Polyphylly of the calyx; see CALYCINARIS.

calycinous. Calyx-like, calycoid.

calycle. An epicalyx, a whorl of bracts forming a secondary or accessory calyx outside the true calyx, a calicle.

calycostemon. A stamen seated on the calyx.

calycosus. Calyx-like.

calycular. Cup-shaped, of the nature of or belonging to a calyx.

calyculate. Having bracts around the calyx or involucre imitating an outer calyx, having a calycule or additional bracts outside the calyx forming what looks like a double calyx.

calycule. 1. A group of small leaf-like organs placed close beneath the calyx. 2. An epicalyx. 3. A cup or calyx-like structure below a sporangium in myxomycetes.

calyphyomy. Adhesion of the sepals to the petals.

calypso. A plant or flower of the genus *Cytherea*.

calypter. A calyptra.

calyptra. 1. A covering. 2. The cap or lid covering the developing spore case of a moss formed by the enlargement of the archegonium after fertilization. 3. The root cap. 4. The hood, sometimes applied to that part of the volva covering the top of the pileus of mushrooms.

calyptra thalamogena. A structure of the capsule and stalk in some *Hepaticae* acting as a covering for the young sporangium.

calyptrate. Capped, having a calyptra, hoodlike.

calyptriform. Shaped like a calyptra or candle extinguisher.

calyptrogen. 1. The group of meristematic cells from which the root cap is formed. 2. The layer of tissue covering the young embryo as in ferns.

calyptron. The squama or scale of a calyptra.

calyx. The outer floral envelope of the flowering plants usually green in color and composed of sepals, the sepals considered collectively, the outer set of the floral envelope. When there is but one set, it is considered the calyx.

calyx adherens. A calyx not separable from the ovary.

calyx calyculatus. The calyx surrounded by a ring of bracts.

calyx communis. The involucre of the composites.

calyx inferior. The calyx fastened below the ovary.

calyx liber. The calyx free from the ovary.

calyx superior. The calyx adherent above the ovary.

calyx teeth. The tips of the calyx lobes or divisions.

calyx tube. The hollowed receptacle of a perigynous flower from which the petals and stamens grow. The tube is formed by the union of the sepals.

camara. 1. A fruit having more or less membranous carpels, as in *Ranunculus* and apple. 2. The hard and durable fruit of a tonka bean tree and other related species. 3. The single carpel of a fruit.

camarius. Resembling a simple carpel, as the berry-like fruit of *Actaea*.

cambial zone. The layer of variable width in a stem or root composed of the formative tissues and their undifferentiated derivatives.

cambiform. Resembling the form and character of cambium cells, as the parenchymatic tissue of primary phloem excepting companion cells.

cambiform cell. A parenchymatous cell occurring in the phloem. It is elongated and pointed at both ends.

cambiogenetic. Producing cambium.

cambium. The thin layer of formative tissue beneath the bark of dicotyledons and gymnosperms from which new wood and bark originate, a sheath of generative tissue ordinarily between the xylem and phloem, the meristematic zone from which new growth develops, the secondary tissue from which secondary growth arises in stems and roots.

cambium, fascicular. The cambium within the vascular bundles.

cambium fibers. The immediate derivatives of the cambium, partly formed woody fibers.

cambium, initial. One of the permanently meristematic cells of the cambium.

cambium, interfascicular. The cambium which is formed between the vascular bundles and the primary medullary rays.

cambium layer. The layer of cambium which is the formative tissue during active growth.

cambium ring. The complete system of the cambium separating the wood from the bast in the shoot.

Cambrian. The earliest division of the Palaeozoic Era.

Cambrian system. A series of very ancient Palaeozoic rocks between the Laurentian and the Silurian, formerly thought to be the oldest fossiliferous rocks.

cambricus. Of Cambria, Wales.

camelinous. Tawny.

cameration. The division into a large number of separate chambers.

camerula. A small camara.

camnium. A succession due to cultivation; see CULTURE COMMUNITY.

campanaceous. Bell-shaped, usually applied to a corolla.

campaniliform. Campanulate.

campanulaceous. Belonging to the genus *Campanula*, the bell flower.

campanulastrum. A small campanula or bell-shaped flower.

campanulate. Bell-shaped.

Campanulatae. An order of dicotyledons.

campeachy wood. Logwood, so-called from Campeche, Mexico.

campestral. Growing mainly in uncultivated fields, inhabiting open country.

campestrian. Of the Northern Great Plains area, the arid transition of Merriam life zones.

camphor. A solid essential oil distilled from the wood of *Cinnamomum camphora*.

camphoric. Pertaining to or of the nature of camphor, derived from camphor.

campine. Of the African Congo savannah.

campo. A Brazilian savannah, low open woods with ground vegetation, the transition from grass steppe to savannah comparable to the prairies of North America.

campo vero. The treeless savannahs in Brazil.

campschaticus. Of Kamchatka.

camptodrome. Leaf venation in which secondary veins bend forward and anastomose before reaching the margin.

camptodromous. With venation in which the secondary veins curve toward the margins but do not form loops.

camptotropal. Like an orthotropal ovule but curved like a horseshoe.

camptotropism. The tendency to resume a normal position after being forced out of it.

campulitropal. Curved, descriptive of an accessory fruiting structure in lichens.

campulitropous. Campylotropous, curved.

campyllidium. A fungus parasite once thought to be a fructification in lichens.

campylocarpous. With curved fruits.

campylodromous. Having venation in which the primary veins are curved toward the leaf apex in a more or less bowed form.

campylospermous. Having the albumen curved at the margin so as to form a longitudinal furrow, as in sweet cicely and others of the *Umbelliferae*.

campylotropism. The condition of being bent back.

campylotropous. Said of ovules or seeds having the nucellus and its integuments so curved that the apex is brought near the base; of an ovule, curved in such a way that the chalaza and the micropyle do not lie in a straight line.

cañada. A small canyon.

canada balsam. A turpentine from the balsam fir, *Abies balsamea*, which is a pale yellowish viscid liquid which solidifies to a transparent mass. It is used in varnish and lacquers and as a cement, especially in microscopy.

canadensis. Canadian.

Canadian life zone. A portion of the boreal life zone exclusive of the transcontinental coniferous forest and beyond timberline areas, the southern limit defined by a mean normal temperature of 64.4°F during the hottest weeks of the year.

canal. 1. A duct, tubular passage or channel. 2. A passage in the archegonial neck. 3. An elongated intercellular space containing resins, oils or other substances. 4. A water duct on the inner side of the xylem opposite a ridge on the surface of the stem of *Equisetum*.

canal, air. A passage on the inner side of the xylem and opposite a ridge on the stem surface.

canal of bordered pit. An elongated and narrow part of bordered pit.

canal cells. The short-lived cells in the central cavity of the neck of the archegonium the connecting septa of which disappear, forming a canal filled with mucilage for the passage of the antherozoids.

canal raphe. A modification of the raphe in diatoms by a longitudinal fissure.

canalicular. Pertaining to canals or canaliculi, having a canaliculus or canaliculi.

canalicular apparatus. A term used by those who consider the Golgi apparatus to be essentially a system of intracellular canals.

canaliculate. Marked longitudinally by a channel or groove, furrowed or fluted.

canariensis. Of the Canary Isles.

cancellate. Lattice-like, having an open network, reticulated, veined in the form of a lattice, cross-barred.

cancellous. Consisting of spongy or porous structures.

candelabra. A many-branched structure of spores and sporangia in some fungi that resembles the lighting fixture.

candelabra hairs. Stellate hairs in one or more tiers.

candicans. White, hoary, or growing white.

candicant. Whitish to shining white, albescent.

candidous. Pure white.

candlenut. The fruit of *Aleurites moluccana*, a plant growing in the Pacific. It is used for light by the natives. The oil has many uses.

cane. 1. Any hollow or pithy jointed stem, including the stems of reeds, large grasses, and small palms. 2. In horticulture it applies to stems of the raspberry, the black-berry, and the one-year-old stems of grape vines.

cane freckle. A fungus disease of cane.

cane rust. A fungus disease of cane.

cane soot. A disease caused by the fungus *Macrosporium*.

cane sugar. Sucrose, the crystallized product of sugar cane (*Saccharum officinarum*).

cane, spume sugar. A disease caused by *Strumella Sacchari*.

cane undershrubs. Plants having lignified but commonly monocarpic shoots, as various species of *Rubus*.

canella bark. The bark of a tropical American tree, *Canella*, which is used as a tonic, stimulant, and spice; wild cinnamon or cinnamon bark; see CINNAMON.

canellaceous. Resembling cinnamon in taste or shape.

canescence. Hoariness, a grayish-whiteness.

canescent. Having a hoary appearance due to a covering of short inconspicuous hairs, covered with hoary down.

canker. 1. Various diseases of trees caused by fungi, usually having localized patches of dead bark surrounded by swollen margins. 2. A disease of plants which causes slow decay.

cannabinous. Like *Cannabis*, hemp or marijuana.

cannaceous. Of the genus *Canna* or related forms.

cannon-ball tree. A South American tree which bears a large globose fruit with a hard woody rind.

canopy. 1. The layer of branches, twigs, and leaves formed by woody plants at some distances above ground level. 2. A characteristic membrane within the testa surrounding the free part of the nucleus.

canopy trees. Trees having well-branched crowns and abundant leafage.

canous. Whitened with pubescence, grayish-white.

cantabricus. From Cantabria, Spain.

cantaloupe. Any muskmelon, *Cucumis melo*.

cantharelloid. Shaped like *Cantharellus*, a white-spored agaric; more or less vase-shaped.

cantharophilae. Plants having showy colors and an abundance of pollen which are fertilized by beetles.

cantoniensis. Of Canton, China.

canus. Ash-colored, grayish-white.

caoutchouc. 1. An elastic substance obtained from the milky juice or latex of a large number of tropical plants. 2. Raw rubber.

caoutchouc bodies. Small particles in the latex.

cap. 1. The pileus in hymenomycetes, the umbrella-shaped fruitbody of a mushroom. 2. The husk of a nut.

cap cell. The cell which surmounts the antheridium of a fern and is thrown off when the antheridium liberates the sperms.

cap fungi. Fungi which have pilei.

Capensis Region. A floral region including the Cape of Good Hope.

capillaceous. Resembling hair, having long filaments; see CAPILLARY.

capillament. The stalk of a stamen supporting an anther.

capillamentosis. Comose.

capillare. Hair-like.

capillaries. Minute, thin-walled vessels which are channels for the conduction of liquids; fine, hair-like or thread-like vessels.

capillarity. The rise of water in a tube with a very narrow bore due to the forces of cohesion and adhesion.

capillary soil water. Water held between the particles of the soil by capillarity, i.e., by cohesion or adhesion.

capillatae radices. Roots with root hairs.

capillaturous. Having a mass of hair.

capilliform. Hair-like, having the form of a hair.

capillipes. Slender-footed.

capillitial. The width of a hair, about 1/12 of a line or 0.17 mm.

capillitium. A mass of thread-like sterile hyphae mixed with spores in the fructification of myxomycetes and gasteromycetes.

capitalist. A plant which has a large reserve of material and is insect-fertilized.

capitate. Head-shaped, having a globose head.

capitate hairs. Thicker hairs on a head-shaped surface.

capitate incrusted. With the incrustation at the apex only.

capitate stigma. A stigma which is broad and flat.

capitellate. Having a very small knob-like termination.

capitellum. The capsule of mosses, a little head of any sort bearing spores inside or outside.

capitiform. Shaped like a head.

capitular. Capitellate, growing in small heads.

capitulate. Resembling a head.

capituliform. In the form of a small head, like a capitulum.

capitulum. 1. A close, rounded, dense cluster or head of sessile flowers; the flower head of composites. 2. The globose apical apothecium of lichens in the *Coniocarpineae*. 3. A dense tuft of branches at the apex of a gametophyte in *Sphagnidae*.

capnodic. Smoke-colored, capnoid.

capoe. A palm thicket in the campos veros in Brazil.

capoeira. A plain of the Amazon Valley; see SELVA.

capparinous. Brownish-green.

capreol (e). A tendril.

capreolate, capreolatus. Having tendrils.

capreolus. A slender appendage which serves for support by coiling around some other object.

capricornis. Of the Tropic of Capricorn.

caprification. 1. The custom of hanging branches of the wild fig in the cultivated trees so as to insure pollination by means of the gall insects thus introduced. 2. Hand-pollination of figs.

caprificous. Like the uncultivated male form of the common fig.

caprifig. A race of figs which does not produce edible fruits but provides food for the wasps which pollinate the cultivated figs, the wild fig.

capsella. An achene.

capsicin. An acrid alkaloid substance found in some species of *capsicum*, the hot red pepper used as a spice.

capsomania. 1. A multiplication of pistils. 2. An unnatural development of pistils either in alteration of form or impairment of function.

capsulate. Enclosed in a capsule.

capsules. 1. Dry dehiscent fruits formed from a compound ovary with various types of dehiscence to release the seeds, the most common seed structures. 2. The theca or spore cases of mosses and ferns. 3. The perithecia or receptacles of fungi, the sporangia.

caput. 1. The peridium of some fungi. 2. A knob-like swelling at the apex. 3. A head.

caput florum. The capitulum.

caput radicis. 1. The crown of the root.

2. An obsolete term for the stem or bud of herbaceous plants.

caraguata. Fiber.

caraway seed. A seed of the herb *Carum Carvi* grown for its seeds which are used in flavoring breads, cakes, cheese, etc. The young shoots and leaves are also used in salads.

carbo. Carbon or charcoal.

carbohydrase. A carbohydrate-splitting enzyme.

carbon assimilation. Photosynthesis.

carbon cycle. The circulation of carbon in nature. Inorganic carbon in the air is utilized by plants to form organic carbon compounds through photosynthetic and other anabolic processes; such carbon atoms may then be assimilated into the bodies of one or more successive animals; excretion, respiration, burning, and bacterial action on dead plants and animals return the carbon atoms to the inorganic state.

carbon-nitrogen ratio. The relation between the carbon and nitrogen content of a plant. Often written C/N ratio.

carbonaceous. Consisting chiefly of substances in which carbon predominates; rigid, blackish, and brittle; like coal; dark-colored, almost black.

carbonate. A salt or ester of carbonic acid.

carbonicolous. Living on burned-over ground or charcoal.

Carboniferous Age. The geological age of carbon or coal deposits when a warm, damp climate produced great forests of large ferns and primitive gymnosperms from which rich seams of coal were formed.

carbonized. Turned into nearly pure carbon by slow combustion, as wood burned to charcoal.

carbonous. Like coal or carbon, carbonaceous.

carbozymase. An enzyme found in yeasts.

carcerule. 1. A dry indehiscent fruit formed from a polycarpellate superior ovary, the carpels of which separate when ripe into indehiscent, few-seeded, lobed fruits, e.g., the hollyhock. 2. The sporangium of some fungi. See SCHIZOCARP.

carcinodes. Cancerous diseases.

carcinoma. Cancer, canker, and similar diseases.

carcithium. A mycelium, carcyte, or carcythium.

carda. A seed.

cardaminefolious. Cardamine-leaved.

cardaminetum. An association of *Cardamine*, the herb bitter cress.

cardamon. An aromatic herb of the tropics from two sources: *Elettaria Cardamon*, the true cardamon, the dried capsules of which are used in medicines; and *Amomum Cardamon*, a plant with aromatic leaves and seeds used for flavoring, supposed to have tonic qualities.

cardinal grade. The highest and lowest temperature at which plant functions can be performed.

cardinal points of temperature. The minimum, optimum, and maximum temperatures affecting plant growth.

cardiochilous. Heart-shaped.

cardiopetalous. With heart-shaped petals.

carduaceous. Thistle-like.

carene. The keel or midrib in the leaves of grasses.

caribaeus. Of the Caribbean.

caricetum. An association of *Carex*, the sedges.

caricography. The study of the *Cyperaceae*, sedges, of the genus *Carex*.

caricosous. *Carex*-like.

caries. Putridity, decay.

carina. 1. The keel or boat-shaped portion of a papilionaceous flower formed by two lower petals which enclose the stamens and the pistil. 2. A longitudinal ridge or projection on the glumes of certain grasses. 3. The principal nerve of a sepal.

carinal aestivation. The condition in which the carina embraces the other parts of the flower.

carinal air spaces. Certain cavities in the fibrovascular strands of *Equisetum*.

carinal canal. A lacuna in the xylem of a fibrovascular bundle as in *Equisetum*, a water canal in *Equisetum* on the inner side of the xylem and opposite a ridge on the surface of the stem.

carinalis. Keeled, as in the umbellifers in which the side of the fruit represents the principal nerve (carina) of the adherent calyx.

carinate. 1. Having a keel or projecting ridge on the lower surface. 2. Shaped like a keel, as the glumes of many grasses.

carinato-plicate. With leaves so plaited that each fold resembles a keel.

cariopside. Caryopsis.

cariopsideous. Having a caryopsis as fruit.

cariopsis. See CARYOPSIS.

cariose. Decaying or decayed.

cariosocancellate. Said of lichens which become latticed by decay.

carissa. Straggling by axillary branches.

carminative. Promoting perspiration.

carmine. The purest red pigment having no blue or yellow in it.

carnation. 1. Flesh-colored. 2. The flower or plant of that name, *Dianthus Caryophyllus.*

carnea. Flesh-colored, pale red.

carneous. 1. Flesh-colored, very pale red. 2. Fleshy in texture, as the trama of fungi.

carniolicus. Of Carniola in South Central Europe.

carnivorism. The flesh-digesting capacity of insectivorous plants.

carnivorophyte. A flesh-digesting plant.

carnivorous plants. Plants which capture animals (chiefly insects) and get nourishment from them.

carnose. Fleshy in texture, firmer than succulent or pulpy.

carnulose. Somewhat fleshy.

caro. The flesh, as the pulp of a melon and/or the fleshy part of a drupe (rarely applied to the tissue of some fungi).

carob. *Ceratonia siliqua* (St. John's bread), a tree of the Mediterranean region, cultivated elsewhere for the edible pods which are used for forage and sometimes for man. The seeds were formerly used as a standard of weight (carat).

Carobe di Ginde. The turpentine gall-apple found on *Pistacia Lentiscus.*

carolinianus. Pertaining to the Carolinas.

carotene. The yellow pigment of blood derived from carotin in plant food.

carotin. Xanthophyll, a yellow pigment found in plants, from *Daucus carota*; the red coloring matter found in chromoplasts.

carotinoids. The collective name for the red and yellow pigments in plastids, carotins.

caroubin. A carbohydrate first observed in the carob.

caroubinase. A hydrolytic enzyme formed during germination of seeds of *Ceratonia siliqua*; see CAROB.

carp. An abbreviation for carpel, a fruit.

carpadelium. The fruit of the umbellifers and maples; see CREMOCARP.

carpadelus. A carpodelium.

carpathicus. Of the Carpathian region in Europe, carpaticus.

carpels. Modified floral leaves in the seed plants which form the simple or compound gynoecium of the flower in which the seeds are formed (usually along the junction lines of the floral leaves). A carpel usually consists of three parts: the ovary (a swollen basal portion containing the ovules), the style (a filamentous prolongation of the apex of the ovary), and the stigma (the specialized tip of the style on which the pollen lodges and germinates).

carpel disk. The ovuliferous expansion, as in the fossil plants *Williamsonia.*

carpel, solid. A fibrovascular strand with a few lateral veins or reticulations.

carpel valve. A midrib with inconspicuous reticulate venation more or less leaf-shaped.

carpellary scale. A bract scale.

carpellate strobili. Strobili composed of megasporophylls or carpels.

carpellody. The change of a floral leaf into a carpel.

carpellotaxy. The arrangement of carpels in the fruit.

carpellum. A diminutive carpel, the small parts from which compound fruits are formed; see CARPEL.

carpet. A ground-covering of plants.

carpeting plants. Very low plants covering the ground.

carphospore. A plant whose seeds are disseminated by means of a scaly or chaffy pappus.

carpid. A small carpel.

carpidium. A carpel or carpid.

carpinifolious. Leaved like *Carpinus*, the ironwood tree.

carpium. The oogonium modified by fertilization which remains as an envelope around the embryo.

carpo-. A prefix meaning fruit.

carpo-asci. The more complex ascomycetous fungi (all except the *Exoascaceae*).

carpocephalum. A specialized, erect, sporangium-bearing branch in the *Marchantiales* (*Hepaticae*). The archegoniophore.

carpoclonium. The case or receptacle of spores found in certain algae.

carpodermis. The pericarp.

carpodes. Abortive carpels as in *Typha.*

carpogam. The female organ in a procarp which produces a cystocarp.

carpogamy. The process of producing fertile cells.

carpogenic, carpogenous. 1. Producing fruit or fertile cells. 2. Producing cells which form the carpogonium. 3. Living on fruit.

carpogon, -e, -ium. 1. The primordial stage of fructification. 2. The female organ of some algae and some common fungi. 3. The archicarp in ascomycetes. 4. The part of the procarp which develops into a sporocarp after fertilization. See OOGONIUM.

carpogonidium. A carpospore.

carpography. The description of fruits.

carpohylile. A dry forest community.

carpolite. A fossilized fruit found in coal, a lithocarp or carpolith.

carpolochmis. A dry thicket community.

carpology. The study of the structure of fruits and seeds.

carpoma. A collection of spermangia, a compound sporocarp.

carpomania. Grittiness in fruit.

carpomany. The substitution of pistils for stamens.

carpomorpha. The apothecia in some lichens which resemble fruits.

carpomycetes. The higher fungi which produce fruit bodies, as the ascomycetes and basidiomycetes.

carpon. Fruit.

carpophagous. Feeding on fruits and seeds.

carpophore. 1. The stalk which bears the carpels or gynoecium or sporocarp. 2. A slender stalk to which the mericarps of the umbelliferous fruits are attached. 3. The stalk of a pistil extending between its carpels. 4. The stipe, pileus, and lamellae of fungi.

carpophore-stalk of a sporocarp. A carpophore.

carpophyll. A fruit leaf or a carpel.

carpophyte. A thallophyte or phanerogam which forms sporocarps.

carpophytic fungi. Fungi which produce conidia.

carpopodium. A fruit-stalk.

carpoptosis. The abnormal falling of fruit.

carpos. Fruit.

carposoma. The fruit bodies of certain fungi.

carposperm. The impregnated oosphere in certain thallophytes.

carposphere. The oosphere in some algae before impregnation.

carposporangia. Differentiated sporangia found in the cystocarp of the red algae.

carpospore. 1. A plant which produces spores after fertilization. 2. A spore formed in a sporocarp or a sporophyte. 3. A spore formed at the end of a filament developed from a carpogonium. 4. A uninucleate nonmotile spore formed in red algae as a result of growth and division of the zygote.

carposporiferous. Bearing carpospores in red algae.

carposporophyte. 1. A plant which has carpospores. 2. A cystocarp of the red algae when considered to be an asexual spore-producing generation parasitic on the sexual generation.

carpostome. The opening in a sporocarp through which the spores are discharged.

carpostrotes. Plants whose distribution is effected by means of their fruits.

carpotropic movement. A curving of the fruit stalk after fertilization bringing the fruit into a favorable position for ripening the seeds or liberating them in a place where conditions will favor germination.

carpotropism. The movement of fruits before or after pollination.

carpozygote. A zygospore.

carr. An association of scattered trees and shrubs progressing from fen to scrub.

carr fen. The ultimate stage of fen formation.

carr swamp. Swampwood occurring on the edge of the water.

Carragheen moss. A mucilaginous seaweed, kelp, *Chrondrus crispus*, from which gelatin is extracted. It is widely used in foods, cosmetics, water-base paints, etc. First used in Ireland, it is obtained from the North Atlantic Ocean. Carrageenin, Irish moss.

carrasco. Low brush communities found on rock wastes in Brazil.

carrier. Any individual that harbors and excretes pathogenic bacteria.

carrion flower. A flower with the odor of carrion which attracts carrion flies.

carse. A fen.

carthamine. Red coloring matter from flowers of *Carthamus tinctorus*, the safflower.

cartilaginous. Like cartilage, tough but pliable.

caruncle. A localized outgrowth of the seed coat, a small hard aril, an excrescence or appendage at or about the hilum of a seed.

caryallagic. Involving a nuclear change in reproduction.

caryo. See KARYO.

caryoid. A minute spherical mass of protein of obscure significance found in some algal cells.

caryophyllaceous. Resembling the pink family, *Caryophyllaceae*; having connate-perfoliate leaves and stems swollen at the nodes; having petals with long tapered bases or claws, as *Dianthus caryophyllus*, the carnation.

caryophyllatous. With long claws, caryophylleous.

caryopsidous. Like a caryopsis.

caryopsis. A one-seeded dry fruit with the thin pericarp adherent to the seed, as in most grasses and cereal grains; an achene with the pericarp adherent to the seed coat.

caryotaefolious. With leaves like those of *Caryota*, the East Indian palm.

cascarillous. Having the color of the inner bark of *Cascarilla*.

casein. See PLANT CASEIN.

cashmerianus. Of Cashmere.

Casparian dots. Certain suberized markings on the walls of the endodermis in *Dianthera*.

Casparian strips. 1. A secondary thickening which develops on the radial and end walls in some rhizomes and some cotyledons. 2. A band of peculiar impervious cellular tissue in the endodermis of certain water plants.

Caspar's band. The Casparian strip or band, Caspary's band.

caspicus. Of the Caspian Sea.

casque. A process or structure like a helmet, an arched sepal or petal resembling a helmet, a *galea*.

cassiarabicus. Arabic *Cassia*, senna, an herb grown for flowers and its medicinal uses, as senna leaves.

cassideous. Helmet-shaped, with an irregular corolla having the upper petal broad and helmet-shaped as in *Aconitum*.

cassinoid. Like *Cassine*, an African climbing shrub the wood of which is used for making small articles.

cassus. Empty, as an anther containing no pollen; sterile.

castaneous. Chestnut brown.

castanhal. See SELVA.

casting. The premature shedding of leaves or fruits.

castor oil. A mild cathartic fixed oil which is expressed or extracted from the seeds of the castor plant, a nondrying oil used commercially obtained from *Ricinus communis*.

castrate. To deprive of the androecium, to lack anthers or viable pollen, to be anantherous.

castration, amphigenous. A transformation in either the stamens or pistils.

castration, androgenous. The removal of anthers from flowers.

castration, thelygynous. The production of pistils in the male host.

casts. Fossils which show the impressions of the structures from which their forms are derived.

casts, medullary. The impressions of the internal cavities of the fossil plants *Calamites*.

casual. An occasional weed in cultivation which is not naturalized.

casual species. An alien species occurring in a plant community of which it is not a regular inhabitant.

casuarinoid. Of *Casuarina*, a primitive Australian dicot.

cata-. See KATA-.

catabolism. Chemical changes which take place in plant tissues which result in degeneration into simpler chemical composition, destructive metabolism, the opposite of anabolism, katabolism.

catabolite. An organism in which the catabolic processes predominate over the anabolic processes, a katabion.

catacladous. Deflected, bent, or curved.

cataclesium. A one-celled, one-seeded fruit within a hardened calyx as in *Mirabilis*; a diclesium.

catacorolla. A second corolla formed inside or outside the true one, a phenomenon observed in *Gloxinia* and *Datura*.

catadromous. Said of the form of branching or veining in ferns, having the lowest inferior segment of a pinna nearer the rachis than the lowest superior one, having the first vein in each leaf segment come off on the basal side of the midrib, katadromous, the opposite of anadromous.

catagenesis. Retrogressive evolution, modification by loss of attributes or by simplification of structure.

catakinetic. Katakinetic.

catalase. An enzyme present in plant tissue which hastens the decomposition of hydrogen peroxide while being slowly destroyed itself.

catalpifolious. Leaved like *Catalpa*.

catalysis. The acceleration or retardation of a chemical reaction by a substance which itself undergoes no permanent change or which may be recovered when the action is completed.

catalyst. A substance which aids in breaking down other substances.

catametadromous. Sometimes catadromous and sometimes metadromous in the same species.

catapetalous. Having the bases of the petals of a polypetalous corolla adherent to the base of the stamens, having the petals united only by cohesion with the united stamens.

cataphasia. The functional decline of a cell.

cataphyll. A scale-like leaf as found in buds, cotyledons, rhyzomes, etc.; any rudimentary scale-like leaf which precedes the foliage leaf; the German Niederblätter, an underleaf; a leaf present at the beginning of growth. A cataphyllary leaf.

cataplasm. A diseased, abnormal growth.

cataplastic. Of cataplasy, degeneration of tissue combined with an increase in size.

catapult fruits. Fruits in which the dispersal of seeds or fruit segments is due to the elastic reaction of the resilient peduncles or pedicels.

catapult mechanism. A means of seed dispersal depending on sudden jerks due to the stiffness of the long stalk as the fruit sways in the wind.

catarobic. Having an adequate medium in which slow decomposition of organic matter occurs using a relatively large amount of oxygen but not enough to reduce the oxygen concentration below the amount required by most aerobic organisms; see OLIGOSAPROBIC, POLYSAPROBIC, and MESOSAPROBIC.

cata-species. A species of the *Uredinales* which lacks a pycnidial stage.

catathecium. An inverted thyriothecium, the fruit body of *Trichothyriaceae* with a pseudo-ostiole and asci arranged in a fan-like manner but not radiating from the base of the fruit body, a catothecium.

catch-fly. Any of the various plants which have a viscid substance on the stems or inflorescences to which small insects adhere.

catchment. A watershed or a unit of drainage area.

catechin. A crystallizable constituent of catechu.

catechu. 1. The heart wood of *Acacia Catechu*, which is very astringent due to its rich tannin content. 2. Any of the several dry, resin-like astringents obtained by decoction from wood, leaves, and fruits of certain tropical Asiatic plants.

catenation. Arrangement in chains or rings.

cateniferous. Having or bearing chains, arranged like a chain, linked to look like a chain.

catenulate. Formed of parts united or linked as in a chain, catenate, catenuliform. See CONCATENATE.

caterva. A heap or crowd.

cathayanus. Of Cathay, China.

cathedrous. Growing between the angles of a stem.

cathodic. Turned away, said only of that half of a leaf which is turned away from the course of the ascending spiral; kathodic.

catkin. A specialized type of inflorescence of several flowers borne on a single stalk, usually pendant with all staminate or all pistillate flowers. The catkin usually falls as a unit after pollen is shed or the seeds are liberated. An ament, amentum, or catulus.

catocladous. Deflexed, bent outwards or downwards.

catothecium. An inverted perithecium in which the asci hang down from the base of the organ. Catathecium.

catulus. A catkin.

caucasicus. Of the Caucasus Mountains.

cauda. A tail or tail-like appendage.

caudescens. Becoming stem-like.

caudex. The perennial base of an otherwise herbaceous plant, the axis of a woody plant, the stem or trunk of a palm or tree fern.

caudex columnaris. An erect columnar stem or a main trunk.

caudex descendens. The root.

caudex radicis. The root tip.

caudex repens. A rhizome.

caudicicontinuous. Having leaves which have no articulation with the stem but are continuous with it.

caudiciform. Having a tree-like stem, like a caudex in form.

caudicle. 1. A small stem or stemlet. 2. A mucilaginous thread-like stalk of orchids which attaches the pollinium to the rostellum.

caudicula. A caudicle.

caul. 1. An enclosing or investing membrane, as the pericardium. 2. A stem.

caulescence. The development of the stem.

caulescent. Having a stem which arises out of the ground, with an obvious stem above ground.

cauliatatous. Wing-stemmed.

caulicle. 1. A small stem. 2. The initial stem in an embryo, the part of the stem lying between the radicle and the cotyledons.

caulicolous. 1. Having a stem. 2. Living or growing on the stem of another plant, as some fungi. Caudicole, caulicole.

caulicule. A caulicle.

caulid. The main shoot or stem of the bryophytic gametophyte which supports the vegetative and reproductive organs.

caulidium. The leaf in the oophore generation as an analagous term to caulome in the sporophore generation.

cauliferous. Having a stalk, caulescent.

cauliflorous. Flowering on the trunk or on specialized spurs from it or from the larger branches.

cauliflory. The production of flowers from old stems, as in the redbud and many tropical trees.

cauliform. Having the shape of a stalk.

cauligenous. Arising from a stem.

cauline. Growing on or belonging to a stem, especially on the upper portion.

cauline bundle. A vascular bundle that remains within the stem and does not pass into the leaves, a fibrovascular bundle confined exclusively to the stem and not directly connected with one in the leaves.

caulis. The stem or stalk of a plant.

caulis deliquescens. A stem which branches irregularly.

caulis excurrens. A stem growing straight upwards and having side branches.

caulis suffruticosus. A suffruticose stem, a stem which is shrub-like rather than tree-like.

caulocaline. See CALINE.

caulocalyx. The pseudoperianth of the liverworts.

caulocarpic. Perennial, living to flower and fruit more than once or indefinitely.

caulocarpous. Producing fruit on a permanent stem as do ordinary trees and shrubs.

caulocystidium. Cystidium-like cells on the stipe which may form a sort of skin on the stipe of agarics.

caulode. The portion of a thallophyte which simulates a stem.

cauloma. The stem of a palm or the stem-like portion in some algae.

caulome. 1. A general term denoting all organs belonging to the shoot. 2. The stem-structure of a plant whether or not it has the usual stem form and function.

caulomer. One of the secondary axes which form a sympodium.

caulotaxis. The arrangement of the branches upon a stem.

caustic. 1. Any substance or means which applied to organic tissue burns, corrodes, or destroys it by chemical action. 2. Biting to the taste like cayenne pepper.

caval. Tufted at the apex, comose.

cavernarius. Growing in caves, cavernicolous.

cavernose. With hollows.

cavernula. A little cavity.

cavernuli. The pores of polypores.

cavitate. Hollow.

cavitus. The perithecium of some fungi.

cavity. The depression in the stem end of an apple or other pome fruits.

cavum. Any hollow or chamber.

cavus. The peridium in certain fungi.

cavus superus. The hymenium of certain fungi.

cayennensis. Of Cayenne, French Guiana.

cecidiology. The study of galls and their origins.

cecidium. A gall or hypertrophy on a plant-member due to the stimulating action of a fungus or an insect.

ceinture. Zonation.

celastrinous. Like *Celastrus*, the type genus of the family *Celastraceae*, a family of tree shrubs and woody climbing vines.

cell. A microscopic unit of protoplasm, a protoplast with or without a cell wall, the fundamental unit of structure and function of all living things, a nucleus with its most intimately surrounding cytoplasm, a mass of protoplasm containing a nucleus or nuclear material, the cavity of the anther or ovary; see LOCULE.

cell bridge. One of the delicate strands of protoplasm connecting the sieve tubes.

cell bundle. A band or bundle or similar cells, as in the bast fibers of dicotyledons.

cell cap. A structure in *Oedogonium* which is caused by intercalary surface growth.

cell community. A cell.

cell contents. The material inside the cell wall, the protoplasm and its contents.

cell division. The formation of daughter cells from a mother cell, the process by which cells multiply, amitosis, meiosis, mitosis.

cell, erect. Vertically placed cells in contact with the rays in the phloem of pines.

cell family. A group of cells of common origin chiefly appearing among the lower algae, a colony, a coenobium.

cell fibers. The achromatic filaments which form the nuclear spindle during the process of nuclear division; see NUCLEAR FIBRILS and CHROMATIC THREADS.

cell formation. The construction of a new cell by the reorganization of the protoplasm which may not involve a division of the cytoplasm.

cell fusion. The union of cells either by absorption or by perforations of the transverse walls.

cell growth. The enlargement and multiplication of cells.

cell, helicoid. The apical coenocyte in *Pithophora*.

cell inclusion. Any non-living material present in the cytoplasm whether organic or inorganic.

cell kernel. The nucleus.

cell lineage. The history of the division of the cell from the earliest cleavages until the time the definite fundamentals of the organ are laid down.

cell masses. Masses of cells without any definite arrangement.

cell membrane. The cell wall.

cell multiplication. The increase in cell number, cell division.

cell nucleus. An organized structure within the living cell by means of which cell-

division takes place. It is usually spherical in form, richer in protoplasm, and of higher refractive power than the remaining cell-contents.

cell organ. Any special structure within the cell which has some special function in the life, growth, and reproduction of the cell.

cell plasm. Cytoplasm.

cell plate. 1. A delicate membrane formed across the equator of the achromatic spindle as cell division proceeds which provides the foundation of the cell wall separating the daughter cells resulting from the division. 2. An aggregation of cells in one plane which is formed by a series of thickenings of the spindle fibers called dermatosomes.

cell, primordial. The cell before the formation of a cell wall, a naked cell.

cell, prolific. The disjointed part of the thallus of *Cladophora*.

cell rows. The arrangement of cells in contact by their ends forming a filament.

cell sap. The colorless liquid filling the vacuole of the plant cell; a watery solution containing various substances—salts, sugars, alkaloids, and the like.

cell surface. A single layer of cells as found in some algae.

cell theory. A theory developed by Schleiden and Schwann that all plants and animals are composed of cells and products of cells and the cells are units of structure and function.

cell tissue. A group of cells formed by the division of one or a few original cells which remain associated and function as a whole, the tissue composed of cells as distinguished from vessels.

cell wall. The non-living supporting material which forms a wall between adjacent protoplasts, a sac-like structure enclosing the living contents of a cell, the outer covering of a protoplast.

cella. A cell or a form of perithecium in fungi.

cellase. An enzyme which reduces cellose.

celled. Divided into cells, contained or enclosed in a cell, sometimes used to denote the chambers of an ovary, referring to the number of seed cavities in a fruit.

celliferous. Bearing or producing cells.

cellifugal. Moving away from a cell.

cellipetal. Moving toward a cell.

cellobiose. A reducing sugar said to have essentially the same composition as cellulose, cellose.

cells of the protective sheath. Cell walls characterized by a narrow strip of lignified material giving rise to Casparian dots.

cellul. An anther.

cellular. Composed of cells; made up of short, thin-walled cells rather than of fibers or tubes; parenchymatous.

cellular bark. The middle or green layer of the bark between the liber and the outer epiphloem, the cellular envelope; see MESOPHLOEM.

cellular envelope. See MESOPHLOEM and CELLULAR BARK.

cellular plants. Plants which contain no fibrovascular tissue, such as fungi, algae, and mosses which are composed exclusively of cellular tissue; the lower plants or non-vascular cryptogams.

cellular spore. A compound spore composed of more than one cell, each of which is frequently capable of germination.

cellular system. The fundamental or typical cells as distinct from the cells which form the vascular system.

cellular tissue. Tissue in which none of the cells are modified into ducts or vessels, in contradistinction to the vascular cells; see PARENCHYMA.

cellulares. All plants which are composed of cells in contrast to non-cellular or unicellular plants.

cellulase. An enzyme found in the large intestine of herbivorous animals which assists in the digestion of cellulose. It is important to saprophytes and parasites, and is found in wood-destructive fungi. Cytase.

cellule. A small cell, cistula, or cellula.

celluliferous. Producing cellules.

celluliform. Cell-shaped.

cellulin. A refractive substance probably resembling cellulose in composition which is present in the hyphae of some aquatic fungi.

cellulin grains. Certain bodies sometimes found in vegetative hyphae.

cellulosae. Sporidesm.

cellulose. The carbohydrate which composes the cell membranes; the primary cell-wall substance; an amorphous white compound which is isomeric with starch and insoluble in ordinary solvents; the raw material for the manufacture of paper, artificial silk, laquers, films, etc.

cellulose, fungus. The cellulose found in the hyphal walls of the fungi; see CHITIN.

cellulose, reserve. Cellulose stored as food.

cellulose trabecula. A strand of cellulose which crosses the lumen of a cell.

celluloses. A generic name for plants containing cellulose.

celluloside. A mixture of cellulose and pectose of which the primitive cell wall is composed.

cellulosoplicate. Folded so as to form small cells.

cembretum. An association of *Pinus cembra*.

cement disk. The glandular disk or retinaculum of orchids.

cementation. The union of membranes by a cementing substance so that hyphae are inseparably grown together, a concrescence.

cen-, ceno-. A prefix meaning recent, fresh, or new.

cenanthy. The suppression of both stamens and pistils in a flower.

cenchrus. Millet, a generic name for grasses with spiny involucres forming troublesome burrs.

ceneostrate. A cenophytic eostrate.

cenisius. Of Mt. Cenis, between France and Italy.

cenobiar. Of the cenobium.

cenobium. The peculiar four-parted fruit (or the four nutlets around a common style) which distinguishes *Labiatae* and *Borraginaceae*, a coenobium.

cenocyte. A mass of cells or protoplasts with a common limiting wall but without walls delimiting the individual cells, a coenocyte.

cenogenesis. A type of ontogeny in which the nonancestral characters appear as a result of secondary adaptation of the offspring to the particular environmental conditions in which they grow, the appearance of characters in the development or adaptation of an organism which its ancestors did not show, a form of development of an organism in which the evolutionary history of the group is not repeated. The opposite is palingenesis.

cenogenetic. Of recent origin.

cenomorphism. The development of new simple modifications from more complex organisms.

cenophytic. Referring to those plants of the most recent era of plant life.

cenosere. The geologic period marked by the change in plant dominance from gymnosperms to angiosperms, the eosere of the Cenozoic Period, ceneosere.

cenosis. A community having several dominants.

Cenozoic Era. The era of geological history following the Mesozoic Era and including the Tertiary and Quaternary Periods in which mammals and man developed.

censer action. The action in certain capsules which open partially by valves permitting the seeds to be shaken out by the wind.

censer holes. Apertures or openings in capsules.

censer mechanism. A means of seed liberation by which the seeds are shaken out of the fruits as the stems of the plant sway in the wind.

center of dispersal. An area in the range of a species from which it spreads in large numbers. This area may or may not be the center of origin or distribution.

center of distribution. A common region where the ranges of several unrelated species overlap and have an environment at this point suitable for all species in question.

center of origin. The area from which a taxonomic group of organisms has originated and spread. The theory that the region of greatest genetic variation of a species contains its center of origin.

centgener. A 100-plant plot in which each seed was planted a certain distance from every other seed.

centifolious. Hundred-leaved, with very many leaves.

centonate. Applied to leaves resembling patchwork because of the presence of blotches of different colors.

centrad. 1. Centripetal wood. 2. A unit of angular measure about 0.57°, one-hundredth of a radian.

central area. A hyaline portion of a diatom valve which sometimes surrounds the central nodule.

central body. The structure at the center of the aster during mitosis including the centriole and centrosome, the incipient nucleus.

central cell. 1. The cell in the dilated base of an archegonium which divides to form the primary ventral cell and the primary canal. 2. The cell in the venter in gymnosperms which develops into the ventral canal and the egg.

central cord. A cord or bundle of elongated thin-walled cells at the center of the leaves, stems, and fruit-stalks of many mosses which serves in the transfer of water; tissue cord.

central cylinder. The stele or portion within the endodermis.

central fibers. 1. Fibers in the central area. 2. A band between bundles and especially phloem regions with thick walls and tannin contents characteristic of *Pinus*.

central granules. Granules in the incipient nuclei in *Cyanophyceae*.

central placentation. The attachment of the ovules to a compound placenta that rises as a column from the base of the ovary.

central spindle. The group of fibers situated in the axial part of the spindle of an amphiaster distinguished from the surrounding contractile mantle fibers.

central strand. The middle of many stems in mosses made up of a bundle of much narrower and more slender cells similar to the vascular bundles in the higher plants.

centranthifolious. Leaved like *Centranthus*, a cultivated flower in the Mediterranean regions, red valerian.

centrarch. Solid xylem with protoxylem elements in the center.

centraxonia. Syngramme.

centraxonia center. The middle point of the pervalvar axis in diatoms with linear symmetry.

centric. 1. Circular in section with tissues distributed evenly all around. 2. Of leaves which show little difference between the internal structure of their upper and under sides. 3. Cylindrical or terete.

centric diatom. A diatom in which the valves are built on a radial plan.

centric fusions. Mutual translocations of large segments or whole arms of chromosomes resulting from breaks at or near the kinetochore.

centric oosphere. A fungal oosphere in which one or two layers of small globules of oil completely surround the central protoplasm.

centrifugal. 1. Produced or expanding from the center outward. 2. In inflorescence when the central flower or a cyme precedes the other, i.e., the flowering commences at the center and extends successively to the circumference, as is typical of flowers of determinate inflorescence.

centrifugal growth. Growth from the center outward.

centrifugal inflorescence. Determinate inflorescence. See CYME.

centrifugal thickening. The depositing of layers of wall material on the outside of a cell wall which is possible only when the cell lies free and not touching its neighbors. The sculpturing on the walls of pollen grains is formed by centrifugal thickening.

centrifugal xylem. The xylem in which differentiation proceeds in succession towards the periphery of the stem or roots.

centrifugally. Away from the center.

centriole. A central granule in most centrosomes which undergoes division with the rest of the centrosome.

centripetal. Pointing to the axis; toward the center; developing or opening successively from the outside toward the center, as in the case of the flowers of an indeterminate inflorescence; the reverse of centrifugal.

centripetal growth. Growth proceeding from the periphery toward the center.

centripetal thickening. The depositing of layers of wall material on the inner side of the wall of a cell, a common process in a developing cell.

centripetal xylem. Xylem in which differentiation proceeds in succession toward the center of the axis.

centrodesmose. The central spindle or axis of an achromatinic spindle.

centrodesmus. A connection between the centrioles after their division from which in some cases the central spindle arises. The attraction spindle.

centrogene. A fragment of a centromere which can grow by itself after being divided from the main body.

centrogenesis. The development of peripheral or rotate-forms in plants.

centrogenous. Meeting in a common center and growing outward.

centromere. The point of spindle attachment of the chromosomes during cell division. It is believed to be a determining factor affecting chromosome movement by variation in protein composition. The chromocenter, kinetochore, or kinomere.

centron. A spur.

centronucleus. A nucleus whose centrosome is active during division and is intranuclear.

centroplasm. 1. The substance composing the centrosome. 2. A mass of plasm lying in the center of cells in one of the *Myxophyceae*.

centroplast. An extranuclear spherical body forming a division center of mitosis in certain lower organisms.

centrosome. 1. A minute body believed to have directive influence in nuclear division. 2. A self-propagating body in the cytoplasm consisting of a central granule (centriole) surrounded by the centrosphere. In the prophase of mitosis it divides and the daughter centrosomes move to opposite sides of the nucleus where they apparently influence the formation of the spindle.

centrosphere. The hyaline or alveolar material which with the centriole makes up the centrosome, an astrosphere or attraction sphere.

centrospores. Plants having spiny disseminules or spurred fruits.

centrostigma. A synstigma.

centroxyly. A centrifugal woody structure.

centrum. 1. A group of asci and the nutritive cells associated with them found in the perithecium of some pyrenomycetes. 2. The central portion of a solid body, as the air space in the stem of equisetum.

century. A set of 100 dried plants.

century plant. *Agave americana*, a plant of the southwestern United States formerly said to bloom only once in a century.

cepaceous. Having the taste or smell of garlic or onions, alliaceous.

cepaeform. Onion-shaped.

cephal-. A prefix meaning head.

cephalanthium. The capitulum or head of composites, an anthodium or the head of a flower.

cephalic. Of the head.

cephalium. The woody, head-like stem end of certain cacti which bears the flowers and fruits.

cephalization. A simplification of floral elements.

cephalobrachial. Having branches tipped with rounded heads, applied to chromosomes.

cephalodine. Forming a head.

cephalodium. 1. A peculiarly branched or convex outgrowth on a lichen thallus in which algal cells are localized. 2. The capitulum of composites.

cephaloid. Capitate or head-shaped.

cephalonian gall. A sac-like gall jointed to a leaf by a narrow neck.

cephalonicus. Of Cephalonica, one of the Ionian Islands.

cephalophore. A conidial fructification wherein the spores are held together in a mass by mucilage, e.g., in a cephalosporium.

cephalophorum. The receptacle or stipe of some fungi.

cephalosporial. Of or possessing cephalosporia.

cephalosporium. A spore ball or a spherical mass of spores held in mucilage, as in the genus *Cephalosporium.*

ceraceous. Waxy.

ceramicus. Pottery-like.

ceramidium. The ovate or urn-shaped capsule containing the spores in red algae, a cystocarp.

ceranoid. Bearing branches shaped like horns.

cerasiferous. Bearing cherries.

cerasin. A gummy exudate from plum and cherry trees which swells in water but does not dissolve.

cerastioid. Like *Cerastium,* a genus of silenaceous plants.

cerat-. A prefix meaning horn.

ceratenchyma. A tissue composed of sieve tubes which becomes horny.

ceratium. A siliquiform capsule as that of *Corydalis, Cleome,* etc.

ceratocaulis. Horn-stalked.

ceratomania. Excessive production of horn-like or hooded structures in the flower.

ceratonian gall. A hollow, thick-walled, horn-like gall belonging to the mantle galls.

ceratophylletum. An association composed of *Ceratophyllum,* a genus of aquatic herbs.

ceratophyllous. Having stiff, sharp, upward-curved, linear leaves like plants belonging to the genus *Ceratophyllum,* aquatic plants with finely divided, whorled leaves.

ceratrin. The bitter substance found in Iceland moss, *Cetraria islandica.*

cercidium. The mycelium of some fungi.

cereal. 1. Any grass yielding farinaceous seeds suitable for food, as wheat, corn, rice, etc. 2. The seeds or grains so produced, either in their original state or in a commercially prepared state.

cerale. Pertaining to Ceres, the ancient Greek goddess of agriculture.

cerealia. The cereal grasses, generally corn plants.

cerebriform. Brain-like in appearance and form, as the kernel of a walnut.

cerebro-convolute. With brain-like folds.

cerebrose. 1. Convoluted like a brain. 2. Galactose, a sugar.

cerebrosides. A group of lipases containing fatty acids, nitrogen, and a sugar but no phosphorus.

cerefolious. Wax-leaved.

cereum. Cerium, ceria; see CARYOPSIS.

cereus. Waxy.

ceriferous. Producing or bearing wax.

cerin. Cerine, a waxy substance extracted from cork.

cerinous. A yellow wax color.

cerinthoid. Like *Cerinthe,* a boraginaceous flower thought by the ancients to be the source of wax for bees.

cernous. Nodding, drooping, pendulous, or inclined; curved near the top, as the flower of the *Narcissus;* cernuous, ceruus.

cerrusate. White like white lead.

certation. The competition in rate of growth of pollen tubes of different genetic types.

cerumin. Wax.

cervine. 1. Dark, tawny, or fawn-colored. 2. Horned; cervive.

cervix. 1. A rhizome, a neck or constricted portion of an organ or part. 2. The elongated neck of a bulb.

cesious. Pale bluish-gray; see CAESIOUS.

cespititious. In tufts or dense bunches.

cespitose. Growing or aggregated in tufts but not grown together; forming matted tufts or cushions; growing from the roots in tufts, as in many grasses; caespitose.

cespitulose. Cespitose.

cesspool. A contrivance for the anaerobic decomposition of the organic matter in sewage.

cetrarin. A substance from several species of the fungus-lichen *Cetraria.*

ceylanicus. Of Ceylon.

cH. The hydrogen ion concentration in the soil; see pH.

chaet-. A prefix meaning hair.

chaeta. A spine, bristle, or seta.

chaetomallous. Having flowing hair, thick-maned.

chaetoplankton. A plankton composed of diatoms with awn-like processes.

chaetotaxy. The pattern of bristle arrangement.

chaff. Small membranous scales or bracts on the receptacle of composites, the floral parts of cereals usually separated from the grain during threshing or winnowing, the glumes of grasses.

chaff scale. Palea.

chain channel. A depression around the anterior schizont of the *Peridineae*.

chain formation. Diatoms and *Peridineae* in attachment resembling a chain.

chain-gemma. In *Mucorales* septate confervoid filaments the segments of which are capable of growth, a sprout gemma.

chalaza. The point at which the nucellus and the integuments of the ovule are united, the place where the seed coat unites with the rest of the ovule, the basal part of the ovule where all the parts grow together.

chalazogams. Plants which are fertilized through the chalaza and not through the micropyle.

chalcedonicus. Of Chalcedon on the Bosporus.

chalepensis (Halepensis). Of Aleppo.

chalicad. A plant which grows on gravel slides.

chalice. A flower cup, as the buttercup.

chalicium. A community established on a gravel slide.

chalicodium. A chalicium.

chalicodophyte. A chalicad.

chalicophytia. Gravel plant formations.

chalicosporeae. Plants disseminated by movements of earth and soil.

chalk glands. Multicellular glands which deposit calcareous matter, the secretion escaping through a special channel, the water pore, as found in some saxifrages.

chalonic. Denoting internal secretions which depress, inhibit, or restrain activities.

chalybeous. Lead-colored or steel gray.

chamae-. A prefix meaning ground.

chamaedrys chamaedrifolius. An ante-Linnaean name meaning dwarf oak (an allusion to the shape of the leaves).

chamaephyte. A plant whose surviving buds or shoot-apices are borne on shoots very close to the ground.

chamaephyte climate. The cold zone.

chamaephytion. An association of chamaephytes.

chamaesiphoneous. Pertaining to dwarf algae.

chamber-fluid. The Kammerflüssigheit of Crato composed of cell sap and enchylema between lamellae of protoplasm.

chambered fibers. Fibers which have become septate and seemingly multicellular, as in the secondary wood of the dicotyledons.

chambered ovary. An ovary with the margins of the carpels projecting into the interior to form incomplete longitudinal dissepiments, the ovary remaining unilocular.

chamisal. Chaparral.

chañar steppe. Regions in Argentina predominating in legumes and composites.

channel-leaved. Folded together so as to resemble a channel for conducting water.

channels. 1. Longitudinal grooves. 2. The interstices between the ribs on the fruits of umbelliferous plants.

chapadas. Flat elevated grassy table lands.

chaparral. 1. The xerophytic scrub vegetation consisting of dwarf oaks, currants, buckeye, roses, etc. 2. Any dense impenetrable thicket composed of stiff thorny shrubs and dwarf trees. 3. Chamisal.

chaplet. A series of objects arranged like beads on a string, as the spores of *Cystopus*.

characetum. An association of plants of the genus *Chara*.

characine. A substance resembling camphor found in some terrestrial algae such as *Palmella*, *Ocillaria*, etc., which smell like *Chara*.

characinous. Resembling *Chara*, a genus of freshwater algae with heavily calcified walls and whorls of short branches at the nodes.

character. A trait or quality which is the essential mark of a species, genus, family, etc., which distinguishes it from all others; any trait of an individual; any trait, faculty, or physical feature of the individual or species that can be identified and more or less accurately described; in heredity, a single definable character which can be transmitted to offspring.

character, dominant. The more prominent of two mutually exclusive characters which therefore characterizes three-fourths of the offspring of hybrid parents.

character plants. Species occurring only in the community under consideration; characteristic species, exclusive species, etc.

character, recessive. The less conspicuous of two characters which are mutually exclusive which characterizes one-fourth of the offspring of hybrid parents.

character species. Species which prefer a given situation and show the character of the community of plants found there.

characteristic species. Species which occur in particularly large numbers in a community but are not necessarily confined to it.

charad. A charophyte.

charetum. A characetum.

charophyte. A plant allied to or having the aspects of the genus *Chara.*

chartaceous. 1. Having the texture of writing paper. 2. Thin, hard, and stiff.

chart quadrat. A plot of ground used for detailed ecological plant study, usually one meter square, in which every plant is accurately plotted on a chart.

chasmantheric. Denoting those cleistogamic flowers when the anthers open and liberate their pollen.

chasmanthery. The condition in which the stamens are exserted from otherwise closed flowers.

chasmochomophyte. A plant growing in the crevices of rocks.

chasmocleistogamous. Having cleistogamic flowers accompanied by others which are chasmogamic.

chasmogamic. Having pollination take place during the expansion of the floral envelope; open, not cleistogamic.

chasmogamy. The opening of the perianth at flowering time.

chasmopetaly. The persistent opening of the floral envelope.

chasmophile. A plant inhabiting crannies.

chasmophyte. A plant growing in the crevices of rocks, the opposite of lithophyte.

chathamicus. Of Chatham Island, near New Zealand.

cheilanthifolious. Resembling the fern *Cheilanthes,* the lip-fern or lip-flowered fern, so-called because of the method of attachment of the indusium.

cheilanthous. Allied to or resembling *Cheilanthes.*

cheilobasidium. A basidium occurring on the edge of a gill.

cheilocystidia. Cystidia arising from the face of the lower edges of gills in agarics.

cheilodromous. Craspedodromous.

cheilomania. The doubling of the lip in orchids.

cheirostemonous. Having five stamens united at the base.

chelate. Bifurcate.

chelidonioid. Resembling *Chelidonium,* the celandine or swallowwort of the poppy family.

cheliform. With claw-like petals or other parts.

chemauxism. Incitement to growth by certain reagents or compounds.

chemical messengers. Hormones.

chemoaesthesia. The capacity of a plant to respond to chemical stimuli.

chemoanalysis. The breaking down of complex compounds with the release of energy.

chemoautotrophic. Obtaining energy through the oxidation of simple inorganic molecules by bacteria; e.g., oxidation of hydrogen sulphide to sulphur.

chemokinesis. The action of zoospores which is induced by chemical attraction.

chemolysis. A decomposition by chemical reagents, chemical analysis.

chemomorphosis. A change in shape resulting from a chemical reaction such as plant galls caused by insect stings.

chemonasty. The response to chemical stimuli resulting in curvature.

chemoreflex. A reflex caused by a chemical stimulus.

chemosynthesis. The synthesis of organic compounds by energy derived from chemical changes or reactions in place of reactions as in respiration.

chemotaxis. The sensitivity and reaction of cells or organisms to chemical stimuli.

chemotaxis, negative. The repulsion by a chemical solution, apochemotaxis.

chemotaxis, positive. Attraction by a chemical solution.

chemotropism. The curvature of a plant toward or away from a chemical stimulus.

chemozoöphobe. A plant which is protected from insects or other animal attack by the presence of an inhibiting substance such as tannin.

chena. A scrub forest produced by the burning of low-country forest.

chenopodiaceous. Of the *Chenopodiaceae,* salt-loving herbs.

cheradad. A wet sandbar plant.

cheradium. A wet sandbar formation or community.

chermesine. Crimson or reddish purple.

chernogens. Continental soils which develop with little rainfall and are permanently grass-covered, as the Russian black soils.

chersad. A plant of dry wasteland.

chersic. Of communities of wastelands.

chersium. A dry waste formation.

chestnut soil. A shallow grassland soil with a calcium carbonate base near the surface. It is formed in extremely dry conditions so that no leaching takes place.

chiasma. The exchange of material between chromosomes during nuclear division, a crosswise fusion at one or more points of paired chromosomes or chromatids which are twisted about each other in meiosis; an exchange of partners in a system of paired chromatids, a visible genetic cross-over between chromosomes and chromatids; pl. chiasmata.

chiasma, compensating. A chiasma which restores an association interrupted by another fusion.

chiasma, complete. A fusion which occurs before the conjugating chromosomes split so that all four chromatids are involved.

chiasma, imperfect. A chiasma in which one of the four associations in a chiasma is broken prior to the anaphase.

chiasma, incomplete. A chiasma which occurs after the conjugating chromosomes have split apart so that only two of the four chromatids are involved.

chiasma, interstitial. A fusion which occurs between the ends of the paired chromosomes or chromatids, one in which there is a length of chromatid on both sides of the chiasma.

chiasma, lateral. A chiasma which is terminal as to two chromatids and interstitial as to the others, symmetrically or asymmetrically.

chiasma, multiple. A terminal chiasma in which three or four pairs of chromatids are engaged.

chiasma, terminal. A fusion which occurs at the ends of the paired chromosomes or chromatids, an association of four chromatids end to end which results from the shifting of a chiasma until it reaches the end of the bivalent or multivalent.

chiasma theory of pairing. The hypothesis that whenever two chromosomes have been paired at pachytene and remain as-sociated until the metaphase, they do so by virtue of the formation of a chiasma or visible exchange of partners among their chromatids.

chiasmatype hypothesis. The part of the chiasmatype theory which supposes that chiasmata are determined by crossing over between two dissimilar chromatids of the four involved.

chiasmatype theory. The theory that chiasmata are connected with crossing-over either as a cause or as a consequence.

chiasmatypy. A recombination of chromosome material in synapsis, the crosswise fusion at one or more points of paired chromosomes or chromatids which are twisted about each other and through which points of separation later occur along a new plane so that each of the two chromosomes or chromatids is made up of more parts (crossovers) from its mate. Chiasmatype.

chiastobasidium. A club-shaped basidium in which the spindles of the dividing nuclei lie at the same level across the basidium.

chicory. *Cichorium intybus*, a perennial plant native to Europe which is grown for the roots and used as salad.

chilarium. The boundary of a small pit in the testa of *Phaseolus* of two movable valves which by hygrometric movements cause the rupture of the testa.

chilary layer. The investment of the seed which contains the chilarium.

childing. 1. Proliferous. 2. Of flowers, producing younger or smaller blossoms around an older blossom.

chilensis (chiloensis). Belonging to or related to Chile.

chilile. In shore lake bottoms, down to 6 meters; see PYTHIC.

chilling. Exposing of perennial plants to wintry cold necessary for early growth in the following spring, induced dormancy.

chimaera. A plant composed of two genetically distinct types as a result of mutation, segregation, irregularity of mitosis or artificial fusion (grafting), etc.; the product from a bud with mechanical coalescence of two parent forms; a chimera.

chimaera, chromosomal. A chimaera in which the nuclei do not all contain the same number of chromosomes.

chimaera, dichlamydeous. A diplodichlamydeous chimaera.

chimaera, diplodiclamydeous. A periclinal chimaera consisting of an outer skin two layers thick which represents one constituent and surrounds a core representing the other.

chimaera, haplochlamydeous. A periclinal chimaera in which one component is present in a single cell layer forming the epidermis.

chimaera, mericlinal. A chimaera in which one component does not surround the other, an incomplete periclinal chimaera.

chimaera, monochlamydeous. A haplochlamydeous chimaera.

chimaera, periclinal. A chimaera in which one component is completely enclosed by the other.

chimaera, polychlamydeous. A periclinal chimaera in which the skin is more than two layers of cells in thickness.

chimaera, polyclinal. A chimaera which is made up of more than two components.

chimaera, sectional. A chimaera in which the mutants arise from mixed cells.

chimaera, sectorial. 1. A chimaera in which the plant consists of two or more distinct types of tissue arranged in sectors which come to the surface, i.e., the composite tissue in cross section takes the form of a sector of a circle. 2. Bud variation which results in obviously mixed tissue in a branch of a tree or shrub.

chimiosis. The change or alteration in the time of action of the digestive fluid in a carnivorous plant.

chimiotropism. Chemotropism.

chimney. The protrusion of the epidermal cells around the guard cells of a stoma producing a long respiratory cavity.

chimnopilous. With the chief development taking place in the winter season, hiemal.

chimonochlorous. With thin herbaceous leaves persisting through the winter.

chimopelagic. Found on the water surfaces only in winter.

china. Quinine.

china-grass. The fiber from the tropical plant *Boehmeria nivea*.

chinensis. Belonging to or related to China.

chinin. Quinine or cinchona bark.

chionad. A plant growing in snow.

chionic. Living in snow fields.

chionium. A snow-plant community, a snow-plant formation.

chionophilous. Bearing winter leaves, as *Helleborus foetidus*.

chionophobe. A plant shunning snow.

chionophyte. A snow plant.

chionophytia. A snow-plant community, a chionium.

chionophytium. A niveal or snow-plant association.

chironym. The assigned name of a type specimen.

chirophyllous. Having hand-shaped leaves.

chiropterophile. A plant pollinated by bats.

chirotype. The specimen on which a manuscript name is based, a type specimen.

chitin. A substance similar to horn characteristically found in insects which has the same composition as fungus cellulose. In micrography, a cell-wall substance called chitin is colored by iodine solution acidulated with sulphuric acid after previous heating to 160° C in a solution of potash.

chittamwood. *Bumelia languinosa*, the American smoke tree of the southern United States.

chive. 1. One of the *Alliaceae*, the onions. 2. An anther or an offset of a bulbous plant.

chlamydate. Having a mantle.

chlamydeous. With a perianth.

chlamydia. The bud scales or the floral envelopes.

chlamydobacteria. Iron bacteria covered with ferric or manganese oxides which reproduce by swarm spores. They are closely allied to algae.

chlamydogonidium. A relatively large, thick-walled unicellular gemma of certain fungi which is adapted for a rest period before germinating.

chlamydomonad. An alga resembling the genus *Chlamydomonas*.

chlamydomonetum. A community of *Chlamydomonas* and diatoms which lie loosely on sand and are not cemented together.

chlamydomonous. Resembling the simple alga *Chlamydomonas*, which is a green, unicellular, biflagellate, motile alga from which the vascular plants are thought to have evolved.

chlamydomorphic soil. A loosely aggregated soil containing grains with a colloidal coating.

chlamydospores. The asexual, thick-walled resting spores produced within the hyphae of fungi which usually develop into sporangia or conidiospores.

chlamydosporicous. With chlamydospores.

chlamydozoa. An obsolete phylum used to include the viruses.

chlamys. A cloak or covering.

chledad. A ruderal plant.

chledium. A waste community or ruderal formation.

chledocolous. Inhabiting waste places.

chledophilous. Dwelling in waste places.

chledophyte. A plant of waste places.

chloraefolious. Green-leaved.

chloralbino. Variegated with green and white markings in the leaves.

chloramylite. A chlorophyll granule which is transformed from starch.

chloranthous. Having inconspicuous green flowers.

chloranthy. The production of green flowers, a supposed reversion of floral structure to a primitive foliar condition.

chlorascens. A green color tending toward yellow.

chlorenchyma. Tissue whose cells contain chlorophyll.

chlorin. The green constituent of chlorophyll.

chlorina. A plant deficient in chlorophyll, xanthein, and carotin.

chlorinous. Yellowish-green like young grass.

Chloris. 1. A title sometimes used for a work on the plants of a district, analogous to Flora. 2. A large genus of grasses. 3. The Roman goddess of flowers.

chlorites. The chlorophyllous plastids.

chloro-. A prefix meaning light yellowish green.

chlorobacteria. Green-pigmented sulphur bacteria which do not produce oxygen but photosynthesize in hydrogen sulphide and deposit sulphur outside the cell.

chlorocarpous. Having green fruits.

chlorochilon. Green-lipped.

chlorochrous. With a green skin.

chlorococcine. Resembling the *Chlorococcales*, motile unicellular algae which have lost their vegetative motility and their ability to divide vegetatively except for the production of reproductive cells; chlorococcinous.

chlorococcoid. Resembling the algal genus *Chlorococcum*.

Chlorocyperacea. The *Cyperaceae*, which have much assimilatory tissue and numerous stomata but little sclerenchyma in the cortex.

chlorocyst. A chlorophyll cell.

chlorofucine. A chlorophyll which has a clear yellowish green color.

chloroglobin. The green coloring matter of chlorophyll.

chlorogonidium. In lichens, the green gonidium.

chlorogonimus. The green gonidial layer in lichens.

chloroleucite. A chlorophyll granule, a chloroplastid, an autoplast.

chlorophaeus. Yellow-green, as the coloring matter of algae.

chlorophore. A chloroleucite, a chlorophyll granule.

chlorophyceous. Like the green algae *Chlorophyceae*.

chlorophyll. The mixture of the two green and yellow pigments present in the chloroplasts of all plants which are able to synthesize carbohydrates from carbon dioxide and water. It is composed of chlorophyll a, chlorophyll b, carotin, and xanthophyll.

chlorophyll body. The proteid body containing chlorophyll in the cells of green plants.

chlorophyll corpuscle. A chloroplast.

chlorophyll grain. A proteid body in the cells of plants.

chlorophyll granule. A granule containing chlorophyll in the chloroplast.

chlorophyll vesicle. A chlorophyll granule.

chlorophyllaceous. Consisting of or containing chlorophyll.

chlorophyllan. Hypochlorin, the first visible product of constructive metabolism in plants.

chlorophyllase. An enzyme occurring in association with chlorophyll in plants and able to decompose it.

chlorophylligerous. Having chlorophyll.

chlorophyllin. A water-soluble fluorescent constituent of chlorophyll, chlorophyllan.

chlorophyllogen. Potential chlorophyll produced without light which develops into chlorophyll when exposed to light.

chlorophylloplast. A chromoplast containing chlorophyll as coloring matter, a chloroplast.

chlorophyllose cells. The small cells in the

leaves of *Sphagnum* and other mosses which contain chlorophyll.

Chlorophyta. The green algae.

chloroplastid. A plastid containing chlorophyll, a chloroplast.

chloroplastin. A proteid constituting the ground substance of the chlorophyll granule.

chloroplasts. Minute flattened granules or plastids containing chlorophyll developed in great numbers in the cytoplasm near the cell wall in cells exposed to light which possess the ability to form starch by photosynthesis.

chlororufin. A reduced chlorophyll, a red pigment of the *Chlorophyceae*.

chlorosis. 1. An unhealthy condition due to a deficiency in the chlorophyll in which green parts turn yellow. 2. A condition in which colored parts turn green.

chlorospermous. Of or belonging to the algae which have green spores.

chlorostatoliths. Chloroplasts containing starch.

chlorotiderm. A plant with a greenish-yellow subepidermal layer and a green core.

chlorovaporization. A function which is analogous to transpiration but proceeding only from the chloroleucites under certain light.

choana. A funnel-shaped opening.

choanocyte. A cell with a funnel-like rim or collar around the base of a flagellum.

choline. A crystalline base derived from lecithin found in plants and animals.

chomopophyte. A ruderal plant, a chomophyte.

chomophyte. A plant growing on ledges or in fissures, a ruderal plant, a plant growing on ledges where rock debris has accumulated.

chondriocont. A chondriosome in the form of mitochondria from which chromoplasts are derived; see CHROMIDIA. A chondrikont.

chondriokinesis. The division of chondriosomes during mitosis and meiosis.

chondriolysis. The dissolution of mitochondria.

chondriome. All the chrondriosomes in a cell.

chondriomere. A plastomere.

chondriomite. A chondriosome which has the form of a linear series or chain of granules.

chondriosomal mantle. An accumulation of small cytoplasmic particles associated with a dividing nucleus.

chondriosomes. 1. Small structures in the cytoplasm whose functions are not definitely known. 2. A generic term including all forms of mitochondria, chondrioconts, chondriomites, and other cytoplasmic bodies of the same nature. See MITOCHONDRIA.

chondriod. Having thick-walled, hard and tough hypha layers in the thallus of a lichen.

chondriosphere. A spherical chondriosome.

chondroblast. A cartilage-producing cell.

chondroclast. A large multinucleate cell which destroys the cartilage matrix, a chondrioclast.

chondrogenesis. The production or formation of cartilage.

chondroid. Like cartilage, applied to the strengthening strands of the hyphae of lichens which are hard and tough.

chondrome. A granular mass in the fluid contents of cells.

chorda pistillaris. A line of tissue reaching from stigma to ovary.

chordaceous. Like a rope.

chordorrhizal. With the rootstock producing a number of flowering stems, one before the other on its sides, as in *Carex chordorhiza*.

-chore. A suffix meaning an agent of migration.

chori-. A prefix meaning distinct and separate.

chorion. 1. The pulpy matter in a young ovule. 2. A tough membrane secreted around an egg by the surrounding cells.

chorionarius. An etaerio, an aggregate fruit.

Choripetalae. A subdivision of the archichlamydeous dicotyledonous plants in which the corolla is divided into separate and distinct petals, a term for both the *Polypetalae* and *Incompletae*.

choripetalous. Having separate and distinct petals, polypetalous, choriopetalous.

choriphelloid. Having suberized cells and lenticels.

choriphyllous. Having perianth parts separate and distinct.

chorisepalous. Having separate and distinct sepals, polysepalous.

chorisepaly. The condition in which the sepals are separate and distinct.

chorisis. The separation of normally united parts or where two or more parts take the place of one, the separation of a leaf or phyllum into more than one, doubling.

chorisis, collateral. Chorisis when the plane of separation is anteroposterior.

chorisis, parallel. Chorisis when the plane of separation is lateral.

chorisolepideous. Having the scales of the involucre distinct from each other as in the *Compositae.*

choristate. Unlined, exhibiting chorisis.

choristophyllous. Having separate leaves.

chorization. Chorisis.

choroid. Having delicate vascular membranes or structures.

chorologic. Topographic.

chorology. The study of migration and of the areas of distribution of life, biogeography.

chortonomia. The art of making an herbarium.

chott. A salt spot in the Algerian desert, a shot.

chresard. The total amount of available water in the soil which can be used by plants, the physiological water content of soil.

chromaphobe. A nonstainable cell or tissue.

chromasic. Showing an increase of chromatin in the nucleus and the formation of the nucleoli.

chromatic. Said of the deeply staining contents of the nucleus, colorable by staining reagents, applied to the materials which form the chromosomes.

chromatic adaptation. A variation in coloration in relation to the amount of light reaching a plant.

chromatic sphere. The body formed by the coalescence of the chromosomes after the anaphase in mitosis.

chromatic thread. The filiform body in nuclear division which breaks up into chromosomes, chromatic fiber.

chromatid. 1. One of the two threads formed by longitudinal splitting of a chromosome in somatic mitosis. 2. One of the four threads similarly formed from paired chromosomes between diplotene and the second metaphase of meiosis.

chromatid bridge. The extension of a dicentric chromatid (one having two kinetochores) from pole to pole in meiotic division.

chromatidium. The coloring matter of plants.

chromatin. Nuclein, the minute granular masses of which the chromosomes are composed which are stained readily by basic dyes, the material which forms the most conspicuous part of the nuclear network and of the chromosomes. It is rich in desoxyribonucleoprotein, the protoplasmic substance found in the nucleus which is considered the physical basis of heredity.

chromatin diminution. The elimination, usually in early cleavage, of a portion of the chromatin in the formation of the primordial germ cells.

chromatin granules. The granular bodies composing the chromatin.

chromatin network. The granular network of threads in the nucleus.

chromatism. The abnormal coloration of the normally green parts of plants.

chromatoid bodies. The intensely staining cytoplasmic bodies of unknown function found in the spermatocytes and passed on to certain spermatids.

chromatoid grains. Readily stainable grains in cell-protoplasm, probably of an albuminous nature.

chromatoid granules. Granules like those containing chromatin.

chromatology. The science of vegetable coloring matter.

chromatolysis. The condensation or disintegration of nuclear chromatin in a homogeneous mass.

chromatomere. The chromosome.

chromatophile. Any part or organ which is easily stained.

chromatophores. 1. A general term for all bodies in plants containing coloring matter, pigment-bearing sacs or structures. 2. A specific term applied to the chloroplastids in the algae. Chromatoplasts.

chromatophyll. The coloring matter of plant-like flagellates.

chromatoplasm. The peripheral region of the protoplast in *Myxophyceae* which contains the pigments of the cell.

chromatospherite. A nucleolus.

chromidia. Fragments of chromatin which lie free in the cytoplasm and are not massed together to form a nucleus. Chromatidia.

chromidia, generative. The chromidia which may replace or be re-formed into nuclei.

chromidia, vegetative. The chromidia which

are extruded for metabolism or accumulated in nucleus-like structures.

chromidiocentrum. The structure formed when the chromidia are grouped into a well-defined mass in a cell.

chromidiogamy. The union of chromidia from two conjugating cells.

chromidiosome. The smallest chromatin particle of which the chromidial mass is composed with some particles inside and some outside the nucleus.

chromidiosphere. The chromidiocenter.

chromidium. The algal component of a lichen.

chromidosomes. The minute, especially stainable, bodies in the cytoplasm of many cells.

chromioles. The smallest visible organized parts of the chromosomes grouped to form chromomeres, the minute granules which form the chromomeres.

chromism. An abnormal coloring of leaves.

chromoblast. A chromoplast.

chromocenter. The deeply staining part of the chromosome in the nuclear reticulum of a resting cell.

chromogen. The material in plants which will develop into coloring matter.

chromogenesis. Color production.

chromogenic. Forming pigments, color-producing, or chromogenous.

chromoleucite. A protoplasmic color granule.

chromolipoid. A fatty color allied to carotin.

chromomeres. The chromatic thickenings of granules of definite size and position arranged in linear order on the spireme threads of a chromosome during cell division; regions of tight coiling; the genes or ids.

chromonena. The longitudinal thread of a chromosome making up the nuclear reticulum at various stages of nuclear division. The inner core of the strand is composed of DNA covered with protein; the chromonene, orgenonema.

chromoparous. 1. Exuding color, as colorless bacteria. 2. Secreting colorless material, as some bacteria.

chromophil. A living organism which stains very easily.

chromophilous. Staining readily.

chromophobe. Staining slightly or not at all.

chromophore. Any chemical group or residue to whose presence decided color in a compound is attributed.

chromophorous. Having natural coloring matter, applied to bacteria.

chromophyll. Any substance which colors plant cells.

chromoplasm. The pigmented outer region surrounding the centroplasm in the blue-green algae.

chromoplast. 1. A pigmented plastid (other than a chloroplast) which may be red, yellow, brown, or orange. 2. An embryonic cell giving rise to a pigment cell. 3. A chromoplastid.

chromoproteid. A substance formed by the combination of a proteid with a pigment.

chromosomal chimaera. A chimaera in which the nuclei do not all contain the same number of chromosomes.

chromosomal vesicle. A swollen chromosome of inter-division stages.

chromosomes. The rod-like, deeply staining bodies, constant in number for any given species, into which the chromatin of the nucleus becomes condensed during meiosis or mitosis. The chromosomes carry the genes, linearly arranged, which bear the hereditary material.

chromosome arm. One of the two parts of a chromosome to which the spindle fibers is attached along the side.

chromosome complement. The set of chromosomes characteristic of the nuclei of any one species of plant or animal.

chromosome cycle. The whole of the changes in the chromosomes during the complete life-cycle of an organism.

chromosome hypothesis. The hypothesis that factors or genes are arranged in a definite manner in the chromosomes.

chromosome map. A diagram of the relative order of genes or of geneloci in a particular chromosome of an organism. The order is determined in part from crossover percentages which are proportional to the distances between the loci.

chromosome matrix. A covering of stain-resistant material surrounding the readily stainable portion of the chromosome.

chromosome threads. The threads found in various stages of cell division, as the threads of chromomeres, the achromatic connective threads, the pellicle at prophase, the spindle threads, etc.

chromosomes, daughter. Chromosomes derived from other chromosomes, secondary chromosomes.

chromospire. A spireme-like thread formed from nuclear granules in haplomitosis, the folds of the spireme in nuclear division.

chromotropism. Tropistic response to color.

chromule. The coloring matter of the plant other than chlorophyll, applied especially to petals.

chronisporangium. A structure producing chronispores.

chronispore. A resting spore, a microgonidium produced by hydrodictyon which rests before germinating.

chronizoöspore. A chronispore.

chronology. The appearance of plants in the history of the earth, the study of the historical transformations of the vegetation of the earth.

chronotropism. A change, such as the position of leaves, due to age.

chroococcaceous. Of or pertaining to the genus *Chroococcus*, a blue-green alga.

chroolepoid. Covered with yellow scales, like the genus *Chroolepsis* of the lichens.

chrys-, chryso-. A prefix meaning golden or golden yellow.

chrysaloid. Rolled and folded at the same time.

chrysanthemoid. Like a chrysanthemum.

chrysanthine. Having yellow flowers.

chrysellous. Of a golden hue.

chryseus. Golden yellow.

chrysocarpous. Having golden fruit.

chrysochlorophyll. One of the constituents of chrysochrome.

chrysochrome. A characteristic golden-brown pigment in *Chromulina Rosanoffi*.

chrysochrous. Having a yellow skin or pellicle.

chrysocomous. Golden-haired.

chrysogonidia. 1. Yellow algal cells, as in some lichens. 2. Yellow gonidia.

chrysogonimus. A layer of yellow gonidia in some lichens.

chrysohermiden. A labile chromogen in *Mercurialis*, euphorbia.

chrysolepis. Having golden scales.

chrysoleucus. Gold and white.

chrysolobous. Golden-lobed.

chrysophan. Gold-colored crystals found in *Physcia parietina*, a lichen.

chrysophanic acid. Chrysophan.

chrysophyll. A yellow coloring matter in leaves.

chrysophyllous. Golden-leaved.

chrysophyta. A group of algae including *Chrysophyceae* and diatoms.

chrysorhamnin. A yellow substance found in unripe buckthorn berries.

chrysostomous. Golden-throated, golden-mouthed.

chrysotannin. The coloring matter in plants which gives rise to brown tints in autumn foliage after oxidation.

chrysotaxum. Golden-arched.

chrysoxanthophyll. A constituent of chrysochrome.

chylocaula. Plants with succulent stems.

chylophyllae. Plants with succulent leaves.

chymifera Vasa. An imaginary sap thread rolled around a tube to form a tracheid or spiral vessel.

chytrid. One of the *Chytridiales*, the simplest parasitic or saprophytic fungi.

chytridiosis. A disease caused by the chytrid *Cladochytrium viticolum*.

chytridium. 1. The spore vessel of certain fungi. 2. The generic name of some *Chytridiales*.

cicatrice. A scar left by a fallen organ, such as that left by a fallen leaf, a broken stem, or the hilum of a seed; a cicatrix.

cichoriaceous. Of *Chichorium*, chicory.

cicinnus. Sympodial branching in which, from heterodromy of the phyllotaxis of the axes of limited growth that build up the system, the median plane of each successive axis is placed alternately right and left of the median plane of the preceding axis, and therefore the branches form a double row on one side of the sympodium or false axis.

cicutaefolious. Having leaves like *Cicuta*, genus of poisonous hemlock.

cicutarious. Of or like *Cicuta*.

cienchyma. A system of intercellular spaces.

cilia. Minute protoplasmic threads on the surface of a cell which produce movements in the surrounding medium by moving back and forth; organs of motion which propel zoospores, gametes, and many unicellular organisms from place to place.

ciliaris. Ciliate, fringed with hairs on the margin.

ciliate-dentate. Having teeth fringed with hairs.

ciliate-serrate. Having serratures resembling cilia.

Ciliates. A subphylum of the Protozoa having cilia in the immature stages or throughout life.

ciliatifolious. Having ciliate leaves.

ciliatulate. Slightly ciliate, with small cilia, ciliolate.

cilicicus. Of or from Cilicia, in southern Asia Minor.

ciliicalyx. A ciliated calyx.

cilliiform. Like cilia.

ciliograde. Moving by means of cilia.

ciliola. Secondary or minute cilia.

ciliospore. A swarm spore with a coat of cilia, a type of zoospore.

cinicimous. Having the odor of bugs, like coriander.

cinchonaceous. Of or pertaining to *Cinchona*, trees and shrubs of the Andes from which quinine is obtained.

cinchonine. A white crystalline alkaloid formed in various species of *Cinchona* and *Remijia* extracted in the preparation of quinine.

cincinnal. Curled or with curled inflorescences.

cincinnal cyme. A cyme having the successive flowers on alternate sides of the pseudaxis.

cincinnal dichotomy. The condition of cymes in which alternate branches develop.

cincinnus. A form of cymose inflorescence, a one-sided cyme, a curl, a uniparous scorpoid cyme which is cincinnal.

cinctus. Girdled or surrounded, as albumen when surrounded by an annular cyme.

cinenchyma. Lactiferous tissue.

cinenchymatous. Having latex vessels.

cineraceous. Ashy gray. Cinereous, cinerus.

cinerariaefolious. Having leaves like *Cineraria*.

cingalese. Of or pertaining to Ceylon.

cingulate. Surrounded, bordered, or having a girdle.

cingulum. 1. The girdle in *Peridineae* which separates the epivalve from the bivalve. 2. The neck of a plant which is between the stem and the root. 3. Any structure which is like a girdle.

cinna. Grass.

cinnabar. Vermillion red.

cinnabarine. Pertaining to, like, consisting of, or containing cinnabar.

cinnamic. Pertaining to cinnamon.

cinnamomeous. Cinnamon-colored.

cinnamonifolious. Leaved like a cinnamon, a tropical laurelaceous tree with handsome foliage.

cinnamon. A light brown with a little pink; a spice.

cinquefoil. Members of the genus *Potentilla* having digitate leaves with five leaflets.

cion. The bud or branch used in grafting, a cutting set into a plant rather than into the soil, a scion.

cionospermae. Plants whose ovules develop on a central and a more or less columnar placenta.

circinate. Coiled from the top downward, as the young frond of a fern; rolled on an axis so that the apex is the center; coiled like a watch spring; circinal.

circle, migration. The migration of plants from a parent individual or group.

circle of vegetation. The totality of the communities and associated species that are confined to a natural vegetation region; see COMMUNITY and ZONATION.

circulation. The streaming movements of cytoplasm from the cell periphery to the nucleus.

circulation of protoplasm. The streaming movements of protoplasm not only in a primordial utricle but also along threads passing from the utricle to a mass of protoplasm investing the cell nucleus in the cell cavity.

circumaxile. Surrounding a central axis which separates when the fruit splits open.

circumcinct. Having a band around the middle.

circumcision. 1. A division by a circular cut or fissure as in the apothecia of some lichens. 2. The ringing of trees.

circumfloral. With nectaries on the outer side of a flower.

circumlateralism. The tendency in plant phylogeny to develop a circular arrangement of parts.

circummedullary. Perimedullary.

circumnutation. The irregular elliptical or spiral movement exhibited by the apex of a growing stem or shoot, any movement of the growing points around the axis.

circumposition. The placement of a branch in the earth while still attached to the parent stock to produce a new plant by rooting.

circumscissile. Opening or dehiscing by a line around the fruit or anther, the valve usually coming off as a lid; dehiscing by a transverse fissure around the circumference; circumcissle.

circumscription. 1. The outline of an organ. 2. The definition of a form or group of forms, as of species, genera, order, etc.

circumsepiens. Surrounding as a protection.

circumsepientia folia. Leaves which surround the stem to protect the young growth.

circumvallation. Layering by ringing the stem and surrounding it with soil kept moist while the stem remains erect, pot layering.

cirrhate. 1. Applying to those parts which assume the functions of a tendril. 2. Curled, applied to leaves on drying. 3. Cirrate, cirose.

cirrhiferous. Producing or bearing tendrils, cirrhose.

cirrhiform. Formed like a tendril.

cirrhoids. Balls of *Cladophora* which are formed of coiled shoots which do not alter their shapes.

cirrhose. Having a cirrus or tendril, having tendrils or terminating in a tendril.

cirrhosely pinnate. Pinnate with the terminal leaflets replaced by a tendril.

cirrhositas. The state of producing tendrils.

cirrhus, cirrus. 1. A tendril. 2. A tendril-like curl of exuded spores. See SPORE HORN.

cirrhus capreolus. A tendril.

cirrhus costalis. A projecting or excurrent midrib modified as a tendril.

cirrhus foliarus. A leaf modified as a tendril.

cirrhus peduncularis. A flower-stalk modified as a tendril.

cirrhus petiolaris. A petiole or leaf-stalk modified as a tendril.

cirrhus radicularis. A root modified as a tendril.

cirrhus rameanus. A tendril which is a modified branch.

cirrhus stipularis. A tendril which is a modified stipule.

cissus. 1. The host of *Rafflesia*, a fleshy parasite of the tropics. 2. A genus of climbing vines, mostly tropical.

cistella. An apothecium of a lichen which is globular at first but which bursts at maturity, a cistula.

cistern epiphyte. An epiphyte in which the roots are mere supports or are altogether suppressed, and the entire nourishment is supplied by the leaves.

cisterna. A reservoir or cavity within a cell enclosed by a membrane.

cistifloreae. The cistern epiphytes.

cistifolious. Having leaves like *Cistus*, the rockrose.

cistolith. A cystolith.

cistome. A stomatic chamber when it exists as a kind of sac lined by a special layer of cells, a membranous sac beneath the stomatic guard cells.

cistophorum. The stipe of certain fungi.

cistula. A cistella.

cistus-maqui. A mass of mostly evergreen vegetation composed of *Cistus*, the rockrose found in the Mediterranean region.

citrange. A fruit in the *Rutaceae* family, a hardy hybrid orange.

citrangequat. A fruit in the *Rutaceae* family, a hybrid kumquat.

citratus. Citrus-like.

citreous. Lemon yellow.

citric acid. An acid found abundantly in lemon juice and other citrus fruits.

citric acid cycle. The formation of carbon dioxide and water by the breaking down of acetyl-S-coenzyme A in the mitrochondria during cellular respiration, Kreb's cycle.

citrifolious. Having leaves like citrus trees.

citriform. Lemon-shaped.

citrin. Vitamin P, an antiscorbutic vitamin in paprika and lemon peel.

citrine. Lemon yellow.

citrinellus. Yellowish.

citrinin. An antibiotic obtained from some *Penicillium* ssp.

citrinous. Citron-colored, citron-like.

citriodorous. Lemon-scented.

citroid. Like citrus.

citron. A large lemon-like fruit, *Citrus Medica*, with a very thick peel and a small amount of pulp. The peel is candied and used as a confection and in cooking.

citronella, oil of. An oil from citronella, *Collinsonia canadensis*.

citrulline. A precursor of the basic amino acid, arginine, obtained from decomposing vegetable tissues.

citrus. A member of the *Rutaceae* family.

cladanthous. Having terminal archegonia on short lateral branches, cladocarpous.

cladautoicous. 1. Having the male organs on a special stalk. 2. Having the male inflorescence of a moss on a separate branch.

cladenchyma. Branch parenchyma.

cladietum. An association of *Cladium*, a sedge.

cladina heaths. Tundra, barren peaty lands with large quantities of the lichen *Cladina*.

cladinosus. Said of heaths having a substratum of the lichen *Cladina*.

clado. A cladophyll, a phylloid shoot, a branch.

clado-, clados-. A prefix meaning branch.

clado-androgonidium. A male androspore or merid which is terminal or intercalated.

clado-autoicous. Cladautoicous.

cladocalyx. A club calyx.

cladocarpi. Mosses which have their fruit on short lateral terminal branches.

cladocarpous. Having the fruit borne at the ends of short lateral branches in mosses, cladanthous.

cladode. A cladophyll.

cladodium. A flat expansion of the stem.

cladodystrophia. The loss of branches.

cladofied. Becoming branched.

cladogenous. Producing the inflorescence at the ends of branches.

cladogonidium. The gonidium which gives rise to a merid either intercalated or subterminal.

cladogynogonidium. A female merid.

cladomania. An extraordinary production of branches.

cladophora balls. Rounded accumulations of shoots of the alga *Cladophora*.

cladophore. The portion of the stem in *Hieracium* giving rise to the branches of the inflorescence.

cladophyll. A branch having the form and function of a leaf, a stem having the appearance and function of a leaf, a cladade, cladode or phylloclade.

cladophyllum. 1. A cone scale. 2. A flattened leaf-like branch functioning as foliage, as in many acacias and asparagus. 3. A bract or branch resembling a leaf.

cladophyllum ocreaeform. Horn-shaped and more or less attached.

cladophyllum utriculiform. Approaching the normal appearance of the utricle.

cladoptosis. The annual shedding of twigs.

cladosclereids. Stellate bodies containing calcium oxalate in leaves and floral envelopes of *Euryale ferox*, an Asian water-lily.

cladose. Branched.

cladosiphonic. Having a tubular stele interrupted at the insertion of branches, i.e., having branch gaps not leaf gaps on the siphonostele.

cladosporoid. Like the fungus *Cladosporium*.

cladostemon. The semi-connate filaments in willows.

cladostroma. A receptacle or growing point covered with carpels each of which has a free placenta.

cladothrix. 1. Straight and slender forms of bacteria. 2. A bacterial genus of that name.

clamp. On mycelium of some *Basidiomycetes*, the small semicircular hollow protuberance laterally attached to the walls of two adjoining cells and arching over the septum between them by means of which the pseudogamous sexual process takes place. A clamp-connection.

clamp cell. A papilla-like cell by which an epiphyte root adheres to the substratum, a clamp connection.

clamp connection. A small protuberance attached to the walls of two adjoining cells in the hypha of a fungus mycelium covering the septum between them like a clamp.

clan. A small community of subordinate importance but of distinct character, frequently the result of vegetative propagation; a colony.

clapper. The water sac or lobule of *Hepaticae* or the gynoecium of a flower.

clasileucite. The part of the protoplasm differentiated in nuclear division to form the spindle and centrosomes or spheres.

clasper. A tendril or climbing shoot of vines.

clasping. Having a leaf partially or completely surround a stem, growing around, amplexicaul.

class. A comprehensive group of plants or animals forming a category ranking above an order and below a phylum, the highest category in the Linnaean system.

class of variates. A group all of which show a particular value falling between certain limits.

classification. A systematic distribution of individuals into groups or the systematic arrangement of plants.

clastotype. A fragment from the original type or a relict.

clathrarian. With the characteristic markings of the fossil *Clathraria*, now referred to as *Sigillaria*.

clathrate. Latticed or cancellate, net-like.

clathrate cell. A sieve tube resembling lattice-work, a cribform cell.

clathroid. Latticed, resembling the fungus *Clathrus*.

clathrospores. The glands in the pitchers of *Nepenthes*.

clathrus. A membrane pierced with holes and forming a grating.

clausilus. A macropodal embryo when its radicle is united by its edges and entirely encloses the rest.

clava. A club or the club-shaped fruiting structure of certain fungi, such as in *Cordyceps*.

clavacin. An antibiotic substance produced by *Asperigillus clavatus* and species of *Penicillium*, clavatin, claviformin, patulin, expansin.

clavaria-like. Club-shaped, or like the fungus *Clavaria*, clavarioid.

clavate. Club-shaped, slender at the base and gradually thickening upward.

clavate-bulbous. Of a stipe, with a bulb which gradually tapers upward.

clavellate. In the form of a little club.

clavicle. A tendril or a cirrhus.

claviculate. Having tendrils or hooks.

clavillose. Clubbed or markedly club-shaped.

clavis. An artificial key which contrasts characteristics of plants or groups of plants and facilitates their identification.

clavule. A club-shaped sporophore in certain fungi as in *Clavaria*.

clavus. An ergot disease in grasses with the young grains aborted to club-shaped sclerotia caused by *Claviceps purpurea* (obsolete).

claw. The slender, tapered base or petiole of a petal or sepal.

claw hook. The petiole of a well-developed leaf which is transformed into a hook after the fall of the lamina.

clay color. Cinnamon-brown.

clearing. 1. The use of a clearing agent in microtechnique. 2. An area which has been cleared of vegetation or deforested.

clearing agent. A solution used to prepare material to make it transparent for examination under a microscope.

cleat. A small outgrowth of silica from the secondary hoop of certain diatoms.

cleavage. 1. The series of mitotic divisions by which the fertilized ovum is transformed into a multicellular embryo or blastula. 2. Cell division in the xylem, pith, and medullary rays to form strands.

cleavage nucleus. 1. The nucleus of a fertilized ovum produced by fusion of male and female pronuclei. 2. In parthenogenetic forms, the nucleus of the ovum.

cleavage plane. A separation layer produced in leaves, stems, and other organs by means of which they are separated from the plant.

cleavage, polyembryony. The formation of several embryos resulting from splitting of basal tier cells in the proembryo.

cleft. Having narrow sinuses which reach about halfway to the midvein, cut into lobes.

cleft grafting. The insertion of a scion into a cleft made into a stock; the method of grafting in which the stock is cut squarely across and split, and the wedge-shaped scion inserted and sealed.

clefts. See LIRELLAE.

cleistanthery. The failure of the anthers in a partially cleistogamous flower to become exserted.

cleisto-. A prefix meaning closed.

cleistocarp. An ascocarp which is completely closed with the spores escaping through a rupture; see CLEISTOTHECIUM.

cleistocarpic, cleistocarpous. Opening of a capsule by rupture instead of by a lid.

cleistogamy. The production of small, inconspicuous, often simple, self-fertilized flowers.

cleistogene. A plant which produces cleistogamic flowers.

cleistopetaly. The permanent closing of the floral envelopes, thus insuring cleistogamy.

cleistothecium. 1. A closed fruit body with no ostiole. 2. An ascocarp which remains closed and produces its spores internally.

clema. A branchlet.

clematideous. Of or like *Clematis*.

clepsydroid. Denoting pinna-traces in fossils when they are in two rows.

clepsydroid trace. A band of centrifugal xylem separating into halves, each having parenchyma and dying out; the remains of centripetal xylem.

clepsydropsis. The condition of having clepsydroid traces.

cleptobiosis. Synclopia, the stealing of food.

clestines. The large parenchymatous cells in which raphides are frequently deposited.

clethroid. Like *Clethra*, a genus of subtropical trees and shrubs.

clianthus. 1. A semiprostrate leguminose shrub or vine of Australia and Asia. 2. A generic name, a synonym for the genus *Donia*.

climacorhizae. Gymnosperms and all dicotyledons except the *Nymphaeaceae* whose root hairs have an epidermal origin.

climacteric phase. The optimum phase in the development of fruit which is followed by deterioration.

climactic. Pertaining to a climax.

climagraph. 1. A diagram in which the mean monthly temperature is plotted against the mean monthly humidity (or rainfall). 2. A line surrounding the plottings of all twelve months which gives a graphic expression of the climate at any given station.

climate. The general or average conditions in relation to atmospheric phenomena, such as temperature, moisture, etc.

climatic climax. A climax in which climate is the controlling factor.

climatic community. A plant community determined by the climate of the region in which it exists.

climatic factors. Factors of climate which result in a stable plant formation.

climatic formation. A complex of associations which are linked by climate.

climatograph. A climagraph.

climax. A plant community which has reached a relatively stable condition in which it is able to reproduce itself indefinitely under existing conditions; a mature plant community.

climax association. A plant association which is stable under the influence of any given set of ecological factors.

climax community. A stable community which does not undergo change unless the surroundings change.

climax complex. A group of seres of the same climactic makeup which generally develop under the same climatic conditions and therefore occupy a wide territory corresponding to a climatic region, as deciduous forests in the North Temperate Zone.

climax dominant. A species which dominates a climax community.

climax, edaphic. A climax due to soil or some other local condition.

climax leaves. The most developed and complete leaves of a given plant.

climax species. Any species which is a characteristic member of a climax community.

climax, temporary. A temporary period of balanced growth.

climax unit. An association, a consociation, a society, a clan, etc.

climax vegetation. A type of vegetation which will undergo little further change under the controlling climate.

climax zone. A belt of stable plant communities which have reached the climax stage by gradual development from variant associations.

climb. To ascend in growth by twining around a support or by attaching to a support by aerial roots, etc.

climber. A plant which supports itself on surrounding objects.

climbing bogs. Bogs which occur on sloping ground such as sphagnum bogs which hold water and slowly cover slopes by spreading upward.

climbing ferns. Mostly tropical species of ferns which are vine-like. Lygodium is a genus of subtropical eastern U.S. Others belong to the Schizaeaceae family.

climbing plants. Usually large and woody tropical plants, lianas. There are four chief groups: twiners (whose tips nutate in search of support), climbers with sensitive organs (usually tendrils which may be modified stems), hook climbers (sprawling and catching by hooks), and root climbers which adhere to a support.

climograph. A climagraph.

clinandrium. The part of a column of an orchid which contains the anther, a cavity in orchids in the apex of the column between the anther sacs which often contains the stigmatic surface.

clinathium. The receptacle of the composite flowers.

cline. The rate of change in a measurable hereditary character within a group of organisms related to the rate of change in the climate, geography, or ecology of the groups.

clingstone. Applied to those varieties of peach and other drupes in which the ripe flesh is not readily separable from the seed.

clinidium. A filament in a pycnidium which produces spores, the stalk supporting the stylospore.

clinism. The situation in which there is an inclination of the axis due to each unit bending an angle to its original direction.

clinium. The receptacle of a composite flower or the sporophore of some fungi.

clinode. The conidiospore of certain fungi, as *Uredinales*.

clinomorphous. Of asymmetric organs without definite relation to the horizon.

clinosporangium. A pycnidium.

clinospore. A stylospore.

clinostat. An apparatus which eliminates the action of external agents (such as light and gravity) by means of a slowly revolving disk regulated by clockwork, a klinostat.

clinotropism. The oblique placement of an organ so that it has no vertical plane of symmetry.

clip. A seizing mechanism in certain flowers as *Asclepias*.

clisere. A successional development from one climax to another.

clistase. The climax layer of a given stase which differs from the preceding or succeeding stase.

clistogamy. Cleistogamy.

clistrate. The transition layer between two climaxes.

clitochore. A plant distributed by gravity, by falling or sliding.

clivus. A slide or incline.

clonal. Propagated from a bud; see CLONE.

clonarium. The ripe spiral-coated nucule or nutlet of *Chara*.

clone. 1. A group of cultivated plants which have been propagated vegetatively from a single original individual to preserve desirable characteristics which do not come true from seed. 2. A sub-culture of an isolate in a bacterial culture. 3. A clon.

clonotype. A specimen propagated from the original type by buds or cuttings.

close. 1. Of gills, midway between crowded and subdistant. 2. Having lamellae close together. 3. Of leaves, appressed.

close daughter skein. A figure produced by the chromatin during karyokinesis in which the chromosome loops are more or less jointed by connecting strands.

close fertilization. Self-fertilization or the action of pollen upon the pistil of the same flower.

close mother skein. An early stage in karyokinesis when a continous spireme is

present which has not yet folded into definite loops or broken apart.

close pollination. The transfer of pollen to the pistil of the same flower, self-pollination.

closed bundle. A fibrovascular bundle in which the procambium cells become permanent tissue, a fibrovascular bundle containing no cambium and therefore incapable of further growth.

closed collateral bundle. A bundle with phloem toward the outside of the stem and the xylem toward the center typical of monocot stems.

closed communities. Areas which are so crowded that invasion by other species is difficult or impossible.

closed fertilization. Close fertilization.

closed flowers. Cleistogamic flowers.

closed forest. A forest with a closed arboreal canopy commonly with lianas but without grasses.

closed formations. Areas with the component plants so crowded that invasion by other species is difficult.

closed nucleus. The nucleus of higher plants.

closed savannah. A savannah consisting of densely crowded grasses.

closed vascular bundle. A simple bundle without cambium or a closed bundle.

closing bands. Layers of coherent cells with intercellular spaces in the lenticels.

closing layer. The sheet of closely packed cells lying across a lenticel which permits diffusion of gases through the lenticel.

closing membrane. The original unthickened cell wall at the center of a pit.

closter. An elongated cell with points at each end frequently found in wood.

closterospore. A multinucleate structure (which may be a degenerate ascogonium or antheridium) resembling the gametangium of the primitive *Endomycetales* which divides into 2-5 cells with each cell behaving like a thin-walled chlamydospore and found chiefly in *Trichophytoneae*.

clostridia. Boat-shaped cells of certain spore-forming bacteria as in the genus *Clostridium*.

clouded. With colors unequally blended.

cloud forests. Forests about 2200 feet on mountains similar to tropical rain forests but cooler and more humid.

clove. 1. A gardener's name for a young bulb developed by the side of the mother bulb. 2. The spice of that name.

clover. A common name of a species of *Trifolium.*

club. One of the elements composing the pulp in the seed cavities of the lemon and orange, a basidium.

club moss. *Lycopodium.*

club root. A malformation or disease of certain crucifers caused by *Plasmodiophora Brassicae.*

club-shaped. Larger at the top than at the bottom, clavate.

clubbed. 1. Referring to the stem of an apple when its base is enlarged and fleshy. 2. Said of cabbage affected by the club root disease.

clusium. A succession of plants on flooded soil, a clysium.

cluster. An inflorescence of small, closely crowded flowers.

cluster crystals. Aggregates of crystals.

cluster cups. Aecia or aecidia.

cluster gall. A gall with a stunted axis and densely crowded, leaf-like appendages.

clustered inflorescence. Several flowers collected into a bunch.

clypeate. Shield-shaped or buckler-shaped, clypeastriformis, clypeatus, clypeolar.

clypeola. One of the sporophylls in the spike of *Equisetum*, a shield-shaped sporophyll.

clypeus. A shield-shaped disk of tissue around the mouth of a perithecium in certain fungi.

clysium. A clusium.

clysotremic. Of a tide pool.

cnicetum. An association of roadside weeds with the genus *Cnicus* predominant.

coacerrate. Heaped together or coacervate.

coadaptation. The correlated variation in two mutually dependent organisms.

coadnate. Adnate, connate, cohering, coadnite.

coadunate. United at the base, connate.

coaetaneous. Existing or appearing at the same time.

coaetaneous flowers. Flowers which appear at the same time as the leaves.

coagulase. An enzyme which can precipitate starch in solution.

coagulation. The change from a fluid to a thickened, congealed condition, as in the clotting of blood; curdling; the changing from a liquid to a viscous or solid state by chemical reaction.

coagulin. An agent capable of coagulating albuminous substances.

coagulum. A coagulated mass or a hard jelly.

coal balls. Calcareous masses in coal seams containing fragments of fossil plants.

coal, mother of. The charred wood found in the seams of coal.

coalescence. 1. Of hyphae, the complete fusion of the membrane of two originally separate hyphae or hyphal branches. 2. The union of parts or organs of the same kind, cohesion, symphysis.

coalescence of cells. The absorption or disappearance of cell walls between cells.

coalescent. Uniting by growth or fusing, with the organic cohesion of similar parts.

coalescent apertures. The slit-like inner apertures united into spiral grooves.

coalitus. Joined, running together, contracted, brought close together.

coar. A core.

coarctate. Crowded compactly together, contracted, brought close together.

coarcture. 1. The neck or collum. 2. The junction of the root and the stem at ground level.

coat. 1. The successive layers of a bulb. 2. The integument of an ovule. 3. A testa.

coat bulb. A tunicated or layered bulb.

coated. Composed of layers or having a rind or bark, furnished or covered with a coat, having integuments.

coaxial. With a common axis.

cob. The spike on which maize grows, a corncob.

cobaltine. Light chalky blue.

cobwebby. 1. Of a veil, composed of threads as fine as those of a cobweb. 2. Bearing long and soft entangled fibers, arachnoid.

cocaine. An alkaloid from the leaves of *Erythroxylum Coca.*

coccidium. A cystocarp, a sporocarp.

cocciferous. Bearing berries.

cocciform. Having lichen spores shaped like the insect which affords the scarlet dye from *Quercus coccifera.*

coccine. Bright red, scarlet.

coccinellus. Light scarlet.

coccineous. Carmine tinged with yellow, scarlet.

coccochromatic. With color distributed in granular patches.

coccodes. Pills like spherical granulations.

coccogone. A reproductive cell found in certain algae as the propagative cell like a sporangium in *Cyanophyceae.*

coccoid. Spherical or globose, pertaining to or resembling a coccus.

coccoid bodies. Certain reproductive bodies occurring in *Spirochaetes* which are equivalent to bacterial spores.

coccoid state. The unicellular state of algae.

coccoliths. Calcareous spicules in certain flagellates, the plates making up coccospheres.

coccoloba association. An association in which the shrub *Coccoloba*, the seaside grape, is predominant.

coccospheres. Spherical masses originating from protoplasm which have coocoliths on their external surface.

coccule. A portion of a divided coccus.

coccus. 1. A bacterium having spherical or near spherical form. 2. A one-seeded carpel into which compound fruits split when ripe. 3. A spore mother cell of certain hepatics. 4. A mericarp.

-coccus. A suffix used to designate bacteria.

cochenilliferous. Bearing cochineal.

cochlea. 1. A spirally coiled legume. 2. A spirally coiled body or organ.

cochlear. 1. Spoon-shaped, rounded and concave like a spoon. 2. Having a form of aestivation in which one larger petal or sepal covers all others.

cochlearispathous. Spoon-spathed.

cochleate. 1. Screw-like. 2. Spirally coiled or shaped like a snail shell.

cochlidiospermata. Seeds convex on one side and concave on the other from unequal growth or structure.

cockscombed. Fasciated, resembling a rooster's crest.

coconut. The fruit of *Cocos Nucifera*, a common palm.

cod. A seed pod.

codeine. An alkaloid in the opium poppy.

codiophyllous. Having leaves covered with a woolly pubescence.

cod-like. Follicular, having a seed pod which opens along one side only.

codominant. A plant species which shares dominance in a plant community with other equally dominant species.

codwar. The pulse plant.

coefficient of association. The degree of association.

coefficient of community. The similarity of species lists of two regions or communities expressed in percentages.

coefficient of destruction. The percentage of progeny which must normally be eliminated in order to keep the species at a given level.

coefficient of variability. A relative index of variation obtained by expressing the standard deviation in percentage of the mean.

colenterate. A pitcher plant of carnivorous habit.

coelestinous. Sky-blue.

coeline. Caerulean blue.

coeloblast. A noncellular alga or fungus.

coeloma. The body of *Vaucheria*, a nonseptate coenocyte.

coelomycetes. A large group of *Fungi Imperfecti* which form their spores within a cavity in the matrix upon which they grow.

coelonemata. The myxogasters having a hollow capillitium.

coelosperm. A seed-like carpel of certain apiaceous plants, as *Coriander*, having a hollow surface on the inner side.

coelospermous. With hollow or boat-shaped seeds.

coen. See HOLOCOEN.

coenanthium. An inflorescence with a nearly flat receptacle having upcurved margins, a clinanthium.

coenobe. A colony of separate organisms or structures united by a common investment, such as the algal colony of *Volvox* or the four nutlets of the fruit of the *Labiatae* and *Boraginaceae*, etc.; a carcerule, cenobium, or coenobium.

coenobiology. Biocoenology.

coenocarpium. The collective fruit of an entire inflorescence, as the fig or pineapple.

coenocenter. A dense, deeply staining mass of granules which seem to attract the egg nuclei in *Albugo* and certain other fungi.

coenocladia. Natural grafting, as where branches have grown together.

coenocyst. A multinucleate nonmotile spore.

coenocyte. 1. A multinuclear plant body enclosed within a common wall. 2. A bit of cytoplasm with many nuclei not separated by walls. 3. A multinucleate cell.

coenocytic. Having a nonseptate structure, as in molds and many other types of plants.

coenogametangium. A gametangium in which a coenogamete is formed.

coenogamete. A multinucleate gamete.

coenogenesis. A development by adjustment to the environment, cenogenesis, caenogenesis, cainogenesis, kenogenesis.

coenomonoecia. Polygamous plants the same

individual having male and female flowers or the normal hermaphrodite flowers.

coenopodous. Coinopodous.

coenopterid. A Palaeozoic fern previously called *Botryopteridae*.

coenosis. A population system held together by ecological factors in a state of unstable equilibrium.

coenosium. A community of plants, further divided as biocoenosium, isocoenosium, permanent coenosium, temporary coenosium, etc.

coenospecies. 1. A variable hybrid of two Linnaen or ecospecies. 2. The total sum of possible combinations in a genotype compound. 3. A species incapable of genetic recombination with similar species.

coenosphere. A coenocenter.

coenozygote. A zygote formed by the union of coenogametes each containing many nuclei.

co-enzyme. An organic substance closely associated with an enzyme but sometimes separable from it. The presence of the coenzyme is required for the proper activity of the enzyme.

coeruleous. Sky-blue.

coesius. Caesious.

coetaneous. Appearing or existing at the same time, of the same age.

coetonium. The outer glumes of a multifloral spikelet in grasses, caetonium.

coffeate. Coffee-like, shaped like a coffee bean of the genus *Coffea*.

cogeneric. Congeneric.

cognoles. 1. Grasslands as a consequence of cultivation. 2. Small portions of second-growth forest which have been cleared and cultivated and then abandoned and burned. 3. Grasslands of the pasture type in the Hawaiian Islands.

cohabitants. Plant which can survive in the same area.

coherence. Cohesion; sometimes used for partial cohesion.

cohesion. The congenital union of like parts, as petals which unite to form a gamopetalous or monopetalous corolla. Adnation, coalescence, fusion.

cohesion mechanism. A plant structure which depends on some liquid substance for its operation, as a seed pod or sporangium which ejects its contents when the moisture content is decreased or lost.

cohort. A group of families or orders which are closely related to one another, allied plants. Earlier classifications considered a cohort a group of somewhat indefinite limitation.

coincidence, coefficient of. The proportion of unplanned crosses which produce desired hybrids in relation to planned double crossovers.

coinopodous. Terminating downward in a cone, as in most embryos; coenopodous.

coir. A product of *Cocos nucifera*, the coconut palm.

colchicine. An alkaloid obtained from the root of *Colchium autumnale*, the autumn crocus.

colchicus. Of Colchis in the eastern Mediterranean region.

cole. The colewort, a species of *Brassica*.

-cole, -coleous. A suffix meaning living on or inhabiting.

colein. The red coloring matter of *Coleus Verschaffeltii*.

colenchyma. Collenchyma.

coleogen. A ring-shaped group of cells surrounding the mestome of *Dicksonia*.

coleophyllum. A membranous or fleshy sheath investing the plumule in monocotyledons, the first leaf in germination of monocotyledons which sheathes the succeeding leaves.

coleopteroid. Resembling a beetle or bug, as the seeds of some *Euphorbiaceae*.

coleoptile. A coliophyllum.

coleorhiza. The root sheath in endogens through which the caulicle bursts at germination. The coleorrhiza.

colesule. 1. A membranous bag-like organ enclosing the sporangium of *Hepaticae*. 2. The perichaetal sheath, usually termed the vaginule.

colewort. 1. A general name for what may be called the true brassicas as distinguished from the mustards. 2. A variety of cabbage in which the leaves do not form a compact head.

collabent. Collapsing or crumbling.

collapsion. The act of falling or closing together.

collar. 1. The colorless area of the dorsal side of the leaf where the blade and sheath join. 2. Any structure comparable to a collar. 3. A junction of root and shoot. 4. The annulus of an agaric. 5. An encircling outgrowth at the base of the ovule in ginkgo. 6. A collum.

collar of inflorescence. A structure at the junction of the culm and the rachis.

collards. A variety of kale used as a green vegetable, an American form of cabbage.

collare. A ligule.

collariate. Collared or attached to a collar.

collateral. Being side by side, as in a fibrovascular bundle in which the xylem and phloem are side by side in a radial direction.

collateral buds. Accessory buds at the side of the axillary bud, as in the red maple.

collateral bundle. A vascular bundle in which the xylem and phloem strands are in contact on only one side.

collateral chorisis. Having the parts originating by chorisis stand side by side; see CHORISIS.

collateral inheritance. The appearance of characters in collateral members of a family, as when an uncle and a niece show the same character inherited by the related individuals from a common ancestor. Collateral inheritance is characteristic of recessive characters which appear irregularly in contrast to dominant characters which do not skip a generation.

collateral, parallel. The plane of lateral separation.

collateral vascular bundle. A simple bundle containing one xylem and one phloem bundle.

collecting cells. Rounded cells at the base of palisade tissue which do not contain chlorophyll and are densely filled with protoplasm.

collecting hairs. Hairs on the style of some *Compositae* which serve to collect the pollen discharged from the anther.

collective fruit. A fruit which arises from the coalescence of the ripening ovaries of a mass of distinct flowers, as in the mulberry.

collector. A collecting hair, a hair which collects or brushes out the pollen from the anthers.

collenchyma. 1. The first-formed mechanical or strengthening tissue of stems composed of elongated cells thickened only at the angles by material heavy in cellulose. 2. The cellular matter in which pollen is formed which is usually absorbed but sometimes takes a characteristic form as in orchids or as in the delicate threads in *Oenothera*.

collenchyma, bast. Cells in which the thickening involves the whole wall.

collenchyma, cartilage. Tissue with the walls thickened all around with greatly differentiated lamella.

collenchyma, meta. Tissue which results from the slow death of the cell and the metamorphosis of the cell wall.

collenchyma, plate. A form of collenchyma resembling true hard bast tissue.

collenchyma, rift. A thickened portion of a cell wall bordering on an intercellular space.

collenchymatous elements. Living substances which provide supporting tissue at the intersection of cells; see COLLENCHYMA.

collet. A collar.

colleters. Glandular hairs or mucilaginous hairs on the buds of many phanerogams which secrete gum.

colliculose. With small round elevations, colliculous.

colliferous. Bearing a collar, as the stipe of an agaric.

colliform. An ostiole or an orifice lengthened into a neck.

collinus. Growing on low hills.

colliquescent. Becoming liquid by dissolving in moisture.

collococcus. A perianth bract.

colloid. A substance resembling glue or jelly, a noncrystalline, semi-solid substance which is capable of slow diffusion, a state of matter in which particles larger than single molecules are suspended in a liquid.

collum. 1. A collar or neck-like structure. 2. The neck or junction of the stem and root. 3. The tapering basal portion of the capsule in mosses. 4. The lengthened orifice of the ostiole of lichens.

colluvium. An accumulation of soil at the base of a slope, usually washed there by water.

colonal. Relating to a bud.

colonial. Forming or existing in colonies.

colonisation. The occupation of bare ground by seedlings and sporelings; colonization.

colonists. 1. Weeds in cultivated land and about houses which are seldom found elsewhere. 2. Species which enter after the pioneer plants and replace them, forming characteristic and relatively constant communities.

colony. A visible growth of organisms which

has grown from a single bacterium or spore on a culture plate, any collection of organisms living together, a collection of organisms of the same kind in close association with each other, a coenobe.

colony, energid. A temporary union of the meriplasts, the individuality of the protoplasts not being distributed.

colony, motile. An association group of algae that is not fixed to one place.

colony, palmelloid. A colony of non-filamentous algae which are embedded in a gelatinous matrix.

colophony. A form of resin.

color of the reverse. The color of a bacterial culture from the under side.

colorific. Yielding or displaying color.

-colous. A suffix meaning inhabiting.

colpa. In the exine of a pollen grain, a furrow running from one pole to another.

colporate. With both furrows and pores.

colpote. With one to several furrows (colpae) in the same exine.

colpenchyma. Cellular tissue with sinuous cell walls or epidermal tissue composed of cells with sinuous margins.

colubrine. Pertaining to or like a snake.

colum. The united stamens and pistils in the orchid family, a placenta.

columbianus. Columbian, Western North America.

columbine. A ranunculaceous plant of the genus *Aquilegia*.

columel. Lignified tissue formed in place of the fertilized archegonium bearing at its tip the only embryo which develops.

columella. 1. A small column or central axis. 2. A central sterile column extending into a sporangium, as in mosses, lichens, and myxomycetes. 3. A bulbous extension into the sporangium in *Phycomycetes*. 4. The persistent sterile central axis in some fruits around which the carpels are arranged.

columellaris. Pertaining to a small pillar or pedestal.

columelliform. Shaped like a small pillar or column.

column. 1. A small pillar at the top of the ovary made up of the style and filament of the stamens welded together (as in orchids and the mallows). 2. The lower undivided part of the awns of certain species of *Aristida*. 3. The axis or central pillar of a capsule. 4. A columna.

column crystals. Styloids.

coma. 1. The hair on the ends of some seeds. 2. The entire head of a tree. 3. A tuft of leaves at the tip of a stem or branch. 4. A cluster of terminal bracts on a flower stem, as it appears in the pineapple. 5. A head of hair or a tuft of any kind.

comal tuft. A tuft of leaves at the tip of a branch.

comate. Comose.

comate disseminule. A fruit or seed bearing long silky hairs which aid in dispersal by wind, a pappus.

comb grass. Meadow comb grass, *Eragrostis*.

combination-venosus. With joined veins, having lateral veins of a leaf unite before reaching the margin.

combined. 1. United or joined together. 2. United by a continuous longitudinal vein, applied to a peculiar form of venation.

combined bordered pits. Much elongated pits fusing together by means of furrows on the inside of the cell wall which are formed by the sharpedged apertures on inner apertures of the canals belonging to adjacent pits.

combined hybrid. A derivative hybrid in which three or more species or varieties are united, as when one hybrid unites with a new parent form or another hybrid.

combus. A cormus.

comites. Cells occurring in the embryo sacs of *Lupinus*.

commensal. An organism living with another and sharing the food, both species as a rule benefiting by the association, such as the beneficial relationship of algae and fungi in lichens.

commensalism. The state of two commensals living together, living together for mutual benefit, mutualism or symbiosis.

commensual. Said of those species which enter into competition separately and their common relation consists in the fact that they simultaneously utilize the various life conditions of a habitat without benefiting or being injured by the relationship.

comminuted. Pulverized or pounded.

commiscuum. All individuals connected by a genetical possibility of cross-breeding, a convivum.

commissural. The coherence of two carpels by their faces, as in *Umbelliferae*.

commissural arch. A loop of vascular tissue joining the ends of veins of a leaf.

commissural column. The central vascular strand in ferns.

commissural sieve-tubes. Structures which unite the different kinds of sieve tubes with each other.

commissural strand. The structure which unites sieve tubes.

commissure. The face by which two carpels cohere, the line of union between two parts, the place of joining or meeting, a path, cleft, a suture.

common bud. A bud containing both leaves and flowers or one from which more than one flower is produced.

common bundle. A vascular bundle which passes from a stem into a leaf.

common calyx. The involucre.

common involucre. An involucre which extends under an entire inflorescence as under a general umbel.

common name. The name applied to a plant in common usage, not the botanical name.

common parenchyma. A tissue consisting of thin-walled parenchyma cells.

common peduncle. A peduncle which supports several pedicels.

common perianth. A common involucre which surrounds a head of flowers in the *Compositae.*

common petiole. The first and principal leaf stalk in compound leaves.

common receptacle. A receptacle which is common to more than one flower or other organ.

common umbel. A compound umbel.

communal habitat. The general habitat of any recognizable community, such as an association or society.

communal intensity. The degree of the spread of insect or plant diseases depending upon the extent and number of host plants present in a community.

communities. 1. Groupings of plants growing together. 2. A mixture of individuals of two or more species. 3. All the plants and animals of an area.

community complex. A complex or an association complex.

community composition. See ECOLOGICAL STRUCTURE, DOMINANT, INFLUENT, SUB-DOMINANT, SUB-INFLUENT.

commutatus. Changed or changing.

comose. Having a coma or tuft of hairs, being tufted, terminated by small sterile bracts, having a pappus.

comospores. Seeds or other disseminules with a coma or pappus.

compaginate. Packed closely, united, knit, or held together.

compago. A lichen thallus when it is more or less brittle or readily separable into layers.

companion cell. A long, thin-walled nucleated cell associated with the sieve tubes in the phloem; a sister cell of a sieve tube.

companion hyphae. The hyphal cells which accompany the trichogyne of *Polystigma* when it protrudes into the air through a stoma and forms a tuft.

compass plants. Certain plants with a permanent north and south direction of their leaf edges with their leaf surfaces facing east and west.

compatibility. The capability of self-fertilization.

compensation of growth. The lack of development of an organ caused by the suppression of the primordium or by the overdevelopment of another organ.

compensation period. The length of time required for a green plant to be in light to rebuild the carbohydrates consumed by respiration while the plant has been in darkness.

compensation point. The light intensity at which, at any given temperature, respiration and photosynthesis balance in a green plant so there is neither liberation nor absorption of carbon dioxide and of oxygen.

compensation strands. Strands arising from the inner ring of the stele and connecting with the outer ring. A compensating tongue.

competition. The relation between plants occupying the same area and dependent upon the same physical factors, the general struggle for existence in which the living organisms compete for the necessities of life.

competition curve. A curve representing the success of an individual in terms of intensified competition.

competitive association. A group of plants mutually competitive; see CODOMINANT.

competitive society. Those species of plants whose roots occupy the same level in the soil.

compital. 1. Having the veinlets intersect at angles. 2. Having sori at the junction of veins.

complanate. Flattened or compressed; flattened so that several organs lie in one plane or lie against each other, as when leaves lie flat against the stem.

complectens. Comprising or clasping.

complement. 1. The normal number or set of chromosomes in a somatic or gametic nucleus. 2. A substance that will activate the decomposition of dextrin in the presence of heat. 3. An unstable substance necessary for the action of bacterial antibodies.

complementary. Mutually supplying what the other organism lacks, as mosses protect soils and benefit by the shade of the trees above them.

complementary association. An association in which the various species root at different depths and come to the surface at various times of the year, thereby avoiding competition. A complementary society.

complementary cells. Loosely arranged corky cells which occur in the lenticels and allow gasses to diffuse through them. Complementary tissue.

complementary chromatic adaptation. The ability of algae to make effective use of the light which reaches them, complementary to their own coloration.

complementary factor. A gene which when crossed with similar genes produces in the offspring characters resembling the parents.

complementary genes. Genes which are similar in effect when inherited separately but which produce a distinct character when they are inherited together.

complementary society. A relationship in an area when two or more species root in the soil at different levels to each other. It is said to be *seasonal* when different plants use the same ground at different seasons.

complementary tissue. A loose assemblage of thin-walled, unsuberised cells which fit loosely together and lie in the cavity of a lenticel allowing gasses and vapors to diffuse through them.

complementation. The division of a phyllome with each portion acting as a complete whole.

complete. The group of chromosomes derived from a particular nucleus composed of one, two or more sets.

complete flower. A flower having calyx, corolla, stamens, and pistils.

complete leaf. A leaf having blade, petiole, and stipule(s).

complete parasite. A parasite which is entirely dependent on a host.

complete specific assemblage. The sum total of characteristic and companion species showing a high degree of presence in a community at its optimum development.

complex. 1. A group of complicated or interwoven parts or fibers. 2. A mosaic of communities determined by the local diversity and geomorphic factors and repeating itself or occurring in diverse localities.

complex character. A character controlled by many genes which have small but cumulative effects and are likely to vary considerably and to reflect influences of the environment.

complex, formation. A broader classification than a plant formation, a term applied to world-wide formations similar in physiognomy and in ecological characteristics, although the floristic make up may vary or differ.

complex mutation. A mutation with simultaneous changes in several factors in one region of a chromosome.

complex tissue. Tissue composed of cells or elements of more than one kind.

complexus. Having leaves which are folded over each other at the sides and the apex, embraced, encircled.

complexus cellulosus. Cellular tissue.

complexus membranaceus. Ground tissue or elementary membrane.

complexus tubularis. Woody tissue or xylem.

complexus utricularis. Angular cellular tissue.

complexus vascularis. Spiral vessels or small vessels showing secondary deposits.

complicant. Folding over one another.

complicate. Folded over or back on itself.

complicato-carinate. Folded together so as to form a keel.

component grain. A simple grain of a compound starch grain.

composite. A plant of the *Compositae* family, with flowers arranged in a head.

compositicolous. Concerning composites and

herbaceous plants which inhabit an area; see PHYTODYTES.

compound. Formed of a number of similar parts, as a leaf made up of two or more leaflets, or a fruit or pistil made up of several carpels; composed of or produced by the union of several parts.

compound corymb. A corymb with more than one flower on each branch.

compound dichasium. A dichasium in which the primary axis of the cyme divides into secondary dichasia.

compound flower. 1. The flower-head in the *Compositae*, an aggregated cluster or head of florets seated on a common receptacle and surrounded by an involucre or a many-leaved common calyx. 2. A flower with florets with united anthers.

compound fruit. A fruit formed from many closely associated flowers; see AGGREGATE FRUIT, COLLECTIVE FRUIT.

compound fungus body. A growth-form of fungi in which the thallus is constituted by the cohering ramifications of separate hyphae.

compound hairs. Branched hairs.

compound head. A composite flower having an involucre for each individual floret. The whole head usually has a small outer involucre, as the globe thistle, *Echinops*.

compound inflorescence. An inflorescence in which each primary branch bears more than one flower.

compound interest law. The doctrine that the rate of growth of a plant at any time is proportional to the amount of plant material present at the time.

compound leaf. 1. A leaf whose blade is divided into leaflets. 2. A leaf which is divided down to the midrib.

compound medullary ray. A medullary ray which is composed of a vertically alternating uniseriate and pluriseriate layer.

compound oosphere. A multinucleate body occurring in an oogonium, probably composed of a number of female gametes which have not become individualized.

compound ovary. An ovary consisting of more than one carpel.

compound pistil. A pistil having two or more united carpels.

compound pyrenoid. A pyrenoid which is made up of two closely associated portions.

compound spike. A spike in which more than one flower or spikelet occurs on each short branch.

compound spore. A spore consisting of more than one cell each of which may germinate; see SPORIDESM.

compound sporophore. A sporophore formed by the cohesion of separate hyphal branches.

compound starch grain. A starch grain formed by the aggregation of simple grains.

compound stem. A branched stem.

compound tissue. Tissue formed by more than one kind of cell but never formed by the combining of whole parts of plants.

compound umbel. A flat circular inflorescence of simple umbels, each ray being an umbel.

compound vascular bundles. Simple vascular bundles which are separated by medullary commissures.

compression flange. Turgescent parenchymatous cells on the convex side of a coiled tendril.

compression wood. The wood of very dense structure which may be formed at the bases of some tree trunks and on the underside of branches.

comptus. Adorned, ornamented.

concatenate. United in a continuous series like the links of a chain or the beads of a necklace, catenulate, concatenus.

concaulescence. The coalescence of two or more axes, the coalescence of the pedicel of a flower with the stem.

concentration. 1. The ratio, in a dissolved substance, between the molecules of a substance and of the solvent in a given volume. 2. The growth of primordia with the bulk remaining constant.

concentric. 1. Having a common center, used in connection with growth rings in the cross section of a twig when the growth center coincides with the geometric center. 2. Of bundles, when the xylem is surrounded by the phloem or vice versa. 3. Equidistant from a common center.

concentric bundles. See CONCENTRIC, AMPHICRIBAL, AMPHIVASAL.

concentric cells. Certain cells in the *Cyanophyceae* which are destitute of nuclei and yield on slight pressure, resulting in an incurving of cell walls.

concentric starch grain. A starch grain with a central hilum.

conceptacle. 1. A superficial cavity opening

outward within which gonidia are produced, the reproductive cavity in the receptacle of *Fucus*. 2. A pair of follicles of *Asclepiadaceae* and *Apocynaceae*.

conchaefolious. With shell-shaped leaves.

conchate. Shell-shaped.

conchiform. Formed like one-half of a bivalve shell.

concinna. Neat.

concolorous. Of uniform color.

concolorate. Similarly colored on both sides.

concomitant. Applied to the fibrovascular bundles which run continuously side by side without being separated by other bundles.

concrescence. The union of originally distinct organs by the growth of tissue between them, coalescence, growing together or fusion.

concrescent. Having grown together.

concrescent colonies. Colonies resulting from a secondary unit of individuals which are entirely separate for at least a brief period of time.

concretion. A soil formation caused by the accumulation of minerals into rock or marl through the activity of water plants.

condensation. 1. The rearrangement of atoms to form a molecule of greater weight. 2. A concentration or contraction of the chromosomes. 3. The thickening, shortening, and spiralization of the chromatids during the prophase.

condensed. Denoting the inflorescences in which the flowers are crowded together and nearly or quite sessile, crowded.

condensing lens. The epidermal papillae acting so as to focus the available light on the chloroplasts in the palisade cells.

condiments. Spices and other vegetable products raised for their flavor rather than for food value.

conducting bundles. 1. Vascular bundles. 2. The strands of elongated cells in the leaves and stems of mosses which simulate vascular bundles.

conducting cells. Narrow elongated cells associated with sieve-tubes and similar to them but lacking perforated walls.

conducting sheath. 1. The sheath formed by elongated parenchymatous cells which surround the vascular bundles and extend from the stem to the mesophyll of the leaves. 2. The tissues which serve to transfer carbohydrates from the leaves.

conducting strand. See VASCULAR BUNDLE.

conducting surface. The surface in *Nepenthes* upon which the insects can gain no foothold.

conducting tissue. 1. Loose tissue of the style apparently adapted to facilitate growth of the pollen tube down to the ovules. 2. Any tissue made up of conducting cells.

conduction. The transference of soluble matter from one part of a plant to another.

conductive hyphae. Hyphae which convey moisture in dry rot.

conductive tissue. Conducting tissue.

conductivity. The quality or power of conducting stimuli from a receptor to other parts of the body.

conduplicate. 1. With parts folded together lengthwise. 2. Folded along the midrib, as the leaves of grasses. 3. Folded, as the cotyledons around the radicle or leaves in the bud.

conduplication. 1. A doubling. 2. In aestivation the clinging together of organs face to face.

condyle. 1. The antheridium of *Chara*. 2. The basal granule of *Gymnodiniaceae*. 3. A condylium.

cone. 1. The inflorescence of *Coniferae*, *Cycadaceae*, *Lycopodium*, and other plants. 2. The fruit of coniferous trees consisting of a woody axis on which are arranged stiff, leaf-like scales which contain ovules or pollen. See GALBULUS, STROBILUS.

cone, genus. A fossil genus known only by its cones.

cone of growth. The apical growing portion of the stem.

cone scale. The peculiar cone of *Cheirostrobus*.

conein. Conia.

conelet. A diminutive cone or a cone in its first year of growth.

conenchyma. The conical cells which constitute hairs.

conferruminate. 1. Closely united. 2. Stuck together by adjacent faces, as in the case of the cotyledons of the horse chestnut.

conferted. Closely packed, crowded, or clustered.

confervaceous. Composed of threads resembling the genus *Conferva*, green freshwater algae.

confervae. The filamentous weeds of fresh water.

confervoid. Consisting of loose and delicate filaments, like the alga *Conferva*.

configuration. A separate cluster of independent chromosomes found in the anaphase.

conflatus. Swollen.

confluence. An angle of union or the act of flowing together.

confluent. 1. Said of two or more structures which, as they enlarge, grow together and unite. 2. Of sori, those sori which spread so widely that they join those nearest to them. 3. Of mushroom stems, those in which the flesh of the stems and the trama of the pileus is continuous and of similar texture. 4. Of anther lobes, those which are united at the summit of the filament and diverge from that point.

confluent fruit. Collective fruit or compound fruit such as mulberry.

confluent parenchyma. Coalesced aliform parenchyma forming irregular tangential or diagonal bands.

conformed. 1. Similar in form. 2. Closely fitting, as a seed coat to the nucellus.

confused. Mingled so as to be indistinguishable.

congener. A plant belonging to the same genus as another.

congenital. Of the same origin or present at birth.

congeries. A collection of parts or organs; a collection of particles, parts, or bodies into one mass.

conglobate. Ball-shaped or collected into a fleshy mass.

conglomerate. 1. Clustered or crowded together. 2. A rock mass made up of small parts cemented together.

conglutin. A constituent of plant casein, usually with legumin from almonds and lupines.

conglutinate. Glued together into a mass; united, as by some adhesive substance.

congolanus. Of the Congo.

congression. The assemblage of chromosome threads toward the equatorial plate during the metaphase of cell division.

conia. The active principle of the poisonous alkaloid which is obtained from *Conium maculatum*; coniin, conein, koniium.

conico-hemispheral. Between conical and spherical.

conico-ovate. Between conical and ovate.

conidial. Producing or pertaining to conidia.

conidiferous. Bearing conidia or giving rise to conidia.

conidioid. Like conidia in form and/or function.

conidiole. A small conidium usually borne on another conidium.

conidiome. A conidia-bearing body.

conidiophore. A specialized hypha of a fungus mycelium which produces a conidiospore, a hypha-bearing conidium, a gonidiophore.

conidiosporangium. A deciduous zoosporangium which resembles a conidium.

conidiospore. An asexual spore cut off the end of a conidiophore, a conidium.

conidium. An asexual thin-walled spore produced by abstriction from the summit of a conidiophore, an asexual spore developed on mycelium or the hypha of a fruit body, a dust-like spore which is disseminated into the air, a gonidium.

conidium verum. A conidium.

conids. Conidia.

conifer. 1. A general term employed for cone-bearing trees. 2. A tree or shrub of the *Coniferae*.

coniferin. A crystalline glucoside in the cambium of coniferous trees, asparagus, etc.

coniferophyte. A cone-bearing plant.

coniferopsida. A group containing the *Ginkgoales*, *Cordaitales* and the *Coniferae*; an infrequently used term.

coniferous. 1. Cone-bearing. 2. Composed of cone-bearing trees.

coniform. Conical.

conifruticeta. Forests composed of or dominated by coniferous shrubs.

coniin. Conia.

conilignosa. Dominated by trees and shrubs with typical needle-like foliage.

coniocyst. 1. A closed sporangium resembling a tubercle and containing a mass of spores. 2. The oogonium of *Vaucheria*.

Coniomycetes. A large group of fungi including some of the *Sphaeropsidales*, *Melanconiales*, the *Ustilaginales*, and the *Uredinales*.

coniophilous. Benefitting from dust.

coniotheca. The loculus of an anther.

conisilvae. Coniferous forests.

conjoint bundle. A vascular bundle when it is composed of wood and bast elements.

conjugant. 1. One of the two conjugating individuals in partial karyogamy.

conjugate. 1. Coupled, as a pinnate leaf of two leaflets. 2. Joined or arranged in pairs. 3. Fused, as isogametes.

conjugate division. The simultaneous division of the paired sex nuclei or the synchronous division of the dicaryon.

conjugate nuclei. Two nuclei closely associated in one cell which divide simultaneously, a dicaryon.

conjugate spirals. Arrangements of whorled leaves which produce two or more genetic spirals running parallel to each other.

conjugated elements. The tubular lateral processes of adjoining cells meeting each other.

conjugating. Joining the protoplasts of two adjacent cells of some algae by means of the formation of a canal between the two cells.

conjugating tubes. The canals coming from the fertilized trichophore in certain algae which unite with the auxiliary cells.

conjugation. The temporary union of two unicellular similar (isogamic) cells for the purpose of exchanging nuclear protoplasm, the union of two sexual cells (isogametes) to produce a zygote, the most primitive and the simplest form of sexual reproduction in which the male and female cells are alike or nearly so.

conjugation canal. 1. The open tube-like canal formed between the conjugation cells (gametes) of certain algae. 2. A temporary union to complete the fusion of two gametes or unicellular organisms.

conjugation cell. A gamete.

conjugation, cross. A condition in which some cells in a given algal filament are active and others passive.

conjugation, lateral. The conjugation which takes place cell by cell.

conjugation, scalariform. The conjugation in which the entire filament is involved and a ladder-like appearance is presented.

conjugation tubes. The canals between the conjugating cells.

conjugato-palmate. Said of a leaf which divides into two palmate arms.

conjunction. The state of being joined or the pairing of two univalent spiremes to become a heterotype chromosome.

conjunctive parenchyma. The parenchyma cells which occupy space between the vascular strands of the stele.

conjunctive symbiosis. The state of symbionts which are so close that they present the appearance of a single body.

conjunctive threads. The spindle fibers.

conjunctive tissue. The fundamental ground tissue within the stele consisting of the pericycle and mesocycle, nonvascular tissue adjacent to a bundle composed of lignified, usually elongated, cells.

conjunctorium. The operculum of a moss.

conjunctus. The condition in the *Characeae* when the antheridia and oogonia are at the same node.

conk. The fruiting body of a wood-destroying fungus.

connacian. Growing in Connaught.

connascent. Produced at the same time.

connate. 1. United congenitally or subsequently, united with like members in the process of formation. 2. Joined into one organ, as confluent filaments or opposite leaves which are united at the base, as in some *Lonicera*.

connate-perfoliate. Of leaves, with bases united around the stem.

connation. The union of parts of a plant as growth proceeds, applied especially to the union of like parts.

connecting bank. A cingulum.

connecting cell. A heterocyst.

connecting frame. The ridges of pectin substances filling up the corners of the intercellular spaces and surrounding those parts of the cell walls common to adjacent cells.

connecting threads. Delicate strands of protoplasm which pass through fine perforations in the cell wall and unite the protoplasts of the contiguous cells; see DISJUNCTOR.

connecting tissue. The special colorless tissue which adjoins the veins in some leaves.

connecting zone. The hoop or girdle in diatoms.

connectivalis. Having to do with the connective tissue.

connective. The part of the filament which serves to connect the anthers, the stalk or bar connecting the separated lobes of an anther.

connective flaps. The vestigial imbricating laminae in gymnospermic cones.

connective tissue. A mesoblastic tissue with a large amount of intercellular substance in which fibers are developed.

connivent. 1. Coming together but not organically connected. 2. Converging and meeting at the tips.

connubium. The stage of protoplasmic coalescence in the conjugation of filamentous algae.

conocarpium. An aggregate fruit, such as strawberry, consisting of many carpels on a conical receptacle.

conodrymium. An evergreen community, a consilvae or conophorium.

conoid. Cone-like but not quite conical.

conopeus. Conopseus.

conophorium. A coniferous forest community.

conophorophilous. Living in coniferous forests.

conophorophyte. A plant of a coniferous forest.

conopodium. A conical floral receptacle.

conopseus. Gnat-like or canopied, as in the scented orchid *Habenaria conopsea*.

conostroma. A growing point constituting a free central placenta.

consere. A cosere.

conservative organs. The organs (roots, stems, leaves, etc.) concerned with nutrition.

consimilar. With both sides alike.

consimilitude. The resemblance of the valves of diatoms when they are unequal yet similar.

consocial. Said of species which are consistently found together in a given society or community, of species which form consociations or consocies.

consociate. Joined or associated.

consociation. A climax community with a single dominant; a subdivision of an association dominated by one of the co-dominants of the association.

consocies. A developmental stage in the history of a consociation before conditions become stabilized.

consocietum. An association or a community.

consocion. A synusium with essentially uniform species-composition.

consociule. A microcommunity of consocial rank.

consolidated. 1. Having a small surface in proportion to bulk, as in a cactus. 2. With unlike parts coherent. 3. Grown together, said of like or unlike parts.

consortism. Symbiosis or mutualism.

consortium. The mutual association of fungi and algae in lichens.

conspecific. Belonging to the same species.

conspergens. Sprinkled.

conspersus. Scattered.

conspurcate. Polluted.

constance. An expression of the occurrence of a species in several stands of the same kind of community based on a sample area of definite size in each stand.

constance classes. Constant percentages classified on a 5- or 10-parted scale in the same manner as frequency percentages.

constancy. The consistent presence of a species in the plots of a sharply delimited area.

constant. 1. Always present. 2. Always in the same condition or continually recurring. 3. Appearing in at least half of the records of a sampling of a given community. 4. Persistent or uniform.

constellation. The aggregate of conditions which regulate the vital mechanism of the protoplast.

constricted. 1. Contracted suddenly. 2. Narrowed at regular intervals at one or more points along the length, as if compressed by a tightened thread.

constriction. 1. Any sudden narrowing in a cylindrical member. 2. The narrowest portion of a diatom seen from one side. 3. A narrowed region in a chromosome, usually difficult to stain.

constriction, primary or attachment. A constriction which is associated with the spindle attachment.

constriction, secondary. Any constriction other than the primary.

constructive eugenics. A system of securing a superior race through propagation of the fittest individuals.

constructive metabolism. Chemical changes which relate to the formation of new organic material, assimilation.

constructiveness. The dynamogenetic value of the species in the community or communities related in a successional manner.

consumptus. Destroyed or consumed.

consutus. United by a membrane of threads.

contabescence. The abortion of a stamen with the formation of little or no fertile pollen.

contabescent. Shrivelling.

contact cycles. Individual members of a phyllotactic system overlapping to form continuous investments of the axis.

contact lines. Parastichies or the secondary spirals in the leaf arrangement on an axis.

contact parastichies. Contact lines.

contact pressures. The pressures between growing primordia in a concentration system.

contact stimulus. Thigmotropism or the tendency to respond to mechanical contact by clinging and curving, as in tendrils; a response to the stimulus of contact.

contaminate zone. See MESOSAPROBIA.

contematose. With a covering which is described as being between bristly and aculeate.

conterminous. 1. Of equal extent. 2. Said of marginal ray cells which form an uninterrupted row.

context. The layer developed between the hymenium and true mycelium in certain fungi, the flesh or trama of fungi, the sterile inner part of the cap or pileus of fungi.

contextus. Tissue.

contiguum. A continuous noninterrupted area.

continental shelf. The submerged shelf of land that slopes from the exposed edge of a continental land mass, the area where the abrasion by wave action takes place.

continental terrace. A portion of the continental shelf where the material worn away by wave action is deposited.

contingent symbiosis. The condition in which one plant lives inside another for shelter but is not parasitic.

continuity of protoplasm. The connection of protoplasts by threads passing through the cell wall.

continuous. 1. Uniform in structure or outline. 2. Without septa or joints. 3. Confluent. 4. With a common surface.

continuous sori. Fern sori which are confluent or fused.

continuous variation. A series of minute variations, variation shown by such slight individual differences between member specimens belonging to the same lineage that one specimen may shade into another.

contorted. Twisted together, overlapped, bent, convoluted.

contorted aestivation. The spirally folded or twisted overlapping arrangement of leaf buds, flower parts, or other organs around each other and their axis.

contortion. An abnormal twisting of branches or other organs.

contortoplankton. A floating mass of diatoms including *Chaetoceras contortum*.

contortuplicate. Contorted, folded, and twisted, as a morning-glory bud or a plicate leaf bud.

contra-clockwise. Counterclockwise.

contractile. Capable of contracting or being folded in close to the body.

contractile cell. Any cell in a sporangium or an anther wall which by hygroscopic action helps to open the organ.

contractile fiber cells. Cells which give rise to the contractile fibers.

contractile root. A somewhat fleshy root which, as it ages, develops transverse corrugations whereby it is shortened and pulls the plant deeper into the soil.

contractile vacuole. A pulsating reservoir in protozoa into which waste and water flow from metabolism to be expelled to the outside.

contractility. The capacity to alter spontaneously in volume or size, the ability to shrink.

contrary cross. A hybrid with reversed parentage.

contrary dissepiment. A partition not parallel but at right angles or nearly so with the valves of the pericarp.

control, biological. The introduction of natural enemies as a method of control.

control, experimental. The omission of one or more factors of an experiment in a check series in such a manner that the original observations may be checked.

control factor. Any factor which may increase or decrease the development of the organism being used in an experiment.

controls. The less immediate or remote influences which determine the character or amount of factors at work which influence the physical environment of organisms.

controls, geographic. The geographic factors that control biological activity in a given situation.

contusus. Bruised.

conus. A cone, a strobilus, a strobile.

convallarioid. Like *Convallaria*, the lily of the valley.

convariants. Individuals of equal age or the same generation which are likely to vary.

convergence. The development or possession of similar characters by plants or animals of different groups due to similarity in habit or environment.

convergent improvement. A method of bringing together strains of inbred lines to obtain desirable characteristics. The hybrids are backcrossed and the progeny are backcrossed in each inbred line. Selective backcrossing is continued for several generations until the desired characteristic is achieved.

converginervous. Said of simple veins diverging from the midrib and converging toward the margin.

conversion. 1. A change which is the consequence of the destruction and the subsequent progressive development of an area. 2. A modified sere.

convex-expanded. Of a pileus, changing from convex and tending toward flatness, the margin often remaining curved.

convexo-plane. Of a pileus, changing from convex when younger to flat convex when expanded; plano-convex.

convoluted. Coiled, folded, rolled so that one part is covered by another; refers to the lengthwise manner in which organs are wound around each other; cerebrose.

convoluted aestivation. The arrangement of the cotyledons in seeds or the flower parts or leaves in buds in such a manner that the parts are folded lengthwise over each other. *Convoluted* refers to the manner of the folding of the organ itself (a contorted corolla may or may not be convoluted).

convolutions. Surface contours which are coiled or twisted so as to resemble those of the brain or the intestines.

convolutive. Rolled up from the sides or longitudinally.

convolvulaceous. Related to or resembling *Convolvulus*, the morning glory.

conyzoid. Like *Conyza*, a genus of tropical composites.

co-ovarial. Derived from the cells of the same ovary.

copal. A hard resin obtained from tropical trees and used in varnishes.

copiosae. Species mixed with dominants in different proportions but always relatively common, an expression of frequency.

coplin jar. A small glass jar with corrugated insides which are used to support microscope slides containing prepared material during the staining process.

coppice. A dense growth of tree sprouts which has grown from the cut stumps of trees or their roots.

coppicing. In forestry, cropping a plantation by cutting the undergrowth every few years.

copra. The dried endosperm of the coconut from which coconut oil has been pressed.

coprophage. Molds or bacteria which live on feces or dung.

coprophagous. Feeding or living on dung, coprophilous, coprozoic.

coprophyte. A saprophytic organism growing in fecal matter or in the alimentary canal, a coprophil.

copulae. 1. Intermediate bands of cell walls in diatoms. 2. Any bridging or connecting structures.

copulant. An element or individual which copulates, such as a nuclear cell or a thallus.

copulated elements. See CONJUGATED ELEMENTS.

copulation. Conjugation, the union of sex cells, temporary sexual union involving the transference of sperms from the male into the female.

copulation tube. A conjugated tube.

copulative. Showing connections, said of dissepiments not readily separating from the axis or walls of the pericarp.

coque. A coccus.

coracine. Glossy black.

coracoid. Shaped like a crow's beak.

coralliflorous. With flowers resembling coral.

coralliform. Coral-like in form.

coralline. 1. Resembling coral in appearance. 2. Composed of coral. 3. Coral red. 4. Of algae, coralline refers to a calcareous algae or sea weeds of the family *Corallinaceae*.

coralloid. 1. Coral-like. 2. Having the consistency of coral. 3. Branching like coral.

coral spot. A fungus disease caused by the wound parasite *Nectria cinnabarina*.

corbicula. The pollen plate or pollen basket of a bee.

corbula. A stem with alternate branches rising upward and forming a pod-like structure.

corculum. The embryo or miniature of the future plant which is found in seeds, often the plumule and radicle between the cotyledons; a corcle.

cord. 1. Any cord-like structure. 2. The elongated stalk of some seeds. 3. A strand.

cord grass. 1. A fresh water or marsh-grass. 2. A grass with cord-like leaves, *Spartina*.

cord, umbilical. The funiculus.

cordaitean. Of or pertaining to the fossil genus *Cordaites*.

cordate. Heart-shaped.

cordate, clasping. With leaves which are heart-shaped at the base with the lobes overlapping around the stem.

cordate-hastate. Said of leaves intermediate in form between cordate and hastate approaching more nearly to hastate, shaped like a heart below with the apex arrow-headed.

cordate, oblong. Oblong with a cordate base.

cordate-ovate. Between cordate and ovate, approaching more nearly to ovate; of an oval heart shape, broad at the base.

cordate-sagittate. Between cordate and sagittate approaching more nearly to sagittate.

cordiate. Any species of *Cordaites*, a fossil tree.

cordifolious. With cordate leaves or heart-shaped leaves.

cordiform. Having a pointed tip and heart-shaped base (of ovate leaves).

cordilleran. Of or pertaining to the *Cordilleras*.

cord-shaped. Shaped like a funiculus.

core. 1. The hard central portions of the fruits of the apple family consisting of papery or leathery carpels which compose the ripened ovary, the seeds and integuments of a pome. 2. An axial strand of parenchyma in the haustorium of certain parasites.

coreansis. Of Korea.

coremial. Like the fungus genus *Coremium*.

coremiform. Forming a tight bundle of elongated elements, broom-like.

coremioid. Denoting a fasciated form, as *Penicillium* or *Coremium*.

coremium. 1. A rope-like strand of anastomosing hyphae. 2. A tightly packed group of erect conidiophores somewhat resembling a sheath of corn.

coreses. Dark-red broad discoid bodies found beneath the epicarp of grapes.

coriacellate. Somewhat leathery.

coriaceous. Of a leathery texture.

coridifolious. With leaves like the primulas, genus *Coris*; corifolious, coriophyllous.

coridospore. A conidiospore.

cork. A layer of dead cells formed on the outside of a stem or root having suberised walls which are relatively impervious to air and water. The cells are formed by a special cambium layer, the phellogen; the cork protects the inner living cells against dessication, mechanical injury, and attacks of parasites.

cork cambium. See PHELLOGEN.

cork cortex. The corky layers of the bark.

cork crust. A thick layer of corky cells consisting mainly of large, soft-walled cells with some intermingled narrow strips of flattened cells.

cork film. A layer of flattened corky cells two or three cells thick.

cork meristem. The phellogen.

cork porecork. A suberized portion of lenticels with intercellular spaces between the cork cells.

cork warts. Local formations of cork on leaves.

cork wood. A wood of very low specific gravity containing many large, thin-walled, parenchymatous cells.

corky envelope. A corky layer.

corky layer. The bast layer immediately beneath the epidermis which gives rise to cork, the epiphloem.

corky-ridged. With corky ridges or elongated warts on the bark of the twigs in such plants as bur oak, sweet gum, rock elm, etc.

corky scab. A potato disease caused by *Spongospora Solani*.

corky substance. A cell-wall substance which, without being lignified, withstands the action of concentrated sulphuric acid.

corm. A solid, fleshy, underground base of a stem, usually somewhat spherical in shape, covered with thin membranes. It serves for storage of reserve food materials and resembles a bulb in appearance but not in structure.

cormel. A secondary corm produced by old corms.

cormlet. An aerial corm or one borne in the inflorescence or in the leaf axils.

cormodes. Possessing an axis or trunk.

Cormogamae. A division for the *Characeae* and *Muscineae*.

cormogenous. Having a stem or corm.

cormoid. Like a corm.

cormophyllaceous. Referring to the ferns whose fronds are attached to the caudex.

cormophylogeny. The development of families or races showing evolutionary sequences based on corms and other underground parts.

cormophytasters. The mosses.

cormophyte. A plant which has a body differentiated into roots, stem, and leaves; the phanerogams and vascular cryptogams.

cormophytic association. An association dominated by cormophytes.

cormous. Bearing or producing corms.

cormus. A corm.

corn. 1. Any cereal grain plant. 2. The maize plant in America. See POPCORN.

cornaceous. 1. Allied to the cornel tree, *Cornus*. 2. Of a horny consistency.

corneous. Of a texture resembling horn, hard and very dense in texture.

cornet. A hollow horn-like growth, a growth having the general shape of a horn.

cornet-shaped. Cuculliform, hooded.

cornetum. An association of *Cornus*.

corniculate. Having a process or appendage like a little spur or horn, slightly or somewhat horned.

corniculiferous. Bearing horns or protuberances.

corniculum. A small horn-like part or process.

corniform. Horn-shaped.

cornigerous. Horn-bearing.

cornine. A bitter substance in the bark of *Cornus sanguinea*.

cornu. A horn or anything shaped like or resembling a horn.

cornua. A horn-like prolongation.

cornute. Horned or spurred.

cornute leaves. Leaves with a sudden projection of the midrib forming a spine-like outgrowth, often in a different plane.

cornutin. An alkaloid found in ergot which in the form of the citrate is used in medicine as a remedy in uterine hemorrhage.

corol. A corolla.

corolla. The inner circle of petals which is usually the conspicuous part of a flower. The usually colored corolla surrounds the stamens and pistils and is usually surrounded by a green circle of sepals, the calyx.

corollaceous. Of or pertaining to a corolla, petaloid.

corollate. Having a corolla.

corollet. A floret of a composite head or cluster.

Corolliflorae. A group of dicotyledons with the petals united; see SYMPETALAE.

corollifloral. Bearing a calyx, petals, and ovary inserted separately on the receptacle with the stamens inserted upon the corolla.

corolline. Like or belonging to a corolla.

corollule. A diminutive corolla, a floret as in a composite.

coromandelianus. Of or pertaining to Coromandel, India.

corona. 1. A crown or trumpet-like outgrowth from the corolla of a daffodil. 2. Any body which develops between the corolla and the stamens, as the ring of leafy outgrowths in campion. 3. An appendage on the tip of a seed or seed-like fruit, as the coma of milkweed or the pappus of a dandelion seed. 4. The crown of cells on the oogonium of *Chara*. 5. A crown, coronet, a cucullus.

corona seminus. A pappus.

corona staminea. An orbiculus or a corona formed from the transformation of stamens.

corona stipularis. The circle of stipules in *Chara*.

coronal. Pertaining to a corona or lying in the direction of the coronal suture.

coronal roots. Roots that spring from the stem just above the surface of the ground, as in wheat, Indian corn, and other grasses.

coronans. Borne on the summit of an organ, crowning or seated on the apex.

coronarius. Used for or belonging to garlands.

coronary. Crown-shaped or crown-like.

coronate. Crowned or having a corona.

coronate papillae. Growths with the appearance of crown-like cells at their apex.

coronet. A corona.

coronoid. Resembling the beak of a crow.

coronopifolioid. Resembling the foliage of *Plantago coronopifolia*, now merged in *Plantago macrorhiza*.

cornule. 1. A diminutive corona, a floret, a pappus, a cornula. 2. The calyx-like body which crowns the nucule of *Chara*. 3. A set of spines which terminate the fustules in diatoms.

corpora carnosa. The sporangia of certain fungi.

corpus. 1. Any homogeneous structure which forms part of an organ. 2. The inner core of the growing apex of a shoot.

corpus ligneum. The woody tissue in a plant or the corpus lignosum.

corpus medullare. The cellular tissue found in the pith.

corpuscular. Pertaining to or composed of corpuscles or small particles.

corpuscle. 1. A minute mass of protoplasm in a cell which has definite form and function. 2. A small body connecting the pollen masses in asclepiads by means of which the pollen becomes attached to insects to affect cross-pollination. 3. The sporangium in some fungi. 4. The central archegonium in *Coniferae*. 5. The corpusculum.

corpusculum vermiformia. A spiral vessel in a contracted, strangled condition.

correlation. 1. The mutual relationship between cause and effect of external factors in development of plants or plant communities, e.g., the amount of moisture or sunlight needed to support a type of plant or plant community. 2. The relationship between various structures of a plant, as root size and leaf development. 3. The effect of one plant on another. 4. A statistical study of the above and other factors.

correlation of growth. The condition in which one part is developed larger than usual with another part reduced.

correlative characters. Attributes which have been carried along as secondary or incidental features and which may have little significance to the present life of the organism.

correlative differentiation. The differentiation which is due chiefly to the interaction of different parts of an organism.

corrolaris. Having a corolla.

corrugated. With the surface coarsely wrinkled in even or irregular folds.

cor seminus. An embryo.

corsican moss. Dried algae, a mixture of dried seaweeds used medicinally as an anthelmintic.

corsicus. Corsican.

cortex. 1. A cylinder of parenchymatous cells lying between the epidermis and the starch sheath (the endodermis) in a young stem and between the piliferous layer and the endodermis in a young root. 2. A similar cylinder in the older stems and roots,

but less conspicuous. 3. A cellular coating on the outside of the thalli of some algae. 4. The outer layers of the thallus in lichens and in some fungi.

cortex parenchyma. The tissues found in the primary cortex, which in roots is composed almost wholly of parenchyma.

cortical. 1. Of or pertaining to the bark or cortex. 2. Living on bark.

cortical bark. The outer bark.

cortical bundle. A vascular bundle in the cortex of a stem or root.

cortical integument. The cortical layer.

cortical intrusion. The growth of external tissues into stelar or vascular structures.

cortical layer. 1. The investing layers of the bast system. 2. In lichens, a superficial and often double layer of cells forming a pseudoparenchymatous protective tissue at the surface of the thallous.

cortical pore. A lenticel.

cortical rays. The medullary rays found in the phloem.

cortical sheath. The entire primary bast bundle.

cortical stratum. The superficial layer of the lichen thallus.

cortical zone. The outer layer of living protoplasm.

corticate. Having a cortex, covered with bark, covered with an unbroken sheet of interwoven hyphae.

cortication. 1. The formation of cortex. 2. A covering of cells around the main threads of some algae.

corticole. Living or growing on bark, as some algae and fungi; corticolous.

corticose. Having or resembling bark.

cortina. 1. The cobwebby inner or partial veil in certain agarics. 2. Formerly the curtain which hangs down from the edge of the pileus.

cortinate. 1. Provided with or pertaining to the cortina. 2. Having a cobwebby veil covering the gills of an agaric.

cortusoid. Like *Cortusa*, a genus of alpine primulas.

coruscans. Vibrating or glistening.

corvine. 1. Pertaining to the crow. 2. Black.

corydalin. An alkaloid found in the root of *Corydalis tuberosa*.

corydaline. Resembling the genus *Corydalis*, of the poppy family.

corydalis. The common name given to any

plant of the genus *Capnoides*, now the genus *Corydalis*, a large genus of herbs.

coryletum. An association of hazels, the genus *Corylus*.

corylifolious. Having leaves like *Corylus*.

corymb. An indeterminate inflorescence consisting of a central rachis with pedicelled flowers along its sides (the marginal flowers blooming first) with the lower pedicels elongated resulting in a flat or somewhat rounded top.

corymbiflorous. Having flowers in corymbs.

corymbose inflorescence. Any inflorescence in which the outer flowers open first.

corymbulose. Having the flowers in little corymbs.

corynidia. Processes containing spiral threads sunk into the margin of the germinating leaf of ferns.

corynocalyx. A club-like calyx.

coryphad. An alpine meadow plant.

coryphile. A plant of alpine meadows.

coryphium. An alpine meadow formation or community.

coryphophilous. Growing in alpine places.

coryphophyte. An alpine plant.

coryphylly. A monstrosity in which the axis ends in a leaf which is sometimes colored.

coscinocystidium. A projecting tip of a coscinoid, a pseudocystidium.

coscinoid. A long, sieve-like, filamentous conducting element with sponge-like contents, found in the fungus *Linderomyces*.

cosere. 1. A series of unit successions in the same spot. 2. An organic entity.

cosmaesthesia. The sensibility to external stimuli.

cosmobia. Conjoined twins.

cosmophyllous. With leaves like *Cosmos*.

cosmopolitan. World-wide in distribution.

costa. A ridge or midrib of a frond or leaf.

costal nerved. With the nerves arising from the midrib.

costase. Two or more stases which supply a fossil record of former coseres.

costate. 1. Of gills, veined or ribbed. 2. Having one or more longitudinal ribs or nerves. 3. Fluted. 4. Having a costa.

costatovenosus. With the parallel side veins of a featherveined leaf much stouter than those which intervene.

costellate. With small ribs.

costrate. Having a layer of inorganic matter between stases.

costulae. The primary veins of fern segments.

coteau. A hilly upland which divides two valleys, the moraines (hills of glacial or ice deposits) which have characteristic vegetation.

co-terminal. Completing the production of flowers and fruit in the same growing season.

coterminous. Of similar distribution or coextensive.

cotidal line. A line delimiting all areas covered by a tide at any given time.

cotinifolious. With leaves like *Cotinus*, the smoke tree.

cotton. 1. The hairs or fibers of the seeds of the species *Gossypium*. 2. Any downy, cotton-like substance produced by plants.

cotton-grass association. An association in which *Eriophorum*, a sedge, is dominant.

cotylar. Cotyledonary.

cotyledon. The seed leaf, a leaf-like organ within the seed, a leaf-like structure folded within a seed in which food for the new plant is usually stored. The number of cotyledons in a seed is the basis for the primary divisions of the seed plants into monocotyledons and dicotyledons.

cotyledon trace. The common bundle in the stem proper extending to the cotyledon.

cotyledonary. 1. With cotyledons on the placenta. 2. Consisting of, having, or resembling cotyledons.

cotyledonoids. Protonema.

cotyliform. Disk- or wheel-shaped with an erect or ascending border.

cotyloid. 1. Leaf-shaped. 2. Shaped like a cup with a receptacle that is concave, sometimes to the extent of surrounding the carpels.

cotyloid cell. A large single cell which acts as a haustorial organ in *Avicennia officinalis*, a mangrove.

cotylophorous. With a cotyledonary placenta.

cotylvariants. The variations in the number of cotyledons.

cotype. 1. One of several specimens originally described without designation of one as the holotype. 2. An additional type-specimen. 3. A syntype.

coumarin. 1. The fragrant substance of the tonka bean, a white crystalline compound with a vanilla-like flavor. 2. A compound formed by sweet clover and other plants with the characteristic odor of clover. 3. Coumarine, cumarin.

couple-cell. A zygote.

coupling. 1. The association of characters in inheritance due to linkage. 2. The tendency of dominant characters to remain in association.

courbaril. A resin derived from *Hymenaea courbaril*, a leguminous tree which exudes resin used in varnish. The resin is often found underground at the base of the tree.

C.O.V. Cross over value.

covariation. Proportional growth or development, correlation.

coventry bell. The Canterbury bell, a flower.

cover. 1. The operculum. 2. A single species which covers an area.

cover cell. The apical cell of four cells in the neck of a young archegonium of bryophytes and pteridophytes.

cover class. See DOMINANCE CLASS.

cover crop. A crop grown primarily for the covering and protection of land, particularly in orchards after the final tillage in summer until the following spring when tillage recurs; a crop grown to prevent erosion or excess evaporation or to provide humus.

cover glass. A thin, flat glass disk or square used in preparing microscope slides to cover the specimen.

cover scales. The small scales arranged spirally and developed directly on the axis of a cone of the *Coniferae*.

coverage. See DOMINANCE.

covering plate. In ferns, the stegmata.

cowled. Furnished with or shaped like a hood.

crab. A type of malignant growth on larch caused by the mycelium of the fungus *Peziza*.

crab's eye. A type of bean.

cradina. A proteolytic enzyme found in the juice of the common fig tree, *Fiscus*.

cramesine. Of mixed or varied colors.

crampon. 1. An aerial root or rootlet for support in climbing. 2. An adventitious root.

cranberry. The bright red berry produced by an ericaceous plant of the genus *Oxycoccus*.

craspedodromous. Having veins running directly from the midrib to the margin of the leaf without dividing.

craspedote. Having a veil, as some agarics.

crassicaulis. Thick-stemmed.

crassifolious. Thick-leaved.

crassinucellatae. The plants in which the nucellus remains bulky until the embryo is formed.

crassipes. Thick-footed, thick-stalked.

crassulae. Thicker portions of the intercellular layer and the primary walls between primary pit fields (to replace Bars of Sanio and Rims of Sanio).

crataegifolious. Having leaves like *Crataegus*, the hawthorns.

cratera. A cup-shaped receptacle.

crateria. The ascidia which are derived from the surface of a leaf.

crateriform. Cup-shaped, crater-like.

craticular. At the stage in the life history of a diatom when new valves are formed before the old ones are lost.

crazy-weeds. Locoweeds, the poisonous pasture weeds *Astragalus* and *Lupinus*, which cause loco disease in stock.

creaming. The rising of protein particles in the cytoplasm like fat globules coming to the surface of milk.

creatospore. A plant with nut fruits.

creeper. A trailing plant which takes root frequently at the nodes throughout its length.

creeping stem. A rhizome growing flat on or beneath the ground and rooting.

cremeous. Cream-colored.

cremnad. A cliff plant.

cremnion. A cliff community.

cremnium. A cremnion.

cremnophilous. Dwelling on cliffs.

cremnophyte. A cliff plant.

cremocarp. A dry, seed-like fruit which is composed of two one-seeded carpels which are invested by an epigynous calyx and separated into mericarps at maturity; the characteristic fruit of the umbellifer family.

cremoricolor. Cream color.

crena. A rounded tooth or notch.

crenad. A plant growing in or near spring water.

crenate. Of leaf margins, with broad rounded teeth separated by narrow open spaces.

crenatiflorous. Crenate-flowered.

crenato-serrate. Having a scalloped edge with a combination crenate and serrate margin.

crenature. Any of the separate teeth on a crenate leaf, a notch or indentation between crenulations.

crenic. 1. Of springs and the water of their brooks adjacent to their source. 2. Pertaining to or designating a pale yellow, uncrystallizable acid said to occur in vegetable mold.

crenicolous. Dwelling in brooks fed by springs.

crenid. An acid in humus.

crenium. A community of plants around a spring.

crenophilous. Dwelling near a spring.

crenophyte. A plant which grows in or near a spring.

crenulate. With small crenatures.

crenule. A diminutive crena.

creophagous. Carnivorous, as applied to plants.

crepidatus. Sandaled, slippered.

crescograph. An instrument for measuring growth.

crest. 1. An apical appendage in some seeds. 2. A ridge on the summit of an organ.

crest, dorsal. The scale on the underside in some fan-leaved palms.

crest, ventral. The ligule on the upper side of some fan-leaved palms.

cresting. The graded forking of an organ.

cretaceous. 1. With the color and consistency of chalk. 2. A late Mesozoic geologic era.

creticus. Of Crete.

cretin. Referring to the monstrous *Lathyrus* flower with a straight stigma from a cleft in the keel.

cribal tissue. Tissue occurring in secondary phloem having no septa, slight longitudinal growth, thin walls, sieve plates, and living contents.

cribate. Cribrose or crobrose.

cribellum. The network of canals connecting the cells of *Volvox*.

cribose. Perforated like a sieve with small apertures of peristome teeth.

cribriform. Sieve cells.

cribriform tissue. Sieve cells and tubes or sieve tissue.

cribrose. Sieve-like with numerous small apertures, pierced like a sieve, cribrile.

cribrose cells. The sieve tubes.

crinate. Hairy, crested.

criniferous. Hairy.

crinite. Having long, weak hairs or bearded.

crinoid. Lily-like.

crinula. An elater.

crinus. Having stiff hair on any part.

crisp. 1. Wavy at the edge or curled. 2. Brittle.

crispabilis. Having the ability to curl up.

crispate. Crisp, crisped.

crispature. The state of a leaf that is much puckered and crumbled but less than bullate.

crispescens. Able to curl up.

crispifloral. Having curled flowers.

crisping. Having marginal incisions.

crisscrossing. A method of backcross breeding wherein selected offspring from mating A and B are crossed back to A; selected offspring from this mating are crossed back to B, and selected offspring from this mating are crossed back to A, etc.

crisscross inheritance. The inheritance in which maternal characters are transmitted to sons and paternal characters to daughters.

crista. 1. The envelope which protects the young palm leaves. 2. A terminal ridge, tuft, or crest.

cristaeform. With crested appendices.

cristagalli. The cockscomb flowers.

cristarc. A layer of cortical tissue whose arc-shaped cells contain twin crystals and are strengthened by sclerogen.

cristate. Bearing an elevated appendage resembling a crest, bearing elevated and toothed ridges.

critenchyma. The tissue of bundle sheaths, open or closed envelopes which accompany the fibrovascular bundles.

crithmetum. An association of samphire, *Crithmum maritimum*.

crithmifolious. Leaved like *Crithmum*.

critical. Requiring great discrimination and care in classifying.

crocate. Croceous.

crocatus. Saffron yellow.

croceous. Saffron yellow, a deep reddish-yellow.

crocin. The coloring matter producing the saffron yellow pigment.

crocosmaeflorous. Having flowers like *Crocosmia* (*Tritonia*), an African flower with the fragrance of saffron.

cromules. Chromules.

crook. A tendril.

crop hairs. Trichomes occurring in *Cordia* which are usually knobbed at the extremity and have the shape of a bird's crop.

crosier. 1. A young fern frond which is coiled or circinate in venation. 2. The crooked ascogenous hyphae prior to the formation of asci in certain ascomycetes.

cross. 1. A hybrid. 2. To mix through cross-pollination and cross-fertilization.

cross-armed. Brachiate.

crossbreed. A cross between two varieties of the same species; a half-breed, a mongrel, or a variety hybrid.

cross conjugation. See CONJUGATION, CROSS.

cross, double. Mutually crossed with parents mutually crossed.

cross-fertilization. Fecundation effected by pollen from a flower of another individual, fertilization resulting from cross-pollination, the union of an egg cell of one individual with the sperm cell of a different individual.

cross fragment. A fragment of the chromosome which has parted and crossed over to another chromosome.

cross-grained. Having grains or fibers running diagonally, transversely, or irregularly in tissue.

crossover. The interchange of genes usually linked in inheritance, probably due to the exchange of corresponding segments between corresponding chromatids of different chromosomes.

crossover, double. The interchange of linked characters which has occurred twice. It may be reciprocal or non-reciprocal, as between chromatids at meiosis.

crossover gamete. A gamete in which one or the other of a pair of homologous chromosomes has interchanged parts by crossing over, the interchange of factors in chromosomes as opposed to linkage.

crossover unit. A 1% frequency of interchange between a pair of linked genes.

crossover value. The percentage of gametes that show crossing over of a particular gene.

cross-pollination. The deposition of pollen from one flower to the stigma in another by artificial or natural means.

cross section. A section of a body at right angles to its length.

cross septation. The division of the terminal portion of a hypha or of a hyphal branch into a number of spore cells by a transverse septum, the formation of crosswalls.

crossties. Small veins in the leaf which run in a straight course between larger veins giving a ladder-like appearance.

cross timbers. The tree islands which cross the uplands at right angles to the river systems in Texas and Oklahoma.

cross-types. The tetrads in nuclear division.

crossed pits. The cells in the sclerenchyma with the slits on opposite walls at right angles to each other.

crossing. The operation or practice of cross-pollinating or crossbreeding.

crotch. The angle formed by the parting of two branches.

crotonetum. An association of *Croton*, plants of the tropics whose seeds are a source of a medicinal oil.

crotovinas. Animal burrows which have become filled with washed-in surface soil.

crown. 1. A corona. 2. The chaffy scales at the tip of an achene. 3. A tubular or ring-like appendage of a corolla. 4. A part of a rhizome with a large bud suitable for propagation. 5. A short root stalk. 6. A part of a stem at the surface of the ground. 7. The persistent upper leafy part of a tree or shrub. 8. The persistent base of a tufted perennial grass.

crown class. All trees in an even-aged forest-stand occupying a similar position in the crown cover or canopy.

crown cover. The canopy formed by the crowns of all the trees in a forest.

crown density. An expression of the relation of the crown area (or cover) to the land area involved measured by the extent of shading produced by tree crowns with due regard to the habitat of the species, site, and age. It is usually expressed in a decimal fraction of complete coverage.

crown gall. 1. A disease affecting the peach, apricot, grape, rose, and other nursery stock which often results in serious damage. 2. A conspicuous gall caused by the infecting agent.

crown of root. The point where root and stem meet.

crown rust. A disease of cereals caused by *Puccinia coronata*.

crown tuber. A tuber in which the top is stem and the lower part root.

crowned. 1. Having a crown or coronet. 2. Having a circle of projections around the upper part of the tube on the inside of a flower.

crozier. A crosier.

cruciate. Having the form of a cross with equal arms, cruciform.

cruciate basidium. A septate basidium in which the spindles of the dividing nuclei lie on a level across the basidium.

cruciate tetragonidia. The gonidia formed by two divisions at right angles to each other.

crucifer. Any plant of the *Cruciferae*, the mustard family, which has cross-shaped flowers.

cruciferous. Cross-shaped, as the four spreading petals of the flowers of the mustard family; cruciform, cruciate.

cruciform division. Promitosis.

crude fiber. The residues in the soil derived from the woody parts of plants.

cruentatus. Dark purplish red.

crumpled aestivation. The irregular arrangement or folding of the petals in the bud, as in the poppy.

crura. The divisions of the teeth of the peristome in mosses.

crural. Leg-shaped, of or pertaining to the thigh or leg.

crus-galli. 1. Any of the various parts likened to a leg or to a pair of legs. 2. Cockspur or cock's foot.

crustaceous. Crust-like or forming a brittle crust.

crustate. With a crust.

crustose. 1. Crust-like or closely attached to the substratum and lacking a distinct cortex. 2. Forming or having a crust.

crustuline. The color of toast, isabelline.

crymad. A plant of the polar regions, a crymophyte.

crymium. A barren formation in the polar region, a crymion.

crymophilous. Living in the polar barrens.

crymophium. A barren community of the polar regions.

crymophytic. Pertaining to polar plants.

cryophyte. 1. A glacial association of microphytes which is periodically exposed to ice-cold water. 2. A plant often buried in icy, marshy soil (a helophyte) or in water (a hydrophyte).

cryoplankton. Plankton inhabiting polar and glacial ice and snow, phytoplankton.

cryoscopy. A study for determining the freezing points of liquids or of the lowering of the freezing point of a liquid by dissolved substances.

cryotropism. The movements influenced by cold or frost.

crypt. 1. The front cavity of a stoma. 2. A simple gland. 3. A glandular cavity. 4. A tube.

crypta. Sunken glands or receptacles for secretions in plants with dotted leaves.

cryptanthery. The condition of being cryptanthous, i.e., with the stamens remaining enclosed in a flower.

cryptanthous. Cleistanthous, with the stamens remaining enclosed in the flower.

crypthybrid. 1. A hidden hybrid which appears to be a true species but its true reproduction is abortive. 2. A hybrid which shows unexpected characters upon reproduction. 3. A cryptohybrid.

cryptic coloration. Protective coloration to facilitate concealment.

crypto-. A prefix meaning hidden.

cryptobiotic. Said of the simple organisms which appear in geologic times but have left no trace of their existence.

cryptoblast. A kryptoblast.

cryptocarp. A fruit-like structure or the sporophytic phase in red algae.

cryptococcus. A yeast-like fungus which is pathogenic.

Cryptocotyledoneae. The monocotyledons.

cryptocotyledons. A group of syncotyledonous and monocotyledonous plants.

cryptocrystalline. Indistinctly crystalline as the indistinct or imperfect minute crystals in plant cells.

Cryptogamae. The large subdivision of the plant kingdom which includes plants which reproduce by methods other than by flowers and seeds; plants such as the thallophytes, bryophytes, pteridophytes, algae, fungi, etc., which reproduce by means of spores or other more primitive methods; the lower plants.

cryptogamic society. The lowermost layer of a thicket or forest which often consists of mosses, liverworts, lichens, and fungi.

cryptogamic wood. The woody portion in certain fossil *Cycadoxyleae*.

cryptogamist. A botanist who is a specialist in the lower groups of plants.

cryptogams. Flowerless plants which do not produce seeds, such as ferns, mosses, fungi, algae, slime molds, bacteria, viruses, etc.; the *Cryptogamae*.

cryptogams, vascular. The higher cryptogams which have a developed vascular system, such as ferns and their allies.

cryptogamy. The state of having concealed or barely perceptible fructifications.

cryptohybrid. A hybrid which displays unexpected characters.

cryptomere. A factor or gene whose presence cannot be inferred from an inspection but whose existence can be demonstrated by means of suitable crosses, a hidden recessive heredity factor.

cryptomerism. The presence of cryptomeres.

cryptonema. A small cellular thread produced in a cryptostoma.

cryptonervius. With the nervation hidden, as by the hairs or texture of a leaf.

cryptophyte. A plant which forms its resting buds beneath the surface of the soil, a cryptogamous plant.

cryptophytium. An association dominated by hemicryptophytes and geophytes.

cryptoplasm. The part of the protoplasm which seems to be devoid of granular contents.

cryptopore. An immersed stoma or a stoma located below the epidermis.

cryptoporous stomata. Guard cells more or less over-arched by subsidiary cells.

cryptopodsol, cryptopodzol. Infertile soil which must be chemically analyzed to identify as podsol.

cryptostoma. A flask-shaped cavity in the thallus of some large brown seaweeds containing hairs which secrete mucilage.

cryptostomate. Having a barren conceptacle that contains hairs or paraphyses, as in some algae.

cryptozoic. Living in darkness or in caves.

crypts. Stomatal pits.

crystal conglomerate. A cluster of crystals in a cell.

crystal dust. Very small crystals in plant cells.

crystal hairs. Crystals which project inwardly.

crystal idioblast. An epidermal cell of unusual size which contains crystals.

crystal receptacles. All kinds of cells which contain crystals.

crystal sac. An enlarged cell which is almost filled with crystals of calcium oxalate.

crystal sand. A mass of very small and more or less irregular crystals, crystal dust.

crystal sclerenchyma. The tissue of cells with thickened walls which contain single crystals.

crystal sheath. A sheath consisting of crystal cells.

crystal skins. The pouches surrounding crystals consisting of organic cell substances and connected with the cell wall.

crystallid. Crystalloid.

crystalline. Consisting of or resembling crystals (applied to various structures, as the frosted petals of the flowers of the ladies' tresses).

crystallochore. A plant distributed by glaciers.

crystallogenous. 1. Forming crystals. 2. Having crystals in the cells.

crystalloids. Proteinaceous bodies of crystalline form which occur commonly in the aleurone grains, protein crystals less truly angular than normal crystals which swell in water.

cteinomycetes. Fungi which exert only a chemical influence on their hosts.

ctenoid. Comb-like, pectinate.

cubebine. The active substance of *Piper cubeba*, the pepper plant.

cubensis. Cuban.

cubile. A bed.

cuculate. Hooded, with edges curved inward or rolled up like the point of a slipper, cowled, cucullate, cucular.

cucullate calyptra. A calyptra that is hood-shaped and split on one side.

cucullus. A hood or hood-like body.

cucumber. The fruit of *Cucumis sativus*, the common garden vegetable.

cucurbita. 1. Monoecious, tendriliferous, herbaceous plants. 2. A generic name of the squash and pumpkin.

cucurbitaceous. Like gourds, melons, or cucumbers.

cudbear. Orchil or litmus, a dye.

cul-de-sac. A tubular or bag-shaped cavity closed at one end.

culled forest. A cut-over forest from which certain species or sizes have been taken out.

cullion. A tuberous root, as that of certain orchids.

culm. The stem of grasses and sedges; a jointed stem of a grass usually herbaceous, which is hollow except at the nodes; the straw of grasses or sedges.

culmicole. Growing on grass stems.

culmiferous. Producing or bearing culms.

cultiform. A variety of plant which is cultivated.

cultigen. A plant known only in cultivation with no determined nativity.

cultispecies. A species which has risen under cultivation.

cultivar. A botanical variety that has originated under cultivation.

cultohybridoform. A cultivated hybrid of mixed parentage.

cultrate. Shaped like a knife blade, sharp-edged and pointed.

cultriform. Cultrate.

cultural degeneracy. The loss of virility attributed to cultivation or crossbreeding.

culture. 1. The cultivation of microorganisms or tissues in prepared media. 2. Experimental growth in the greenhouse or laboratory.

culture community. A community established or unduly modified from its original condition by man or cultural agencies.

culture medium. A substance or combination of substances that provides a suitable physical and chemical environment for the growth of bacteria and other organisms.

cumaphytism. The modification of a plant by wave action.

cumarin. Coumarin.

cumulate. Heaped in a mass.

cuneal. Wedge-shaped or triangular; cuneate, cuneiform.

cuneifolious. Having wedge-shaped leaves.

cuneiform. 1. Wedge-shaped or triangular. 2. With the stalk attached at the point.

cuniculate. Pierced with a long, deep passage open at one end.

cunix. The cambium region, the separable place which intervenes between the wood and bark in plants which have stems that increase in circumference.

cup. 1. In ascomycetes, a discocarp. 2. A concave involucre enclosing a nut. 3. A corona.

cupellea. 1. A colony of protoplasmic granules which are chemically or vitally active in a cell or which stain deeply. 2. A curved colony of merids.

cupiliform. Shaped like a small cup.

cupola-shaped. Nearly hemispherical, like an acorn cup.

cupping cell. A swollen hyphal attachment formed by some fungi which parasitize other fungi.

cupreate. Coppery.

cupreous. Copper-colored or with a coppery luster.

cupressiform. Shaped like a cypress.

cupressineous. Allied to or resembling *Cupressus*, the cypress.

cupressoid, appressed. Directed toward the apex but sometimes decurrent.

cupressoid, lepidoid. Broad and short.

cupula. A little cup.

cupular. Having a small cup or a cupule.

cupule. 1. A small cup, as the gemma cup of liverworts and the acorn cup. 2. A cup-shaped involucre in which the bracts are indurated and coherent, especially characteristic of the oak and other amentacious plants.

Cupuliferae. A group of amentiferous-dicotyledonous trees including the oaks, chestnuts, beeches, birches, and others now included in the *Betulaceae* and *Fagaceae*.

cupuliform. Dome-shaped, cup-shaped.

curarine. An alkaloid from curare obtained from several species of *Strychnos*.

curassavicus. Of Curaçao, in the West Indies.

curcumine. The coloring matter found in the roots of turmeric, *Curcuma longa*.

curd. In horticulture, the material composing the head of cauliflower or broccoli.

curl. A disease shown by curled and deformed leaves.

curled. 1. Folded or crumpled. 2. Composed of parallel chains in wavy strands, as in anthrax colonies. 3. Sinuous, wavy.

curly grain. A wavy pattern on the surface of worked timber due to the undulate course taken by the vessels and other elements of the wood.

curly greens. A leaf variety of *Brassica oleracea*.

currant. 1. A raisin of Corinth, the dried fruit of a small seedless grape used extensively in cooking. 2. A small, sour, red, white, or black berry used for jellies and jams. 3. The shrub which bears the fruit.

curtain. A cortina.

curvature, Darwinian. The effects produced on growing organs by irritation.

curvature, Sach's. Curvature resulting from a difference in growth on the two sides of a root.

curve-ribbed. Curvinerved.

curve-veined. Curvinerved.

curvembryonic. Said of a curved embryo and of all embryos except the atropous form.

curvicaudate. With a curved tail.

curvicostate. Having curved ribs or veins.

curvidentate. Having curved teeth.

curvifolious. Having curved leaves.

curvinerved. Having curved veins or nerves in the leaves.

curvipetality. The tendency of an organ to curve.

curviserial. In curved ranks or having oblique ranks, with leaf arrangement in which divergence is such that orthostrichies themselves are twisted slightly spirally.

curvuletum. An association composed of *Carex curvula*.

cuscutaeform. Like *Cuscuta*, the dodder, a twining leafless parasite.

cushion. 1. The swollen portion of a fern prothallium on which archegonia are borne. 2. An enlargement at the base of a leaf-petiole. 3. A pulvinus or tuft.

cushion plants. Plants with a finely divided and densely packed shoot system which forms hemispherical cushions, xerophilous plants in which excess evaporation is reduced by their dense growth into tufts.

cushioned fungi. Fungi growing in tufts.

cusp. A sharp, rigid point.

cuspidate. Like the point of a spear, as in the case of leaves tapering abruptly to a point.

cutaneous. Of or pertaining to the skin.

cuticle. 1. A continuous, non-cellular layer (covering the surface of the epidermis of the aerial parts of plants) consisting of cutin and containing no cellulose. 2. A water-repellant outer membrane of plant parts. 3. In fungi, a differentiated tissue consisting of a single layer of hyphae covering the pileus or stipe. 4. A pellicle.

cuticular crests. Formations of cuticle on the epidermis and lower sides of the leaf in certain *Mimosa*.

cuticular crown. A cuticle formation at the apex of papillae in some *Anonaceae*.

cuticular diffusion. The diffusion of oxygen and carbon dioxide through the cuticle of a plant.

cuticular epithelium. The tissue formed of cells of the epidermis and the primary cortex having thickened outer walls.

cuticular layer. A layer of cells immediately beneath the cuticle which is partially impregnated with water-resistant material.

cuticular peg. An intrusion of cuticle into the epidermal cells.

cuticular ridge. A ridge occurring on the flat epidermis between papillae.

cuticular striation. Fine ridges on the outside of the cuticle.

cuticular transpiration. Water loss through the cuticle.

cuticularization. The formation of cuticle or cutinization.

cuticularized cells. Cells provided with a cuticle and sometimes with cuticular layers.

cuticuloid. Resembling skin.

cutin. The waxy substance which impregnates the walls of the epidermal cells and causes them to be almost impermeable to water; the substance, allied to suberins, which repels liquids from passing through the cell walls.

cutinization. The deposition of cutin in external cells making the exposed cells almost impermeable to gases and liquids.

cutinized. Impregnated with cutin.

cutis. The smooth outer skin of the epidermis when thickened or otherwise modified, a pellicle.

cutocellulose. Modified cellulose or the cuticularized layers of the cell wall impregnated with cutin.

cutose. The transparent film covering the aerial organs of plants, cutin.

cut-over forest. A forest from which some or all of the merchantable timber has been cut, a logged-over forest.

cuttage. Propagation by cuttings.

cutting. A piece of stem, root, or leaf which when cut off and placed in contact with the soil or nutrients will form new roots and buds reproducing the parent plant.

cutting, partial. Selective cutting of forest trees.

cut-toothed. Deeply and sharply toothed, cut and toothed at the same time or incised or cut into sharp-pointed lobes.

cyaline. See CYANEOUS.

cyamium. A follicle which resembles a legume.

cyananthous. Having blue flowers.

cyanellous. Almost sky blue.

cyaneous. Bright blue, azure, near Paris blue, cornflower blue.

cyanescent. Turning dark blue.

cyanic flowers. Flowers whose color contains blue.

cyanin. The blue color characteristic of certain plants.

cyanocarp. A blue fruit.

cyanochrous. With a blue skin.

cyanocyst. A cell with starch and chlorophyll taking a blue stain.

cyanogenesis. The formation of cyanogen in plant tissues.

cyanohermidin. A blue compound obtained from *Mercuriales*; see HERMIDIN.

cyanophilous. Readily taking a deep blue stain.

cyanophoric. Yielding cyanogen, as the lotus.

Cyanophyceae. The blue-green algae.

cyanophyceous. Allied to or related to the blue-green algae.

cyanophycin. The blue coloring matter of algae.

cyanophyll. A bluish green coloring matter in plants.

cyanophyllous. Having bluish leaves.

cyanoplasts. Chromatophores or minute granular pigmentary bodies in the *Schizophyceae*, cyanoplastids.

cyatheaceous. Of the fern genus *Cyathea*.

cyathiform. Of a pileus, cup-shaped or bowl-shaped flaring above; shaped like a drinking cup.

cyathium. 1. A peculiar inflorescence in *Euphorbia*, a cup-shaped involucre with stamens and stalked gynoecium, each stamen and the gynoecium being a separate flower. 2. An inflorescence reduced to look like a single flower.

cyathoid. Cup-like or shaped like a wine glass.

cyatholite. A coccolith.

cyathus. 1. The cup-like bodies in *Marchantia* which contain propagules. 2. Any small cup-shaped cavity or organ. 3. A genus of nidulariaceous fungi.

cybele. An estimation of the distribution of plants in a given area, a floristic list, an annotated list.

cycaceous. Sago-gray, from *Metroxylon Sagu*, the sago palm.

cycad. Any plant of the family *Cycadaceae*.

cycadaceous. Belonging to or related to the family *Cycadaceae* or to the fossil cycads *Bennettitales*, cycadeous.

cycadalean. Relating to the *Cycadales*.

cycadean. Allied to or resembling the genus *Cycas*, cycadeoid.

cycadeoidean. Related to the fossil genus *Cycadeoidea*.

cycadofilicinean. Related to or allied to the *Cycadofilicineae*.

cycadophyte. A cycad-like or cycadaceous plant.

cycadopsida. A group including the cycads and cycadeoids.

cycas. Motile male gametes or the genus of gymnosperms of that name.

cyclamine. A substance found in the roots of *Cyclamen europaeum*.

cyclamineous. Like *Cyclamen*.

cyclarch. The first member of a whorl of leaves or flowers.

cycle. 1. The orderly succession of the various stages through which elements pass. 2. One turn of a helix or spire in leaf arrangement. 3. A whorl in the flower envelope.

cyclic. Having floral parts in whorls.

cyclocarpus. A fruit rolled up circularly.

cyclochorisis. The division of an axial organ into a sheaf of secondary axes.

cyclodesmic. Denoting the circular arrangement of the vascular system of typical dicotyledons.

cyclogenous. Having stems growing in concentric circles, exogenous.

cyclogens. Exogenous plants which show concentric circles in the cross-section of their stems, as the annual rings in tree trunks.

cyclogeny. The circular development of organs.

cyclotic interval. The space of the photrum with all grades of illumination up to direct sunlight capable of producing cyclosis or rotation of protoplasm in a plant cell.

cyclome. A ring-shaped cushion of anthers.

cyclopteroid. Having pinnules similar to those of *Cyclopteris*.

cyclosis. The rotation of protoplasm within the cell which takes place in one or more currents.

cyclospermous. Having the embryo coiled around the central albumen.

cyclosporous. Cyclospermous.

cyclura. The last member of a whorl.

cygneous. Said of the seta of mosses when it is curved in such a way as to suggest a swan's neck.

cylinder. A zone or region of a plant stem which is marked by a definite kind of tissue, such as cylinders of pith, wood or bark.

cylindraceous. In the form of a cylinder.

cylindranthera. A circle of anthers in the form of a tube; see SYNGENESIA.

cylindrenchyma. Tissue composed of cylindrical cells.

cylindrical stem. A stem which in cross section is circular and of uniform diameter for its entire length.

cylindrico-campanulate. Cylindrically bell-shaped.

cylindrobasidiostemonous. With anthers united in a cylinder, monadelphous.

cylindrogenic. Having a longitudinal expansion of amoeboid organisms.

cylindrostachys. A cylindrical spike.

cyma. A cyme.

cyma composita. A compound cyme, a definite or centrifugal inflorescence in which the ultimate parts (cymes) are also arranged in a cymose manner.

cymaphytic. Cumaphytic.

cymatium. An apothecium.

cymbaeform. Boat-shaped or cymbiform.

cymbaliform. Cymbal-shaped, as the corolla of the morning glory.

cymbellae. The elliptic locomotive bodies found in some algae.

cymbomorphous. Cup-shaped.

cyme. A few-flowered, flat-topped determinate inflorescence in which the central terminal flowers open slightly in advance of the outer ones. Most cymes appear on plants with opposite leaves or in axillary clusters.

cyme, helicoid. A cyme in which the lateral branches of the successive ramifications always occur on the same side, a bostryx, a drepanium.

cyme, scorpoid. A cyme in which the lateral branches always occur alternately on opposite sides, a cincinnus, a rhipidium.

cymelet. 1. A little cyme. 2. A division of a compound cyme.

cymiferous. Producing cymes.

cymbotryose. With cymes arranged in a botryoid manner similar to a cluster of grapes.

cymbotrys. A mixed inflorescence in which the primary inflorescence is botryose while the secondary is cymose, as in the horse chestnut.

cymose. Bearing or flowering in cymes.

cymose inflorescence. A cyme or other determinate inflorescence.

cymous umbel. An umbel having a centrifugal inflorescence.

cymula. 1. A little cyme. 2. A division of a compound cyme.

cymules. Reduced cymes, cymose clusters, verticillasters.

cynanchicous. Like the genus *Cynanchium*,

an asclepiad which is insect-pollinated by carrion flies; cynanchoid.

cynapine. An alkaloid found in *Aethusa Cynapium*.

cynaroid. Like *Cynara*, a composite.

cynarrhodion. 1. A fleshy, hollow fruit containing achenes. 2. An etaerio with achenes on a concave thalamus or receptacle, as the rose hip.

cynocephalic. Swan-headed.

cynodactyletum. An association of *Cynodon Dactylon*, dog's-tooth or Bermuda grass.

cyon. A scion or cion.

cynosuroid. Like *Cynosurus*, dog's-tail grass.

cyperaceous. Resembling or pertaining to the plants of the *Cyperaceae*, the sedges.

cyperographer. A student of the sedges.

cyphella. A kind of a pit found in the upper surface of the thallus of some lichens, a dimple.

cyphellate. Having cyphellae or pits.

cypress. Any pinaceous tree of the genus *Cupressus*.

cypress knee. A vertical growth from the roots of the swamp cypress which acts as a pneumatophore or breathing structure.

cypripedeous. Allied to or resembling *Cypripedium*, the lady's slipper orchid.

cypsela. An achene-like seed which is derived from an inferior compound ovary characteristic of the composites.

cyriodoche. A perfect or completed plant succession.

cyrrhus. A tendril.

cyst. 1. A sac or cavity, usually applied to a structure whose nature is doubtful. 2. Any cells of nonsexual origin in green algae which reproduce by germination. 3. A bladder or air vesicle in certain seaweeds. 4. An organism around which a resistant wall has formed.

cysta. A berry having a dry membranous envelope.

cysteine. A sulphur-containing amino acid.

cysticarpium. A cystocarp.

cystidium. A large inflated, sterile, thick-walled cell of the hymenial layer projecting beyond the basidia and paraphyses; a large spine-like body among the basidial cells; a cystid.

cystoblast. An organized structure within the living cell by means of which cell division takes place, a cytoblast.

cystocarp. A sporophore in algae (especially the *Florideae*), a cyst containing sexually produced spores, the fruit of the red algae which results from the fertilization of the carpogonium, a cryptocarp.

cystogenous. Producing a cyst.

cystolith. A concentration of carbonate of lime generally deposited on a little tongue or peg of cellulose projecting into the cells of certain plants; a mass of calcium carbonate found in epidermal cells, as in the nettles.

cystophore. The stalk upon which a cyst is borne, an ascophore.

cystosore. 1. A cell with a thick membrane enclosing a group of united cysts. 2. A group of sporangia formed after the division of a single protoplast. 3. A cystosorus.

cystosphere. A pouch or sac enclosing masses of secretions.

cystospore. An encysted zoospore or a carpospore.

cystotyle. A mucilaginous concretion which resembles a cystolith but is uncalcified and usually occurs in pairs.

cystula. A cistella or apothecium of a lichen.

cytase. An enzyme able to break down cellulose. Cellulase.

cytaster. A star-shaped achromatic figure (aster) which lies in the cytoplasm removed from the nucleus, an accessory aster.

cyte. 1. A cell. 2. An oocyte or spermatocyte in the early stage of the formation of gametes.

cytecdysis. The process of shedding useless structures or tissues, ecdysis.

cytenchyma. The fluid which separates from the cell protoplasm to form a vacuole, a vacuole.

cytioderm. 1. The cell wall or the outer layer of the protoplasm next to the cell wall. 2. The primordial utricle.

cytiokinesis. Cytokinesis.

cytioplasm. The cell contents of cytoplasm.

cytisine. An alkaloid found in *Cytisus*, a leguminose plant of the Mediterranean region.

cytoanatomy. The organization of the cell.

cytoaster. The aster in nuclear division.

cytoblast. 1. A colony of bioblasts which has lost its independent existence. 2. The cell nucleus.

cytoblastema. The formative material from which cells are produced and by which they are held together, protoplasm.

cytochemistry. The chemistry of the cell.

cytochorism. The division of living cells.

cytochrome. A pigment occurring in cells which probably plays a great part in respiration.

cytochylema. The contents of the cells composed of plasmochym and cytochym.

cytochym. The watery sap present in the vacuoles of the plant cell.

cytoclastic. Being harmful or destructive to the cell.

cytocoagulase. An enzyme in the cambium of *Prunus* which causes the deposit of insoluble gum in the autumn.

cytococcus. The nucleus of a fertilized egg.

cytode. A non-nucleated protoplasmic mass.

cytoderm. The cytioderma.

cytodieresis. Mitosis, karyokinesis, nuclear division of cells.

cytodynamics. The phenomena of motion, cell division, maturation, fertilization, death.

cytogamy. The sexual union or conjugation of cells.

cytogenesis. The origin and development of cells, cytiogenesis.

cytogenetic. Pertaining to cell formation or the genetics of the cell; cytogenous.

cytogeny. The sexual reproduction by germ cells or cytogenesis.

cytohyaloplasm. The protoplasm of the cell apart from any granules or foreign matter.

cytohydrolist. An enzyme which attacks and breaks up the cell wall by hydrolysis.

cytohydrolysis. The action of a cytohydrolist in breaking down cell walls.

cytokinesis. The cytoplasmic changes or division during mitosis, meiosis, and fertilization in contrast to the nuclear changes (karyokinesis).

cytolist. An enzyme which dissolves the cell wall.

cytolite. A cystolith.

cytology. The study of the internal structure, function, and life history of cells.

cytolymph. The more fluid contents of a cell, the cytoplasm.

cytolysin. A substance which includes cytolysis.

cytolysis. Cell dissolution or disintegration of cell walls.

cytome. The whole of the chondriosomes present in a cell.

cyto-mechanics. The physical properties and behavior in relation to mechanical stimuli.

cytomere. The part of the sperm (especially the flagellum), formed of cytoplasm only, a plastomere, a chondriomere.

cytomere cells. Cells formed by division of schizonts which themselves give rise to merozoites (the non-nuclear portions of sperms).

cytomicrosomes. The cytoplasmic granules or microsomes embedded in the cell protoplasm, chondriosomes which are not of nuclear origin.

cytomitome. The cytoplasmic threadwork in contradistinction to the nuclear threadwork.

cytomixis. The extrusion of chromatin from the nucleus of one pollen mother cell into the cytoplasm of an adjacent mother cell.

cytomorphology. The study of the external form and size of the cell.

cytomorphosis. The structural life history of cells.

cytophil. A cell with an affinity for toxic molecules.

cytophysiology. The study of cellular physiology.

cytoplasm. The substance of the cell body exclusive of the nucleus and certain granules.

cytoplasmic androgamy. The situation in which the male gamete is fertilized by the cytoplasm of the female gamete.

cytoplasmic gynogamy. The situation in which the female gamete is impregnated by the cytoplasm of the male gamete.

cytoplasmic inheritance. Variable inheritance which may be effected by environment because it depends on the cytoplasm and its inclusions rather than inheritance through the genes in the chromosomes.

cytoplasmic stain. Stain which brings out the inclusions in the cytoplasm in contrast to the nuclear material.

cytoplast. The cytoplasmic unit exclusive of the nucleus.

cytoplastin. The proteid which is thought to form the bulk of the cytoplasm.

cytoreticulum. The cytoplasmic thread or the cytomitome.

cytosarc. The body of the cell exclusive of the nucleus.

cytosine. One of the cleavage products of protein, one of the pyrimidine bases found in DNA.

cytosome. The cell body or cytoplasmic mass in contrast to the nucleus.

cytostatic. Having equilibrium in the cell.

cytotaxis. The rearrangement of cells due to stimulation or the mutual relations of cells or organisms.

cytotaxis, negative. The tendency of organisms or cells to separate from each other.

cytotaxis, positive. The tendency of organisms or organs to approach each other.

cytotaxonomy. A system of classification based on a study of cell structure.

cytothesis. The regenerative tendency of cells.

cytotropism. The mutual attraction of two or more cells; see CYTOTAXIS.

cytula. The fertilized ovum or parent cell.

D

D. B. H. Diameter breast high.

D. D. See HOMOZYGOTE.

DNA. Deoxyribonucleic acid, the material in the chromosomes believed to carry the inheritable information of the organism.

dacrydioid. Like *Dacrydium*, a coniferous tree of the tropics, a valuable lumber tree.

dacryoid. Rounded at one end and more or less pointed or narrowed at the other, somewhat pear-shaped, or tear-shaped; see LACHRYMIFORM.

dactyl. A finer or the ultimate ray of a branchlet of *Nitella*, a green alga.

dactyliferous. Having finger-like appendages.

dactylorhiza. The forking of roots.

daedalean. Of or pertaining to the polyporous genus of fungi *Daedalea* or to the labyrinthiform pores which characterize it.

daedalenchyma. The tissue of fungi which is made up of entangled cells.

daedaleous. 1. Having an irregular wrinkled, plaited surface. 2. Having elongated, sinuous tubes or pores, as in the genus *Daedalea*. 3. With leaf-apices which are irregularly jagged but not arcuate. 4. Labyrinthine, daedaloid, daedalioid.

daffodil. A narcissus with large yellow single or double flowers.

dahlia. The common name for the showy flowers of the genus of that name.

dahline. A substance similar to starch which is found in the tubers of the genus *Dahlia*.

dahuricus. Of or related to Dahuria or Dauria in Siberia near the frontier of China.

daikon. Radish, *Raphanus sativus*.

dal. The pigeon-pea, *Cajanus indicus*.

dalmaticus. From Dalmatia or the eastern side of the Adriatic Sea.

damascenus. Of Damascus.

dammar. A hard resin from *Agathis loranthifolia* (*Dammara orientalis*, a coniferous tree of southeast Asia).

damping. A cultivator's term for premature decay in plants, especially in young seedlings.

damping off. The disease of seedlings in seedling beds visible because of the collapse of the seedlings (ascribed to the fungus *Botrytis vulgaris* or *Phythium*).

dandelion. *Taraxacum officinale*, the common weed.

daphnin. A bitter substance found in the genus *Daphne*.

daphnoid. Like the genus *Daphne*.

dark seed. A seed which will germinate only if kept in the dark at the time when other conditions make germination possible.

Darwin. An English naturalist (1809-1882) who publicized the theory of evolution by natural selection; see KNIGHT-DARWIN LAW.

darwinian. Of or pertaining to Darwin or to Darwinism.

darwinian curvature. The bending induced by the irritation of any foreign substance close to the apex of the root.

Darwinism. Evolution in accord with Darwin's theory that the origin of species has taken place by natural selection.

dasheen. An edible tuberous-rooted taro, *Colocasia*.

dasyacanthous. Having thick spines.

dasyanthous. Thick-flowered.

dasycarpous. Thick-fruited.

dasycladous. Compactus, thick-branched.

dasyphyllous. 1. With hairy leaves. 2. With thick leaves. 3. With crowded leaves.

dasystemon. A thick stamen.

date. The fruit of the palm *Phoenix dactylifera*.

datiscin. A substance having the appearance of grape sugar obtained from *Datisca cannabina* which is used as a yellow dye.

daturine. An alkaloid from the genus *Datura*.

daucoid. Like the genus *Daucus*, the carrot.

Dauerhumus. Humus which does not decay, but resists attacks by microorganisms.

Dauergesellschaft. A permanent community.

Dauermodifications. Permanent changes, as cytoplasmic inheritable changes which may be brought about by some treatment.

daughter. An offspring of the first generation with no reference to sex, as daughter cell, daughter nucleus, etc.

daughter cell. Any young cell derived from the division of an older cell (the mother cell).

daughter chromosome. A chromosome which has been derived from the division of an original one; see CHROMATID.

daughter skein. The stage in nuclear division at which the chromatin is in a more or less reticulated condition.

daughter spore. A spore produced directly from another spore or upon a promycelium.

daughter star. One of the groups of chromatic filaments at the poles of a dividing nucleus, the two together with the connecting spindle constituting the dyaster stage.

dauricus. Dahuricus.

davallioid. Related to or like the fern genus *Davallia*.

davuricus. Dahuricus.

daya. A poorly drained area in Algeria, slightly undulating but not salty.

day degrees. A computation to determine the requirements to accomplish a given biological phenomenon: a multiple of the number of days times the number of degrees above or below a threshold.

daylight. In ecology, solar radiation, diffuse sky radiation, and radiation variously reflected from trees.

day plant. A plant requiring a certain number of hours of daylight to develop or blossom.

day position. The position of the leaves during the day.

day sleep. The folding together of leaflets of a compound leaf when exposed to bright light bringing together the surfaces which bear most of the stomata and checking the loss by evaporation from the plant.

dead knot. A knot in timber which is partially or wholly separated from the surrounding wood.

deaf. 1. Wanting essential characteristics. 2. Having imperfect fruit, barren, unproductive, sterile, empty, deadened.

deaf seeds. Imperfect grass seeds.

dealbate. Covered with an opaque white powder, appearing whitewashed, whitened.

deammonification. The reduction of ammonia by soil bacteria.

deassimilation. The conversion of food into digested products in the process of catabolism, catabolism.

death. The cessation of all vital functions without the capability of resuscitation.

death-point. 1. The point at which a spore is rendered permanently incapable of germination. 2. The temperature above which or below which an organism cannot exist.

deasotofication. The action of deasotobacteria in the reduction of nitrogenous substances.

debris. The mixture of leaves, twigs, wood, etc., covering a forest floor.

deca-. A prefix meaning ten.

Decagynia. An obsolete Linnaean order including those flowers which have ten pistils or styles.

decalcify. To treat with acids for the removal of calcareous matter.

decamerous. Having the parts arranged in tens.

Decandria. A class of plants having ten stamens.

decapetalous. With ten petals.

decaphyllous. With ten leaves or segments.

decaploid. Having five double sets of chromosomes.

decarinous. Having ten stamens and one pistil.

decasepalous. Having ten sepals.

decaspermal. Having ten seeds.

decay. 1. The decomposition of dead plant and animal bodies by aerobic saprophytes. 2. The gradual passing from a more or less sound, prosperous, or perfect state to one of imperfection, adversity, or dissolution.

decemdentate. With ten teeth, as the capsule of *Cerastium.*

decemfid. Cut into ten segments.

decemfoliate. With ten leaves.

decemjugate. Having ten pairs of leaflets.

decemlocularis. Having ten cells in an ovary.

decempartite. Divided into ten lobes.

deceptive fly plant. A flower which seems to offer much honey but the apparent glands are dry.

deciduilignosa. Communities of woody plants with protected buds which lose their leaves during unfavorable periods.

deciduous. Falling off at certain seasons or stages of growth; applied to plants which lose parts which fall away, such as leaves, petals, sepals, flowers, etc.; applied to trees which are not evergreen. See CADUCOUS.

Deckunsgrad. The percentage of cover or area. See COVER, DOMINANCE.

declinate. Bent downward, as the stamens in many flowers; directed downward from the base.

declivate. Sloping, declivous.

decoction. An extract obtained from a substance by boiling.

decollate. Having the spine broken or worn off, lacking an apex of the spine.

decolorate. Without color, having lost its color, decolored.

decoloration. The absence or removal of color.

decomposed. 1. Separated into constituent parts. 2. Subjected to decay. 3. Not in contact and not adhering. 4. A term applied to the cortex of the gelatinous, indistinct, or amorphous hyphae of lichens. 5. Divided or compounded several times.

decomposite. Decompound.

decompound. Having divided leaflets compounded more than once, pinnated twice.

deconjunction. The early separation of the network of chromosome threads in meiosis, i.e., early in the prophase.

decorans. Adorning, staining.

decorticated. Destitute of bark, debarked.

decortication. The act of stripping off the bark, rind, hull, or outer coat.

decorous. Elegant, comely, becoming.

decreasingly pinnate. Decreasing in size from the base upward.

decumbent. Reclining at the base but with the top or tips upright; curved upward from a horizontal or inclined base; said of stems lying on the ground but tending to rise at the tips.

decuple. 1. Having ten sets of chromosomes. 2. To multiply by ten.

decurrence. The act of running or extending down or backwards.

decurrent. 1. Of a gill, descending or sloping down the stem. 2. Applied to an organ extending along the side of another. 3. Said of the leaves continued downward on the stem like a wing, as in thistles. 4. Extending below the point of insertion.

decurrent leaf. A leaf with the two edges continuing down the stem like wings.

decursive. Decurrent, running down.

decursively pinnate. With the leaf seemingly pinnate but the leaflets decurrent along the petiole.

decurtation. The spontaneous fall of branches.

decurved. Bent down, deflexed, curved downward.

decussate. In pairs alternately crossing at right angles; applied to leaves and branches arranged in pairs and alternately crossing each other or growing out from the main stem at different angles.

dedifferentation. The loss of differentiation with an apparent approach to the embryonic condition, a return to the embryonic condition.

dediploidization. The process of inducing the development of haploid cells from cells with double the number of diploid chromosomes.

dedoublement. The production of two or more organs in the position of one, branching, doubling, chorisis, deduplication.

deducens. Leading down, as the conduction surface in the pitchers of *Nepenthes*.

deduplication. The production of two or more organs by congenital division, chorisis, dedoublement.

defarination. The suppressed or greatly decreased formation of starch.

defensive. Serving to defend or to protect, as the proteid substances which destroy bacterial toxins in organs or parts of organs in various plants and animals.

deferent. That which carries or conveys.

deferred shoots. 1. Shoots which arise from dormant buds when a stem or branch has been destroyed. 2. Shoots which are produced by buds which have remained dormant for a long time, delayed shoots.

deferricication. The reduction of iron by iron bacteria.

defertilization. Depollination, as when insects clear away the pollen.

deficiency. 1. The loss or deletion of a segment of a chromosome from the diploid complement. 2. The state or quality of being deficient.

deficiency diseases. Diseases which are caused by the lack of vitamins or minerals in diet.

definite. 1. Having a precise or constant number of plant parts, particularly of stamens. 2. Having fewer than twenty stamens (i.e., a number which can be easily counted).

definite growth. The season's growth which ends in a well-formed bud.

definite inflorescence. An inflorescence in which the axis ends in a flower.

definite variation. Any change taking place in a definite direction in the history of a race.

definitive. Fully developed.

definitive nucleus. A nucleus resulting from the fusion of one nucleus from the micropylar end and one from the chalazal end of the embryo sac.

defixed. Immersed.

deflected. Bent, turned abruptly downward, turned aside.

deflexed. Decurved, bent sharply downward or outward, bent gradually downward through the whole length.

deflocculation. The disintegration of small lumps of clay to form a cloudy sticky solution which drastically changes soil structure.

deflorate. Past the flowering state, as an anther after it has lost the pollen.

deflower. To deprive of flowers.

defluent. Running downward, flowing down.

defoliate. Deprived of leaves, having dropped the leaves.

deformation. An alteration from or malformation of the normal state.

defossate. Dug, hidden.

degenerate. 1. Degraded or reverted to an earlier function or form. 2. To undergo progressive deterioration.

degermed. Deprived of an embryo.

degradation. 1. The situation in which the less differentiated and simpler structures take the place of more elaborate structures. 2. The retrograde metamorphosis from complex to simpler forms.

degradation product. The result of catabolism.

degressive. Tending toward degeneration.

dehisce. To open spontaneously for the escape of seeds, spores, pollen, etc.

dehiscence. 1. The natural opening of a fruit capsule or anthers by valves, slits, or pores. 2. The act of splitting open.

dehiscence papilla. The primordial projection which develops a dehiscent pore on the zoosporangium of the primitive fungi *Blastocladiaceae*.

dehydrase. A plant enzyme which induces the reduction of substances.

dehydration. 1. The loss of water. 2. Depriving of water by the use of alcohol, calcium chloride, or some other dehydrating agent.

dehydrogenase. An enzyme produced by some bacteria which catalyzes oxidation by the removal of hydrogen.

deinopore. A cell bridge.

dekasome. Decaploid.

delamination. The division of cells to form new layers or the cleavage into plates or layers.

delayed inheritance. The continued inheritance of a strong character which is passed on through the female parent.

deletion. 1. The loss of a segment of a chromosome from the complement. 2. The act of deleting, blotting out, or erasing.

delignification. The destruction of lignin in plant material by the action of fungi or by an enzyme which breaks down the structure of the wood.

delila. Any color form of *Antirrhinum* with an ivory tube and magenta or crimson lips.

deliquesce. 1. To ramify into fine divisions, as the veins of a leaf or the trunk or branches of a tree. 2. To liquefy, as in the case of some fleshy fungi.

deliquescent. 1. Absorbing water and becoming liquid. 2. Having a large number of fine branches or branching so that the stem is lost in the branches.

deliquescent type. A plant which has its greatest diameter in the upper half.

delphine. An alkaloid present in *Delphinium staphisagria*.

delphinidin. The blue pigment in delphinium flowers.

delphinifolious. With leaves like a delphinium.

delta-leaved. Having triangular leaves.

deltoid. Broadly triangular or delta-shaped.

dematioid. 1. Like the genus *Dematium* in having a felted layer of hyphae bearing perithecia. 2. Black and cobwebby with a dark felted layer of *hyphae*. 3. Dematoid.

dematious. Black and cottony.

demersus. Subaqueous.

demicyclic. With a life cycle lacking only uredia.

demidate. Dimidiate.

demineralization. The removal of extraneous

matter from fossils by the action of hydrofluoric acid.

demoid. Abundant.

demiss. Depressed, low, weak.

demulcent. Softening.

denaturation. Reducing the solubility of a protein by changing it chemically or by heating it to alter its structure.

dendrad. Any orchard tree.

dendriform. Tree-like, tree-shaped, branched like a tree.

dendrio-thamnode. A lichen with a thallus branched like a bush.

dendrite. A fine branch.

dendritic. With a branched appearance, branched like a tree.

dendrium. An orchard formation.

dendrocolous. Dwelling on trees, epiphytic.

dendrogram. A graphic representation of the relationships between related organisms, a family tree.

dendrograph. An instrument used to measure the periodical swelling and shrinking of tree trunks.

dendroid. Resembling a tree.

dendrolite. A petrified or fossil plant or part of a large tree.

dendrologist. A student of trees.

dendrology. The study of trees and shrubs.

dendron. A tree.

dendrophilous. Dwelling in or inhabiting orchards.

dendrophysis. A paraphysoid structure of *Cyphellaceae* which is covered or spotted with crowded, branched spines of various lengths.

dendrophyte. An orchard plant.

denitrification. The freeing of elementary nitrogen from nitrogenous materials in the soil through the action of bacteria which are able to breakdown nitrates and nitrites.

denizen. A plant suspected of foreign origin though maintaining its place; an exotic.

dennstaedtioid. Like the fern *Dennstaedtia*.

densiflorous. Densely flowered.

densifolious. Densely leaved.

density. The relative degree to which vegetation covers the ground surface.

dentate. Having teeth; having a toothed margin; with teeth usually pointing outward; with sharp spreading, rather coarse indentations or teeth.

dentate-ciliate. With dentate and fringed margins.

dentate-crenate. With somewhat rounded marginal teeth.

dentate-serrate. With indentations between dentate and serrate.

dentate-sinuate. Having broad, shallow sinuses between the teeth of a dentate margin.

dentation. The arrangement or direction of the marginal teeth of a leaf.

dentato-ciliate. Having the margin dentate and tipped with cilia.

dentato-laciniatous. Having the teeth irregularly extended into long points.

dentato-serratous. With the teeth tapered and pointing forward.

dentato-sinuate. Scalloped and toothed.

denticle. A small leaf or projecting point.

denticulate. Finely toothed.

denticulations. Small processes or teeth.

denticuligerous. Bearing little teeth.

dentinal. Of or pertaining to dentine.

dentoid. Tooth-shaped.

denudation. 1. The wearing away of the surface of land by water. 2. The removal of the surface covering.

denuded quadrat. A permanent quadrat, usually one meter square, from which all vegetation has been removed so that vegetative invasion may be studied.

deoperculate. Without a lid or operculum.

deoxyribonucleic acid (DNA). The principal, very complex organic acid of the chromosomes, the hereditary material of the cell. It is made up of deoxyribose (a sugar), phosphoric acid, two pyrimidines (thyamine and cytosine), and two purines (adenine and guanine).

depauperate. 1. Undeveloped because of the lack of favorable conditions. 2. To be impoverished as if starved. 3. Diminutive, dwarfed.

depea. A cell with a cap capable of taking in nourishment.

dependent. Hanging down.

dependent communities. Species depending on the presence of more highly evolved communities, as epiphytes in forest communities.

deperulation. The process of throwing off the bud scales in leafing.

deperulation, calyptral. The process of throwing off the calyptra.

deperulation, tubular. The process of throwing off leaf-bud scales but leaving a collar at the base of the shoot.

depigmentation. The destruction of the color in a cell, the removal of pigment from cells or tissues.

depilation. The natural loss of hairy covering by plants as they mature.

deplanate. Flattened.

deplasmolysis. The replacement of liquids by osmosis following the dehydration of the tissues.

depletion. 1. The act of depleting or state of being depleted. 2. The enzyme digestion of the reserve material in the endosperm.

depollination. The eating or brushing off of pollen from anthers by insects.

deposit. 1. A secondary growth on the cell wall more or less covering it. 2. Fresh soil left by flood waters or wind.

deposition, progressive. The continuing process of depositing.

deposition, retrogressive. The gradual removal of fresh earth.

depressant. Anything that lowers functional or vital activity.

depressed. 1. Of a pileus, having the central portion lower than the margin. 2. Having the gills or tubes of fungi shorter in depth next to the stipe.

depressed, globose. Globular with the poles slightly flattened.

depressio-dorsalis. With a depression in the spores of some agarics extending along the back of the spore.

depressio-hilaris. With a depression on a seed above the hilum around the point of attachment.

depresso-truncatus. Having a blunt or rounded apex with a small notch, retuse.

deproteofication. Decay and putrefaction caused by the action of the deproteobacteria.

depside. A product formed from hydroxy-aromatic acids by the condensation of the carboxyl group of one molecule with the phenol group of a second molecule. Depsides are probably concerned with the oxidation of fats and proteins inside plant cells.

depurated. Purified, cleansed.

derased. Rubbed off, smooth.

deregularis. Slightly irregular.

derivative hybrids. 1. Hybrids resulting from the union of a hybrid with one of its parents or its union with another hybrid. 2. Hybrids crossed with one or both hybrid parents.

derived. Alien, coming from other communities.

derived organization. The final stage of development of an organism.

derma. The surface of an organism, bark, rind, or skin.

dermacalyptrogen. A meristematic layer present in the tip of the root of many dicotyledons which gives rise to the root cap and to the dermatogen; the histogen which produces the root cap and the root-epidermis in phanerogams. A dermatocalyptrogen.

dermal appendage. Any outgrowth from the epidermis.

dermal tissue. The tissue composing epidermis and periderm.

dermatine. Living on the bark or epidermis.

dermatioid. Skin-like in function or appearance.

dermatocalyptrogen. Dermacalyptrogen.

dermatocyst. An inflated hair on the surface of the sporophore of young agarics; a dermatocystidium.

dermatocystidium. A cystidium on the cuticle or pellicle.

dermatogen. A hollow sheet of meristematic cells one layer thick covering an apical growing point and giving rise to the epidermis.

dermatophyte. Any fungus parasitic on the skin of man or animals.

dermatoplasm. The protoplasmic content of the cell wall in plants.

dermatoplast. A protoplast having a cell wall.

dermatosome. One of the vital units which unite with protoplasm to form the cell wall or membrane; one of the minute portions into which a cell wall can be resolved by treatment with dilute hydrochloric acid followed by heating.

dermis. A distinctly marked layer above the upper cortex which is composed of flattened cells, the derma.

dermoblast. The layer of the mesoblast which gives rise to the derma.

dermoblastus. The cotyledon which is formed by a membrane which bursts irregularly.

dermocalyptrogen. Dermacalyptrogen.

dermoplast. A monoplast surrounded by a membrane.

dermosymplast. A group of energids, as a latex vessel.

descendant. Standing out from the stem below the horizontal.

descending aestivation. Aestivation in which each segment overlaps the one anterior to it.

descending axis. A root system, a primary root.

descending metamorphosis. The substitution of organs of a lower grade, as stamens for pistils.

descending sap. The soft mucilaginous stage of the cambium.

deschampsietum. An association of *Deschampsia*, a genus of grasses.

desciscent. Leaving, deviating.

descriptive botany. The branch of botany dealing with the systematic description or diagnostic characteristics of plants.

desegmentation. The fusion of segments which were originally separate.

desensitize. To rid of susceptibility of anaphylaxis.

desert. A region with little precipitation and consequently with scant vegetation, such as a steppe, a tundra, a dune, a fellfield, etc.

deserticolous. Inhabiting the desert.

desertion of host. Lipoxeny.

desinens. Ending or closing, as the termination of a lobe.

desmid. A unicellular alga of the *Desmidiaceae*.

desmidian. Related to or allied to the *Desmideae*.

desmidocarp. A specialized structure in *Balbiania*, the fertilized trichogynial cell dividing transversely and each daughter cell in turn branching with terminal oospores.

desmobrya. The division of ferns in which the fronds are adherent to the caudex.

desmochondria. Microsomes.

desmogen. Meristematic or growing tissue.

desmogen, primary. The embryonic tissue from which vascular tissue is afterwards formed.

desmogen, secondary. Tissue formed from the cambium and afterwards transferred into permanent vascular strands.

desmoncoid. Like *Desmoncus*.

desmoplankton. Plankton united into bands or ribbons.

desmos-. A prefix meaning bound or chained together.

desoxyribose nucleic acid. See DEOXYRIBO NUCLEIC ACID, DNA.

despumate. To throw off in froth or scum.

desquamate. 1. Scaleless. 2. Peeled off in the form of scales.

desquamation. The separation or shedding of the cuticle or epidermis in the form of flakes or scales.

destarched. Deprived of starch, as by translocation.

destructive metabolism. The chemical changes which take place during the degeneration of tissues.

destructive parasite. A parasite which seriously injures or destroys its host.

desulphobacteria. Bacteria which carry on the process of desulphofication.

desulphofication. The reduction of sulfates and sulfites by desulfobacteria.

desynapsis. The premature separation of dividing chromosomes before the normal metaphase separation.

detassel. To remove the tassel, as in corn.

detergible. Removable, breakable.

determinant. The unit of heredity, the spearate material particles in the germ cells.

determinants of heredity. The determiners carried in the zygotes.

determinate. 1. Having a fixed, definite limit. 2. Arrested in development. 3. Of an inflorescence, with all the flowers opening at about the same time or the central ones a little in advance. 4. Ending with a bud.

determinate growth. The season's growth ending with a bud.

determinate inflorescence. An inflorescence in which the primary axis is terminated by a flower.

determination. 1. The assigning of any plant to its proper place in the classification. 2. Bringing or coming to an end.

determinator. 1. A heterothallic ascomycete with haploid mycelium which contains potentialities of both male and female sexes. 2. A gene which causes the mycelium or thallus to act either as the male or female sex at the point of fruit body formation.

determiner. The unit of inheritance, a gene, a factor.

detersile. 1. Removable and coming off in such a manner as to leave the stipe clean.

2. Readily falling or easily cleaned off, as the wool on young branches.

detersive. Having the power to clean.

detrivorous. Feeding on animal wastes such as scales, hairs, feathers, wax, etc.

deustate. Scorched.

deuter cells. The row of large parenchymatous cells, empty or containing starch, which occur in the middle nerve of mosses.

deuteroconidia. Spore-like cells resulting from the division of protoconidia in dermatophytes.

deuterogamy. Any process which replaces normal fertilization, as nuclear fusion superposed upon and subsequent to the sexual fusion; secondary pairing.

deuterogonidium. A gonidium in the second generation of a transitorial series.

Deuteromycetes. The Fungi Imperfecti.

deuteroplasma. Paraplasm, deutoplasm, metaplasm.

deuteroproteose. A secondary product from the digestion of the nitrogenous material of plant cells.

deuterostrophies. Spirals of a third degree in the development of leaves.

deutogenotypic. Isogenotypic.

deutoplasm. The more liquid part of the cell contents (the cell sap and its granules) exclusive of the protoplasm; deuteroplasm.

deutoplasmic. Of or pertaining to deutoplasm.

deutoxylem. Metaxylem.

development. The growth or unfolding of the individual from the embryo to maturity.

developmental index. See DEVELOPMENTAL UNIT.

developmental rates. The speed and/or the completeness of development over a known period of time.

developmental total. The sum of the developmental units at the time of completion of a stage in the life history of a community, the number of temperature-humidity-time developmental units required to complete a stage or life cycle.

developmental unit. The difference of development between that produced in one hour at a given degree of medial temperature and the amount produced at the next higher or lower degree as shown by the difference in time to complete a given stage.

deviation, probable. Probable variation.

Devonian. The later Middle Paleozoic geological period.

dewberry. A native species of running, trailing blackberries which root at the joints or tips, mostly *Rubus flagellaris*.

dew leaves. Leaves that slope up and catch dew.

dew point. The temperature at which dew is formed.

dew rust. A discoloration on leaves caused by dew.

dexiotropic. 1. Right-handed or clockwise. 2. Having clockwise spiral cleavage of cells. 3. Having clockwise whorls.

dextrad. Toward the right side, dextral.

dextran(e). A gummy carbohydrate found in the unripe sugar beet and sometimes formed by bacterial action in sugar solutions, wines, etc.; fermentation gum.

dextrin. A soluble substance derived from starch by exposure to high temperature for a short time, a gummy substance produced from starch.

dextrinase. An enzyme present in diastase.

dextrorotatory. Turning to right.

dextrorse. Toward the right, turning in a spiral from left to right as in the stem of the morning glory.

dextrorsum-volubilis. Twining to the right.

dextrose. Grape sugar.

dextrostyle. A condition in which the style curves to the right.

dhal. Pigeon pea.

di-. A prefix meaning two.

di-arched root. A root with two xylem and/or phloem strands.

dia-. A prefix meaning through, transverse.

diablastesis. A special growth from the hyphal layer of lichen.

diacanthous. Two-spined.

diachenium. Each part of a cremocarp, one of the carpids or ripened carpels of a schizocarp.

diachyma. The mesophyll, all the fundamental tissue of a leaf within the epidermis.

diacmic. Having two maximum periods.

diad. A dyad.

diadelphia. Flowers having stamens in two bundles or groups.

diadelphous stamens. Stamens which are united by their filaments into two sets.

diadromous. With veins radiating from a central point in a fan-shaped arrangement, as in the leaves of Ginkgo.

diaceous. Dioecious.

diaegeic. Producing underground stolons.

diageotropic. Growing horizontally under the influence of gravity.

diageotropism. The tendency of certain plant parts to assume a position at right angles to gravity.

diagnosis. A concise description of an organism with full distinctive characters.

diagnostic character. A feature which distinguishes a plant or group of plants from all others.

diagonal plane. Any vertical plane in a flower which is not anterioposterior to the lateral plane.

diagonal symmetry. The symmetry of the valves of diatoms when their torsion amounts to 180°.

diagram. See FLORAL DIAGRAM.

diagrammatic drawing. A drawing showing the relative size, shape, and position of different structures without showing their intimate details.

diaheliotropism. The tendency of organs to become adjusted so that the surface is at right angles to the sun's rays, as in the case of most leaves.

diakenium. A cremocarp.

diakinesis. The last stage in the prophase of meiosis in which the contraction of chromosomes is at its peak, the pairs are spread throughout the cell, the nucleolus disappears or is reduced in size, the major coil is formed.

diallel. Denoting hereditary lines which cross. A diallel cross involves all possible matings of several known males and females.

dialycarpic. Composed of distinct carpels; apocarpous.

dialydesmy. The breaking up of a stele into separate bundles each having its own endodermis.

Dialypetalae. The *Polypetalae*.

diaphyllous. Having separate leaves.

dialysepalous. Polysepalous.

dialysis. The separation of parts which are usually united.

dialystelic. Having distinct steles.

dialystely. A variation of polystely in which the separate steles usually remain separate during their longitudinal courses.

dialyze. To separate, prepare, or obtain by dialysis.

diamesogamous. Being fertilized by some external agent such as wind or insects.

diamines. Compounds containing two amine groups.

diandrous. Having two stamens.

dianthic. Being pollinated by a flower of the same plant.

dianthiflorous. With flowers like *Dianthus*, the pink or carnation.

diaphery. The calycine synthesis of two flowers.

diaphoretic. Having the power to increase perspiration.

diaphototaxis. The arrangement of the filaments of *Oscillatoria* at right angles to incident light of optimal intensity.

diaphototropism. The ability of leaves (or plants) to expose their surface at right angles to the rays of light to get maximum benefit from the rays.

diaphragm. 1. A septum or transverse plate in the pith at the nodes or at intervals between them. 2. A dividing membrane.

diaphragmed-stuffed. Having filled chambers separated by diaphragms.

diaphyllous. Dialyphyllous.

diaphysis. 1. The abnormal growth of an axis or shoot. 2. A proliferation of the inflorescence.

diarch. A tetrandrous flower when the stamens are in pairs with one pair shorter than the other.

diarinous. Diandrous.

diarrhenous. With two stamens.

diarthrodactylous. With dactyls consisting of two cells, as in *Chara*.

diaschistic. Undergoing one transverse and one longitudinal division in meiosis.

diaspasis. The complete division of the daughter cells in amitosis.

diaspore. A general term applied to any means of dispersing a plant, as a seed, fruit, spore, runner, slip, root, bulb, etc. Any part of a plant which can produce a new organism.

diastase. An enzyme which converts starch to sugar.

diastase of secretion. An enzyme formed by the glandular epithelium of the scutellum of grasses which acts by corrosion and attacks parts of the starch grain.

diastase of translocation. An enzyme universally distributed in plants which attacks starch grains uniformly over the surface.

diastasic action. The converion of starch to water-soluble substances by diastase.

diastem. An equatorial modification of protoplasm preceding cell division, a structural modification of the cytoplasm in the equatorial plane through which the cytosome divides.

diaster. A stage in mitosis at which daughter chromosomes are grouped near spindle poles ready to form a new nucleus; a dyaster.

diastole. 1. The slow dilation of a contractile vesicle. 2. The growth and expansion of the nucleus from the end of one mitosis to the commencement of the next.

diastomatic. Freeing gases from spongy parenchyma through stomata or through pores.

diastesiae. The aerial shoots which last the entire year.

diathermancy. The relative conductivity of a medium in the transmission of heat.

diathermotropic. Unaffected by or placing itself transversely to the source of heat.

diathermotropism. The response to the source of heat.

diathesis. Any predisposition or constitutional aptitude for some particular development.

diatmesis. The condition in amitosis when the daughter-cell nuclei become neatly divided.

diatole. The slow dilation of a contractile vesicle.

diatom. A unicellular microscopic form of algae with a regularly shaped cell wall of silica.

diatomaceous. 1. Resembling diatoms. 2. Pertaining to, consisting of, or abounding in diatoms or their siliceous remains.

diatomine. The gold-brown coloring matter of diatoms, phycoxanthin; a buff-colored pigment in diatoms and certain other algae.

diatomist. A student of diatoms.

diatropism. The placement of an organ or organism transversely to a stimulus.

diatrype-like. Having a stroma different from the tissue of the matrix.

diatrypoid. Like the genus *Diatrype*.

diaxon. With two axes.

dibasic. Containing two equivalents of a base, with two replaceable hydrogen atoms in the molecule.

dibotryal. Dibotryoid.

dibotryoid. With a compound inflorescence having the branches of the first and succeeding orders botripoid, such as the compound umbel, panicle, or spike.

dicarotin. A lipochrome pigment.

dicarpellary. Composed of two carpels.

dicaryocyte. A binucleate cell.

dicaryon. A complex of two independent haploid (n) nuclei united in one cell (not a diploid cell). The nuclei divide simultaneously; each nucleus carries its own genotypic chromosomes. A dikaryon.

dicaryon mycelium. A mycelium in which the cells contain two haploid nuclei or dicaryia which divide simultaneously.

dicaryophase. The phase which is characterized by the dicaryon.

dicaryophyte. A dicaryon which has become a new, independent, vegetative entity (the secondary mycelium) of a basidiomycete.

dicellate. Having two prongs.

dicentric. Having two centromeres in a chromosome or chromatid.

dich-. A prefix meaning apart.

dichasial cyme. A cyme in which each branch bears two branchlets.

dichasium. 1. A cyme with two axes running in opposite direction, the type of cyme formed in plants with opposite branching in the inflorescence. 2. A cyme having false dichotomy.

dichastic. Capable of spontaneous subdivision.

dichlamydeous. Having both calyx and corollas, having a double perianth.

dichlamydeous chimaera. See DIPLOCHLAMYDEOUS CHIMAERA.

dichoblastic. Being dichotomous when the repeated dichotomy develops into a sympodium.

dichocarpism. The production in fungi of two distinct forms of fructification, as dimorphism in fruits.

dichodynamic. Having the characters of both plants equally represented in hybrids.

dichogamous. Denoting hermaphrodites in which one sex develops earlier than the other, with stamens and pistils not synchronized in the same flower.

dichogamy. The condition in which the sexual elements mature at different times, thus assuring cross-pollination.

dichogeny. The condition when one of two formative impulses is set in motion and the other inhibited.

dichophysis. The development of anther-like structures in the hymenium and trama of some *Thelephoraceae* which are widely dichotomously branched to form prong-like terminal branches.

dichopodium. 1. A sympodial branch system made up of successive parts of a dichotomous branch system of which only one part assists in forming the axis. 2. An inflorescence with a repeatedly forked axis.

dichotomal. Of, pertaining to, or involving dichotomy.

dichotomal flowers. Flowers seated in the fork of a dichotomous stem or branch.

dichotomia. A forking, as of the branches in an inflorescence.

dichotomia brachialis. The normal forking in *Cladophora* in which the cell wall remains unchanged.

dichotomia connota. The condition in which the basal cells of the forks have grown together.

dichotomia matricalis. The condition when the terminal cell forks and the branch and stem are of equal thickness.

dichotomia spuria. The condition in which the branch and stem are of equal size but the mother cell is bent.

dichotomize. To fork, divide in pairs, or divide.

dichotomous cyme. A dichasium.

dichotomy. Forking in pairs dividing into two branches, branching by repeated divisions in two.

dichotomy, false. Opposite branching which gives the appearance of division; see DICHASIUM.

dichotomy, helicoid. Dichotomy which in each successive forking the branch which continues to develop is on the same side as the previous one, the other branch aborting.

dichotomy, scorpioid. Development of branches on each side in an alternate manner.

dichotypy. The occurrence of two different forms of the same stock.

dichroanthous. Flowered like *Dichroa*, saxifrage, a greenhouse plant resembling Hydrangea.

dichromatic. Having two color varieties.

dichrous. Of two colors.

Dichtigkeit. Density.

dicksonioid. Like *Dicksonia*, a tropical fern.

diclesium. An achene within a separate and free covering of the perianth.

diclinism. The condition of having stamens and pistils in separate flowers, diclinery.

diclinous. 1. Having flowers or fruiting organs of only one sex on a plant. 2. Having stamens and pistils in separate flowers (on the same or separate plants). 3. Having fruiting organs developed on different branches of a thallus.

dicoccous. 1. Splitting into two cocci or closed carpels. 2. Having two one-seeded coherent carpels.

dicoelous. Having two cavities.

dicophysis. Dichophysis.

dicotyl. A plant belonging to the plant class *Dicotylae*, a plant having two cotyledons.

dicotyledon. A plant with two seed leaves, a plant whose embryo has two cotyledons. One of the two great divisions of the flowering plants (angiosperms).

dicotyledonous. Having two seed leaves or cotyledons and other typical characteristics of the group, such as reticulate-veined leaves, a cylindrical arrangement of the fibrovascular bundles, and with flower parts usually in fives.

dicotyledony. The condition of being dicotyledonous.

dicotylous. Dicotyledonous.

dictyate stage. A resting stage succeeding diplotene in oogenesis during which the karyosome and the chromosomes lose their staining capacity and sharp contours, and the nucleus increases in size.

dicranaceous. Resembling the moss *Dicranum*.

dictydin. A granular substance found in the myxomycetes which resists both acids and alkalis. Dictydine granules or plasmodic granules.

dictyodesmic. Having a vascular network in ferns.

dictyodromous. Having reticulated venation, net-veined.

dictyogen. A plant with net-veined leaves.

dictyogenous layer. The layer of meristem in monocotyledonous plants which gives rise to the central body and cortex of young roots.

dictyokinesis. The division of the Golgi apparatus which accompanies division of the nucleus by karyokinesis.

dictyomeristele. A netted strand of vascular tissue enclosed by a sheath of endodermis forming part of a dictyostele.

dictyophyllous. With netted leaves.

dictyosome. An element of the Golgi apparatus.

dictyosporeae. Fungi with muriform spores.

dictyosporangium. A sporangium found in some *Oomycetes* in which the spores encased in the sporangium emit their contents separately and leave a network of empty spore walls.

dictyospore. A multicellular spore divided into segments by both transverse and longitudinal walls, a muriform spore.

dictyostele. A tubular network of vascular tissue wholly encased by an endodermis.

dictyostele, dissected. A perforated dictyostele in which the strands of the stelar network are reduced to thin threads.

dictyostele, perforated. A dictyostele in which gaps other than leaf gaps occur.

dictyostele, siphonic. A dictyostele with a simple tubular network of meristeles.

dictyostelic. Polystelic.

dictyoxylic. Having a network of meristeles or vascular bundles.

dictyoxylon. The cortex of a fossil stem possessing a netted system of hypodermal fibrous strands.

dictyuchous state. The dictyosporangium of *Saprolegniae*.

dicyclic. 1. Having a series of organs in two whorls, as a perianth. 2. Biennial.

dicycly. The condition of having two concentric vascular cylinders.

dicyme. A cyme in which the first axis forms a second cyme.

dicymose. Doubly cymose.

didiploid. Resulting from the fusion of two diploid nuclei.

didromic. Doubly twisted as the awns of *Danthonia*, *Stipa*, etc.

didromy. The condition of double torsion.

didymosporae. Fungi producing spores in pairs.

didymospore. A two-celled spore.

didymous. 1. Twin-like, in pairs of equal parts. 2. Said of fruit composed of two similar parts slightly attached along one edge.

didymous anthers. Anthers in which the lobes are poorly connected.

didynamia. Plants with dynamous flowers.

didynamous. Having stamens arranged in two pairs of unequal length.

didynamy. The state of being didynamous.

die-back. A form of anthracnose disease which results in the death of the tips of the roots of species of *Salic*, *Prunus*, and citrus fruits.

diecodichogamy. The condition which exists in plants having the male and female flowers or organs mature at different times to produce cross-fertilization, dichogamy.

diel. Referring to a 24-hour day.

dientomophily. The condition in some species in which some individuals are adapted for insect-fertilization by one species of insect and other individuals are adapted for other insects.

dieresilis. A dry fruit composed of several cells or carpels connate around a central axis and separating at maturity, as in mallow; a carcerule.

dietesiae. Perennials with persistent short shoots, the long shoots being absent or ephemeral.

differential affinity. The inability of two chromosomes to pair in the presence of a third although they pair in its absence.

differential host. A discriminating plant which is used to test different varieties of parasites.

differential segment. A segment of a chromosome which is lacking in another chromosome that is otherwise homologous.

differential species. Species which appear only in one or two societies but which cannot be designated as characteristic species of any association.

differentiation. The process of becoming structurally and functionally specialized.

differentiation of tissues. The diverse growth and specialization into permanent tissue.

diffluence. Disintegration by vacuolization.

diffluent. Becoming liquid, disintegrating in water.

difform. Irregular, dissimilar, abnormal.

diffract. Broken into areolae and separated by chinks as in some lichens.

diffuse growth. The growth of an alga thallus by the division of any of its cells.

diffuse nucleus. The presence of chromidia in some non-nucleated cells.

diffuse parenchyma. Single parenchyma strands or cells distributed irregularly among the fibrous elements of the wood.

diffuse porous. With xylem vessels scattered uniformly throughout or when there is little

difference between the vessels formed at different times in the growing season.

diffuse porous wood. Wood whose pores are nearly uniform in size and more or less evenly spread through both spring and summer wood.

diffuse stimulus. A stimulus which does not affect the plant from any fixed position.

diffuse tissue. A tissue made up of cells which occur in the plant body singly or in small groups intermingled with tissues of distinct types.

diffusion. The spontaneous intermingling of the molecules of two or more substances; extension, dissemination, circulation, dispersion.

diffusion, static. A botanical designation of the absorption of gaseous bodies through stomata and diffusion through tissues.

digametic. Having both male and female gametes.

digamous. Having the two sexes in the same cluster but in separate blossoms, diclinous.

digency. The condition of being digenous or digamous.

digenesis. 1. Alternation of sexual and asexual generations, i.e., alternating a haploid with a diploid stage. 2. The condition of needing two hosts in some parasitic organisms.

digenic. Controlled by two pairs of genes.

digenetic reproduction. Sexual reproduction.

digenodifferent. Said of hybrids when the genotypes of the two genodifferent gametes are involved and differ on two or more points.

digenous. Containing both sexes or produced sexually.

digestion. The process by which nutrient materials are changed so that they can be absorbed and assimilated.

digestive cells. Cells in mycorrhiza that digest food.

digestive glands. The glands in the lower part of the pitcher of *Nepenthes* which secrete the digestive substances.

digestive pocket. The investment of the secondary rootlets which penetrate the tissues of the primary root until they reach the exterior.

digestive pouch. A layer of cells on the apex of a lateral root which secrete enzymes to help bring about the breakdown of the cortical cells of the parent root as the lateral grows through it; a digestive sac.

digitaliform. Finger-shaped.

digitalin. A poisonous alkaloid obtained from *Digitalis purpurea*.

digitate. Having parts which diverge from the same point like the fingers of an open hand, palmate, finger-shaped.

digitate-pinnate. Denoting a digitate leaf which has pinnate leaflets.

digitate veined. With veins diverging like spread fingers.

digitinervate. With veins which radiate out from base-like fingers of a hand as five or seven-veined leaves.

digitipartite. Having leaves divided in a hand-like pattern.

digitipinnate. Having digitate leaves of which the leaflets are pinnate.

digonous. Having two pistils, styles, or stigmas in a flower.

digynia. Flowers with a gynoecium of two pistils.

digynian. Having two separated styles or carpels.

digynous. 1. Having two carpels. 2. With organs in pairs.

dihaploid. Having two coupled haploid nuclei in the chromosomes.

dihaplophase. The condition of being dihaploid.

diheliotropism. Diaheliotropism.

diheterozygote. An individual heterozygous for two pairs of genes, a dihybrid.

dihybrid. A generic cross in which the parents differ in two distinct characters, an individual which is heterozygous with respect to two pairs of allelomorphs.

dihybridization. The condition of having two pairs of allelomorphs showing the proportion of 9:3:3:1.

dihybridism. Dihybridization.

dikaryon. Dicaryon.

dikaryophase. The part of the life history of many basidiomycetes in which the hyphae are made of segments each containing two nuclei.

dikontan. With two flagella.

dilabent. Breaking apart.

dilacerate. Lacerated, torn asunder.

dilamination. 1. The separation of a layer from a petal. 2. An abnormal absence or diminution of the green coloring in plants, chorisis.

dilatation. Cell division in the parenchyma of the wood, the pith, and the medullary rays causing cleavage of the xylem mass.

dilepidous. Consisting of two scales.

diluent. A diluting agent.

diluted. Pale and faint-colored.

dimerous. 1. Having each whorl of two parts. 2. Bilaterally symmetrical, dimeric.

dimeristele. A pair of meristeles or vascular bundles.

dimery. The dimerous condition.

dimidiate. 1. With only one half developed, lop-sided. 2. Applied to a perithecial wall of a lichen which covers the upper portion only. 3. Said of a capsule split on one side only. 4. Said of an anther which has one lobe aborted or absent. 5. Applied to a pileus with one side much larger than the other, etc.

dimidiato-cordatus. With the lower half of a dimidiate leaf cordate.

dimidiato-cuneate. Divided into two wedge-shaped parts.

dimititic. Having two types of hyphae, generative and skeletal.

dimonoecism. The condition of two out of three kinds of monoecious flowers, having perfect flowers in addition to male, female, or neuter flowers.

dimorphic. Existing in two forms, dimorphous.

dimorphic heterostyly. The possession of styles of different lengths by flowers of the same species.

dimorphism. The condition of being dimorphic as to styles, stamens, leaves, flowers and other plant parts; the development of two forms, as the fertile and sterile fronds of ferns which are unlike.

dimorphous flowers. Flowers which have two forms, as those with long and short styles.

dimorphous species. Flowers differing in the relative position or length of the anthers and stigmas.

dineuroid. Similar to the fossil fern *Dineuron*, which has pinna-traces in four rows.

dinoflagellates. The mobile *Dinophyceae*.

dinomic. Living in only two of the biogeographical divisions of the globe.

diodange. A group of diodes which are surrounded by one or more layers of sterile cells.

diodangium. A sporangium in vascular cryptogams and bryophytes.

diode. A reproductive body peculiar to vascular plants which develops into a rudimentary body or prothallium, the transition between the rudimentary and adult stages.

diodogone. A sporangium which produces diodes in phanerogams (the embryo sac and the pollen sac).

diodon. With two teeth.

diodophyte. A vascular plant.

dioecia. Plants having staminate and pistillate flowers on different individuals.

dioecio-dimorphous. Heterogonous.

dioecio-polygamous. Bearing only unisexual or only hermaphroditic flowers.

dioecious. Having the staminate and pistillate flowers on separate individuals, producing male and female organs on different individuals, unisexual.

dioecious-macandrous. Having the antheridia smaller than the female filaments, as in *Oedogonium*.

dioecious-nannandrous. Having very small male plants.

dioecious species. Species in which the stamens and pistils are situated not only in distinct flowers but also on separate individuals.

dioeciously polygamous. Having perfect and imperfect flowers on different plants.

dioicous. Dioecious.

diosmaefolious. Having leaves like *Diosma*, a South African cultivated heath shrub.

diosmosis. The mutual diffusion of liquids of different densities through membranes.

dipetalous. Having two petals in a flower.

diphorophyll. A leaf differentiated into palisade and spongy tissue from unequal illumination.

diphosphopyridine nucleotide (DPN). Coenzyme, which is reduced in the early stages of respiration by oxidation.

diphotic. Having two surfaces unequally lighted, having leaves set on the stem at an angle to get more light on the upper surface than on the lower.

diphotophyll. A leaf differentiation into palisade and sponge tissue owing to unequal illumination.

diphygenic. Having two modes of embryonic development.

diphyletic. Arising from two distinct ancestral groups.

diphyllous. Having two leaves.

diplanetary. With two distinct types of zoospores.

diplanetic. With two morphologically different phases of the swarm spore stage always separated by a resting period (found in *Saprolegnia*).

diplanetism. The condition in which there are two periods of motility in one life history, as in some fungi.

diplasy. The division of an axial organ into two parts.

diplecolobeae. *Cruciferae* with incurved cotyledons which are folded twice transversely.

dipleuric cambium. Cambium which produces tissue on both sides.

diplo-. A prefix meaning double.

diplobacilli. Bacilli which are composed of two cells or which adhere in pairs; diplobacteria.

diplobiont. 1. A plant flowering or fruiting twice in each season. 2. A plant which includes in its life-cycle at least two different kinds of individuals, and if the species is dioecious, there are three kinds of individuals. See ASPECTION.

diplobiontic. Having thalli of two kinds, one essentially haploid in structure and sexual, the other essentially diplophasic in structure and producing spores with the reduction divisions occurring in each fertilization.

diploblastic. Having two distinct germ layers, the ectoderm and endoderm.

diplocaryon. Syncaryon.

diplocaulescent. Having secondary stems.

diplochlamydeous. Having a double perianth with a distinct corolla and calyx, diplochlamedeous, dichlamydeous.

diplochlamydeous chimaera. A periclinal chimaera consisting of an outer skin two layers thick representing one constituent and surrounding a core representing the outer constituent.

diplochromosome. A chromosome with four chromatids instead of the usual two, with one undivided kinetochore. It is believed to originate from an extra division of the chromatid without nuclear division.

diplococcus. Any spherical bacterium showing paired spheres, two rounded cells having somewhat flattened adjacent walls, a coupled spherule, or the result of the conjugation of two cells.

diploconidium. A binucleate conidium formed in the fructification of *Tremellales*.

diplocyte. A somatic cell which has the full number of chromosomes.

diplodesmic. Having two parallel vascular systems.

diplodisation. The conversion of mycelium composed of uninucleate segments into mycelium composed of binucleate segments. Diploidization.

diploe. The fundamental tissue of a leaf within the epidermis, mesophyll.

diplogamete. The double gametes produced in the same cell in ascomycetes.

diplogenesis. 1. The doubling of those parts which are normally single. 2. A supposed change in germ plasm that accompanies use and disuse, changes occurring in body tissues.

diplohaplont. A plant which has a sexual process with a morphological alternation between a haploid generation and a diploid generation.

diploid. Having the number of chromosomes usually found in the somatic cells of a species; applied to the condition in the 2 X generation, the chromosomes being twice as numerous as in the haploid generation.

diploid apogamety. Euapogamy or diploid apogamy.

diploid apogamy. The development of a sporophyte containing diploid nuclei without any preliminary fusion of gametes from one or more cells of the gametophyte.

diploid cells. The cells having the diploid number of chromosomes.

diploid generation. The sporophyte.

diploid nucleus. A nucleus containing the 2 X number of chromosomes.

diploid set of chromosomes. A group of chromosomes which can be divided into two equal haploid groups.

diploidization. The act or process of inducing a state of diploidy; the fusion of two haploid mycelia, oidia, spermatia, etc., of opposite sex which precedes the formation of special reproductive structures.

diplokaryon. A tetraploid nucleus, one with twice the normal diploid number of chromosomes.

diplonasty. The condition when organs grow faster in the upper and the under surfaces than on the sides.

diplonema. The stage in the mitotic division at which the chromosomes are clearly double.

diplont. 1. An organism with the diploid number of chromosomes in its cells. 2. The sporophytic phase ending with meiosis.

diploperistome. A double peristome.

diploperistomous. Having a double row of teeth or a double peristome.

diplophase. The stage in the life history of an organism when the cell nuclei are diploid, the diploid generation, the diplotene phase of meiotic division.

diplophyll. A leaf which has palisade tissue on both surfaces.

diplophyte. A diplont or sporophyte.

diplosome. A double centrosome which lies outside the nuclear membrane.

diplosis. The fusion of two haploid sets of chromosomes to form a diploid set.

diplosporangiate. Ambisporangiate.

diplospore. A teleutospore.

diplospory. A form of gametophytic asexual reproduction, a condition in which there is no pairing and reduction of chromosomes leading to the formation of a diploid gametophyte.

diplostemonous. 1. Having twice as many stamens as petals or sepals. 2. Having flowers with the outer cycle of stamens opposite the sepals and the inner cycle of stamens opposite the petals.

diplostephanous. With a double circle of stipulodes at the base of each whorl of branchlets in *Characeae*.

diplostephioid. Like *Diplostephium*, a composite of the Andes.

diplostic. Having rootlets in which the mother root has only two xylem bundles.

diplostichous. Two-rowed, in two series.

diplostroma. A well developed stroma as distinguished from the haplostromatic type.

diplotegium. A form of dry dehiscent fruit, as that of *Iris*, differing from the capsule only in that it is developed from an inferior instead of a superior ovary.

diplotene. A phase in the first stage of meiotic mitosis when the contracted homologous chromosomes split, start to form clumps at the center of the cell and start to form coils. It precedes diakinesis.

diploxylic. 1. Having two or more vascular bundles in the leaves. 2. Having vascular bundles in which the centrifugal part of the wood is secondary.

diploxyloid. Of or resemblin the genus *Diploxylon*.

diplozoic. Bilaterally symmetrical.

dipsaceous. Of the teasel, the genus *Dipsacus*.

dipterid. 1. Fly flowers which are visited by

dipterous flies. 2. Resembling the fern genus *Dipteris*.

dipterocarpus. 1. A two-winged fruit. 2. A genus of Asian timber trees.

diptero-cecidia. Galls produced on plants by dipterous flies.

dipterous. Having two wings or wing-like appendages.

dipyrenous. Having two stones or pyrenes, two-seeded.

direct adaptation. An adaptation which does not appear related to natural selection.

directevenosus. Having a feather-veined leaf with secondary ribs passing directly from the mid-rib to the margin, digitinervius.

direct germination. The germination of a spore of any kind directly from a hypha or a filament.

direct nuclear division. See AMITOSIS.

directing leucite. A tinoleucite.

direction cells. Portions of a gamete budded off prior to fertilization; polar cells, corpuscles.

directive movement. The movement of orientation.

directive spheres. Attraction spheres.

directivity. The controlling effect of the vital functions.

direct metamorphosis. Progressive metamorphosis.

direct superposition. The development of an accessory bud in an axil above the leading bud or above first-formed buds.

diremption. 1. The occasional separation or displacement of the leaves. 2. The situation of an organ when it is out of its normal position. 3. Chorisis.

dirinian. Related to or resembling *Dirina*, a lichen.

disappearing. Excess branching.

disarticulate. To separate at an articulation or joint.

disassimilation. Catabolism in plants.

disbudded. With the nascent buds removed.

disc. 1. Any flat, disk-like growth. 2. The central portion of the upper surface of a pileus. 3. The cup-shaped hymenium of a discomycete. 4. The developing torus within the calyx or within the corolla and stamens. 5. The central portion of a head in the composite flowers. 6. A disk, a discus.

disc, adhesive. A modification of a tendril for adhesion aiding a climbing plant.

disc, carpellary. An expansion of the strobilus of fossil cycads bearing ovules.

disc florets. The inner florets borne on an abbreviated and reduced peduncle in many inflorescences.

disc flower. The tubular flower in the center of heads of *Compositae*, as distinguished from the ray flowers.

disc, staminate. The surface upon which the staminate organs were borne in fossil cycads.

discals. An abbreviation for the *Disciflorae*, a series of polypetalous phanerogams.

discentration. The fasciation of the axis or a multiple of a leaf organ.

dischisma. The fruit of *Platystemon*, which divides into longitudinal carpels, each of which again divides transversely.

discifer. 1. Disc-bearing, as in the wood of conifers. 2. Having the shape of a disc.

disciflorous. Having flowers in which the receptacle is large and disc-shaped.

disciform. Discoid.

discigerous frustules. Frustules of diatoms which have valves more or less circular in outline.

disclimax. The climax which is the consequence of a disturbance by man or domestic animals.

discocarp. An ascocarp in which the hymenium lies exposed while the asci are maturing, an apothecium, a cup.

discocarpium. A collection of fruits within a hollow receptacle, as in many *Rosaceae*.

discoid flowers. 1. Flowers arranged in a disc or head. 2. Flowers in a head which have all tubular flowers and lack ray flowers.

discoid glands. The stalked glands in the *Urticaceae* which have a single layer of cells around the head.

discoid head. A head of flowers lacking ray flowers.

discoid marking. A thin spot or opening in a cell wall covered on each side by a thickened convex body having a central perforation; see BORDERED PITS.

discolichens. Discomycetous lichens.

discolith. A coccolith which is shaped like a disc.

discolor. 1. Of more than one color, of two or more colors. 2. To lose color.

discomycete. An ascomycetous fungus in which the fruit body, or ascocarp, is disc-shaped, as in the *Pezizales*; a fungus with an open hymenium.

discontiguous. Resembling rhododendron leaves with gaps between them.

discontinuous distribution. See GEOGRAPHI-
CAL DISTRIBUTION.

discontinuous variations. Abrupt variations
in which there are few or no intermediate
forms; mutations.

discoplacenta. A placenta on a circular disc.

discoplankton. Floating plankton in disc
form, floating diatoms of discoid forms.

discopodium. A disc-shaped floral receptacle.

discus. A disk.

disease. The result of the interaction of an
etiological agent with a host with detriment
to the invaded host; any pathological disturbance or interruption in the process of
nutrition and growth in plants which results in the partial or complete stoppage of
growth or in death.

disepalous. Having two sepals.

disharmonic. Showing evolutionary gaps in
series and having many monotypic genera.

disjunct. With body regions separated by
deep constriction, characterized by separation of parts, formed into separate parts or
groups.

disjunction. 1. The separation of the chromosomes at anaphase, particularly at the first
mitotic division. 2. The act of disjoining,
the state of being disjoined.

disjunctive symbiosis. A situation in which
symbionts derive mutual advantages from
association although there is no direct
union or connection between them.

disjunctive tracheids. Tracheids which are
partly disjoined laterally during differentiation but maintain contact by means of
tubular processes.

disjunctor. A portion of wall material forming a link between the successive conidia in
a chain serving as a weak place where separation may occur.

disk. Disc.

dislocated segments. Homologous pairs of
segments differing in their linear sequence
with other segments.

dislocator cell. The wall cell in gymnosperms
derived from the antheridial mother cell
which frees the spermatocyte from its attachment.

disogeny. The sexual maturity of one and the
same individual in two different conditions
between which a metamorphosis with retrogression of the sex products occurs.

disome. A chromosome set having paired

members, as in normal somatic tissue;
diploid, dissome.

disomic. Having two homologous chromosomes or genes.

disoperculate. Having lost the operculum or
lid.

dispermic. Fertilized by two sperm cells.

dispermous. Having two seeds.

dispermy. The entrance of two sperms into
an egg.

dispireme. A stage in the telophase of cell
division in which the spireme thread of
each daughter nucleus has been formed.

dispirous. Having double spirals.

disporous. Having two spores.

disaccharide. A sugar composed of two monosaccharide molecules.

disseminule. A seed, fruit, or spore modified
for migration.

dissepiment. 1. A partition in a capsule, the
partition between the cells of seed vessels.
2. The trama in certain fungi.

dissilient. Bursting asunder or in pieces,
bursting open or dehiscing violently.

dissimilation. 1. The disintegration of protoplasm, principally by oxidation. 2. The
act of making or the process of becoming
dissimilar. 3. Catabolism.

dissitiflorous. Remotely or loosely flowered.

dissome. A disome.

dissophyte. A plant with xerophytic leaves
and stems and a mesophytic root.

dissymetrical. Biradial.

distachyous. With two styles or spikes.

distal. Remote from the point of attachment,
standing far apart, farthest from the axis,
farthest from the spindle attachment.

disteleology. Purposelessness or frustration
of function.

disterigmatic. Having two spores abjointed
from each basidium.

distichophyllous. With two-ranked leaves.

distichous. In two vertical ranks, producing
leaves or flowers in two opposite rows.

distinct calyx. A calyx with separate sepals.

distractile. With widely separate long-stalked
anthers.

distribution of sexes. See DIOECISM and SEX
DISTRIBUTION.

distromatic. With the thallus in two layers, as
in the alga *Porphyra*.

distrophophytes. Plants of firm soils with
ample moisture.

distrophy. Dystrophy.

distrophic. Dystropous.

distylous. With two styles.

disymmetrical. Biradial.

dithallic. Formed by the union of mycelium from two distinct strains.

dithecal. Having two-celled anthers.

dithecous. With two theca or anther cells.

ditopogamy. Heterostyly.

ditrichotomous. Divided into twos or threes.

ditriploid. Produced by the fusion of two triploid nuclei to form one.

dittany. The fraxinella, the small menthaceous herb *Cunila origanoides*.

diurnal. Opening during the day and closing at night.

diurnal sleep. The power which some leaves have when placed in bright sunlight to place their surfaces parallel to the rays of light, paraheliotropism.

diurnation. The phenomenon of daily fluctuation in the composition of a community within a 24-hour day.

diurnus. Day-flowering.

divaricate. Spreading at an obtuse angle.

divergence, angle of. The angle between succeeding organs in the same spiral or whorl.

divergency. 1. The fraction of a stem circumference, usually constant for a species, which separates two consecutive leaves in a spiral. 2. The separation of parts as they lengthen.

diverginervius. Having radiating main nerves.

diversiflorous. Having flowers of two or more forms.

diversifolious. With variable leaves.

diverticillate. With two whorls.

diverticulum. 1. A blind tube or sac branching off from a cavity or canal. 2. In algae, a protoplasmic protrusion communicating with the fused procarp cells and the placenta, as in *Gracilaria confervoides*.

divided. Cleft to the base or midrib, lobed to the base, cut into lobes or segments; see DISSECTED.

divided leaf. A leaf, almost compound, with incisions extending to the midribs or main veins.

division. The simple process of dividing plants that have rootstocks or tubers.

divisural line. The median line down the teeth of a peristome through which they split.

dixanthous. Double-tinted.

dixeny. The condition in which an autoecious parasite may infect two species but does not require a change of host to ensure its development.

dixylic. Having the xylem in two masses.

dizoic. Having a spore containing two sporozoites.

dizygotic. Originating from two fertilized eggs.

dizygous. Dependent on two rows of chromosomes.

DNA. An abbreviation for desoxyribonucleic acid, which plays an important part in the transmission of hereditary characters.

-doche. A suffix meaning succession.

dodeca-. A prefix meaning twelve.

Dodecagynia. An order of plants with twelve parts.

dodecagynous. Having twelve pistils or styles.

dodecamerous. Having the floral organs or parts in twelves.

dodecandrous. With twelve stamens.

dodecapetalous. With twelve petals (loosely used to describe a flower having from twelve to twenty petals).

dodekasomic. Having six double sets of chromosomes, dodecaploid.

dodonaefolius. A leaf like *Dodonaea*, a tropical tree.

dodrans. A span, 9 inches or 23 cm.

dodrantalis. A span long, about nine inches.

dog's tail, crested. A grass, *Cynosurus cristatus*.

dolabrate. Hatchet-shaped, axe-shaped, dolabriform.

doleiform. Doliform.

doliarious. Rolled inwards from the apex towards the base resembling a crozier in form, circinate, doliatus.

dolichonema. The stage in nuclear division which immediately precedes synapsis in the formation of the reproductive cells.

dolichosis. The retardation of growth in length.

dolichostylous. With long styled anthers.

dolichotmema. A filiform cell which ruptures and frees the gemmae of a moss plant.

doliform. Barrel-shaped.

Dollo's law. That structures or functions once lost to an evolving group of organisms can never be regained.

domatium. A cavity or other form of shelter formed by a plant which harbors mites or insects with which it appears to live in symbiosis.

dome. The growing point of the receptacle of a flower.

domestomycetes. Wood-destroying fungi which attack building timber and grow best at about 21° C.

domin. An organism which exhibits a weak dominance.

dominance. The prevalence of one of a few species in a plant community determining the physiognomy and influencing the rest of the plant population, Dominanz.

dominance area. The region or regions throughout which a species occurs as a frequency dominant.

doninance classes. The classes (usually five) into which vegetation is placed to reflect the percentage of coverage by species as: 1-5%, 6-25%, 26-50%, 51-75%, 76-100%.

dominance, degrees of. The relation of the total numbers of the dominant species to all the plants in a given community.

dominance, hereditary. The expression of a character to the exclusion of its allelic character; see ALLELOMORPH.

dominance, incomplete. An intermediate expression of a character by a hybrid, usually favoring the dominant expression of the character by one of the parents.

dominance modifier. A gene capable of changing the dominance of another gene in inheritance.

dominance, over. See OVER-DOMINANCE.

dominance, partial. The capability of producing a character to an intermediate degree when a mutant gene and its normal allelomorph are present in a hybrid.

dominant. 1. The prevalent character in a hybrid, one member of an allelomorphic pair having the quality of manifesting itself wholly or partly to the exclusion of the other member of the pair. 2. An organism which controls the habitat, an organism or organisms which characterize the community in its larger aspects.

dominant character. A character inherited from one parent which develops to the exclusion of a contrasting character of the other parent.

dominant percentage. 1. The number of dominants expressed as a percentage of the number of species. 2. The numerical percentage of the dominants.

dominants. Generations which have per-

sisted through geologic times to the present.

Dominanz. Dominance.

dominule. The dominant of a microhabitat, a dominant organism in any community in a serule.

domitoform. A cultivated form of which the original is unknown or dissimilar.

donacinus. Reed-like.

dormant buds. Buds which do not develop unless stimulated to growth by special conditions.

dormant eyes. Dormant buds.

doronicoid. Like *Doronicum*, a cultivated composite.

dorsal. Referring to the back or outer surface of an organ, the surface most distant from the axis, the surface turned away from the axis.

dorsal pneumatic tissue. The loose mesophyllic tissue of the leaf.

dorsal suture. The midrib of a carpel, the line of opening on the back of a carpel.

dorsal trace. The median vascular supply to a carpel.

dorsally compressed. Flattened on the back.

dorsicumbent. Lying flat with face upward, supine.

dorsiferous. Borne on the back, as the sori of most ferns.

dorsifixed. Attached to the back of an anther; adnate.

dorsinasty. Epinasty.

dorsiventral. Extended horizontally so as to have dorsal and ventral surface, having a distinct upper and distinct lower surface, having both front and back surfaces, bifacial.

dorsiventral structure. A structure having two distinct sides.

dorsiventral symmetry. The symmetry in an organ or shoot which develops unequally on two sides in relation to gravity, light, etc.

dorsiventrality. The condition of possessing upper and lower faces of an organ.

dorsocentral. In the middle of the back.

dorso-umbonal. Lying on back near the umbo.

dorsoventral. Dorsiventral.

dorsum. 1. The back of an organ. 2. The curved convex side of the girdle in forms of diatoms which are more or less lunately curved.

dorty. Delicate, difficult to cultivate.

dothideaceous. 1. Of, pertaining to, or belonging to the *Dothideales*, with asci in cavities. 2. Loculate without true perithecia. 3. Dothideal, dothideoid.

dothioraceous. Having the characteristics of the fungus *Dothiora*.

dot. 1. A minute speck or tubercle. 2. A pit in the cell wall. 3. A receptacle of oil in leaves.

dotted ducts. Pitted ducts, vessels with pit-like markings on the walls.

dotted tissue. Bothrenchyma, pitted ducts or cells.

double. Said of flowers with more than the normal number of petals which are frequently monstrously increased at the expense of other organs.

double diploid. Having a total number of chromosomes equal to the sum of the chromosomes in the diploid parents, the parents differing in their chromosome numbers; see AMPHIDIPLOID.

double fertilization. The situation in angiosperms in which one male cell from the pollen tube fuses with the egg nucleus, and the second male nucleus fuses with the fusion nucleus of the embryo sac (made up of two polar nuclei) and produces the primary endosperm nucleus.

double flower. A flower in which petal numbers are increased greatly resulting in an apparent lessening in number of the other parts.

double flowering. The abnormal condition sometimes shown by plants which flower in the spring and again in the autumn.

double fructification. Dimorphism in the fruiting bodies of certain algae.

double heterozygote. An individual that has inherited two unlike genes (dominant and recessive) which control one or more characters.

double needle. A dwarf branch without bud scales in the conifer *Sciadopitys* in which the two leaves are fused at the edge into one needle.

double recessive. A diploid homozygote for a recessive gene.

double reciprocal cross. The offspring obtained by recrossing previously crossed hybrids.

double reciprocal roots. Lateral roots of monocotyledons when they occur in the interval between two protoxylem bundles.

double reduction. See NONDISJUNCTION.

double rosette. A dyaster.

doubling. Chorisis.

doubly crenate. Having crenations which are themselves crenate.

doubly dentate. With the teeth of a dentate leaf also dentate, having dentate teeth.

doubly ternate. Divided into three parts each of which is divided into three.

doubly toothed. Having teeth which are toothed themselves.

down. 1. A dune or hill. 2. The coma of certain seeds. 3. The pappus of a composite flower. 4. A soft pubescence.

DPN. Diphosphopyridine nucleotide.

dR. See HETEROZYGOTE.

drabifolious. With leaves like *Draba*, a crucifer.

dracaenoid. Like *Dracaena*, a liliaceous house plant with variegated foliage.

dracanth. Gum tragacanth.

dracocephalous. Dragon-headed.

draconine. A red resinous substance obtained from dragon's blood, *Dracaena*.

dracunculoid. Tarragon-like.

draining point. The drip point of a leaf.

draw. A young shoot or sprout; see ALVEUS.

dreen. A woodland swamp which separates the marginal islands from the mainland.

drepaniform. Scythe- or sickle-shaped, falcate.

drepanium. A sickle-shaped cyme.

drepanocladous. Having sickle-shaped branches.

drepanophyllous. Having sickle-shaped leaves.

drimad. A plant of an alkaline formation.

drimium. An alkali plain or salt basin community.

drimophilous. Salt-loving, drimyphilous, halophylous.

drimyphyte. A salt plant.

driodad. A plant of a dry thicket.

driodium. A dry thicket formation.

drip point. The acuminate apex of a leaf from which point water drips.

drip tip. A marked elongation of the tip of the leaf said to facilitate the shedding of rain from the surface of the leaf.

dromotism. Spiral curvature.

dromotropic. Bent in a spiral.

dromotropism. The spiral growth of plants caused by their irritability.

drop-disease. A disease of lettuce ascribed to *Botrytis vulgaris* and *Sclerotinia libertiana*.

drop-seed, Mexican. A common American grass, *Muhlenbergia Mexicana.*

dropper. A young immature bulb.

dropping point. The drip point.

drosophile. Pollinated by dew.

drought, physical. A condition in which the soil contains very little available water.

drought, physiological. A condition in which the soil contains a considerable amount of water which, by reason of the nature of the soil or of the chemical factors present, cannot enter the roots.

drought resistance. The degree of fitness of a plant to withstand drought.

drupa. A drupe.

drupaceous. Resembling or bearing drupes.

drupe. A one-seeded, usually indehiscent, fleshy fruit in which the endocarp is stony, the mesocarp fleshy, and the exocarp skin-like.

drupe, false. A nut-like fruit in which the lower persistent part of the perianth becomes fleshy.

drupe, spurious. A fleshy body enclosing a stone.

drupel. A diminutive drupe (the fruit of the blackberry is an aggregation of drupels); a drupelet, a drupeola.

drupetum. A cluster of drupes.

drupiferous. Drupe-bearing.

drupose. One of the constituents of the stone cells of the flesh of pears.

druse. A globose mass of crystals of calcium oxalate formed around a central foundation of organic material occurring in some plant cells.

drusy. 1. Having the appearance of the stigma of *Orobanche caryophyllea.* 2. Covered with minute crystals. 3. Having a bloom. 4. Pruinose.

Drüzenzotten. Glandular hairs.

dry fruit. Fruit with little or no pulp.

dry rot. A disease caused by *Merulius lacrymans,* which is very destructive to cut timber.

dry wall. A wall of tissue which is relatively hard and tough.

dryad. A shade plant.

dryadetum. An association of *Dryas,* a rosaceous alpine plant.

drymophytes. Bushes and small trees of the chaparral and woodland.

drynarioid. Resembling *Drynaria,* an East Indian fern.

dryon. A scrub climax.

dryophantin. A pathologic coloring matter from galls produced by *Dryophante divisa,* on leaves of British oaks.

dryophilous. Living on, under, or near oaks.

dryopterid. Like the fern *Dryopteris.*

dsaengael. Loose scrubland with scattered trees, found in Arabia.

dual hypothesis. The hypothesis that two organisms are present in the lichen thallus.

dual phenomenon. The association of genetically unlike nuclei within a single mycelium. See HETEROKARYOSIS.

duces. The character cells in mosses, the deuter cells.

duck's meat. Duckweed, the genus *Lemna.*

ducts. 1. Continuous tubes or vessels formed by a row of elongated cells which have lost the intervening partitions and serve for the passage of water in the stems of plants, the tracheids. 2. Narrow linear vessels separating the cellules of the leaves of sphagnum.

ducts, annular. Ducts in which secondary thickening occurs more or less in the form of rings.

ducts, closed. Long cells which are not continuous but which have the intervening septa remaining.

ducts, dotted. Bothrenchyma, pitted ducts.

ducts, reticulated. Ducts in which the markings seem to form a network.

ducts, scalariform. Ducts with ladder-like markings, as in some ferns.

ductule. The fine thread-like terminal portion of a duct.

duff. The top layer or mat of forest humus which has not been incorporated into the soil, the decomposed and decomposing vegetable matter on the forest floor.

dulcite. A sweet, white crystalline substance $C_6H_8(OH)_6$ occurring in various plants and obtained from cell sap.

dumetose. Bushy, dumose.

dumetum. A thicket.

dun. A yellowish or grayish brown color.

dune. A hill made up of undulating banks of wind-blown sand and having characteristic vegetation usually found on the shore or coast and in sandy deserts.

duodecuple. Twelve pairs of chromosomes.

duodichogamy. The condition of flowering in which there are two periods of pollen-shedding from two kinds of catkins with the maturing of the pistils taking place between the periods and resulting in cross-pollination.

duplex. 1. Having two similar dominant genes for a given character, one from each parent resulting in a formula AAaa, as in an autotetraploid. 2. Having a pileus which is soft above and firm next to the gills or tubes.

duplex factors of character. The condition in which the determiners for a character are derived from both parents.

duplicate-crenate. Doubly crenate.

duplicate-dentate. Doubly toothed, duplico-dentate.

duplicate factors. Two or more factors either of which alone produces the same result.

duplicate genes. Two or more pairs of genes having similar effects on one character.

duplicate parasitism. Self-parasitism, as in the case of mistletoe growing on mistletoe.

duplicate-pinnate. Bipinnate.

duplicate-serrate. Biserrate.

duplicate-ternate. Biternate.

Duracinus. Having hard berries.

duramen. 1. The heartwood of tree trunks (the older, dead, more strongly colored inner part of the secondary xylem of dicotyledonous stems). 2. The outer and harder part of monocotyledonous stems.

durifruticeta. A sclerophyllous scrub formation, an association composed of macchia and garigue.

duriherbosa. Grasses and herbs which die in winter.

durilignosa. Trees and shrubs which have sclerophyllous leaves or green axes which serve as leaves.

duriprata. A meadow (consisting chiefly of grasses and sedges) in which the dominant species are strengthened by mechanical tissue.

durisilvae. A broad sclerophyllous forest formation of trees with firm, durable leaves.

dust. 1. Granules resembling dust. 2. Pollen.

duvet. A soft, thick, finely matted nap; a tomentum, a duvetyn.

dwarf branch. A shortened, highly specialized and reduced shoot or twig; a short branch with many internodes.

dwarf male. A short-lived filament of a few cells in *Oedogoniaceae*, the upper cells of which are antheridia which grow epiphytically on the female filaments.

dwarf-shoots. Spurs.

dy. 1. A soupy type of peat. 2. The mush of lake bottoms largely composed of plant detritus. 3. A type of deposit having a pronounced effect on the fauna of the area.

dyad. The two-celled stage which may exist during a long interphase.

dyadocyte. A second spermatocyte or auxocyte which contains dyads, a homeocyte.

dyaster stage. The stage in nuclear division in which the rays of linin split longitudinally into two stars which move apart and form the daughter skeins, the amphiaster stage.

dyblastous. Two-celled.

dyclesium. Diclesium.

dyclosium. Diclesium.

dycotyl. Dicotyl.

dyhybrid ratio. The Mendelian proportions of 9:3:3:1.

-dynamous. A suffix indicating the degree of development of stamens, as didynamous flowers, with two stamen filaments longer or more mature than the others, or tetradynamous flowers, with four filaments longer or more mature than the others.

dynamic behavior. The influence of a species on the development of the communities of its sere. A species may be constructive, conserving, consolidating, neutral, or destructive.

dynamic cell. Any thick-walled prosenchymatous part having its molecules or micellae in transverse rings and undergoing marked longitudinal contraction in water.

dynamic center. The actual seat of various vital activities in a cell.

dynamic status. The condition of a unit or system with regard to its degree of relative equilibrium. The initial stage of the cycle is the condition of stress or pressure; the response to the pressure is the process of adjustment to the strain and leads to the condition of adjustment known as relative equilibrium.

dynamoplasm. The active portion of the protoplasm of a cell in contrast to the inert paraplasm.

dynamostatic elements. Hygroscopic motor cells.

dyplostemonous. Diplostemonous.

dyplotegium. Diplotegium.

dysanthic. Denoting fertilization by the pollen from a different plant.

dyschronous. Said of a species, genus, or family which does not overlap in period of blooming, or a group which does not contain species which overlap in blooming period.

dysgenesis. Infertility between hybrids from a cross which are fertile with either parent strain.

dysgenic. Detrimental to the racial qualities of future generations, impairing the hereditary qualities of an organism.

dysgenics. The study of racial degeneration and the factors contributing to it.

dysgeogenous. Growing on soils or rocks which do not readily yield detritus.

dysmerism. An aggregate of unlike parts.

dysmerogenesis. Segmentation resulting in unlike parts.

dysphotic. Living in deeper water where the light is at a minimum; dysphotistic.

dysphototropic. Adapted to a limited amount of light.

dysploid. Having an irregularity in the number of chromosomes in an organism.

dyssophytes. Plants which are sometimes hydrophytes and sometimes aerophytes.

dysteleologic. Evading the teleologic end, as a bee which obtains nectar by means which do not lead to pollination.

dysteleology. The doctrine of purposelessness in nature or the frustration of function.

dystrophic. Said of lake habitats in which humic acids and iron reduce the dissolved oxygen content and produce brown water, the condition found in peat bogs.

dystrophy. The damage to flowers caused by an insect which does not enter the flower in the usual way but perforates the perianth to remove the nectar without working the pollen mechanism, thereby damaging the flower and failing to achieve pollination of the stigma; distropy.

dystropous. Damaged by insect visitation without pollination.

dyticon. An inhabitant of the aqueous portion of partially moving media, as mud.

E

e-. A prefix meaning without or out of.

ear. 1. A large, dense or heavy spike or spike-like inflorescence, as the ear of corn.
2. The spike of a cereal. 3. A prominent lobe in some leaves.

ear cockles. A disease of wheat due to nematodes which infest the ear and cause the formation of a gall in which the larvae develop.

ear drop. The garden fuchsia.

ear-formed. Auriculate.

early wood. The less dense, larger-celled, first-formed part of a growth ring.

ebetate. With a dull, blunt, or soft point; hebetate.

ebony. A hard, heavy, durable wood obtained from several species of *Diospyros* in tropical Asia and Africa.

eborine. 1. Ivory white. 2. Of a consistency like ivory.

ebracteate. Without bracts or bracteoles.

ebracteolate. Destitute of bracteoles or bractlets.

eburneous. White like ivory.

ecad. A habitat form arising as a result of adaptation.

ecalcarate. Without a spur.

ecarinate. Without a carina or keel.

ecaudal. Without a tail or similar appendage, ecaudate.

ecballium. A succession of plants following lumbering.

ecblastesis. 1. The proliferation of the main axis of the inflorescence. 2. The production of buds in a flower in consequence of lateral proliferation.

eccentric. 1. Of a pileus, not attached in the center. 2. Out of the center or axis. 3. Not having the same center. Excentric.

eccentric oosphere. An oosphere in fungi which has one large fatty drop to one side, or several large drops included in the protoplasm to one side, or a crescentic set of small drops lying to one side.

ecdemic. Of foreign origin.

ecdysis. The act of shedding an outer cuticular layer.

ecesis. The germination and the establishment of invading plants.

echard. The soil water not available to plants.

echinate. With prickles or spines.

echinocarpous. Prickly-fruited.

echinosepalous. With prickly sepals.

echinulate. With minute and finely pointed spines.

echioid. Like *Echium*, a borage, viper's bugloss.

echlorophyllose. Without chlorophyll, scarious.

echma. The hardened, hook-shaped funicle in most *Acanthaceae* which supports the seed.

ecidio-climate. The climate of a very small place, a micro-climate.

ecidium. An aecidium.

eciliate. Without cilia.

ecize. To colonize.

ecoclimate. 1. The actual climate of the individual. 2. The total of the metereological factors within a habitat.

ecoclimatic forecasting of pests. The forecasting of pests taking into consideration the physiological life history and the seasonal course of the weather.

ecoclimax. The climax of a given period of dominance of a given plant group.

ecocline. 1. The aspect of a slope of a community. 2. The differentiation in community structure as a result of slope exposure as on two sides of a high ridge or mountain.

ecodichogamy. Monoecious asynchronism in fertilization.

ecogenesis. The origin of ecologic factors.

ecograph. An instrument to measure the physical factors of a station or habitat.

ecological. Pertaining to ecology, the science of organisms in relation to their natural environments; referring to the habitat or surroundings of a plant.

ecological-edaphic series. A series connected with a change of the nature of the soil within the limits of a given region.

ecological factor. Any environmental factor affecting a plant and plant community.

ecological optimum. The condition which offers the most favorable situation for the maximum development of a given organism.

ecological structure. All peculiarities in vegetation which are of ecological significance.

ecology. The study of the relations between the organism and its environment, including other living beings; the science of communities; ecologism.

ecology, physiographic. The study of the distribution of plants according to climate and soil.

economic botany. Applied botany, botany which treats of the botanical application of plants and plant products, the study of plants in the service of man.

economic coefficient. The percentage of weight produced by the consumption of 100 parts of a nutrient material.

ecoparasite. A specialized form of a parasitic fungus growing on one or more host species to which it is confined under normal circumstances.

ecophene. A plant developing from an ecotype in response to extreme habitat factors.

ecoprotandry. The maturation of the staminate flowers before the pistillate flowers.

ecoproterogyny. The maturation of the pistillate flowers before the staminate flowers.

ecornutous. Hornless.

ecorticate. Destitute of bark or covering.

ecospecies. An ecological race or subspecies which shows physiological differences brought about by environmental influences. They often exhibit reduced fertility. Okotypes.

ecostate. Without ribs or costae.

ecosystem. The entire system of life and its environmental and geographical factors which influence all life.

ecotone. The transition area on the ground between two plant communities, an area of mixed communities formed by the overlapping of adjoining communities in the transition area.

ecotype. A habitat type of plant, a sub-unit of the ecospecies produced by the reaction to its particular environment.

ecronic. Estuarine.

ecrustaceous. Without a thallus.

ect-, ecto-. A prefix meaning outside.

ectal layer. A thin membrane at the extreme edge of an excipulum.

ectauxesis. The growth of an organ outward through the parent shoot.

ectendotrophism. A combined type of parasitism, exterior and interior.

ectexine. The outer layer of exine of pollen grains or spores of vascular plants and bryophytes.

ectoascus. An outer ascus.

ectoblast. The outer envelope of a cell, the epiblast.

ectocarpoid. Resembling *Ectocarpus*, a genus of algae having gonads of ectodermal origin.

ectocyclic. Between the epidermis and the ring of sclerogen.

ectodynamic soil. Soil whose formation is predominantly conditioned by climate and the resulting vegetation.

ectogenesis. Variation induced by the influence of conditions outside the plant.

ectogenous. Capable of living outside a host, capable of living an independent life, ectogenic.

ectogeny. The effect of the pollen on the tissues of the female organs of the parent, ectogony.

ectokinetic. Dehiscing by an epidermal mechanism, as in a sporangium.

ectoparasite. A parasite that lives on the exterior of an organism.

ectopeptase. An enzyme in the excretions of plants (such as the pitcher liquid of *Nepenthes*) which peptonizes the more complex proteins.

ectophloeodal. Living on the outside of the bark, ectophloedic, ectophlocodal.

ectophloeodes. The organisms living on the surface or bark of other plants.

ectophloic. Lacking internal phloem.

ectophloic siponostele. A stele in which there is a zone of phloem outside the xylem but not inside.

ectophyte. An external plant parasite.

ectoplacodial. Having the placodium originating from the ectostroma.

ectoplasm. The plasma membrane of somewhat more dense protoplasm surrounding cells or unicellular organisms, the thin layer of hyaloplasm surrounding the cell contents, exoplasm.

ectoplast. 1. The edge of the cytoplasm where it comes into contact with the cell wall, the protoplasmic film or plasma membrane just within the true wall of a cell. 2. The cyanophycin granules in blue-green algae.

ectopy. The condition of having an organ in an abnormal position.

ectosarc. The outer surface of the cytoplasm of a plant cell lying against the inner surface of the cell wall, the ectoplast.

ectospore. A spore produced exogenously as at the tip of each sterigma in basidiomycetes, a basidiospore.

ectosporium. The outer layer of a spore in bacteria.

ectosporous. Having spores formed exogenously, exosporous.

ectostroma. The epistroma.

ectothecal. Having an exposed or naked hymenium, as in the ascomycetes.

ectothiobacteria. Bacteria which form sulfur outside the cells.

ectothioleukaceae. Colorless bacteria with the sulfur outside the cells.

ectothrix. A parasite which grows on the surface of hair such as the organism which causes barber's itch.

ectotroph. A parasite feeding from the outside of its host.

ectotrophic. 1. Finding nourishment from the outside. 2. Living on the surface of the host.

ectotrophic infection. See ECTOTROPHIC MYCHORRHIZA.

ectotrophic mycorrhiza. 1. A fungus which lives outside the tissue of the host. 2. A mycorrhiza which surrounds the roots of its host plant with a close web of hyphae and seldom enters the root hairs.

ectotropic. 1. On the outside. 2. With outward curvature.

ectotropism. Outward curvature, as the course of the pollen tube through the micropyle to the embryo sac or as the hyphae running between instead of through the epidermal cells.

ecyphellate. Destitute of cyphellae (in lichens).

edaphic characters. The nature of the physical and chemical condition of the soil and other local physiographic factors.

edaphic climax. See EDAPHIC FORMATION.

edaphic climax association. 1. An association complex which is related to a specific physiographic area. 2. The culminating development of a specific plant succession within the regional climax association.

edaphic factors. 1. The conditions due to the physical structure or chemical nature of the soil or water or in whatever medium plants grow. 2. All factors other than atmosphere. See PHYTOBIOTIC FACTORS.

edaphic formation. An association complex which is related to a specific physiographic unit area.

edaphic formation type. Edaphic formations correlated with a common type of physiognomic unit area.

edaphon. The biota of the soil and humus layers of a community, the qualities of the soil as regards plant growth, edaphos.

edaphonekton. The organisms living in free soil water.

edaphophytes. Plants which root in the earth with organs of assimilation in the air.

edaphotropism. Tropistic responses to soil water.

edema. Oedema.

edentate. Without teeth.

edestin. A crystalline globulin found in many edible seeds, as in oats, maize, wheat, rye, etc.

edged. Having a margin differing in texture, form, or color from the remainder of the surface.

edible products. Foodstuffs (in a wide sense) which are obtained from stores of reserve foods in plants, the seeds, cereals, roots, etc.

edobole. A plant whose seeds are scattered by propulsion through turgescence of fruits or sporangia.

edominant. Denoting secondary or accessory species which exert little or no dominance in a community.

edominule. An edominant of a micro-community.

edulis. Edible.

eel-trap hairs. Hairs found in structures which detain insect visitors.

eel-grass. A sea plant (*Zostera marina*) whose grass-like leaves are used for sound insulation and for the correction of acoustical defects.

effete. Functionless from age, no longer productive or fruitful, effoetus.

efficiency index. The rate at which dry matter accumulates in a plant.

efficient difference. The amount of a physical factor necessary to produce a change in the response.

effigurate. Having a definite form or distinct shape.

effigurations. Outgrowths of the receptacle or torus.

efflorescence. The production of blossoms, anthesis, the season of flowering; see ASPECTION.

effluent. Outflow, purified or partly purified sewage running from the filter beds.

effoetus. Effete.

effoliation. Exfoliation.

effuse. Loosely spreading, very diffuse, spread out with a poorly defined edge.

effuse-diatrypoid. Having broadly erumpent stroma of the diatrypoid kind; see EUTYPOID.

effused-reflexed. Spreading out over the substrate and turned back at the margin to form a pileus.

effusion. 1. The act of effusing or pouring out. 2. An intermingling of gases under different pressures through openings in membranes.

eflagelliferous. Having no flagella.

efoliolate. Without leaves, scales, or squamae; efoliolose.

efoveolate. Having no pits or depressions.

efulcrate. With buds from which the customary leaf or bract has fallen.

egg. The female gamete, the female germ cell, the oosphere.

egg apparatus. A group of three primordial cells at the micropylar end of the embryo sac consisting of two synergids and the egg cell (found in plants with enclosed seeds).

egg cell. The oosphere or gynogamete, the female gamete.

egg nucleus. The nucleus of the egg cell.

egg plant. A solanaceous plant of East Indian origin related to the potato.

egg sac. The mesochite and endochite of the *Fucaceae*, the membranes which enclose the egg.

egg spore. The oospore.

eglandular. Without glands, eglandalose.

egranulose. Without granules.

egret. Any feathery crown or tuft attached to the seed, the pappus or coma.

ehilatous. Imperforate, as pollen grains without perforations.

Einzelbestände. A representative example of an association.

eisodal. The anterior or outer pore of stomata.

eisodal aperture. The enlargement of the stomatal pore nearest the surface of the leaf.

ejaculation of spores. Forceful expulsion of spores from a sporangium or from a capsule. Ejection of spores.

ektexine. The exine or extine.

ektodynamorphous soil. A soil changed by external factors.

elaborate. To change from a crude state to a state capable of assimilation, to form complex organic substances from simple materials.

elaboration. The total of the changes which take place after the absorption of food material to fit it for the use of the plant; see ASSIMILATION.

elaeagnifolious. With leaves like *Elaeagnus*, the oleasters.

elaeoclaphines. Certain bodies in spongy and palisade parenchyma similar to elaioplasts, probably oil bodies.

elaeodic. Olive green, brownish green.

elaioleucite. An elaioplast.

elaioplankton. Plankton which floats by means of fatty material.

elaioplast. A plastid which forms oils and fats in plant cells.

elaioplastid. A plastid which stores reserve food in the form of fat.

elaiosomes. An outgrowth from the surface of a seed containing fatty or oily material (often the food attractive to ants) and serving in seed dispersal; see MYRME-COCHORY.

elaisospheres. Bodies similar to elaioplasts which are found in spongy and palisade parenchyma.

elaphines. Tawny or fulvous.

elaphinous. 1. Fawn colored. 2. Pronged like a fawn's horns.

elastic limit. The maximum load which a vegetable fiber can support without permanent stretching.

elastin. An albuminoid which forms the chief constituent of elastic tissues.

elata. Tall.

elater. A sterile, elastic, spirally twisted, hygroscopic filament found mixed with the spores of some liverworts which assists in expelling the spores from the spore case; a free capillitium thread, strap-shaped bands around the spores of *Equisetum*.

elaterin. The active principle of the fruit of the squirting cucumber.

elaterium. 1. A cathartic and diuretic drug obtained from the squirting cucumber (*Ecballium elaterium*) which forcefully discharges its seeds and mucilaginous contents from a turgid fruit. 2. One of the carpels of a compound fruit which contains a single seed (a coccus).

elaterophore. 1. The organ which bears the elaters in the *Hepaticae*. 2. The central core of sterile tissue in the sporangium of the *Jungermaniales*.

elcotropism. See ELECTROTROPISM.

election. The selection of the fittest as opposed to the elimination of the unfit specimens.

elective. See SELECTIVE SPECIES.

electosome. A chondriosome which is regarded as a center for elaborating and fixing chemical constituents of protoplasm.

electrine. Amber yellow.

electro-culture. The stimulation of the growth of plants by electrical means.

electrotropism. The electric impulse which governs certain plant functions such as the inflection of roots or shoots toward the cathode, a reaction to an electric current.

electrosis. Reaction from an electric current.

electrotaxis. The orientation or movement within an electric field, a response induced by electric currents.

electrotonic. Pertaining to the state of electric tension.

electrotonus. A latent period of electric stress.

electro-vegetometer. An apparatus made of wires above plants to be electrified by atmospheric electricity.

electuaries. Medicines of conserves and powders in honey.

element. The simple chemically indivisible substances of which all matter consists.

elementary association. See FACIES.

elementary organs. The constituents of cellular and vascular tissue.

elemi. A fragrant oleo-resin obtained from various tropical trees which is used in making varnish and medicinal ointments and plasters, balsams.

eleoplast. An elaioplast.

elephant's ear. A very common tropical plant so-called because of the extremely large leaves found in many species.

elephant's foot. A common name for any species of *Elephantopus*, asteraceous herbs.

elepidote. Destitute of scurfy scales.

eleutherantherous. With the anthers distinct and not united.

eleuteropetalous. Having petals free or separate and distinct, polypetalous, choripetalous.

eleutherophyllous. Having the components of the perianth whorls free.

eleuthero-. A prefix meaning separate and distinct.

eleutherosepalous. Having sepals free and separate.

eleutherotepalous. With free tepals, polytepalous, eleutherophyllous.

elevated. 1. Of a pileus, raised at the margin. 2. Raised above the surface of the matrix as in lichens.

elfin trees. An alpine forest composed of trees distorted from living in a mountain climate.

elfin wood. An alpine forest distorted by mountain climate.

eligulatae. The lycopods which have no ligules.

elitriculus. An elytriculus.

elittoral. The coastal region below the sublittoral extending as far as the light penetrates.

elleborin. An acrid resin obtained from *Eranthus hyemalis*, a ranunculus.

ellipsoid. A solid body which is elliptic in section used to denote the shape of certain inflorescences.

elliptic. 1. With the outline of an ellipse, about twice as long as wide. 2. Oblong and rounded at the ends.

elliptic-fusiform. Said of the shape of spores which are fundamentally fusiform but somewhat elliptical.

elliptic-lanceolate. Intermediate between elliptical and lanceolate but approaching the latter.

ellitoral. Ellittoral.

elocular. Being without divided locules, unilocular.

elodioid. Denoting a linear leaf.

elongate-acuminate. Long and drawn out to a point.

elongating stage. The period of growth when an organ increases in length before secondary thickening starts.

eluviation. The separation of the finer particles from the heavier by a stream of water, elutration.

eluvium. Sand-blown dunes.

elymetum. An association of *Elymus arenarius*, wild rye.

elymus. 1. Rolled up or enveloped. 2. The genus of that name.

elytriculus. A floret in the composites.

elytriform. Similar to the wing case of a beetle, resembling an elytrum.

elytron. An elutron, cover, or sheath.

emarcid. Flaccid, withered, decayed.

emarginate. 1. Having a notch or a sinus at the end. 2. Of gills, notched near the stipe.

emasculation. 1. The act of removing the anthers from a flower. 2. The removal of the stamens before they open and shed their pollen.

embedded veins. Veins which are surrounded on all sides by assimilatory tissue.

embolic. Pushing or growing in.

embolus. 1. Anything pointed so as to be put or thrust in. 2. A plug which covers the foramen of the ovule.

embossed. Having a slight central nodule or a small central hump.

embracing. Clasped by the base.

embryo. 1. The young plant developed from the fertilized egg cell. 2. A rudimentary plant still enclosed in the seed, the young sporophyte resulting from the union of male and female sex cells.

embryo bud. A rudimentary bud.

embryo cell. One of two cells formed from the first division of the fertilized egg in certain plants which develops into the embryo (the other develops into the suspensor), the oosphere.

embryo cord. A single row of cells which connects the embryo with the outer surface of the albumen.

embryo, fixed. A leaf bud.

embryo nodules. Small knots found beneath the bark in certain trees sometimes containing one or more rudimentary buds, the embryo buds.

embryo sac. In seed plants the great, thin-walled cell in which the fertilization of the ovum and the development of the embryo takes place.

embryo, secondary. The embryo-sac tubes.

embryo tubes. Tubular upgrowths and compartment walls within which the female nuclei of *Welwitschia* are conducted to the nucellar cone.

embryoblastanon. The suspensor in cycads.

embryogenic. Of or pertaining to the development of the embryo.

embryogenic bodies. Naked masses of protoplasm at the end of the zygospore (in mucors) derived from the nuclei which ultimately fuse to become embryonic spheres surrounded by a double wall.

embryogenic spheres. Embryogenic bodies.

embryogeny. The formation of the embryo.

embryogeny, direct. The condition in which a spore gives rise to an embryo which resembles the adult form.

embryogeny, heteroblastic. A condition in which the embryo differs widely from the adult form and is not borne direct but as a lateral outgrowth.

embryogeny, holoblastic. Embryogeny in which the whole of the ovum takes part.

embryogeny, homoblastic. Direct embryogeny.

embryogeny, indirect. Heteroblastic embryogeny.

embryogeny, meroblastic. The development in which only a portion of the ovum is involved.

embryology. The study of the embryological development of organisms.

embryon. The rudimentary plantlet formed in a seed, the embryo.

embryonal. Belonging to or related to the embryo.

embryonal cell. The oospore before fertilization.

embryonal tube. A tier of cells produced by a basal tier of suspensor cells in the embryo of vascular plants, the secondary suspensors.

embryonic vesicle. The oosphere previous to fertilization.

embryonary sac. The embryo sac.

embryonate. With an embryo.

embryonic. Rudimentary, in an early undeveloped stage.

embryonic appendage. The apical portion of the suspensors in grasses.

embryonic development. The growth and development of the embryo.

embryonic sac. The embryo sac.

embryonic shield. A shield-like thickened area of the walls of the blastodermic vesicle in which the embryo proper is formed.

embryonic tissue. The meristematic tissue.

embryonic vescicle. The egg, the oospore previous to fertilization.

embryophore. 1. A suspensor having the lower cell cut off by a septum in the oosphere and then further divided into two quadrants one of which becomes the foot and the other the first root. 2. A ciliated envelope which encloses the embryo.

embryophyta siphonogamia. Plants having pollen tubes, as have practically all flowering plants.

embryophyta zoidiogamia. Cryptogams having ciliated spermatozoids.

embryophyte. A plant which forms an embryo.

embryophytic branches. Peculiar branches in *Chara* which resemble an embryo and which become separate and grow into new plants.

embryophytic spheres. Embryogenic spheres.

embryotegium. A small callose cap which covers the micropyle in certain seeds and which is detached by the radicle on germination. Embryostegium.

embryotropha. Perisperm.

embryotrophy. Nourishment of the embryo by perisperm.

emergences. Growths such as thorns on plant roots, stems, or leaves which lack vascular tissue and arise from subepidermal or cortical tissues and never function or develop into roots, stems, or leaves.

emergent. Suddenly appearing, as capsules which rise slightly above the perichaetum.

emerging belt. The belt extending landwards from the low-tide mark above the high-tide mark to a distance proportionate to the force of the water.

emersed. Raised above and out of the water, emerging, rising out of the water instead of floating on it.

emersiherbosa. Communities of fens, sedge swamps, reed swamps, and salt marshes; the upper portion of moist meadows.

emersiprata. 1. Marsh plants which root in water-covered or -saturated soil but have their leafy shoots erect above the surface. 2. The upper portion of moist meadows.

emetin. An alkaloid supposed to appear in *Psycotria Ipecacuanha* and similar emetic roots.

eminence. A ridge or projection on the surface of leaves.

emissaria. Hydathodes, water glands.

emissivity, thermal. The interchange of heat between a leaf and its surroundings.

emmenagogue. A medicine which produces menstruation of which many are plant derivatives.

emodin. A glucoside obtained from buckthorn and a species of rhubarb, an orange red crystalline purgative.

emophytes. Plants which are entirely submerged and have no functional stomata.

empaled. Hemmed in, as the flowers by the calyx.

empalement. The calyx.

empalers. Segments of the calyx.

empennate. Pinnate.

empetrifolious. With leaves like *Empetrum*, the crowberry.

emphysematose. Bladdery, emphysematous.

emphytism. The inheritance of a simple type of growth force.

emphytogenesis. The origin of the inherited growth force.

emphytogenous. Denoting graft hybrids.

empirical thresholds. Any threshold assumed or calculated which is not approximately correct for the organism in question, an imaginary threshold.

empiric diagram. A scheme to show the relative number and position of parts of a flower.

emprosthrodromous. Having a flower with the genetic spiral on its shortest way from the bract to the outermost perianth segment passing outside the flower farthest from the axis.

empty glumes. Sterile glumes, as those of a spikelet whose axiles are without flowers or the glumes which subtend a spikelet in grasses and enclose one or more flowers.

emulsin. An enzyme which acts upon glucosides. It is abundant in almonds, fungi, and other plants.

emulsoid. A colloid which is liquid under ordinary environmental conditions.

-en. A suffix indicating larger societies or layer societies.

enalid. A submerged marine plant which grows on the loose soil of the sea bottom, as eel grass, *Zostera*.

enantioblastae. Plants which have the embryo at the end of the seed diametrically opposite the hilum.

enantioblastic. Of or pertaining to the enantioblastae, enantioblastous.

enantiostylous. Having styles protruded to the right or left of the axis with the stamens opposite, enatiostylous.

enantiostyly. The condition of being enantiostylous.

enate. Growing out.

enation. 1. An outgrowth from another organ. 2. An outgrowth from the veins on the underside of a leaf.

enation theory. A theory of the evolution of vascular plant structures which proposes that a simple leaf evolved from a bud or outgrowth from a leafless stem. As evolution progressed, the structures enlarged and a vascular system developed and extended until a leaf or fern frond was eventually produced.

enaulad. A sand draw plant.

enaulium. A sand draw community.

enaulophilous. Dwelling on sand dunes.

enaulophyte. A plant which inhabits sand draws.

encapsuled. Enclosed in a firm envelope.

encarpium. A sporophore.

encasing. Being enclosed by cellulose caps of protoplasm in the cells of certain trichomes.

enchylema. The more fluid portion of the cell contents.

enclaves. Openings of prairies in forests.

encyonemetum. An algal association, *Spirogyra* (*Encyonema*).

encyst. To enclose or become enclosed in a cyst or capsule.

encystment. The formation of a walled, nonmotile body from a swimming spore.

endarch. 1. Having the first-formed woodsubstance nearest the center, i.e., having the xylem with the protoxylem nearer the center of the axis, as in seed plants. 2. Having a single simple protoxylem surround a central parenchyma.

endarch primary xylem. A bundle with protoxylem turned inward in the stele and the metaxylem turned outward.

endauxesis. Growth on the inner side of an organ relative to the main shoot.

end bud. The bud at the end of the twig in case the terminal bud is self-pruned, the characteristic growing tip of a stem or its branch.

end bulb. A minute cylindrical or oval body consisting of a capsule containing a semifluid core in which the axis cylinder terminates either in a bulbous extremity or in a coiled plexiform mass.

endeca-. A prefix meaninng eleven.

endecagynian. Having eleven pistils or styles, endecagynous.

endecandrous. Having eleven stamens.

endecaphyllous. Having eleven leaves or leaflets.

endemic. Occurring in one limited locality or region only, indigenous.

endemic disease. A disease confined to a relatively localized area and apparently having no tendency to spread.

endemism. A situation in which a species is limited to a restricted area.

enderon. The inner or endodermal layer.

enderonic. Of or pertaining to the endodermal layer.

endexine. The inner layer of the exine of pollen grains or spores.

endhymenine. The intine, the innermost coat of a pollen grain.

endistem. Young pith.

endive. *Cichorium endivia*, a vegetable used as salad or greens.

endiviaceous. Light blue like the flower of endive or chicory.

endo-. A prefix meaning within.

endoascus. An inner ascus.

endobasidial. 1. Having a sporophore with a secondary sporiferous branch. 2. With an enclosed basidium.

endobasidium. An enclosed basidium as in the gasteromycetes.

endobiotic. 1. Growing or living inside another plant. 2. Formed inside the host plant.

endoblast. The hypoblast.

endoblem. Tissue beneath the dermatogen made up of small-celled parenchyma.

endocarp. The usually woody-textured inner layer of the pericarp.

endocarpanthous. Superior, as applied to a flower or its parts.

endocarpoid. Having disc-like covered ascocarps embedded in the thallus, resembling the lichen genus *Endocarpon*.

endocaryogamy. The last stage of sexual degeneration in which no foreign nuclear material is introduced from without and cytological development is wholly internal and intracellular, endogamy; see EXOCARYOGAMY.

endocatadromous. With the stronger veins and pinnules of a fern frond nearer the rachis.

endocellular enzyme. An enzyme which is excreted by an organism when it is no longer needed.

endochite. The innermost membrane of the egg in *Fucaceae*.

endochlorites. Chlorophyllous plastids contained in achroocysts.

endochroa. The inner layer of the cuticle.

endochrome. 1. The coloring matter other than chlorophyll in cells. 2. The colored cell-contents of a spore.

endochrome plate. A band of yellowish chromatophores found in the protoplasm of certain diatoms.

endochyle. A plant having its water-tissue within the assimilating tissues.

endochylous. Of or pertaining to endochyles.

endococcoid. Resembling the lichen genus *Endococcus*.

endoconidia. 1. Thin-walled asexual spores abstricted internally. 2. Conidia formed inside a hypha. 3. Endogonidia.

endoconidiophore. The organ which produces endoconidia.

endocortex. The innermost layer of the cortical region.

endocribrose. Inside the sieve tubes.

endocyst. A probable sex organ in the frustules of certain diatoms.

endodermal pressure. Root pressure.

endodermis. A firmly built sheath of cells one layer thick which surrounds the stele. The cells develop characteristic bands of thickening (the Casperian strip) which influence the horizontal movement of water in roots and stems.

endodermogens. The vascular cryptogams.

endodermoid. Like the endodermis.

endodynamomorphic soils. Soils whose formation is conditioned chiefly by the character of the underlying soils.

endo-ectothrix. Growing both on the surface and within a hair of hypha.

endo-form. Of *Uredinales*, having only aecial and pycnial stages.

endogamous. Of or pertaining to endogamy.

endogamy. 1. The union of two or more female gametes. 2. Pollination between two flowers from the same plant. 3. Sexual union of haplonts derived from the same diplonts or the same zygote. 4. Inbreeding.

endogelatin. A mucilaginous or pectin-like layer found in the megasporium of some brown algae which when swollen is effective in expelling the megaspore.

endogenesis. The development from within.

endogenous. 1. Forming new tissue within the plant. 2. Originating from internal tissues. 3. Forming inside another organ of a plant. 4. Growing throughout the substance of the stem (as in monocotyledons) rather than by successive consecutive layers (as in dicotyledons).

endogenous cell formation. Free cell formation.

endogenous multiplication. Spore formation.

endogenous origin. The development of a new part from deeply seated tissue.

endogenous plants. An old name for monocotyledonous plants, the plants which grow by central deposits of new tissue (as in the monocotyledons) rather than by growth in an outer ring of tissue as in the dicotyledonous plants.

endogenous spores. The spores formed within a cell or sporangium.

endogenous structure. Stem structure in which pith and woody fibers are indiscriminately mingled.

endogenous thallus. The thallus of a lichen in which the alga predominates.

endogens. Plants which were presumed to grow by internal growth within the stem because of the scattered arrangement of the bundles; the endogenae, the monocotyledons.

endogeny. The development from a deep-seated layer.

endogonidium. A gonidium formed within a receptacle or gonidangium.

endogonium. The contents of the nucule of *Chara*.

endohaustorium. A body resembling a young haustorium within a cell of a plant infected by rust fungi.

endokaryogamy. Endogamy.

endokinetic. Opening by mechanisms of internal organs as in some fruiting bodies.

endolithic. 1. Growing below the surface of limestone rock. 2. Embedded in rock or penetrating rock. 3. Endolithophytic.

endolysin. An intracellular substance of leucocytes which destroys engulfed bacteria.

endome. The inner layer of the pachyte, the phelloderma.

endomeristem. The meristem in a moss which produces the central strand.

endomesoderm. Mesoderm derived from primary endoderm.

endomitosis. The production of more than double the haploid number of chromosomes without nuclear division.

endomixis. The intermingling of nuclear and cytoplasmic substances in the cell resulting in a reorganization without conjugation.

endonastic. Having an antropous or campylotropous ovule in which the curvature is horizontal toward the edge of the carpel.

endonucleolus. A space inside the nucleolus.

endonucleus. The nucleolo-nucleus.

endoparasite. A parasite which lives inside the body of the host.

endoperidium. The inner layer of the peridium, the inner peridium.

endopetrion. A plant growing in the interstices of rocks.

endophelloderm. The inner phelloderm formed outside the cortex of a stem and inside the phelloderm.

endophloem. The inner bark.

endophloic. Of the inner bark.

endophragma. A partition found in the fronds of some seaweeds.

endophyllous. Enclosed in a leaf or sheath as the young leaves of monocotyledons.

endophytal. Growing within other plants.

endophyte. A plant which grows within another plant upon which it may or may not be parasitic.

endophytic. Living in cavities of other plants.

endophytic mycorrhiza. See ENDOTROPHIC MYCORRHIZA.

endoplacodial. A hardened layer of hyphae edging the opening of some perithecia which has developed from beneath the epistroma.

endoplasm. The inner or central granular portion of the cytoplasm in a cell, the endosarc.

endoplast. 1. The granular protoplasmic contents of a cell. 2. Bodies in the centroplasm in the blue-green algae.

endoplastid. A plastid which contains one starch granule which may be simple or compound.

endopleura. The inner seed coat, integument, tegmen.

endoprothalleae. The phanerogams.

endoptile. An embryo whose plumule is rolled up in the cotyledon.

endorhizae. Monocotyledons.

endorhizal. Having an embryo with the radicle sheathed by the cotyledon or with the plumule wrapped around it which gives rise to secondary rootlets instead of lengthening as in many monocotyledons.

endorhizoid. A rhizoid formed at the base of a seta of a bryophyte which penetrates the gametophyte.

endorhizus. An embryo in monocotyledons which has the radicle sheathed by the cotyledon or plumule wrapped around it.

endosaprophytism. The destruction of the algal contents of lichens by the enzymes of the fungus.

endosarc. Endoplasm.

endosclerotium. A persistent tuber-like mycelium of endogenous origin.

endoscopic. Having the apical pole of a plant embryo turned towards the base of the archegonium, as in seed plants.

endoskeleton. An internal skeleton.

endosmometer. An instrument to measure endosmosis.

endosmose. To pass as a liquid or gas through a differentially permeable membrane into a cell.

endosmosis. Osmosis into a cell.

endosome. A chromatinic mass near the center of the vesicular nucleus, a karyosome.

endosperm. 1. The multicellular food-storing tissue formed inside a seed of flowering plants following the double fertilization of the embryo sac by the second sperm nucleus. 2. The prothallus of the female gametophyte of gymnosperms.

endosperm nucleus. The nucleus of the angiosperm embryo sac from which the endosperm of the embryo sac develops.

endospermic. Having endosperm (albumen) or associated with it.

endosphaerine. Related to or resembling *Endosphaera*, a genus of the *Protococcaceae*, green algae.

endosphaerosira. A small stunted form of the male plant of the alga *Volvox*.

endospore. 1. The innermost layer of the wall or membrane of a spore or pollen grain, the intine of a pollen grain. 2. A spore formed inside a mother cell. 3. A spore without sex.

endosporous. Having endogenously formed spores.

endostere. The timber of an exogen without the pith.

endostome. 1. The orifice in the inner coat of an ovule. 2. The inner row of teeth of the peristome.

endotesta. The hard liquefied inner integument of the seed of *Cordia*.

endotheca. The oval surface of cystidia.

endothecial. 1. Of or pertaining to an endothecium. 2. Having asci enclosed in an ascocarp.

endothecium. 1. The inner tissue of a young sporogonium. 2. The inner fibrous layer of an anther.

endothelium. The endodermis.

endothermic. Denoting the internal changes of heat within a plant.

endothiobacteria. The bacteria which temporarily store sulfur within their cells.

endothioleukaceae. The colorless sulfur bacteria.

endothrix. A group of fungi found growing within a hair, the ringworm fungi.

endotoxin. Toxin produced within the cell.

endotroph. A parasitic fungus feeding internally on its host.

endotrophic. 1. Having parasites or commensals within the cells of a host. 2. Nourished from within.

endotrophic mycorrhiza. A mycorrhiza in which the fungus occupies the living cells of the host.

endotrophy. The condition of thickened growth of a shoot in the direction of the parent shoot.

endotropic. 1. Exhibiting inward curvature. 2. Fertilized by pollen from another flower of the same plant. 3. Following the path of the pollen tube in basigamic fertilization.

endotrypase. A proteolytic enzyme in yeasts.

endouredinales. See ENDOFORM.

endoxylophyte. A parasite living in plants.

endoxylous. Within wood.

endozoic. 1. Living in an animal. 2. Referring to dispersal of seeds by animals who have eaten and voided them at some distance from the plant.

endozoochory. The dispersal of seeds by animals after passing through the digestive tract.

endozoophyte. An organism living in animals, frequently a pathogen.

endotrypsin. A proteolytic enzyme in yeast.

endysis. Development of a new coat.

eneilema. The inner skin of a seed.

energesis. The process by which energy is liberated through catabolic action; see RESPIRATION.

energetics. The science which treats of the transformation of energy.

energid. 1. Any living uninucleated protoplasmic unit with or without a cell wall. 2. The nucleus and protoplasm as a vital unit.

energy, kinetic. The energy of actual motion.

energy, potential. Energy of position.

enervious. Without veins.

enervis. Nerveless, without visible ribs or veins, enervose.

Eng-forest. Forests of India dominated by *Dipterocarpus* (Eng is the local name for the tree).

English type of distribution. The distribution of plants whose range in Great Britain is central in England proper.

engram. A character impression in the mnemonic theory of heredity: the tendency in the nucleus of a somatic cell to be transferred to a sexual cell so as to transmit the special structure or function.

engraved. With irregular linear grooves on the surface.

enhalid community. Plants in the loose soils of the littoral region, a salt area community.

enhalid formation. Spermatophytes and larger algae growing on loose soil in salt water where *Enhalus*, a marine plant of the *Hydrocharitaceae* family, occurs.

ennea-. A prefix meaning nine.

enneacanthous. Nine-spined.

enneagynous. With nine separate styles or carpels.

enneandria. Plants having nine stamens.

enneandrous. Having nine stamens.

enneapetalous. Having nine petals.

enneaphyllous. Having nine leaves.

enneasepalous. With nine sepals.

enneasome. With nine chromosomes.

enneaspermous. With nine seeds.

ennobling. An old term for inarching.

enodal. Without a node or knots.

enphytotic. Refers to a disease regularly occurring in a locality and not likely to vary in destructiveness, the opposite of epiphytotic.

ensate. Shaped like a sword with a straight blade; ensiform.

ensifolious. Having sword-shaped leaves, as the iris.

ensiform. Sword-shaped, having sharp edges and tapering to a slender point.

ensporulation. The reproduction of bacteria.

entelechian. Of or pertaining to entelechy.

entelechy. The vital element that controls and directs the response of organisms to stimuli.

enterokinase. An enzyme which converts trypsinogen into trypsin.

enterophleodes. The lichens which can thrive in bark, wood, etc., only after it has undergone weathering.

enterophloedal. Of or pertaining to the enterophleodes.

entire. Concerning leaf margins or gills without teeth or marginal divisions; with a continuous, even margin.

entire frond. A fern leaf or frond consisting of one piece.

entire margin. A margin without indentations of any sort.

ento-. A prefix meaning within.

entocycle. The sieve tubes on the inner side of the ring of the sclerenchyma in the *Cucurbitaceae*.

entocyclic. Referring to the sieve tubes.

entoderm. Endoderm.

entodiscalis. Inserted within a disc as in some stamens.

entomochoric. Depending upon insects for dissemination.

entomochory. Dissemination by insects.

entomogamy. Pollination of flowers by insects.

entomogenous. Said of fungi which are parasitic on insects.

entomophagous. Denoting organisms parasitizing insects.

entomophilae. Plants in which pollination is carried on by insects.

entomophilous. Being pollinated by insects, adapted to insect pollination, having spores disseminated by insects.

entomophilous flowers. Flowers which are insect-pollinated.

entomophilous plants. Plants in which pollen is transported to the stigma by insects.

entomophily. State of being entomophilous.

entomophytal. Entomogenous.

entomophytous. Growing on insects.

entoparasite. A parasite living entirely within its host.

entoparasitic. Being parasitic within the host.

entophytal. Endophytic.

entophyte. An endophyte.

entophytic. Endophytic.

entoplacodial. Originating at least in part from the entostroma.

entoplasm. The inner surface of the cytosome as opposed to ectoplasm.

enterhizoid. The root-like structure of the sporophyte in mosses, a rhizoid from the foot of the seta of a moss which grows down into the tissue of the gametophyte.

entosphere. The inner portion of the attraction sphere.

entospore. A spore which has its own membrane which is formed inside another cell.

entostroma. Hypostroma.

entozoic. Endozoic.

entrance. The outer aperture of a stoma.

enucleate. 1. Without a nucleus. 2. To remove a nucleus.

enucleation. The manipulatory removal of a nucleus from a cell.

envelope. The perianth or calyx and corolla, an integument or cover.

envelope apparatus. All of the ascocarp except the ascus apparatus.

envelope cell. The common hyaline envelope of a colony of *Stephanasphaeria.*

envelopes, floral. The perianth or its analogues.

environmental resistance. The resistance imposed upon the numerical increase of a species by the physical and biological factors of the environment.

enzootic. Affecting animals.

enzymatic. Of or pertaining to enzymes.

enzymatically. In the manner of an enzyme.

enzymes. Organic catalysts which are produced by living cells which bring about specific (usually intracellular) transformations. Each enzyme catalyzes only one reaction or type of reaction within a very limited range.

enzymes, amylolytic. Enzymes which convert starch into sugar.

enzymes, fat. Enzymes which convert olein into oleic acid and glycerine.

enzymes, genetic. Formative substances.

enzymes, glucoside. See EMULSIN.

enzymes, heterolytic. Enzymes which split substances into more than one substance.

enzymes, homolytic. Enzymes which turn a substance into more of the same nature.

enzymes, hydrolytic. Enzymes which split due to hydrolysis.

enzymes, invert. Enzymes which turn cane sugar into grape sugar.

enzymes, oxidizing. Enzymes which assist in the oxidation of various substances.

enzymes, proteolytic. Enzymes such as trypsin which decompose protein.

enzymoid. Resembling an enzyme.

enzymology. The study of enzymes.

enzymolysis. The breaking up of a substance by the solvent power of an enzyme.

enzymosis. The changes induced by the action of an enzyme.

enzymotic. Acting as an enzyme.

Eocene. The earliest or oldest division of the Tertiary Period in the Cenozoic Era.

eocladous. Having leaves which in development become branched in the meristematic state.

eolian erosion. Erosion by wind.

eophytic. Designating the earliest plant life.

eoplasm. The theoretical primitive substance which precedes protoplasm.

eosere. A great era of succession, the development of vegetation during an eon or era.

eosin. A common dye named from the fine rose-red color it imparts to tissue. It is obtained by the action of bromine on fluorescein.

eosin-singed. Referring to a type of fruit fly with easily recognized characters used to demonstrate hereditary patterns in linkage experiments.

eosinophil. Tissue which stains with eosin.

eostase. The series of geological layers resulting from an eosere.

eostrate. 1. The total of all the strates in the same great vegetative era. 2. A succession after a stase when the inorganic matter exceeds the organic.

epacme. The stage in the phylogeny of a group just before it reaches its summit.

epactile. In the upper littoral zone of the ocean.

epanody. The reversion from an irregular to a regular condition, as in flowers.

epanthous. Growing on flowers, as certain fungi.

epapillate. Having no papillae.

epaxial. Above the axis, dorsal, having an axis formed by a vertical column.

epedaphic. Pertaining to or depending upon climatic conditions.

epeirogenic. Said of earth movements raising continents.

epelliculose. Without a covering or pellicle.

epenchyma. The fibrovascular tissue, the cambium.

ephaptomenon. A major life-form division referring to adnate types and including several life-form classes.

epharmonic adaptation. Change in form or physiology beneficial to an organism evoked by the operating of some stimulating factor in the environment.

epharmonic convergence. Resemblance in external appearance and in structure between plants which are not closely related in their systematic positions.

epharmonism, physiologic. The methods by which the plant adapts to sun and drought.

epharmony. A growth form in contradistinction to its systematic form, the process of adaption by organisms to new conditions of environment, the process of changing form due to environmental conditions.

ephebic. Being in a stage in phylogeny between childhood and the old age stage of a group.

ephebogenetic. Matured, applied to the development of sperm cells.

ephemer. 1. An introduced plant which is unable to exist and soon disappears. 2. A flower which closes after a short term of expansion.

ephemeral. Continuing only for a day or less, evanescent, short-lived.

ephemeral movement. A change in position of a structure of a plant which can take place only once, as a flower which opens and blooms for one day only.

ephemeral petals. The petals which last for one day.

ephemerophyte. A plant which is very short-lived.

ephydrogamicae. Plants in which the flowers are pollinated on the surface of the water.

ephydrogamy. The condition of being pollinated on the surface of water.

epi-. A prefix meaning upon, above, beside, or on the outside.

epiachene. An achene developed from an inferior ovary, i.e., developed above the ovary.

epiascidium. A funnel formed from a leaf with the inner surface corresponding to the upper surface of the leaf.

epibasal. In front of the basal wall, as in the anterior half of a proembryo or the upper segment of an oospore which ultimately gives rise to a shoot.

epibasal cell. The upper cell of an oospore in the bryophytes and pteridophytes.

epibasal half. The anterior portion of an embryo.

epibasal hemisphere. The part of an embryo lying above the basal wall.

epibasal octants. The subsequent divisions of the epibasal cell.

epibasidium. The four appendages which are frequently separated from the basal cell or hypobasidium by a septum. The hypobasidium and the epibasidia make up a heterobasidium.

epibenthos. Plants and animals found living below the low-tide mark and above 200 meters in depth.

epibioses. Organisms living on the surface of water.

epibiotic. 1. Existing in a contracting or smaller area than formerly, as in a relic community. 2. Surviving but not contribut-

ing to floral evolution. 3. Being survivors of a lost or almost extinct flora. 4. Growing on the outer surface of another plant or animal.

epiblast. A small scale-like appendage in front of the embryo which is opposite the scutellum in seeds of rice and many other grasses. It is believed to be an aborted second cotyledon.

epiblastous. Of the epiblast.

epiblasteme. A superficial outgrowth from leaves, a tuft of glandular emergences which act as collectors and whose cells secrete a viscid substance.

epiblastesis. The growth of lichens from gonidia which develop in the parent lichen.

epiblema. The outermost layer of root tissue and of stems of submerged aquatics.

epibole. A growth of one part over another in embryonic stages.

epiboly. The growing of one part about another so as to enclose it.

epibranchial. Of the second upper element in the branchial arch.

epicalycious. With stamens upon the calyx.

epicalyx. A secondary calyx, a group of bracts formed beneath the calyx of a flower, a series of small sepal-like structures alternating with the sepals and growing from under their sides.

epicarp. The outer layer of the ovary wall, the superficial layer of the pericarp especially when it can be stripped off as a skin, the epicarpium.

epicarpanthous. Being superior, as applied to a flower or its parts; epicarpous.

epichil. The terminal part of the labellum of an orchid when it is distinct from the basal portion.

epichroa. The supposed external layer of the cuticle.

epiclinal. Being seated on a torus or a receptacle.

epicline. A nectary when on the receptacle of a flower.

epiclysile. Of upper tide pools in which the temperature of the water rises to more than 3° C above that of the sea.

epicopula. An intermediate band of a cell wall in the upper or large valve of diatoms.

epicormic. Growing from a dormant bud, said of the branches which develop on the trunk of a forest tree after surrounding trees have been removed.

epicorolline. Inserted upon the corolla.

epicotyledonary. Situated above the cotyledons but below the first foliage leaves.

epicotyledonary node. The place where leaves ordinarily arise above the seed leaves.

epicotyl. The portion of the stem of a seedling between (above) the cotyledons and the first true leaves.

epicotyllary. Belonging to the epicotyl.

epictesis. The ability of a living cell to accumulate salts in higher concentration than the solution from which it is being received by diffusion from adjacent cells.

epicutis. The superficial layer of cuticle in agarics.

epicyte. The investing membrane of a cell.

epidemic. Spreading widely or found generally over a considerable area.

epidermal layer. The outer layer of the cortex.

epidermal tissue. Tissue composing the epidermis.

epidermis. The thin external layer of protective cells of a plant; a sheath of closely united cells, usually one cell thick, which forms a layer over the stems and leaves. It is usually continuous except where stomata perforate it.

epidermoidal layer. The exoderm of roots, an outer layer of cortical cells bordering on the epidermis.

epidiphyllum. A double leaf when the growth of a lamina has been interrupted at a particular spot.

epiendodermal. Having cells with thickening ridges immediately outside the endodermis in the roots of many crucifers.

epigamic. 1. Denoting the species in which sex is determined during the later stages of development. 2. Tending to attract the opposite sex.

epigeal. 1. Germinating with the cotyledons appearing above the surface of the ground. 2. Living on the surface of the ground.

epigean. Occurring on the ground.

epigeic. 1. Having stolons above ground. 2. With shoots that do not protrude from the soil but rest upon it.

epigenesis. The theory, now universally accepted, that the creation of an embryo consists of the gradual production and organization of parts as opposed to the theory of preformation which supposed that the future organism was already present in complete but miniature form in the germ.

epigenous. 1. Growing on the surface as fungi on leaves. 2. Growing upon or above the surface of the ground.

epigeotropism. Growth on the surface of the soil.

epigone. 1. The cellular layer covering the young sporophore in *Hepaticeae*. 2. A similar tissue in mosses after the formation of the capsule, which is frequently ruptured, the upper portion carried up as the calyptra, the lower portion remaining as the vaginule. 3. The nucleus in *Chara*.

epigynicous. Having the calyx or corolla superior.

epigynophorious. Located on a gynophore or stipe of an ovary.

epigynous. 1. Having the calyx, corolla, and stamens grow from the top of an inferior ovary, having the concave receptacle surround the ovary and fuse with it so that the other flower parts arise from above it. 2. Having the antheridia grow above the oogonium.

epilimnile. 1. Of the water above the thermocline of a lake. 2. Of that portion which is warm and well-aerated by circulation. 3. Of the upper layer of a body of water which is affected by wind.

epilithic. Growing on rocks, as do many lichens.

epilithophyte. A plant growing on stones or rocks.

epilittoral zone. A zone on the coast bordering the ground occupied by plants which cannot withstand exposure to salt.

epilose. Destitute of hairs.

epimatium. The ovuliferous scale of the conifers.

epimenous. Having a superior perianth.

epimorphosis. The type of regeneration in which proliferation of new materials precedes development of a new part, the mode of regeneration of organisms in which a multiplication of cells on an injured surface precedes other development.

epinasty. 1. The downward curvature of a plant member occurring when the upper side develops faster than the lower. 2. The eccentric thickening of a more or less horizontal branch or root.

epinemus. The upper part of the filament which bears the anther in *Compositae*.

epinyctous. Referring to flowers which begin to open in the evening.

epiontology. The developmental history of plant distribution.

epipactoid. Like *Epipactus*, a terrestrial orchid.

epiparasite. An ectoparasite.

epiparasitism. Superparasitism.

epipedochorisis. The division of an axial organ in one plane, frequently resembling fasciation.

epipeltate. Having a phyllome in which the base of the limb is on the superior face.

epiperidium. The exoperidium.

epiperispermicous. Having no perisperm or albumen.

epipetalous. Having the stamens seated on the petals or corolla, borne on or adnate to the petals, arising from the upper surface of a petal.

epipetreous. Growing on rocks.

epiphloedic. Growing on the surface of bark, epiphloedal.

epiphloem. The outermost or corky bark.

epiphlosa. The epidermis.

epiphragm. 1. A delicate membrane closing the cup-like sporophore in *Nidulariales*. 2. A membrane closing the capsule in mosses. 3. Any membrane covering the mouth of a deoperculate capsule.

epiphragma. An upper wall or division.

epiphyll. The upper portion of a leaf from which the petiole and blade develop.

epiphyllae. Epiphyllous algae and lichens.

epiphyllospermous. Bearing seeds or spores on leaf-like organs.

epiphyllous. Growing on leaves, particularly on the upper side.

epiphysis. A protuberance around the hilum or foramen.

epiphytaceous. Epiphytic.

epiphyte. 1. A green plant which is attached to or depends upon another plant for physical support but is able to manufacture its own food. 2. An air-plant.

epiphytoid. Resembling a phanerogamous parasite presumed to have been derived from an autogamous epiphyte.

epiphytoid parasites. Partly parasitic plants as *Viscum*, the mistletoe, and the *Santalaceae*, semiparasitic shrubs and herbs.

epiphytotism. The occurrence of any destructive epidemic in plants.

epiplankton. 1. The plankton from the sur-face to a hundred fathoms. 2. Floating organisms attached to pelagic organisms.

epiplasm. The residual cytoplasm which remains in the ascus after the ascospores have been formed. It may play a part in the subsequent nutrition of the developing spores. See GLYCOGEN MASS.

epiplast. A spherical body within the cytoplasmic lamellae in the blue-green algae.

epipleura. The outer half of the diatom girdle.

epipodium. 1. The apical part of a leaf. 2. The apical portion of an undifferentiated leaf axis or phyllopodium. 3. A form of disk consisting of glands upon the stipe of an ovary. 4. The stalk of the ovarian disk.

epipolyarch. The division of the median protoxylem in a triarch stele.

epiproteoid. Having leaves with sclerogamous cells on the upper surface.

epipterous. Having wings at the apex.

epirhizous. Growing on roots.

epirrheology. The study of the effects of external agents on living plants.

episematic. Aiding in the recognition of a species.

episematic colorations. Recognition markings.

episepalous. On a sepal, adnate to a sepal, standing before a sepal or opposite to a sepal.

episperm. The testa or outer coat of seeds.

epispermicous. Exalbuminous.

episporangium. An indusium.

epispore. The outer wall or coat of a spore often characterized by a deposit of ridges, spines, or other irregularities on the surface; the covering on the exospore.

epistameneous. Having stamens upon the calyx or other parts.

epistaminalis. Located on the stamens.

epistasis. The dominant action of a gene over a nonallelic gene located on a different chromosome or at a different locus on the same chromosome.

epistatic. 1. Applied to a unit character becoming invisible but not inactive. 2. Said of a character which is dominant to another to which it is not the allelomorph.

epistomeous. Spigot-shaped.

epistroma. A hyaline pseudoparenchymatous crust formed in the outer layers of the primary cortex of the host which ruptures the bark or epidermis and produces conidia, the ectostroma.

epistrophe. 1. The arrangement of the row of chloroplasts at right angles to the incident light. 2. The position assumed by the chloroplasts upon the upper and under faces of the cell walls upon exposure of the plant to diffuse daylight.

epistrophion. The range of intensity of sunlight which is needed to produce epistrophe.

epistrophy. The reversion of a monstrous form to the normal.

epitactic. Arranged one behind the other.

epiteospore. A spore in a sorus surrounded by prominent paraphyses.

epiterranean. Above-ground.

epitetrarch. A triarch stele in which the third protoxylem group is divided.

epithalline. Growing on the thallus.

epithallus. The cortical layer in lichens which serves to protect the gonidia.

epitheca. The outer and larger half-frustule of diatoms, the older of the two valves forming the wall of a cell of a diatom.

epithecium. A thin colorless layer over the asci in an apothecium, particularly in lichens, formed from the tips of the paraphyses.

epithelium. 1. The layer of elongated cells forming the boundary of the scutellum in grains. 2. A layer of parenchymatous cells surrounding an intercellular canal. 3. Any cellular tissue covering a free surface or lining a tube or cavity.

epithem. A group of cells (usually devoid of chlorophyll) found in the mesophyll of leaves which exude water.

epithem hydathode. A hydathode which is directly connected with the vascular system of the leaf.

epithet. The specific or second part of the Latin name of a plant. An adjective used as a noun, it may be capitalized if formed from the name of a person, deity, or a genus but it is usually lower case.

epitriarch. A triarch stele in which the third protoxylem group is uppermost.

epitrophic. 1. Having buds on the upper side. 2. Growing more on the upper side than on the under side.

epitropic. Below the axis.

epitropism. Geotropism.

epitropous. Having an anatropous ovule which has its raphe averse when ascending and adverse when suspended.

epivalve. The valve of the epitheca of a diatom.

epixyloneae. Plants, such as the fungi and lichens, which grow on wood.

epixylous. Growing on wood.

epizoarius. Growing on dead animals.

epizoic. 1. Growing on living animals whether parasitic or not. 2. Dispersing seeds by adherence to passing animals.

epizoochory. The dispersion of plants whose seeds adhere to passing animals and are thereby scattered.

eplicate. Not folded or plaited.

epoikophyte. A plant that is somewhat naturalized but is confined to roadsides and paths.

eporose. Without pores.

eprophyllate. Without prophylls or small bracts below the flower in addition to the floral bract at the base of the pedicel.

epruinose. Without whitish dust or bloom, not pruinose.

equal dichotomy. A dichotomy giving two branches of the same size.

equalling. The condition when the tips of several organs or of organs of diverse kinds are at the same level but the lengths of the several organs differ.

equally pinnate. Having no terminal leaflet.

equation division. An ordinary nuclear division in which each chromosome divides equally.

equatorial plane. 1. The line which passes through the mother star of the nucleus. 2. The plane of division.

equatorial plate. The plate formed by a group of chromosomes lying at the equator of the spindle during mitosis.

equi-. See AEQUI-.

equicellular. Composed of equal cells.

equinoctial. Having flowers which expand and close at particular hours of the day.

equisetaceous. Of or pertaining to *Equisetum*, the horsetail or scouring rushes, equisetic.

equisetetum. A plant association of *Equisetum*.

equisetosis. Poisoning from *Equisetum* which has been used as fodder.

equitant. 1. Straddling, overlapping each other. 2. Having conduplicate leaves whose bases successively overlap.

equitorial plate. In cell division, the line

formed by the delicate fibers of the nucleus halfway between the poles where the spindle widens and where the chromatin threads are arranged during the metaphase. It is in this area that the dividing cells separate. The equatorial plane.

equivalvular. Having a fruit with valves equal in size.

equivocal generation. Spontaneous generation, the development of living organisms from dead or inorganic matter.

eradiculose. Without rootlets or rhizoids.

eramose. Unbranched.

erectopatent. Between spreading and erect.

eramacausis. The gradual oxidation of organic material from exposure to air and moisture.

eremad. Any desert plant.

eremion. A desert formation or community, eremium.

eremoblasts. Cells which are at first united and then separate as unicellular plants.

eremobrya. Ferns having articulated fronds not adherent to the stem or rhizome.

eremus. 1. A carpel separate from its sister carpels. 2. A desert community.

erepsin. An enzyme capable of converting proteoses into amino acids.

ereptase. Any peptonizing enzyme.

erg desert. A type of desert found in the Sahara region characterized by the formation of sand dunes.

ergasialipophyte. A plant relic of cultivation.

ergasiapophyte. The colonist of cultivated fields.

ergasiophygophyte. A fugitive from cultivation.

ergasiophyte. A foreign cultivated plant which has reached its habitat by the conscious action of man.

ergastic. Said of the nonliving products of metabolism in the cell.

ergastoplasm. Protoplasmic filaments in the embryo sac of certain *Liliaceae* whose origin and formation are uncertain. Endoplasmic reticulum.

ergesis. The ability of an organ to react.

ergodic hypothesis. A theory concerning worldwide vegetation, that under similar environmental conditions the same or similar types of vegetation will develop or that the types of plant succession will be similar.

ergogenesis. The exhibition of growth energy.

ergology. Biology.

ergonomy. The division of labor.

ergoplastic nucleus. The vegetative nucleus.

ergot. A fungus disease on rye and other cereal grains caused by *Claviceps purpurea*.

ergotin. An extract from the ergot fungus, ergotic acid, ergosterin.

ergotisized. Infected with the ergot fungus.

ergotism. The effect produced by eating bread which has been made from ergotized grains.

eriacanthous. Having woolly spines.

eriantherous. Having woolly anthers.

erianthous. Having woolly flowers.

ericaceous. Heath-like.

ericaefolious. With leaves like *Erica*, evergreen shrubs (heaths).

ericetal. Growing upon moors, such as heather.

ericetinous. Heath-like in form and habit.

ericetum. 1. A heath plant association. 2. A monograph on heaths.

ericifruticetum. A heath community.

ericilignosa. A community of woody heaths.

ericimaqui. Arboreal heaths with *Ulex* and *Sarothamnus* (*Cytisus*), as in certain areas of France.

ericoid. 1. Having heath-like leaves which are tough, narrow, needle-like, or rolled back. 2. Pertaining to or resembling the genus *Erica*.

erigens. Used of a branch which is horizontal at first and then rises at the point.

erine. An abnormal growth on the epidermis of plants caused by mites, particularly the genus *Phytaptus*.

erinous. Prickly rough with sharp points, hedgehog-like.

eriobotryoid. Like *Eriobotrya*, a genus of Asiatic rosaceous trees.

eriocarpous. Having woolly fruit.

eriocephalous. Woolly-headed.

eriophoretum. A plant formation of cotton grass.

eriophorous. Wool-bearing, cottony, tomentose.

eriophyllous. Having leaves with a cottony appearance, woolly-leaved.

eriospathous. Woolly-spathed.

eriostachyous. Woolly-spiked.

eriostemon. A flower with woolly stamens.

eripleogamic. Having a variety of flowers

some perfect, some staminate, some pistillate.

erisma. The rachis in grasses.

ermineous. Ermine color, white with a yellow tinge in places.

eroded. Of gills, edged as if gnawed, irregularly notched, erose.

erosion, progressive. The deposit of materials, soil, etc.

erosion, retrogressive. The removal of materials, soil, etc.

eroso-dentate. With jagged teeth.

erostrate. Not beaked, said of anthers.

errantia. Mobile organisms.

erratic lichens. Unattached and drifting lichens.

Errera's law. The proposition that a cell membrane at the moment of its formation tends to assume the form which would be assumed under the same conditions by a liquid film destitute of weight.

Ersatzfasern. An intermediate form between woody fibers and parenchyma.

erubescent. Bluish-red.

erucacalform. Having a caterpillar-like appearance, of lichen spores.

erucoid. Like *Eruca*, a genus of the mustard family.

erumpent. Breaking through the surface and spreading.

eruption year. See OUTBREAK.

erysimin. A glucoside found in *Erysimum*, a genus of the mustard family.

erysiphoid. Cobwebby, like *Erysiphe*, a genus of the powdery mildews.

erythrin. A red coloring matter found in certain algae.

erythrism. A condition due to an excessive amount of red coloring in flowers which are usually white, the reverse of albinism.

erythrobacteria. A group of bacteria with a deep red color.

erythrocarpous. Red-fruited.

erythrocephalous. Having a red head.

erythrophilous. Having a special affinity for red dyes.

erythrophore. The chlorophyll granules which are red, as in certain algae.

erythrophyll. The red coloring matter in plants; see ANTHOCYANIN.

erythropodous. Red-footed, red-stalked.

erythropterous. Red-winged (seeds).

erythrosorous. A red sorus.

erythrostromum. An etaerio, an aggregate fruit like the raspberry.

erythrozym. An enzyme from the root of the madder which acts on glucosides.

escape. A plant originally cultivated and now found wild.

escharotic. Having the power to scar or to burn the skin, corrosive or caustic.

eschatophyte. Any member of a climax vegetation.

esculin. Aesculin, an alkaloid from the horse chestnut.

eseptate. Without septa or cross walls, aseptate.

esetulose. Without bristles.

esker. An extensive ridge of sand and gravel deposited by a stream coming from a glacier. An os (pl. osar).

esorediate. Without soredia.

esoteric. Arising within the organism.

espalier growth form. 1. A natural form assumed by many subglacial plants whose stems are often spread flat on the ground and are often covered by the ground mosses with only the tips directed upwards and exposed. 2. A trained form of fruit trees or shrubs with the stems grown against a trellis or railing to obtain better exposure to sunlight and air.

espartetum. Any association of esparto grass, *Stipa tenacissima*.

espathaceous. Lacking a spathe.

espinal formation. A thorny xerophytic woodland, a maquis.

espino. Any of numerous tropical American thorny or spiny shrubs or trees, especially various rutaceous trees of the genus *Zanthoxylum*.

esquamate. Having no scales.

essential aggregations. Communities of species which have a real value for the individuals composing them.

essential character. A feature or group of features which distinguish a plant or group of plants from all others.

essential element. A chemical element without which a plant cannot complete its development.

essential organs. The stamens and pistils of flowers or organs essential to a function.

establishment. A successful germination and subsequent growth of a plant, particularly in a new locality.

esterases. Fat-splitting enzymes like lipases, enzymes that facilitate the splitting of esters.

esteros. The salt wastes of western Argentina.

esters. Derivatives of acids many of which have a fruity smell and are used in artificial fruit flavors.

esthesis. The perception of or sensibility to stimuli.

estipulate. Without stipules.

estivate. To pass the summer in a dormant condition.

estivation. See AESTIVATION.

estriate. Without lines or markings.

estrophiolate. Without caruncle, strophiole, appendage, or protuberance.

etaerio. The fruit composed of several drupelets, as in the blackberry; a fruit composed of achenes or drupelets developed on an enlarged receptacle.

ete. See SELVA.

etesiae. Herbs with perennial persistent roots, the above-ground portion being annual.

ethanol. Ethyl alcohol.

etheogenesis. The parthenogenesis of male individuals.

Ethiopian region. The region including Africa south of the Sahara and Madagascar.

ethnobotanic. Relating to those plants which illustrate or are typical of the customs of a given race or people.

ethnobotany. Folk botany.

ethomeric. Having the normal number of chromosomes.

etiolation. The blanched condition produced in plants by the lack of light or by disease.

etiolin. A yellowish pigment formed in chloroplasts of plants grown in darkness.

etiology. The science of the causes of disease.

etrabeculatous. Lacking cross bars, as when the peristome teeth of mosses lack crossconnections.

etuberosus. Without tubers.

eu-. A prefix meaning true or typical.

euacranthic flower. A terminal flower which springs immediately from the apex of a shoot which has produced leaves of other lateral structures.

euanthic. Having a typical monothalamic flower.

euanthrostrobilus. The typical flowering of angiosperms.

euapogamy. The development of a diploid sporophyte from a cell or cells of the gametophyte (not from a zygote resulting from gametic fusion), a sporophyte developed without fertilization.

euapospory. 1. The condition of having no sexual fertilization. 2. Complete failure to form spores.

euaster. An aster in which the rays meet at a common center during mitosis.

eubacteria. The true bacteria.

eucalyptoid. Like the eucalyptus tree.

eucarotin. Yellow carotin.

eucarpic. 1. Having both vegetative and reproductive organs separate and functioning at the same time. 2. Having only a part of a body of the plant involved in the formation of a sporangium. 3. Said of fungi which produce several successive fructifications from the same thallus.

euchromatin. The part of the chromosome which contains the hereditary material. During some phases it stains more lightly than the euchromocenters.

euchromocenters. True chromocenters. Separate globular bodies which stain deeply and are scattered throughout the nucleus during interphase.

euchromosome. A typical chromosome or autosome.

eucyclic. Composed of alternate isomerous whorls, having the members in each whorl of floral parts equal in number and alternating with those in an adjoining whorl.

eudiometer. An instrument for measuring the quantity of gas in fluid.

eudipleural. Bilaterally symmetrical.

eudominant. 1. A dominant of a true prairie. 2. Typical of an association.

euephemerous. Having flowers which open and close within twenty-four hours.

eufluent. An influent more or less peculiar to or typical of an association.

euforms. Uredinaceous fungi whose spores develop on the living host but only germinate after the death of the host, usually after a resting period.

eugamophyte. A cryptogam which supports dependent sporophytes.

eugenioid. Like *Eugenia*, a genus of tropical shrubs, family *Myrtaceae*.

eugenol. The chief constituent of oil of cloves obtained from myrtaceous plants.

eugeogenous. Said of those rocks which yield detritus easily and the plants which grow on it.

eugeopenous. Weathering readily to form soil.

eugeophytes. Plants which have a resting period due to want of warmth or light.

euglenoid. Resembling *Euglena*, a genus of algae.

eugonidium. A bright green algal cell forming part of the thallus of a lichen and belonging to the *Chlorophyceae*.

euhymenial. With an hymenium in which the collective development of the parallel hyphal ends proceeds at a uniform rate.

euisogamy. The union of a gamete with any other similar gamete.

eulimnetic. Growing in pools.

eumeiosis. True meiosis or reduction division, the opposite of pseudomeiosis.

eumeristelic. Having reduced eusteles, as some species of *Primula*.

eumerogenesis. The segmentation in which the units are similar at least for a certain time.

eumitosis. A typical mytosis.

eumitotic. Applied to bivalents or tetrads which undergo two longitudinal cleavages in the course of the meiotic divisions, anaschistic.

eumorphic. Well-formed.

eumycetes. The so-called true fungi.

eunuchs. Flowers destitute of stamens, as double flowers.

eunucleoli. 1. Nucleoles which persist in nuclear division after the pseudonucleoli have disappeared. 2. Nuclei which stain red readily, erythrophilous nuclei.

euparthenosperm. A plant in which both embryo and endosperm are parthenogenetic.

eupatorine. An alkaloid occurring in *Eupatorium cannabinum*, the boneset.

eupatorioid. Like *Eupatorium*, the boneset.

eupelagic. Of or pertaining to plankton confined to the ocean.

euphemera. Flowers which open and close within twenty-four hours; see EPHEMERAL.

euphorbioid. Like *Euphorbia*, a very large and diverse genus often having milky juice.

euphorbium. Very acrid yellowish or brownish gum resin derived from various species of *Euphorbia*.

euphotic. Applied to hydrophytes which receive an abundance of light.

euphotic zone. That section of a body of water (to about 100cm.) which can receive adequate light for plant development.

euphotometric. Denoting leaves which place themselves so as to obtain the maximum of diffused light, as the foliage of forests; euphototropic.

euphyll. An ordinary foliage leaf, a true leaf.

euphyllode. The flattened primary axis of a bipinnate leaf which has lost its pinnae.

euphytoid parasites. Erect land plants which are parasitic in habit.

euplankton. Free-floating organisms.

euplastic. Readily organized to form a tissue.

euploid. Having an exact multiple of the monoploid or haploid chromosome number.

eupontic. Inhabiting a range slightly westward from Pontus in the northeast of Asia Minor.

eupotamic. Inhabiting running or standing inland waters; eupotamous.

eupuccinia. See EUFORMS.

euradulan. Similar to *Rubus Radula*.

europhytia. Leaf mold communities, eurotophytia.

eurotaphilous. Dwelling in leaf mold or humus.

eurotophyta. Leaf-mold plants.

eurybathic. Referring to the species which can extend a long way vertically in water.

eurychoric. Having a wide distribution in varying climates and several plant formations.

eurycladous. Adapted to varying conditions of salinity, indifferent to degree of salinity.

eurycoenose. Widely distributed.

euryhaline. Peculiar to nonmarine brackish water and resistant to great changes in salinity.

euryoecic. Not broadly limited by ecological conditions.

euryphotic. Adapted to light of varying intensity.

eurysynusic. Of or pertaining to widely distributed groups of plants.

eurysynusic species. Species due to constant and solid groupings.

eurythermal. Having wide distribution due to the ability to withstand diverse temperatures.

eurotope. An organism which spends one or more stages in several varying habitats.

eurytropic. Adapted to varied conditions.

euschist. A gamete which is formed by successive complete divisions from the parent cell, the gametogonium.

eusigillarian. Resembling the ribbed stems of *Sigillaria* found in the carboniferous formation.

eusporangiate. Having sporangia which arise from a group of epidermal cells, as ferns which possess special sporangia of a primitive type.

eusporangium. A sporangium derived from a group of superficial cells.

eusporophyta. Cryptogams which are self-supporting and do not nourish the gametophytes.

eustathe. The outermost layer of a cell.

eustele. The typical dicotyledonous arrangement of vascular tissue in collateral bundles with conjunctive tissue between the bundles.

eustomatous. Having a distinct mouth-like opening.

euthallophytes. Thallophytes exclusive of the myxogasters or sometimes restricted to *Chlorophyceae* and fungi only.

euthenics. The system of improving individuals by good environment.

eutherophyte. An annual seed plant.

euthybasids. Basidia which arise directly from the sporophore.

euthymorphosis. The rapid succession of members of different forms on the same stem.

euthyschist. A brood division when each nuclear division is accompanied by cell division.

eutrophic. 1. Said of lakes characterized by the paucity or absence of oxygen in the bottom waters. 2. Of waters poor in humus, often richest in calcium, and with a broad zone of rooted plants. 3. Of submerged plants which are adapted to live at the expense of the nutritive substances present in the soil.

eutropic. Twining or turning from left to right following the sun.

eutropy. A characteristic of flowers to which only a restricted class of specialized insects can gain access.

eutype. An effuse stroma similar to the tissue of the matrix.

evaginate. 1. To be without a sheath. 2. To turn inside out. 3. To protrude or cause to protrude.

evagination. 1. The process of unsheathing or the product of this process. 2. An outgrowth or protrusion of some part or organ usually away from a closed cavity. 3. The unequal outward growth of a surface layer, one of the processes by which the differentiation of organs is produced.

evalvular. Lacking valves, not opening by valves.

evaniscentivenose. The condition when the lateral veins of a leaf do not reach the margin.

evaporimeter. An instrument used to measure the amount of moisture given off by plants, an atmometer.

evection. The condition in *Cladophora* in which the initial cells of the branches arise from the sides of the upper end of the mother cell, elevation.

even-aged. A term applied to a stand of trees in which only small age differences appear.

even-pinnate leaf. 1. An abruptly pinnate leaf. 2. A pinnate leaf without a terminal leaflet and usually with an equal number of leaflets.

everbearer. A plant which bears fruits over a long period of time.

ever-bloomer. A plant which vegetates and flowers for a long period of the growing season.

evergreen. Having green foliage at all seasons, not deciduous, losing leaves at all seasons but never all of them at one time.

everlasting flowers. Flowers which may be dried without losing form or color.

everniaeform. Similar to the thallus of *Evernia*, a genus of lichens.

evernine. Like the genus *Evernia*, with a fruticulose or pendulous thallus with cottony medulla.

eversion. 1. The protrusion of organs from a cavity turned backwards or outward. 2. The act of turning or state of being turned inside out.

eversporting race. A race of plants which does not breed true and gives mixed progenies.

everted. Turned outward abruptly.

evident plasmolysis. The stage in plasmolysis when the protoplast is shrunken from the cell wall.

evittate. Without vittae or oil reservoirs.

evolution, saltatory. The sudden appearance of sports, mutation.

evolvate. Without a volva.

exalate. Wingless.

exalbescent. Becoming white, turning pale. *Note*: from the Latin *exalbesco*—to grow white, to turn pale.

exalbuminous. Without albumen, lacking endosperm and reserve food stored in the cotyledons.

exannulate. Without an annulus or ring in the sporangium of ferns, without an annulus on the stipe of a fungus.

exanthema. 1. A blotch on leaves, looking as though it is eruptive. 2. An eruptive disease.

exanthium. A bractlet immediately external to the flower incapable of forming axillary buds.

exapophysatous. Without an apophysis or swelling below the capsule of a moss.

exappendiculate. Without appendages, fragments of a veil, pellicle, etc.

exarate. Furrowed.

exarch. With protoxylem strands in touch with the pericycle as in roots, applied to primary xylem in which the progressive development of the elements is centripetal.

exarch primary phloem. Protophloem turned outwards in the stele and the metaphloem turned inwards.

exarch primary xylem. Protoxylem turned outwards in the stele and the metaxylem turned inwards.

exareolate. Not marked into small areas.

exarillate. Without an aril.

exaristate. Without awns or arista.

exasperate. Covered with hard, stiff, short points.

excentric. See ECCENTRIC.

excentric starch grain. A starch grain with an eccentric hilum.

exciple. The outer covering or rim of the apothecia or perithecia of lichens. The excipulum.

exciple, thalloid. A portion of a lichen thallus supporting or surrounding the apothecium.

excipuliform. Wart-like, cup-shaped.

excitonutrient. A stimulus causing or increasing the production of nutrient activities.

exclusive species. Species completely or almost completely confined to one community.

excoemum. A fringe or tuft of hair at the base of the glumes in some grasses.

exconjugant. An organism which is leading an independent life after conjugating with another.

excoriate. To strip the bark or skin, to break and remove the cuticle.

excrescence. A warty outgrowth, protuberance, or gnaur.

excreta. The waste or deleterious substance formed within a plant.

excrete. To eliminate useless materials from the place of most active metabolism in a plant.

excreting cell. A cell through which the secretion is exuded from the plant.

excurrent. 1. Extending from base to tip without dividing, as spruce or cedar stems. 2. Running out, as a vein of a leaf projecting beyond the margin.

excurved. Curved outward from center.

exemplarium. A specimen or example.

exendospermous. Having reserve food materials stored in the embryo of the seed, exalbuminous.

exendotropic. Fertilized by another flower of the same plant or of a different plant.

exesous. Having the surface irregularly sculptured as if by corrosion.

exfoliate. To peel off in thin layers, to cast off layers or plates, to scale or flake off.

exfoliation. The shedding of leaves or scales from a bud, peeling off, the process of exfoliating or the state of being exfoliated.

exhalantia vasa. The imaginary vessels in the epidermis which are really the sides of confluent cells.

exhalation. The function discharged by stomata in passing off vapor, a loss of vapor through the stomata.

exhomotropic. Fertilized by the anthers of the same or a different plant.

exhymenine. See EXINE.

exilis. Lank and straight, meagre, thin.

eximious. Conspicuous, select, extraordinary.

exindusiate. Without an indusium, said of an uncovered sorus in ferns.

exine. The outer thick layer of spores and pollen grains which consists of cutin and no cellulose (there is an outer layer, the ectexine, and an inner layer, the endexine); the extine.

exintine. The third or middle coat of a pollen grain which is between the intine and the intexine.

existem. The tissue of protomeristem which is not young pith, the mesistem (the thickening ring) and the peristem (the young cortex).

exit. The inner aperture of the slit of a stoma.

exit papilla. An outgrowth from a zoosporangium through which the zoospores escape into the surrounding water, the exit tube.

exitiosus. Pernicious, destructive.

exo-. A prefix meaning outward, out of, or outside.

exobasidial. 1. Separated by a wall from the basidium. 2. Having a sporophore without a secondary sporiferous branch. 3. With basidia.

exocarp. The outer layer of the pericarp or fruit coat.

exocaryogamy. Caryogamy of the usual type which involves the union of two nuclei from different cells or thalli, exogamy.

exocatadromous. Denoting nervation of ferns with their stronger pinnules anadromous and their weaker pinnules catadromous.

exochite. The outer membrane of the egg in *Fucaceae*.

exochomophyte. A plant which is surface-rooting and mat-forming.

exocortex. 1. The outermost portion of the cortex. 2. A special layer in the root of saprophytic orchids. 3. Rhizomorphs which are pervaded by hyphae.

exodermis. The outermost cortical layer of the adult root.

exoenzyme. An enzyme produced by a plant (chiefly bacteria and the lower fungi) which is exuded into the surrounding area and breaks down potential food material which can then be assimilated by the plant.

exogamete. A reproductive cell which fuses with one derived from another source.

exogamy. 1. The tendency of closely allied gametes to avoid pairing. 2. The union of two gametes of a different brood, outbreeding.

exogen. An old name for dicotyledons because of the increase in diameter of the stem through the successive additions of annular layers outside the older tissues.

exogenous. 1. Produced on the outside of another body. 2. Produced externally, as the spores on tips of hyphae. 3. Growing by outer additions to annular layers, as the wood in dicotyledons.

exogenous expulsion. The violent discharge of basidiospores from the sterigmata of certain gasteromycetes.

exogenous origin. The development of new parts from superficial tissue.

exogenous plants. Plants that have two cotyledons and increase in diameter by annual additions of new wood between the old wood and the bark.

exogenous-sessile. Being without sterigmata and sessile on the outside of the basidia.

exogenous spore. A spore formed on the end of a hypha, not inside a sporangium.

exogenous-sterigmate. Having nonpropulsive sterigmata on the basidium.

exogenous thallus. A lichen thallus in which the fungus predominates.

exogynous. Having the style exserted beyond the corolla.

exohadromatic. Exterior to the woody portion of a stem.

exoisogamy. The condition when a gamete pairs only with a similar gamete of another plant.

exolete. Without contents, as a mature fruit-body without visible contents.

exolithophytes. Mosses and lichens growing on rocks.

exome. A secondary inner bark.

exomeristem. The meristem which produces the cortex and the epidermis of a moss.

exonastic. Having anatropous or campylotropous ovules with the curvature horizontal towards the median nerve of the side of the upper face of the carpel.

exoneurosis. The separation of veins in appendicular organs and their reappearance as teeth, spines, or bristles.

exoperidium. 1. The outer layer of the peridium in certain fungi which peels off at maturity. 2. The outer layer of the spore case.

exophelloderm. The tissue formed outside of and next to the cork cambium.

exophylaxis. The protection afforded plants against pathogenic organisms by skin secretions.

exophyllous. Having naked cotyledons which lack a foliose sheath.

exoplasm. See ECTOPLASM.

exopleura. The testa.

exoprothallae. Vascular cryptogams.

exoptile. Having a naked plumule upon or between cotyledons and not rolled up in a cotyledon.

exorhiza. See EXOGEN.

exorhizal. Having the radicle in germination unsheathed.

exosclerotes. Sclerotia which are external to the surface of agarics.

exoscopic. Visible from without, as the apical

pole of an embryo when turned towards the neck of the archegonium.

exoscopic embryology. The condition when the apex of the embryo is turned toward the neck of the archegonium.

exosmose. The process of the diffusion outwards through the differentially permeable membrane.

exosmosis. The diffusion of materials from the inside of the cell to the outside, outward osmosis.

exospore. 1. The outer wall of a spore. 2. A spore which is not produced within a sporangium, as basidiospores and conidiospores.

exosporinium. The outer integument of a pollen grain; see EPISPORIUM.

exosporous. 1. With spores borne exogenously. 2. With scattered spores.

exostome. 1. The outer row of teeth of the peristome. 2. The orifice in the outer coat of the ovule.

exostosis. 1. The formation of knots in the surface of wood. 2. The formation of nodules on roots of legumes. 3. The formation of any indurated protuberance.

exostylus. The fruit composed of four seemingly naked nutlets, as in *Labiatae*.

exoteric. Arising from outside the organism.

exotesta. The hard outer layer of a seed coat.

exothecial. Pertaining to the outer layer of cells of the capsule wall.

exothecium. 1. The outer wall of the anther. 2. The extine (outer layer of pollen grains).

exothermic. Heated from the outside and not by vital action.

exothiobacteriaceae. The ectothiobacteriaceae, bacteria which form sulfur outside the cell.

exotics. A plant which is not indigenous.

exotoxin. A toxin secreted in the medium in which it grows by the bacterial cell during its metabolism.

exotrophic. Having an organ or lateral shoot more strongly developed than the mother shoot.

exotrophy. The development of lateral shoots instead of the main axis.

exotropic. Pollinated from anthers of the same plant.

exotropism. The curvature of a lateral geotropic organ away from the main axis.

exotropy. The condition in which roots arise from the small extremities of a flattened root.

expansion of protoplasm. The normal condition resulting in a turgid cell.

expansion theory. A theory that the cylinder of parenchymatous cells in the center of roots and stems (the pith), which is surrounded by a hollow tube of vascular tissue (the stele), has developed by growth rather than by differentiation of tissues. The supposition that the pith is part of the stele.

explanate. Spread out flat.

explantation. A tissue culture away from the organism of its origin.

explodiflorae. Wind-pollinated flowers which expel their pollen by explosive action.

exponential law. The concept that development follows a normal curve on which the two critical points are the point beyond which development is not completed and the point at which death occurs.

expulsive fruits. Fruits which forcibly expel their seeds or spores.

expressivity. The degree of control exhibited by a gene over its allelomorph, modifying genes and environment also play a part.

exraphidian. Without raphides.

exscapous. Without a scape.

exsculptate. 1. With the surface marked with more or less regularly arranged raised lines with grooves between. 2. Having small linear depressions.

exscutellate. Without a scutellum.

exsiccatae. Collections or series of dried botanical specimens often available in sets prepared by herbaria.

exsiccate. To arrange and label dried botanical specimens.

exsiccation. The process of furthering desert conditions through human agency or change of climate.

exstipulate. Without stipules.

exsuccate. Without milk or juice.

extended aperture. An inner aperture which appears in a surface view to extend beyond the border.

extension factor. A factor (gene) which extends the action of the primary gene.

external plasma membrane. The ectoplasm.

external sheath. A modification of the bundle sheath.

extine. The outer coat of a pollen grain; the exine.

extra-. A prefix meaning outside, beyond, in addition to.

extra-axillary. 1. Arising above the axil of a leaf. 2. Beyond or out of the axil.

extracapsular. Outside of the capsule.

extracellular. Outside of the cell.

extracellular digestion. The digestion of material outside the cell by enzymes secreted by it.

extracted. A term applied to the individuals in the second hybrid generation from a cross which resemble the parent forms that were mated to make the cross.

extraembryonic. Situated outside the embryo proper.

extrafascicular. Outside the vascular bundle.

extrafloral. Situated outside the flower.

extrafloral nectary. A nectary appearing on or in some part of a plant other than a flower.

extrafoliaceous. Not situated on or near the leaves.

extramatrical. Outside of the matrix.

extrameability. The capacity of protoplasm to permit substances to pass outward from the vacuole.

extranuptial. Said of nectaries or honey glands which are not part of the floral organs.

extranuptial nectary. See EXTRAFLORAL NECTARY.

extraovular. Outside the ovule.

extraprothallial. Originating outside the prothallus.

extrasaccal. Said of the embryos which arise outside the cells of the embryo sac.

extraseminal. Outside the seed.

extraseminal development. Development outside the seed after it is sown.

extrastelar. Having ground tissue outside the central cylinder of the vascular tissue.

extratropical. To the north or south of the tropics.

extravaginal. 1. Bursting through the enclosing sheath as the shoots of many grasses. 2. Beyond or outside the sheath.

extravaginal innovation. The development which results when a branch splits the sheath and grows outward like a stolon or root stock.

extravasation. The unnatural flow of a liquid from a tissue or organ like the bleeding of a vine.

extrorse. 1. Opening away from the center of a flower. 2. Facing outward. 3. Having an anther open away from the axis of the flower.

extrorse anthers. Having the cells turned outward or away from the pistils with the filament or connection extended up the inner side.

extrorse-marginal. Directed or turned outward from the margin.

exudases. Exudations from tissues.

exudation. 1. Any discharge through an incision or pore. 2. The loss of liquid through hydathodes.

exudation pressure. Root pressure.

exunguiculate. Lacking a claw.

exutive. Denoting seeds which lack the usual integuments.

exuviae. Cast-off parts.

exuviation. The operation of shedding effete material.

eye. 1. A pigment spot in various animals and lower plants. 2. An undeveloped bud. 3. A conspicuous spot in a flower. 4. The cavity enclosed by the calyx in an apple.

eye, dormant. A bud which does not develop.

eyespot. A pigmented spot, believed to be light sensitive, found in some motile forms of the dinoflagellate algae.

F

F. A class of flowers pollinated by moths or butterflies.

F_0. A pure parental type.

F_1. The first filial generation, the first hybrid offspring of a given mating of genetically unlike parents.

F_2. The second filial generation produced by intercrossing or self-fertilizing the members of an F_1 generation.

F_3. The third filial generation.

fabaceous. Bean-like, having the characteristics of a bean.

fabiform. Bean-shaped.

faciation. 1. A local variation of the major dominant species in an association. 2. A portion of an association in which one or more dominants have dropped out or have been replaced (the general aspect of the association remains unchanged). 3. The local climatic differences within an association which result in the recombination of the dominants of the association.

facicle. A cluster proceeding from a common plant, like the leaves of a larch.

facies. A local variation in the dominant vegetative make-up of an association as it progresses in its development, a difference in quantity or distribution of the dominant species or the companion species, the changing aspect of a developing association.

facilitated diffusion. Diffusion which is made easier by the action of substances in the membrane which can alter and increase the solubility of the particles passing through the membrane.

factor. 1. An immediate influence affecting organisms directly. 2. A special germinal cause of a developed character, the unit of heredity transmitted in the germ cells, a unit of inheritance, a gene.

factor hypothesis. An assumption that organisms may contain various heredity units which do not appear in their body cells.

factor-pair. See GENE.

factors of habitat. Any factors in the environment which exert a direct or indirect effect on the life of a plant.

facultative. Having the power to live under different conditions.

facultative aerobes. Bacteria which ordinarily develop under anaerobic conditions but which may develop in the presence of free O_2.

facultative anaerobes. Organisms which are able to exist in the presence of combined oxygen although the preferred habitat provides free O_2.

facultative gamete. A zoospore which can function as a gamete.

facultative parasite. A saprophyte which is able to live under parasitic conditions at least for a certain part of its life cycle.

facultative saprophyte. A parasite which is able to continue its life processes under saprophytic conditions.

facultative symbiont. An organism which can exist and reach maturity independently or in symbiosis with another organism.

faecula. Any powdery farinaceous matter; see FECULA.

fageta asperulosa. Beech forests with ground vegetation and *Asperula*.

fageta myrtillosa. Beech forests with *Vaccinium myrtillus* in place of *Asperula*.

fagetum. An association of beeches, the genus *Fagus*.

fagion. A formation of beeches.

fairy ring. A circular patch of mushrooms which have grown centrifugally and whose effect is shown by greener vegetation where they have appeared.

falcate. Sickle-shaped; falciform.

falcato-secund. Falcate and turned to one side of the stem.

falciphore. A hypha which bears a falx.

falcula. A curved, scythe-like claw.

falling starch. See STATOLITH.

fallow. Uncultivated for an entire growing season.

false. Similar in appearance but different in structure and origin, spurious.

false annular ring. A growth ring caused by arrested and recurring growth within a single season.

false axis. A pseudoaxis; see SYMPODIUM.

false bark. A layer of cellular tissue on the outside of endogens into which fibrous tissue passes obliquely.

false berry. A fleshy fruit looking like a berry but with some of the flesh developed from the receptacle of the flower.

false dichotomy. 1. Any dichotomous branching which does not arise from a terminal division on a main axis. 2. Branching in which the terminal bud is self-pruned and the two daughter branches of equal rank develop from terminal axillary buds. 3. Dichasium.

false dissepiments. Additional partitions in certain fruits which are not formed by the edges of the carpels.

false foot. The base of the seta in some bryophytes which becomes dilated.

false fruit. A pseudocarp, as a strawberry.

false germination. An appearance of germination in a dead seed due to swelling of the embryo as it takes up water.

false hybrid. A plant developed after cross-fertilization which has characteristics from one parent only.

false indusium. The recurved margin of the pinnules of some ferns which serves to protect the sori.

false parenchyma. Parenchyma-like tissue in fungi which is formed by interlacing and united hyphae, pseudo-parenchyma.

false partition. An ovary partition not formed by infolding of the edges of the carpel but growing from the middle of the placenta or formed by the ingrowth of placentae.

false plankton. Plankton attached before breaking loose and floating.

false raceme. See HELICOID CYME.

false ray. A band or aggregation of uniseriate rays in the wood of certain *Cupuliferae.*

false septum. See SPURIOUS DISSEPIMENTS.

false stomata. The pores in the epidermis of *Equisetum.*

false sympodial type. A type of branching which develops when a terminal bud fails to develop and a daughter branch develops from a lateral bud some distance behind the tip of the stem.

false tissue. Hyphal or mycelial felted tissue.

falsinervis. Having nerves formed from cellular tissue without fibrovascular bundles, as in mosses.

falx. A sickle-shaped fertile hypha.

family. 1. A term in classification which includes related genera. 2. A more or less natural assemblage or association of plants placed together because of a few common bold resemblances. 3. Occasionally applied to a group of plants belonging to one species or the descendents of a single plant.

fan. A rhipidium.

fan-nerved. Having the nerves and veins radially disposed.

farctate. 1. Stuffed or plugged. 2. With a soft center.

fariam. In rows.

farina. Meal, flour, pollen, starch, mealy powder.

farinaceous. 1. Covered with a fine meal-like dust. 2. Like fresh meal. 3. With the odor and taste of fresh meal.

farinose. Covered with a meal-like powder, having a mealy surface.

farious. In rows.

fascia. 1. An ensheathing band of connective tissue. 2. A broad or well defined band of color. 3. A fascicle.

fasciated. 1. Having parts which have coalesced and flattened. 2. Having broad parallel bands of stripes. 3. Malformed. 4. Fused together.

fascicle. 1. A bundle. 2. A loose cluster. 3. A tuft of plant parts.

fascicled roots. Roots arranged in clusters and approximately equal in size.

fascicle sheath. A tubular envelope at the base of a fascicle.

fascicular. 1. Of or pertaining to fascicles. 2. Connected or drawn into a fascicle.

fascicular cambium. The cambium located within the bundle between the xylem and the phloem, the vascular cambium.

fascicular secondary xylem. The xylem formed by the cambium of a simple vascular bundle.

fascicular system or tissue. The fibrovascular system.

fascicular xylem. The hadrome or the wood elements of a bundle.

fasciculate. 1. Crowded into bundles, tufts, or clusters. 2. Having several similar parts originating at the same spot and collected close together. 3. Growing in spiral or whorled fascicles.

fasciculus. A dense cymose inflorescence, a fascicle.

Fasergrubchen. Cryptostomata.

fastigiate. 1. Having branches which are erect and close together with many branches parallel to the stem. 2. Tapering to a narrow point like a pyramid. 3. Parallel and upright. 4. Bunched or clustered.

fastigiate cortex. The cortex formed of clustered parallel hyphal branches vertical to the long axis of the thallus in lichens.

fastigiate trees. Trees with shoots growing erect and forming an acute angle with the stem.

fat. Vegetable oils, non-nitrogenous reserves in seeds or the volatile oils which perfume many flowers and leaves.

fat bodies. The fatty oils in plants.

fat cells. The specialized hyphal cells containing fat or oil.

fat enzyme. An enzyme which breaks up oils or fats.

father plant. The pollen parent.

fatique substances. The substances thrown off by plants which act in a restraining or poisonous way.

fatiscent. Disappearing, breaking up.

fatuoid. 1. Like a mutation from *Avena sativa,* the cultivated oat. 2. Resembling *Sativa fatua,* a wild species of oat.

fauces. The throat of a gamopetalous corolla, the jaws or gaping orifice of a monopetalous flower.

faucial. Situated in the throat or mouth of the tube of the perianth.

Faulschlamm. Foul-smelling slime on a lake bottom due to anaerobic decomposition of organic matter which has been covered or sealed by the deposit of fine soil.

favella. A structure containing sex organs in

some red algae, a spore-bearing structure in the red algae containing an irregular mass of spores embedded in more or less gelatinous material.

favellidium. A cystocarp.

faveolate. Having cavities or cells, alveolate, favose.

favic. See FAVUS.

favoid. Like a honeycomb, favoloid.

favose. Honeycombed, alveolate, deeply pitted.

favoso-areolate. Areolate in a manner suggesting a honeycomb.

favoso-dehiscens. Appearing honeycombed after dehiscence.

favosus. Pitted or excavated like the cells of a honeycomb, as the receptacles of many *Compositae*.

favularian. Resembling a ribbed surface separated by zigzag furrows in certain genera of fossil lycopods.

favus. A disease of the skin resulting in the loss of hair caused by the parasite *Achorion Schönleinis*.

feather-veined. Having lateral veins which branch at regular intervals from the midrib.

febrifuge. A remedy used in moderating or curing fever, often a vegetative derivative.

fecula. Any farinaceous matter, a starch extracted from plants by agitation with water.

feculent. Thick with sediment, muddy, turbid.

fecundation. Fertilization.

federation. The whole of the plant association of the biosphere.

federion. A stable synusium composed of one or more independent associations dominated by a definite group of species.

feeder. 1. A host plant. 2. An outgrowth of the hypocotyl serving as a temporary organ of absorption. 3. An organ that gives or provides food.

Fehling's solution. A solution of cupric sulfate and potassium sodium tartrate in alkali used as on oxidizing agent.

fellent. Bitter as gall.

fellfield. An alpine formation in the European mountains; districts of dwarfed, scattered plants, chiefly cryptogams found in arctic conditions.

felling subsere. A developmental series of communities started by the felling of trees.

felted. Matted with intertwined hairs; having hairs, filaments, or hyphae closely woven or closely matted together.

felted tissue. Hyphal tissue in which the filamentous cells are not regularly united but cross over one another irregularly and are often more or less grown together, the tela contexta.

female flower. A flower bearing only pistils.

female gamete. The egg cell or oosphere.

female organ. The pistils, archegonia, oospheres, etc.

femineus, flos. A flower which contains pistils but no stamens.

feminine. Pistillate, seed-bearing when the sexes are separate.

fen. A low, moist, level, humus-rich tract with peat, generally alkaline or neutral in reaction.

fence. An involucre.

fenchone. A ketone, the essential oil in oil of fennel.

fenestrae apicales. Apical openings in outer membranes, fenestrae basales.

fenestrate. Perforated.

-fer. A suffix meaning bearing.

feral. Wild or escaped from cultivation and reverting to a wild state.

ferment. 1. The act of fermentation. 2. An old name for enzyme. 3. A substance causing fermentation.

fermentation. The decomposition of carbohydrates by living cells or enzymes, any transformation of organic substances through the action of enzymes.

fermentation, acetic. The production of acetic acid.

fermentation, alcoholic. The production of alcohol from sugar by yeasts.

fermentation, butyric. The production of butyric acid.

fermentation, diastatic. The conversion of starch to sugar by diastase.

fermentation, lactic. The production of lactic acid from sugars.

fermentation, peptic. The action of the enzyme papain on protein as the tenderizing of meats.

fermentative energesis. The disruptive process of fermentation by which energy is released.

fern. Any plant of the *Filicales*.

fern allies. Plants closely related to or resembling the ferns.

feroces. Spines.

ferox. Very thorny.

ferrification. The action of the iron bacteria.

ferrobacteria. The bacteria which oxidize ferrous to ferric salts.

ferrugineous. Rust-colored.

ferruginous. Rusty, rust-colored, ferrugenous.

ferrugo. The rust disease caused by the uredo stage of various species of the genus *Puccinia.*

fertile cells. The binucleate basal cells in an aecidium which produce aecidiospores.

fertile flowers. Female flowers, those which have pistils.

fertile hypha. A conidiophore.

fertile, self. Having flowers which develop fruits or seeds in the absence of insects.

fertile stamens. Stamens which produce pollen capable of fertilizing the ovules.

fertilization. The union of the male and female reproductive cells, the fusion of the sperm and egg, the conjugation of isogametes.

fertilization, breech. Chalazogamy.

fertilization, close. The inbreeding of successive progeny of closely related parents.

fertilization, cross. 1. Fertilization between flowers on different plants. 2. Progeny from parents not closely related.

fertilization, double. The fusion of one of the male generative nuclei with the egg nucleus and the fusion of the second with the fusion nucleus to form the endosperm.

fertilization, generative. The sexual union of germ plasm of different parentage and different potentialities.

fertilization, post-. The stage after fertilization before the seeds ripen.

fertilization, pre-. The stage of the ovules prior to fertilization.

fertilization, reduced. The partial fusion of a female cell with a vegetative cell or the fusion of two female cells.

fertilization, self-. The fusion of a female gamete of an individual with a male gamete of the same individual.

fertilization tube. A tube or branch from the male gametangium through which the gonoplasm passes to the female gametangium.

fertilization, vegetative. The stimulus to growth resulting from the fusion of the two nuclei or other masses of protoplasm.

ferulaceous. 1. Resembling the genus *Ferula*, a giant fennel. 2. Being hollow like a reed or cane.

fervidarium. The stove in a botanic garden.

feste. See SELECTIVE SPECIES.

festuca. The stalk or straw.

festucare. A community of *Festuca*, a grass.

festucetum. An association of the genus *Festuca.*

festucine. Straw-colored, as in the dry culm of *Festuca.*

feuillemort. Of the color of a faded leaf.

Feulgen stain. A stain used for staining chromosomes to identify DNA. It stains purple and is one of the few specific dyes.

fiber, elementary. The thread or secondary deposit in a spiral vessel or tracheid.

fiber tracheides. See TRACHEID FIBERS.

fibers. Elongated sclerenchyma cells; slender, thick-walled cells many times longer than wide; prosenchyma.

fibertracheid. A fiber-like tracheid, a cell intermediate between a fiber and a tracheid.

Fibonacci series. Braun's series of numbers formed thus: 1, 2, 3, 5, 8, 13, 21, 34, 55, etc., by successive additions of the last two; they occur in phyllotaxis and were formulated by Leonardo Fibonacci of Pisa.

fibril. 1. A small thread-like branch. 2. A secondary fiber. 3. In sphagnum, the thickenings of the hyaline cell walls.

fibril of nucleus. A chromosome.

fibrillae. 1. Thread-like branches of roots. 2. Little threads.

fibrillate. Having fibrillae or hair-like structures.

fibrillate layer. The two outer layers of closely woven hyphae in the fungus *Geaster.*

fibrillate mycelium. See FIBROUS MYCELIUM.

fibrillose. 1. Having a finely lined appearance as if composed of fine fibers. 2. Covered with minute fibers. 3. Glabrous.

fibrillose-glabrose. Smooth to the naked eye but fibrillose under high-power magnification.

fibrillose mycelium. See FIBROUS MYCELIUM.

fibrils. Small fibers or filaments lining the utricles of *Sphagnum.*

fibrin, vegetable. A substance found in gluten which forms a tough, horny mass when dry.

fibro-cellular. Composed of spiral cells.

fibrolein. A very delicate membrane of the spirals of protoplasm.

fibrose. The cellulose of woody fiber.

fibrosin. A reserve substance resembling fibrose found in the form of discs embedded in protoplasm in the conidia of certain fungi.

fibrosis. An exaggerated development of fibrous strands.

fibro system. The whole of the fibrous portion of a plant exclusive of the purely cellular structures.

fibrotype. The condition of a root of the orchid *Cephalenthera* with a reduction and fusion of the stelar compounds and radially elongated cortex.

fibrous. Composed or covered with tough string-like tissues.

fibrous cells. Cells which are effective in opening the anther to shed the pollen.

fibrous cortex. A layer formed of hyphae parallel to the long axis of the thallus.

fibrous flaking. Flaking in narrow shreds.

fibrous layer. A layer of parenchyma cells having more or less reticulate thickening of the wall and occurring in anthers below the epidermis.

fibrous mycelium. Mycelium in which the hyphae unite to form long branching strands.

fibrous roots. Tough roots in tufts of uniform length, as in grasses.

fibrous tissue. Tissue formed of elongated, thick-walled cells.

fibro-vasal. Fibrovascular tissue.

fibrovasal bundles. String-like bundles found in the pith of the corn stalk, vascular bundles surrounded by a sheath of sclerenchyma fibers.

fibrovascular. Composed of both fibers and ducts.

fibro-vascular bundle. A vascular bundle; an association of vessels characteristic of the higher plants usually consisting of phloem and xylem which is often surrounded by a special layer of cells (the bundle sheath).

fibrovascular cord. A fibrovascular bundle in monocots.

fibrovascular cylinder. The fibrovascular system in the stem of the *Lycopodiaceae*.

fibrovascular system. The fibrovascular tissues considered collectively.

fibry. Fibrous.

fibula. A cylindrical stalk terminated by apothecia.

ficifolious. With leaves like *Ficus*, the fig.

-fid. A suffix meaning cleft or lobed.

fidelity. The degree to which species are confined to certain communities.

field stream. A layer of vegetation formed by grass, herbs, and dwarf shrubs.

fig. 1. Any tree of the genus *Ficus*. 2. Any fruit of the fig tree.

fig insect. The fig wasp (*Blastophaga*), the fertilizing agent in caprification.

fila adductoria. The abortive pistillidia of mosses.

fila succulenta. Paraphyses.

filament. 1. The microsporangiophore or stalk of the stamen. 2. A separate thread of mycelium. 3. A separate fiber.

filamenta ostiolaria. The delicate colorless threads lining the perithecium around the epithecium of *Verrucaria*.

filamentous fungus. A growth form of a branched hypha without the union with other hyphae.

filamentous mycelium. A mycelium composed of loosely interwoven free hyphae, floccose mycelium, fibrous mycelium.

filamentous sporophore. A sporophore which consists of a single hypha or hyphal branch.

filamentous thallus. See FRUTICOSE THALLUS.

filar-filamentous. Thread-like.

filarious. Filamentous.

filar plasma. Kinoplasm.

filatus. Wand-shaped, twiggy, streaked.

filberts. The fruit of *Corylus*.

filemot. Having the color of a faded leaf, feuille-morte.

files. A series of *Navicula*-like frustules, as in *Micromega*.

file trichome. A trichome covered with small knobs formed by the cuticle or small crystals.

filial cell. A daughter cell.

filial generation. The first crossbred generation, indicated as F_1.

filial regression. The tendency of the offspring of outstanding parentage to revert to the average for the species.

filical. 1. Fern-like. 2. Allied to the ferns.

Filicales. The ferns and fern allies, one of the chief divisions of the *Pteridophyta*, the *Filices*.

filicauline. With a thread-like stem.

filices. The *Filicales*.

filicifolious. Fern-leaved.

filiciform. 1. Shaped like the frond of a fern. 2. Thread-like.

filicinean. Relating to the ferns.

filicoid. Fern-like.

filicology. Pteridology, the study of ferns.

filiferous. Thread-bearing, filamentous.

filifolious. With leaves cut into thread-like divisions.

filiform. Having the shape of a thread or filament, thread-like.

filiform apparatus. A homogeneous, strongly refractile cellulose cap which is often found at the apex of each synergid, especially in monocotyledons.

filigerous. Bearing filaments.

filipendulinous. Like *Filipendula*, a small genus of rosaceous herbs.

filipendulous. 1. With tuberous swellings in the middle or end of filiform roots. 2. Hanging by or strung upon a thread.

filipes. Thread-like stalks.

filobacteria. Thread-like bacteria.

filoplasmodium. A net-like pseudoplasmodium.

filose. Terminating in a thread-like process.

filter. Any porous substance through which water or other liquid is passed to separate it from matter held in suspension or in some cases dissolved impurities or coloring matter.

filter beds. Especially constructed filter systems found in water purification systems or in sewage systems.

filter passers. Organisms which can pass through filters.

filtrable virus. A virus that can pass through a filter.

filtrate. The liquid and its contents which have passed through a filter.

filum. A filament or thread-like structure.

fimbria. A fringe or fringe-like border, as is found in the peristome of a moss.

fimbriate. Having the edge minutely fringed.

fimbricate. Fimbriate.

fimbrilla. A diminutive fringe.

fimetarius. Growing on or in dung.

fimicole. An organism dwelling on dung, fimbricolous.

fimus. Dung.

finger-and-toe. A disease of cabbage, club-root.

finger-parted. Divided into lobes having a resemblance to the five fingers of a hand.

finiform. A form whose nearest relations have completely died out.

finishers. Chemicals which may be used to further purify filtered sewage.

first division. The first of the two meiotic divisions, formerly known as the heterotypic or reduction division.

firstling cell. The first of a new generation from an auxospore in diatoms.

fisetin. The yellow coloring matter of *Rhus cotinus*.

fissifolious. Split-leaved.

fissile. 1. Tending to split. 2. Capable of being split.

fission. 1. The cleavage into new organisms or cells. 2. The division of one-celled organisms into two equal parts during asexual reproduction.

fission fungi. *Schizomycetes*.

fissiparity. The act of multiplication among the lower forms by breaking into living portions, reproducing by fission.

fistula. 1. A reed. 2. A pipe.

fistula, medullary. The central cavity in the stem of *Equisetum*.

fistula spiralis. The trachea.

fistular. Tubular, fistulose.

fixation. The process of killing and coagulating a cell by means of some chemical or physical agency.

fixation of nitrogen. The formation by soil bacteria of nitrogenous compounds from elementary nitrogen.

fixative. A reagent which will permanently fix the structure of a specimen in a life-like condition.

fixed oils. Nonnitrogenous reserves in seeds released by pressure.

fixity. A condition characterized by little or no response to stimuli.

fjaeld. 1. A barren Scandinavian upland. 2. An arctic stone desert. 3. A plant community which occupies most of the arctic land which is free of ice, including all stages between ground with an abundance of plants and the barren waste where only a more careful search can disclose a tiny tuft of moss under a stone.

flabellate. Fan-shaped, flabelliform.

flabellinerved. With radiating straight veins or nerves.

flacheric. A disease of the silk worm caused by bacterial fermentation of the food in the intestinal tract.

Flachmoor. A fen; see EMERSIHERBOSA.

flag apparatus. The anthers which become petaloid as a signal for insect visitors.

flagella. The thread-like organs of locomotion on bacteria.

flagellar pore. An aperture in the cell wall of the *Peridineae* through which the two flagella pass as they leave the protoplast.

flagellata. Algae which possess whip-like flagella by which they move through the water.

flagellate. 1. Having flagella. 2. Having the shape of a flagellum or whip.

flagellary. Caused by flagella, as in the motion of zoospores.

flagellispore. A swarm spore which has flagella.

flagellosis. A disease caused by flagellates.

flag leaf. The uppermost leaf of a plant.

flagon-shaped. Flask-shaped.

flake. 1. A gland bearing nectar. 2. A bicolored race of carnations having petals with large stripes.

flame-shaped. Wavily branching from the pith toward the bark, as applied to the direct pattern of such woods as chestnut and oak when seen in cross section.

flank curvature. The unequal growth of climbers.

flap. The pileus of an agaric.

flaps. See CONNECTIVE FLAPS.

flask. The utricle of *Carex*.

flask cell. The stalk-cell of the antheridium in *Characeae*.

flat sour. A type of spoilage of certain canned foods caused by the formation of acid without gas.

flattening. The fasciation of a stem.

flavedo. A disease of plants in which the green parts become yellow.

flavicin. An antibiotic obtained from *Aspergillus flavus* which is effective against bacteria but not against fungi.

flavicomous. Yellow-woolled, yellow-haired.

flavispinous. Yellow-spined.

flavone. A colorless crystalline substance occurring in plants which gives rise to certain yellow pigments.

flavous. Nearly pure yellow.

flavovirent. Yellowish green.

flavus. Pale yellow.

flax. The plant producing flax fibers, the genus *Linum*.

Flechtenserien. A lichen series.

fleshy disseminule. A seed or fruit consisting in large part of fleshy material.

fleshy fruit. An indehiscent fruit with pulp.

fleshy root. A root thick in diameter with much stored food.

flexicaulis. With a pliant stem.

flexuose-recurved. Bent backward in a flexuous or undulating manner.

flexuous hyphae. Haploid rust hyphae which after fusion with pycniospores or spermatia are diploid.

flexuous veins. Winding tortuous veins.

float. A hollow, inflated organ or air sac for making aquatic plants buoyant, as in *Fucus*.

floating respiration. Respiration in which the carbohydrates and other reserve materials are used.

floating tissue. Air-containing tissue in the seeds of plants dispersed by water currents.

flocci. 1. Small points or tufts resembling cotton. 2. Any woolly hairs or a tuft of such filaments. 3. Masses of filaments of mycelium.

flocculation. The aggregation of precipitated particles into large, soft masses remaining suspended in a medium.

flocculence. The adhesion in small flakes, as a precipitant.

flocculose-crenulate. Having minute flocculose markings on the edges.

flora. 1. The plants peculiar to a country, area, or period. 2. A catalogue of the plants growing in a country.

floraecology. The ecology of flowers.

florae horologicae. Flowers which expand at particular hours and can be used as an approximate timekeeper.

florae horologium. A floral clock of certain plants arranged in the order of the hours of opening or closing.

floral apex. The mamelon, the apex or tip of a flower.

floral axis. See RECEPTACLE.

floral diagram. A diagram to show the relative position and number of the constituent parts of typical flowers.

floral envelope. The perianth of a flower.

floral formula. A convenient mode of registering the component parts of a flower.

floral glume. The lower glume of the flower in grasses.

floral kingdoms. Regions characterized by the possession of a considerable number of local (endemic) forms. The greater their number and the higher their systematic rank, the more natural the region.

floral leaves. Bracts or parts of the flower, especially the calyx and the corolla.

floral mechanisms. Mechanisms which encourage fertilization of a flower to insure that the visiting insect shall receive pollen or touch the stigma.

floral organs. The parts of a flower: sepals, petals, stamens, and pistils.

floral regions. See FLORAL KINGDOM.

floral symmetry. The symmetry of a flower which indicates whether the flower is zygomorphic (divisible into two halves) or asymmetrical.

florealbo. With white flowers.

florepleno. With full or double flowers.

florescence. The opening of flowers, anthesis, the state of being in bloom.

floret. A small, often imperfect flower, usually one of a cluster of flowers, as one of the small flowers of a composite or one of the small flowers in a spike.

floribund. Having or producing many flowers.

floricole. Living on flowers.

floricome. A branched hexaster spicule.

Floridanus. Of Florida.

Florideae. The larger of the two classes of red algae characterized by cells composing the thalli united by protoplasmic threads.

floridean starch. A solid carbohydrate resembling starch formed by red algae as a product of assimilation staining reddish or brown with iodine.

florie. The perianth.

floriferae gemmae. Flower buds.

florigen. A hormone, presumed to be produced during photosynthesis, which stimulates flower production.

florigerous. Flower-bearing, producing flowers.

floriglume. The flowering glume in grasses.

florilege. A treatise on flowers.

floriparous. Producing flowers.

floristic composition. The compiled species lists of a number of samples of a given community.

florula. A small flora or botanic account of a restricted area.

flos. 1. A flower. 2. An anther in *Coniferae*. 3. An assembly of the organs essential for fertilization, as stamens and pistils with a protecting envelope.

flos aquae. Floating algae.

flos compositus. The capitulum.

flos plenus. A double flower with stamens or pistils or both converted into petals.

floscule. A little flower, a floret.

floscule, semi-. A composite floret.

flosculous. 1. Having tubular corollas like the florets of *Compositae*. 2. Composed of florets. 3. Discoid.

floss. 1. The styles or silk of the pistillate flowers of maize. 2. Any downy or silky substance.

flossification. The expansion of flowers.

flourish. A disk floret of *Compositae*.

flourish, half-. To bear ligulate or strap florets.

flower. A collection of sporophylls with the perianth; an axis bearing stamens or pistils, or both, and usually having a calyx and a corolla; the modified spore-bearing branch of the seed plants.

flower axis. The receptacle.

flower bud. An unopened flower.

flower cup. A hollow receptacle, a calyx, the cup-like interior of a flower.

flower-de-luce. The *Iris*, the fleur-de-lis.

flower, doubling of. The change of stamens into petals or, as in the composites, the change of tubular to ligulate flowers.

flower fence. The Pride of Barbados, the dwarf poinciana, *Caesalpinia pulcherrima*.

flower head. 1. A capitulum or head, as that of a daisy. 2. A cluster of flowers.

flower mechanism. See FLORAL MECHANISM.

flower movements. The bending of the stem and the closing of the petals.

flower pride. See FLOWER FENCE.

flower scar. The scar which remains after a flower has fallen.

flower tube. The concrescent portion of a flower.

flowering. The opening of floral envelopes and the maturity and exposure of the flower organs.

flowering glume. The lower of the two bracts which subtend the flower in grasses.

flowering plants. The phanerogams.

flowerless plants. The cryptogams.

flowers of tan. An aethalium of a myxomycete, the frothy body produced by the fungus.

flowers of wine. The growths of *Saccharomyces mycoderma* during fermentation.

fluctuating variations. Deviations from type which can be related to external conditions.

fluitantes. Floating plants.

fluminales. Growing in running water.

fluorescence. The property possessed by certain organic compounds of emitting light in the presence of certain rays whereby the compound appears to be of different colors by reflected and transmitted light.

fluorescence of chlorophyll. The shifting of the spectrum by the coloring matter contained in chlorophyll.

fluorescigenic. Causing fluorescence, as do certain bacteria.

flush. A shallow rivulet covered with vegetation, a sluggish channel.

flush, snow. The tracks of channels leading from snow patches.

fluvatile lakes. Lakes which are appendages to river systems often situated in river bottoms and connected during heavier flows of water.

fluviomarine. Inhabiting rivers and seas.

fluvioterrestrial. Found in streams and on the banks.

fluviruption. The act of tearing or carrying away by flowing or running water.

fly-flowers. Flowers which are especially adapted for fertilization by flies.

fly poison. A plant which produces a bulb which has been used as a poison for flies.

fly traps. Natural contrivances by which insects are caught, as in pitcher plants, the tentacles of *Drosera*, etc.

flywood. Oakwood which has been destroyed by the fungus *Stereum*.

flying hairs. Hairs which aid seeds in dispersal.

flying membrane. The expanded structures in winged seeds.

flying organ. Any structure attached to or associated with fruit or seed which facilitates dispersal by the wind.

flying tissue. The tissue making up the flying organs.

foedate. Dark or soiled.

foeniculaceous. Fennel-like, like the genus *Foeniculum*.

folded. 1. Conduplicate, said chiefly of leaf blades. 2. In vernation when the two halves of a leaf are applied to one another.

folded tissue. Endoderm with a suberified or lignified membrane located in a band on the lateral and transverse faces of the cells.

folded vernation. The condition in which the leaf is folded about the midrib with the two faces brought together.

Folds of Sanio. See SANIO'S RIMS.

foliaceae. The frondose vascular cryptogams, structures which are leaf-like in texture or appearance.

foliaceous thallus. In lichens, a flat, leaf-like, lobed, crisped thallus which spreads over the substratum but is attached at one or several scattered points and may be separated from the substratum without injury; a frondose thallus.

foliage leaf. The ordinary green leaf of a plant.

foliage sprays. Twigs which finally fall away carrying the small leaves with them.

foliar. 1. Leafy or leaf-like. 2. Consisting of leaves.

foliar gap. A break between vascular bundles of the stems which runs continuously from one internode into another and through which certain bundles of the stem pass out into the leaves.

foliar ray. A secondary ray.

foliar shoots. A foliage spray.

foliar spur. The dwarf shoot in a pine tree which bears a pair of leaves.

foliar trace. A leaf trace, the remains of the vascular bundle or bundles which entered a leaf.

-foliate. A suffix meaning having leaves.

foliation. The development of leaves, foliage, or petals.

folicaulicole. Growing on leaves and stems.

folicole. Living on leaves either as a parasite or an epiphyte, folicolous.

foliiferae gemmae. Leaf buds.

foliiparous. Producing leaves.

foliolae. Leaf-like appendages.

foliolar. Related to a leaflet.

-foliated. A suffix meaning having leaflets, pertaining to leaflets, or leaf-like. Used with prefixes bi-, tri-, etc.

foliole. A little leaf.

foliolean. Growing from the end of a leaf.

foliolose. Closely covered with flattened leaflets.

foliose. 1. Bearing numerous leaves. 2. Having the nature or appearance of a leaf, as lichens with a leafy form and layered in structure.

folious. Having leaves intermingled with flowers.

follicetum. A whorl or aggregation of follicles.

follicle. A dry, one-celled, capsular fruit dehiscing longitudinally by a suture on one side.

folliculate. 1. Having follicles. 2. Enclosed in follicles.

folliculose. Resembling a follicle.

fomes. An agent, usually inanimate, by which infection is spread.

fontanus. Growing in or near a spring.

food-bodies. 1. Small pear-shaped bodies on or near the leaves of certain plants which are used by ants as food. 2. A soft mass of food attached to a seed coat which attracts ants which move the seed and thereby assist in its dispersal.

food cycle. A fairly complete analysis of the food relations between the species in an association showing where each species obtains its food and what other organisms in turn derive their food from it.

food of the gods. *Ferula*, a giant fennel, used as a condiment in Persia and as a stimulant in medicine (as afoetida).

food pollen. The pollen formed by some flowers which attracts insects.

food vacuole. One of the temporary cavities in the protoplasm of many protozoa into which solid food is received and in which it is digested.

foot. 1. The portion of a sporophyte which fastens it to the gametophyte and absorbs materials from the gametophyte. 2. A development from the hypobasal part of an embryo.

foot cell. The spore of *Guttulina rosea* arising from a naked cell of protoplasm from the aggregated plasmodium.

foot embryo. An arrested terminal growth of the embryo of *Cutleria* differing from the protonematoid embryo of the same species.

foothill. See PAGOPHYTIA.

foot rot. A disease of ungrafted citrus caused by *Fusarium limonis*.

foot stalk. The stalk of either flowers or leaves, a pedicel, a petiole, or a peduncle.

foramen. 1. The opening through the coats of an ovule. 2. Any small perforation.

foraminated. Pitted with small holes or perforations.

foraminose. Perforated.

foraminula. The ostiolum of certain fungi.

forb. 1. An herb other than a grass or sedge. 2. A weed found in pastures.

forcing. The procedures by which cultivators produce fruit and vegetables out of season, early or late.

forcipate. Forked.

foredune. The surface of a dune exposed to the prevalent wind.

fore leaf. A bracteole or prophyllum.

foreolate. Pitted.

fore-runner point or tip. A form of leaf apex which performs all duties of assimilation before the basal portion is mature.

foreshore. The area traversed daily by the oscillating water-line of the tide.

forespore. A clear area in the cytoplasm of a bacterial cell which becomes surrounded by a refractile wall in the endospore formation.

forest climax. A climax community composed of trees.

forest cover. All trees, other woody plants (underbrush) covering the ground in a forest, and the litter on the forest floor.

forest edge. The thicket at the edge of an undisturbed forest composed of the forest reproduction and shrubs.

forest floor. The ground layer of a forest including dead vegetable matter, duff, litter, and the upper humus.

forest influences. All effects resulting from the presence of the forest upon health, climate, streamflow, and economic conditions.

forest oak. *Casuarina*, in Australia.

forest type. A forest stand essentially similar throughout in floristic composition, physiognomy, and ecological structure.

forestian. A type of peat formation in which trees are dominant, *Pinus* in the upper layers and *Betula*, *Corylus*, and *Alnus* in the lower stages.

forewold. The thicket zone bordering a forest, the forest edge.

forficate. Deeply notched, scissor-shaped, forficulate.

form. 1. A slight variety or variation in plant structure, usually transient, caused by some local environmental situation. 2. A variation occurring sporadically in a species population not forming a distinct regional or local facies of it and differing from other biotypes of the species population in one or more distinct characters.

form family. A botanical family consisting of form genera.

form genus. 1. A group of species which have similar morphological characters but which are not certainly known to be related in descent. 2. A group of organisms classified by their sexual reproductive structures or form species. 3. In fungi, a generic name based on the morphology of the asexual structures. 4. In fossil plants, a name for parts with the same form or morphology.

form order. In fungi imperfecti, an order based on the imperfect (i.e., asexual) structure.

form species. Species constituted by a single life cycle of a pleomorphous species and supposed to be the complete representative of the species.

form spore. A body simulating a spore but without germinating power or remaining attached to its sporophore.

formae-oxydateae. In crustaceous lichens those forms which have a rusty color from an infiltration of iron salts.

formation. A fully developed or climax community of a natural area in which the essential climatic regions are similar. It usually includes the developmental stages within its borders. An association.

formation, closed. A formation in which the plants are so crowded that invasion is difficult, a closed community.

formation dominants. Species which occur everywhere within a formation with a frequency of more than 80 per cent.

formation, mixed. An association in which two or more distinct formations compose a mixture.

formation, open. A formation in which the plants and groups are scattered.

formations, secondary. Formations which have arisen through human interesference.

formative area. The area in which development and differentiation may take place.

formative irritability. The capacity of tissues to respond to stimuli and to produce outgrowths.

formative materials. Materials such as sugars, starches, fats, etc., that are utilized in building and development.

formative region. 1. A growing point. 2. A developing area.

formative stimulus. Any agent stimulating the capacity of microorganisms to form outgrowths of determinate form.

formative stuffs. Hypothetical substances which are formed in one part of an organism and transported to another part to produce or to influence the production of new organs.

formative stage of growth. The stage in development when a cell is formed from a pre-existing cell.

formicaeformis. Ant-shaped, ant-like.

formicarian. Applied to plants producing sweet fluids which attract ants.

formion. A stable synusium composed of one or more stable and independent federions indicating their affinity by the presence of certain species common throughout.

fornicate. 1. Provided with scale-like appendages in the corolla tube. 2. Arching over.

fornix. 1. A small arching crest in the throat of the corolla. 2. One of the arched scales in orifices of some flowers. 3. A vault.

fossil botany. Palaeobotany, the study of fossil plants.

fossula. 1. A small groove found in some diatom valves. 2. A space found between the ridges of an oospore of *Chara*. 3. A sulcus.

fosterplant. A host plant.

fourcroid. Like *Fourcroya*, an amaryllis.

fourfold pollen grains. Pollen grains which form coherent tetrads.

four o'clock. *Mirabilis Jalapa*, a garden flower which opens in late afternoon.

fovea. 1. A small pit or fossa. 2. A small hollow at the leaf base in *Isoetes* containing a sporangium. 3. The seat of the pollinium in orchids.

fovillae. Minute granules in a liquid, as in the protoplasm of the pollen grain.

foxglove-shaped. Shaped like the corolla of *Digitalis*, digitaliform.

foxtail. Any of several grasses with brush-like spikes, especially species of *Alopecurus* and *Chaetochloa*.

fractional cultures. See SEPARATION CULTURES.

fragariform. Strawberry-shaped, after the genus *Fragaria*.

fragarioid. Strawberry-like.

fragmentation. Nuclear division by simple splitting, the direct division of a nucleus without the formation of a spindle, the condition of breaking up before crossing over in nuclear division.

frangulin. A yellow crystalline glucoside extracted from the parenchyma of *Rhamnus frangula*, the buckthorn.

fraternity. See ADELPHOUS.

fraxinetum. An association of ash trees, the genus *Fraxinus*.

fraxinin. An extract from the bark of ash trees.

free basal placentation. Ovules arranged in a basal placenta in a one-celled ovary.

free cell formation. The production of new

cells from several nuclei within the mother cell, endogenous cell formation.

free central placenta. A placenta running through the center of a unilocular ovary which looks like a multilocular ovary that has lost its septa.

free central placentation. A situation in which the ovules are on a central placenta reaching from the bottom to the top of a one-celled ovary, the attachment of ovules to the central axis of an ovary.

free nuclear division. Nuclear division which takes place without the development of cell walls, as the early development of endosperm in seeds.

free stock. A seedling tree of the same species used for grafting as opposed to a stock of a different species.

freestone. Having drupes in which the flesh separates readily from the pit when ripe.

frenching. A fungus disease of uncertain nature affecting plants in the course of which the leaves lose color and die.

frequency classes. The frequency percentages or indices of the component species of a community divided into equal classes on a 5 or 10 parted scale.

frequency curve. See LAW OF FREQUENCY.

frequency dominant. Dominant species with the highest degree of frequency.

frequency factor. The percentage of occurrence of a species in a plant community.

frequency index. The percentage of uniformity with which the plants of a species are distributed throughout a community.

frequency, law of. The distribution of the frequency percentages of the species of a community through the five classes reveals a double peak in classes A and E. The law of distribution of frequency figures can be expressed thus: A>B>C><D<E.

friable. Easily crumbled or breaking into a powder.

frigidarium. 1. The temperate house in a botanic garden in which there is simple exclusion of frost. 2. A cold place for cold storage.

frigideserts. Cold deserts or tundras.

frigofuges. Plants which shun low temperatures.

frill. An annulus in the form of a plaited frill in certain mushrooms; see ARMILLA.

fringe. 1. A fimbriate border. 2. The peristome of mosses.

fringing forest. A rain forest which exists as a continuous belt along water courses of certain parklands.

frond. 1. A general term for the leaf of a fern which differs from a typical leaf in that it bears reproductive organs on its surface. 2. The leaf-like thallus of a liverwort or seaweed. 3. The leaf of a palm.

frond genus. Of ferns, referring to any genus described solely from fronds.

frondescence. The development of leaves, vernation, phyllody.

frondiparous. 1. Bearing fronds. 2. With monstrous production of leaves instead of fruit.

frondose. 1. Said of a forest or woods of broad-leaved trees. 2. Having the character of bearing fronds.

frondose thallus. A foliaceous thallus, the thallus in lichens when flat and leaf-like.

frondula. The main stem of *Selaginella*.

front chamber. The part of the pore in stomata below the upper projecting ridges.

frost cracks. Longitudinal cracks in the bark due to sudden reduction in temperature.

frost rib. A callus formed over a wound caused by a frost crack.

fructescent. Bearing fruit.

fructicolous. Living on fruits or parasitic on fruits.

fructifer, calyx. A fruiting calyx.

fructification. 1. The body which develops after fertilization and contains spores or seeds. 2. Any spore-bearing structure whether formed after fertilization or by purely vegetative development.

fructification, double. The dimorphic fructification in algae.

fructification, organs of. 1. Stamens and pistils. 2. The fruiting organs.

fructosans. Plant storage products produced by the condensation of fructose.

fructose. A fruit sugar, levulose, a keto-hexose sugar.

frugivorous. Feeding on fruit.

fruit. A fructification, the structure which develops from the ovary of an angiosperm after fertilization with or without additional structures formed from other parts of the flower.

fruit bearer. The carpophore.

fruit bodies. 1. The well defined groups of fungal spores and the hyphae which produce and surround them. 2. The spore-bearing bodies of the nonflowering plants. 3. The sporophores.

fruit bud. A bud producing flowers and fruit.

fruit dots. The sori of ferns.

fruit galls. The diseased growth caused by *Ustilago treubii*.

fruit spur. In orchard fruit trees, as apple or pear, a short, stout branch bearing fruit buds.

fruit, spurious. A pseudocarp.

fruit stalk. 1. The peduncle. 2. The seta in mosses.

fruit sugar. Levulose.

fruit wall. The pericarp.

fruiting body. A complex spore-bearing structure which usually has a definite shape.

frumentaceous. 1. Producing or pertaining to edible grain. 2. Made of or resembling wheat or other grain.

frumentum. Grain or cereal.

frustilla. See FRUSTULE.

frustraneous. Resembling *Frustranea* composites with hermaphroditic disk flowers and neuter or imperfect ray flowers.

frustulation. The formation of a frustule.

frustule. A diatom cell made up of valves, girdle, and contents.

frutescent. Becoming shrubby or shrub-like.

frutex. A shrub or bush.

frutical. With a soft-wooded stem.

frutice. Shrubs.

fruticeta. A scrub forest; see LIGNOSA.

fruticose. 1. Shrubby, with woody persistent stems and branches. 2. Of lichens, having an upright or pendulous thallus with a radiate structure.

fruticose thallus. A thallus in lichens which is attached to the substratum at one point only by a narrow base and grows upward as a simple shrub-like body.

fruticulose. Somewhat shrubby, resembling a small shrub.

fruticulus. A small, minute, or low shrubby plant.

frutlet. A low tufted evergreen plant such as a *Saxifrage*.

frutose. Fruit sugar, fructose.

fucaceous. Of or pertaining to the genus *Fucus*, the brown algae or rockweeds.

fucan. Fucosan.

fucatus. Painted, dyed, colored.

fuchsioid. Like *Fuchsia*, a cultivated tender plant with conspicuous reddish purple flowers.

fucin. A special substance in the cell wall of *Fucus*, a seaweed.

fucioid. Resembling *Fucus*.

fucivorous. Feeding on *Fucus* or other seaweeds.

fucoid. 1. Pertaining to or resembling algae of the family *Fucaceae*. 2. Loosely resembling or having the nature of seaweeds.

fucosan. A product of carbon assimilation in brown seaweeds in the form of semifluid particles, fucan.

fucose. A sugar found in brown algae.

fucoxanthine. The brown pigment which is characteristic of the brown algae.

fugacious. Ephemeral, evanescent.

fugitive. Said of plants that are not native but which recur here and there but apparently do not become established.

fulcra. 1. The appendages of leaves, as prickles, tendrils, or stipules. 2. In lichens, the sporophores.

fulcrum. A structure which provides support, as the sporophore in lichens, the supporting cells of a zygospore in molds, stipules or tendrils in climbing plants, etc.

fuliginose. Sooty.

full. Denoting a double flower in which the stamens and pistils are transformed into flowers.

full meristem. A meristem forming a complete organographical part.

fulmineus. Fulvous, almost brown.

fulvic acid. An acid present in humus and in the pigment of *Penicillium fulvis*.

fulvid. Yellow mixed with grey, tawny brown, fulvous.

fumaginous. Smoky, sooty.

fumagoid. Resembling the fungus *Fumago*.

fumariaceous. Pertaining to the genus *Fumaria*, a poppy.

fumaroid. 1. Of or pertaining to the poppy genus *Fumaria*. 2. Resembling fumaric acid.

fumarole. A hole or spot in a volcanic region through which fumes arise. The surrounding flora is xerophilous.

fumid. Smoky.

fumigacin. An antibiotic obtained from some species of *Aspergillus*.

fumigatin. An antibiotic effective in the control of bacteria which does not deter fungus growth.

funalis. Funiliform, like a rope or cord.

functional metabolism. The kinetic effects of certain chemical changes in a plant.

fundamental cells. The parenchyma.

fundamental organs. The nutritive organs essential to the existence of the plant: root, stem, and leaf.

fundamental spiral. The genetic spiral.

fundamental stage of growth. The formation of new protoplasm.

fundamental system. The cellular system, the portion of the substance of higher plants which is not included in the fibrovascular and epidermal system.

fundamental tissue. The ground tissue, meristematic tissue and the undifferentiated parenchymatous tissue forming the greater part of the initial plant body.

fundamentum. The hypocotyl.

fundiform. Looped.

fundus. The bottom or base of the internal surface of a hollow organ.

fungaceous. Fungoid or fungus-like.

fungal. Relating to fungi.

fungal cellulose. Fungus cellulose.

fungales. An absolute term for lichens and fungi.

fungi imperfecti. The group of fungi with septate hyphae for which the knowledge of the life cycle is incomplete and for which no sexual stage is known.

fungic. Relating to mushrooms.

fungic acid. A mixture of citric, malic, and phosphoric acids.

fungicide. Any substance which kills fungi.

fungillus. A diminutive fungus, a small parasitic fungus.

fungin. A variety of cellulose found in the cell walls of fungi.

fungistatic. Able to arrest the growth of fungi but does not kill them.

fungisterol. A sterol in fruiting bodies of the *Polyporus Sulphureus.*

fungo cellulose. Fungus cellulose.

fungoid. Fungus-like.

fungo lichens. Plants considered transitional between fungi and lichens.

fungology. Mycology.

fungose. Spongy in texture, like a fungus.

fungs. A little-used term for fungi.

fungus. A thallophyte lacking chlorophyll.

fungus cellulose. A carbohydrate which is horny in texture which adds rigidity to cell walls of some fungi and lichens. It is similar to cellulose. Chitin, fungal cellulose, fungo cellulose.

fungused. A little-used term meaning attacked by fungus.

fungus gall. A malformation produced by a parasitic fungus.

fungus stone. The hard, almost stony sclerotium of *Polyporus Tuberaster* which when warmed and watered yields an edible crop. Used in Italy.

fungus traps. Catch crops: quickly growing crops to secure attacks from *Plasmodiophora Brassicae* which are then removed with the fungus and the land is presumed to be free for that season for a later crop of crucifers.

funicle. 1. The funiculus or stalk of an ovule or seed. 2. The cord which attaches the peridiole to the peridium wall in the *Nidulariaceae.*

funicular cord. The cord which attaches the stalk of an ovule or seed to the placenta.

funiculose. In ropes or bundles, rope-like.

funiculus. In *Nidulariales*, the structure attaching the peridiole to the inner surface of the wall of the peridium; see FUNICLE.

funiliform. Applied to organs which are tough, cylindrical, and flexible, as in the case of the roots of the arborescent monocotyledons.

funkia. Sporophytic budding in the ovule.

funnel. A passageway in some plants which permits the passage of gases.

funnel cells. Short and broad cells which are shaped like a funnel often found in the palisade layer of a leaf.

furcate. Forked.

furcellate. Minutely or slightly furcate or forked.

furfur. Bran or scurfy particles.

furiotile lakes. Oxbows and sloughs which are connected with the main stream at periods of high water but disconnected at low water.

furrowing. Cell division by the development of a furrow beginning at the cell periphery and extending inward until the cell is cut into two cells.

furrows. Grooves or channels (common on old bark of many trees).

fusariosis. A disease induced by *Fusarium*, a parasitic fungus causing serious plant diseases as the dry rot of potatoes, etc.

fuscate. Darkened.

fuscifolious. Fuscous-leaved.

fusco-lutea. Brown yellow.

fusco-pubescent. With reddish green hairs or scales.

fuscous. Dusky grayish brown.

fusco-viride. Dusky green.

fuseau. A spore of the fungi causing hair or

skin disease; see TERMINAL CHLAMYDO-
SPORE.

fusel oil. An acrid, oily, poisonous product of insufficient fermentation.

fusiform. Spindle-shaped.

fusiform-elliptical. Fundamentally elliptical but somewhat fusiform, more elliptical than fusiform.

fusiform initial. A cambial initial which gives rise to a vertical or axial element of xylem and phloem which appears fusiform in tangential section.

fusiform wood parenchyma cell. A wood parenchyma cell derived from a cambial initial without subdivision.

fusion. The complete union of vessels as in lactiferous tissue.

fusion cell. A double cell as found in uredineous fungi formed by the conjugation of a pair of fertile hyphal cells without their nuclei fusing.

fusion nucleus. The nucleus near the center of an embryo sac formed by the fusion of polar nuclei.

fusion sori. Sori which have spread and appear joined.

fusion, triple. Double fertilization.

fusisporous. Having spindle-shaped spores.

fusoid. Fusiform or shaped like a spindle.

fustic. 1. The wood of a common tropical tree, *Chlorophora tinctoria*, which yields a light yellow dye much used in art. 2. A name applied to other dyewoods.

future generations. Successive generations of basidia.

Fynbosch. See MAQUIS and DURIFRUTICETA.

G

galacifolious. Galax-leaved.

galactans. The gums, agar, fruit pectins, mucilages, etc., found in algae, lichens, mosses and fruits which are anhydrides of galactose.

galactase. A trypsin-like enzyme occurring in milk and important in the ripening of cheese.

galactin. A substance in the juice of *Brosimum Galactodendron* and in leguminous seeds like gum arabic, an acacia.

galactite. Milky white.

galactose. A white crystalline sugar present in certain gums and seaweeds as a polysaccharide galactan.

galactosidase. An enzyme which catalyzes the change from galactose to galactans.

galbalus. The fleshy and ultimately woody cone of junipers and cypresses.

galbanum. A fetid yellowish or brownish gum resin derived from certain species of *Ferula* and other Asiatic plants which is used in making varnishes and medicines.

galbanus. The greenish-yellow color of galbanum.

galbulus. The more or less fleshy strobile of the cypress and the juniper.

galea. A helmet-shaped petal or other structure.

galegifolious. Leaved like *Galega*, a leguminose plant (goat's rue) commonly cultivated.

galericulate. Covered with a small cap or cup, galerculate.

galiod. Resembling *Galium*, the bed straw weed.

gall. 1. An excrescence on plants which is caused by disease. 2. A large growth caused by insect puncture.

gall flower. An imperfectly developed flower of the fig tree in which the eggs of the gall wasp are laid.

gallic acid. An astringent derived from oak galls.

gallicus. Of Gaul or France.

gallivorous. Feeding on galls.

gallorubrones. Red pigments from plant galls.

gallotannin. A glucoside found in the bark of oak.

galochrous. Milky white.

Galtonian curve. A graph devised by Galton resembling the curve of probability and representing graphically the deviations of any given characteristic from the norm of that characteristic in the species under consideration; see NEWTONIAN CURVE.

galvanotaxis. A response to an electrical stimulus.

galvanotaxis, negative. The attraction of organisms toward the cathode.

galvanotaxis, positive. The attraction of organisms toward the anode.

galvanotropic. Showing a curvature when subjected to an electric current (usually toward the positive electrode).

galvanotropism. See GALVANOTAXIS.

gamboge. A yellow resinous gum used for

yellow paint pigments which is derived from several species of *Guttiferae*, chiefly tropical plants.

gamboge, fungus. A gum found in fungi which resembled gamboge.

gametangial copulation. The conjugation of gametangia where the differentiation of gemetes is suppressed.

gametangium. A specialized cell in which gametes are produced, a structure producing sex cells.

gametangy. The type of sexuality in which the copulation is between gametangia and not between the gametes.

gamete. A reproductive cell of either sex prior to conjugation. The union of gametes produces a sexual spore or zygote.

gametic number. The number of chromosomes usually found in reproductive cells represented by "n" in haploid gametes (one in each of a pair), or "2n" in diploid or fused gametes (zygotes).

gametids. The primary sporoblasts which develop into gametes.

gametoblast. A formative substance, the plasson.

gametocyst. An envelope which encloses one or more gametes.

gametocyte. The mother cell which gives rise to gametes.

gametocytogony. Sexual reproduction.

gametogenesis. The process of producing or forming gametes.

gametogenic. Arising from spontaneous changes in the chromosomes of gametes, said of the production of gametes.

gametogenous. Having organs or cells which produce gametes.

gametogeny. The production of gametes.

gametogonidium. The initial plastids of gametes in *Volvox*.

gametogonium. A gametocyte.

gametoid. An apocytial structure which unites like a gamete and produces a zygotoid.

gameto-nucleus. The nucleus of a gamete.

gametophore. A structure upon which gametes are borne, a modified branch bearing sex organs or gametangia.

gametophyll. A modified leaf bearing sex organs.

gametophyte. The phase in the life cycle of plants which bears the sex organs and gives rise to the gametes.

gametophyte budding. The situation in which the gametophyte is reproduced by buds or gemmae from a parent gametophyte.

gametoplasm. The protoplasm of gametes.

gametozoospore. The biciliate zoospore in *Ulothrix*.

gametrophic. Having movement of organs before or after fertilization.

-gamic. A suffix signifying a sexual union.

gamicae. Algae.

gamo-. A prefix denoting sexual union or coalescence.

gamobium. The gametophyte.

gamocentres. Centers of grouped chromatin granules during synapsis which afterward become the reduced number of bivalent chromosomes.

gamodesmic. Having the vascular bundles fused together instead of separated by connective tissue.

gamoecia. The inflorescence of bryophytes.

gamogastrous. Having a pistil which is formed by the more or less complete union of ovaries with the styles and stigmas remaining free.

gamogemmie. The intimate association of two or more floral rudiments.

gamogenesis. Sexual reproduction.

gamogony. Sporogony, sexual reproduction.

gamoid. Having sexual as opposed to vegetative reproduction.

gamomeristele. The lateral fusion of individual bundle sheaths.

gamomeristelic. Gamodesmic.

gamomerices. Flowers in which the parts are united by their edges.

gamomery. The condition of normally distinct petals when joined into a gamopetalous corolla.

gamomites. The conjugated filaments in karyokinesis.

gamont. A sporont, a gamete-producing form.

Gamopetalae. Flowering plants which have the petals united.

gamopetalous. Said of a corolla with the edges of the petals wholly or partially united, monopetalous, sympetalous.

gamophase. The haploid phase in the life cycle.

gamophyllous. Having the perianth members united, composed of coalescent leaves or leaf-like organs.

gamophyte. A sexual plant.

gamosepalous. 1. Formed of united sepals. 2. With the calyx of one piece. 3. With a calyx tubular at least at the base.

gamosomes. The aggregation of chromatin granules formed from portions of the thread during synapsis.

gamosperms. Plants which have seeds without parthenogenetic embryos.

Gamosporeae. Algae which produce zoogonidia or zygospores, as the *Conjugatae*.

gamostelic. Having the steles of a polystele fused together to constitute a gamostele.

gamotropism. 1. The tendency of a plant to respond to the mutual attraction of similar conjugating gametes. 2. The responsive movement of flowers before fertilization. 3. The movement of flowers when expanding.

gandavensis. Relating to Ghent, Belgium.

gangeticus. Relating to the Ganges River.

ganglia. The various enlargements on the mycelium of certain fungi some of which are rudimentary fructifications.

gangligerous. Bearing knots, gangliform.

ganglioneous. Having hairs which bear branchlets on their articulations.

gap. See LEAF GAP.

gaps, branch, foliar or leaf. Openings in the siphonosteles to permit the passage of vascular tissue to form branches or leaves.

garganicus. Of or pertaining to Gargano in eastern Italy.

garide. The bushland composed of deciduous shrubs occurring in the Jura and Rhone valleys.

garique. 1. An open type of vegetation in dry localities which is transitional between fell-field and woodland, usually composed of perennial herbs. 2. Waste tracts in southern France in which remnants of the former forest occur.

gas vacuoles. Special floating organs in certain *Cyanophyceae*.

gas plankton. Organisms which float by means of air vacuoles.

gasterolichens. Gasteromycetes in symbiosis with algae.

gasteromycetes. A group of *Basidiomycetes* in which the hymenium is enclosed in a sac-like envelope called the peridium.

gasterospore. A thick-walled, globose spore borne within the tissues of a fruit body, an internal conidium.

gasterothalameae. Lichens which have sporangia which are always closed and which burst through the cortical layer of the thallus.

gastric bacteria. Bacteria found in the digestive tracts of animals.

gastronasty. See HYPONASTY.

gattine. A disease of silk worms caused by parasitic fungi.

gaultherase. An enzyme which produces oil of wintergreen and glucose.

gaultherin. A substance which occurs in *Gaultheria*, an evergreen ericaceous plant.

ge-. A prefix meaning earth.

Gebiet. A complex climatic plant formation.

Gegenpol. The pole of a resting nucleus which lies farthest from the centrosome.

geitonembryosperm. A parthembryosperm with the endosperm fertilized by pollen from a flower on the same plant.

geitonendosperm. A parthendosperm with the embryo fertilized by pollen from a flower on the same plant.

geitonocarpy. The production of fruit as the result of geitonogamy.

geitonogamy. Pollination of one flower by another growing on the same plant.

geitonosperm. A plant whose embryos arise by geitonogamy.

gel. A colloid which assumes a jelly-like state under ordinary environmental conditions which offers little resistance to liquid diffusion. Some gels (like gelatin, which contains 90% water) react more like solids than like liquids.

gel water. The water held in the interstices of the gel-structure of a soil.

gelate. To become coagulated.

gelatin. A colorless, odorless, tasteless substance derived from animal and plant materials which is soluble in hot water and forms a jelly-like substance at normal temperatures and is scarcely soluble in water; gelatine, agar, gelose.

gelatina hymenea. A gelatinous substance surrounding the asci and paraphyses in some lichens.

gelatinization. The process in which a membrane breaks down into a jelly-like mass.

gelatinous felt. Gelatinous tissue.

gelatinous matrix. The jelly-like matrix around certain *Cyanophyceae*, the blue-green algae.

gelatoids. Protein-like substances resembling gelatin.

gelineae. Cells in algae which secrete vegetable jelly.

gelose. An amorphous gelatin-like carbohydrate found in agar.

gem. See GEMMA.

geminate. United in equal parts or pairs, twins.

gemini. Twins.

gemini, synaptic. The pairing of somatic chromosomes in prophase of the first or heterotypic meiotic division.

geminiflorus. A plant whose flowers are arranged in pairs.

geminispinous. Twin-spined.

geminus. See BIVALENT.

gemma. 1. A small multicellular body (consisting of thin-walled cells) produced by vegetative means and able to separate from the parent plant and form a new individual. 2. A nonmotile asexual spore in some algae. 3. A thick-walled resting spore formed by some fungi. 4. A leaf bud.

gemma cup. A cup-like structure in which gemmae are produced, as the cyathus in *Marchantia*.

gemmaecorm. A bud corm, applied to herbaceous plants with a root crown which increases by sidebuds.

gemmate. To produce or propagate by buds.

gemmation, nuclear. The budding of the nucleus, as in *Synchytrium*, and the establishment of a definite group of nuclei.

gemmidium. A tetraspore.

gemmiparous. 1. Producing buds or gemmae. 2. Having leaves arise from adventitious buds.

gemmule. 1. A diminutive gemma. 2. A plumule. 3. An ovary.

-gen. A suffix meaning producing.

gene. The hereditary unit which controls the appearance of definite characters.

gene complex. The interlacing system produced by the whole of the genetic factors of an organism.

gene mutation. A change in a genetic factor.

geneagenesis. The occasional production of true spores or seeds without fertilization, parthenogenesis.

genecology. Ecology concerned primarily with species; see AUTECOLOGY.

genepistasis. The graduated evolution brought about by the unequal development of some individuals.

general involucre. A universal involucre.

generalized root system. A root system in which the tap root and the lateral roots are well developed.

generating spiral. A genetic spiral.

generating tissue. The meristem or cambium.

generation. The individuals of a species equally remote from a common ancestor; see ALTERNATION.

generation time. The time required to complete a life cycle, or in unicellular organisms, the time between one cell division and the next.

generative apogamy. The asexual origin of a sporophyte from the vegetative tissues of the gametophyte when the nucleus of the mother cell of the sporophyte has only haploid chromosomes.

generative cell. 1. The cell in a pollen grain which develops into male gametes. 2. A sexual cell of any kind.

generative nucleus. The nucleus in a pollen grain which is actively concerned in fertilization.

generative parthenogenesis. The asexual origin of a sporophyte from a germ cell when the nucleus of the latter has haploid chromosomes only, the formation of an embryo without fertilization from a haploid egg.

genes, complementary. Genes which inherited separately produce similar effects but inherited together produce qualitatively different effects.

genesiology. The doctrine of the transmission of qualities from the parent in vegetative or sexual reproduction.

genetic balance. A result of the counteraction of the many genes which determine the hereditary characters of organisms resulting in the fairly equal distribution of opposing qualities which balance each other in total effect.

genetic coefficient. The part played by the species in the development of the community.

genetic complex. All the factors in the chromosomes and the cytoplasm of an organism which are involved in inheritance of characters.

genetic equilibrium. The state reached by interbreeding organisms in which specific genotypes and genes are developed in the same frequencies in successive generations.

genetic sociology. Syngenesis.

genetic spiral. A spiral line which passes through the point of insertion of all equivalent lateral members of an axis in order their age.

genetic system. The structures concerned with reproduction and heredity.

genetic variation. Variation due to differences in the gametes.

genetics. The science of breeding from the standpoint of the transmission of hereditary characters without regard to the influence of environment.

genevensis. Relating to Geneva.

genic. Genetic.

geniculate. Bent abruptly like a knee.

geniculum. A node of a stem, especially when the stem is bent.

genistifolious. Having leaves like *Genista*, a legume.

genitalia. In plants the stamens and pistils or their analogues.

gennylangium. An anther.

gennyleion. An antheridium.

genoblast. A mature male or female germ cell.

genocentric. See REPRODUCTOCENTRIC, MONOGENOCENTRIC.

genodifferent. Having gametes which form a monohybrid.

genoholotype. The one species on which a genus is founded, a type genus.

genolectotype. The one species subsequently selected out of a series as typical of a genus if there is no genoholotype.

genome. A complete haploid set of chromosomes as it is inherited from each parent, a genom.

genomere. A hypothetical particle which with other similar particles makes up a gene.

genophene. A reaction type of a genotype.

genoplast. A genotype, the fundamental hereditary combination of the genes of an organism.

genoplastic. Denoting one of a series of species upon which a genus is founded, no one species being the actual type.

genospecies. A genotypical construction of a Linnaean species, a homozygotic biotype.

Genossenschaft. An association.

genosyntype. One of several species included within a genus at the time of its proposal if none was designated as the genotype.

genotype. 1. A group of individuals which are alike with respect to their hereditary factors. 2. The entire genetic constitution of an organism. 3. The single species upon which the genus is based.

genotype compounds. The products of recombined Mendelian factors.

genotype conception. The Mendelian subunits of the genospecies.

genotypic control. The control of chromosome behaviour by the hereditary properties of the organism.

genotypist. A student of biotypes.

-genous. A suffix meaning producing or yielding.

gens. A tribe in botany.

gentiacauline. A glucoside from *Gentiana acaulis*, the stemless gentian.

gentianin. A bitter derivative of *Gentiana*.

gentianose. A sugar from *Gentiana lutea* which occurs with saccharose.

genuine tissue. A tissue derived from the division of a mass of related cells with subsequent differentiation of the daughter cells.

genus. The principal subdivision of a family, a more or less closely related and definable group of plants comprised of one or more species. The generic name becomes the first word of the binomial employed in horticultural and botanical literature.

genus hybrid. A hybrid between genera, a bigener or bigeneric cross.

geo-. A prefix meaning earth.

geoaesthesia. The capacity of a plant to respond to the stimulus of gravity.

geobenthos. The portion of a stream bottom not covered by vegetation.

geobion. A plant community of the land as distinguished from one in water.

geobiont. An inhabitant of the soil.

geobios. Terrestrial life.

geoblast. An embryo whose cotyledons remain under ground in germination.

geobotany. The study of plant distribution, phytogeography.

geocalycal. Resembling the hepatic genus *Geocalyx*.

geocarpic. Producing fruits underground.

geocarpy. The formation of subterranean fruits.

geocentric. Pertaining to or measured from the earth's center, as opposed to geotropic.

geocryptophyte. A flowerless plant which multiplies by means of underground buds, a geophyte.

geodiatropism. The tendency of an organ to place itself at right angles to the force of gravity.

geodistomycetes. The wood-destroying fungi which are more or less xerophytic which can grow in situations above the ground but grow best above 29°C; see DOMES-TOMYCETES and GEOPROXIMYCETES.

geodynamism. The influence of soils as agents of growth.

geodyte. A ground inhabitant; see TER-RICOLOUS.

geogenetic. Derived from the ground.

geographic botany. The study of plants in their geographic relations, phyto-geography.

geographic plant units. Units of plant associations in climatic zones which are characterized by special climax formations.

geoheterauxecism. The variation in the relative growth of opposite sides of an organ due to gravity.

geoid. Of the earth.

geologic botany. Paleobotany, fossil botany.

geomalism. The tendency of an organism to grow symmetrically in a horizontal plane.

geomorphic. Of or pertaining to the figure of the earth or to the form of its surface, taking its shape from the earth.

geonasty. Curvature toward the ground.

geonomaeform. Formed like *Geonoma*, Central and South American palms.

geonyctinastis. A sleep movement which is influenced by the stimulus of gravity.

geoparallelotropism. The condition of an organ placing itself parallel to the surface of the earth.

geoperception. See GEOAESTHESIA.

geophagous. Feeding on soil.

geophilae. Soil-loving species, as algae growing on barren or mossy ground.

geophilous. Living in or on the ground as a rosette or a subterranean organism. Earth-loving, geophilic, geocarpic.

geophilous fungi. Fungi which grow saprophytically on decaying vegetable matter in or on the ground.

geophyte. 1. A terrestrial plant. 2. A plant which produces underground buds with perennial development.

geophytia. Land plant communities.

geoplagiotropic. Growing at an angle to the ground surface.

geoponic. Growing in soil.

geoproximycetes. The wood-destroying fungi which normally grow in rather moist situations and which grow best at about 26°C.

georgianus. Of or from Georgia.

geosere. The total plant succession of the geological past.

geosphere. The earth.

geostrate. The entire series of strates subdivided into ceno-, meso-, and paleostrate after the geologic periods.

geostrophism. The tendency of a plant to twist in response to the rotation of the earth.

geosylvacolous. Ground-inhabiting; see TER-RICOLOUS.

geotaxis. The response to the laws of gravity.

geothermometer. A thermometer for measuring temperature below the surface of the ground.

geotome. An instrument for obtaining samples of soil.

geotonus. The normal state of an organism with reference to gravity.

geotortism. The torsion caused by the influence of gravity.

geotrophy. Unilateral inequality in growth due to gravity.

geotropism. Movement toward the earth in reaction to gravity.

geotropism, lateral. Horizontal curvature, as in twining stems.

geotropism, negative. Growth away from the earth, as in stem growth.

geotropism, positive. Growth toward earth's center, as in roots.

geotropism, transverse. The neutralization of the force of gravity by the attraction of light, diageotropism.

geoxyl. A woody plant with numerous stems which arise from a subterranean rhizome.

geraniaceous. Of, pertaining to, or like *Geranium*.

geranioid. *Geranium*-like.

geratology. A study of the factors of decadence.

germ. 1. A microorganism. 2. A bud or growing point. 3. A reproductive cell. 4. An embryo in a seed. 5. An embryo in its early stage.

germ cell. A cell which has the perpetuation of the race as its function, a reproductive cell, a gamete.

germ-cell determinants. Cytoplasmic inclusions which are unequally distributed in cleavage but pass into the daughter cells of the germ line.

germ disc. A small, green cellular plate of the

germ tube of liverworts from which the adult thallus develops.

germ layer. The earliest simple strata of cells out of which all the later tissues and organs are developed.

germ nucleus. The nucleus resulting from the fusion of male and female pronuclei.

germ plants. Stages in the life of *Hepaticae.*

germ plasm. Reproductive or sex cells, the generative substance contained in the body of a parent from which new individuals arise.

germ pore. A pit on the surface of a spore membrane through which a germ tube makes its appearance.

germ sporangium. A sporangium formed at the end of a germ tube produced by a zygospore.

germ theory. The theory that living organisms can be produced or developed only from living organisms, the theory stating that diseases arise from etiological agents called germs, biogenesis.

germ track. The course which determines the direction of the development of cells in the early cleavage stages, as the early development of the primordial germ cells; the direction of descent of the germ cells. The German Keimbahn.

germ tube. A filament put out by a spore in germination, the first shoot formed in the germination of a fungus spore or spore of hepatics.

german tinder. Amadou.

germanic. 1. German. 2. Showing close relationship or descent, germane.

germarium. An ovary.

germen. 1. An ovary. 2. The capsule of mosses. 3. A bud.

germen, inferior. Fruit produced below the flower.

germicide. An agent which kills bacteria or spores.

germiculture. Bacteriology.

germinability. The capacity to germinate.

germinal. Relating to a seed, germ cell, bud, or reproduction.

germinal aperture. See GERM PORE.

germinal apparatus. The egg apparatus.

germinal cells. The cells concerned in reproduction which are set apart early in embryonic life.

germinal corpuscle. The oosphere which produces the oospore.

germinal disk. The germ disk.

germinal dot. The centrosome in diatoms.

germinal lid. A separable area of a pollen grain which breaks away to permit the pollen tube to grow out.

germinal pore. 1. A thin, usually rounded area in the wall of a pollen grain through which the pollen tube emerges. 2. A similar spot in a spore wall from which the germ tube develops.

germinal process. A part belonging to an ovary or coming from an ovary.

germinal slit. A small break in a seed coat of some monocots.

germinal spot. The nucleolus of the egg nucleus.

germinal tube. The germ tube.

germinal units. Hypothetical parts of germ cells which are supposed to have specific functions in development.

germinal variations. Variations which owe their origin to some modification in the germ cells.

germinal vesicle. An oosphere.

germination. The development in a plant embryo in changing from a resting to an active condition, the development of a spore or seed into a plant, the beginning of growth.

germination by repetition. Germination by the formation of conidia rather than by a germ tube.

germinative area. The region in the embryo from which development proceeds.

germinative nucleus. See GENERATIVE NUCLEUS.

germiparity. The reproduction by germ formation.

germules. Small seeds or other reproductive bodies.

gerontogaeous. Denoting the plants of the Old World or the eastern hemisphere.

gerosere. The total plant succession of the geological past.

Gesamtschaetzung. An expression of plant dominance for areas of considerable extent combining abundance and dominance.

Geselligkeit. See SYNECOLOGY.

Gesellschaftshaushalt. See SYNECOLOGY.

Gesellschaftstreue. The fidelity of the ties by which plants are restricted to certain communites.

getah. Gutta (Malay).

gherkin. The small immature fruit of the common garden cucumber which is used in making pickles.

G-horizon. The gley horizon.

giant culture. The usual type of culture on a large scale over extended periods of time.

gibber. A pouch-like enlargement of the base of an organ.

gibberellin (gibberelic acid). A plant-growth stimulant extracted from molds (Gibberella or Fusarium).

gibberose. Humped, hunchbacked.

gibbiflorous. Gibbous-flowered.

gibbous. With an unsymmetrical convexity or umbo, with a convexity on one side, irregularly rounded, gibbose.

gibbsite. A clay soil, a constituent of bauxite. Hybrargillite.

gibraltaricus. Of Gibraltar.

giganthous. With giant flowers.

gigastylosporous. With very large stylospores.

giliare. A community of *Gilia*, a *Polemoniaceae*.

gill. The lamella or knife-blade-like structure which bears the spores on the underside of the cap of an agaric mushroom.

gill cavity. A ring-shaped hollow in the young agaric in which the early stages of the organization of the gills are completed.

gill cover. An operculum.

gill fungi. The *Agaricaceae*.

gill trama. The tissue of a gill between the two hymenial layers.

gilly flower. Gilliflower, a *Dianthus* (clove pink) or *Chorispora* (stock).

gilvous. Isabelline or dirty reddish yellow.

gimped. Crenate.

ginger beer plant. A mixture of fermentation organisms used in a sweet ginger-flavored liquid to produce ginger beer.

ginglymoid. Like a hinge or joint.

ginkgoaceous. Resembling the maidenhair tree, *Ginkgo biloba*; ginkgoalean.

ginkgophyte. A plant resembling the modern *Ginkgo*.

ginseng. Species of *Panax* grown for the roots which are much prized by Chinese for medicinal uses.

girder. An arrangement of the mechanical tissue of a stem or leaf which provides effective support to the entire structure.

girder sclerenchyma. Strengthening tissue in section resembling a T or H girder.

girdle. The overlapping edge of one of the two valves in diatoms.

girdle band. The hoop, girdle, or cingulum of a diatom frustule.

girdle canals. Narrow intercellular air spaces around the palisade cells parallel to the leaf surface.

girdle structure. Vascular bundles surrounded by radially elongated photosynthetic cells.

girdle view. The front or back view of a diatom in distinction to a lateral view.

girdling. The ringing of trees; cutting through the cambium layer to prevent passage of sap to upper parts, thus killing the tree.

githagineus. With red or purple streaks on a green or greenish red background.

gitonogamy. See GEITONOGAMY.

glabellous. Smooth.

glabrescent. Having few very fine hairs when young which are lost at maturity.

glabrism. The smoothness of normally hairy parts.

glabrous. Without hairs, bristles, or scales; smooth but not to be confused with "even," which describes general topography or configuration.

glabrum. A smooth surface destitute of pubescence.

glacial. Denoting distinctively northern plants influenced by glaciers.

glacial zones. Zones of vegetation in the arctic regions or high elevations.

glacier. A field or body of ice formed in a region of perpetual snow moving slowly down the mountain slope or valley.

gladiate. Sword-shaped, ensiform, ancipital.

gland. 1. A secreting cell; usually tissues or structures that secrete mucilage, volatile oils, balsams or resins. 2. An acorn or acorn-like fruit.

gland, attractive. The gland in *Nepenthes* which secretes nectar to attract insects.

gland, chalk. A gland which exudes salt solutions and gives a whitish deposit on drying.

gland, dermal. External secreting cells or groups of cells.

gland, digestive. The gland in *Nepenthes* which produces a peptic ferment.

gland, epidermal. A gland on the external surface.

gland, external. A gland not immersed in the tissues.

gland, intramural. The tubular, curved, or sinuate secreting elements in *Psoralea*.

gland, marginal. A gland formed inside the upper part of the pitchers of carnivorous plants.

gland of the torus. A rudimentary sterile stamen usually in the form of a nectar gland or petaloid scale; see LEPAL.

gland salt. A gland which excretes solutions of hygroscopic salts which are dry in day time and deliquesce at night.

glandaceous. The color of a ripe acorn, raw sienna yellow, glandulaceous.

glandulaceous. Glandaceous.

glandular-bristly. With stiff gland-tipped hairs.

glandular cells. Cells which excrete special substances often in a fluid state but not pure water.

glandular ciliate. Fringed with small glands.

glandular disk. A glandula or gland.

glandular hairs. 1. Epidermal cells which bear glands. 2. Hairs tipped with a gland or head.

glandular-hispid. Hairy or pubescent with hairs tipped with glands.

glandular-pubescent. Covered with fine gland-bearing hairs.

glandular-secrete. With a margin consisting of short teeth tipped with glands.

glandular tissue. Tissue of single or massed cells which are parenchymatous and filled with granular protoplasm adapted for secretion of aromatic substances.

glandular woody tissue. The pitted tissue in conifers.

glandulation. The arrangement and position of the glands on a plant.

glandule. 1. A viscid gland in orchids and asclepiads which holds the pollen masses in their place. 2. The retinaculum; the sticky, dot-like structure on tubes or stipes of higher fungi usually consisting of cystidia which secrete a sticky fluid.

glandulose. Glandular.

glandulose-serrate. Having the serrations tipped with glands.

glans. 1. A nut enclosed by or seated in an involucre, the acorn or mast of oaks and similar fruits. 2. A secreting surface or structure.

glareal. Growing on dry exposed ground, chiefly gravel or sand.

glasswort association. An association formed of various species of *Salicornia*.

glassy fir. Fir wood with a glassy appearance due to the wood cells being filled with water and then frozen.

glastifolious. With leaves like dyers' woad, *Isatus tinctoria*, formerly called *Glastum*.

Glastonbury thorn. A variety of hawthorn.

glaucine. With a bluish hoary appearance.

glaucogonidium. The bluish-green gonidium of lichens.

glaucous. Covered with fine white or sea green bloom which is easily rubbed off, silvery.

gleba. 1. The spore-bearing tissue composed of chambers lined with the hymenium and enclosed by the peridium in *Gastromycetes*. 2. The gelatinous spore mass in *Phallales*. 3. A glebe, a glebula.

glebula. 1. A small prominence on a lichen thallus. 2. A small gleba.

gleichenioid. Resembling or allied to the fern genus *Gleichenia*.

glenoid. Having the form of a smooth and shallow depression.

gleocystidium. A structure found in *Hymenomycetes* of gelatinous or horny consistency with oily granular contents.

gleolichens. Lichens with gonidia which belong to the *Chroococcaceae* or *Gleocapsa*.

gley, glei. Soil built up in areas of excessive moisture, it is bluish gray or greenish in color, sticky and compact.

gliadin. A vegetable glue which forms part of gluten, a protein in wheat grains.

glian. The alcohol-soluble part of gluten.

gliding growth. The overlapping of growing cell walls as the cells elongate.

gliotoxin. An antibiotic obtained from *Aspergillus fumigatus*.

globes. Pollen grains.

globi spermatici. The spores of some fungi.

globoids. Small globular inclusions of aleurone grains consisting chiefly of phosphate, calcium, and magnesium.

globule. The antheridium or male organ of *Characeae*.

globulet. 1. A glandular hair. 2. A pollen grain.

globulin. Any of a group of proteids, as fibrinogen, myosin, musculin, etc., which are insoluble in water but soluble in dilute solutions of neutral salts.

globulose-glabrous. Glabrous with the cuticle made up of globular cells.

globulus. 1. The fruit of *Hepaticae*. 2. The deciduous shield of some lichens. 3. A soredium.

glochid. A small barbed hair or bristle.

glochidium. A hair-like appendage with a

hooked tip formed on the spore masses of the water fern, *Azolla*.

glochis. A barb, a barbed hair, a bristle.

gloea. An adhesive secretion of some *Protozoa* and other low organisms.

gloeocarpous. Having the fruits immersed in mucus.

gloeocystidium. See GLEOCYSTIDIUM.

gloeolichens. See GLEOLICHENS.

gloeophyte. A thallophyte, a gleophyte.

gloeospore. A viscid disseminule.

gloiocarpus. A tetraspore.

glome. A rounded head of flowers.

glomerate. Densely clustered in small heaps or irregular heads, in compact clusters or clustered into a head.

glomerule. 1. A cyme of almost sessile (usually small) flowers condensed to form a head or a capitate cluster. 2. A small ball-like cluster of spores.

glomus. A number of glomerules run together.

glory of the snow. *Chionodoxa*, a widely cultivated flower.

glossopode. The sheathing leaf base of the quillworts, *Isoetes*.

gloxinoid. Resembling *Gloxinia*, the cultivated hothouse flower.

glucan. Glucosan.

glucase. A plant enzyme which converts maltose into glucose and decomposes certain glucosides.

glucokinin. A substance produced by some plants which is able to reduce blood sugar.

glucoproteins. Compounds formed by a protein with a substance containing a carbohydrate group other than nucleic acid, e.g., mucin.

glucosamine. An amino sugar which represents a link between the carbohydrates and the proteins.

glucosan, glucan. Carbohydrates which are found in plants, as starch, dextrin, cellulose.

glucose. 1. The common sugar produced in plants. 2. A group of carbohydrates, crystallizable and soluble in water, occurring in fruits, as grape sugar. 3. A commercial term for syrups made from starch or grain.

glucoside. A chemical substance which on decomposition always yields glucose or an analogous compound.

glucoside enzyme. An enzyme such as synaptase or emulsin.

glucostacty. The secretion of a sugary fluid as in the case of maize seedlings.

glue, bud. Blastocolla, the gummy substance found on some leaf buds.

glumaceous. Like paper, thin and brown.

glumales. Grasses, sedges, etc.

glume. 1. A chaff-like bract, specifically one of the two empty chaffy bracts at the base of the spikelets in grasses. 2. A scale, valve, chaff, or husk which makes up the calyx and corolla of grasses.

glume, barren. A glume which subtends a spikelet which does not include a flower, an empty glume.

glume, fertile. The glume in grasses which includes a flower.

glume, floral. The glume in grasses which includes a flower, the palea.

glume, fruiting. The mature fertile glume.

glume, sterile. A glume subtending other glumes but having no flower.

glumella. 1. A diminutive of glume. 2. An inner or secondary glume. 3. An obsolete term which has been applied to both the palet and lodicule in grasses.

glumellule. One of the small scales at the base of the grain between the stamens and the palet in many grasses, a palea; see LODICULE.

glumiflorous. Having flowers with glumes or bracts at their bases, having flowers subtended by glumes.

glutamine. An amide allied to asparagine which is found in the juice of beets.

glutelins. Simple proteins insoluble in water but soluble in acids and dilute alkalis.

gluten. 1. A reserve protein found in plants (chiefly in grains after the removal of starch). 2. A sticky coating on the pilei of some agarics. 3. The resilient protein (chiefly glutenin and gliadin) remaining after starch has been washed from dough.

gluten cells. Cells which contain numerous minute aleurone grains.

glutenin. A proteid substance found in the seeds of cereals which interacts with gliadin to form gluten.

glutinium. The flesh of certain fungi.

glycase. An enzyme, glucase.

glyceria. Sweet.

glycerietum. An association of *Glyceria*, a genus of grasses.

glycerrhizin. A saccharine substance from

the roots of *Glycerrhiza glabra*, licorice, glycion.

glycinioid. Glycine-like.

glycocol. A protein found in fungi.

glycodrupose. A lignocellulose which forms the hard concretions in the flesh of pears.

glycogen. A carbohydrate storage product of plants and animals, an animal starch found in certain bacteria and other fungi. A glucosan.

glycogen mass. The cytoplasm in the ascus which is permeated with glycogen.

glycolignose. A presumed glucoside from pine wood.

glycolysis. The decomposition of sugar by hydrolysis.

glycophytes. Plants which react to alkaline soils.

glycosecretory. Connected with the secretion of glycogen.

glycosic. Resembling the action of the enzyme glucose.

glykophytes. Plants forming glycogen.

glypholecine. With wavy longitudinal canals or grooves.

gnaphalioid. Pertaining to or resembling the genus *Gnaphalium*, a genus of woolly herbs widely distributed.

gnaurs. Burrs or knotty excrescences on trunks or roots probably caused by adventitious buds.

gnesiogamy. Fertilization between different individuals of the same species.

gnetalean. Allied to the genus *Gnetum*, gymnosperms found chiefly in tropical Africa and Asia.

gnomonical. Denoting an appendage which is abruptly bent at an angle to its attachment, geniculate.

gnotobiotics. Germ-free life, axenic life.

Golgi bodies or apparatus. A series of vesicles or scattered particles found in cells which are involved in cell metabolism. They undergo changes in secreting cells and are presumed to be involved in the secreting processes, although their exact function is not known. Dictyosomes, lipochondria.

gomphocephalic. Club-headed.

gonad. A mass of undifferentiated generative tissue from which the male and female productive glands originate, the gamete-producing gland, an ovary.

gonadin. The active substance of sex glands which control secondary sexual characteristics.

gonangium. 1. A closed structure, as a cystocarp or scyphus, in which reproductive or regenerative units are formed. 2. A spherical colony of *Palmella*, etc., overgrown with thick-walled brown lichen hyphae.

gonel. A floral reproductive apparatus subdivided into amphigonel, acrogonel, and anthogonel.

goneoclinic. Being a hybrid which approximates one parent and is not intermediate.

gones. 1. Asexual spores and gametes. 2. The group of four nuclei or cells which are the product of meiosis.

gonglyodic. Knob-like, gongylodes.

gongrosiroid. Resembling the genus *Gongrosira* (applied to the resting stage of *Vaucheria*).

gongylus. 1. A globular body in the thallus of lichens. 2. A rounded corpuscle-like body in certain algae which becomes detached and germinates as a separate individual. 3. A spore, a sporidium, a speirema of lichens.

gonia. A general term which includes both spermatogonia and oogonia, the cells resulting from the division of primordial germ cells before the end of the growth period.

goniangium. The cystocarps and scyphi of *Hepaticae*.

goniatus. Angled, cornered.

goniautoecious. Having the male inflorescence of a moss bud-like and axillary on a female branch.

gonid. A gonidium.

gonidangium. A structure which produces or contains gonidia.

gonidema. The gonidial layer in lichens.

gonidial layer. The green algal layer in a lichen thallus which forms a cushion-like layer or crust.

gonidimium. 1. A small algal cell occurring in the hymenium of some perithecia. 2. The gonidial layer.

gonidiophore. 1. A stalk bearing a gonidium. 2. A conidiophore.

gonidiophyll. 1. A gametophyte leaf-bearing gonidia. 2. The sporophyll of the alga *Alaria*.

gonidium. 1. An algal cell occurring in the thallus of a lichen, a chromidium. 2. A gemma in some liverworts. 3. An old term for conidium or brood cell.

gonimic layer. The algal layer in certain lichens.

gonimium. The blue-green algal cells of a lichen thallus.

gonimoblasts. Filamentous outgrowths of the fertilized carpogonium of certain algae.

gonimolobes. The terminal tufts of gonimoblasts.

gonimon. The gonidial layer of lichens.

gonimous. Related to gonidia.

gonioautoicous. Bearing the antheridium as a bud-like outgrowth from a branch bearing archegonia.

goniocyst. A sporangium, a nest of gonidia.

goniosporous. With angular spores, as in a subdivision of *Inocybe*.

gonoblast. A reproductive cell.

gonocyst. A metamorphosed gonidium of peculiar appearance extruded on the outside crust.

gonocyte. A gamete-producing cell.

gonohyphema. The hyphal layer of lichens.

gonomeres. The theoretic separate chromosomes of maternal and paternal nuclear parts.

gonomery. The theory of the existence of separate paternal and maternal chromosomes that remain in separate groups throughout life.

gonophore. A stalk elevating the stamens and pistils.

gonoplasm. The generative part of protoplasm, the ooplasm.

gonosphaeridium. A gonidium.

gonosphere. The contents of the female gametangium of some species of *Polyphagus* which are fertilized after being extruded as an oval vesicle, a gonosphaerium, an oosphere.

gonotaxis. The movement of antherozoids toward the female organ.

gonothallium. The gonidial layer of lichens.

gonotocont. The organ in which meiosis occurs or originates, an auxacyte, a gonotokont.

gonotome. An embryonic segment containing the primordium of the gonad.

gonotrophium. A soredium.

gonotropism. The movement of antherozoids and pollen tubes toward the female organ.

goosefoot. Any plant of the genus *Chenopodium*.

gosling. An ament or catkin.

gossypine. Cottony, like the genus *Gossypium* (cotton).

gossypol. A pigment from the seeds of cotton (*Gossypium*).

gourd. A fleshy, one-celled, many seeded fruit with parietal placentas, as a melon; the fruit of any cucurbitaceous plant.

gourmandiser. A strong, coarsely growing sucker, especially from the stock of a grafted plant.

gowan. The English daisy.

gracilis. Slender.

gradatae. The definite succession in time and space in the production of sori in homosporous ferns, the dominant ferns of the present.

gradate sorus. A fern sorus in which the sporangia develop from the apex of the receptacle downward.

gradient. The condition when the intensity of a stimulus acting on a plant increases or decreases towards the plant.

graecus. Greek.

graft. 1. A branch or bud made to grow on another plant. 2. To insert buds or scions taken from one plant within the bark of another so that a permanent union is affected by the two cambium layers.

graft chimaera. A plant which is composed of two sorts of tissue differing in genetic constitution and assumed to have arisen as the result of a nuclear fusion following grafting.

graft hybrid. An individual formed from graft and stock showing the characteristics of both.

graft symbiont. One member of a graft union.

graftage. The multiplication or increase by grafting.

grained. 1. Having grain-like tubercles or processes as in the sepals of the dock. 2. Having a grain as in wood.

graining. The fibrous arrangement of the particles in wood determining its hardness, splitting qualities, smoothness, etc.

gram. The chick pea.

Gram-positive. Said of bacteria which stain when treated with methyl violet followed by iodine and then by acetone or ethyl alcohol. Bacteria which do not stain are termed Gram-negative (from the Danish scientist, H. Gram).

gramen. Grass.

graminicoious. Living on grass, i.e., parasitic on grass.

grammicus. Lettered, marked as though inscribed.

grammitoid. Resembling the fern genus *Grammitis*.

grammopetalous. Having striped or marked petals.

grammopodious. Having a striped stalk.

gramnicolous. Inhabiting grass.

grana. The colored drops in chloroplasts which hold in solution various chlorphyll pigments.

grana tetrasticha. The four-parted spores of certain fungi.

granatine. Pale scarlet between peach red and scarlet.

grandifoliate. Having leaves which are much more conspicuous than the usually shortened stems.

grandipunctatus. Having large spots.

grandmother axis. The primary axis in a series of three.

grandmother axis cell. The first cell of a third generation.

grand period of growth. The period in the life of a plant under constant conditions during which growth slowly begins, rises to a maximum, falls off, and comes to an end.

graniferous. Bearing a grain or a grain-like structure, monocotyledonous.

graniform. Shaped like grains of corn.

graniticus. Growing on granite, as some lichens.

granose. Having the appearance of a chain of grains.

granula. 1. Any small particles as pollen, chloroplast, etc. 2. The sporangia in fungi. 3. The nucleolus, etc.

granula gonima. The gonidia in lichens.

granular protoplasm. Hyaloplasm containing microsomes.

granule cells. A variety of cells occurring in connective tissue in which the cytoplasm contains coarse granules staining deeply with aniline dyes.

granuloma. A growth resembling granulation tissue.

granulose. 1. Finely roughened as with grains of sand, granular. 2. A starch-like

substance found in some species of bacteria. 3. A true starch.

granum. A minute globule of pigment in the colorless stroma of a chromoplast.

grape-sugar. A sugar found abundantly in grapes, dextrose.

-graph. A suffix meaning written.

graphidioid. Like the lichen genus *Graphis*, long and cleft.

grascilatio. Etiolation.

grass-heath. A tussock peculiar to the southern hemisphere.

grass moor. A moor intermediate between *Scirpus* moors and silicious grassland mainly of grasses, rushes, and sedges.

grass steppe. A prairie or pampa where rain is moderate in amount and falls only a few days of the year.

grass waste. A dry meadow where deep-rooted perennials usually dominate over the grasses due to edaphic factors.

grassland. Land which is kept in perennial grass and not tilled.

grassland climate. A climate with rainfall favorable to the development of grasslands.

grassland climax. A climax community consisting of grassland.

grassveld. A grassy prairie in South Africa.

graveolent. Having a strong, unpleasant odor.

graviperception. See GEOAESTHESIA.

gravitational induction. The development of a structure from the underside of a plant member.

grazing capacity. The number of cattle of a given kind which a range unit will support.

greaved. See OCREATE.

green algae. The CHLOROPHYCEAE.

green cell. A cell of the alga *Chlorella* which lives inside certain simple animals.

greengage. A type of plum which remains green in color when ripe.

greenhouse. A glass house or structure in which tender plants are maintained or grown.

green layer. See MESOPHLOEM.

green rot. A disease in wood which is characterized by the tissues becoming verdigris green.

greens. Pot herbs which are cooked as a vegetable.

greffe des charlatans. A fraudulent apparent graft, the scion being passed through a hole bored in the stock.

gregariae. Species occurring in groups.

gregarinulae. Spores which glide along.

gregarious, solitary. A single or isolated clump of one species.

gregiform. A variable or polymorphic finiform.

grey blight. A disease of tea caused by *Pestallozzia Guepini.*

griseofulvin. An antibiotic produced by *Penicillium griseofulvum.* Effective against the ringworm fungi.

griseous. Gray, bluish gray, dull gray, or white mottled with black or brown.

grit cell. A sclerotic cell, as in the flesh of pears; a parenchymatous cell having walls strongly thickened or cuticularized.

groenlandicus. Of Greenland.

grosse-crenatus. Coarsely crenate or serrate.

grosse-serratus. Large-toothed.

grossification. The swelling of the ovary after fertilization.

grossulaceous. Of or pertaining to gooseberries, *Ribes Grossularia.*

grossuline. An acid found in certain fruits.

grossus. An unripe fig.

ground cover. The vegetation cover.

ground form. An elementary form as distinguished from a growth form.

ground mass. Woody tissue.

ground meristem. A primary meristem which develops into ground tissue.

ground stratum. The layer of the soil about 5 centimeters deep.

ground tissue. Fundamental tissue or fundamental parenchyma (pith, medullary rays, and cortex).

ground vegetation. The plants which cover the soil.

ground water. The water in the ground which is collected above the impermeable stratum and moves in response to gravity.

group society. A plant community within an association which differs from the predominant species which form the association.

grove. A smaller group of trees than a forest without underwood.

growing point. The group of meristem cells at the growing tip of an organ from which various tissues develop.

growing zone. The portion of an organ in which elongation or expansion takes place.

growth. Increase by new cell formation or the extension of old cell; the progressive development of an organism or member from its earliest stages, usually accom-

panied by an increase in size with its approach to maturity.

growth curvature. A curvature in an elongated plant organ caused by one side's growing faster than the other.

growth enzyme. A ferment which accelerates growth by breaking down other tissue in advance of the growth.

growth form. A vegetative structure marked by some easily recognized feature of growth and characterizing individuals or stages in the life cycles of types which have no necessary genetic affinity.

growth inhibiting substance. A substance formed inside plant cells which slows or stops growth in some part of the plant.

growth layer. A layer of wood produced during one growing period.

growth ring. The annual ring, a growth layer as seen in a cross section of tree trunks.

growth ring boundary. The outer limit of a growth ring.

growth water. The percentage of soil moisture in excess of that present when wilting occurs.

gruinalis. Shaped like the bill of a crane.

grumose. 1. Formed of clustered grains or granules. 2. Clotted. 3. Knotted.

Grundform. The original form, sometimes hypothetic, from which other forms have been derived by morphologic variation.

guaiacinus. Greenish brown.

guanin. A substance like uric acid found in some plants and certain mammalian glands. A purine found in DNA. Guanine.

guanophore. A cell bearing yellow pigment, an iridocyte.

guanylic. Having nucleic acid which yields guanin.

guaranine. A bitter substance from Guarana bread or Brazilian cocoa which is isomeric with caffeine.

guard cell. One of the two kidney-shaped cells by which a stoma is opened and closed.

guardian cell. See GUARD CELL.

gubernaculum. The posterior flagellum which is used for guidance in movement.

guianensis. Of Guiana.

guides. A term applied to the large parenchyma cells seen in cross section of the costa of many mosses (*Dicranum*).

guild. A group of plants resembling one another ecologically, such as saprophytes, epiphytes, lianas, etc.

guimauve. The marsh mallow plant.

gullet. A longitudinal groove present in some *Cryptophyceae* and *Euglenophyceae*.

gum. An exudation of certain plants and trees, vegetable mucilage, an exudate characterized by its tendency to swell in water.

gum arabic. A fine yellow or white powder soluble in water used in pharmacy and in glues and pastes. It is obtained from *Acacia sengal* or *A. arabica*. The chief source is the Sudan and Senegal. It is often called *Acacia* gum or Senegal gum.

gum canals. Thin-walled sacs in the pith of *Lygenodendron*, now regarded as secretory sacs.

gum cells. See OIL CELLS.

gum lac. The excretion by an insect, *Carteria lacca*, on various trees.

gum passage. A glandular intercellular passage containing gum.

gum resin. An exudation similar to a gum or resin.

gummosis. A pathological condition, usually physiological, or caused by bacteria. The cells dry out causing an enzymatic breakdown of the cell walls to form a gum.

gunneraefolious. Having large leaves like *Gunnera*, chiefly tropical plants.

gusset. An intercellular space, either filled or hollow, at an angle where more than two cells meet.

guts. Stony stream beds.

gutta. A vacuole, a drop.

gutta-percha. A rubber-like substance obtained from various latex-bearing plants which softens with heat.

guttate. 1. Spotted as if by drops of liquid. 2. To eliminate water from the leaves of plants in liquid form.

guttation. The exudation of droplets of liquid from the edges or tips of leaves. This sometimes takes place through modified stomata (hydathodes).

guttifer. A plant which produces gum or resin.

guttuate. 1. Finely guttate. 2. Containing or composed of fine drops or drop-like particles. 3. Said of spores containing an oily globule or guttula.

guttula. 1. The oil globule in spores resembling a nucleus. 2. A small drop or drop-like particle.

guttulate. 1. Resembling or containing small drops of oil or resin. 2. Marked or covered with guttulae.

guttules. 1. Small drops or drop-like particles. 2. Oil globules in spores which resemble nuclei.

gyalectiform. Urceolate like the apothecia of the lichen genus *Gyalecta*, urn-shaped.

gymnanthous. Having no floral envelope, naked flowered, achlamydeous.

gymnaxony. A monstrous condition in which the placenta protrudes through the ovary.

gymneosere. The eosere of the Mesozoic geological period, a mesosere or a sere dominated by gymnosperms.

gymno-. A prefix meaning naked or uncovered.

gymnoblastous. Having a superior exposed ovary.

gymnocarp. A naked fruit.

gymnocarpous. 1. With naked fruit, i.e., free from the perianth or other covering. 2. In lichens, with uncovered apothecia. 3. In mosses, with an expanded hymenium. 4. In fungi, with the spores exposed during their development.

gymnocaulon. A naked stem.

gymnocephalous. Bareheaded.

gymnochlorites. Those chlorophyllous plastids contained in cyanoplasts which ordinarily become detached from the protoplasmic layer of their formation.

gymnocidium. The swelling sometimes formed at the base of the moss capsule, the apophysis.

gymnocycads. The cyads having naked flowers.

gymnocyte. A cell without a limiting cell wall.

gymnocytode. A cytode without a cell wall or a nucleus.

gymnodinium stage. The stage at which the mobile flagellate bodies of certain *Peridineae* resemble the algal genus *Gymnodinium*.

gymnogams. 1. The heterosporous and isoporous cryptogams. 2. All plants having naked motile male cells.

gymnogamy, cytoplasmic. The condition in which the female gamete is impregnated by the cytoplasm of the male gamete.

gymnogamy, nuclear. The condition in which the female gamete is impregnated by the nucleus of the male gamete.

gymnogen. A gymnosperm.

gymnogrammoid. Of or resembling the fern genus *Gymnogramma* which lacks a sorus and has sporangia scattered over the under surface of the leaf.

gymnogynous. Having a naked ovary.

gymnophyllous. Having branchlets destitute of cortex.

gymnoplasm. An amorphous mass of protoplasm.

gymnoplast. A monoplast which has no covering, a cell or mass of protoplasm without a distinct cell wall.

gymnoplastid. A plastid similar to gymnochlorites which may be found in pith of certain shrubs.

gymnopodal. Denoting those peculiar branches of *Chara* partially or wholly without cortex in the lowest whorl.

gymnosperm. 1. A seed plant bearing seeds in open receptacles, any plant of the *Gymnospermae* (the conifers).

Gymnospermae. One of the two main divisions of the seed plants with about 500 species, mostly conifers. They are distinguished by the production of their ovules and seeds on the surface of a fertile leaf, not enclosed in an ovary.

gymnospermia. An artificial order of *Didynamia* in which the nutlets resulting from four divisions of an ovary were regarded as naked seeds.

gymnospermism. The real or supposed condition of plants with naked seeds.

gymnospore. A naked spore, a spore which is not borne in a receptacle.

gymnostomatous. Naked mouthed, having no peristome.

gymnostome. The naked orifice of the capsule which lacks a peristome.

gymnosymplast. A plasmodium, naked protoplasm.

gymnotetraspermous. Having a four-lobed ovary as in the *Labiatae*, once considered naked-seeded.

gymnotremoid. With a bare open spot or space.

gyn-, gyno-. A prefix meaning female.

gynacandrous. With staminate and pistillate flowers in the same spikelet, usually the pistillate ones above; gynaecandrous.

gynaeceum. See GYNOECIUM.

gynaeocentric theory. A concept of evolution which emphasizes the more important role of the female sex.

gynander. A gynandrous individual, a plant with stamens inserted on the pistil.

gynandria. Plants with gynandrous flowers.

gynandrism. Hermaphroditism.

gynandromorph. 1. Any individual in which male and female characters are blended. 2. A female plant assuming the appearance of a male one.

gynandrophore. A stalk supporting the stamens and pistils above the insertion of the corolla, any axial prolongation bearing a sporophyll.

gynandrospore. A fern spore.

gynandrosporous. Bearing both male and female spores as in *Oedogonieae*, where certain female plants also produce androspores.

gynandrous. 1. Having the stamens borne upon the pistil. 2. Having the stamens and styles grown together to form a column.

gynantherous. Having stamens converted into pistils.

gynase. A female determining factor in the form of an enzyme or hormone.

gynecium. See GYNOECIUM.

gynecogenic. Parthenogenetic.

gynecology. The ecology of species or autecology.

gynerium. A woolly female floret.

gynixus. The stigma in orchids, the gynizus.

gynobase. An enlargement or prolongation of the receptacle forming a short stalk to the ovary, a dilated base or receptacle bearing the gynoecium, a gynobasis, a gynophore.

gynobasic style. A style which arises from the base of the ovary.

gynodimorphism. The occurrence of small female flowers on a gynodioecious plant.

gynodioecious. Having pistillate flowers only on one set of plants and perfect flowers on another set, dioecious.

gynodioecism. The state of being gynodioecious.

gynodynamous. Having the female aspects preponderant.

gynoecism. The presence of female flowers without male flowers.

gynoecium. 1. The single or compound carpel in a flowering plant, the female organs of a flower. 2. A group of archegonia in mosses.

gynoecy. The occurrence of purely female individuals in a plant.

gynogametangium. An archegonium, an organ in which female sexual cells are formed.

gynogametes. Egg cells.

gynogametophore. The female gametophore.

gynogenesis. The development of an egg activated by the sperm but lacking paternal chromosomes, pseudapogamy in which the egg develops without being fertilized by the sperm although the sperm enters the egg.

gynogonidium. An oospore.

gynomonoecious. Having pistillate and hermaphroditic flowers on the same plant but lacking staminate flowers.

gynophore. 1. The stalk supporting the ovary. 2. The stipe of an ovary prolonged within the calyx. 3. A stalk supporting the gynoecium above the stamens.

gynophylly. The virescence or phyllomorphy of the ovary.

gynophyte. The female plant of the sexual generation.

gynoplasm. Protoplasm in female gametes.

gynopleogamy. The condition of one individual having pistillate flowers, another with perfect flowers, and a third gynomonoecious.

gynosporangium. A sporangium producing gynospores.

gynospore. A macrospore or a megaspore, one of the larger reproductive bodies in the *Isoetaceae*.

gynostegium. A sheath or protective covering of the gynoecium.

gynostemium. 1. A compound structure resulting from the union of the stamens and the pistil. 2. In orchids the union of the stamens and the style to form a column.

gynosynhesmia. See SYNHESMIA.

gyno-zoogonidium. The female filament derived from zoogonidia in *Oedogonium*.

gypsophiles. Plants growing on chalk or limestone.

gypsophytia. Limestone plant formations.

gypsum crystals. Crystals occurring in the epidermis of certain species of the tropical plants, *Capparis*; sulfate of lime.

gyrogonites. The fossil fruits of *Chara*.

gyroliths. Presumed fossil fruits of *Chara*.

gyroma. 1. The annulus of ferns. 2. The button-like shield of the lichen *Gyrophora*.

gyrose. 1. Having a folded surface. 2. Marked with sinuous lines or ridges.

gyrus. A ridge between two grooves, a gyroma.

gyttja. The jelly-like ooze on the lake bottoms.

H

H. (Flower class) usually zygomorphic flowers with a tube 6-15 mm. long, suited to bees.

H+. See *pH*.

H—layer. See HUMUS.

H—pieces. The halves of neighboring cells of the yellow-green algae *Tribonema* which are formed like the letter H, a short lateral hypha connecting two longer hyphae to form an H-like structure.

habitually. 1. Having the habit of another plant. 2. Resembling another with respect to habitat.

habitat complex. An edaphic formation.

habitat form. The form given to the plant by the habitat.

habitat group. Plants having common habitats although they are not related.

habitat, partial. The habitat of an individual species during one period or stage of its existence or its life history.

habitat races. Parasites which are adapted to respective species of host; see BIOTYPE.

habitat types. Types formed from parallel series of habitats.

habitation. The entire locality or geographical range within which a species is found.

habituation. The adjustment effected in a cell by which subsequent contacts of the same stimulus produce diminishing effects.

hadriaticus. Adriatic.

hadrocentric bundles. A concentric vascular bundle in which the xylem is surrounded by phloem.

hadromal, hadromase. An enzyme present in some fungi, particularly *Merulius lacrymans*, which attacks the hadrome and destroys the cell walls; ligninase.

hadrome. The conducting tissue of the xylem, the hadromestome.

haemanthous. Having blood-red flowers.

haemastomous. Red-mouthed.

haematein. The blood-red coloring matter obtained from *Haematoxylon* (logwood or campeachy wood).

haematine. Purpureous, reddish purple, blood red.

haematocalyx. A blood-red calyx.

haematochrome. A red coloring matter found in several green algae in drought conditions, the pigment of *Haematococcus pluvialis*.

haematocyanin. Haemocyanin.

haematogen. A pseudonuclein containing iron.

haematoid. Bloody.

haematophyte. A plant microorganism of the blood.

haematoxylin. The red coloring matter from logwood, a dye used to stain tissues, haematoxylon.

haemophile. A plant organism living in the blood.

haemorrhagia. Excessive loss of sap through an external wound in a plant.

haemotropic. Affecting or acting on blood.

haerangium. An organ of spore formation and spore dispersal of some fungi.

haft. 1. A green-winged leaf stalk or stem. 2. The stem of a spoon-shaped leaf. 3. The claw or stem of the petal of a flower.

Haidenhain. Haidenhain's iron alum haemotoxylin dye.

hair cystoliths. Structures resembling cystoliths which occur in trichomes.

hair grass. Any grass with wiry culms or leaves.

hairs, mucilage. Hairs found in certain algae.

hair pit. See CRYPTOSTOMA.

hairs, sheathed. Of the brown algae *Sphacelariaceae*, said when the apical cell dies and the cell below proliferates through the cavity leaving a basal sheath.

hakeoid. Like *Hakea*, a genus of Australian shrubs cultivated in greenhouses in northern climates.

halarch. Saline conditions which prevail at the beginning of the development of a sere.

halberd-form. Like an arrowhead in form with the basal lobes turned out at right angles, hastate.

halepense. From Aleppo, Syria.

half anatropous. Amphitropous.

half-bordered pit-pair. An intercellular pairing of a simple pit with a bordered pit.

half-breed. The product of cross-fertilization, half-blooded.

half-compound starch grains. A starch grain consisting of two or more simple grains held together by common enveloping layers.

half-cordate. Heart-shaped on one side.

half-culture communities. Communities owing their existence to the presence of man, such as the meadows, heaths, etc.

half cylinder. A stem flattened on one side.

half-equitant. Said of opposite leaves whose margins are folded forward and enclose the stem and one edge of the opposite leaf leaving one margin of each leaf outside.

half Galtonian curve. See NEWTONIAN CURVE.

half-humus plants. Semisaprophytes.

half-hybrid. The product of a cross between one species and a variety of another species.

half-inferior. Perigynous, i.e., with the calyx and stamens partly adherent to the ovary.

half-monopetalous. With petals united so slightly that they separate easily.

half-netted. With only the outer layer netted.

half race. A form intermediate between a species and a variety of it which produces few seedlings of the racial character, the majority reverting to the specific type.

half-shrub. A suffruticose perennial plant in which the stems are more or less woody, especially at the base.

half-siblings. Plants from the ovaries of the same parent or fertilized by pollen of the same parent.

half-stamen. In *Cucumis*, the stamen which has only one loculus.

half-stem clasping. See SEMIAMPLEXICAUL.

half-superior. See HALF-INFERIOR, PERIGYNOUS.

half-terete. Semicylindrical.

halic. Saline.

halimifolious. With leaves like *Halimium*, a genus of the rockrose family.

halion. A saline scrub climax.

halion bacteria. Bacteria growing on marine fish.

haliplankton. The floating organisms in the sea, haloplankton.

halm. See HAULM.

halo-. A prefix meaning salt.

halo of bordered pit. The boundary of the widest part of the pit chamber.

halobion. A community of marine plants.

halobios. The life of ocean waters.

halodrymium. A mangrove community.

halogenic. Salty.

halolimnetic. Belonging to the sea or salt lakes.

halolimnic. Pertaining to marine organisms which are modified to live in fresh water.

halonate. With a colored circle surrounding a spot like a halo.

halonereid. 1. Of or pertaining to salt water. 2. A marine association of algae or plankton.

halonial. Denoting the fertile branches or tubercles of the fossil *Lepidophloios*, formerly considered as belonging to *Halonia*.

halophilous. Thriving in the presence of salt.

halophobe. A plant which does not tolerate salt.

halophyte. A plant growing in a saline habitat.

halophytia. The plant associations of salt marshes.

haloplankton. The floating vegetation of salt water.

haloplankton, neritic. Haloplankton confined to the coast.

haloplankton, oceanic. The plankton of the open sea.

halosere. A hydrosere of salt water origin or a hydrosere with salt contents.

halospore. A haplospore.

hamada. A stony desert, as in Algeria.

hamate. Hooked or curved at the end.

hammock. An island of vegetation in a swamp.

hamulate. With small hooks.

hamulus. A hooked bristle in the flowers of *Uncinia*, the cypress.

handle. The manubrium of the antheridium of *Characeae*.

handle cells. The sterile cells inside the antheridial globules of *Chara* which extend the outer covering to form spaces where antheridial filaments are borne.

hanger. A woodland on the side of a steep hill.

hapanthous. Flowering once and then dying.

hapaxanthic. Having a single flowering period in a lifetime.

haplanthe. The hypothetic anemophilous type of flowers of the *Gentianaceae*.

haplo-. A prefix meaning half.

haplo-diploid sex differentiation. The differentiation in which the sexes are distinguished by the males being haploid and the females being diploid.

haplo-synoecious. With a form of physiological heterothallism in which there is no segregation of the sexes on separate thalli but in which both sexes are on the same haploid, self-sterile mycelium and fertility is exhibited only between certain compatible thalli.

haplobacteria. The true bacteria which reproduce by simple division.

haplobiontic. 1. Having only one form of plant or thallus in a life history, i.e., having a haploid sexual thallus with the reduction division taking place immediately after fertilization. 2. Being a plant which fruits only once in a lifetime.

haplocaulous. Having a simple unbranched stem.

haplocheilic. Having the stomatal apparatus develop the two guard cells from a single initial cell while the subsidiary cells develop from epidermal cells.

haplochlamydeous. Having a single perianth with rudimentary leaves in connection with sporophylls, monochlamydeous.

haplochlamydeous chimaera. A periclinal chimaera in which one component is present as a single cell layer forming the epidermis.

haplochromosomes. Single chromosomes which combine into a pair of myxochromosomes.

haploconidium. A uninucleate conidium formed on the mycelium of *Tremellales*.

haplocyte. A cell containing nuclei with the reduced number of chromosomes.

haplodioecious. Heterothallic.

haplodiplont. A sporophyte in which the cells contain the haploid chromosome number.

haplogenesis. The origin of new forms by evolution and the development of new characters.

haplogenous. See HETERONEMOUS.

haplogonidium. An algal gonidium in lichens which resembles *Protococcus*.

haplogonimia. Gonimia occurring singly.

haploheteroecious. Heterothallic.

haploid. With only one member of each chromosome pair present, having the *n* number of chromosomes in the nucleus of the gamete in contrast to the $2n$ number (diploid) present in a zygote.

haploid, double. Having two haploid sets of chromosomes, one from each of two parental species.

haploid, true. An organism having one set of chromosomes.

haplolepidous. Having a single row of teeth or scales in the peristome.

haplomeristele. A simple stele consisting of an axial series of trachea surrounded by a ring of phloem.

haplomitosis. The type of division in which the nuclear granules form spireme-like threads which withdraw in two groups and divide transversely in the middle to form chromospires instead of chromosomes.

haplomonoecious. Homothallic.

haplont. An organism with the haploid number of chromosomes in each somatic nucleus, the zygotic nucleus only is diploid.

haploperistomous. Having a peristome with a single row of teeth.

haplopetalous. Having petals in a single row.

haplophase. The stage in the life history of an organism when the nuclei are haploid.

haplophyll. The primitive universal leaf as in *Tmesipteris* and the lycopods.

haplophyte. A haplont, a gametophyte.

haplopolyploid. Having half the chromosome number present in a polyploid parent, brought about by haploid parthenogenesis.

haplos-. A prefix meaning simple.

haplosis. Halving the number of chromosomes at meiosis.

haplospore. A simple spore in lichens, an asexual spore.

haplostele. A simple stele consisting of xylem surrounded by phloem.

haplostemonous. 1. With only one whorl or series of stamens. 2. With half the usual number of stamens. 3. With only one whorl of the perianth or androecium.

haplostephanous. Having a single circle of stipulodes at the base of each whorl of branchlets.

haplostichous. Having one row of cortex cells to each branchlet or bract cell of *Chara*.

haplostromatic. Having the rudimentary type of stromatic development in which the entostroma disappears and the perithecial initials develop within or near the base of the ectostroma.

haplosynoecious. Homothallic.

haplotype. A single species in its original place of publication.

haploxylic. Having a single vascular bundle in a leaf.

haptera. 1. Organs of attachment which do not contain vascular tissue. 2. Special disc-like outgrowths from the stem-like portion of certain algae which serve as organs of attachment. 3. Holdfasts.

haptomorphism. A tendency of an organism to be influenced in growth by gravitation so that one side or lateral organ balances with another.

haptonema. The coiled cell organelle for attachment occurring in some *Chrysophyceae*.

haptophore. The combining qualities of the molecule of a toxin.

haptotaxis. The curvature induced in climbing plants by a rough surface.

haptotropism. 1. The one-sided growth leading to curvature (haptotropic curvature). 2. The response of an elongated plant organ which has been stimulated by touch or slight pressure.

hard blast of the phloem. The sclerenchyma tissue of the phloem consisting of bast fibers.

hardwood. Lumber derived from broad-leaved, deciduous trees.

hare-bell. *Campanula rotundifolia*.

harmonic. Developing large groups of plants characteristic of continents.

harmosis. The response to stimuli comprising both adjustment and adaptation.

harpidioid. Resembling or allied to the lichen genus *Harpidium*.

harpophyllous. Sickle-leaved.

Hartig net. An intercellular growth associated with a fungus mantle on the roots of conifers.

hastate. See HALBERD-FORM.

hastate-lanceolate. Between halberd-shaped and lanceolate.

hastate-sagittate. Between halberd-shaped and arrow-shaped.

hastilabium. A halberd-shaped lip.

hat. A pileus.

hatchet-shaped. Dolabriform.

haulm. The dried culms or stems of grasses or herbaceous plants, straw, haum.

haustoria appendiculata. Haustoria which

arise from a protrusion of the hyphae, appressors.

haustoria exappendiculata. Haustoria which arise directly from the hyphae without contortion at the point of their origin.

haustoria lobulata. Lobed appressors.

haustorium. 1. An absorptive structure of a fungus mycelium or a modified root or shoot of a higher plant which serves as an attachment to obtain food through penetration of the host cells. 2. The foot of the embryo of a fern.

haustrum. The bulbous nursing foot of developing plants, an organ of attachment and of temporary nutrition.

Hautschicht. Ectoplasm.

head. 1. A dense, round inflorescence of sessile or nearly sessile flowers. 2. A close terminal collection of flowers surrounded by an involucre as in the *Compositae*. 3. A shortened spike reduced to a globular form. 4. A group of sterigmata and conidia crowded into a dense mass of rounded outline. 5. A capitulum.

head cell. The capitulum of *Chara*, one of the rounded cells borne on the manubria in the antheridium of *Chara*.

heart rot. The decay of the heartwood or central cylinder of trees caused by various species of parasitic fungi.

heartwood. The innermost and oldest wood next to the pith, the duramen, the dead central portion of the tree trunk.

heartwood rot. A rot which attacks the wood near the pith and spreads toward the sapwood.

heath. 1. A member of the *Ericaceae*. 2. A community typically treeless characterized by dwarf shrubby *Ericaceae*.

heath association. A stable plant community principally of heather, usually without trees.

heather. *Calluna vulgaris.*

heather-moor. A plant formation in which *Calluna* is dominant, often accompanied by *Vaccinium myrtillus*.

heathland. A delayed or abortive stage of moorland.

heautotype. A specimen of a previously described and named species selected by an author not otherwise recognizable and meant to supersede the autotype.

hebecarpous. Having fruiting structures covered with a downy pubescence.

hebephyllous. Having pubescent leaves.

hebetate. Having a dull, blunt, or soft point.

hecistothermic. 1. Being able to withstand cold winters and to mature in short summers. 2. Being able to withstand cold dry winters.

hederaceous. Of or pertaining to *Hedera*, English ivy.

hederose. A sugar contained in ivy, *Hedera helix*.

hedium. A plant succession on residuary soils.

heel. The base of a tuber, cutting, or other part of a plant separated for propagation especially when it includes a part of the wood or stem of the parent branch.

hegemon. Fibrovascular tissue.

hekistothermic. See HECISTOTHERMIC.

helad. A marsh plant.

helcotropism. See ELECTROTROPISM.

helenioid. Pertaining to or resembling the genus *Helenium*, aster-like weeds.

heleocharetum. Heleocharitetum, an association of *Heliocharis*.

heleoplankton. The floating vegetation of marshes which overpowers the animal plankton (potamoplankton).

heliad. A sun-loving plant (heliophyte) which is adapted to full exposure.

helianthaceous. Pertaining to or related to the genus *Helianthus*, the sunflowers.

helias. A heliad.

helic. Of marsh communities.

helichrysetum. An association of *Helichrysum*, aster-like plants.

helichrysin. The yellow coloring matter of several species of *Helichrysum*.

heliciform. Coiled like a snail shell.

helicine. Spiral or convoluted like an ear.

helicism. A torsion which usually becomes evident at an advanced period of plant life as in tendrils and fruit of *Streptocarpus*.

heliocarp. A fruit whose carpels are arranged in a spiral.

helicogyrate. Having a circular line carried obliquely around an object, as the annulus on the spore case of some ferns.

helicoid cells. The terminal cells which are usually branched, as in *Pithophora*.

helicoid cyme. A scorpoid inflorescence produced by the suppression of successive axes on the same side causing the sympodium to be spirally twisted.

helicoid uniparous cyme. A bostryx.

helicoid dichotomy. A dichotomy in which only one branch on the same side in each successive bifurcation continues to develop.

helicoid inflorescence. An inflorescence in which the flowers are in a single row.

helicomorphy. The young and the adult forms of the leaf in heteroplastic plants.

helicospore. A cylindric, spiral, or convolute spore, usually septate.

helio-. A prefix meaning sun.

heliogyrate. See HELICOGYRATE.

helion. A swamp scrub climax.

heliophilous. Adapted to full exposure to the sun.

heliophobic. Avoiding the sun.

heliophyll. A leaf of a heliophyte.

heliophyte. A sun plant.

heliophytia. Sun plant communities.

helio-sciophyte. A plant which can live in shade but does better in the sun.

heliosis. The production of discolored spots or markings on leaves through concentration of sun upon them.

heliostrophism. A tendency to twist in response to light.

heliotaxis. The turning of an organ toward light.

heliotortism. Torsion caused by light.

heliotropic. Responding to the light stimulus.

heliotropic angle. The angle of the incidence of light at which it has the most stimulating effect.

heliotropism. The tendency of certain growing organs to respond to the stimulus of sunlight by movement or curvature.

heliotropism, negative. Shunning light.

heliotropism, positive. Growing in the direction of light.

heliotropism, transverse. Diaheliotropism.

helioturgotropism. Becoming turgid in response to light.

helioxerophilous. Adapted to strong sunlight and dryness.

helioxerophyll. Leaves which are able to withstand drought and strong sunshine.

heliozooid. Amoeboid but possessing distinct ray-like pseudopodia.

helmet. A name given to the upper sepal of an aconite, a galea.

helminthoid. Worm-shaped, vermiform.

helminthosporoid. Resembling the genus *Helminthosporium*, especially as to its pluriseptate, worm-like spores.

helobios. The inhabitants of the shore zone of stagnant bodies of water.

helobious. Living in marshes.

helodad. A marsh plant.

helodrad. One of the plants in a marsh thicket.

helodium. A swampy open woodland.

helodric. Pertaining to a swamp thicket community.

helodrium. A thicket community.

helohydrad. A marsh forest plant.

helohylium. A swamp forest community.

helohylophilous. Dwelling in wet forests.

helohylophyta. Wet forest plants.

helolochium. A meadow thicket, a helolochmium.

helolochymophilous. Dwelling in meadow thickets.

helolochymophyta. Plants of a meadow thicket.

helophilous. Marsh-loving.

helophytium. A formation of marsh plants.

helophyte. A marsh plant.

heloplankton. The floating vegetation in a marsh.

helorgadium. Swamp formation, a swampy open woodland.

helorgadophilous. Dwelling in swampy woodlands.

helostadion. Plants submerged at the base only.

helotism. A state of servitude used to describe the symbiotic relations of fungi to the algae in lichens.

helveous. Pale yellow.

helveticus. Swiss.

hematine. Haematin.

hemeranthy. Day-flowering.

hemeroecology. The ecology of areas modified by man, such as cultivated fields, parks, and gardens.

hemerodiaphorous. Varied under cultivation.

hemerophilous. Readily cultivated.

hemerophobous. Hard to cultivate.

hemerophytes. Plants which man has introduced.

hemialbumose. A mixture chiefly of proto- and hetero-albumose.

hemiamphicarpous. Having two kinds of fruit, one of which is both aerial and subterranean.

hemianatropous. Half anatropous, the ovule being partially bent back with half the raphe free.

hemiangiospermeae. Hypothetical ancestors of angiosperms.

hemiangiocarp. A sporocarp closed at first but opening at maturity to disclose the hymenium.

hemiascospore. An ascospore of a hemiascus (an atypical structure); see HEMIASCUS.

hemiascus. The ascoid sporangium or atypical multinucleate ascus of *Ascoidea* and *Dipodascus.*

hemiautophyte. A chlorophyll-bearing parasite.

hemibasidiomycetes. The basidiomycetes producing promycelia.

hemibasidium. The promycelium of the *Ustilaginales*, etc.

hemicarp. A half carpel or one carpel of a cremocarp.

hemicellulose. The cellulose of cotyledons and endosperm tissue of seeds, reserve cellulose, pseudo-cellulose. It does not color blue with chlor-zinc-iodide.

hemichimonophilous. Able to grow above ground before the ground is thawed.

hemichlamydeous. Half-coated, as ovules when borne on an inverted symphyllodium in the *Coniferae.*

hemicleistogamy. The conditions of plants whose flowers open slightly.

hemicryptophyte. A plant with surviving buds or shoot apices situated in the soil surface.

hemicryptophyte climate. The climate of the greater part of the cold temperate zone.

hemicryptophytosynusium. A community of life forms which are morphologically similar but differ genetically.

hemicycadales. Plants similar to *Cycas* but which are bisexual instead of dioecious.

hemicyclic. 1. Having half of the usual number of whorls of floral organs. 2. Having some of the flower parts arranged in spirals and some in whorls.

hemidystrophia. Partial nourishment, semistarvation.

hemiendobiotic. Usually living within the host, but sometimes outside.

hemiendophyte. A fungus parasite which is sometimes external and sometimes internal.

hemiendozoic. Disseminated by animals which have eaten the seeds of the plants or needing to pass through the intestinal tract of animals to assure the germination and dissemination of seeds.

hemiepiphyte. A plant which roots first in soil and develops aerial roots later.

hemiform. Having only uredial and telial stages (in the *Uredinales*) with the teleutospores germinating after a resting period.

hemigamotropous. Said of flowers which open and close imperfectly.

hemigonaris. The condition in which some of the stamens and some of the pistils are changed into petals.

hemigymnocarpous. Producing spores in closed receptacles which open for dispersal.

hemigyrus. A follicle.

hemihelicoid. Hemicyclic.

hemiheterothallism. Semidioecism.

hemihomothallism. Semimonoecism.

hemikaryon. A nucleus with a gametic or haploid number of chromosomes.

hemimetatropic. Having the interchange of male and female genes from different plants or flowers only partly complete.

hemiorthomorphic. Developing organs symmetrically in a vertical plane.

hemiorthotropy. The vertical symmetry displayed by naturally placed organs.

hemiparasite. A parasite which can exist as a saprophyte, a facultative saprophyte.

hemiparthenosperm. A plant having either embryo or endosperm but not both, parthenogenetic.

hemipelic. Said of plants in areas where there are rocks which yield a moderate amount of clay detritus.

hemipeloric. Having flowers partly peloric but nearly regular, as in *Linaria.*

hemipentacotyl. A seedling which has partial division of its cotyledons so as to appear as if it had five.

hemiphloeus. Half-barked.

hemiphyll. A hypothetic segment of a carpel.

hemiphyll, ovular. Carpels formed by modified leaves.

hemiplankton. The plankton which is the mingled vegetation of shallow and deep water forms in land-locked pools.

hemipsammic. Having sandy porous soil with the vegetation which it supports.

hemisaprophyte. A partial saprophyte, a facultative parasite, a plant living partly by photosynthesis and partly saprophytically.

hemischist. A brood cell formation in which only the nucleus divides while the cytoplasm remains whole.

hemispore. A protoconidium; a spherical,

globose-to-clavate cell at the apex of a filament which later divides to form several conidia.

hemisyncotyly. The condition in which seedlings have their cotyledons partially fused with one another or some other organ.

hemisyngynicus. Half-adherent.

hemitelioid. Having a resemblance to *Hemitelia*, tree ferns.

hemiteria. A monstrosity of elementary organs or of appendages of the axis.

hemitetracotyledonous. 1. With both cotyledons divided into two. 2. With one cotyledon divided, the other normal.

hemitrichous. Half covered with hairs; see FLAGELLAR ARRANGEMENT.

hemitricotyly. The partial division of one cotyledon into three.

hemitrimerous. Denoting seedlings with a whorl of three cotyledons with a normal pair of primordial leaves.

hemitropal. 1. With the ovule more curved than in the anatropous condition (amphitropous). 2. Having flowers which are limited to certain insects for honey-gathering. 3. Having flowers with moderate adaptions to insect visitors.

hemitropal herkogamy. Having an hermaphroditic flower which requires insects for fertilization.

hemitropous. Half anatropous; see AMPHITROPOUS.

hemizygous. Having haploid genes, having genes present in one chromosome but its allele absent or deficient in the homologous chromosome, half-yoked.

hemlock. *Tsuga*, any of several poisonous herbs.

hemp. 1. A tall herb of the *Moraceae*, producing a bast fiber which is used for making cloth and cordage. 2. The fibrovascular tissue of *Cannabis sativa*.

hen-and-chickens. Proliferous flowers in which the center flower or head is surrounded by subsidiary flowers.

hendecaploid. Hendekasome, having eleven sets of chromosomes.

Henslovian membrane. The cuticle.

hepatic. 1. A liverwort. 2. Pertaining to or resembling the *Hepaticae*. 3. Liver-colored.

hepaticologist. An expert in *Hepaticae*, the liverworts.

hepedochae. A secondary succession, a subsere, a hepodoche.

heptagynia. Plants having seven pistils.

heptamerous. 1. Having whorls of flowers in sevens. 2. Having seven parts.

heptandra. A monstrosity in *Digitalis* where the three divisions of the corolla are transformed into stamens, making seven in all.

heptandrous. Having seven stamens.

heptagynous. Having seven pistils.

heptapetalous. Having seven petals.

heptaphyllous. Having seven leaves.

heptaploid. Having seven sets of chromosomes.

heptarch. A fibrovascular cylinder or stele with seven rays or bundles.

heptarinus. Heptandrous.

heptasome. Having seven sets of chromosomes.

heptasterigmatic. Having seven sterigmata.

heptastichous. With leaves arranged in sevens.

heptose. A monosaccharide with seven carbon atoms.

heracleifolious. With leaves like *Heracleum*, an umbelliferous herb.

herarchs. Successions which originate in wet habitats progressing toward the moist status.

herb. A seed plant without a woody stem.

herbaceous perennial. A plant having annual stems from a perennial root.

herbal. A book in which plants are named, described, and often sketched.

herbalism. The use of herbs in magic or medicine.

herbalist. 1. A writer of herbals. 2. One who collects and studies herbs.

herbarist. A botanist.

herbarium. An identified collection of dried specimens of plants systematically arranged.

herbicolous. Living on herbs.

herbivorous. Feeding on vegetation.

herborist. A collector of plants for medical uses.

herborize. To botanize.

herbosa. Herbaceous vegetation communities of grasses and herbs.

hercogamy. The condition of hermaphroditic flowers in which the structure precludes self-pollination and requires insect pollination.

hercogamy, absolute. The condition in which self-pollination is always excluded.

hercogamy, concealed. The condition in

which self-pollination is as frequent as insect pollination.

hercogamy, contingent. The situation in which accidental and occasional self-fertilization is possible.

hercogamy, half. The condition in which hercogamy exists at first, but with growth and development of the flower parts self-pollination becomes possible.

hereditary character. A structure, peculiarity, or process which develops as the result of the normal activity of one or more hereditary factors.

hereditary complex. The total set of transmissible factors in any species conceived as a reaction system in which the factors display harmonious interrelations with one another.

hereditary factor. The property or ability possessed by a cell through which an hereditary character is developed either independently by its own activity or in connection with other properties or factors.

hereditary symbiosis. The presence of mycobacteria in the tissues, including seeds.

hereditary transmission. The passing of genes from one generation to another.

heredity. The organic relation between successive generations, the sum total of hereditary characteristics, the appearance in offspring of characters whose differential causes are in the germ cell.

heredity, bisexual. Heredity in which the qualities of both parents are transmitted.

heredity, unisexual. Heredity in which the qualities of only one parent are transmitted.

herkogamy. Hercogamy.

hermaphrodism. See HERMAPHRODITISM.

hermaphrodite. 1. A plant with stamens and pistils in the same flower. 2. An organism with both male and female reproductive organs.

hermaphroditism. The condition of having both male and female reproductive organs in one individual.

hermidin. A colorless extract from *Mercurialis* yielding by oxygenation a blue compound (cyanohermidin) and a yellow one (chrysohermidin).

herpes tonsurans. Ringworm, a disease of the skin ascribed to *Trichophyton tonsurans.*

herpism. Creeping by means of variously shaped pseudopodia, as in *Flagellata.*

herpoblast. A confervoid prothallium lying flat on its substratum.

Hertzotropism. The movement due to the influence of the Hertzian waves.

hesperidium. A berry with a hard or leathery rind like the orange and lemon.

hesperius. Western.

hetaerio. A collection of distinct indehiscent carpels produced by a single flower, dry or fleshy, as the strawberry or raspberry.

heter-, hetero-. A prefix meaning diverse or dissimilar.

heteracanthous. Various spined.

heteracmy. Dichogamy.

heteradelphic. Having two adherent carpels which develop unequally with one being more or less atrophied.

heterandrous. Having stamens of different lengths or shapes.

heteranthery. The condition of having distinct kinds of stamens.

heterauxesis. The irregular or asymmetrical growth of organs.

heteraxial. With three unequal axes.

heteraxon. A diatom in which the transverse axes are unequal.

heterecism. See HETEROECIOUS.

heterephaptomenon. The life form of more or less parasitic plants.

heterism. Normal diversity.

heteroalbumose. Composed of proteids, phytalbumose.

heteroauxin. A growth-promoting substance for plants found in urine.

Heterobasidiomycetes. The *Basidiomycetes* producing heterobasidia and basidiospores which germinate to form secondary spores or a sprout mycelium instead of forming a true mycelium directly.

heterobasidium. A basidium often indefinite in form and usually septate which arises as a probasidium and is typically composed of two parts.

heteroblastic. 1. Having offspring which are not similar to the parents. 2. Having the young stage of an organism differ from the mature stage.

heterobolite. A catabolic product with absorption of other bodies.

heterobrachial. Having two chromosome parts which differ in length and size.

heterocarpicus. An inferior fruit.

heterocarpinus. An inferior or partially inferior fruit, as the acorn.

heterocarpous. Producing more than one kind or form of fruit.

heterocary. A strain of a pure line from a single spore.

heterocaryotic. Having a mycelium develop from the union of genetically different nuclei or different strains of mycelium, as the + and − strains of some fungi.

heterocatalysis. A chemical change without the agent itself suffering loss.

heterocellular. Having cells of more than one type.

heterocephalous. Having pistillate and staminate flowers on separate heads, having heads of more than one kind.

heterochlamydeous. With a perianth whose inner and outer series are differentiated as to color, texture, etc., as is the case in the majority of flowers, i.e., calyx and corolla of two different whorls.

heterochoric. Having species which inhabit two or more closely related communities.

heterochromatin. Segments of chromosomes which are genetically relatively inert. It can be deleted from a chromosome without producing any obvious phenotypic change.

heterochromatism. A change in the coloring or marking of petals, sometimes due to seasonal differences.

heterochromosome. A chromosome other than an ordinary or typical one, an aberrant chromosome; see ALLOSOME.

heterochromous. Said of the disc florets in *Compositae* which differ in color from those of the ray florets.

heterochromy. The color differences between individuals of the same species.

heterochrony. Irregularity of occurrence of development in organisms due to difference in time of starting or seeding or climatic influences or in a broader sense a variation in evolutionary deviations from the typical sequence in the variation of parts or organs.

heterochrosis. Abnormal coloration.

heteroclema. Heterophyllous.

heteroclinous. Having the male and female members on separate receptacles, heterocephalous.

heteroclite. A deviation from the common rule or form.

heterocotylous. With cotyledons unequally developed.

heterocyclic. Differing in the number of whorls of floral organs.

heterocyst. 1. A cell which differs in size and content from the other cells in the filament of certain blue-green algae. 2. The cell which marks the limits of hormogonia in *Nostocineae*.

heterodesmic. Having some vascular bundles of phloem only.

heterodichogamy. Dichogamy.

heterodiode. A macrospore or microspore.

heterodiody. The condition when reproductive bodies are differentiated into macrospores and microspores.

heterodistyly. The condition which exists when short and long styles exist in the same plants, dimorphism.

heterodon. Variously toothed.

heterodromous. Having spirals change directions, as in some tendrils or leaf spirals.

heterodymanic. Resembling one parent more than the other.

heterodynamous. Having forms of the same annual cycle exhibiting dissimilar biological activity.

heteroecious. Said of a parasitic fungus which forms one or more kinds of spores on one host and one or more kinds of spores on a second host which is not of the same species as the first host.

heteroecismal. Heteroecious.

heteroecium. A metoecious parasite, a fungus passing its stages on more than one host plant.

heteroeuform. Heteroform.

heterofertilization. The fertilization of the endosperm and embryo nuclei by gametes of different genetic constitution.

heteroform. Any of the *Uredinales* which have all spore stages but which are heteroecious.

heterogametangic. Having more than one kind of gametangia.

heterogamete. One of dissimilar conjugating gametes, an anisogamete, one of two unlike sex cells.

heterogametic. Producing gametes of more than one sex or kind.

heterogametic sex. Dissimilar sex chromosomes.

heterogamous. 1. Bearing pistillate, staminate, hermaphroditic, and neutral flowers in one inflorescence (or any two or more in one inflorescence). 2. Producing two kinds of gametes.

heterogamous heads. Heads of syngenesious flowers containing florets of different structures and sexual characters.

heterogamous plants. Plants reproducing by the fusion of unlike gametes.

heterogamy. The reproductive process in plants in which dissimilar gametes fuse.

heterogene. The offspring of hybrid parents or parents of different types.

heterogeneous induction. Sensitive movements caused by two or more distinct stimuli.

heterogeneous ray. A xylem ray which is composed of cells of different morphological types.

heterogenesis. 1. Alternation of generations. 2. Origination from different genera or orders. 3. Origination by sports or bud variation. 4. Spontaneous generation.

heterogenetic fertilization. Cross fertilization.

heterogenetic variation. Mutation.

heterogenism. Heterogenesis.

heterogenous induction. Sensitive movements caused by two or more distinct stimuli.

heterogeny. Several distinct generations succeeding one another in a regular series.

heterogeophyte. A saprophytic or parasitic cryptogam.

heterogeophytic enzyme. An enzyme in which the power of chemical change is not restricted.

heterogone. A plant whose flowers are dimorphic or trimorphic in the length of the stamens or styles.

heterogonic growth. Disproportionate growth of the parts of an organism.

heterogony. The state of having two or more kinds of perfect flowers varying in relative length of stamens and styles.

heterogynous. With two kinds of female organs.

heterohabitum. See MESOHABITUM.

heterohomotype. The entire stage of hetero- and homo-type karyokinesis.

heteroicous. Heteroecious, on two hosts.

heteroid. Diversified in form.

heterokaryotic. Said of spores in which both male and female nuclei are found; see HETEROCARYOTIC.

heterokinesis. The qualitative or differential division of chromosomes, heterotypic meiosis.

heterokont. A motile plant or spore bearing flagella or cilia which are unequal in length.

heteroleptic. Variable-scaled.

heterolichens. Lichens in which the gonidia are stratified in the thallus.

heteromallous. Spreading or turned in different directions, as leaves and branches.

heteromastigate. Forming two different types of flagella with one or more anterior flagella and a trailing one.

heteromerals. The heteromerae, part of the *Gamopetalae*.

heteromericarpy. Heterocarpy which occurs between parts of the same fruit, a binary fruit the halves of which differ from each other.

heteromericus. Stratified, as some lichens.

heteromerous. 1. Having the whorls of floral organs differ from similar whorls in the number of parts produced. 2. In lichens, having an algal layer divide the hyphae into an outer zone and an inner (medullary) stratum.

heteromesogamy. The variation of individuals in the method of fertilization.

heterometabolic. Having a partial or incomplete metamorphosis.

heteromistic. With varying floral formulae, as in the same group of *Rubiaceae*, where the corolla lobes vary from four to ten.

heteromorphic. 1. Having chromosomes of different sizes and shapes at different times. 2. Varying from normal structure.

heteromorphic colony. A polymorphic colony.

heteromorphic incompatibility. Differences in structure which interfere with or hamper normal fertilization and reproduction.

heteromorphism. Heterogony.

heteromorphosis. 1. A type of regeneration in which the part produced is different from that which is lost. 2. The production of a part in an abnormal position.

heteromorphous. 1. With an irregular structure or departure from the normal. 2. Of two or more shapes.

heteronomous. Denoting plants which on germination produce thread-like growths from which the leafy axis is formed.

heteropetalous. Having dissimilar petals.

heterophagous. Attacking a variety of plants, attacking plants of several genera.

heterophagy. Sexual protoplasmic unions which leave a residue.

heterophils. Nonspecific antigens and antibodies present in an organism affording natural immunity.

heterophyadic. Producing separate shoots, one vegetative and one reproductive.

heterophylletum. An association of *Potamogeton heterophyllus*.

heterophyllous. 1. Having leaves of more than one form, bearing leaves of different shapes on different parts of the plant. 2. Having dissimilar gills.

heterophyte. 1. A plant which is dependent upon other organisms (either living or dead) for its food. 2. A parasitic plant without chlorophyll. 3. A plant which bears leaves and flowers on separate stems.

heteroplanobios. Organisms which are passively transported in river floods.

heteroplasia. The development of one tissue from another of a different kind, the development of abnormal tissue.

heteroplasm. Tissue formed in places where it does not usually appear.

heteroplasma. Plasma from a different species used as a medium for tissue culture.

heteroplasmic. Heterocaryotic.

heteroplastic graft. Transplantation of tissue from an individual of one species to an individual of a different species or even a different genus.

heteroplastids. Organisms which have differing cells perform different functions.

heteroplasy. All forms, cells, and tissues arising from abnormal growth after a wound.

heteroploid. Having an extra chromosome through nondisjunction of a pair in meiosis, not diploid.

heteropodous. Variously footed or stalked.

heteropolar. Said of the axis of *Diatomaceae* when the extremities differ.

heteroproteose. One of the primary products formed by the action of gastric juices on proteids.

heteroprothally. The production of unisexual prothallia.

heteropycnosis. The condensation of sex chromosomes during growth-period stages of gonia, the property of contrasting or condensing at a different rate from the majority of the chromosomes in the nucleus.

heterorhizal. Having roots which seem to arise from no fixed point.

heteroschizis. Simultaneous fragmentation of the mother nucleus giving rise to many nuclei.

heterosepalody. The change of one sepal into another.

heterosis. Cross-fertilization, hybrid vigor, the increased growth vigor exhibited by a hybrid.

heterospermic. Producing two kinds of seeds, as plants which bear seeds with and without endosperm.

heterosporangic. Having male and female gametes produced by different sporangia.

heterosporangy. The formation of more than one kind of sporangium containing more than one kind of spore.

heterospore. A spore containing both male and female energids in variable proportions mixed but not fused.

heterospory. The presence of two kinds of spores, microspores and megaspores.

heterostaminody. The change of a stamen of one type into another type.

heterostemonous. Having unlike stamens.

heterostrophy. The condition of being coiled in the direction opposite to the normal.

heterostyled. Having unlike or unequal styles, heterogonous.

heterostylia. Heterogamous plants.

heterostylous. Having styles of one length in some flowers and of a different length in others of the same species.

heterosymbiontic. Denoting those lichens whose algae are diverse in the same specimen.

heterosynapsis. A synapsis or pairing of two dissimilar chromosomes.

heterotactic. Having more than one system or type in the same inflorescence.

heterotaxis. An abnormal or unusual arrangement of organs or parts.

heterotaxy. The deviation of organs from their normal position.

heterothallic. 1. In phycomycetes and basidiomycetes, having thalli separable into two or more morphologically similar strains with conjugation occurring only when compatible mating types are paired. 2. In ascomycetes, the term has been used for hermaphroditic self-sterile species but is more properly applied only to fungi that lack distinguishable male and female gametangia.

heterothermic. Denoting porous silicious soil which readily absorbs and loses warmth.

heterotic. Unlike in formation.

heterotomy. The condition in which perianth parts are unequal or dissimilar.

heterotopic. Said of plants found on soils apparently very different from their normal stations, changing locality.

heterotopism. The alteration of the location of certain structures in embryonic development.

heterotopy. Displacement.

heterotrichous thallus. An algal thallus consisting of a prostrate portion lying on a substratum and a series of filamentous branches standing out into the water.

heterotristylic. Having styles of three lengths, trimorphic.

heterotropal. 1. Turned in more than one direction or in an unusual direction. 2. Lying parallel to the hilum. 3. Amphitropous, heterotropous.

heterotroph. 1. A plant that requires an external source of one or more organic compounds as an energy source. 2. A true saprophyte. 3. An organ which is developed more on one side than on the other.

heterotrophic. 1. Getting nourishment from without, as a parasite and saprophyte which cannot carry on photosynthesis. 2. Said of plants found on soils very diverse from their normal habitats.

heterotrophy. 1. The symbiotic habit of lichens, nutrition by ingestion. 2. The compound position of a shoot with regard to the horizon and the mother shoot.

heterotropic chromosome. A sex chromosome.

heterotype. 1. A peculiar nuclear division connected with or of the chromosomes marked by the early fission of the chromatic thread. 2. A special form of the chromosomes themselves.

heterotype division. Nuclear division in meiosis in which the number of chromosomes is halved, reduction division.

heterotypic. Referring to the cell division which involves the reduction of chromosomes from the diploid to the haploid number, i.e., the first reduction division.

heterotypic division. The meiotic or true division by which homologous chromosomes are separated into different gametes, the first meiotic division.

heteroxenous. Occurring on or infecting more than one kind of host, heteroecious.

heterozone organisms. Organisms which are not restricted to a single habitat during their environmental stages.

heterozygosis. Hybridization, crossbreeding.

heterozygote. An individual which has inherited from two parents unlike genes (dominant and recessive) controlling one or more particular characters.

heterozygote, complex. One whose gametes have numerous differences which segregate as a unit.

heterozygous. Possessing both the dominant and the recessive genes of an allelomorphic pair.

heterozygous sex. The sex in which the members of the chromosome pair that determine sex are unlike.

heterphaptomenon. The life form of more or less parasitic plants.

hex-. A prefix meaning six.

hexacoccus. A fruit having six cells.

hexacotylous. Having what seems to be six cotyledons due to fission of the two normal ones.

hexactine. A spicule with six equal rays meeting at right angles.

hexacyclic. Arranged in six whorls.

hexad. A group or series of six, an unequal bivalent (not trivalent) formed by pairing of one chromosome with its homologue which has fused with a third nonhomologous chromosome in a fusion heterozygote.

hexagonienchyma. Cellular tissue which exhibits hexagonal cells in section.

hexagonoid. Having hexagonal areolae on ferns which are bordered by veins.

hexagonopteris. Having six angled wings.

hexagynia. Plants possessing six pistils.

hexalepidous. Having six scales.

hexander. Having six stamens.

hexapetalous. Having six petals.

hexaphyletic. Being hybrids which are the products of six forms or species.

hexaphyllous. Having six leaves.

hexaploid. Having six sets or six times the normal number of diploid chromosomes.

hexapyrenous. Having six kernels.

hexarch. With six radiating fascular strands.

hexarinous. Hexandrous.

hexasepalous. With six sepals.

hexasomic. Hexaploid.

hexaspermous. Having six seeds.

hexasporous. With six spores.

hexastemonous. Hexandrous, with six stamens.

hexasterigmatic. Having basidia with six sterigmata.

hexastichous. Having parts arranged in six rows.

Hexenbesen. Witches broom, an abnormal brush-like growth of small branches on trees.

hexicology. Bionomics.

hiascent. Gaping or opening wide.

hibernacle. 1. A winter bud. 2. A hibernaculum or winter quarters in botanic gardens. 3. The habitat in which hibernation takes place.

hibernicus. Of or pertaining to Ireland.

hibiscifolius. Hibiscus-leaved.

hidden-veined. With veins embedded in tissue and not visible.

hidebound. Barkbound, having bark which does not yield to the growth of the stem.

hidroplankton. See HYDROPLANKTON.

hiemefruticeta. Tropical scrub and deciduous shrubs which shed their leaves in dry seasons.

hiemilignosa. Vegetation in which leaves are shed during the hot dry summer.

hiemisilvae. Woods in which the trees shed their leaves in the hot dry season, monsoon forests.

hieraciarch. A person who is an expert on the genus *Hieracium*, an hieraciologist.

hieraciology. The special study of the genus *Hieracium*.

hierochunticus. Of Jericho.

hieroglyphicous. Hieroglyphic, marked as if with signs.

higher plants. A relative term, the spermatophytes.

high moor. A moor arising in water but emerging from it and depending upon rain for its supply of water.

high yeast. Barm, the yeast which forms on the surface in fermentation.

hilar. Pertaining to or designating the hilum.

hile. Hilum.

hiliferous. Having a hilum on the surface.

hilofera. The internal integument of a seed.

hilum. 1. The scar at the point of attachment of the seed, the eye of a seed. 2. The nucleus or organic center of a starch grain.

himalaicus. Himalayan.

himantioid. Like the fungus *Himantia*, velvety.

hing. *Asafoetida, Ferula.*

hinge. 1. The isthmus of diatoms. 2. The delicate lamellae of cellulose upon which the mobility of the guard cells usually depends. 3. In some plants a special part near a node which is capable of movement.

hinge cells. Cells lying in furrows on the upper face of the leaves of grasses deeper than the epidermal cells and folding easily as the leaf curls.

hinge plants. Plants susceptible to curvature because of hinge cells.

hinnuleous. A tawny cinnamon, fulvous.

hinoid. Having the secondary veins parallel and at right angles to the midrib and undivided.

hinoideous, venuloso-. With veins arising from the midrib which are parallel and connected by cross veins.

hip. The fruit of the rose, a succulent hollow receptacle.

hippocrepiform. Shaped like a horseshoe.

hippophaetum. An association of *Hippophae*, sea buckthorn.

hippuridetum. An association of *Hippuris*, water plants.

hircinous. Smelling like a goat, hircosus.

hirtelliforms. Plants which have hairs on the midribs of the leaves.

hirtiflorous. With hairy flowers.

hirtiforms. Plants in the genus *Rosa* having the lower leaf-surface and the entire leaf hairy.

hirtipes. Hairy-stalked, stemmed.

hispanicus. Spanish.

hispid. Having stiff bristly hairs.

histioid. Arachnoid, tissue-like, histoid.

histiology. Histology.

histoblast. One of the morphological units composing a tissue, a cell.

histochemistry. The chemistry of the tissues and structural elements of organisms.

histocyte. A tissue cell as distinguished from a germ cell.

histodialysis. The separation from each other of the cells of a tissue.

histodine. An amino acid.

histogen. A particular area where definite tissues or organs are formed by differentiation.

histogen theory. The theory that particular

tissues of a plant form definite regions called histogens.

histogenesis. The formation and development of meristematic tissue, histogeny.

histogenic plasma. The tissue-forming protoplasm.

histogenous. Of conidia, produced directly from tissue without conidiophores.

histoid. Resembling the normal tissues like a spider web.

histology. The science which treats of detailed structures of tissues, microscopic anatomy.

histolysis. The decay and dissolution of organic tissues.

histometabases. Changes by which tissues have been fossilized.

histonal. Tissue-forming.

histones. Simple proteins which often occur with nucleic acids.

histophyly. The phylogenetic or ontogenetic history of a group of cells.

histophyta. Parasites.

histophytia. Parasitic communities.

histrophic. Pertaining to tissue formation or repair.

hiulcus. Gaping, split.

hizometer. An instrument for measuring gravitation waters.

hoarhound. *Marrubium vulgare*, a mint.

Hochblatter. Bracts.

Hochmoor. A moss moor.

Hof. 1. The areola of a bordered pit. 2. A clear, granule-free space surrounding the nucleus or nucleolus.

Hofporen. Of *Sphagnum*, the cell membranes within the thickened ring around the pore.

Hohengleider. Altitudinal facies.

holarctic. Of or pertaining to the arctic regions collectively.

holard. The total water content of the soil whether available or not.

Holde. Preferential species.

holdfast. 1. A differentiated basal structure consisting of one or more cells by which thalli may be attached to a substrata. 2. The sucker or disc of algae and fungi. 3. Any root-like structure that attaches a plant to another surface.

holendobiotic. Producing spores in other organisms.

holendophytes. The fungi that are limited to a parasitic life within other species.

holendozoa. Fungi which live within animals.

holeraceous. Used for food (especially garden vegetables), oleraceous, esculent.

hollandicus. Of or from Holland.

holly. A tree or shrub of the genus *Ilex*.

hollyhock. A tall malvaceous perennial herb native of China and cultivated in gardens, genus *Althaea*.

holo-. A prefix meaning complete or whole.

holobasidiate. Having nonseptate basidia.

holobasidium. A basidium in which nuclear division is not followed by the formation of septa.

holobenthic. Living in the depths of the sea.

holobiont. A homophyte, a holophyte.

holoblastic. Having the type of egg structure in which cleavage divides the entire egg, undergoing total or complete cleavage.

holocarp. An entire fruit resulting from a number of carpels.

holocarpic. 1. Reproducing by having the entire thallus (in a unicellular plant) become a fruiting body (sporangium). 2. Having the pericarp entire. 3. Being whole-fruited.

holochlamydeous. Denoting the ovules which have integuments which are practically complete.

holochrysous. Golden.

holocoen. An organization with its living and nonliving components.

holocyclic. Denoting stems with amplexicaul leaves, regarded as encircling the stem and ending at the node in a leaf, evergreen.

holodactylous. Composed of a single cell, as the ultimate rays of *Chara*.

holoenzyme. A complete enzyme, made up of an apoenzyme and coenzyme.

hologamy. A fusion between two mature cells each of which has been completely changed into a gametangium.

hologenesis. The theory of descent by species developing and then dividing with the mother cell disappearing.

hologonidium. Algal gonidium.

hologymnocarpous. Permanently gymnocarpous, with the fruits entirely free.

holometabolism. The state of complete metamorphosis.

holomorphosis. Regeneration in which the entire part is replaced.

holoparasite. A parasite completely dependent on its host and incapable of utilizing inorganic food material.

holopetalarious. See OLOPETALARIOUS.

holophyte. A plant capable of manufacturing its own food from the simplest beginnings.

holoplankton. The plankton of the open sea.

holosaprophyte. A true saprophyte which depends on humus for its food.

holoschisis. The direct division of the nucleus without formation of a spindle and chromosome, amitosis.

holosericeous. 1. Completely covered with silky hair-like structures. 2. Having a silky lustre or sheen.

holotrichous. Having a uniform covering of cilia over the body.

holotype. The one specimen used by the author of the name as the nomenclatural type.

homalochoric. Denoting species confined to one country.

homalocladous. Straight-branched.

homalotropous. Growing in a horizontal direction.

holozoic. Devouring other organisms.

homeokinesis. Mitosis with equal divisions of chromatic elements to daughter nuclei.

homeomorphs. Plants genetically different which resemble each other because of conditions of the environment.

homeoplasy. See HOMOPLASY.

homeosis. The occurrence of a homologous appendage in a part of the body to which it does not belong.

homeostasis. The stabilization of the internal balance of an organism.

homeosynapsis. Synapsis between like chromosomes.

homeotely. The evolution from homologous parts but with little resemblance to them.

homeotype division. The division following the heterotypic division.

homeotypic division. The second division in meiosis which is similar to mitosis.

hometerostyly. Homoheterostyly.

homiodromous. Homodromous.

homo-. A prefix meaning alike or of one sort.

homobasidiomycetes. Basidiomycetes which have homobasidia and basidiospores which germinate to form a true mycelium instead of secondary spores or sprout mycelium. Most conspicuous fungi (mushrooms, puffballs, and bracket fungi) belong to this group.

homobasidium. A basidium always definite in form and nonseptate, the typical basidium not divisible into hypobasidium and epibasidium.

homobium. An interdependent association of algae and fungi as in lichens.

homoblastic. Showing direct embryonic development from the earliest stages to maturity, originating from similar cells.

homocarpous. Having one kind of fruit.

homocaryotic. Having mycelium in which all the nuclei have the same genetic makeup, having mycelium with + and − nuclei only, unisexual, homokaryotic.

homocentric. Concentric.

homocephalic. Having anthers fertilize the stigma of another flower in the same inflorescence.

homochlamydeous. Having the outer and the inner perianth whorls alike, not distinguishable as a corolla or a calyx.

homochromatism. The constancy of color of the flower.

homochromous. With capitular florets all of one color.

homoclinic. Having the type of homogamy in which the anthers fertilize the stigma of the same complete flower.

homodermic. Originating from the same germ layer.

homodesmic. Having the vascular bundles of an atactostele of the same type.

homodichogamy. The condition in which homogamous and dichogamous individuals exist in the same species.

homodromous. Having all the leaves or other organs inserted in spirals all running in a uniform direction, homodromal.

homodynamic. 1. Being hybrids with parental characters equally transmitted. 2. Having no definite life cycle, the number of generations depending on weather conditions.

homodynamic hybrid. A hybrid having an equal grouping of characters derived from both its parents and so differing from both in appearance.

homodynamy. Metameric homology.

homoeandrous. With one kind of stamen.

homoeomorphous. Of similar structure.

homoeogamy. The impregnation of an antipodal cell instead of the oosphere.

homoeokinesis. Homotypic meiosis, equal division of chromatin between daughter nuclei.

homoeolichens. Lichens which have conidia scattered throughout the thallus.

homoeomerous. Said of lichens in which

hyphae and gonidia are uniformly distributed in the thallus.

homoeomorphs. Genetically different organisms which resemble each other due to similar environmental conditions.

homoeophyllous. Having only one form of branchlets.

homoeosis. A variation in plants in which one organ takes on the characteristics of another, as when petals are changed into stamens.

homoeosis, inward. A variation in which an inner whorl of organs assumes the form of an outer whorl, as stamens to sepals.

homoeosis, outward. A variation in which the forms of outer organs are assumed by those typically found inside the whorl, as when sepals become stamens.

homoeotype. A specimen which has been carefully compared to and identified with an original or primary type.

homoetic. Metamorphic.

homoetype. Homotype.

homogametic. Producing gametes which are alike as to their chromosome makeup, particularly as to the sex chromosomes.

homogamous. 1. Having all the flowers of an inflorescence alike, being all staminate, pistillate, hermaphroditic, or neuter. 2. Having the anthers and stigmas mature at the same time. 3. Inbreeding due to isolation. 4. Homoclinic. 5. Monoecious.

homogamous head. A head or a cluster with flowers all of one kind.

homogene. One of a group having a common origin, the condition of offspring whose parents are pure and of the same type.

homogeneal. Having successive generations resemble the parent form (the reverse of heterogenesis), homogenetic.

homogeneity. The regularity in distribution of individual species, especially the dominant species, in a community or association; uniformity of distribution.

homogeneous ray. A xylem ray which is composed of radially elongated cells.

homogenetic. Having successive generations resemble the parent form without alternations of generations.

homogone. A plant bearing only one kind of flowers.

homogonous. Homomorphous in respect to the stamens and pistils, as opposed to dimorphous.

homogony. The condition of having one type of flower with stamens and pistils of equal length.

homoheterostyly. The occurrence of similar and dissimilar styles in the same species.

homoicous. On one host.

homoimerous. Homoiomerous.

homoio-. A prefix meaning alike or similar.

homoiochlamydeous. 1. Having the perianth uniform. 2. With leaves of only one kind.

homoiogamous. 1. Having the stamens and stigma ripen together. 2. Having two sexually similar nuclei fuse.

homoiogeneous. Homogenous.

homoiologous. Equivalent by descent or of similar origin although differing in function.

homoiomerous. Said of a lichen thallus in which the fungal and algal components are mixed and not arranged in layers with the gonidia and hyphae in about equal proportions.

homoiomorphous. Uniform in shape.

homoiotherms. Plants whose vital temperatures are approximately the same as those of their surroundings.

homoiotransplantation. The transplantation of tissue from one organism to another, possibly unrelated.

homokaryotic. See HOMOCARYOTIC.

homokinesis. Homotypic mitosis.

homolichens. Homoeolichens, lichens which are homoiomerous.

homolecithal. Having little deutoplasm, which is equally distributed.

homolepis. Homologous scales.

homologous. 1. Having the same position and development. 2. Having the same function. 3. Related in origin and morphology.

homologous alternation of generations. The theory that the sporophyte originated as a modification of the gametophyte, not as a new phase introduced into the life cycle.

homologous chromosomes. A pair of chromosomes, one maternal and one paternal, which contain the same inherited chracters.

homologous variation. Parallel variations, similar variations in allied species.

homology. The fundamental structural similarity between organs based on the common embryological origin.

homolytic enzymes. Enzymes which cause irreversible chemical actions.

homomallous. 1. Curving uniformly to one side or turned in the same direction. 2. Originating all around a stem but all bent or curved round to one side.

homomeric. Having the same number of parts.

homomorphic. 1. Having chromosome pairs of similar size and structure. 2. Uniform with all parts alike.

homomorphic colonies. Colonies of essential aggregations having all the individuals morphologically similar.

homomorphic incompatibility. The inability of organisms which are similar in structure to reproduce, e.g., strains of fungi which appear identical in structure but differ physiologically.

homomorphism. The condition of having perfect flowers of only one type or kind.

homomorphosis. The regeneration of a removed part in the same form as the original part.

homonemeae. An old name for the algae and fungi.

homonomy. The homology existing between plants arranged on a transverse axis.

homonym. A name of a species or genus, etc., which has been used for an earlier species, genus, etc., and is therefore rejected.

homonymy. The use of a specific name in another genus.

homoogonous. Breeding true, anisogonous.

homoomerous. Homoiomerous.

homooplasy. The condition in which an abnormal growth consists of the same elements as the part from which it arises.

homopetalous. With all petals alike.

homophyadic. 1. A term applied to the species of *Equisetum* whose fertile and sterile stems are similar in form. 2. Producing only one kind of shoot.

homophyllic. Resembling one another because of a common ancestry.

homophyllae. Groups of plants bearing leaves of one kind or shape.

homophyllous. With leaves all of one kind.

homophyte. A plant growing in fissures or crevices in rocks and on ledges where rock debris has accumulated.

homophytic. Having bisexual sporophytes.

homoplasia. Abnormal tissue formed by the increase of the elements.

homoplasmy. The state of being similar in form but not of similar origin.

homoplast. An organ composed of similar plastids.

homoplastic. Being equivalent in structure and in mode of origin but of parallel, not common, descent. 2. Of or pertaining to homoplasy.

homoplastids. Organisms derived from similar cells.

homoplasty. Convergence, homoplasy, resemblance in form or structure between different organs or organisms due to evolution along similar lines.

homoplasy. The correspondence between parts or organs not due to their modifications from their common ancestral types but acquired independently, parts molded alike but of different origin, abnormal growth composed of normal elements.

homopolar. 1. Relating to the same pole. 2. Having the poles of the primary axis alike.

homoproteoid. With leaves which have sclerotic cells which are uniformly distributed.

homosporangic. Giving rise to only one kind of spores.

homosporangium. A sporangium which produces spores which develop bisexual sporangia.

homosporic. Derived from one kind of spore.

homosporous. Having asexually produced spores of only one kind, isosporous.

homospory. 1. The condition in plants which produces only one kind of asexual spores. 2. The condition in which a sporophyte produces spores of the same size.

homostatic period. The period during which the present vegetation developed after the Pliocene formation.

homostyled. With uniform styles, homogonous.

homostylia. Homogonous plants.

homostylism. The condition of having homostyled flowers.

homostyly. The condition in which there is the same relation of length between all styles and anthers of the same species.

homosynapsis. The pairing of two X or two Y chromosomes.

homotactic. Having only one system of arrangement in an inflorescence.

homothalamous. Resembling a thallus (lichen) or flower receptacle (thalamus).

homothallic. 1. Bearing both male and female sex organs. 2. Forming zygospores from two branches of the same mycelium. 3. Monoecious.

homothallium. The medullary layer of a lichen.

homothermic. Denoting firm earth or rocky soil which absorbs heat and loses it slowly.

homothermous. See HOMOIOTHERMS.

homotropal. Applied to organs having the same direction as the body to which they belong, as an embryo in a curved seed when it is curved in the same manner as the seed.

homotropic. Fertilized by anthers from the same flower.

homotropous. 1. Erect. 2. Having the micropyle and chalaza at opposite ends. 3. Curved or turned in one direction, used of an anatropous ovule having the radicle next to the hilum.

homotropy. The homotropous condition, the condition in which secondary rootlets branch in the same direction from the axis.

homotype. 1. In nuclear division a term applied to cases resembling ordinary karyokinesis except in minor respects. 2. A part homologous with another.

homotype division. The second division in the spore tetrad carried out like any somatic division.

homotypic. 1. Said of the second nuclear division of sporogenesis in plants. 2. Having the same nature or character, homologous.

homotypic division. See MITOSIS.

homotypical association. An association composed of homotypes.

homotypical societies. Societies composed of a single species.

homotyposis. The principle of the likeness and diversity of homotypes.

homotypy. 1. The relation existing between homotypes. 2. The correspondence of parts which are in a series.

homozygocity. The condition of producing homozygotes.

homozygosis. Genetical stability as regards inheritance of a given factor, the condition of inheriting a given character from both parents and therefore producing gametes of one kind only as regards that factor.

homozygote. 1. A zygote resulting from the fusion of like gametes. 2. An individual whose allelomorphic pairs are composed of similar elements. 3. An animal or plant in which the characters are stable, having been received in the dominant form from both parents or in the recessive form from both parents.

homozygotic. Originating from the same strain, of pure line.

homozygous. Having both parents transmit identical genes for a particular character, being genetically pure (for pairs of genes).

honesty. Satin pod or virgin's bower, a garden plant *Lunaria*.

honeycomb cells. The hexagonal hollows in diatoms.

honey cup. A nectary.

honeydew. A sweet substance found on the leaves of plants, usually a secretion from plant lice.

honey feeding. See MELLIPHAGOUS.

honey guides. Lines or streaks of honey or color leading to the nectary.

honey leaves. Nectaries such as those of *Aquilegia*, the columbine.

honey pore. The pore in flowers which secretes honey.

honey scales. The scales in flowers which secrete honey.

honey spots. 1. Honey guides, marks on flowers believed to designate the locality of nectar to insects. 2. Spots in flowers which secrete honey.

hood. A color marking, crest, hood-like expansion, helmet, or cucullus.

Hoogeveld. A treeless area caused by wind and drought on typical soil at an elevation of 4,000 to 5,000 feet in South America.

hook climbers. Plants which climb by means of prickles, as the climbing rose, bedstraw, and many tropical lianas.

hooked-back. Curved in a basal direction from the apex.

hooked disseminule. Any fruit, seed, or spore which bears outgrowths in the form of hooks.

hoop. The girdle of a diatom.

hop meal. See LUPULIN.

hordeaceous. Pertaining to or resembling *Hordeum*, barley.

hordein. A proteid occurring in barley related to the gliadin in wheat, hordinine.

horizon. A layer or stratum of soil. The A horizon is the surface horizon.

horizontal ovules. Ovules which, when projecting from the side of the cell, point neither to the base nor to the apex.

horizontal partitions. Walls at right angles to the longitudinal axis of the vessel.

horizontal system. The cellular rather than fibrovascular system.

hormesis. A stimulus received by an organism by the administration of a toxic substance in small nontoxic concentrations.

hormocyst. A short hormogonium enclosed in a thick stratified sheath.

hormogones. Short filaments of blue-green algae (separated from adjacent parts by heterocysts) which are capable of a gliding motion and develop into independent organisms capable of reproduction.

hormogonimium. Gonimia arranged in a necklace fashion.

hormon. Anchored plants in the sea without absorptive roots.

hormone, plant. An internal secretion (such as auxins) formed in the actively growing parts of plants which diffuse to other tissues and regulate and influence development.

hormophorous. Arranged as a necklace.

hormospores. Spores which are similar in origin to the stylo- or teleutospores of fungi.

horn. 1. An awn. 2. Any pointed projection or process in plants. 3. The antheridium of the alga *Vaucheria*.

horn blast. A thickened tissue of obliterated groups of sieve tubes having a horny texture.

hornlet. The male organ of *Vaucheria*, a papilla or projection from the filament.

hornworts. The *Anthocerotae* of world-wide distribution which are close relatives and resemble the thallose liverworts except that the gametophytic stage forms a rosette and usually lacks dichotomous branching.

horological. Denoting those flowers which open and close at stated hours; see PHOTOPERIODISM.

horologium florae. A timetable of the opening and closing of certain flowers.

horridus. Provided with spines or barbs.

horse nettle. A coarse prickly weed having white or pale purple flowers and bright yellow berry-like fruit, a *Solanum*.

horse radish. The root of *Amoracia rusticana* used as a condiment and stomachic.

hortinus. The present year's growth.

hortus. A garden.

hortus siccus. An herbarium, a classified collection of dried plants.

hortus vivus. A collection of living plants.

hose in hose. A duplication of the corolla having a second inserted in the throat of the first.

host. An organism which temporarily or permanently supports another organism at its own expense.

host cells. The cells in mycorrhiza of *Neottia* which are associated with the digestive cells.

host selection principle. The theory that if a species has been reared for several generations on one of several host plants, the progeny tend to grow on the same host plant on which they were reared.

hotel. The portion of an organism's habitat which can provide facilities to the organism for every purpose—resting, breeding, or feeding.

hover fly. A fly that hovers over flowers, as the *Syrphus* fly.

hover fly flowers. Flowers adapted for pollination by the *Syrphidae*.

Hudsonian life zone. The zone which includes the northern portion of the transcontinental coniferous forest of North America and the cold summits of the higher mountains.

hukwin. A white ring in the corolla of *Ipomoea hederacea* in Japan.

hull. 1. The lemma and palea when they remain attached to the caryopsis after threshing, the outer shell of a grain.

humble-bee flowers. Flowers which are adapted for the visits of species of the *Bombus* bee, bee flowers.

humectate. Wet, moist.

humi-. A prefix meaning in or on the ground.

humic acids. Those acids derived from and found in humus.

humicole. A plant growing on soil or humus.

humic water. Water which is strong in acids of vegetable origin, as in peat moss.

humicular. Saprophytic.

humidity, absolute. The maximum amount of water vapor in suspension in the air.

humidity, relative. The ratio of the vapor actually present as compared with the greatest amount the air could contain at any given temperature.

humification. The reduction of dead plant substances by fungi.

humifuse. Spread on the surface of the ground.

humilifolious. Hop-leaved.

humilis. Dwarf, low-growing.

humistrate. Laid flat on the soil.

humor. Sap.

humoral. Having to do with natural body fluids.

humose. Earthy.

humulin. The oleoresin of the hop.

humus. The mixture of decayed vegetation and soil found in many forests and fields, decaying organic matter in the soil, the mold or soil formed by the decomposition of vegetable matter.

humus cover. A cover composed of unincorporated organic matter.

humus lake. Dystrophic lakes which are very rich in humic acids and floating life.

humus layer. The top layer of the soil including a large amount of organic matter.

humus plants. Saprophytes.

humus soils. Garden soils with manure or humus.

humusnecron. Decayed vegetable matter.

husk. The outer coating of various seeds and fruits.

hyacinth. *Hyacinthus*, widely cultivated for its flowers.

hyacinthine. Dark purplish blue.

hyalescent. Becoming or appearing hyaline or glassy.

hyalicolor. Lacking color.

hyaline. Colorless, glass-like.

hyaline area. The smooth part of a diatom valve.

hyalodictyae. Fungi which have translucent, uniform, or netted spores.

hyalodidymae. Didymosporae with clear spores.

hyalogen. A particle or substance secreted by a cell.

hyaloid. Glassy, transparent.

hyalom. Hyaloplasm.

hyalophragmiae. Fungi having multiseptate spores.

hyaloplasm. The hyaline matrix or clear nongranular portion of protoplasm.

hyalosome. A nucleolar-like body in a cell nucleus only slightly stainable by nuclear or plasm stains, colorless granules which do not take stain.

hyalosporae. Organisms having colorless spores.

hyalosporous. Having hyaline or one-celled spores.

hyalostaurae. Fungi with cruciate spores without color.

hybernacle. Hibernaculum.

hybrid. The offspring of two different varieties, species, or genera; a heterozygote.

hybrid, bisexual. The offspring which shows the characters of the parents combined in pairs.

hybrid, derivative. A hybrid which is the result of a self-cross or a cross with a parent.

hybrid, double. The product of dihybridization.

hybrid, double reciprocal. The product of the crossing of reciprocal hybrids.

hybrid, graft. A hybrid showing the reciprocal influences of the scion and stock on each other.

hybrid, heterodynamic. A hybrid showing the characters of male and female parents in varying degrees.

hybrid, homodynamic. A hybrid showing an equal combination of the characters of both parents.

hybrid, mosaic. A hybrid showing traces of each parent, as special color patches.

hybrid, numerical. A hybrid whose parental gametes differed in respect to the number of chromosomes.

hybrid, reciprocal. A hybrid obtained from the same parents but transposing the male and female elements.

hybrid, secondary. A hybrid resulting from a cross with a hybrid.

hybrid, sesquireciprocal. A hybrid obtained when a hybrid is crossed with one of the parental types.

hybrid, structural. A hybrid whose parental gametes differ in the structure of their chromosomes.

hybrid, twin. One of twin hybrids that are identical but from reciprocal crosses.

hybrid, unisexual. A hybrid in which a certain character is found in one parent but does not occur in the other.

hybrid vigor. The increased vigor of a hybrid when it is greater than that of either of the parents.

hybridiform. A hybrid between finiforms.

hybridization. 1. The result of crossing of more or less dissimilar parents. 2. The act or process of hybridization.

hybridogamy. The formation of hybrids between different species.

hybridoproliform. A fertile hybrid of hybridoforms.

hydathode. The glandular structure which exudes water from the leaf during guttation.

hydathode, substitute. Oedema.

hydatophytia. Submerged plant communities.

hydra-. A prefix meaning wet.

hydracellulose. See CELLULOSE.

hydrad. A hydrophyte.

hydragogue. A purgative drug which produces watery evacuation, sometimes obtained from *Euphorbia*.

hydralgae. Hydrophytes.

hydrangeoid. Like *Hydrangia*, a genus of shrubs.

hydrarchs. Successions which originate in hydric habitats and progress toward mesophytism or toward a developmentally more advanced condition.

hydras. The wet forms of species; see ECAD.

hydrase. An enzyme which stimulates the addition or diminution of water in a structure without chemical changes.

hydrastin. An alkaloid found in *Hydrastis canadensis*, a crowfoot.

hydrate. A compound containing a definite proportion of water in chemical combination.

hydration. Physical or chemical absorption of water.

hydric. Watery.

hydrion. Hydrogen-ion concentration.

hydro-. A prefix meaning water.

hydrobios. Organisms of isolated waters.

hydrocarpic. Denoting the aquatic plants which are fertilized above the water but withdraw the fertilized flowers below the surface for development.

hydrocellulose. A product formed by treatment of cotton with sulfuric or hydrochloric acid; see CELLULOSE.

hydrocharetum. An association of *Hydrocharis*.

hydrocharid. A formation of macrophytes floating on or in water, as the water plant *Hydrocharis*.

hydrochimous. Adapted to rainy winters or weather.

hydrochore. A plant dispersed by water.

hydrochrome. The pigments of the fungus *Russula*.

hydrocleistogamous. Having flowers which do not open after submersion.

hydrocryptophytes. Plants which have the vegetative parts permanently in water.

hydrodynamic. Being distributed by the action of tides and waves.

hydroecium. A closed tube at the upper end of a siphonophore.

hydrogams. Cryptogams.

hydrogenic soils. Soils which form under water or in saturated conditions in cold climates.

hydrogers. 1. Water-bearing tissues. 2. Threads in the spiral vessels which were once presumed to conduct liquids in plant stems.

hydroharmose. Responding to a water stimulus.

hydroid. A water-conducting strand in aerial stems.

hydroid areas. Algal climaxes in pre-Devonian time.

hydrolated. Combined with water.

hydroleucite. Types of vacuoles in cell sap.

hydrolist. A cytohydrolist.

hydrolysis. The chemical decomposition of a compound which follows the absorption of water, the act of being hydrolyzed.

hydrolyst. A hydrolizing agent.

hydrolyte. Any substance which undergoes hydrolysis or fermentation.

hydrome. Any tissue which conducts water.

hydrome cylinder. The vascular tissue which carries and supplies water.

hydrome mantle. A structure composed of elements identical with the hydroids of the leaf tissues.

hydrome sheath. A separation layer between hadrome and leptome.

hydrome stele. A cylinder for conduction of liquids.

hydrome strand. A unit of the water-vascular tissues.

hydromegatherm. A plant which must have both moisture and considerable heat to develop fully.

hydromegathermic. Tropical.

hydromorphosis. A change due to water, such as submersion.

hydronardetum. An association of *Nardus stricta*, a water plant.

hydronasty. The change produced because of

the changes of fluid relationship in the tissues, such as curvatures, etc.

hydrone. The simple fundamental molecule (H_2O) of which water is formed.

hydropermeable. Specialized for water absorption.

hydrophilae. A group including water-pollinated plants.

hydrophilous. 1. Dwelling in wet land or in water. 2. Having water pollination. 3. Aquatic.

hydrophilous fungi. Fungi living in water, such as *Saprolegnia*.

hydrophily. 1. The state of having an aquatic habit. 2. The condition of being disseminated by water.

hydrophyll. A leaf of a hydrophyte.

hydrophyllaceous. Of or pertaining to *Hydrophyllum* or its allies.

hydrophyllium. One of the leaf-like transparent bodies arising above and partly covering the spore sacs in the *Siphonophora*.

hydrophyte. 1. An aquatic plant of any kind. 2. A phanerogam with reproductive organs under water.

hydrophytia. Water communities.

hydrophytic forest. A forest that thrives in saturated soil or in soil that is saturated in spring and dries out in late spring or summer.

hydrophytium. A plant community of bog and swamp plants.

hydropic cells. Enlarged cells in the *Cyanophyceae*.

hydroplankton. Microorganisms floating in water.

hydroplast. An apparent vacuole in which the aleurone grains appear.

hydroplastids. Vacuoles in the endosperm of *Ricinus*, the castor bean.

hydropleon. An aggregate of molecules smaller than a micella, a water of crystallization.

hydroponics. The cultivation of plants which depend on solutions for nutrients. The growth of plants in water instead of soil.

hydropote. A cell or cell group in submerged leaves easily permeable by water and salts.

hydrorhiza. The root stock or decumbent stem by which a hydroid is attached to other objects.

hydrose. Having internal moisture.

hydrosere. A plant succession starting in a wet or moist situation and developing to a climax in the same sort of situation, a hydrarch succession.

hydrospheric. Using water as an agency of dispersion.

hydrospore. A plant whose seeds are distributed by water.

hydrostatic. 1. Completing plant succession under hydric conditions. 2. Completing successions in conditions which do not require greater moisture as the climax is approached.

hydrostereids. Prosenchymatous thick-walled elements with conspicuous pits lacking spiral thickening in the walls.

hydrosterome, transverse. The transverse parenchyma of the gymnosperms *Podocarpus* and *Cycas*.

hydrotaxis. The response of organisms to the stimulus of moisture.

hydrotherm. A graph of the annual course in temperature and precipitation used in the study of climate.

hydrotribium. A badlands formation or community.

hydrotribophilous. Inhabiting badlands.

hydrotribophyta. Badland plants.

hydrotrophy. The unequal growth due to a difference in moisture supply.

hydrotropic. 1. Of a plant organ curving towards moisture, applied to successions which become mesophytic. 2. Changing to a greater water content in a succession.

hydrotropism. The growth response of plants stimulated by moisture.

hydrotropism, negative. The turning away of a plant organ or structure from moisture.

hydrotropism, positive. The turning of a plant organ or structure toward the source of moisture.

hygrochastic. Said of plants in which the bursting of the fruit and the dispersal of the spores are caused by the absorption of water.

hygrocolous. Inhabiting wet ground.

hygrodiffusion. The entrance of moist air by diffusion and its subsequent loss from the looser tissues of the leaf.

hygrodrimium. A tropical forest formation, a rain forest.

hygrometric. Hygroscopic, moving under the influence of moisture.

hygromorphism. 1. The form of plants determined by the moisture of their surroundings. 2. The state of little water absorption and equally little evaporation from plant tissues.

hygropetrobios. An inhabitant of submerged rocks.

hygrophanous. Darkening in color following the entry of water into or between the cells, having a soaked appearance.

hygrophile. A plant which lives where moisture is abundant.

hygrophobe. A plant living best where moisture is scanty.

hygrophorbium. A moist pasture, a fen, a low moor community.

hygrophorous. Moisture-bearing, saturated.

hygrophyte. A plant living where moisture is plentiful, a hydrophyte.

hygrophytia. Formations of hydrophytes, hydrophytic communities.

hygroplasm. The fluid portion of the protoplasm.

hygropoium. A meadow formation or community, an evergreen meadow.

hygroscopic. 1. Readily absorbing moisture from the atmosphere. 2. Measureable only with a hygroscope.

hygroscopic cells. Cells in grass leaves which cause a modification of shape in dry weather.

hygroscopic mechanisms. The means by which movements of plant organs are achieved by the uneven swelling or shrinking of tissue following intake or loss of water.

hygroscopic movement. Movement due to changes of moisture.

hygrosphagnium. A high moor.

hylacolous. Tree-inhabiting species.

hylad. A forest plant.

hylea. Luxuriant flood forests of the Amazon.

hyloin. Hylium, a forest climax.

hylium. A series of forest communities.

hylobios. Inhabitants of solid media.

hylocolous. Forest-dwelling.

hylocomniosus. Mossy, composed of *Hylocomnium* or similar mosses in a formation.

hylodad. A plant of an open, dry, wooded formation.

hylodium. A dry, open woodland community.

hylodophilous. Living in dry woods.

hylodophyte. A dry woodland plant.

hylogamy. The fusion of a sexual nucleus with a vegetative nucleus.

hyloids. The crystals in *Gouania* leaves shaped like logs.

hylophagous. Wood-eating.

hylophilous. Dwelling in forests.

hylophyte. A plant growing in the woods.

hylotomous. Wood-cutting, as certain insects.

hylum. Hilum, hylus.

hymenanthous. Having membranaceous flowers, as straw flowers.

hymenial. Of or pertaining to the hymenium, the reproductive organ of cryptogams.

hymenial algae. In lichens, algal cells in the sporocarp, hymenial gonidia.

hymenial gonidia. Algal cells in the hymenium.

hymenial layer. The hymenium.

hymeniferous. Having a hymenium.

hymenium. The spore-bearing surface of asci or basidia in certain fungi, the fruiting surface of mushrooms and certain other fungi.

hymenoid. Having a membranous texture.

hymenolichens. Lichens which are symbiotically associated with a hymenomycetous fungus.

hymenomycete. A fungus with an exposed hymenium or hymenophore, a member of the *Basidiomycetes*.

hymenomycetous. Having the hymenial layer exposed early in development of the fungus and the spores borne on basidia.

hymenophore. The portion of the fruit body bearing the hymenium.

hymenopode. The hypothecium.

hymenopterid. A flower which can be pollinated only by *Hymenoptera*.

hymenopterous. Having membranous wings.

hymenorrhizous. Membranous-rooted.

hymenosepalous. Having membranous sepals.

hymenulum. A disc or shield containing asci but without an excipulum.

hyoscyamine. An alkaloid obtained from henbane, *Hyoscyamus niger*, and jimsonweed, *Datura stramonium*.

hypactile. Uncovered by the tide for less than one-fourth of the time.

hypallelomorphs. Allelomorphs which under certain conditions are themselves compound, the constituents of compound allelomorphs.

hypanthium. 1. The tube of the receptacle

upon which the calyx, corolla, and stamens are borne; the calyx tube. 2. A fruit-like body formed by the enlargement of the torus and bearing the proper fruits on its upper and inner surface. 3. The cup-shaped receptacle of a cotyloid flower.

hypanthodium. An inflorescence with a concave capitulum on whose walls flowers are arranged, the synconium.

hyperanisogamic. With the female gamete active at first and much larger than the male gamete.

hyperbasal cell. A cell from which the seta and foot of a sporophyte develop in bryophytes and pteridophytes.

hyperchimaera. A plant resulting from a chimaeral fusion which produces abnormal fruits; see CHIMAERA.

hyperchromasy. Superabundant supply of chromatin in a cell.

hyperchromatic. 1. Readily susceptible in taking color. 2. Of intensive coloration.

hyperdiploid. Having more than the normal diploid number of chromosomes or having extra segments of chromosomes.

hyperdispersion. An irregular mode of distribution of individuals resulting in crowding.

hyperdromy. The condition in which andromous and catadromous venation occurs on one side of a fern frond.

hyperhydric. With water overflowing from tissue.

hypericifolious. Leaved like *Hypericum*, a large genus of herbs or shrubs.

hypericoid. Like *Hypericum.*

hypermetamorphosis. A protracted and thoroughgoing metamorphosis.

hypermetatropic. Having flowers exchange pollen for fertilization, i.e., having the ovary of one flower fertilized by pollen from a second flower and the pollen of the first fertilize the ovary of the second.

hyperparasite. A parasite which is parasitic on or in another parasite.

hyperplasia. Excessive or hyperplastic overgrowth.

hyperploid. Having a chromosome number in excess but not a multiple of the basic chromosome number.

hyperplasy. Hyperplasia.

hyperstomatic. Having the stomata on the upper surface of the leaf.

hypertely. A high degree of imitative coloration or ornamentation not explainable on the ground of utility.

hypertonia. Excessive tonicity.

hypertonic. Having a greater osmotic concentration than the cell sap.

hypertrophic. Morbidly enlarged.

hypertrophy. An abnormal, usually pathological, enlargement of a plant cell or a plant member.

hypertrophytes. Parasitic fungi which cause hypertrophy in the tissues.

hypha. 1. One of the simple or branched thread-like filaments that compose the web-like mycelium of fungi which develops by apical growth and usually becomes transversely septate as it develops. 2. A simple or branched filamentous outgrowth from internal cells in the thallus of a large seaweed.

hypha, sieve. A special form of thread-like structure found in algae bulging at each septum.

hyphal body. A short thick hypha which produces conidiophores.

hyphal peg. A compound hyphal fasciculate projection extending beyond the general level of the hymenium.

hyphal rhizoid. A hypha which penetrates the substratum and performs the function of a rhizoid.

hyphal tissue. Interwoven hyphae which constitute the tissues of the larger fungi.

hyphalmyroplankton. The floating organisms of brackish water.

hyphasma. 1. Mycelium. 2. Barren mycelium. 3. An agaric thallus.

hyphema. The hyphal layer in lichens.

hyphenchyma. A tissue-like structure formed of felted hyphae.

hyphidium. Spermatium.

hyphadrome. A form of nervation in certain thick coriaceous leaves in which the veins are not visible on the surface.

hyphoid. Resembling hyphae, hypha-like.

hyphomycetes. A group of imperfect fungi.

hyphomycetous. 1. Denoting the fungi which bear their spores on simple or branched hyphae. 2. Of or pertaining to the *Hyphomyces*. 3. Mold-like, cobwebby.

hyphopode. 1. An appendage on the mycelium of *Meliola* which bear the perithecia. 2. A branch, generally unicellular and more or less lobed, by which the epiphytic aerial mycelium of the *Erysiphaceae* and *Hemisphaeriales* clings to the leaf.

hyphostroma. Mycelium.

hyphydrogamicae. Plants whose flowers are pollinated under water.

hyphydrogamy. Reproduction of flowers pollinated under water.

hypnetum. A plant association composed of mosses, especially of *Hypnum* and its allies.

hypnocyst. A cyst in which a contained organism rests. In *Pediastrae*, etc., a dormant stage is assumed when conditions for growth are unfavorable.

hypnoid. Moss-like.

hypnoplasy. The state of arrested development due to various inhibiting reactions which prevent the cells or tissues from attaining normal size.

hypnosis. The state of dormant vitality shown by seeds while they still retain their power of germination and growth.

hypnosperm. An asexually-produced resting spore in algae, a hypnospore.

hypnosporangium. A sporangium containing resting spores.

hypnospore. A zygote that remains in a quiescent condition during winter, a thick-walled resting spore.

hypnote. An organism in a dormant state.

hypnothallus. The structure resulting from hypnocysts by cell division.

hypnotic. Dormant, as in seeds.

hypnozygote. 1. A dormant zygote. 2. A dormant stage after the union of two sex cells.

hypo-. A prefix meaning under.

hypoachene. An achene from an inferior ovary.

hypoascidium. A funnel-shaped growth, the inner surface corresponding with the lower surface of the metamorphosed leaf.

hypobasal. Below the basal wall, as the posterior half of a proembryo.

hypobasal half. The posterior portion of an embryo.

hypobasal tier. The part of the embryo lying below the basal wall.

hypobasidial. With the characters of the hypobasidium of the heterobasidiomycetes.

hypobasidium. The matured probasidium or primary basidial cell. The hypobasidium

and the epibasidium compose the heterobasidium.

hypobenthile. On the sea bottom below 1000 meters, abyssal.

hypoblast. The cotyledon of a grass.

hypocarpium. An enlarged growth of the peduncle beneath the fruit.

hypocarpogean. Producing fruit under the surface of the ground, e.g., the peanut; hypogean.

hypochil. The basal portion of the labellum or lip in the flower of orchids.

hypochlorin. A constituent of chlorophyll corpuscles which is supposed to be the first visible product of constructive metabolism.

hypochromyl. Hypochlorin.

hypoclysile. Of low tide pools in which the water temperature does not rise more than 3° C above that of the sea.

hypocnoid. Resembling the fungus genus *Hypochnus*, which has felt-like resupinate hyphae.

hypocopula. The lower or intermediate band of cell wall in the lower and smaller valve of certain diatoms.

hypocotyl. The short stem of an embryo seed plant, the portion of the axis of the embryo seedling between the attachment of the cotyledons and the radicle.

hypocotyledonary. Below the cotyledons.

hypocrateriform. 1. Salver-shaped, said of flat corollas. 2. Having a gamopetalous corolla with long narrow tube and limbs at right angles to the tube.

hypocraterimorphous. Hypocrateriform.

hypocreaceous. Fleshy and bright colored like the fungus *Hypocrea*.

hypoderm. The outer cortex immediately below the epidermis, as in *Begonia* and fossil plants, tissue under the epidermis in plants. 2. The inner layer in the capsule of mosses.

hypodermal cell. 1. The apical cell in the nucellus giving rise to the embryo sac. 2. A cell lying beneath the epidermis.

hypodermic. Under the epidermis.

hypodermic zone. A structure in the scales of the rhizome of certain mosses distinct from the bundle in the midrib.

hypodermis. The tissue just beneath the epidermis which serves to strengthen itself.

hypodispersion. The regular mode of distribution of plant individuals.

hypogeal. 1. Germinating with the cotyledons remaining in the seed or under the ground. 2. Subterranean, hypogeous.

hypogenesis. Development without the occurrence of alternation of generations.

hypogenous. Growing on the lower surface, borne on the torus or under the ovary.

hypoglaucus. Glaucous beneath.

hypogynium. The structure supporting the ovary in some sedges.

hypogynous. Having the floral parts (calyx, corolla, and stamens) borne at the base of or below the free ovary and not attached to the calyx, having the antheridium develop below the stalk of the oogonium.

hypogyny. The state of being hypogynous.

hypohaeus. Grey.

hypohaploid. Having fewer than the haploid number of chromosomes.

hypoleucus. Whitish.

hypolimnile. Below the thermocline.

hypolimnion. The portion of certain lakes below the thermocline which receives no heat from the sun and no aeration by circulation.

hypolithic. Growing beneath stones.

hypomenous. Arising from below an organ without adhesion to it.

hypomiclia. The mycelium of certain fungi.

hypomorphic. Having a gene mutation producing an effect similar to but not so great as that produced by a gene loss.

hyponasty. 1. The more vigorous growth of the underside of a flattened organ usually resulting in its upward curvature. 2. Eccentric thickening of the lower side of a more or less horizontal stem or root.

hyponym. A generic or specific name not based on a type species or specimen.

hypopeltate. Having the base of the limb on the inferior face of a phyllome.

hypopetalous. With the corolla inserted below and not adherent to the gynoecium.

hypophloeodal. Living beneath the bark or periderm.

hypophyll. 1. An abortive leaf or scale growing under a leaf or leaf-like organ. 2. The lower portion of the leaf from which stipules develop which adhere to the leaf axis to form the leaf scar.

hypophyllopodous. Having radical leaves present when flowering.

hypophyllous. Growing on the underside of a leaf.

hypophyllum. An abortive or scale-like leaf subtending an organ.

hypophyse cell. The cell from which the primary root and root cap of the embryo in angiosperms is derived.

hypophysis. 1. In seed plants, the cell between the suspensor and the embryo which gives rise to the root tip. 2. In mosses, a swelling of the seta just beneath the capsule.

hypoplasia. Defective development due to insufficient nourishment and consequent cessation of growth.

hypopleura. The inner half-girdle of the frustule of a diatom.

hypoploid. Lacking the basic number of chromosomes.

hypopodium. The basal part of a leaf, the stalk or support.

hypopolyploid. Having fewer than the polyploid number of chromosomes.

hypoproteoid. Having sclerotic cells on the lower surface of leaves.

hyposathria. Secondary ripening (bletting), as in medlars.

hyposperm. The lower part of an ovule or seed below the level where the integument becomes free from the nucellus.

hyposporangium. The indusium of ferns when it arises below the sporangium.

hypostase. 1. A disc of lignified tissue at the base of the ovule in certain orders. 2. Tissue containing chromatic substance in the chalazal region.

hypostasis. The recessive condition of a gene due to the masking or inhibiting action of another (nonallelic) gene located on a different chromosome or at a different locus on the same chromosome, the suspensor of an embryo.

hypostate. See HYPOSPERM.

hypostatic. Exhibiting hypostasis, recessive.

hypostomatic. Having the stomata on the under surface.

hypostomium. The cells which form the lower portion of the stomium of the annulus of a rupturing sporangium in the ferns.

hypostroma. 1. A stroma formed by a parasitic fungus beneath the epistroma. 2. The root-like base of a stroma. 3. The entostroma.

hypostyle. The free portion on the ventral side of the stone in *Crataegus* and *Co-*

toneaster differing conspicuously in texture from the rest of the stone.

hypotetrarch. The division of the median protoxylem in a triarch stele.

hypothallinic. Situated beneath the thallus of a lichen.

hypothallium. The basal rhizoidal layer in calcareous algae.

hypothallus. 1. A net-like film of material left on the substratum by myxomycetes. 2. The weft of hyphae formed by a developing lichen thallus which often persists as a colored layer around the thallus, the prothallus of lichens.

hypotheca. The younger of the two valves in the cell wall of a diatom.

hypothecium. The layer of hyphal tissue immediately beneath the hymenium of apothecia in lichens.

hypothetical units. The ultimate component parts of protoplasm.

hypotonic. With a lower osmotic concentration than the cell sap.

hypotriarch. A triarch stele with the median protoxylem group lowest.

hypotrichous. Having cilia mainly restricted to the undersurface.

hypotriploid. Having fewer than the triploid number of chromosomes.

hypotrophic. More nourished and developed on the lower side, as in the horizontal branches of the yew.

hypotrophy. The condition when the growth of cortex or wood is greater on the lower side of the branch.

hypotype. A described, figured, or listed specimen.

hypovalve. The valve of the inner shell or hypotheca of a diatom, the antapical plate.

hypoxanthin. A substance related to xanthin which has been found in germinating seeds and muscle tissue.

hypoxyloid. Forming a cushion-shaped or crust-like stroma, like *Hypoxylon*.

hypsiu. A plant succession in response to elevation, hypsion, hypsium.

hypso-. A prefix meaning high.

hypsophyll. A bract, scale, or floral leaf below a sporophyll or inflorescence; Hochblätter.

hypsophyllary leaf. A bract.

hyrcanium. Hyrcanian, near the Caspian Sea.

hysgine. Reddish.

hyson. Chinese green tea, the early leaves or crop.

hyssopifolious. With leaves like hyssop, a fragrant blue-flowered plant of the mint family, used in medicines and rituals (in America a thistle plant).

hysteranthous. With leaves appearing after the flower.

hysteriaceous. 1. Belonging to the *Hysteriales*. 2. Having a hysterothecium or a similar structure.

hysteriaeform. Hysteriform.

hysteriform. Boat-shaped, with a longitudinal opening along the top, resembling the ascomycete *Hysterium*, hysterioid.

hysterogenic. Of later development or growth.

hysterolysigenous. With the ultimate formation of a cavity by the dissolution of cells.

hysterophyme. An elementary organ which has been mistaken for an independent organism.

hysterophytal. Fungus-like.

hysterophyte. A plant living on dead matter, a saprophyte.

hysteroplasma. The more fluid part of protoplasm.

hysterostele. A stele reduced in structure.

hysterothecium. An oblong or linear perithecium opening by a cleft.

hystrella. A carpel.

hystrix. Bristly.

hytherograph. A plotted diagram of mean monthly temperature and rainfall, a line surrounding the plotted points being a graphic expression of the climate of the area; a climagraph.

I

I_1, I_2, I_3, etc. 1. Symbols for the stages of rust development. 2. Symbols for the first, second, third, etc., generation by inbreeding.

ianthine. Bluish purple.

ibericus. Of Iberia, the Spanish peninsula.

iberidifolious. With leaves like *Iberis*, the candytuft.

iced. With a glittering papillose surface, covered with particles like crystals.

ichneumon. A flower which is visited by *Ichneumonidae*, flies or wasps.

icones. Colored plates or pictorial representations of plants.

icos-. A prefix meaning twenty.

icosandria. Plants with twenty or more stamens inserted on the calyx.

icosandrous. Having twenty or more perigynous stamens.

icotype. A type which is used in identification but which has not been previously used in literature.

icterine. Yellowish.

icterus. Vegetable jaundice, a form of chlorosis characterized by yellowness.

id. A hypothetical structural unit of the nucleus resulting from the successive aggregations of biophores and determinants and assumed to be represented by the chromomeres.

idaeus. Of Mt. Ida, in Asia Minor.

idant. 1. A unit resulting from an aggregation of ids. 2. A chromosome.

ideal angle. A theoretic angle for a central station of rest in leaf arrangement.

identify. To determine the species of a plant by the study of its characters.

-ides. A suffix meaning similar.

idioandrosporous. Said of the condition when dwarf males of *Oedogoniaceae* are produced from zygospores contained in certain cells of neuter individuals.

idiobiology. The biology pertaining to the individual organism, autobiology.

idioblast. 1. A cell which differs in form, content, and wall-thickening from its neighbors. 2. A nonchlorophyllous, thick-walled cell having supporting functions, usually occurring among cells with chlorophyll.

idioblast, oleoid. The long sinuous sclerenchyma cells occurring in the olive, *Olea*.

idioblast, proteoid. Idioblast cells found in the tropical plant *Protea*.

idiocalyptrosome. The outer zone derived from idiosphaerosome in sperm cells.

idiochorology. Autochorology, applied to self-distribution of plants as distinct and separate units.

idiochromatin. 1. Temporarily dormant generative chromatin. 2. Chromatin concerned especially with the reproductive functions as distinguished from the nutritive or somatic.

idiochromidia. Generative chromidia, chromidia derived from idiochromatin which are predominantly of generative functions

and may enter into the formation of gamete nuclei.

idiochromosome. A special chromosome believed to convey sex tendency, an additional chromosome with a relation to sex observed in certain germ cells.

idioecology. Autecology.

idiogynous. Not having a pistil.

idiomeres. Structures evolved during the resting stage in nuclear division and believed to be the sexual elements of the resultant nucleus.

idiomorphosis. A special kind of metamorphosis, as the development of petals of *Camellia* from bundles of stamens.

idiopher. A gene.

idioplasm. The hypothetical part of the germ cells which is supposed to be alone responsible for hereditary transmission.

idioplasm, chromatin. The generative or germinal part of a cell, the active organic part of the protoplasm identified with chromatin.

idioplast. A cell with special contents, an idioblast.

idiosome. A cell which differs markedly in size, form, or contents from its neighbors; an idioblast.

idiotery. A monstrosity which is peculiar to the individual.

idiothalamous. Having different coloration from the thallus.

idiotype. A specimen identified by the describer but not from the original locality.

idorgan. A purely morphological multicellular unit which does not possess the feature of a soma.

-ies. A suffix meaning consocies.

igapu. See REBALSA.

igarapis. Sluggish channels choked with palm forests; see REBALSA.

igneus. Flame-colored.

igniareous. Of the consistency of German tinder or amadou derived from wood-destroying fungi or puffballs.

-ile. A suffix meaning society.

ilicifolious. Holly-leaved.

illecebrosus. Of the shade.

illegitimate pollination. The transfer of pollen to the stigma of the same flower when the species seems to be adapted for cross-pollination.

illinitus. Varnished.

illustris. Lustrous.

illyricus. Of Illyria in Greece.

imaginary threshold. See EMPIRICAL THRESHOLD.

imbedded. Almost or entirely covered.

imberbifolious. Beardless with flowers.

imberbis. Without a beard or other hairs.

imbibition. A forceful absorption of water which is accompanied by a swelling to an abnormal size due to the forcing apart of the micellae in the cell walls of the object which has absorbed water, the addition of moisture to organized bodies in a manner that causes them to swell.

imbibition theory. The theory that water ascends in plants by a chemical process in the cell walls and not by actual passage upwards by vessels.

imbricate. Overlapping like the shingles on a roof.

imbricate aestivation. Aestivation in which the perianth leaves overlap at the edges.

immaculate. Without spots or marks.

immarginate. Without a border or margin.

immunity. The power of an organism to resist invasion by a parasite or infection.

immortelles. Plants which retain their original shape and appearance when dried.

immotiflorae. Wind-fertilized plants whose flowers are steadily fixed.

immune. Not susceptible to a particular disease or to the etiological agent causing it.

immunology. The study of immunity.

impaler. A division of an impalement, a sepal, or a bract.

impalpable. Not readily apprehensible, minute.

impari-pinnate. Pinnate but having an old or single leaflet at the apex.

imperfect flowers. Flowers which are unisexual, flowers which have either stamens or pistils but not both.

imperfect fungi. See FUNGI IMPERFECTI.

imperfect hybridization. The abortive attempt to form zygospores between the hyphae of two distinct species of zygomycetes.

imperfect stage. 1. An asexual stage of a fungus in which spores may or may not be produced. 2. The conidium-bearing stage of a fungus.

imperfect succession. A succession in which one or more of the usual stages are omitted anywhere in the sere and a later stage ap-

pears before its usual turn; see *Xenodochae.*

impermeable. Not permeable, not permitting passage.

implant. An organ or part transplanted to an abnormal position.

implicate. Tangled, as the branches of the panicles of *Panicum implicatum.*

impotence. Sterility including floral abortion and arrested development.

impregnating tube. An outgrowth from the antheridium of *Pythium* which penetrates the periplasm to the surface of the oosphere.

impregnation, generative. The fusion of the generative nucleus with the egg.

impregnation, vegetative. The fusion of the polar nuclei either with each other or with one of the generative nuclei.

impressed. Bent inward, hollowed, or furrowed as if by pressure.

impressed veiny. With sunken veins or veinlets.

impressus. Marked with slight depression.

impubes. Not mature, before impregnation is possible.

inadhering. Free from adjacent parts.

inaequalifolious. Unequal-leaved, inequalifolious.

inaequihymeniiferous. See INEQUIHYMENIIFEROUS.

inaequimagnus. Not the same size.

inaequinervius. With different-sized veins.

inaequipolaris. With unequal poles.

inaequivalved. Showing inequality in valves of glumes.

in-and-in. Breeding for successive generations from closely related individuals; mating, breeding, etc., that is done or takes place repeatedly in the same or closely related stock.

inanthecate. Bearing no anthers, as abortive or sterile filaments.

inappendiculate. Without appendages.

inarching. The natural union of stems or roots which grow in contact, natural grafting, grafting by bringing scion and stalk into contact while both are growing on their own roots.

inborn. Innate, said of characteristics which are especially rooted in the constitution of the individual.

inbreeding. 1. The mating of a male and female of the same or closely related parentage for a number of generations. 2. In plants, self-fertilization (the most efficient and rapid method to produce homozygous genes to obtain a pure line).

inbreeding coefficient. A measure of the intensity of inbreeding which is expressed in the percentage of the genes in the plant which have changed from being heterozygous to being homozygous after inbreeding for one or more generations.

incaliculate. Lacking a calicle.

incanescent. Becoming grey.

incanous. Hoary with white pubescence.

incarnate. Flesh colored.

incasement theory. The preformation theory.

incept. The rudiments of an organ.

incerate sedis. Of uncertain position.

incidental species. Species occurring only in small numbers and probably of little ecological significance, occasional species.

incipient nucleus. 1. The central body. 2. An achromatic ground substance occupying the alveoli of a reticulum in which there are minute granules.

incipient plasmolysis. The stage in plasmolysis in which the cell wall is fully contracted before the protoplast has shrunk away from the wall at any point.

incise. To cut sharply and deeply on the margin.

incisifolious. Cut-leaved.

incisodentate. Slash-toothed.

incisolobate. With lobes deeply cut or divided.

inciso-pinnatifid. So deeply cut as to approach a pinnate form.

inciso-serrate. With the edges sharply cut in tooth-like form.

inclaudens. Never closing.

included. 1. Not projecting beyond the surrounding parts enclosed. 2. Entirely contained within a tube or cavity.

included aperture. An inner aperture whose outline in surface view is included within the outline of the border.

included phloem. Phloem strands or layers included in the secondary xylem of certain dicotyledonous wood.

included sapwood. Masses of concentric zones included in the heartwood which retain the appearance and technical properties of sapwood.

included stamens. Stamens which do not protrude from the corolla tube.

includentia folia. Alternate leaves which in the sleep position approach buds in their axils and seem to protect them.

inclusion. 1. A foreign body included in a cell. 2. Nonprotoplasmic substances in the form of granules, droplets, crystals, etc.

inclusive. Permitting the entrance of individuals of other species.

incoctus. Not cooked.

incognita. Plants whose origins or distribution is unknown.

incolens. Dwelling in.

incoloratus. Without color.

incompatible, self-. Self-sterile.

incompatibility. 1. Differences in the physiological properties of a host and a parasite which limit or stop the development of a parasite. 2. Physiological differences which prevent fertilization and seed development and seed development or reproduction. 3. The inability of a graft to unite with the stock because of physiological or structural differences. 4. The inability of a pollen tube to reach the ovules because it is arrested in the style. 5. Sterility, infertility.

incompatibility, anatomical. Incompatibility due to structural differences, as hercogamy.

Incomplete. An artificial grouping of dicotyledons which completely lack a perianth or have only one whorl (usually sepals), such as the *Monochlamydeae*.

incomplete. 1. Of the annulus, forming a partial ring. 2. Of flowers, with one or more whorls missing.

incomplete flower. 1. A flower lacking a calyx or corolla. 2. A flower in which any of the four series of floral parts is missing.

incomptus. Unadorned.

inconditus. Confused, unformed.

incrassate. 1. Thickened upward or toward the summit. 2. Of cells, thick-walled.

increscent. Growing, enlarging.

incretion. An internal secretion.

incrustation. The fossilization by incasement in mineral substance, the act of incrusting or state of being incrusted.

incubation. 1. The period in disease between exposure and the first symptoms. 2. The placing of organisms in culture in suitable places for them to develop.

incubous. Having the tips of one leaf overlap the base of the one above it.

incumbent. Having a radicle which is bent

over and lies on the back of one of the cotyledons.

incumbent anther. An anther which lies against the inner face of its filament.

incurvation. The doubling back on itself of a structure or organ, as in the case of a spirochete about to divide.

incurve-recurved. Bending inwards and then backwards.

indeciduous. Not falling off at maturity, evergreen.

indefinite. Of no fixed number, very numerous (as above twenty stamens or petals).

indefinite growth. 1. Continuous growth and not the mere extension of a limited organism or bud, applied to all stems which have no terminal bud. 2. Indeterminate growth.

indefinite inflorescence. See INDETERMINATE INFLORESCENCE.

indehiscent. Not opening naturally at maturity, not splitting regularly.

independence. The separation of organs that are usually together.

independent assortment, principle of. The random combination of characters in the offspring as the result of the random alignment of the chromosomes on the equator of the spindle at the reduction division; their random combination in eggs and sperms, and independent union at fertilization. It occurs only when the genes affecting such characters are on separate (nonhomologous) chromosomes.

indeterminate growth. The growth of a stem, branch, or shoot not limited or stopped by the development of a terminal bud.

indeterminate inflorescence. 1. The indefinite branching of a floral axis because of the absence of a terminal bud. 2. An inflorescence with axillary buds which continue to develop indefinitely.

indican. A nitrogenous glucoside forming indigo when it decomposes.

indicators. 1. Plants which by their presence indicate the general nature of the habitat, such as type of soil or other edaphic factors. 2. Substances whose color indicates the presence of certain properties, such as the color test for acidity or the iodine test for starch, etc.

indicus. Indian.

indifferent. Not specialized or differentiated, as plants which grow equally well in acid or neutral soil.

indifferent species. Species growing more or less abundantly in many diverse communities.

indigenous. Native to a country.

indigo. A deep blackish blue dye which is obtained from various species of *Indigofera*.

indigogene. White indigo.

indigoticus. Indigo blue.

indigotine. Pure blue indigo.

indimulsin. An enzyme producing indigo in the leaves of *Indigofera*.

indirect venosus. Having lateral veins combined within the margins and giving rise to other little veins.

indirect nuclear division. Mitosis.

individual cross. The offspring of two crossed flowers.

individual fertilization. Cross-fertilization between different flowers on the same plant.

individual habitat. The habitat of an individual organism whether solitary or forming a part of a community.

individualism. 1. The capacity for separate existence. 2. Symbiosis in which the total result is wholly different from any of the symbionts.

individuation. Development of interdependent functional units as a colony formation, individualism.

indolylacetic acid. A plant hormone which causes elongation of cells when it is present in suitable concentrations.

induction. 1. The production of sensitive movements or conditions due to the action of an external factor. 2. A change brought about in the germ plasm which temporarily affects the first generation but does not bring about a permanent change in the inherited characters.

induction, heterogeneous. Induction due to two or more causes.

induction, isogamous. Induction due to one cause.

inductive stimulus. 1. An external stimulus which influences growth or behavior of an organism. 2. An external force or stimulus which by its actions produces internal changes in an organism.

indumentum. A hairy covering.

indumentum, bistrate. A two-layered hairy covering, the outer layer being caducous.

indumentum, unistrate. A one-layered hairy covering.

induplicate. With edges folded in, turned inward, or folded cross-wise.

induplicate aestivation. Valvate aestivation in which the edges of the perianth segments are turned inward.

induplicative. Having induplicate sepals, petals, or leaves.

indurate. Hardened.

indusial. 1. Having indusia. 2. Of or pertaining to the indusium.

indusial flaps. A false indusium.

indusiate. 1. Having an indusium. 2. Like an indusium or small cup.

indusioid. Having an indusium-like covering, in ferns.

indusium. 1. A covering protecting the sorus of a fern composed of hairs or scales. 2. A cup-shaped structure around the base of the sorus or umbrella-like scales completely covering the sorus. 3. In phalloid fungi, an appendage or veil on the stipe beneath the pileus.

indusium, false. A recurved margin of the fronds in ferns covering the sporangia, as in the genus *Pteris*.

induviae. 1. Persistent portions of the perianth. 2. Leaves which wither but do not fall off. 3. Scale leaves.

induviate. 1. Covered with scale leaves or induviae. 2. Covered with old and withered parts.

inembryonatus. Lacking an embryo.

inencyma. A fibro-cellular tissue in which the cells have the appearance of spiral vessels.

inequihymeniiferous. Resembling the development of the fruit body in agarics in that the hymenium develops in an unequal manner, i.e., with the basidia producing spores in zones on each gill starting at the bottom end of each gill and developing upward.

inequilobate. Unequally or irregularly lobed.

inequipolar. With unequal poles.

inequivalve. Having unequal valves.

inerm. Unarmed, without spines or prickles.

inert chromosome. A chromosome all or most of whose genes are physiologically inactive.

inextensible. Not elastic.

ineye. 1. To inoculate. 2. To bud.

infarctate. Turgid, solid, without vacuities.

infection. 1. The entrance and growth of a parasite in a host. 2. The communication of disease from one organism to another.

infection layer. A layer of hyphae near the base of the scutellum in the grass *Lolium temulentum*.

infection thread. The continuous chains of bacteria which pass from cell to cell.

infection tube. 1. A germ tube. 2. The germ tube which penetrates the host from the germinating spore of a parasitic fungus.

infection vesicle. The haustorium of an invading fungus.

infection zone. A series of cells in which the infection threads pass from cell to cell.

infectorius. 1. Used for dyeing. 2. Pertaining to dyes.

inferagarian arctic zone. The lowest division of the arctic region in Great Britain.

inferagarian zone. The lowest portion of cultivated land in Great Britain.

inferior. 1. Of the annulus, below the middle of the stipe. 2. Of an indusium, below the sporangium.

inferior annulus. An indusium or veil below the middle of the stipe in agarics.

inferior calyx. A calyx placed below and free from the ovary.

inferior corolla. A corolla which is attached below the ovary.

inferior indusium. A fern indusium attached below the sporangium.

inferior ovary. 1. An ovary with the calyx tube adnate to it and with the stamens, sepals, and petals inserted upon it. 2. An inferior gynoecium.

inferoanterior. Below and in front of.

inferolateral. Below and toward the side.

inferomedian. Below and about the middle.

inferoposterior. Below and behind.

infest. To trouble greatly by numbers or by frequency of presence.

inflected. Curved or abruptly bent inward or toward the axis, inflexed.

inflorescence. 1. A reproductive shoot composed of or bearing a number of shoots of limited growth. 2. An arrangement of flowers on a stem or axis, a cluster of flowers or a single flower. 3. A cluster of reproductive organs in bryophytes.

inflorescence, cymose or sympodial. An inflorescence in which the main axis terminates in a flower and subsequent flower development takes place in outward succession in the lateral axes; see CYME.

inflorescence, definite. An inflorescence in which each axis in turn is terminated by a flower, as in a cyme; a determinate inflorescence.

inflorescence, indefinite. A floral axis which is capable of continuous extension, as in a raceme; an indeterminate inflorescence.

inflorescence, mixed. An inflorescence with both cymose and racemose flower arrangements.

inflorescence, mono-, di-, or pleiochasial. A cymose inflorescence which bears one, two, or more branches of flowers.

inflorescence, monopodial or racemose. An inflorescence in which the main axis does not terminate in a flower but continues to grow onwards; see CATKIN, CORYMB, HEAD, PANICLE, RACEME, SPIKE, and UMBEL.

inflorescence, scar. The scar left on a stem by an inflorescence after it has fallen.

influent. 1. An organism which has important relations in the biotic balance and interaction. 2. An exerting influence.

infoliate. To cover with leaves.

infossate. Sunken.

infra-axillary. 1. Branching below the axis. 2. Inserted below the axis.

infracortical. Beneath the cortex.

infracted. Incurved, inflexed.

infracutaneous. Subepidermal.

inframarginal. Submarginal.

infranodal. Below a node.

infranodal canals. Marks below the node leaving prints on the casts, as the medullary rays of the fossil *Calamites.*

infrapetiolar. Below the petioles.

infraspinal. Below the spine.

infrastipular. Below the stipules.

infructescence. 1. The inflorescence after the petals have fallen and fruits have developed. 2. Collective fruits.

infructuose. Barren.

infundibular. Funnel-shaped.

infundibulum. A funnel-shaped corolla.

infuscate. Of a brownish tint.

infusion. 1. Water containing substances extracted from plant or animal matter. 2. The steeping or soaking in water of any substance to extract the desired substances.

infusoria. Organisms living in stagnant water or water rich in organic matter, as in hay infusions, etc.; diatoms.

ingest. To convey food material into the food cavity or body.

inherited character. A character the determiner for which was received from the parent or parents.

initial cell. A cell which remains meristematic, divides repeatedly, and gives rise to many daughter cells from which the permanent tissues of the plant are ultimately differentiated.

initial layer. The middle layer of the cambium.

initial spindle. The netrum.

initial stage. The stage during which a minute spindle (the netrum) forms within the centrosome during the division of the centriole.

injection. The forceful filling of intercellular spaces with water or other substances; the forcing of some substance, such as inoculum, into tissues.

innate. 1. Growing inside or inclosed. 2. Borne on the summit of a filament. 3. Not superficial. 4. Inherited.

inner aperture. The opening of the canal into the cell lumen.

inner bark. The tissue between the stellar cambium and the cork cambium.

inner endodermis. The endodermis inside the vascular tissue in a solenostele.

inner glume. A pale or palea of a grass flower.

inner lamina. The lignified layer of a lignified cell wall which is next to the inside of the cell.

inner peridium. A differentiated inner layer of the peridium in certain fungi, peridium internum.

inner tunic. A colored membrane which surrounds the hymenium in *Verrucaria* beneath the perithecium.

innervation. 1. An offshoot from a stem. 2. A mode of budding producing offshoots.

inocuous. Unarmed, spineless.

innovantes gemmae. The fixed or persistent buds of mosses.

innovation. 1. A newly formed shoot which in mosses becomes independent of the parent stem. 2. A new growth. 3. A young or basal shoot.

innovation shoot. A vigourous shoot which causes further growth of the plant.

innucellatae. Phanerogams which lack nucellus and integuments.

inoculation. 1. The introduction of bacteria, immune serum, or some other antigen into living organisms to secure immunity from future infections. 2. Grafting by inserting buds.

inoperculate. Having no operculum, as the fungi in the *Inoperculatae*.

inophyllous. With thread-like veins in the leaf.

inorganic. 1. Having no organs. 2. Not being or not having origin in a living organism.

inorganic ash. The ultimate residue after complete combustion, the mineral portion of a vegetable tissue.

inorganic compounds. Compounds which are derived from mineral sources and which may form part of an animal or plant structure.

inorganic ferments. Enzymes as opposed to organic ferments such as bacteria.

inosculation. Anastomosing, blending, budding, grafting.

inosite. A saccharine aromatic substance occurring in many seeds and other parts of plants.

inotagmata. Hypothetical contractile elements of protoplasm.

inovulatae. Phanerogams which have no discernible ovules at the time of fertilization.

inquinate. Dirty, blackish, polluted.

inrolled. Rolled inward.

insculpt. 1. Embedded in rocks, as some lichens. 2. Having holes or depressions in the surface.

insect pollination. The carrying of pollen from anthers to stigmas by insects.

insectivorous. Feeding on insects.

insect vector. Any insect which is actively or passively responsible for the dissemination of a disease-producing organism or any other etiological factor.

inseminatae. Plants which do not contain separate or distinct seeds at maturity.

inseparation. Coalescence.

insert. To attach by natural growth processes.

insertion of leaves. The union of leaves with stems.

insertion region. The part of a chromosome which is attached to a spindle fiber.

insition. The placing of a scion into a stock, grafting.

insolation. 1. Exposure to direct rays of the sun. 2. Exposure to intense heat and light.

inspersed. Having granules which penetrate the substance of a thallus.

inspissate. Thickened by drying.

instipulate. Exstipulate.

institius. Grafted.

integer. Entire; not serrated, lobed, or divided.

integminatae. Plants in which the nucellus is devoid of integuments.

integra radix. An unbranched root.

integra vagina. Sheathing petiole which forms a continuous tube, as in sedges.

integrifolious. Having entire leaves.

integument. 1. One or more cell layers covering the ovule leaving only a small pore, the micropyle. 2. The covering or testa of a seed.

integumental glands. Peltate glands which have an abundant secretion which causes the integument to be raised like a bladder.

integumental tissue. The epidermis and the hypoderm.

intenerate. To soften or make tender.

interalveolar. Between the surface pits of a plant.

interascicular pseudoparenchyma. The sterile filaments in the fructifications of fungi or groups of cells resembling parenchyma between asci.

interaxillary. Situated within or between the axils of leaves.

interbiomoric. Being of clear, nongranular protoplasm; hyaloplastic.

interbreed. To breed by crossing different stocks, varieties, or species of animals or plants.

intercalary. Lying between other bodies in a row or placed somewhere along the length of a stem, filament, or hypha.

intercalary bands. Bands in the girdle region of diatoms which separate the two frustules and may form a wide girdle area.

intercalary branching. Intermediate branching below the apex.

intercalary cell. A small cell between two aecidiospores which disintegrates as the spores ripen and breaks down as they are set free.

intercalary growth. Growth resulting from the development of new tissues between old tissues.

intercalary inflorescence. Flowers which bloom along the side of the main axis which continues to grow after the development of the flowers.

intercalary meristem. A meristem situated

some distance from the apex of the stem between the permanent tissue.

intercalary plates. Posterior or anterior plates found in *Peridineae.*

intercalary valves. The top or bottom surfaces of diatom frustules which have longitudinal septa.

intercalary vegetative zone. The zone lying between mature tissues which begins to grow as if it were a growing point.

intercarpellary. Between carpels.

intercellular. Between or among cells.

intercellular canals. Canals of any kind formed from intercellular spaces and serving as a repository for resins, gums, etc., that are secreted by the adjacent cells.

intercellular layer. The layer between adjacent cells often merging insensibly into their primary walls.

intercellular mycelium. The mycelium of a parasitic fungus living only in the intercellular spaces of the host plant.

intercellular passage. A continuous opening between the cells.

intercellular space. 1. The space between cells. 2. Any cavity within the plant.

intercellular substance. Material extruded from the cells of a plant into the space between the cells.

intercellular system. The intercellular spaces of a plant considered as a whole.

interchange. An exchange of segments between nonhomologous chromosomes.

interchromosomal. Between chromosomes.

intercostal. Between the veins or nerves of a leaf.

intercotyledonary. Between the cotyledons.

intercrescence. Growth into each other, as of tissues.

intercrossing. Cross-fertilization.

intercutis. The hypoderm of the root.

interfascicular. Between the vascular bundles.

interfascicular cambium. The strand of cambium between two adjacent vascular bundles the formation of which is the first stage in the normal thickening of a stem.

interfascicular conjunctive tissue. Interfascicular cambium.

interfascicular phloem. Phloem formed between the bundles.

interfascicular secondary phloem. Phloem formed by the interfascicular cambium of a medullary commissure.

interfascicular secondary xylem. Xylem formed by the cambium of a medullary commissure.

interfascicular xylem. Xylem formed from the cambium and located between bundles.

interference. The condition which reduces the probability of more than one cross-over or chiasma to take place in contiguous parts of the chromosomes.

interfertile. Able to interbreed.

interfibrillar spaces. The spaces between the tiny fiber-like threads or branches of a cell wall which contain solutions of pectins.

interfilar. Between filaments (as the resting spores in the conjugating tube of *Mesocarpus*) or the fluid portion of protoplasm in the hypothetical fibrillar network.

interfilar substance. The ground substance as opposed to the fibrillar substance.

interfoliaceous. Between the leaves of a pair, situated or arising between two opposite leaves.

interfoliar. Situated between two opposite leaves.

interfoyles. Bracts, scales, and stipules.

intergranum area. The area between the grana of a chloroplast, the stroma.

intergranum lamellae. The plates or submicroscopic layers found in a chloroplast which contain the green pigments.

intergerinum lignum. The dissepiment of a fruit.

interkinesis. An interphase or resting period between the two meiotic divisions of a cell.

interlaced. Twisted or linked into each other.

interlamellar. Between lamellae.

interlaminar. Between laminae.

interlobular. Between lobes or lobules.

interlobule. The small subulate or triangular form between the lobule and the stem in some *Hepaticae.*

interlocular. Between loculi.

intermediate bands. See CLOSING BANDS.

intermediate bundles. Later bundles.

intermediate parietal cell layer. The layer below the fibrous layer in anthers.

intermediate tissue. The fundamental tissue in exogens except the epidermis and vascular bundles.

intermediate type. A plant of Great Britain whose distribution is of a local or doubtful range.

intermediate zone. 1. The active zone between the pith and epidermis which contains the vascular bundles in monocots. 2. The elevation between the agrarian and arctic zones.

intermicellar. Between the micellae.

intermitosis. The interphase or resting phase.

intermolecular. Between the molecules.

internal factor. Any factor which depends on the genetic constitution of the plant and which influences its growth and development.

internal gland. One or more secreting cells inside the plant, such as those containing essential oils which form the translucent dots in the leaves of the orange.

internal pericycle. The procambium retained on the inner side of the vascular bundle.

internal phloem. Primary phloem internal to the primary xylem.

internerves. The spaces between nerves, said of glumes and lemmas.

internode. The space between nodes or phalanges.

interosculant. Having characteristics of more than one species.

interpetiolar. Between the petioles.

interpetiolar stipules. Stipules situated or originating between the petioles of opposite leaves.

interphase. The period between mitotic cell division; intermitosis, interkinesis, a resting stage.

interplacental. Between the placentae, as the vascular bundles which are present in the capsule.

interplastidic. Between plastids and uniting them.

interpolation of plants. The appearance of extra primordia in spaces which are normally unoccupied.

interpolation theory. A name suggested to replace the antithetic theory.

interposed members. Plant parts which have arisen in a whorl after its earlier members.

interposition. The formation of new parts between those already existing in a whorl.

interprotoplasmic. Having gaps in the reticulum of *Myxogastres.*

interramal. Between branches or rami.

interrupted. Asymmetrical, irregular, not continuous.

interrupted growth. An alternation of scanty and abundant development appearing as constrictions in an organ, such as a fruit or taproot.

interrupted leaf. A leaf on which small leaflets are interposed.

interrupted sori. Sori which are not continuous.

interruptedly pinnate. Having pairs of small leaflets (pinnae) alternate with large ones.

interseminal. Between or among seeds.

interseptal. Between septa.

intersex. An organism having characteristics intermediate between the typical male and the typical female of its species.

intersexualism. Alternative development of either sex organs.

interspace. Of gills, the space between the attachment of the gills to the pileus.

interspecies group behavior. The relation of various species to each other as regards their functions.

interspecific hybrids. Hybrids resulting from a cross between two given species.

interspicular. Between spicules.

interspinal. Between spines.

intersporal. Between the spores in a sporangium.

interstaminal. Between stamens.

intersterility. The incapacity to interbreed.

interstices. Small air spaces between surfaces or bodies.

interstitial. 1. Occurring in interstices. 2. Applied to that method or theory of growth which consists in the interposition of new particles between the older ones rather than additions to the surface.

interstitial bodies. Mucilaginous discs which occur in some pollen grains.

interstitial growth. The interposition of new particles between the older portions.

interthecial. Of stroma, having a portion of the stroma between ascigerous locules.

intertidal. Living between high and low tide marks.

intertriginous. Between two faces or surfaces which are not separated very far from each other.

intertropic. 1. Situated within the tropics. 2. Related to the torrid zone.

intervaginal scales. Squamules which are found between the leaves of aquatic monocotyledons.

intervarietal. Applied to crosses between two distinct varieties of the same species.

intervenium. A portion of the parenchyma between the veins of a leaf, the area lying between one or more veins or veinlets in a leaf blade.

intervenose. Having the veins of gills on the surface and extending various distances into the interspaces or crossing to the next gill.

interweaving of hyphae. The union of hyphae by growing among each other without cohesion.

interwoven. With hyphae of the trama intermingled.

interxylary phloem. A strand of secondary phloem surrounded by secondary xylem.

interzonal fibers. The connecting fibers of the mitotic spindle that extend between the two daughter groups of chromosomes during the anaphases and telophases.

interzone. 1. A strip separating two larger communities which contains species absent from either of them. 2. The portion of a diatom frustule which lies between the girdle and the valves.

intexine. Intextine.

intextine. The inner membrane when two are present in the extine or the outer covering of the pollen grain.

intine. 1. The inner layer of the wall of a pollen grain. 2. The endospore in spores of bryophytes.

intodiscal. Inserted within the disc of a flower.

intorted. Twisted upon or around itself.

intortion. Torsion, the bending of any part of a plant toward one side or another.

intra-. A prefix meaning within or inside.

intra-axillary. Within the axil, as many leaf buds.

intrabiontic. Having selection occur in a living unit.

intracambial. Within the cambium.

intracarpellary. Within or produced within the carpels.

intracellular. Inside a cell.

intraclonal. Within the limits of bud variation.

intracuticular. Within the cuticle.

intradiel. Of or pertaining to the phenomena which take place within a single 24-hour day.

intrafascicular. Within the vascular bundle.

intrafertile. Said of two species fertile between themselves.

intrafilar. Within a filament.

intrafloral. Within the floral organs.

intrafoliaceous. 1. Having stipules which encircle a stem and form a sheath, within a leaf. 2. Intrapetiolar.

intraglobular. Situated in or occurring within a globule.

intralamellar tissue. Tissue within special layers of lamellae, as in hymenomycetes; a trama.

intralobular. Within lobules.

intramarginal. Within or near the margin.

intramatrical. Inside a matrix or nidus.

intrameability. The capacity of protoplasm to permit substances to pass into its vacuoles.

intramedullary. Within the pith.

intramolecular. 1. Existing or acting within the molecule. 2. In plants, applied to respiration by splitting up of complex substances within the cell.

intramolecular respiration. Anaerobic respiration.

intramural. Between the walls of cells.

intramural glands. Multicellular organs of secretion whose product appears in the limiting walls.

intramycelial. Within the mycelium.

intranucellular. Within the nucellus.

intranuclear. Within the nucleus.

intraovular. Within an ovule.

intrapalear. Referring to the fertilization of grasses which usually takes place within the flower before the exsertion of the anthers.

intraparietal. Enclosed within an organ.

intrapetalous. In a petaloid area.

intrapetiolar. Inside or beneath the petiole (subpetiolar) or between the petiole and the stem (intrafoliaceous).

intrapetiolar buds. Buds which are completely closed by the petiole.

intrapetiolar stipules. Stipules which are situated within or above the petioles usually sheathing the branch.

intraprothalloid. Within the prothallus or immersed in its tissue.

intraprotoplasmic. Within the protoplasm.

intrarious. 1. Turned inward toward the axis. 2. Of flowers, opening toward the center.

intraselection. The selection within an organ of the cells most fitted to survive.

intraseminal development. The entire development of the embryo during the conversion of the ovule into a seed.

intrasporangial germination. The growth of the embryo within the sporangium.

intrastamineal. 1. Within the stamens. 2. Inside or between the whorls of stamens.

intrastelar tissue. Conjunctive tissue within the stele.

intrasterility. The infertility between two closely related species.

intravaginal. Within the sheath, said of branches growing parallel to the culm and emerging from the sheath, as in bunch grass.

intravaginal innovation. The condition in which the new shoot starts inside a basal sheath and continues to grow between it and the stem.

intravalvularis. Within valves, as the dissepiment in many *Cruciferae*.

intricate. Entangled, intertwined.

intricate cortex. The cortex composed of densely interwoven hyphae which have not coalesced.

intrinsic factors. Factors which reflect highly efficient adjustment of the individual to environmental conditions, such as structures and habits peculiar to the species.

introflexed. Inflexed, bent strongly inward.

introitus. An opening, an orifice.

intromarginal. Having veins which run just inside the outer margins of a leaf.

introrse anthers. Anthers with the cells turned inward or toward the pistils and the filament or connective tissue extending up the outer side.

introsporangial germination. The growth of an embryo within a sporangium.

introvenius. With the veins hidden.

introxylary. Within the wood or xylem.

introxylic. Within the xylem.

intrusion, cortical. Abnormal growth of cortex in other tissues.

intumescence. The abnormal or pathological swelling on the exterior of plants, chiefly parenchymous.

intussusception. Growth and development of organisms by the deposition of sub-microscopic amounts of food in and between the cell walls.

intybaceous. Akin to or part of *Cichorium intybaceum*, chicory.

inulase. An enzyme found in plants which converts inulin into levulose.

inulenin. A subordinate constituent of inulin.

inulin. A carbohydrate resembling starch which has been isolated from the roots and rhizomes of many *Compositae*.

inuncant. Having the surface covered with glochidia or hooked hairs, inuncate.

inundatal. Growing where inundation takes place in wet weather but dry conditions prevail in summer.

invader. 1. A plant occurring in a community to which it does not belong. 2. A plant entering an area where it has not been before.

invaginate. To involute or draw into a sheath.

invasion. The intrusion and establishment of alien plants into a new community.

invasion theory. A theory promulgated to support the idea that the pith is non-vascular because the vascular tissue has been invaded by tissue from the cortex to form pith.

inverse. Said of the condition of an embryo in which the radicle is turning toward a point in the seed at the opposite end of the hilum.

inverse symmetry. The state of having the right half of one asymmetrical individual equivalent to the left half of another, mirrored symmmetry.

inversion. 1. The reversal in position of a portion of a chromosome. 2. The turning inside-out during development of a colony in some algae that form coenobes. 3. The hydrolysis of cane sugar. See INVERTASE.

invertase. An enzyme which hydrolyzes cane sugar, which is present in most yeasts. Sacchrase, sucrase.

inverted sugar. The mixture of fructose and glucose by the action of invertase on cane sugar.

inverted superposition. The position of accessory buds below the principal bud.

invertin. Invertase.

investment. The outer covering of a cell, part, or organism.

involucel. A secondary involucre as that of secondary bracts of some *Umbelliferae*.

involucellate. Having an involucel.

involucral. Belonging to or like an involucre.

involucral bract. One of the leafy bracts forming an involucre.

involucrate. Having an involucre.

involulucre. 1. A cluster of modified leaves or bracts at the base of a flower cluster or capitulum. 2. A short tube around the archegonia and the calyptra in bryophytes. 3. A peridium.

involucre, general. An involucre at the base of a compound umbel.

involucre, partial. The involucre which surrounds a partial or secondary umbel, the concentric zones of growth in exogens, an involucel.

involucret. An involucel or partial involucre.

involucrum. A velum, an involucre, an involucel.

involute. 1. Having the upper surface of a leaf rolled inwards. 2. In a pileus, being rolled inward, especially when young.

involution. 1. The act of rolling inward. 2. The return of an organ or tissue to its original state following the removal of an unfavorable condition.

involution form. 1. A swollen bladder-like form of schizomycetes presumed to be a diseased condition. 2. Bacterial cells of unusual size, shape, or development due to unfavorable growth conditions.

involution period. The resting period of a spore, seed, or other plant organ which remains inactive for a time.

involution spore. A resting spore.

involution stage. A resting stage, a dormant period.

involvens. Rolled together.

iodic. 1. Violet in color; violaceous. 2. Pertaining to, caused by, or containing iodine.

iodophilic. Staining darkly in iodine solution.

ioensis. Of Iowa.

ionandrus. Violet-anthered.

ionanthus. With flowers like violets.

ionid. Violet-colored.

ionopterous. Having wings like the violet.

iridiflorous. Iris-flowered.

iridile. A society of iris.

irpiciform. Having teeth resembling those of the fungus *Irpex*.

irregular. Asymmetrical, not arranged in an even line or circle; not divisible into halves by an indefinite number of longitudinal planes.

irregular corolla. A corolla having the upper and lower sides unlike.

irregular flower. A flower in which some parts are different from other parts of the same whorl in size or shape, an unsymmetrical flower.

irregular nutrition. The condition of obtaining organic substances by some process other than photosynthesis.

irregular peloria. A monstrosity in which an irregular form has become regular by symmetric development.

irregularly compound leaf. A compound leaf which has leaflets of various and more or less indefinite shapes and sizes.

irrepens. Creeping in.

irritability. One of the characteristics of living matter, the ability to receive and to respond to external sitmuli.

irrorate. As if covered with dew, covered with minute grains or with small specks of color.

isabelline. Tan, tawny, pinkish-cinnamon, alutaceous.

isadelphous. 1. Having an equal number of stamens in each adelphia. 2. Equal brotherhood, as when the number of stamens in two phalanges is equal.

isandrous. With equal stamens.

isarioid. Like the fungus *Isaria*, having a cylinder of hyphae.

isatin. The woad or coloring matter obtained from the crucifer *Isatis tinctoria* prepared from the leaves by grinding them to a paste and fermenting them. It was widely used before the introduction of indigo and is also called false indigo or isatine.

isidiiferous. 1. Having a thallus which resembles the genus of corals from which it derives its specific name. 2. Having coral-like protuberances (isidia) on the lichen thallus. 3. Coralloid, isidioid.

isidiose. Having coral-like protuberances or powdery excrescences.

isidium. A rigid protuberance of the upper part of a lichen thallus which may break off and serve for vegetative reproduction.

islands. Isolated strands of phloem in the xylem.

iso-. A prefix meaning equal.

isoandrospore. A spermatozoid of *Marchantia*.

isobilateral symmetry. The condition of flowers and other parts of plants which can be divided into symmetrical halves by two distinct planes.

isobiochore. See BIOCHORE.

isobrachial. Said of a chromosome which is bent into two equal arms.

isobriatus. Dicotyledonary.

isobrious. 1. Having equal strength. 2. Applied to the embryo of dicotyledons because both are equally developed. 3. Isodynamous.

isocarpic. Having the number of carpels equal to that of the parts of other floral sets.

isocheim. The isotherm of the coldest months.

isochimereal. Applied to the hypothetical lines connecting places on the earth's surface with the same mean winter temperatures.

isochomous. Said of branches springing from the same stem at the same angle.

isochromous. All of one color, tint, or hue; uniform in color throughout.

isocies. 1. Similar communities having similar characteristics in different parts of the globe. 2. Synusia showing resemblances but of various affinities. 3. Habitat groups.

isocoenosis. A group of phytocoenoses physiognomically more or less consistent.

isocoenosium. A community composed of isocies.

isocotylous. Having equally developed cotyledons.

isocryma. A winter isotherm.

isocyclic. 1. Having a flower with the same number of parts in each whorl. 2. Having similar whorls.

isocytic. With all cells equal.

isodiametric cells. Cells having an equal diameter in each direction – longitudinal, transverse and perpendicular.

isodiodes. Diodes which are all of one kind, either all macrospores or all microspores.

isodiody. The production of diodes which give rise to unisexual prothallia.

isodynamic. Of equal strength.

isodynamous. Equally developed, isobrious.

isoetoid. Having a leaf which is linear, undivided, terete, often tubular, and sessile resembling the genus *Isoetes*.

isofogs. Isopracts surrounding areas having the same degree of injury by insects or mammals.

isogametangial copulation. Conjugation in which the gametangia and nuclei are alike.

isogametangic. Producing gametangia all of the same size and form.

isogametangium. The organ which produces isogametes.

isogametes. Gametes of similar size and appearance which conjugate to form a zygote which develops into a zygospore. The male cannot be distinguished from the female.

isogamous. Denoting plants whose pairing gametes are similar, being a gametophyte-producing isogamete.

isogamy. The sexual union of two like gametes.

isogenetic. Having the same or similar origin.

isogenic. Propagating entirely by means of apogamy.

isogenetypic. Having two or more generic names applied to the same type species.

isogenomatic. Having complementary sets of chromosomes made up of similar genomes.

isogenous. 1. Having individuals belonging to the same genotype. 2. Having the same origin.

isogenous induction. The sensitive movements arising from a single cause.

isogonous. Said of hybrids which combine the parental characters in equal degree.

isogynospore. The egg of *Marchantia*.

isogynous. Having similar pistils.

isogyrous. Forming a complete spire.

isohabitu. A continuous area where there is no important variation in any environmental factor.

isohaplont. A haplont with genotypically similar cell nuclei.

isohologamy. The condition in which the coalescent individuals are entirely alike.

isoholotype. A later specimen taken from the type plant.

isohydrics. Isopracts surrounding areas having similar hydrogen ion concentration.

isohyet. An isopract delimiting equal rainfall over a given area, a line of equal rainfalls.

isohyp. An isopract surrounding land areas of the same elevation, a contour line.

isokont. Having flagella of equal length.

isolateral leaves. Leaves which have palisade tissue on both surfaces and have both sides exposed to light.

isolation transect. A belt of land to which grazing animals are admitted under observation so that the effect of grazing on the vegetation may be studied.

isolectotype. A specimen taken from a chosen type long after publication.

isomaltose. A product of amylodextrin which changes by fermentation into maltose.

isomastigate. Having two or four flagella of equal length.

isomer. A substance which has the same chemical composition as another substance but possesses different chemical and physical properties.

isomerogamy. The conjugation of isogametes, as in many algae.

isomerous. Having the same number of organs in each floral whorl.

isomorphism. Apparent similarity of individuals of different race or species.

isomorphs. Organisms which are superficially similar to each other although phylogenetically different.

isonif. An isopract surrounding areas having equal heights of snow.

isopetalous. Having similar petals.

isophagous. Attacking one or several allied species.

isophase. A situation which develops when hereditary factors are overwhelmingly influenced by one single factor.

isophene. A theoretical line along which seasonal phenomena occur at the same date, an isophane.

isophenous. Belonging to the same phenotype.

isophotic. Equally illuminated on all sides.

isophotophyll. A leaf in which both halves of the chlorenchyma are alike because of equal illumination.

isophyllous. Alike in shape and size, bilateral.

isophyte. An isopract surrounding areas having equal height of vegetation above the ground.

isophytoid. Being an individual of a compound plant not differentiated from the rest.

isophytotonus. Having the same temperature requirements.

isoplanogametes. Motile sexual cells of equal size found in algae.

isopleth. An isopract surrounding areas having the same numbers of a given species or number of species.

isopolar. An axis of diatom frustules when its extremities are similar.

isopract. A line indicating the boundary of like frequency of expression of a given factor, as contour lines indicate similar areas of elevation.

isoprothally. The condition in which prothallia are alike in sexual characters.

isoreagent. A variety or a microspecies.

isoschist. One cell of a related group all of which are equal in size and function.

isosmotic. Passing by osmosis in or out of the cell with equal facility, exhibiting or exerting equal osmotic pressure.

isospore. A swarm spore or gamete.

isosporous. Having sexually produced spores of one kind only, homosporous.

isostemonous. Having the same number of stamens as other parts in the flower (sepals and petals).

isostic. Having a mother root with more than two xylem bundles.

isostichous. Having the ridges in the stem cortex of *Chara* of equal size.

isostomous. Having the calyx and the corolla of unequal size.

isostylous. With the styles similar and equal in size.

isotely. Homoplasty.

isoterra. An area which shows uniformity of habitat conditions on a large scale.

isothere. An isotherm showing equal temperatures of the hottest months.

isotomy. Bifurcation repeated in a regular manner.

isotonic. 1. Of equal tension. 2. Having the same osmotic concentration as the cell sap.

isotonicity. The normal tension under pressure or stimulus.

isotrophic. With equal growth all around.

isotrophyte. A parasitic fungus whose influence is only chemical, causing slight changes in the host.

isotropous. Being equally influenced from all directions, as in contorted aestivation.

isotype. 1. A plant common to different countries. 2. A specimen believed to be a duplicate of the holotype.

isotypic. Described from more than one species all of which are congeneric.

isthmus. The constricted portion between the two half-cells in most desmids or the girdle in diatoms.

istrian. Of Istria, in southern Europe.

italicum. Italian.

iteology. The study of the genus *Salix*, willows.

iterato-proliferous. Repeatedly bearing proliferations.

ithyphyllous. Having straight and stiff leaves.

ixioid. Like *Ixia*, a South African iris-like plant.

ixocarpous. Having sticky or glutinous fruits.

ixous. Sticky or viscous.

J

jacket cells. Cells surrounding the nucellus in *Thuja*, arbor vitae.

jaculator. A hook-like process on the placenta of certain fruits which aids in the expulsion of the seeds.

jaculiferous. With dart-like spines.

jaggery. A coarse dark sugar from the coconut and other palms which produces arrack by fermentation, palm sugar.

jalap. The dried tuberous root of *Ipomoea purga*, a Mexican morning glory widely collected near Jalapa and used as a purgative.

jalapin. A resinous glucoside found in jalap.

jamaicensis. Of Jamaica.

jamaicin. An alkaloid occurring in the tropical cabbage tree, genus *Andira*.

Jaminian chain. A series of short threads of water separated by bubbles of air in the vessels of plants, Jamin's chain.

japonicus. Japanese.

jarales. Maquis in the Iberian peninsula, a shrub transitional zone between steppe and forest.

jarovisation. The shortening of the vegetative period of plants by seed treatment.

jasmineous. Jasmine-like.

jasminoid. Jasmine-like.

jaspideous. Having a mixture of many colors arranged in small spots.

javanicus. Javanese.

jessamine. Jasmine, yellow or Carolina jessamine.

jodicus. Of iodine or jodus.

joint. 1. A node or articulation as in grasses and some other plants. 2. The septum between two cells in a filament.

jointed. Said of an elongated plant member which is constricted at intervals and separates into a number of portions by breaking at the constrictions.

jonquilleous. Light yellow, jonquil-colored.

jordanism. An excessive multiplication of so-called species usually considered varieties.

jordanon. A variety, a form which breeds true to type but does not differ enough to be considered a separate species, a race or strain.

jowar. Guinea corn.

juba. A loose panicle having a deliquescent axis.

jubate. Crested with a mane.

jugate. 1. With pairs of leaflets. 2. Having a jugum.

jugum. 1. A pair of opposite leaflets resembling a yoke or collar of a pinnately leaved plant. 2. A ridge on the fruits of the umbellifers.

juice vessels. Vascular tissues.

julaceous. 1. Resembling a catkin or ament. 2. Smooth and cylindrical.

julianiales. Woody plants with alternate usually pinnate exstipulate leaves and dioecious flowers.

juliform. Like a catkin or ament.

julus. A catkin, spike, or ament.

juncetum. An association of species of *Juncus*, rushes.

junceous. Rush-like, juncoid, juncaceous.

juncifolious. With rush-like leaves.

junctures. The points at which one season's growth is succeeded by the next, the interrameal regions.

jungate. Having a pair of leaflets.

Jungermanniales. The order of liverworts the plant bodies of which are either cylindrical stems or shortly stalked thalli of simple construction with the antheridia and archegonia on or (rarely) in them. The capsules open by four valves.

Junin waste. The salt wastes of Argentina; see ESTEROS.

juniperetum. An association of junipers.

juniperifolious. Juniper-leaved.

juniperinous. 1. Juniper-like. 2. Bluish brown like juniper berries.

Junquillo-pampa. Pampas characterized by the grass *Sporobolus arundinaceus*.

jute. The glossy fiber of East Indian tiliaceous plants.

juvenile form. A young plant which has leaves and other features differing markedly from those of a mature plant of the same species.

juvenile organ. An organ which is normal and functional in the early stages of the individual but disappears later.

juvenile stage. A particular stage in the life history of some plants from which the vegetative stage develops.

K

K. See also C.

kaffir thorn. The African tea plant, *Lycium*.

kafir. Grain sorghums grown for feed, *Sorghum*, kaffir.

kale. 1. A hardy, cool-season plant grown for greens, a member of the cabbage family. 2. Sea-kale, a crucifer the shoots of which are blanched and eaten in the early spring.

kalidion. A cystocarp, a form of sporocarp, a kalidium.

kaliform. Shaped like *Salsola kali*, a sea-coast plant, glass wort.

kalloplankton. Organisms which float in gelatinous envelopes.

kammenaia tundra. A tundra of Siberia which is bisected by mountain ranges or raised into plateaus which becomes rocky and rugged.

kamptodromous. Camptodromous.

kamtchaticus. Of Kamtchatka.

kangaroo thorn. The acacia.

Kanker. Caliche.

Kar. A community transitional between a heath and a moor characterized by a lack of raw humus.

Kar herbage. Plants occurring in glacial hollows high in the mountains.

karenchyma. The nuclear sap or karyochylema.

karpotropic. Carpotropic.

karroid. Karroo-like.

karroo. A dry region in South Africa which has a continental climate.

kary-, karyo-. A prefix meaning nucleus or nut.

karyaster. A group of chromosomes arranged like the spokes of a wheel or star.

karyenchyma. Nuclear sap, achromatin, karyochylema, karyolymph.

karyodermatoplast. The kinoplasmic asters of *Synchytrium*, a simple fungus.

karyogametes. Gametonuclei.

karyogamy. The fusion of two sex nuclei following the fusion of protoplasts, plasmogamy.

karyoid. A minute spherical body attached to the chlorophyll plate of conjugatae and desmids.

karyokinesis. Nuclear division, cell division, mitosis.

karyology. Nuclear cytology; the science of the nucleus, its development and vital history.

karyolymph. A colorless watery fluid occupying most of the space inside the nuclear membrane, nuclear sap.

karyolysis. The supposed dissolution of the nucleus in mitosis.

karyomere. 1. A swollen mass sometimes seen in chromosomes toward the end of nuclear division. 2. A compartment or vesicle in the resting nucleus which usually contains one chromosome.

karyomerites. Karyomeres or partial nuclei whether formed from one or several chromosomes.

karyomicrosome. A nuclear granule.

karyomite. A chromosome.

karyomitome. A nuclear network of fibers, the nuclear as opposed to the cytoplasmic fibrillar formation.

karyomitosis. Indirect nuclear division, mitosis.

karyomixis. The fusion of the two nuclei as in the teleutospore.

karyon. The cell nucleus.

karyophagy. The destruction of a nucleus by a special parasite.

karyophyte. A plant which has a nucleus.

karyoplasm. The protoplasm of the nucleus, a cytological name referring to the substance or plasm distinctive from the cell nucleus, nucleoplasm.

karyoplasmic ratio. The ratio between the volume of the nucleus and the volume of the cytoplasm in the same cell.

karyoplast. The entire nucleus.

karyorhexis. The fragmentation or rapid dissolution of a nucleus.

karyosome. A body within the nucleus containing all or most of the chromatin, an aggregate of chromatin within the nucleus, the nucleolus which furnishes material for the chromosomes during mitosis.

karyosphere. 1. The large nucleolus in protista from which all or most of the chromosomes arise. 2. The part of the nucleus into which the chromosomes have contracted.

karyosymphysis. Nuclear fusion.

karyota. Cells having nuclei.

karyotheca. The nuclear membrane.

karyotin. The nuclear substances which make up the nuclear reticulum, the chromatin.

karyotype. The morphological type or the phenotypical appearance of the chromosomes of an individual or related groups.

kashmirianus. Of Cashmere.

kata-. See CATA-. A prefix meaning down.

katabion. A catabolite.

katablast. A shoot from an underground stock.

katabolism. The destructive chemical processes in living organisms, the breaking down of body tissues, catabolism.

katabolite. Any product of destructive metabolism.

katachromasis. The sum total of the telophasic transformations by which the daughter chromosomes reconstruct the daughter nuclei.

katadromous. Said of the venation in the royal fern where the first nerves in each leaf segment arise on the basal side of the midrib.

katagenesis. Retrogressive evolution.

katakinetic. Leading to the discharge of energy.

katakinetomeres. Unreactive stable atoms or molecules of protoplasm.

kataklinotropism. Negative clinotropism.

katalase. Catalase.

katalysator. A substance which causes katalysis.

kataphase. The stages of mitosis from formation of chromosomes to the division of a cell.

kataphoric. 1. Denoting passive action or the result of lethargy. 2. Having the power to carry away.

katastate. Any product of katabolic activity of protoplasm.

katatonic. Tending to decrease a stimulus.

katatropic. Negatively tropic.

katelectrotonus. The heightened stimulation in plants due to an electric current.

katharobia. The organisms living in clean water.

kathodic. Not arising in conformity with the genetic spiral, applied to leaves which turn in the opposite direction of the genetic spiral.

katothecium. The fruit body of *Trichothyrium* with the asci arranged as an inverted fan, an inverted thyriothecium.

katylytic. Catalytic.

keel. 1. The boat-shaped petals of a legume or the glumes of some grasses. 2. The narrow outgrowth from the underside of some leaves. 3. A prominent ridge. 4. A carina.

keel puncta. The nodulated thickenings on one margin of the valves of the fungus *Nitschkea*.

kefir. An effervescent liquor-like kumiss made from fermented milk and used as a food and as a medicine in the northern Caucasus.

keimplasm. Germ plasm.

kelp. A general name for large seaweeds.

kenopophytes. Plants which colonize cleared land.

kenenchyma. Permanent tissue which has lost its living contents, as cork tissue.

keramidium. A cystocarp, the ovate or urn-shaped capsule containing the spores in the red algae.

keratinization. The state of becoming horny.

keratogenous. Producing horny tissue.

keratoid. Resembling horny tissue.

kermesine. Carmine red.

kernel. 1. The seed inside the stony endocarp of a drupe. 2. An old term for the nutritive tissue and asci inside a perithecium. 3. The matured body of an ovule. 4. The seed within the coat. 5. The centrum or nucleus.

ketones. A class of ethereal oils as camphor, organic chemical compounds.

ketose. A hexose sugar.

kettle trap. A flower such as *Aristolochia* which imprisons insects until pollination is effected.

kewensis. Of Kew (the Royal Botanical Gardens, Kew, England).

key. A dry, winged, indehiscent fruit.

key fruit. The samara or winged fruit of the ash, elm, maple, etc.

khor. A waste or stony desert.

kidney-shaped. Crescent with ends rounded.

kinase. A substance that incites enzymic activity, a substance that converts a zymogen into a enzyme.

kinesis. Karyokinesis, movement.

kinetic bodies. Small areas in a chromosome where the spindle fibers are attached. They appear to take an active part in chromosome movements during mitosis and meiosis. The kinetochores.

kinetic energy. The energy of actual motion as distinguished from potential energy.

kinetic elements. Special bodies and fibers in a cell which have to do with movement and with the transmission of stimuli to motile organs.

kinetochore. The portion of a chromosome where the attachment is made to a spindle fiber. It appears to influence chromosome movement in cell division. The centromere.

kinetomeres. Molecules of protoplasm which may be energy-rich and reactive or be energy-poor and stable; see ANAKINETOMERES, KATAKINETOMERES.

kinetosome. 1. One of a group of granules occupying the polar plate region in moss sporogenesis. 2. A small polar plate or body of kinoplasm present before mitosis presumably material for the formation of the spindle fibers.

kingdom. One of the highest divisions of living things, as the plant kingdom.

kinic. Of or pertaining to *Cinchona*, a source of quinine.

kinic acid. An organic acid found in *Cinchona* bark.

kinins. Plant hormones which effect the rate of cell division. They are abundant in young tissue and embryos.

kino. A resin-like substance soluble in water, astringent, and used medicinally and in tanning; a dark red or blackish tanniferous product similar to catechu obtained from various tropical trees.

kinoplasm. The protoplasm which appears to be composed of fibrils and which in cell division composes the spindle fibers, the attraction sphere, and the astral rays.

kinosphere. The astral system surrounding the central bodies in cell division.

kinospore. A spore resulting from a simple process of division.

kladodium. A cladode.

kleistogamous. Fertilized in closed flowers, cleistogamous.

Klimax-Gebiet. A climax complex.

klinogeotropic. Said of an organ which takes up a stable position lying at an angle to the vertical.

klinomorphy. The condition of an organ determined by the simultaneous oblique position of the principal and median planes so that the right and the left halves may be distinguished as upper and lower, resulting in a different shape of the two halves.

klinorrhombic. A mineralogic term applied to the oblique rhombic crystals in plants.

klinostat. A mechanical arrangement for slowly rotating a plant under experiment to study its reaction to gravity and other controlled stimuli, a clinostat.

klinotropic. Slanted or angled toward the direction of a stimulus.

klinotropism. Clinotropism.

knaur. A swollen outgrowth from the trunk of a tree, a growth on a tree trunk which will grow when removed as a cutting, a gnaur, nawr, or knur.

kneepan-shaped. Concave-convex; in the form of a watch crystal or shallow saucer, especially when thickened like a kneepan.

knees. 1. Growths from the roots of some swamp trees, as the bald cypress which rise above the water level to serve as organs of strength and for aeration. 2. Joints or articulations in some grass stems.

knephopelagile. The middle pelagic area of the ocean from the depth of 30 meters to the extreme limits of light.

Knight-Darwin law. The concept that nature abhors inbreeding: no organic being fertilizes itself for many generations.

knob. A root tuber in some orchids, a cephalodium.

knorria. Lepidodendroid stems when their cortex has been stripped off to a considerable but a variable depth.

knot. 1. A node or swollen joint in a grass stem. 2. A small particle of chromatin where meshes cross in nuclear meshwork. 3. A hard and often resinous inclusion in timber formed from the base of a branch which has been buried in secondary wood as the trunk developed.

knot, black. A disease caused by *Plowrightia morbosa*.

knot phase. A phase in nuclear division also known as the skein stage or the knot stage.

knur. See KNAUR.

kohlrabi. A kind of edible cabbage in which the stem becomes greatly enlarged, fleshy, and turnip-shaped.

koleochyma. Kritenchyma.

kollaplankton. Organisms which float encased in a gelatinous envelope.

Konspecies. Subspecies.

kopraphagous. Copraphagous.

koraianus. Of Korea, coreanus.

kormogene association. Colonies in which the different individuals remain morphologically attached to each other, an aggregation.

kormogene society. A homotypical society having the individuals composing it originally connected with each other.

Krautschicht. An herbaceous stratum.

Kreb's cycle. A complicated series of reactions which take place during cellular respiration. It involves the formation of citric acid and its breaking down to be used again by the plant. The citric acid cycle.

kremastoplankton. Floating organisms having appendages which aid in floating, as cilia, etc.

kremnophyte. A plant which grows against a steep wall.

kritenchyma. One or more layers of cells which form a sheath for a vascular bundle.

Krogh's law. A law which states that an increase in temperature results in a corresponding increase in the rate of a biological process.

Krummholz. Elfin wood, the stunted growth of trees in alpine regions; a type of forest characteristic of certain alpine regions of southern Europe in which the knee pine or the mountain pine is the predominating tree.

kryptoblast. A preventitious bud.

kryptocotyledons. Cryptocotyledons.

Kunchangraph. An apparatus to measure longitudinal contraction.

kutine. Cutin.

kyanophilous. Having tissues readily stained by a gentian blue dye.

kyanophyll. Nearly pure chlorophyll freed from its associated yellow pigment xanthophyll.

L

label. The pinnule or ultimate segment of a fern frond, a labellum.

labellate. Furnished with labella or small lips.

labelloid. Like a labellum.

labellum. 1. The posterior petal of an orchid flower which appears to be anterior due to twisting of the flower during development. 2. A similar petal in other flowers. 3. A lip.

labellum, pelory. 1. An abnormal petal, one which is usually irregular that is formed as a regular petal. 2. A symmetrical orchid flower.

labia. Lip-like structures.

labial. Pertaining to or resembling a lip.

labiate. 1. Having one part of the corolla or calyx overlap the other like a lip. 2. A plant which has labiate flowers, many of which belong to the mint family (*Labiatae*).

labiatiflorous. Having the corolla divided into two lip-like portions, having flowers with a bilabiate corolla.

labile. Plastic, easily modified, perishable, transient.

labioscopic. Said of certain orchids when the sepals are combined with an extension of the axis.

labiose. Said of a polypetalous corolla which appears two-lipped.

labium. The lower lip of a labiate flower.

laboulbenomycetes. The *Laboulbeniaceae* and their allies, ascomycetous fungi which are parasitic on insects.

labrosus. Large-lipped.

labrum. A lip or edge.

laburnifolious. Laburnum-leaved.

labyrinthiform. Like a labyrinth, with intricately winding lines or passages.

lac. A resinous excretion of scale insects on tropical plants which is widely used in commerce in the manufacture of shellac and other purposes.

laccase. An enzyme occurring in many plants which has the property of inducing the oxidation of certain polyatomic phenols, the enzyme which produces lacquer from fluid lac.

laccate. Appearing as if varnished.

laccatus. Milky.

laccine. A substance insoluble in water, alcohol, and ether, which occurs in lac.

lacertiform. Lizard-shaped.

lachrimiform. Tear-shaped.

lachrymose. Bearing tear-shaped appendages, as the gills in certain fungi.

lacinia. A segment of an incised leaf, a slender lobe.

laciniate. Cut into deep narrow segments or shreds, jagged, slashed, lacerated.

laciniation. Fission.

laciniform. Fringe-like.

lacinule. A diminutive lacina or lobe, the incurved point of the petal in many *Umbelliferae*.

lacrima. A drop of gum or resin exuded from a tree.

lacrimose. With tear-shaped appendages as in the gills of certain fungi, lacrimoid, lacrimiform.

lactalbumin. An albumin found in milk.

lacteal. Lactiferous.

lacteous. Milky.

lactescence. An abundant flow of sap, especially white or milky sap.

lacteous. White with a tinge of blue, milky white.

lactic. Pertaining to milk, the lactic bacilli, or to lactic acid found in sour milk.

lactic acid bacteria. Bacteria capable of transforming milk sugar and other sugars into lactic acid.

lacticolor. Milk-colored.

lactiferous. 1. Of trama, having a milky juice. 2. Producing or having latex. 3. Lacticiferous.

lactiferous cell. A cell or vessel which contains or conducts latex.

lactiferous duct. A duct containing a milky sap or latex.

lactiferous tissue. A tissue whose cells and ducts bear milk-like fluid.

lactiferous vessels. Special anastomosing tubes containing the latex in the plants which have milky juice, latex tubes.

lactific. Producing latex or milky juice.

lactiflorous. With milk-colored flowers.

lactiginous. Filled with milk or milky.

lactoflavum. A yellow pigment.

lactucarium. The condensed juice of the common lettuce, a mild hypnotic and antispasmodic which is sometimes used instead of opium.

lactucine. An active substance found in *Lactuca*, lettuce.

lacuna. 1. A depression on the surface of a plant or a cavity within a plant. 2. A cavity formed in the rapidly elongating stem by breaking down of the protoxylem. 3. A large intercellular air space.

lacunar. 1. Pertaining to, arising from, or having a lacuna. 2. In pilei, covered with pits or indentations.

lacunar tissue. Thin-walled cells which form regular crossbars radially transversing the intercellular cavity of the stem of *Selaginella*.

lacunorimose. Marked with irregular cracks or excavations.

lacunose. Perforated with small holes, having numerous cavities, pitted or furrowed.

lacunosorugose. Having deep furrows or pits, as some seeds and fruits, e.g., walnut seed and peach seed, lacunorugose.

lacuster. The central zone of a lake.

lacustrine. Living in or beside lakes or ponds, lacustral.

lacustrine peat. Peat formed under anaerobic conditions from decomposing vegetable material.

ladanifera. Bearing resinous juice (ladanum).

ladanum. A dark resin obtained from *Cistus*, a rockrose; labdanum.

ladder cells. A vessel marked with elongated transverse bordered pits, as in many ferns.

laeotropic. Inclined, turned, or coiled to the left.

laetevirens. Light or vivid green.

laeticolor. Bright colored.

laetiflorous. Bright or pleasingly flowered.

laeve. Smooth.

laevicaulis. Smooth-stemmed.

laevigate. See LEVIGATE.

laevipes. Smooth-footed, smooth-stalked.

laevulose. Levulose, fruit sugar.

lag period. The period needed to establish normal growth after inoculation of a culture medium.

lag phase. The initial phase in the growth curve of yeasts and bacteria.

lagenarius. Like a bottle or flask, from the generic name of the bottle gourd, *Lagenaria*.

lagenate. Flask-shaped.

lagenian. Of or pertaining to Leinster.

lageniform. Having the form of a Florence flask, gourd-shaped like *Lagenaria*.

lagenostome. The free apex of the nucellus in *Lagenostoma*.

lagging. The slow movement toward the poles of the spindle by one or more chromosomes in a dividing nucleus with the result that these chromosomes do not become incorporated into a daughter nucleus.

lagopous. Densely covered with long soft hairs, hare-footed.

lair flora. The flora growing on ground manured by animals.

lair herbage. Plants growing about the over-manured areas near alpine dairy huts.

lake. A purplish red pigment prepared from lac or cochineal by precipitating the red coloring matter with a metallic compound.

lalang. A type of savannah vegetation in eastern Asia.

Lamarckian doctrine. The theory that the effects of use and disuse of the organs of an individual are transmitted to its offspring and that the changes induced in an organism by its environment are inherited by its progeny, the theory of inheritance of acquired characters.

lamel. A thin plate, as one of the gills of a mushroom; a gill of an agaric; a lamella.

lamella, middle. 1. The membrane or primary septum between any two cells. 2. A thin plate, particularly the flat plate on the dorsal surface of many peristome teeth.

lamellate. Made up of lamellae or plates, having lamellae.

lamellose. Lamellate, composed of thin plates or scales, stratified.

lamellulae. The gills of fungi, a diminutive of lamellae.

lamiation. A stratal or layer society of an association.

lamies. A strata or layer society of an associes.

lamina. 1. A layer. 2. The blade or extended part of a leaf, the leafy portion or blade of the frond.

lamina proligera. Lamina sporigera.

lamina sporigera. The disk or center of the apothecium of a lichen.

laminar. Consisting of plates or thin layers, laminous.

laminarian. 1. Pertaining to algae of the genus Laminaria. 2. Designating that zone of the sea (from 4 to 15 meters in depth) in which seaweeds occur.

laminarietum. An association of the marine algal genus Laminaria, a large, tough, leathery seaweed having ribbon-like segments 50 feet long.

laminarioid. Resembling or akin to Laminaria.

laminaris. Leaf-like.

laminated bulb. A tunicated bulb; a bulb with broad, thin scales which form successive overlapping coats, as an onion.

lanate. Covered with fine, long hair or hairlike filaments; having a woolly surface.

lanceate. Somewhat lanceolate but wider at the base than at the middle.

lance-linear. Between lanceolate and linear in form.

lance-oblong. Oblong with tapering ends.

lanceolate. Resembling a lance, much longer than broad, widest in the middle and tapering to a pointed apex.

lanceolate-acuminate. Lance-shaped, narrow and tapering at each end.

lanceolate-hastate. Broad at the base and tapering to a pointed apex.

lanceolate-sagittate. With a pointed lanceolate tip and with an arrowshaped base.

lanceolate-subulate. Between lanceolate and awl-shaped.

lance-ovate. Between lanceolate and ovate, broader than lanceolate and narrower than ovate.

lance-ovoid. Egg-shaped, having a broad base and a tapering apex.

lancet-shaped. Short and bluntly lanceolate.

lancifolious. With lanceolate leaves.

landes. Tracts of ericamaquis in the south of France which lack raw humus.

languescent. Drooping, wilting, withering.

laniger. Wool-bearing.

lanipes. Woolly-footed, woolly-stalked.

lanose. Woolly, lanate.

lanthanin. An antipyretic substance obtained from species of Lantana, a large genus of verbenaceous shrubs.

lanuginose. Covered with down or fine short hair, woolly, cottony.

lanulose. Woolly.

lapideus. Stony, as the seeds of stone fruits.

lapidose. Growing among stones.

lappaceous. Prickly, bur-like, hamate.

lapponicus. Of Lapland.

larch. A tree of the genus Larix.

large secondary medullary rays. Medullary rays which reach from the pith to the cambium or from the pericycle to the cambium, interfascicular rays.

laricetum. An association of Larix.

laricifolious. Larch-leaved.

laricine. Of or pertaining to the larch.

laricophilous. Living under or near the larch.

larrea scrub. A scrub association of Larrea, creosote bush of deserts.

larval stage. 1. The resting stage, as in the sclerotium of ergot. 2. The early form of certain conifers in which the perfect and adult forms vary.

lasiacanthous. Pubescent-spined.

lasiandrous. With pubescent stamens.

lasianthus. Woolly-flowered.

lasio-. A prefix meaning woolly or hairy.

lasiocarpous. With pubescent fruit.

lasiodontus. Woolly-toothed.

lasioglossus. With a rough, hairy tongue.

lasiolepis. With woolly scales.

lasiopetalous. With rough, hairy petals.

lata-type. A mutant with one or more supernumerary chromosomes as compared with its parent (Oenothera lata).

latebrose. Hidden.

latent. Not visible or apparent until brought out in a hybrid generation by crossing, dormant but capable of development.

latent bud. An adventitious bud, a concealed bud which may develop when conditions become favorable.

latent development. The metabolic activity during quiescent stages, dormancy.

latent factors. Characters which are not expressed by a plant because the genes normally controlling the characters are recessive or in a hypostatic condition.

latent period. 1. The resting or dormant period. 2. The time between the incidence of a stimulus and the first signs of a response.

lateral. Situated or produced on the side or sides.

lateral area. A smooth place in a diatom valve sometimes parallel to the axis but nearer the margin.

lateral buds. 1. Buds on the side of a branch. 2. Buds borne in the axils of leaves or leaf scars. 3. Adventitious buds.

lateral chain theory. See SIDE-CHAIN THEORY.

lateral conjugation. The conjugation of adjacent cells in the filament, as in *Spirogyra*.

lateral dehiscence. Dehiscence along the side.

lateral frond. A frond attached on one side.

lateral geotropism. The lateral movement of plants climbing to a support showing neither positive nor negative geotropism.

lateral meristem. A meristem located on the side of a plant member.

lateral nucleolus. One of the additional or secondary nucleoli in a nucleus.

lateral plane. A vertical plane passing through a leaf, flower, or other organ at right angles to the median or antero-posterior plane.

lateral plantation. The erosion of a stream along the sides of its course, undercutting.

lateral view. The view of a diatom frustule when the valves are seen in front view, the girdle being seen in side view.

laterality. The excess of development on one side.

laterally compressed. 1. Flattened from the sides. 2. Having the lateral edges pressed toward each other.

latericious. Darker than brick red.

lateriflorous. With flowers on the side.

laterifolius. Growing on the side of a leaf at the base.

laterinerved. Having lateral veins or straight veins as in grasses.

lateripes. Having a lateral stalk.

lateristipulus. Having stipules growing on the sides.

laterite. A porous reddish clay of the tropics where rainfall reaches about fifty inches a year.

lateritious. Brick, red.

late wood. The denser, smaller-celled, later-formed tissues of a growth ring.

latex. The milky or colored juice of some plants, especially of the rubber tree.

latex duct. An elongated, branched, aseptate system of anastomosing hyphae containing latex found in some of the larger agarics.

latex granules. Starch or other granules floating in the latex.

latex hairs. The hairs continuous with latex tubes which break easily and liberate drops of latex.

latex sacs. Special cells containing latex.

latex tube. One of the special anastomosing tubes containing the latex.

latex vessels. Anastomosing vessels containing latex, latex cells.

latexosis. Abnormal secretion of latex caused by pathological conditions.

lati-. A prefix meaning broad.

laticiferous. Bearing or containing latex.

laticiferous cells. The peculiar thin-walled cells containing latex in certain families of seed plants.

laticiferous coenocytes. Branched cells or vessel-like cells containing latex.

laticiferous duct. A cavity into which latex is secreted.

laticifers. Laticiferous cells or vessels.

latiflorous. Broad-flowered.

latifoliate. Broad-leaved.

latifrons. Broad-fronded, broad-leaved.

latilabrus. Broad-lipped.

latilobus. Having broad lobes.

latimaculate. Broad-spotted.

latipes. Broad-footed, broad-stalked.

latiseptal. Having broad septa in their silicles, as some crucifers.

latiseptate. Having a broad septum or partition.

latispinous. With broad spines.

latisquamous. With broad scales.

latticed cell. A sieve tube.

lattices. Abortive and lateral sieve plates in angiosperms.

laurad. A plant of a drain or sewer.

laurifolious. Laurel-leaved.

laurifruticeta. Thickets with a preponderance of evergreens, thickets or scrub of laurel or other broadleaved evergreens.

laurilignosa. 1. Laurel vegetation. 2. Woods with a dominance of broad-leaved evergreens.

laurin. An acrid substance obtained from the

berries of *Laurus nobilis*, laurel or sweet bay.

laurinoxylon. Any fossil dicotyledonous wood resembling that of the genus *Laurus*.

laurion. An association of laurels.

laurisilvae. Laurel forests where the dominant trees are dicotyledons with glossy evergreen leaves and protected buds and conifers of the more mesophytic types:the knysna forests of South Africa, the temperate rain forests of Chile and New Zealand, the mesophytic coniferous forests of the western coast of the United States.

laurium. A drain or sewer formation.

laurophilous. Dwelling in sewers and drains.

laurophyta. Sewer plants.

lavandulaceus. Like lavender plants.

lavateroid. Like *Lavatera*, the tree mallows.

lavender. Pale purple or pale bluish gray.

laver, purple. *Porphyra*, a red alga gathered as food (one of the most valuable industries in Japan); nori.

lavigate. Smooth as if polished.

law of acceleration. A generalization that organs of greater importance develop more quickly than others.

law, natural. A description of a uniformity in the sequence of events the actual existence of which has been proven and accepted.

laxiflorous. With loosely arranged flowers.

laxifolious. With loosely attached leaves.

layer. 1. A soil-covered attached branch which takes root and gives rise to an independent plant. 2. The stroma or receptacle of fungi. 3. A stratum of vegetation, as the shrubs or the herbs in a woods.

layer, absciss. The layer of corky tissue found when a leaf is pulled from the branch.

layer, lignified. Of leaves, the lignified layer of tissue at the base of leaves before leaf fall.

layer, protective. A suberized layer of tissue which serves to protect the tissue beneath.

layer, separation. The absciss layer in leaf fall.

layer societies. Layers, as of stands of trees with bushes beneath and herbs at the bottom forming horizontal strata; societies in which there is a tendency of various species of smaller size than the dominant form to display their foliage at more or less definite levels.

layer transect. See BISECT.

layerage. The rooting of branches which are still a part of the parent, propagation by means of layers.

laying. A gardener's term for layering.

lazuline. Ultramarine blue.

leaching. The removal of mineral salts from soil by percolating water.

leader. The terminal branch or primary shoot of the tree trunk.

leaf. A foliage appendage from the stem of a plant, usually green, in which photosynthesis (food manufacture) and transpiration (loss of water vapor) takes place. Leaves are usually borne at the tip or nodes of the stem and are composed of a veined blade and a petiole or stalk. They vary in complexity, being either simple or compound in structure; and in shape and size.

leaf appendage. A small or miniature leaf-like structure occurring at the base of the leaf stalk.

leaf arrangement. The order of arrangement of leaves on a stem, phyllotaxis.

leaf axis. The rachis.

leaf base. The base of the leaf stalk where it joins the stem.

leaf blade. The lamina or expanded portion of a leaf.

leaf blister. A disease of pear leaves caused by *Taphrina bullota*.

leaf blotch. The black patches on maple leaves caused by *Rhytisma acerinum*.

leaf, branch. A branch leaf, as in *Sphagnum*.

leaf bud. An embryonic shoot which bears the undeveloped vegetative leaves only.

leaf cast. Pine leaves diseased by *Lophodermium pinastri*.

leaf climber. A climbing plant which supports itself by means of leaves and/or leaf modifications.

leaf, compound. A divided leaf composed of distinct parts called leaflets.

leaf curl. A very common disease of peach leaves caused by *Exoasus deformans*.

leaf cushion. 1. In conifers, the basal part of the leaf which is decurrent on the stem. 2. A raised base on which leaf scars frequently occur. 3. A swollen leaf base.

leaf cycle. In phyllotaxis, a spiral which passes through the insertions of intermediate leaves until the next leaf is exactly above its starting point.

leaf divergence. The angle at the intersection

of the planes passing longitudinally through the middles of two successive leaves.

leaf fall. Defoliation, the result of plants dropping leaves for any cause.

leaf fixed position. A more or less horizontal position.

leaf gap. An interruption of the vascular tissue of a stem brought about by the insertion of a leaf on the stem, a foliar gap.

leaf green. Chlorophyll.

leaf incept. The earliest recognizable rudiment of a leaf.

leaf mosaic. The arrangement of leaves on a plant stem in such a way that as much leaf surface as possible is exposed to light and as little as possible is shaded by other leaves.

leaf pores. The stomata.

leaf primordium. Meristematic tissue that develops into a leaf.

leaf scar. The scar left on the twig at the point where a leaf has fallen. It is usually covered with a thin layer of corky tissue, periderm.

leaf, simple. A leaf with a blade in one piece and not divided into leaflets.

leaf scorch. A fungus attack on leaves causing them to appear scorched.

leaf sheath. The base of the leaf which surrounds the stem.

leaf-size classes. More or less natural leaf-size classes bearing a geometrical relationship: leptophyll, nanophyll, microphyll, mesophyll, macrophyll, megaphyll (according to Raunkiaer).

leaf skin theory. The theory that the superficial layers of the shoot are formed by the downward growth of leaf rudiments.

leaf spine. A spine developed from a leaf instead of a branch.

leaf spot. Any disease of plants in which discolored spots appear upon leaves, due to certain species of parasitic fungi.

leaf stalk. The petiole.

leaf tendril. A tendril which is a modified or transformed leaf.

leaf trace. The group of fibrovascular bundles which connect the veins of a leaf with the fibrovascular system of the stem.

leafing. The unfolding of leaves.

leafit. A leaflet.

leaflet. One of the component parts of a compound leaf blade.

leafy raceme. A raceme in which the bracts differ little or not all from ordinary foliage leaves.

leather yellow. Tan, alutaceous.

leaves, mantle or pocket. Specialized leaves which accumulate humus, as bird's nest fern.

Lebensgemeinschaft. A biotic community.

lecanorine. Resembling the apothecium of the lichen genus *Lecanora*, which has a paler margin arising from a thallus.

leceideiform. With a margin of the same color as the disc, like the apothecium of *Lecidea*.

leceideine. Having an apothecium which is usually dark-colored or carbonaceous and without a thalline margin.

lecideoid. Resembling the apothecial structure of *Lecidea*.

lecithalbumin. A substance consisting of albumin and lecithin.

lecithin. An important component of protoplasm; a white, waxy, phosphorous-containing substance found in seeds and animal tissues, particularly membranes; lipsin.

lecostachys. White-spiked.

lecotropal. Shaped like a horseshoe.

lectotype. A specimen of the original series upon which a revised description of the species is based.

lecus. A corm.

ledifolious. Having leaves like *Ledum*, Labrador tea.

leek. An onion-like plant grown in vegetable gardens for seasoning (*Allium porrum*).

leek green. Vivid green.

legitimate fertilization. Fertilization in the usual or natural manner by its own kind of pollen.

legume. 1. A fruit formed from a single carpel opening by two sutures. 2. A plant of the family *Leguminosae*. 3. A legumen.

legumin. A proteid found in the seeds of *Leguminosae*.

leguminous. 1. Bearing legumes. 2. Having the characteristic of legumes.

leianthous. With smooth flowers.

Leibig's law. A statement that when a number of factors is present and only one is near the limits of toleration, this factor will be the controlling one.

leimocolous. Inhabiting moist grassland or meadows.

leimonapophyte. A plant introduced into grasslands.

leio-. A prefix meaning smooth.

leiocarpous. With smooth fruit.

leiodermarian. Having external markings resembling the skin disease leiodermia, characterized by abnormal glossiness and atrophy.

leiogynous. Having smooth pistils.

leiophyllous. With smooth leaves.

leiosporous. Having smooth spores.

leiotropic. With leftward spiral cleavages, laeotropic.

lemma. The lower of two chaffy bracts or scales enclosing the flower in grasses, the flowering glume or palea of grasses.

lemma, sterile. The third glume.

lemnetum. An association of duckweed, *Lemna*, the smallest seedplant.

Lemurian realm. The islands of Madagascar.

lendiger. Having an inflorescence resembling insects.

lenetic. Living in still waters.

lens cells. Cells of the integuments which are capable of focusing light and other rays.

lens, condensing. Epidermal papillae causing photosynthetic activity.

lens-shaped. Doubly convex, lentil-shaped, lenticular.

lenticel. A small breathing pore in the bark of trees and shrubs, a corky aerating organ which permits gaseous diffusion between the plant and the atmosphere.

lenticellatus. Having lenticels.

lenticule. A lenticel or a spore case in fungi.

lenticular. Lens-shaped or resembling a lentil, orbicular and convex on both faces.

lentiform. Doubly convex, lens-shaped.

lentiginose. Freckled.

lentil. The lens-shaped fruit or seed of one of the legumes.

lentiscifolious. With leaves like *Lentiscus* or *Pistacia*, the pistachio tree.

lento-capillary point. The point just above the wilting coefficient at which the flow of water toward root hairs is impeded because of surface tension resistance.

lenzitoid. Like the agaric *Lenzites*.

leocarpine. Of fruit bodies, usually myxomycetes, like *Leocarpus*.

leochromous. Tawny, leonine, fulvus.

leontoglossus. Lion-tongued, lion-throated.

leopardinus. Spotted like a leopard.

lepal. 1. A nectary which originates in a barren transformed stamen. 2. A sterile stamen.

lepalum. A stamen which is transformed into a scale or a nectary.

lepanthium. An apetaloid nectary.

lepicena. The glume in grasses.

lepides. Epidermal scales attached at their centers.

lepidium. The ovuliferous lamina in the *Coniferae*.

lepidodendroid. Pertaining to or resembling the fossil genus *Lepidodendron* or its allies.

lepidoid. Scaly.

lepidophyllous. Lepidoid, with scaly leaves.

lepidophyte. Any Paleozoic fern or fern ally, a fossil fern.

lepidopterid. Having flowers which are adapted for pollination by moths or butterflies.

lepidopterophilae. Flowers adapted for pollination by lepidopterous insects.

lepidospermae. Lycopods which bear seeds.

lepidostroboid. Of or pertaining to the fossil genus *Lepidostrobus* in form or marking.

lepidote. Covered with small scurfy scales, having a scale-like structure as that on the shoots of *Tillandsia*, Spanish moss.

lepis. A scale.

lepisma. A membranous scale in some *Ranunculaceae*, as an aborted stamen in *Peonia* which encloses the ovary.

leporinus. Of a hare.

lepra. A white mealy matter extruded from the surface of some plants.

leprarioid. 1. Resembling the genus *Lepraria*, a lichen. 2. Having a whitish scurfy surface.

lepta-, lepto-. A prefix meaning small, thin, slender.

leptanthous. Thin-flowered.

leptocaulis. Thin-stemmed, thin-branched.

leptocentric vascular bundle. A concentric vascular bundle in which a central strand of phloem is surrounded by xylem.

leptochloa. A slender grass.

leptocladous. Slender-branched, thin-stemmed, liptoclemous.

leptodermatous. Thin-coated, said of moss capsules when pliable; leptodermous.

leptoform. Applied to *Uredinales* having only microteliospores which germinate as soon as they are mature.

leptogioid. Like the lichen genus *Leptogium*.

leptogonidium. A microgonidium.

leptoids. Groups of six to eight polygonal cells resembling sieve tubes found in the leptome of some mosses.

leptolepsis. Thin-scaled.

leptoma. A thin region of exine at the distal

pole of a pollen grain which usually functions as the point of emergence of the pollen tube.

leptome. The conducting tissue of the phloem, the food-conducting cells of the fibrovascular bundle, the haplomestome.

leptome mantle strand. A modification of the leptome cylinder, a fusion of several leptoids into a single layer.

leptomestome. The phloem-like portion of the vascular bundles in vascular plants.

leptomiasis. A flagellate disease attacking *Euphorbiaceae*.

leptomin. A substance found in the leptome of some plants, especially in the sieve tubes and laticiferous vessels.

leptonema. The delicate thread formed during the transition from a reticulum to a spireme in synapsis, the leptotene stage in meiosis.

leptonization. The reduction of the nucleus into a finely filamentous condition from reticulum to spireme.

leptopetalous. Thin-petaled.

leptophloem. The rudimentary bast tissue or phloem used for storage or conduction of food materials.

leptophyll. The smallest leaf classified by Raunkiaer.

leptophyllous. Having small, slender leaves.

leptopuccinia. A group of the genus *Puccinia* which produces only teleutospores.

leptopous. With thin or slender stalks.

leptosepalous. With thin sepals.

leptosome. Tall and slender, the opposite of eurysome.

leptosporangiate. Having sporangia which arise from single cells of the epidermis.

leptosporangium. A sporangium derived from one superficial cell, as in the true ferns.

leptostachyous. With thin spikes.

leptotene stage. The earlier part of the prophase of meiotic division in which the chromatin forms threads before uniting in synapsis.

leptotichous. Composed of thin-walled tissue.

leptoxylem. 1. Rudimentary wood tissue. 2. The water-conducting tissue of the sporophyte of mosses.

leptozygonema. The transition of the meiotic nucleus between the leptonene and zygo- tene stages by parallel fusion of thin threads.

leptozygotene. A transition stage between the delicate single threads or the leptonema of the nucleus and their paired arrangement in the zygonema.

lepturpid. Like *Lepturis*, a grass.

lepyrophylly. The arrest of the testa in the leaf stage.

leskeoid. Resembling the moss genus *Leskea*.

lethal coefficient. The lowest or highest temperatures which are fatal to the vital functions of a given organism.

lethal factor. A factor or gene that brings about the early death of a gamete or zygote.

lethal gene. A gene which renders an organism inviable when it is present.

lettered. Having spots resembling letters.

lettuce. Varieties of *Lactuca* used as a salad vegetable.

leu-. A prefix meaning white.

leucanthemifolious. *Leucanthemum*-leaved.

leucanthous. With white flowers.

leucine. 1. A white nitrogenous substance found as a constituent of various tissues and organs. 2. Any of a series of amino acids formed in the decomposition of proteids. 3. Leucin or leuceine.

leucite. A colorless plastic, a leucoplast.

leucobotrys. White clusters.

leucocarpous. With white fruit.

leucocaulis. With white stems.

leucocephalous. With white heads.

leucochilous. With white lips.

leucocyan. A white pigment found in certain algae.

leucodermis. With white skin.

leuconervious. With white nerves.

leucophaeus. Dusky white.

leucophyllgrain. A leucoplast.

leucophyllous. Having white leaves.

leucoplasts. Colorless plastids, leucoplastids, protoplasmic bodies, or granules found in the interior of a plant (roots, stems, etc.) around which starch accumulates. Leucoplasts often develop into chloroplasts when exposed to light.

leucorhizous. With white roots.

leucosin. A substance in algae of unknown composition resulting from photosynthesis which appears as glistening granules in the cells.

leucosomes. Small spherical bodies apparently composed of albuminoids enclosed in the leucoplasts of *Commelinaceae*, subtropical monocots.

leucosporous. Having white spores.

leucotriche. With white hair.

leucoxanthous. Whitish yellow.

leucoxylon. With white wood.

leukoplasts. Leucoplasts.

levigate. Having a smooth polished surface, laevigate, laevis.

levulose. Fruit sugar, fructose.

ley. Planted pasture land which is plowed up for other uses after a short period.

liana. The luxuriant woody climbers in the tropics which become entangled in other plants.

lianoid. Like a liana.

libanoticus. Of Libania.

liber. The inner bark of exogenous stems having no cohesion with the adjoining parts, bast fibers.

liberoligneous. Having a conjoint bundle composed of bast and wood elements.

libriform. Having wood fibers, having the form or resembling liber or bast.

libriform fiber. An elongated thick-walled part of the xylem formed from a single cell.

libriform wood fiber. An elongated, commonly thick-walled cell with simple pits.

libroplasts. Elaeoplasts which are free on the median line of diatoms.

liburnicus. Of Liburnia (west of the Adriatic Sea).

lichen. A cryptogam composed of an alga and a fungus in intimate association, usually an ascomycete but rarely a basidiomycete.

lichen acids. Organic acids peculiar to lichens.

lichen algae. The algal cells or green bodies in the lichen thallus.

lichen fungi. The hyphae which are usually interwoven with the algal gonidia in lichens.

lichen starch. Lichenin.

lichen tundra. The flat or gently undulating northern land upon which lichens are the predominant plants.

lichenicolous. Dwelling in or on a lichen.

lichenin. A gelatinous carbohydrate isomeric with starch which is extracted from several species of mosses and lichens.

lichenism. The symbiotic relationship between certain algae and fungi which results in lichens.

lichenography. The study of lichens.

lichenoid. Resembling lichens, lichen-like.

lichenology. The study of lichens.

lichenose. Pertaining to or resembling lichens.

lichnoerythrine. The red coloring matter in lichens.

lichnoxanthine. The yellow coloring matter in lichens.

Licopoli glands. Chalk glands.

lid. 1. The operculum or the transversely dehiscent top or cap on the moss capsule. 2. The calyx which falls from the flower in a single piece.

lid cells. The terminal cells of the neck of the archegonium which temporarily close the canal.

life cycle. The various stages through which an organism passes from fertilized ovum to fertilized ovum of the next generation.

life form. The characteristic form and structure by which a plant is adapted to cope with various conditions of the environment, as size, habit of growth, etc., e.g., single cells, trees, herbs, grass, etc.

life form dominance. The condition in which no one species (or a small number of species) exerts strict dominance, but collectively several species all of the same life form dominate a plant community.

life history. The life cycle, the sum of events in the life of a plant.

life zones. The names applied by Merriman to certain types of vegetation found in the various ecological areas of the earth.

ligamentum. A raphe, a suture.

ligases. Enzymes which catalyze organic substances.

light absorption. The ratio of the whole of daylight to that of the place in which a plant grows.

light-absorption traps. Lens cells.

light requirement, relative. The relation of the light intensity of the habitat to full sunshine measured at the same time.

light seed. A seed which requires exposure to light in order to germinate.

lign-aloes. The wood of *Aquilaria Agallocha*, rich in resin and used in India and Burma for perfumes and medicines.

lignatile. 1. Growing on wood. 2. Woody.

lignescent. Developing woody tissue.

lignicole. Living on timber, growing on or in wood.

lignicolor. Tawny, the color of fresh cut wood.

ligniferous. Having branches which form wood but no flowers.

lignification. The hardening or thickening of the cell wall by secondary deposits, the formation of wood.

lignified layer. The layer of cells immediately above the separation layer in leaf fall.

lignin. The substance which is deposited in cell walls to produce woody tissue, a secondary deposit which forms the greater part of the bulk of ordinary wood, lignine.

ligninase. A wood-destroying enzyme, hadromal, hadromase.

lignireose. A constituent of lignin which is only slightly soluble in water.

lignivorous. Eating wood.

lignocellulose. 1. An essential constituent of woody tissue, lignin and cellulose combined. 2. Several closely related substances constituting the essential part of woody tissue.

lignone. A substance which differs from lignin by being insoluble in water, alcohol, and ether but soluble in ammonia, potash, and soda.

lignosa. Woody vegetation.

lignose. Woody, ligneous.

ligno-suberization. The disappearance of protoplasm from the cells surrounding the leaf scar after the fall of the leaf and the subsequent lignification and suberization of the scar tissue.

lignosum. A type of vegetation in which there are several layers conditioned by the dominant trees or shrubs.

lignous. Woody.

lignum. Woody tissue, wood within the cortex.

ligular. Of or pertaining to a ligule.

ligulate. 1. Having a ligule. 2. Strap-shaped, flat and linear, ribbon-shaped.

ligulate florets. The marginal flowers of a head in *Compositae* bearing a ligulate or strap-shaped corolla.

ligule. 1. A strap-shaped corolla bract of the ray flowers in composites. 2. A membranaceous appendage at the tip of the leaf of most grasses. 3. An elongated triangular stipule-like organ situated above the sporangium on the leaf of *Isoetes*. 4. An envelope which protects the young leaf in palms.

liguliflorae. Flowers having only ligulate corollas.

liguliform. 1. Strap-shaped. 2. Having a ligule.

ligustcifolious. Having leaves like *Ligusticum*, herbs of the temperate region.

ligusticus. Of Liguria, a province in Italy (Genoa).

ligustrifolious. Privet-leaved.

ligustrinus. Like *Ligustrum*, privet.

lilac. Pale warm purple.

lilaceous. Of or like the color of the purplish lilac.

lilacine. A bitter substance from the bark of the lilac.

lilacinus. Lilac, lilac-colored.

liliaceous. 1. Belonging to the *Liliaceae*. 2. Resembling the lily.

limaciform. Shaped like a slug or shell-less snail.

limax-shaped. Shaped like a slug.

limb. 1. The expanded part of a petal, sepal, or sympetalous flower. 2. The expanded portion of a gamopetalous perianth. 3. A large primary branch or bough of a tree. 4. An expanded part or blade of a leaf.

limbate. Bordered or margined with color, surrounded by an edging of another color.

limbus. A border, a blade, a limb.

lime. 1. Calcium carbonate. 2. A citrus fruit with globose greenish fruits which is quite acid.

lime cell. A hard shell around the oospore due to a secretion of lime in the spirals of the oogonium in *Chara*.

lime chlorosis. The yellowing of the leaves of a plant due to chlorophyll deficiency caused by excess calcium carbonate in the soil.

lime knot, lime granule. A widening in the threads of the capillitium of myxomycetes containing calcium carbonate.

lime scales. The chalk glands which excrete lime, as in certain saxifrages.

limequat. A small citrus fruit, a hybrid between a lime and a kumquat.

limes communis. The column or neck of a plant.

limicolous. Living in mud, growing in mud as on the margins of pools.

limit of trees. The area beyond which trees are unable to survive due to cold and other factors caused by elevation or latitude.

limitate. Limited or bounded by a distinct line of hypothallus in lichens.

limiting cell. A heterocyst, an intercalated cell.

limiting factor. The growth factor which determines the rate or extent of growth.

limiting lamella. See CLOSING MEMBRANE.

limnad. A lake plant.

limnaea. Aquatic plants with a loose substratum of soil.

limnaen. An association formed by submerged plants.

limnetic. Living in or close to marshes or fresh-water lakes.

limnicolous. Growing in lakes.

limnium. A lake formation or community.

limnobion. An organic association occurring in fresh water.

limnocryptophyte. A marsh plant with surviving buds buried below the surface, a halophyte.

limnodad. A plant of a salt marsh.

limnodium. A salt-marsh community.

limnodophilous. Marsh-loving.

limnodophyta. Pond or marsh plants, limnophyta.

limnology. The scientific study of fresh waters, especially ponds and lakes, dealing with all chemical, physical, meteorological, or biological aspects.

limnonereid. A fresh-water algal subformation.

limnophilous. Living in fresh-water marshes, pond-loving.

limnoplankton. The floating animal and plant life living in fresh-water ponds and marshes.

limo-. The blade of a petal or leaf.

limoniform. Lemon-shaped.

limonile. Far beneath the surface of the ground.

limonious. Lemon or citrine color.

limosequisetum. An association of *Equisetum limosum*.

limosphere. A hollow sphere enclosing a vacuole in the spermatid of a bryophyte.

limosus. Of muddy or marshy places.

linamarin. A glucoside found in linseed or flax, *Linum*; phaseolunatin.

linariifolious. With leaves like *Linaria*, toad flax.

linase. An enzyme in flax.

linden. A tree of the genus *Tilia*.

Lindleyan. Of or pertaining to John Lindley, the English botanist, or his system of plant classification.

lindsayoid. Like *Lindsaya*, tropical ferns.

line breeding. Mating selected members of successive generations among themselves to fix desired characteristics.

line survey. A record of plants occurring along a line taken across a designated area.

line transect. A chart showing the position and names of all the plants occurring on a line drawn across an area.

linear-ensate. Between linear and ensiform in shape, long, sword-shaped.

linear-filiform. Cylindrical with margins parallel and many times longer than broad.

linear-lanceolate. Narrowly lanceolate.

linear-oblong. Between linear and oblong in shape.

linear-tape. Thread-like.

linear tetrad. The row of four megaspores usually found in flowering plants.

linearifolious. Linear-leaved.

linearilobous. Linear-lobed.

lineate. Marked with lines.

lineatipes. Having a lined or striated foot stalk.

lineolate. Marked with fine lines or striae.

lines of growth. The limits of each year's growth in woody stems.

lines of vegetation. Lines plotted on a map which join the limits of the distribution of a species.

ling. *Calluna vulgaris*, the ling heath or heather.

linguiform. Tongue-shaped.

lingulate. Tongue-shaped; shorter, broader, fleshier, and with a more blunt apex than ligulate.

liniflorous. With flowers like *Linus*, flax.

linin. The nonstaining material of the reticulum of the nucleus along which the chromatin granules are formed and which holds them in formation, linine.

linkage. 1. The physical segregation of genes on a chromosome resulting in their frequent association in inheritance of characters. 2. The tendency of genetical characteristics to be inherited together.

linkage groups. Series of linked pairs of genes on the same chromosomes.

linkage map. A diagram showing the related positions of known genes in the chromosomes of a species, a chromosome map.

Linnaean species. A wide concept of a species in which many varieties are included.

Linnaean system. The system of classification devised by Linnaeus, a system founded on the number and arrangement of stamens and pistils.

linnaeoid. Like the genus *Linnaea*, the abelias.

linnaeon. The group usually designated as species, perhaps in the Linnaean sense, a linneon.

linoid. Flax-like.

linolein. The glyceride of lineoleic acid found in linseed oil.

linom. Linin.

linophyllous. Flax-leaved.

linosporous. Linear-spored.

liorhizae. A name for monocotyledons and *Nymphaeaceae*, the root hairs being of exodermic origin.

lip. A large projecting lobe of a bilabiate calyx or corolla, the labellum in orchids, a labium.

lip cell. One of the narrow lignified cells of a fern sporangium at the point where dehiscence takes place.

lipalian era. An era of marine deposit when pelagic life was adapted to littoral conditions, the time of the appearance of the species of the Lower Cambrian Period.

lipase. The enzyme which splits fats.

lipaseidin. The fat-splitting enzyme of the cytoplasm in castor bean seeds.

lipids, lipides. Lipins. Fatty acids in combination, divisible into (a) crebrosides, with nitrogen and sugar, and (b) phosphatides, with phosphorus and nitrogen. Lecithin is one of the three known lipins.

lipochondria. Golgi apparatus.

lipochrome. A yellow pigment of certain flowers.

lipocyanin. The blue pigment found in some plants.

lipogenous. Producing or tending to produce fat.

lipoids. A series of fatty bodies found in plants in association with protoplasm, e.g., cytolipoid, tropholipoid, etc.

lipolytic. Dissolving fats, as lipase.

lipoplast. A fatty globule.

lipoprotein. Compounds found in membranes composed of protein and fats.

liposome. A fatty or oily globule in cytoplasm.

lipoxenous. Abandoning its host, said of a parasite which develops independently at the expense of reserve food provided from its host.

lipoxeny. The desertion of a host and living independently on food appropriated from the host.

liquefaction. The conversion of a solid or semisolid into a liquid.

lirella. A linear sessile apothecium in some lichens which has a ridge in the middle.

lirellate. Like a lirella or furrow.

liriogamae. Monocotyledons with a perianth which is never glumaceous.

lisigenetic. Lysigenic.

lissoflagellate. Without a collar around the base of the flagellum.

list-quadrat. An enumeration of the plants found in a designated square space or quadrat.

litharch. A succession or adsere on hard rock.

lithic. Of or on rocks.

lithobiblion. A lithophyl, a fossil leaf.

lithocarp. A fossil fruit.

lithocyst. A cell with crystals, a cystolith.

lithodomous. Living in rocks.

lithophilous. Growing on rocks, using stones as a shelter, lithophytic.

lithophilous formation. A formation of aquatic plants fixed to stones or rocks, as the marine algae.

lithophilous benthos. The algae attached to the harbor bottom.

lithophyll. A fossil leaf or leaf impression.

lithophyte. A plant growing on rocky ground.

lithophytic. Lithophilous.

lithosere. A rocky adsere, a sere having its origin on rock.

lithospermous. Having hard stony seeds.

lithoxyle. Fossil wood.

litmus. 1. A violet-colored dye derived from several species of lichens. 2. A reagent by that name which turns red in acids and blue in alkali.

litoral. Littoral.

litorideserta. 1. Seashore deserts. 2. Open stands of halophytes.

litter. The upper and only slightly decomposed portion of the forest floor under which lies the humus.

littoral. 1. Growing near the seashore, growing between the tide marks. 2. The seashore.

littoral belts. Subdivisions of the littoral area: sublittoral, -6 to $+2$ feet; lower littoral, 2 to 7 feet; upper littoral, 7 to 14 feet from the tide marks.

littoral zone. The part of the seashore inhabited by plants which is below the average lowtide level.

littorelletum. An association of *Littorella*, a shore weed.

lituate. Forked with points turned slightly outward.

lituiflorous. Trumpet-flowered.

liturate. With spots formed by an abrasion of the surface.

litus. A strand community, a sandy seashore or beach.

liverworts. 1. Usually small plants, the *Hepaticae*, which possess flattened branching thalli or have bilaterally arranged leaves one layer thick without a midrib. 2. A flowering plant with liver-shaped leaves (*Hepatica*).

livetype. A biotype.

llano. An extensive short-grass plains area with few trees, often wet at one season and very dry in others, which produces a xerophytic aspect; the savannah of Venezuela.

llano estacado. The semi-arid short-grass plains of western Texas in the United States.

loam. A noncoherent mixture of sand, clay, and organic matter.

lobate. Having lobes.

lobe. A rounded division of a plant organ, such as a deeply cut part of a leaf, petal, stigma, etc.

lobe, middle. A small conical or tongue-shaped growth arising from between the two side-lobes of a fern prothallus.

lobelioid. Like *Lobelia*, a genus of herbs and shrubs.

lobing. The division of the blade of a leaf or of a flat thallus, when the separation does not extend much more than halfway in but is deeper than is necessary to cut out teeth.

lobiolus. One of the small lobes into which some lichen thalli are divided.

lobocarpous. Having lobed fruit.

lobophyllous. With lobed leaves.

lobular. Like a lobule or a small lobe.

lobulate. Divided into small and shallow lobes.

lobule. 1. A small lobe. 2. A secondary division of a doubly pinnatifid frond.

locality. 1. The ground occupied by a single community. 2. An approximate geographical position of an individual specimen or an individual association.

localization. The genetic property of restriction of chiasmata to one part of the paired chromosomes, proximal or distal.

localization of sensation. The identification on the surface of a body of the exact spot affected.

locellate. Divided into small compartments, chambered.

locellus. 1. A little cavity. 2. One of the compartments of an ovary or of a pollen sac.

lochmad. A thicket plant.

lochmium. A thicket community.

lochmocolous. Dwelling in thickets.

lochmodium. A dry thicket community.

lochmodophilous. Dwelling in dry thickets, lochmophilous.

lochmodophyta. Dry thicket plants, lochmophytes.

lociation. A local variation in the important subdominant species of an association.

locies. A variation in the important subdominant species of an association as it progresses in its development.

lock. A locule or cavity in plant ovaries.

locoform. A form which differs from its nearest allies because of peculiarities of the climate or soil.

locoweeds. Leguminose weeds that poison stock.

loculament. The loculus of a carpel, the partition or cell of a seed vessel.

locular. Relating to locules in leaves, ovaries, etc.; having chambers or hollows.

loculate. Having locules.

locule. A cell or cavity, a compartment or cell of a pistil or anther.

loculicidal. Of dehiscence, splitting down the back between the divisions; splitting down through the middle of the back of each cell; splitting along the midrib of the carpel of a fruit.

loculiferous. Containing hollows or locules.

loculiform. Chamber-like, loculoid.

loculose. Cellular, divided, partitioned, locular, loculous.

loculus. 1. The cavity of the ovary or anther. 2. One portion of a septate spore. 3. One compartment in a synangium.

locus. 1. The position of a gene on a chromosome in a linkage group or on a chromosome map. 2. The hilum of a starch grain.

locus change. A change in position of a chromosome that appears first in the heterozygous condition. It is restricted to one pair of chromosomes without affecting its allelomorphic mate.

locusta. The spikelet in grasses.

lodger arrangements. Arrangements in flowers which detain insect visitors.

lodicule. One of the small scales present below the stamens in the flowers of grasses which become distended with water and assist in the separation of the glumes.

Loeb effect. The action of an inhibitor (probably a single active substance) in an early bud before later growth.

loess. A wind-blown deposit of very fine loam which forms extensive deposits.

loganberry. A hybrid between the raspberry and blackberry.

logarithmic phase. The second stage in the growth of the yeast plant and other microorganisms.

logotype. A type determined historically from two or more original species.

logwood (Campeachy). *Haematoxylum campechianum*, the heartwood of a Central American leguminous tree which is used for dye.

loiseleurietum. An association of *Loiseleuria procumbens*, an alpine azalea.

loliaceous. Like *Lolium*, rye grasses.

loliophyll. Chlorophyll from *Lolium* and other grasses.

loma. 1. A thin membranous flap forming a fringe around an opening. 2. A grasslike steppe in Peru in which the growing season is the moist winter season.

lomarioid. Resembling a fern genus *Lomaria*.

lomastome. Having the margin of the lip recurved.

loment. An indehiscent segmented pod, a legume which is constricted and usually separates into one-seeded articulations, a lomentum.

lomentaceous. Resembling or having loments.

lomentaceous legume or pod. A loment.

long day plant. A plant which needs alternating periods of comparatively prolonged periods of light and relatively reduced darkness for the proper development of flowers and fruit.

long moss. *Tillandsia*, Spanish moss or old man's beard.

long styled. With styles longer than the stamens.

longebracteatus. With long bracts.

longepedunculatus. With long peduncles.

longicaudatus. With a long tail.

longicaulis. With a long stem.

longicollous. With a long beak.

longicomus. With long hair.

longicuspis. With long points.

longiflorous. Having long flowers.

longifolious. With long leaves.

longihamatous. With long hooks.

longilaminatus. With long laminae or plates.

longilobous. With long lobes.

longimucronatus. Having a long, sharp, terminal point.

longipedunculatum. Having a long peduncle or stalk.

longipes. With a long foot or stalk.

longipesplankton. A summer association of the alga *Ceratium longipes* found in the north.

longipetalous. With long petals.

longipinnatus. With long pinnate leaves or with long pinnae.

longiracemose. With long racemes.

longirostris. With a long beak.

longiscapous. With a long scape.

longisepalous. With long sepals.

longispathous. With a long spathe.

longispinous. With long spines.

longistamineae. Flowers which are wind-fertilized and have long stamens.

longistylous. With long styles.

longitrorse. Longitudinally, parallel with the axis.

longitudinal. Lengthwise, parallel with the axis from the base toward the summit or apex.

longitudinal system. A fibrovascular system.

longitude. Extension in the direction of growth.

looped mother skein. The stage in karyokinesis in which the spireme is arranged in definite loops just before it breaks into pieces.

loose daughter skein. The stage in karyokinesis in which the separate daughter chromosomes are beginning to unite after the daughter star.

loose smut. A smut disease of cereals caused by *Ustilago*.

lophad. A hill plant.

lophanthous. With flowers resembling a crest.

lophiostomate. Having crested apertures or openings like the fungus *Lophiostoma*.

lophium. A hill-crest community.

lophophilous. Dwelling on hills.

lophophyta. Hill plants.

lophospore. A plant having a plumose disseminule.

lophotrichous. Having a tuft of flagella at one end of the cell.

lophus. A crest.

lopped. Truncate.

loranthaceous. Akin to, or resembling the *Loranthaceae*, a family of chiefly tropical shrubs in the mistletoe family.

lorate. Strap-shaped, ligulate, linear, thong-shaped.

lords and ladies. *Arum maculatum*, a calla lily.

lorica. 1. A hard, protective case or shell, as the entire silicious covering of the frustule in diatoms. 2. A testa or seed covering.

lorifolious. With strap-shaped leaves.

lorulum. The filamentous and branched thallus of some lichens.

lotase. An enzyme from *Lotus arabicus*.

lotic. Growing in rapidly flowing streams or currents.

lotifolious. With leaves like *Lotus*.

lotoflavin. A yellow coloring matter found in *Lotus*.

lotusin. A yellow crystalline glucoside from *Lotus*.

lough. A lake or pool.

Louisianian zone. The Sonoran zone exclusive of the Gulf strip.

Louisianus. Of Louisiana.

low moor. A swampy formation in which peat develops.

low yeast. The yeast at the bottom of a fermenting liquid.

lower. Recessive.

lower beach. The area which lies between low tide and mean high tide and is twice daily exposed to air and submergence.

lowered. Having the lip of a bilabiate corolla inclined at about a right angle to the tube.

lows. The narrow valley between the dune ridges, the slacks between the west coast dunes of Britain.

lucenus. With a shining surface.

luciferase. An oxidizing enzyme which acts on luciferin to cause luminosity.

luciferin. The substance oxidized by luciferase, causing luminosity.

lucifuge. A form which does not inhabit light areas, a deep-water form avoiding or turning away from light, a photophobe.

lucifugous. Shunning light, living in deep waters or deep woods, photophobous.

luciphile. A plant growing in full light, a photophile.

luciphilous. Seeking light.

lucky nuts, lucky knots. Woody structures embedded in the bark of the beech, the olive, etc., representing loosely attached rudimentary branches that are comparable to burls.

lucus. A grove or park, a place grown with trees and grass.

ludovicianus. Of Louisiana.

lugdunensis. Of Lyons.

lumbrical. Having the shape of an earthworm.

lumbricous. Shaped like an earthworm.

lumen. 1. A cell cavity. 2. The cavity of a tubular organ.

luminous line. A line on the testa of certain seeds which is due to a modification of the outer layer.

luminous organs. Specialized organs which produce light and are found in various plants and animals.

lunar plants. The plants which twine with the moon against the sun, sinistrorse plants.

lunate. Crescent-shaped.

lunule. A crescent-shaped marking, a lunula.

lunulet. A small lunule.

lupinine. A weakly poisonous alkaloid in the flower buds of *Lupinus luteus*.

lupinite. A bitter substance found in the leaves of the white lupin, *Lupinus albus*.

lupulin. A bitter, acrid compound obtained from resinous glandular scales of hops, *Humulus lupulus*.

lupulinic glands. Resinous glandular bodies within the scales of the female flower of hops.

lupulinous. Resembling the head of hops or strobile of hops.

lupulite. A lupulinic gland.

luridic acid. An acid occurring in the fungus *Boletus luridus*.

lusiform. Reproducing only by vegetative increase, not by seeds.

lusitanicus. Of Portugal.

lusus. A sport, a variation from seed or bud.

lusus naturae. A monstrosity, a mutation.

lutein, luteol. Xanthophyll, the yellow coloring matter found in plants, chiefly in leaves and flowers.

luteo-ciliata. Yellowish hair tufts.

luteofuscous. Blackish yellow.

luteolin. A yellow coloring matter found in dyer's weed or weld, *Reseda lutea*.

lutetianus. Parisian.

luteus. Yellow.

luticole. Growing in miry places.

lutose. Muddy, covered with clay.

luzuletum. An association of *Luzula*, wood rush.

lyases. Enzymes active in the decomposition of complex molecules into more simple ones without hydrolysis.

lychinidiate. Luminous.

lychnetum. An association of *Lychnis*, campion; lychnidetum.

lychnidifolius. *Lychnis*-leaved.

lycoetonum. Wolf-poison.

lycoperdaceous. Like the *Lycoperdaceae*, the puffball fungi.

lycoperdioid. Resembling a puffball.

lycopersicin. A red pigment allied to carotin which occurs in tomatoes (*Solanum Lycopersicum*), red peppers (*Capsicum*), bugleweed (*Lycopus*), etc., lycopin.

lycopod. A plant of the genus *Lycopodium*, the club mosses.

lycopodinean. Having structures similar to *Lycopodium*.

lycopodioid. Like a club moss, like *Lycopodium*.

lycopsid. Having sporangiophores like the cryptogams in the *Lycopodiales* and *Equisetales*.

lycotropal. Having an orthotropous ovule bent like a horseshoe.

lymph. Sap.

lymphatic. Clear, pellucid.

lyophils. Solutions which after evaporation to dryness go readily into solution when fluid is added.

lyophobe. Solutions which after evaporation to dryness are not restored upon the addition of fluid.

lyotropic. Said of solutions which are dependent on changes of the solvent itself.

lyrate. Lyre-shaped.

lyrate sectus. Lyrately pinnate.

lyrately pinnate. With the pinnae decreasing in size toward the base of the leaf in pinnately compound leaves.

lyrati-partitus. Lyrately pinnate.

Lysenkoism. Doctrines of the Russian Lysenko which state that acquired characters are inherited, that heredity is not based on germ plasm, and that all parts of the plant, vegetative as well as sexual, are the materials of heredity.

lysigenic. Having a cavity formed by the disorganization or dissolution of cells; lysigenetic, lysogenous.

lysimachioid. Like *Lysimachia*, a genus of primulaceous herbs.

lysin. A substance which can destroy cells of bacteria.

lysine. An amino acid needed for animal growth.

lysis. 1. The metamorphosis of a part or organ. 2. The bursting of a bacterial cell when attacked by a bacteriophage.

lysogenesis. The destructive action of lysin.

lysozyme. A substance present in some plants which has the power of killing bacteria, resembling an enzyme in some respects but apparently is not able to reproduce itself.

lysozyme cell. A cell containing lysozyme which can reproduce itself.

lytic. 1. Of or pertaining to lysis or lysin. 2. Dissolving cells.

lytic 'phage. A bacteriophage which causes lysis.

M

macaedium. See MAZAEDIUM.

macchia. Shrubby mostly evergreen growth, macchia or maqui in the Mediterranean region and Africa, Fynbosch in South and Southwest Australia, chaparral in California.

mace. 1. The aril of the nutmeg. 2. A kind of spice constituting a dried arilode or external fibrous covering of the nutmeg.

macedonicus. Of Macedonia.

maceration. 1. The process commonly used in isolating elements of a tissue. 2. The decomposition by steeping in water or other liquid. 3. The softening or wearing away by digestive or other physiological processes.

macilent. Lean, meager.

macracanthous. Having large spines.

macrandrous. 1. Having large or elongated male plants (in algae). 2. Said of antheridia developed in male filaments of *Oedogonium* which are nearly as large as the filaments themselves. 3. With large anthers.

macrodenium. A large gland.

macranthus. With long flowers, with large flowers.

macro-. A prefix meaning large or long.

macroaerophilous. Having great avidity for oxygen, as in the case of *Clostridium*.

macroandrospores. Macrospores of *Selaginella* which have a male function.

macroaplanosporangium. A sporangium in which macroaplanospores (large, nonmotile cells) are produced.

macroaplanospores. Aplanospores of large size.

macrobiocarpy. The property of certain fruits which are able to retain their seeds for a number of years.

macrobiosis. Long life.

macrobiostemonous. With persistent stamens.

macrobiostigmatic. Having stigmas remain capable of fertilization until the anthers are mature.

macroblast. A normal wood bud.

macrobotrys. With large clusters.

macrocarpous. Producing large fruit.

macrocephalous. 1. Having a big head. 2. Having thickened or consolidated cotyledons.

macrocladous. Having long or large branches.

macroclema. A long cutting or twig.

macroconidium. A large asexual spore or conidium produced at a different time or in a different sporocarp from the microconidium.

macroconjugant. The larger individual of a conjugating pair, the larger gamete.

macrocyclic. In *Uredinales*, long-cycled (with mycelium occurring in both the haploid and diploid phases).

macrocyst. 1. A large reproductive cell of certain fungi, a cell or case in which spores are borne. 2. The resting condition of a young plasmodium, a mass of protoplasm with nuclei in a double-walled cell.

macrocytase. The enzyme of the macrophages or endothelial cells.

macrocyte. The larger of the two forms in dimorphic flagellate algae.

macrodactylous. With the long rays as *Nitella*.

macrodiodange. A macrosporangium.

macrodiode. A macrospore.

macrodontous. With large teeth.

macrogamete. The larger usually female gamete.

macrogametocyte. The mother cell of a macrogamete considered female and used mainly in connection with protista.

macrogametophyte. The fern plant which produces the female gamete.

macrogamy. Conjugation between full-grown individuals of a species, halogamy.

macroglossate. With a large tongue.

macrogonidium. A large gonidium, a macrospore, a megalogonidium.

macrogynospore. A gynospore of *Selaginella* which presumably has a female function.

macromere. One of the larger blastomeres in eggs with unequal cleavage.

macromicrosporophyll. A carpel.

macromitreous. Resembling the tropical moss *Macromitrium*, having large spores which produce the female gametophytes.

macronucleus. The larger nucleus in infusoria presumed to control the vegetative functions of the cell.

macropetalous. With large petals.

macrophage. A large mononuclear leucocyte.

macrophanerophyte. A tree.

macrophyll. A long leaf, shorter than a megaphyll.

macrophyllous. Having long or large leaves or lobes.

macrophyte. Marine algae of great length, visible floating plants.

macrophytoplankton. Floating angiosperms, large algae, etc.

macroplast. The large disc-like plastids in *Bacterium rubescens*.

macroplectron. With large spurs.

macropodous. 1. Having a long stalk, as a leaf or leaflet. 2. With a hypocotyl which is large in relation to the rest of the embryo.

macroprothallium. A prothalloid growth from a microspore of *Selaginella* having a female function.

macropteres. The wings on the stems of plants with reduced leaves.

macropterous. With large wings.

macroptilous. Longibracteate.

macropycnid. A spore borne on a filament.

macropycnospores. The long spores of certain fungi.

macrosclereids. The long stone cells which have blunt ends.

macroscope. 1. A hand microscope. 2. A hand lens of about ten diameters.

macroscopic. Visible to the naked eye without magnification.

macrosepalous. With especially large sepals.

macrosomatous. Possessing an abnormally large body.

macrosome. A large alveolar sphere or granule in protoplasm.

macrospadix. A large spadix.

macrospartinetum. A saltmarsh plant formation in which *Spartina* is dominant.

macrospermous. With large seeds.

macrosporange. A sporangium containing macrospores.

macrosporangiate flowers. Pistillate or carpellate flowers, flowers without stamens.

macrosporangiophore. A structure bearing a macrosporangium.

macrosporangium. A structure in which macrospores are produced, a megasporangium, an ovule.

macrospore. The larger spore in heterospory, the spore producing the female gametophyte, the embryo sac in phanerogams, the megaspore.

macrosporioid. Resembling the genus *Macrosporium*, especially its muriform spores.

macrosporophore. An organ in which macrospores are produced.

macrosporophyll. A sporophyll which produces megasporangia, a carpel, a megasporophyll.

macrosporophyllary. Carpellary.

macrostachyous. With large spikes.

macrostemous. With large filaments.

macrostomatous. With a very large mouth or opening.

macrostylospore. A large stalked spore.

macrostylous. 1. With long styles and short filaments. 2. With large styles.

macrosymbiont. The larger of the associated organisms in symbiosis.

macrotherm. A tropical plant requiring heat and moisture which dies at freezing or near freezing temperatures, a megatherm.

macrothermophilous. Living in the tropics.

macrothermophyte. A tropical plant.

macrothermophytia. Tropical plant communities.

macrourous. Large-tailed.

macrozoogonidium. A large zoogonidium, as in the alga *Ulothrix*.

macrozoospore. A large motile spore or large zoospore.

maculation. The pattern or the arrangement of the spots in a plant.

macules. Patches or spots of color or small shallow pits as the aerolated pits of the *Coniferae*, maculae.

maculicolous. Dwelling on spots.

maculiform. 1. Spot-shaped. 2. Having apothecia which appear as irregular spots.

madar. See MUDAR.

madefact. Moistened, as plants in an herbarium previous to examination.

madid. Moist, wet.

madreporic. Like a madrepore or branching coral.

madura. A disease of man which is characterized by the swelling and degeneration in feet and hands, a fungus disease of the feet caused by *Chionyphe Carteri*, an actinomycete.

maesiacus. Of Moesia, the ancient name of Bulgaria and Serbia.

magellanicus. Of or pertaining to the region of the Straits of Magellan.

magmaphilae. Algae which thrive in warm and well-lit waters forming a colored mixture.

magmoid. Consisting of spherical green cellules in lichens.

magnetotropism. The effect of a magnet upon responsive particles in a plant.

magnigrade. With a large variation or a noticeable mutation.

magnigrade evolution. A mutation great enough to constitute an evolutionary change.

magniguttate. With one or two large globules.

magnocariceta. Associations of tall species of *Carex*.

mahogany. A tropical tree yielding beautiful lumber.

mahonia. Thornless evergreen shrubs, *Berberis*.

maiden. 1. A tree or other plant of one year's growth from the bud or graft. 2. Any plant which has not fruited.

maidenhair fern. *Adiantum*, a fern with slender stipes and delicate fronds.

maiosis. Meiosis.

majalis. Of May.

major quadrat. A square of four quadrats usually four meters square.

makroflora. The luxuriant vegetation found in some of the valleys in the Caucasus.

malabaricus. Of Malabar.

malaceous. Resembling the apple, the subgenus *Malus*, genus *Pyrus*.

malacogamy. Fertilization by snails.

malacoid. Soft in texture, mucilaginous, having soft or fleshy leaves.

malacophiles. Plants which are fertilized by snails or slugs.

malacophyllous. Xerophytic, having fleshy leaves with much water-storing tissue, with soft or fleshy leaves.

malacospermous. With soft seeds.

male cell. The smaller of two unequal gametes.

male flowers. Staminate flowers lacking a pistil.

male gametes. Male sexual cells, sperms.

male organs. Organs producing the male gametes or sperms.

male prothallium. A prothallium producing antheridia only.

male system. All the parts of the flower belonging to the stamen.

malezales. Deep swamps in Paraguay.

malic. Pertaining to apples, *Malus*.

malic acid. An acid frequently found in cell sap, unripe fruits, and wines; an unstable acid which changes to maleic and fumeric acid under heat.

malicorium. The rind of a pomegranate.

maliform. Apple-shaped.

mallee scrub. A scrub steppe in Australia composed of *Eucalyptus* about the height of a man.

malleolus. An attached shoot or twig of a woody plant which is bent and partly covered with earth so that it may take root, a layer.

mallococcous. With downy fruit.

malol. A constituent of apple wax.

Malpighiaceous hairs or pili. Stellate leaf-hairs attached at the middle and tapering toward each end characteristic of the tropical herbs and shrubs of the genus *Malpighia*.

Malpighian. Of, pertaining to, or described by the Italian anatomist Malpighi.

Malpighian cells. A closely packed layer of cells found in the testa of some seeds which show as radial light lines under the outer skin.

malt. Partially germinated barley rich in amylase.

maltase. An enzyme found in germinating cereals and yeasts which converts maltose into dextrose, maltin.

Malthusian parameter. A projection of the relative change in population in relation to the established stabilized population.

malting. The process of germinating the seeds of barley until the radicle is produced, at which time the action is stopped with heat.

maltodextrin. A substance intermediate in properties between maltose and dextrin.

maltose. Malt sugar, a sugar formed by the action of diastase on starch.

malus. The apple, a subgenus of *Pyrus* in the *Rosaceae*.

malvaceous. Resembling the *Malvaceae*, the mallow family.

mamelon. The floral axis.

mamelon, ovular. The papilla which precedes the formation of the nucellus in *Cycas*.

mamilla. Mammilla.

mammiform. Breast-shaped, conical with a rounded apex.

mammilla. A nipple, a projection.

mammillar. Having a nipple.

mammilliform. Applied to those papillate protuberances on a petal which give it a velvety appearance, nipple-shaped.

mammose. Breast-shaped.

mammulose. Having small nipples or protuberances.

mandschuricus. Of Manchuria.

mangel-wurzel. A beet with large roots grown for forage, *Beta vulgaris*.

mango. A well-known, widely-cultivated fruit of the tropics, *Mangifera indica*, considered one of the most delicious fruits of the tropics.

mangosteen. A handsome tropical tree, *Garcinia Mangostana*, with delicious fruits about the size of a mandarin orange with a thick rind of rich reddish color difficult to cultivate.

mangroves. Swamp communities of the tropics found in the swampy lands and estuaries along the coasts composed of several genera of which *Rhizophora* is the most common. The trees have spreading branches which send down more trunks causing a very dense growth over a large area. Many of the trees show viviparous germination.

manicate. With pubescence so dense and interwoven that it can be stripped off like a sleeve; having a coating of tangled, interwoven hair.

manifest. Said of anthers which are visible at the mouth of the corolla tube but neither exserted or inserted.

manna. Hardened sweetish exudate from various trees, as from the European flowering ash, *Fraxinus Ornus*.

mannan. A semicellulose.

mannite. A white crystalline substance belonging to the class of alcohols called hexites and occurring in three different optical forms, the chief constituent of manna.

mannitose. A sugar obtained from the pith of ash, oak, and alder; a sugar obtained by the careful oxidation of mannite.

mannocellulose. A constituent of gymnosperm wood which yields mannose on hydrolysis.

mannose. A sugar which results from the hydrolysis of cellulose, a sugar obtained by the oxidation of mannite.

manocyst. The receptive papilla protruding from the oogonium, as in *Phytophthora*.

manoxylic wood. Wood of a loose texture containing much parenchyma as the wood of cycads.

mantle. 1. An ocrea or tubular stipule. 2. A cover or cloak.

mantle cavity. The space between the mantle and the body proper.

mantle cell. A cell of investing tissue of a sporangium, a tapetal cell.

mantle fibers. The spindle fibers which extend from one pole to the other in karyokinetic figures.

mantle layer. A layer of tapetal cells.

mantle leaf. The prostrate, half-enveloping barren frond as distinct from the fertile frond.

manubrial. 1. Handle-shaped. 2. Of or pertaining to a manubrium.

manubrium. 1. A cylindrical cell borne on the inner surface of the eight shields which compose the globular antheridium of the *Characeae* which bears the head cells upon its summit. 2. A cell which projects inward from the center. 3. A part which resembles a handle or clapper.

many-headed. Having many distinct buds on the crown of the root.

manzanita. Any of various California shrubs of the genus *Arctostaphylos*.

maqui. A Chilean shrub of commercial value.

maquis. A Corsican term for dense thickets of shrubs, mostly evergreen; the copse association of the Mediterranean coast; macchina, Fynbosch, mesothamnium, etc.

marattiaceous. Of or pertaining to *Marattia*, a genus of ferns.

marcescent. Withering but not falling off.

marchantiaform. Resembling *Marchantia*, a genus of liverworts, as do the prothalli of ferns.

marcid. Withered or shrunken but not falling off.

marcor. Flaccidity caused by lack of water.

margaritaceous. Pearly or of pearls.

margella. The elliptic ring around a stoma formed by the guard cells.

marginal bast. The strong development of a hypoderm on the edges of leaves in certain families as *Myrsinae*, tropical plants.

marginal community. A plant community which borders on another community of slightly different character.

marginal glands. The glands formed on the incurved margin of the pitchers of *Nepenthes*.

marginal growing point. The marginal cells which remain embryonic and capable of growth.

marginal ovule. An ovule borne on the margin of a carpel.

marginal pits. Pits which traverse the outer walls of the epidermis in leaves.

marginal ray cell. A more or less specialized cell which occurs with others of the same kind on the edge of a vascular ray.

marginal species. Species of plants which grow along the edge of woodlands.

marginal veil. A membrane closing the hymenium in young agarics, the partial veil of the velum partiale.

marginate. Having a distinct margin in structure or coloring, with a well-defined border.

marginate-depressed. Having a narrow circular, horizontal platform on the upper side of the bulb of a mushroom.

marginicidal. Dehiscent along the line of union of the carpels.

margothallode. The rim of the shield of a lichen formed by the thallus.

marilandicus. Of Maryland, Marylandicus, Marianus.

maritime vegetation. Vegetation that is free-floating, submerged in salt water, or subjected to periodic inundation.

marmorate. Marbled, mottled.

marmorophyllous. With marbled leaves.

marram-grass association. An association formed of *Ammophila* on sand dunes.

marrow. The pith or the pulp of a fruit.

marsh. A tract of soft wet land commonly covered wholly or partly with water and supporting aquatic herbaceous vegetation, a fen, a swamp, a morass.

marsh plants. Helophytes in fresh water, halophytes in salt water.

marsupium. 1. A nursing sac surrounding certain archegonia. 2. The fruiting receptacle of certain liverworts.

marvel of Peru. The four-o'clock, *Mirabilis*.

marylandicus. Of or pertaining to Maryland.

masculine. Male, staminate.

mash. A decoction of grains or fruit, a mass of mixed ingredients made soft and pulpy by beating or crushing.

masked. Having a corolla with the throat nearly closed by a projection in the lower lip, personate.

mass. A sorus; see MAST.

massa. The mass or substance of a body.

massa seminalis. The flesh of some fungi.

massa sporophora. The sporangia of some fungi.

massula. 1. A hardened frothy mucilage enclosing a group of microspores. 2. A massed group of microspores in orchids. 3. A mucilaginous mass in the water fern (*Azolla*) formed from the tapetal cells of the microsporangium and enclosing a number of microspores.

mast. 1. The fruit of forest trees like acorns and other nuts. 2. A heap of nuts.

master factor. An ecological factor which plays the main part in determining the occurrence in a given area of a plant community of major rank.

mastic. A resinous exudation from *Pistacis Lentiscus*.

mastigocladous. Flagellate, having runners.

mastigonemes. Fine hairs on flagella.

mastigopod. 1. A stage in the development of *Myxogastres* when the contents of each spore escapes as a zoogonidium enclosing a nucleus and a contractile vacuole with a single cilium. 2. A swarm cell of *Myxogastres*.

mastigospore. A plant with ciliate or flagellate disseminules.

mastoid. Resembling a nipple or breast.

mat. 1. Closely intertwined vegetation with roots and rhizomes intermixed. 2. The fabric of rushes, straw, etc.

mat geophytes. Closely intertwined vegetation of perennial spot-bound plants, mostly monocotyledons.

maternal inheritance. Inheritance solely from the mother.

mates, synaptic. Leptotene threads.

math. A crop or a second crop (aftermath).

matonioid. Resembling the fern genus *Matonia*.

matorral. A xerophilous scrub formation in Spain and Portugal.

matricariaefolious. With leaves like *Matricaria*, a genus of asteraceous herbs.

matrix. 1. The body upon which lichens and fungi grow. 2. The ground substance of connective tissue.

matrix, gelatinous. A jelly-like matrix.

matrix pollinis. The pollen mother cell, the cell in which pollen grains develop.

matroclinal inheritance. The inheritance in which the offspring resembles the mother more closely than the father.

matroclinous. Having more of the characters of the female parent and therefore resembling the mother, matroclinic.

mattae. Mats or plants which form matted growths.

matteuccioid. Resembling the fern genus *Matteuccia*.

mattula. The fibrous material surrounding the petioles of palms.

maturation. The final series of stages in the formation of the egg or the sperm by which its nucleus is prepared for union, the final stages of a germ cell just before it becomes functional, ripening.

maturation divisions. Meiosis.

mature cells. Adult cells.

maturescent. Approaching maturity.

matutinal. Flowering in the morning like the morning glory.

matzoon. Milk fermented by yeasts and bacteria.

mauritanicus. Of Mauretania.

maxillary. Of the jaw, as in orchid flowers, etc.

maximum temperature. The temperature above which an organism cannot survive.

mays. Maiz or mahiz, the native name of Indian corn.

mazaedium. A dough-like mass of spores and

paraphyses, the powdery spore mass in *Caliciaceae*.

mbuga. The periodically moist alluvial sunken lands in Tanganyika.

mchaka. Deciduous scrub in Tanganyika.

mead. A wet meadow.

meadow. A grassland artificially maintained by mowing and grazing; a low prairie; a lowland covered with coarse grass, composites, or other herbage; a grassland which is cut for hay.

meadow moor. A fen.

meadow thicket. A lowland covered with thickly set trees and shrubs.

mealy. Farinaceous, covered with meal-like powder, having the qualities of meal.

mean sample tree. A tree of representative form which in diameter, height, and volume is an average of the trees in a group or stand.

meandriform. Having a winding direction as the anther cells of *Cucurbitaceae*.

meatus, intercellularis. An intercellular passage.

meatus, pneumaticus. An air passage.

mechanical tissue. A tissue composed of thick-walled cells.

mechanistic theory. The view that all vital phenomena are subject to physical and chemical laws.

mechanomorphoses. The mechanical changes in structure produced in the larger groups of plants by similar external causes.

mechanotropism. The movements in plants in response to mechanical stimuli.

meconine. An alkaloid contained in opium.

meconium. The juice of *Papaver somniferum*, the opium poppy.

medanos. Sand dunes on marsh or salt deserts in Argentina.

mediad. Situated at or near the middle of the stipe.

medial humidity. The mean humidity accompanying mean temperatures under outdoor weather conditions.

medial temperature. The range of temperature within which the increase in the rate of development under constant temperature is directly proportional to the rise in temperature.

median. A midrib or vein of a leaf running lengthwise from the base to the tip.

mediananisophylly. The form of leaves on the median shoots as seen when the twigs are normally decussate.

median anterior. The first sepal in phyllotaxis.

median bracteole. A small bract inserted at the middle of the pedicel.

median chorisis. The multiplication of a single organ in the median plane.

median optical view. A view halfway between the upper and lower surface of a structure.

median plane. The plane including the axis and the midrib of the bract in floral diagrams. The median plane of a leaf would pass through the midrib above and below.

median posterior. The second sepal in the quincuncial calyx.

median wall. The wall or plane in archegonia which bisects the pro-embryo at right angles to the basal wall.

median zygomorphous. Having structures capable of division into similar halves by a plane passing through the middle.

medicagophyll. The characteristic chlorophyll of alfalfa, *Medicago sativa*.

mediocortex. The central layer or layers of the bark.

medioform. An intermediate form which is not due to genetic crossing.

mediolocoform. A local medioform.

mediopictous. Pictured or striped at the center.

medioventral. In the middle ventral line.

mediterraneus. 1. Of the Mediterranean. 2. Inhabiting spots far from the sea.

medium. The artificial substance (fluid, gelatinous, or solid) used to grow organisms in the laboratory under controlled conditions.

medivalvis. On the middle of the valves.

medulla. 1. Pith. 2. A tangle of loose hyphae in a sclerotium, rhizomorph, or other massive fungal structure. 3. A loose hyphal network in the interior of a lichen thallus.

medulla seminis. The albumen of seeds.

medullary. Belonging to the pith or medulla.

medullary axis. The medullary layer.

medullary bundle. One of the lateral leaf-trace bundles in monocotyledons.

medullary casts. The impression of the internal cavity of *Calamites* in solid material.

medullary commissure. The medullary rays between the bundles in the stele.

medullary conjunctive tissue. The pith.

medullary crown. A sheath.

medullary fistula. See FISTULA, MEDULLARY.

medullary layer. A thick subcortical layer of

the thallus of some lichens, usually hyphal elements without gonidia.

medullary phloem bundles. Independent phloem bundles which are developed just within the ring of normal vascular bundles.

medullary ray cells. Cells in the medullary rays which are parenchymatous but which show no fibrous shape, the silver grain of wood.

medullary rays. The strands of connective tissue, parenchymatous cells, separating the vascular bundles which extend from the pith to the bark or pericycle in woody dicotyledons or gymnosperms; the vascular rays or silver grain of wood seen in cross section of stems which conduct food and water transversely.

medullary sheath. A ring of protoxylem around the pith of certain stems, tracheids forming a sheath around the pith, the primary xylem bundles projecting into the pith from the cambium.

medullary spot. An accumulation of parenchymatous cells in certain woods.

medullary stele. A meristele lying in the central tissues of a fern stem.

medullary system. The whole ground tissue or more appropriately only the pith and medullary rays.

medullate. Having pith or a medullary sheath.

medullation. The formation of the central tissue of a stele.

medullin. Cellulose from the pith of the sunflower and the lilac.

Medusa's head. *Hydnum caput-medusae*, an edible fungus, so-called from its long twisted and interwoven spines.

mega-. A prefix meaning large or extended.

megacalyptra. A large cap.

megacanthous. With large spines.

megacarpous. With large fruits.

megacephalous. With a large head.

megachloroplast. The compound chlorophyll granules in *Tillandsia*, Spanish moss.

megaconids. Large conidia borne in the pycnidia of certain ascomycetes.

megagamete. The larger of two uniting cells or gametes, the egg.

megagametocyte. A cell producing a megagamete.

megagametogenesis. The development of megagametes.

megagametophyte. The gametophyte produced from megaspores.

megalanthous. With large flowers.

megalogonidium. A macrogonidium, a large gonidium, a macrospore.

megalophylla. Extremely large leaves.

megalophylly. The bipinnation of a fern frond.

megalospores. The large female spores of some fern allies.

megamere. A macromere.

meganucleus. The vegetative nucleus in infusoria (microscopic organisms).

megaphanerophytes. Trees more than 30 meters tall.

megaphylls. The largest leaves in Raunkiaer's classification, meiophyll and meirphyll classes combined.

megaphyllidae. Ferns which have broad fronds.

megaphyllous. Having relatively large leaves with many veins.

megaphytes. Spermatophytes.

megaplankton. Plankton which includes megaphytes and algae of special groups, pleuston.

megaplanogamete. A large planogamete presumably female.

megapotamicus. Of a large river.

megaprothallus. A prothallus which produces archegonia.

megarchidium. A nucellus.

megarhizous. With large roots, megarhyzous, megarrhyzius.

megascopic. 1. Visible to the naked eye. 2. Of or pertaining to the megascope or the projection of images of opaque objects.

megasome. A macrosome.

megasorome. The sporangial apparatus of the vascular plant with its receptacle or stalk.

megasorus. A sorus in which megasporangia are formed.

megaspermous. With large seeds.

megasporangium. A relatively large structure containing one to four megaspores which are the result of reduction division, the ovule in seed plants, a megasporange, a meiosporangium, a megasporium.

megaspore. The larger spore produced in heterosporous plants which gives rise to the female gamete or megagametophyte, the larger meiospore.

megaspore mother cell. The cell producing megaspores.

megaspore, primary. A megaspore mother cell.

megasporium. The megasporangium.

megasporocarp. The developed megasporangium in the water fern *Azolla* which contains the single perfect megaspore.

megasporocyte. The early stage in development of the embryo sac.

megasporogenesis. The development of the megaspore, the cell division which leads to the development of the megasporangium.

megasporophyll. 1. A leaf-like plant organ which bears or encloses megasporangia, a carpel. 2. The female cone of *Cycas*.

megastachyous. With large spikes.

megastigmous. With a large stigma.

megastrobilus. The female flower and cone of *Cycas* and its allies.

megatherm. A tropical plant which grows only where temperatures are high throughout the year (usually with abundant moisture).

megazooids. Large motile daughter cells produced in certain unicellular algae.

megazoosporangia. 1. The special sporangium in *Hydrodictyon* (of the green algae) which contains a swarm of megazoospores. 2. The protoplasm of a cell which gives rise to a large number of spores with four cilia.

megazoospore. A large zoospore or asexual swarm cell, as that found in some thread-like algae.

megecad. A group of several ecads of close affinity.

megistotherms. 1. Plants which require a uniformly high temperature. 2. Extinct plants which lived in temperatures of 30°C.

meiacanthous. With small flowers.

meiocyte. A cell in which meisosis has begun, a meiospore mother cell or a cell in which meiospores are produced.

meiogyrous. Rolled slightly inward.

meiomerous. 1. Having a small number of parts. 2. Having fewer than the normal number of parts.

meiophase. The phase in cell division during which the diploid nucleus undergoes reduction.

meiophyll. A simply elaborated leaf as in the fossil *Pseudobornia*, a plant with whorled leaves arranged at the nodes of the stem.

meiophylly. A diminution in number of the leaves as compared with a preceding whorl.

meiosis. Reduction division, the reduction of the chromosome number from diploid (2n) to haploid (n).

meiosporangium. A structure in which spores are produced by meiosis (reduction division), a meiosporange.

meiospore. The spore produced by meiosis with reduction in the chromosome number from diploid to haploid (the spores are usually produced in fours).

meiostates. Intermediate products of metabolism.

meiostemonous. Having fewer stamens than petals or sepals.

meiotaxy. The complete suppression of entire whorls or organs.

meiotherm. A plant inhabiting cool temperate regions.

meiotic. Of or pertaining to meiosis.

meiotic euapogamy. A condition in which the nuclei of the mother cells of the sporophyte have the haploid number of chromosomes; see REDUCED APOGAMY.

melampsoraceous. 1. Having the characteristics of the rust family. 2. Implying a more primitive condition as regards sori, spores, pores, etc., as compared with *Pucciniaceae*.

melampyrine. Dulcite, a substance occurring in *Melampyrum nemorosum*, an herbaceous annual.

melananthous. With black flowers.

melancholicous. Hanging or drooping.

melangeophilous. Dwelling in loam or black soil.

melangeophyte. A loam plant.

melangeophytia. Loam or alluvium communities.

melanin. A dark brown or black pigment.

melanism. The excessive development of black pigment (the opposite of albinism) due to disease.

melanocarpous. With black fruits.

melanocaulon. With a black stem.

melanochlorous. Blackish green, atrovirens.

melanococcus. A black berry.

melanoleucus. Black and white.

melanphore. A cell containing black pigment.

melanophyll. The chief black pigment of diatoms.

melanophyllous. With dark leaves.

melanose. A disease of grapes causing leaf fall.

melanospermous. Having dark seeds or spores.

melanosporous. Having black spores.

melanotic. Developing black pigment.

melanoxylon. With black wood.

melantherous. With black anthers.

melasmatic tissue. A group of large cells around the vascular bundles in the stems of *Calamites* with dark brown or black contents.

melastomaceous. Of or pertaining to *Melastoma*, showy flowered tropical shrubs.

meleagris. Like a guinea fowl, speckled.

melezitose. Sugar from the larch.

melibiase. Raffinase, an enzyme.

meline. Quince-colored, dull yellow.

melioloid. Like *Meliola*.

melitose. Sugar from *Eucalyptus manna*, raffinose.

melittophilae. Flowers which are adapted for pollination by the larger bees.

melizitase. An enzyme from *Sterigmatocystis nigra*.

melizitose. A sugar from *Alhagi Mauroram*.

mellarose. A variety of orange.

melleous. Like or pertaining to honey in taste, smell, or color.

melliferous. Producing or bearing honey.

melligo. Honey dew, an exudation from aphids.

melliodorous. Scented like honey.

melliphagous. Feeding on honey.

melon. A very large berry-like fruit, the muskmelon, etc.

melon-shaped. Oval-shaped.

melonida. An inferior many-celled fruit such as an apple.

meoniform. Shaped like a melon with projecting ribs.

membrana gongylifera. The hymenium of fungi.

membranaceous. Membranous.

membrane. A thin expanded tissue or film covering, separating, or protecting a cell or unicellular organism; a pellicle of homogeneous tissue; a membrana.

membranella. An undulating membrane formed by the fusion of rows of cilia found in *Protozoa*.

membraniferous. Enveloped in or bearing a membrane.

membranogenic. Producing a membrane.

membranoid. Resembling a membrane.

membranous. Thin, flexible, and more or less translucent; with the texture of a membrane or parchment.

membranous layer. The interwoven hyphae forming a layer.

membranous mycelium. Mycelium in which the hyphae form a membranous layer by becoming interwoven.

membranula. The indusium of ferns.

memnonious. Brownish black.

mendel. A genetical measure named for Gregor Mendel which designates fifty units of distance in a chromosome which is equivalent to fifty percent of crossing over.

Mendel's laws. The enunciation of the basic principles of heredity which state that a unit character is inherited in an alternative manner (as a dominant or recessive character) and is controlled by a pair of factors: each gamete bears one or the other of these factors which segregate at random in the gametes formed by the individual and recombine at random when gametes of the opposite sex fuse to form a new individual. The offspring of parents that show contrasting characters (one dominant and one recessive) resemble the dominant parent in such a character. In the second filial generation resulting from a cross of these hybrids, 25 percent of the individuals will resemble the dominant grandparent, 25 percent will resemble the recessive grandparent, and 50 percent will resemble the hybrid individuals of the first filial generation.

Mendelian. Referring to Mendel and his work or to the characters which behave according to the results of Mendel's laws.

Mendelian hybrid. A hybrid the parents of which differ in a particular character controlled by one or only a few pairs of genes.

Mendelize. To follow Mendel's law of inheritance, to work in accordance with Mendelism.

meneblastema. The soredium of lichens.

meniscate. Bent into a half circle, crescent-shaped, shaped like a watch crystal, meniscoid.

meniscifolious. With crescent-shaped leaves.

meniscus. 1. A crescent-shaped body. 2. A bubble found in the woody tissues of plants.

menispermine. An alkaloid derived from the genus *Menispermum*, a genus of climbing herbs.

menstruum. 1. A liquor used as a dissolvent. 2. Any substance which dissolves a solid body.

mentagra parasitica. Sycosis, a skin or scalp disease caused by fungi.

mentagraphyte. A fungus causing the disease mentagra or sycosis.

menthol. A white crystalline substance forming a principal constituent of the oil of peppermint.

menthologist. A specialist on the genus *Mentha*, the true mints.

mentum. An extension of the base of the column in some orchids.

menyanthetum. An association of *Menyanthes*, a genus of bog plants.

mercury. Any plant of the genus *Mercurialis*, dog's mercury.

merenchyma. 1. Spherical cellular tissue. 2. Fungous tissue built up by the welding of hyphal elements.

merenchyma cells. Unpitted cells in the pith of trees with intercellular spaces greatly elongated radically.

merenchymatic. With many cells.

merenchymatous. Of or pertaining to merenchyma.

mericarp. A one-seeded portion of a fruit which splits at maturity, one of the achene-like carpels of *Umbelliferae*.

mericlinal chimaera. A chimaera in which one part does not completely surround the other, an incomplete periclinal chimaera.

mericyclic. Having spirally arranged leaves or other organs which occupy only a part of the diameter.

merid. A solitary or colonial asemblage of plastids formed by successive divisions from one.

meridian. 1. In diatoms, the plane of the pervalvar axis. 2. Apparent noon. 3. Pertaining to or characteristic of the highest point or culmination.

meridional. Southern.

meridisk. A growth upon the receptacle apart from the floral organs whether glandular or not.

meriphyll. The complex meriphytic leaf of the ferns leading to angiosperms.

meriphyte. The vascular tissue of a leaf.

meriplast. A protoplast of a polyplast which remains distinct and does not fuse with the others.

merism. 1. The repetition of parts to form a symmetrical pattern. 2. The division of cells or cellular structures, or dichotomous division of organs. 3. A primordial assemblage of cells.

merismatic. 1. Dividing or separating into cells or segments, dividing into symmetrical parts by the formation of septa. 2. Pertaining to or consisting of meristem.

merismatic tissue. Formative tissue; see MERISTEM.

merismatoid. Having a pileus which is made up of many smaller pilei or laciniately divided pilei, merismoid.

merispore. One segment or spore of a multicellular spore body, a segment of a sporidesm.

merisporocyst. A simple or branched sporocyst, a departure from the type of fructification of the *Mucoraceae*.

meristele. 1. A strand of vascular tissue enclosed in a sheath of endodermis forming part of the dictyostele. 2. The branch of a stele supplying a leaf, one of the leaf bundles in a monostelic stem. It is sometimes further identified as eu-, haplo-, or mono-, di-, tri-, or tetra-meristele.

meristem. The undifferentiated formative or generative cells of plants which give rise to daughter cells capable of further division, the cells found in the cambium or growing points capable of further development.

meristem phialospore. A spore borne at the tip of a phialide which is abstricted in succession from the tip.

meristem, primary. The growing developing cells of a young organ, the primary tissue which forms the whole tissue of very young organs.

meristem, secondary. The meristem in an organ or part of one after its first development is completed by means of which further growth is effected, as in cambium. It occurs in very young tissue in thin layers.

meristem spore. One of the spores that are abstricted in basipetal succession from the tip of a conidiophore, phialide, or hypha, which tip may be considered as a growing point.

meristematic cells. Cells with large cell nuclei but little differentiation.

meristic. Segmented.

meristic differences. Differences in the fundamental number of parts in different flowers.

meristic variation. Merism, a variation in the number of parts and the geometric relation of parts.

meristogen. The meristogenous primordium in a pycnidium.

meristogenetic. 1. Developing from actively dividing cells. 2. Arising from the division of a single hypha with the aid of the neighboring hypha of the same branch. 3. Meristogenous.

merithall. An internode.

meroblastic embryogeny. The condition which exists when only a portion of the ovum or spore is involved in the formation of the embryo; see MEROGOMY.

meroconidia. Conidia which arise from the simultaneous septation of a hypha in zygomycetes and mature together other than in succession.

merogamy. The conjugation of two specific gametes not closely related which have arisen as daughter cells or gametangia, a form of amphimixis.

merogenesis. The production of similar parts, segmentation.

merogenic. From a portion of an egg.

merogony. The development of an organ or an organism from a portion (usually a portion of the female unit), the development of a nonnucleated egg fragment upon its fertilization by a sperm.

merokinesis. The formation and division of a thread-like chromosome in the karyomeres.

meromorphosis. The regeneration of a part with a new part less than that lost.

meront. A uninucleate or multinucleate product of schizogony, one of the daughter myxamoebae cut off successively as short blunt parts by the parent myxamoeba or plasmodium.

meroplankton. 1. Plankton which live only part-time near the surface. 2. Plankton found only at certain seasons of the year. 3. Plankton found at different levels at different times.

merosporangium. A thread-like growth from the enlarged tip of a sporangiophore in *Mucorales*. Chain-like spores are produced in it.

merotomy. The segmentation or division into parts.

merotype. A later specimen collected from the original type cultivated by means of vegetative reproduction.

merotype, synchronous. A specimen collected at the same time as the original type specimen.

-merous. A suffix which taken with a numerical prefix indicates the number of each of the floral parts.

Merrian's life zones. Alpine, timberline, Hudsonian, Canadian, yellowpine, pinon, and deserts were originally recognized.

merulioid. 1. Like *Merulius*, a polypore, especially as to fruiting surface. 2. With pit-like depressions or shallow tubes.

mesa. A dry tableland capped by a more resistant stratum which keeps the top flat by retarding erosion except at the sides.

mesad. A mesophyte.

mesaprobe. A plant living in foul water.

mesarch. Having the protoxylem (oldest xylem) surrounded by the metaxylem (newer xylem) in all directions.

mescal. A colorless intoxicating drink made in Mexico from the leaves of various species of *Agave*, maguey or maguly.

mesectoderm. The parenchyma formed from the descendants of ectodermal cells which migrated inward.

mesenchyma. 1. The tissue which separates the xylem and the phloem elements in root bundles. 2. The loosely scattered, more or less branching cells of the mesoderm. 3. Mesenchym.

mesendobiotic. Living partially on dead organic material.

mesendozoa. Animals which resemble fungi.

mesenterica. The mycelium of certain fungi.

meseosere. The eosere plant succession corresponding to the Mesozoic Period, a mesophytic eosere or gymneosere.

meseostrate. A mesophytic eostrate.

mesh. A spikelet.

mesic. Mesophytic.

mesidium. A strongly developed, thickened portion of the mesochil in the flower of certain orchids.

mesistem. A contraction of mesomeristem.

meso-. A prefix meaning middle or intermediate.

mesobenthile. The sea bottom at a depth of 200-1000 meters.

mesoblast. 1. The middle layer of an embryo. 2. An organized structure within a living cell in which cell division takes place. 3. The ovule containing the embryo sac. 4. The nucleus. 5. Any organic center.

mesoblastesis. The medial growth from lichen hyphae.

mesoblastic. Developing from the middle layer, the mesoblast.

mesocarp. The middle layer (between the endocarp and the exocarp) of the pericarp which consists of three layers.

mesocauleorhiza. The lines of demarcation between the ascending systems (stems) and the descending systems (roots) in plants.

mesochil. The intermediate or middle part of the lip of orchids when the lip is separated into three parts.

mesochite. The middle layer which surrounds the egg in *Fucaceae* composed of cellulose and attached at the base.

mesochthonophilous. Growing in the midlands or inland.

mesochthonophytia. A midland plant formation or an inland plant community.

mesocladous. Having branches of medium length.

mesocline. A moist, cool slope; a mesic slope supporting mesophytic plants.

mesocolla. A supposed layer of cuticle between the upper and lower surfaces.

mesocortex. The middle cortex.

mesocotyl. A node in the seedling of grasses interpolated so that the sheath and cotyledon are separated by it.

mesocycle. A layer of tissue between xylem and phloem of a monostelic stem which is a part of the conjunctive tissue.

mesocyst. The definite central nucleus of the embryo sac with which the second antherozoid fuses to form a trophime.

mesoderm. 1. The middle germ layer of the formative tissue composing it. 2. The middle layer of tissue in the capsule of a moss.

mesodes. The two medium cells of the embryo sac of angiosperms which contain the polar nuclei.

mesodesm. Part of the mesocycle.

mesogamy. The fertilization process in some of the *Urticaceae*, nettle family, intermediate between basigamy and acrogamy.

mesogelatin. A gelatinous substance in sea weeds, particularly *Fucales*.

mesogenous. Borne in the middle.

mesogonidium. A gonidium partially developed in new tissue.

mesogonimicous. With the gonidial layer in the center.

mesohabitum. Local or limited variations in an otherwise uniform habitat.

mesohydrophytic. Growing in temperate regions and requiring much moisture, intermediate between mesophytic and hydrophytic.

mesohygromorphic. Mesophytic.

mesohylile. Of moist forests or woodlands.

mesoleucous. Mixed with white.

mesolochmis. Moist thicket associes.

mesology. Bionomics, the study of the relation between an organism and its environment.

mesomelitae. A series of *Gentianeae* which have honey glands in the central portion of the flower.

mesomere. A blastomere of a size intermediate between a macromere and a micromere.

mesomeristem. The thickening Rims of Sanio, markings on the tracheids; mesistem.

mesometatropic. Having an ovary fertilized by pollen from another flower.

mesomitosis. Mitosis which takes place within the nuclear membrane without the cooperation of the cytoplasmic elements.

mesomorphous. Not specifically protected against dessicating influences.

mesomycetes. Fungi intermediate between the *Phycomycetes* and the higher fungi.

meson. The central plane or a region of it.

mesopetalum. The labellum or lip of an orchid.

mesophanerophyte. 1. A perennial plant from eight to ten meters high. 2. According to Raunkiaer, a tree eight to thirty meters high.

mesophanerophytium. A community of perennial plants eight to thirty meters tall.

mesophilic bacteria. Bacteria which grow best at temperatures 10-40° C.

mesophilous. Growing in moist soil or in moist areas.

mesophloem. The middle or green bark, the layer between the liber and the outer (usually dry) epiphloem or corky layer.

mesophorbium. An alpine meadow formation or evergreen meadow.

mesophyll. The soft tissue (parenchyma) between the upper and the lower epidermis of the leaf which is chiefly concerned in photosynthesis.

mesophyllous. Having leaves of medium length or of average size for the genus.

mesophyte. 1. A land plant which is adapted to average moisture conditions. 2. A plant inhabiting moist or humid places.

mesophythmile. Inhabiting offshore lake bottoms at six to twenty-five meters.

mesophytia. Moist land communities or inland communities.

mesophytism. The power to withstand a certain amount of aridity.

mesophytium. A mesophytic formation.

mesophytum. 1. The collar or juncture of a stem and root. 2. The demarcation between the internode and petiole.

mesoplankton. Floating animal and plant life from a hundred fathoms down.

mesoplasm. The middle layer of the cytoplasm.

mesoplast. The nucleus of the cell.

mesopod. A fungus which has a central stipe.

mesopodal. Having a central stipe.

mesopodial. Of or pertaining to the mesopodium, the leafstalk or petiole of a leaf.

mesopodium. A leafstalk or petiole of a leaf.

mesopoium. A steppe.

mesoproteioid. Having sclerous cells derived from the middle zone of the mesophyll.

mesopteridetum. An association of *Pteris* (bracken fern), *Holcus lanatus* (fog grass), and *Scilla festalis* (blue bell).

mesopus. With a central stalk or central stem.

mesosaprobia. Organisms which require a small amount of impurity, as algae growing in contaminated water.

mesosaprophyte. The fungus which has its mycelium completely within the host but which produces external fruit bodies.

mesosere. The eosere of the Mesozoic Period, a mesophytic eosere.

mesosperm. 1. The second membrane or middle coat of a seed, the sarcoderm. 2. The secondary or inner coat of an ovule called the tegmen in the seed.

mesospore. 1. The middle portion of the spore in *Isoetes* which develops inside the outer layer and sometimes has ridges or other ornamentation. 2. The one-celled teliospore found among the two-celled spores of the rusts. 3. An urediospore which germinates after a long resting period (an amphispore).

mesosporinium. The middle coat of a pollen grain in angiosperms.

mesostate. An intermediate stage in metabolism.

mesostatic. Developing a mesophytic succession under conditions with adequate moisture.

mesostylous. Having flowers with styles of intermediate length.

mesothamnium. A maquis formed of hard-leaved shrubs, partly laurifruticeta, partly durifruticeta.

mesothecium. 1. The middle covering layer of an anther sac. 2. The ascigerous thecium of lichens.

mesotherm. A plant thriving in moderate heat and moisture, a plant of the temperate regions, a mesothermophyte.

mesothermophilous. Dwelling in the temperate zone.

mesothermophytia. Temperate plant communities.

mesotriarch. A triarch stele resulting from the fusion of the two principal xylem bundles.

mesotrophic. Moderately provided with nutrients, as the peat of transitional moors.

mesotropic. Of a mesic succession which tends toward hydrophytism.

mesoventral. In the middle ventral region.

mesoxerophytic. Midway between mesophytic and xerophytic.

mesoxylic. Mesarch.

Mesozoic. The middle or secondary geological era, the age of reptiles.

mesquite. *Prosopis glandulosa*, a desert shrub.

messmates. 1. Symbionts. 2. A usual association of different species of eucalypti.

mestome. The conducting portion of a vascular bundle including the hadrome and leptome, the functional tissue in distinction from the cortical tissue which chiefly gives support, mestom.

mestome bundle. A fibrovascular bundle.

mestome sheath. A bundle sheath, a fibrovascular bundle without either wood or bast fibers.

metabasidium. A degenerate basidium or one no longer exhibiting its typical form, that stage of development of the basidium when the diploid nucleus divides.

metabiont. A polyplastid, a many-celled individual.

metabiosis. 1. The condition in which one organism lives only after another has prepared its environment and has died. 2. The dependence of one organism upon another.

metabiotic. Of or related to metabiosis.

metablast. The nucellus.

metabolic force. Vital activity.

metabolic nucleus. A resting nucleus, i.e., when the chromatin is in the form of a network and is not dividing.

metabolic stage. The resting stage.

metabolism. 1. The sum total of the continuous chemical processes taking place in a living organism. 2. The physico-chemical processes within a cell that build up and tear down protoplasm.

metabolite. A product of metabolism.

metabolize. To change by metabolism.

metaboly. The power possessed by some cells to alter their external form.

metacellulose. The cellulose found in fungi and lichens, fungine.

Metachlamydeae. The *Compositae* or *Gamopetalae.*

Metachlamydeae, Age of. A term for the present geological age subsequent to the Glacial Age.

metachlorophyllin. A class of chlorophyll derivatives, the crystallizable chlorophyll.

metachromasy. The condition of certain tissues and cell components which, when treated with basic analine stains, show other than the fundamental color constituent; metachromasie.

metachromatic. 1. Changing color. 2. Showing other than basic color constituents after staining. 3. Changing or losing color in flowers from aging or fading.

metachromatic granules. Bodies in bacteria which take a deep stain.

metachromatin. A complicated substance supposed to be a compound of nucleic acid which occurs as granules in cytoplasm, volutin.

metachromatinic. Composed of metachromatin.

metachromatinic grains. Chromatoid bodies found in cells very similar to chromatin in properties and characteristics.

metachromosomes. Certain bodies found in the hyphae of ascomycetes which appear to be chromatin.

metaclinic. With a reversed cross in hybridizing.

metacollenchyma. A result of secondary metamorphosis of tissue which has taken place at a later period.

metacorm. The plant body after the differentiation of the permanent members.

metacrasis. Kinetic metabolism, the transmutation of energy.

metacribal bands of bastparenchyma. Tangential layers.

metacyclic. Exhibiting final infective forms of certain parasitic protozoa which pass on to the next host.

metaderma. A modified tissue which takes

the place of cork in some structures but does not possess the properties of cork.

metadromous. Having the primary veins of each leaf segment arise from the upper side of the midrib.

metagametal rejuvenescence. The ability of individual cells or groups of cells to unite to give rise to new organisms as in the union of gametes which unite to form zygotes.

metagamophytes. The highest group of phanerogams, siphonogamia.

metagenesis. 1. The alternation of sexual and asexual generations in the life cycle of an organism. 2. The production of sexual individuals by nonsexual means, either directly or through intervening generations. 3. Polymorphism.

metagymnospermae. The higher gymnosperms, *Coniferae*, fertilized by means of pollen tubes.

metagyny. The condition in which male flowers mature sexually before the female.

metakinesis. 1. The middle stage of mitosis during which chromosomes are grouped in the equatorial plate. 2. The separation of the threads in the metaphasic stage of nuclear division.

metamere. One of any number of similar parts in a series, a segmented part, a phyton.

metamerism. The state of being made up of metameres or similar segments arranged serially.

metamerization. 1. The multiplication of floral elements. 2. The formation or differentiation of metameres.

metamerous. Segmented or articulated.

metamitosis. Mitosis in which the nuclear membrane disappears and the karyokinetic figure lies free in the cytoplasm, an advanced mitosis in which both the cytoplasmic and nuclear elements take part.

metamorphogenesis. The process by which organs change from their normal to abnormal conditions by means of transitional forms.

metamorphosis. A transformation, an evolution, the sum of various modifications through which primitive plant structures may pass in their development.

metanaphytosis. The formation of floral envelopes.

metandry. The condition when the female flowers mature before the male.

metanema. The second stage in germination of mosses which succeeds the protonema stage.

metanimic. Of a temporary stream.

metanthesis. Retarded floral development, as opposed to proanthesis.

metanym. A taxonomic term used for a synonymous name rendered invalid by the existence of an earlier valid name for the same species or other plant group.

metaphase. The stage in mitosis during which the chromosomes aggregated in the equatorial region of the spindle divide longitudinally and the daughter chromosomes move toward the poles of the spindle.

metaphase plate. The equatorial plate formed during cell division.

metaphasis. The separation of the daughter chromosomes in nuclear division.

metaphery. The condition in which organs are displaced.

metaphloem. The later-formed elements of the primary phloem consisting of sieve tubes, fibers, and parenchyma.

metaphylla. The mature leaf as opposed to the young form.

metaphysis. A thick sterile filament, free above, in fructifications of fungi.

metaphytes. 1. Multicellular plants with differentiated tissue. 2. Plants which develop sexual structures and reproduce sexually.

metaplasia. The conversion of tissue from one form to another.

metaplasis. The mature period in the life of an individual.

metaplasm. The lifeless ingredients of the cell protoplasm such as amides, enzymes, carbohydrates, fats, etc., which may be converted into protoplasmic secretions or cell walls; deutoplasm.

metaplast. A tissue which has taken on a changed appearance due to increased or decreased metabolism.

metaplastic bodies. Grains or granules in protoplasm which are not true protoplasm.

metaplastid. A product of cell activity which remains stored up in the protoplasm.

metaplasy. Any progressive change of cells other than by growth or division, such as by change of cell contents.

metarabin. A substance present in some varieties of gum arabic, possibly identical with the pectose of sugar beets.

metasitism. The change from inorganic to organic food, the change in the assimilation of food as exhibited by plants and animals.

metasperm. 1. An angiosperm or plant having seeds in a closed ovary. 2. The large-celled secondary prothallium in *Selaginella*. 3. The secondary endosperm in gymnosperms.

metaspermous. Angiospermous.

metasporophyte. A cryptogam of the highest specialization, as *Selaginella*.

metastasis. 1. The process by which plants convert one form of vegetable matter into another, metabolism. 2. The shifting of an organ to some unusual position.

metastructure. An ultramicroscopic organization.

metasyndesis. The stage in meiotic reduction in which the chromosomes are united, telosynapsis.

metatonic. Having a stimulus which reverses action.

metatopic. Having an imbricated bud covering which has departed from the course of the normal genetic spiral by secondary development.

metatracheal. Having wood parenchyma which forms tangential bands or layers.

metatracheal parenchyma. Parenchyma occurring in wood scattered throughout the annual ring forming tangential bands.

metatrophic. Living on both nitrogenous and carbonaceous organic matter.

metatrophism. The correlated catabolism of the reserves and the anabolism of the living tissues.

metatrophs. The saprophytic fungi which feed upon decaying matter.

metatrophy. Metasitism, cannibalism.

metatype. A specimen from the original locality recognized as authentic by the describer himself.

metaxenia. The influence exerted by the pollen on the female tissues, the influence of the male germ cell after fertilization on the ovary and adjacent parts.

metaxin. A proteid, the material of the fibrils of the plastids.

metaxylem. The later-formed primary xylem having pitted tracheary elements, the central wood as distinguished from the peripheral xylem strands.

meteoric. Having flowers whose expansion is influenced by the weather.

methane. Marsh gas; an odorless, light, flammable gas accumulated in swamps, mines, oil wells, etc., from the decomposition of organic matter.

methodical selection. The initiation by man of the operation of natural selection as he attempts to secure the favorable development of especially desirable characteristics in domesticated animals and plants.

methyl alcohol. The least complicated alcohol, the esters of which are found in plants. Methanol.

metistoid. Composed of differentiated cells each cell being dependent on the other cells of the organism.

metoecious. Existing on different hosts, heteroecious, metoxenous.

metoecism. Heteroecism.

metonym. A synonymous name rendered invalid by the existence of an earlier valid name for the same species or other plant group.

metoxenous. Parasitic on different hosts at different stages in the life history, metoecious, heteroecious.

metrogonidium. A heterocyst.

metromorphic. Resembling the mother.

Mettenian glands. Organs peculiar to the *Plumbaginaceae* which secrete mucilage and sometimes chalk.

metulae. The outermost branches from which phialides radiate in *Aspergillaceae*.

metuliform. Shaped like a pyramid.

metuloid. A modified cystidium encrusted with lime projecting from the hymenium of hydnums having a velvety appearance under the lens.

mexicanus. Mexican.

miasma. Infectious particles or germs floating in the air.

micaceous. Covered with glistening mica-like particles, glittering, shining, micans.

micella. A hypothetical unit or aggregation of molecules of which organisms are composed.

micellar aggregate. A combination of micellae.

michauxiod. Like *Michauxia* (of *Campanulaceae*).

Michurinism. The principles expounded by the Russian horticulturist Michurin, as: Mendelian genetics are valid only on the condition that both parents and the hybrids are grown in the same environment; dominance is subject to environmental control; the transmission of hereditary characters is dependent on the comparative vigor of the parents; the genetical constitution of a scion of stock may be modified by grafting.

micracanthous. With small spines.

micraeroxyl. A dwarf woody plant with one main axis and with branches free from the soil.

micrander. A dwarf male.

micranthous. With small flowers.

micrembryae. Monocotyledons with very small ovaries or embryos surrounded by endosperm.

microaerophile. An organism which thrives better in a low concentration of oxygen than with the normal concentration of oxygen.

microaerophilous. Needing little oxygen.

microaplanospore. A small nonmotile spore.

microbacteria. Very small bacteria.

microbasis. A small carcerule, as in the *Labiatae*.

microbe. A microorganism or bacterium.

microbiology. The biology of small organisms.

microcarpous. With small fruits, microcarpon.

microcentrum. 1. The dynamic center of a cell which is composed of centrosomes. 2. The granular inclusion of the astrosphere of leucocytes.

microcephalous. Having a very small head.

microchilum. A small lip.

microchloroplasts. The minute granules of chlorophyll in *Tillandsia*, Spanish moss, which make up the megachloroplasts.

microchromosomes. 1. Chromosomes which are much smaller than the other members of the set. 2. Small chromosomes which do not pair or form a chiasma until metaphase.

microcladous. Having small branches.

microclema. Small branchlets.

microclimate. The actual ecoclimate in which an individual lives.

microconidiophore. A conidiophore bearing microconidia.

microconidium. The smaller of two conidia sometimes found to be spermatia.

microconjugant. A motile, ciliated, free-swimming conjugant or gamete which becomes attached to a macrogamete and fertilizes it; a microgamete.

microculture. A microscopic culture, such as a hanging drop, for continuous microscopic observation.

microcyclic. 1. Short-cycled. 2. Having mycelium only in the haploid phase, as some *Uredinales*.

microcyst. A resting stage of the swarm cells in myxomycetes which are surrounded by a wall and become dormant until favorable conditions arise.

microcytase. The enzyme produced by microphages or smaller leucocytes.

microcyte. A detached chromosome.

microdasys. Small, thick, shaggy.

microderm. A microbe.

microdiodange. A pollen sac.

microdiode. A pollen grain.

microdont. Having small teeth.

microfibril. A fine thread of cellulose in a cellulose cell-wall.

microflora. The microscopic flora of a given locality.

microform. 1. A microteliospore which germinates after a resting period. 2. An elementary or Jordan species.

microfungi. Minute fungi.

microgametangium. A gametangium producing microgametes.

microgametes. The smaller or male gamete.

microgametogenesis. The development of microgametes.

microgametophyte. The individual in a dioecious species which bears male sex organs.

microgamy. The fusion between two of the smallest individuals produced by fission or gemmation, merogamy.

microgene. A form of microspecies or variety.

microgeoxyle. A low woody plant with numerous stems which arise from a subterranean root stock.

microgerm. A microbe.

microglossus. With a small tongue.

microgonidia. 1. The smaller gonidia of algae which are usually the male gonidia or androspores. 2. The minute green algae found in the hyphae of lichens.

micrography. The description or study of microscopic objects, micrology.

microhabit. A small habitat within a recognized area, such as a dead tree or fallen log.

microhenad. An organism which is small enough to pass through a filter.

microlepis. With small scales.

microlichens. Minute lichens.

micromelittophilae. Plants whose flowers are pollinated by small bees and similar insects.

micromere. The smaller blastomere of an egg with unequal cleavage.

micromeris. Having a small number of parts.

micrometer. A glass disc ruled with lines in microns to form a metric scale for measuring objects under the microscope.

micromorph. A microspecies or microgene.

micromyiophilae. Flowers pollinated by small flies which are often imprisoned.

micronemeous. Having small or short hyphae.

micronic. Visible under a microscope.

micronucleus. The centrosome, the fragments of the nucleus when it breaks up.

microorganism. Any organism of microscopic size.

microparasite. A parasite of microscopic size.

micropetalous. With small petals.

microphages. Very small phagocytes or leucocytes.

microphagous. Feeding on small objects.

microphanerophyte. A tree two to eight meters high.

microphyle. A micropyle.

microphyll. A small leaf.

microphylline. Composed of small leaflets or scales.

microphyllous. Having small or reduced leaves, as in xerophytic plants.

microphytes. Microscopic plants, bacteria, and smaller algae.

microphytic community. A community composed exclusively of lichens or algae.

microphytology. The study of microphytes, chiefly bacteriology.

micropodous. With a small foot.

microprothallus. A reduced prothallus due to the germination of a microspore in the *Pteridophyta* or gymnosperms.

micropteres. Furrows in the stems of plants.

micropterous. With small wings.

microptilous. Brevibracteate, with small bracts.

micropuccinia. Teleutospores.

micropycnidium. A structure in which small asexual conidiospores (micropycnidiospores) are formed, a small pycnidium.

micropycnidiospores. The asexual spores borne in micropycnidia.

micropylar. Of or pertaining to a micropyle.

micropylar funnel. The lower funnel-shaped part of the micropyle where it joins the seed cavity.

micropylar membrane. The integument lining the micropyle.

micropylar scar. The spot on the ripe seed occupied by the micropyle.

micropylar tube. The passage formed by the micropyle.

micropyle. A tiny opening in the integument at the apex of an ovule through which the pollen usually enters. 2. The corresponding opening in the testa of the seed through which water may enter when the embryo plant starts to develop.

micropyliferous tubes. The foramen of the outer coat of the ovule, the exostome.

microrhabdus. A minute rod-like spicule.

microsclerote. A sclerotium which has become modified by unfavorable conditions which after a resting period develops into a perithecium.

microsepalous. Having small sepals.

microsomes. Granules in protoplasm which have a high degree of refraction and stain deeply with haematoxylin. They are regarded as an essential part of the structure of protoplasm.

microsoroma. The pollen-bearing apparatus.

microsorus. The male sorus in *Azolla*, a water fern.

microspecies. Species found on very minute differences; see JORDANON.

Microspermae. The monocotyledonous order to which the orchids belong.

microsphere. The centrosome in nuclear division, the central region of the aster (centrosphere) at the center of which lie the centrioles.

microsporangiate flower. A male or staminate flower.

microsporangium. The structure in which microspores are developed, the structure in which anther is borne, an anther sac.

microspore. The smaller spore in heterosporous plants, a pollen grain, the spore giving rise to the male gametophyte or prothallium.

microspore mother cell. The cell giving rise to the tetrad of microspores.

microsporocarp. The growth in the water fern *Azolla* from which the microsporangia are formed.

microsporocyte. The mother cell of a microspore or pollen grain.

microsporogenesis. The development of the pollen grain or microspore.

microsporophore. An organ bearing microspores, a microsporange.

microsporophyll. A small leaf-like structure bearing microspores, a stamen.

microsporophyllary flower. A male or staminate flower.

microstemous. Of small filaments or stemlets.

microstome. A small opening or orifice.

microstomous. Having a small opening.

microstrobilus. 1. The microsporangiate cone or the structure producing microsporangia. 2. An aggregate of microsporophylls.

microstylous. 1. Having short styles. 2. Having flowers with short styles and long filaments.

microsymbiont. The smaller of two associated organisms.

microthele. A small nipple.

microtherm. 1. A plant requiring little heat (0-20°C), little sun and uniformly distributed moisture. 2. A plant of the arctic alpine zone. 3. A plant which can endure frost and cold during the vegetative season and usually complete its life cycle in a short time.

microthermophilous. Dwelling in the arctic regions.

microthermophyta. Artic plants.

microthermophytia. Arctic forest communities.

microtome. An instrument for cutting sections of tissue for microscopic examination.

microtrichous. Having a pubescence so minute that a microscope must be used to see it, microtrichal.

microtype. The type-specimen of a microspecies.

microzoid. A male gamete in algae.

microzoogloea. A stage of schizomycetes when they are immersed in a gelatinous envelope.

microzoogonidium. A motile microgonidium having the power of conjugation.

microzooid. One of the minute free zooids in unicellular organisms with dimorphic zooids.

microzoophilous. Pollinated by insects or other small animals.

microzoophobous. Repelling insects and small animals.

microzoospore. A small motile spore.

microzyme. 1. A microscopic organism capable of producing fermentation. 2. A substance found in some tissues which is strongly antagonistic to and destructive of bacteria, a microsome.

mictium. A heterogenous mixture of plants

in an area, as contrasted with zoned areas; see ECOTONE, ALTERNES.

mictohaploidy. The condition of a haplont in which the cells contain differentiated nuclei of different sexes.

mictohaplont. A haplont the cells of which are of a different genotypic constitution, a haplont with sexually differentiated nuclei.

midintermediate. Midagrarian and midarctic zones of vegetation.

midbody. The cell plate in the higher plants formed during the anaphase of mitosis at the equatorial region of the spindle.

miderror. A deviation.

midrace. An intermediate race which may be improved by artificial selection.

midrib. The midvein or the central vein of a leaf.

midseral community. A community below the rank of subclimax communities but above the rank of initial communities.

midsummer growth. An occasional second growth in trees after interruption.

midvein. A midrib.

middle lamella. A thin layer of primary wall forming the middle layer of the wall between two adjacent cells. It often consists largely of pectin and stains differently from the cellulose wall layers on each side of it.

middle lamina. The portion of a lignified cell wall between the middle lamella and the inner lamina.

middle layer of cytoplasm. The bulk of cytoplasm between the ectoplasm and the tonoplast generally consisting of granular protoplasm.

middle piece. A vague designation for the part of the sperm which lies between the head and the main part of the flagellum.

migrant. A plant that is migrating or invading.

migrarc. A migration circle.

migration. 1. The movement of plants into a new area. 2. The passage of a nucleus from a vegetative to a fertile cell.

migration circle. A circle used to measure the extent of plant migration.

migration pseudoplasmodium. The migration phase in *Dictyostelium discoideum* following the aggregation of the *Myxamoebae*.

migrule. The unit or agent of migration, a disseminule.

mikanioid. Like *Mikania*, a composite.

mikroflora. Microflora.

mikrospecies. A variety.

miktohaploidy. See MICTOHAPLOIDY.

miktohaplont. See MICTOHAPLONT.

mildew. A disease of plants produced by various fungi, usually by ascomycetes.

miliaceus. Pertaining to millet, a cereal grass.

miliarius. A minute glandular spot on the epiderm, miliaris.

miliary. Of granular appearance, granulate, resembling many seeds.

miliary glands. Stomata.

milk. Latex, an opaque white juice.

milk sac. A kind of laticiferous vessel existing in some species of maple.

milk sap. Latex.

milk vessels. Laticiferous vessels.

millefolious. 1. With a thousand leaves. 2. With very many parts.

mimeotypes. Forms resembling each other, fulfilling similar functions, and representing each other in different floras.

mimicry. The resemblance of one species to another or to some natural object in such a way as to be protective against possible enemies. The resemblance may be in color or structure.

mimosaceous. Resembling or related to *Mimosa*, a leguminose genus, mimosoid.

mineralization. The deposition of calcium salts, silica, and other inorganic substances on or in a cell wall.

miniate. Vermillion.

minimal area. A minimum area required by a plant community for its normal development, Minimalraum.

minimiareal. The smallest sample area (one quadrat to the stand) which will show most or all of the constant species for the community type.

minimum effective temperature. The lowest threshold of development.

minimum law. Leibig's law.

minimum quadrat area. A quadrat of the least size to provide an adequate sample of the data.

minimum temperature. The temperature below which growth does not take place.

minus. Having spores whose nuclei are presumably female.

minus strain. One of the two distinct strains of a heterothallic mold-strain.

minutiflorous. With minute flowers.

minutifolious. With minute leaves.

Miocene. The geological period between Pliocene and Oligocene.

miombo. The leguminose *Berlinia globiflora* woodland in Tanganyika.

miophylly. Meiophylly.

miostemonous. Meiostemonous, with fewer stamens.

mire. Wet, spongy earth; a marsh, a boggy place.

mischomany. An increase over the usual number of pedicels.

misdivision. A crosswise division of the kinetochore instead of the normal lengthwise split.

mistassinicus. Of Lake Mistassini, Quebec.

mistoform. A hybrid or cross from forms which themselves have varied from the original.

mistoproliform. A fertile hybrid of mistoforms.

mistus. A mixtus or crossbreed.

mitochondria. Protoplasmic inclusions of all living cells (except in bacteria and some algae) which take the form of filamentous or rod-like bodies (chondrioconts) and are believed to play an active part in the production of some types of secretions, as enzymes; protoplasmic particles which play an important part in metabolism of fats and proteins.

mitogenetic rays. Rays which seem to influence plant growth. They are emitted by actively growing plant parts. They are believed to be ultraviolet rays of low intensity.

mitokineticism. Kinesis which reveals itself by thread structures.

mitokinetism. A theoretical special form of energy involved in the formation and action of the mitotic figure.

mitome. The reticulum or network of threads found in the cell protoplasm as distinguished from the ground substance, mitom.

mitoplast. A band appressed to the nuclear membrane of *Selaginella* which divides just before cell division, the successive divisions of which give rise to several chloroplasts.

mitoschisis. Indirect nuclear division, mitosis.

mitosic. Pertaining to, characterized by, or exhibiting mitosis; mitotic.

mitosis. The series of changes through which the nucleus passes during ordinary cell division and by which each daughter cell is provided with a set of chromosomes similar to that possessed by the parent cell, the nuclear division of the somatic cells, the process by which the chromosomes are separated without change into two groups forming two daughter nuclei.

mitosome. A cytoplasmic body presumed to be derived from the spindle fibers of the preceding mitosis, the spindle remnant.

mitotic. Of or pertaining to mitosis, karyokinetic.

mitra. 1. A helmet-shaped part of a calyx or a corolla. 2. The mitriform pileus of certain fungi. 3. The galea of a corolla. 4. The calyptra of a moss.

mitrate. Mitre-shaped.

mitriform. Shaped like a mitre or peaked cap and symmetrically cleft on two or more sides, mitraeform.

Mitscherlich's law. A statement that with a significant increase, decrease, or absence of an essential factor the yield of a plant will be altered according to the proportion of change from the ideal conditions which produce the maximum yield.

mixed bud. A bud with the embryonic shoot bearing both leaves and flowers.

mixed forest. A forest with various kinds of trees, a forest with coniferous and broad-leaved trees or evergreen and deciduous trees.

mixed formation. A plant formation resulting from the mingling of two or more neighboring formations.

mixed inflorescence. An inflorescence in which some of the branching is racemose and some is cymose, a compound inflorescence having both determinate and indeterminate flower clusters.

mixed leaf. A compound leaf containing divisions of various grades or degrees.

mixed pith. A pith consisting chiefly of parenchyma but with isolated tracheids scattered in it.

mixed vessel. A vessel exhibiting both spiral and annular thickening.

mixie. The fusion of two similar nuclei to form the product mixote.

mixochimaera. The artificial mingling of spore material producing plus, minus, and neutral mycelia; heterocaryosis.

mixochromosome. A new chromosome formed by the fusion of a pair of normal chromosomes in syndesis and synapsis.

mixoploid. Having different numbers of chromosomes in contiguous cells or tissues.

mixote. The product resulting from the fusion of two similar nuclei.

mixotroph. A plant with insufficient chlorophyll to insure proper assimilation in photosynthesis.

mixotrophic. Half saprophytic, both holophytic and saprophytic, deriving part of its nourishment from an outside source.

mixtae. Homosporous ferns which produce

sporangia in succession in time but not in space.

mixtinervius. Having veins of various sizes.

mnemon. The elementary factors of heredity.

mnioid. Resembling the moss genus *Mnium*, sometimes used to indicate resemblance to any moss.

mobilideserta. Open plant communities maintained by an unstable substratum, as shifting sand dunes or landslides.

mobility. The ability of a species to move out of the parent area.

mock plums. Abnormal growths also known as bay plums or pocket plums.

modal. Diplobiontic.

mode. The class of greatest frequency or the most common or typical value of a racial character.

mode spores. Modal spore variations in size and shape due to the substratum upon which organisms grow.

moder. Undecomposed organic matter, raw humus, or leaf duff which forms a mat or carpet on top of the mineral soil. It is often held together with fungus hyphae. Mor.

modification. A change in a plant brought about by environmental conditions and lasting only as long as the operative conditions exist, alteration or change of a partial character.

modification forms. Inconstant variations due to alterations in external conditions.

modifier. A hereditary factor which affects the expression of a gene, a modifying factor.

modifying factors. Factors whose principal influence is seen in modifying other factors or the characters to which they give rise.

modioliform. 1. Like the hub of a wheel. 2. Depressed with a narrow orifice, as the ripe fruit of *Gaultheria*, wintergreen.

moesiacus. Of the Balkan region or the ancient Moesians.

moisture equivalent. The moisture equivalent denotes the water content of soil after it has been subjected, usually for 30 minutes, to a centrifugal force 1000 times gravity in a soil centrifuge. The wilting coefficient $= \dfrac{ME}{1.8}$.

mold. 1. A downy or furry growth caused by fungus mycelium. 2. Loose, easily worked soil rich in organic matter, as leaf mold.

moldavicus. Of Moldavia.

molecular sieve theory. An hypothesis that small particles can pass through small pores of a membrane.

molendinaceous. Having large wing-like expansions like the sails of a windmill.

molinetum. A plant succession composed of *Molinia caerulea*, a grass of wet moors.

mollis. Smooth and soft.

moluccanus. Of the Moluccas in the East Indies.

molybdeous. Lead colored, plumbeous.

monacanthous. With one spine.

monacmis. Having only one period of maximum vigor in the year (of diatoms).

monacrorhizae. Roots derived from a single mother cell, as most vascular crytogams except *Lycopodium* and *Isoetes*.

monacrorhize. Having roots derived from a single mother cell.

monad. 1. A primitive organism or organic unit. 2. A minute, simple flagellated organism. 3. A zoospore.

Monadelphia. The Linnaean class containing flowers with monadelphous stamens, i.e., those united by their filaments into a tube or column.

monadelphous. With stamens united into a tube by their filaments.

monadnock. A hill resistant to erosion which stands alone in a peneplane.

Monandria. A class of Linnaeus for plants with one-stamened flowers.

monandrous. 1. Having only one perfect stamen. 2. Having one antheridium. 3. Monandrian.

monangial. 1. With a sorus consisting of a single sporangium. 2. Having a sporangium enclosed by a hood-like indusium. 3. Monangic.

monanthous. With one flower or one flower on a pedicel.

monarch. 1. Having a single strand of xylem and phloem. 2. Having only one protoxylem. 3. A monarch bundle.

monarinus. Monandrous.

monoarthrodactylous. Having one-jointed, finger-like branches, as in *Nitella*.

monaster. A stage in karyokinesis in which the nuclear threads lie in the equator of the nucleus, usually in the form of loops, with their free ends pointing away from the center; the mother star.

monaxon. 1. A type of spicule built upon a single axis. 2. The situation in which the two transverse axes of an organ or organism are equal.

monecious. Monoecious.

monembryonic. Producing one embryo at a time, as in most seed plants.

monera. Hypothetical units of protoplasm postulated as the lowest members of the evolutionary series but for which no evidence has ever been found.

monergic. Consisting of one energid, i.e., one unit or nucleus; monergidic.

moneriod. Like monera, a protistoid body.

mongolicus. Of Mongolia.

moniform. Moniliform.

monile. A chain, a necklace.

moniliferous. Resembling a necklace.

moniliform. Resembling a string of beads, cylindrical with contractions at intervals.

monoascous. Containing a single ascus.

monoaxial. In algae, having one main filament or branch with small filaments attached laterally on all sides, uniaxial.

monobasic. Having a root which is reduced to a small unbranched portion as though it were only the base of the stem.

monoblastesis. Mesoblastesis.

monoblastus. A lichen spore with a single cell.

monocarotin. A lipochrome pigment allied to carotin, the coloring matter in a carrot root.

monocarp. A plant that fruits only once, as an annual.

monocarpellary. Containing a single carpel, monogynous.

monocarpic. Fruiting only once.

monocarpic biennial. A biennial plant fruiting only once.

monocarpic perennial. A plant which lives several years before fruiting and perishing.

monocarpous. Having one ovary in the gynoecium, having one carpel.

monocaryon. The uninucleate phase, the haplont.

monocaryon mycelium. A mycelium in which the cells contain a single haploid nucleus.

monocaryophyte. The primary mycelium of the basidiomycetes each cell of which contains a single haploid nucleus.

monocentric. Having one center of growth and differentiation which becomes a reproductive structure.

monocephalous. 1. Having only one capitulum or head. 2. Applied to an ovary having only one style or to flowers disposed in single umbels or other clusters.

monocerous. Having one horn.

monochasium. A one-sided cyme with one main axis, a uniparous cyme.

Monochlamydeae. A large division of phanerogams which have only one set of floral envelopes, the *Apetalae.*

monochlamydeous. 1. Of or pertaining to the *Monochlamydeae.* 2. Having a flower with only one whorl of the perianth. 3. Having either petals or sepals, not both. 4. Apetalous.

monochlamydeous chimaera. A haplochlamydeous chimaera.

monochromic. Of one color, unicolorous.

monochromosomic. Having only one chromosome.

monochronic. Arising only one time.

monoclimax. A single climax for all series and successions, a climatic climax.

monoclinous. With both stamens and pistils in each flower, hermaphroditic.

monoclonal. In a succession derived asexually from a common ancestor (a single clone).

monocormic. Having one main tree-axis bearing lateral branches of a bilateral structure.

Monocotylae. *Monocotyledoneae.*

monocotyledon. 1. A plant having an embryo with one cotyledon or only one seed leaf. 2. The cotyledon itself.

Monocotyledonae. Angiosperms having a single cotyledon, no consecutive layers of wood in the stem, leaves with parallel veins, and flower parts usually in multiples of three.

monocotylous. Monocotyledonous.

monocyclic. Having one whorl or cycle of floral parts, monocyclous.

monocystic. Having one cell or cavity.

monodactylous. Having only one digit.

monodelphous. Said of stamens united by their filaments into one set, monadelphous.

monodesmic. Having a single vascular bundle or meristele (used of petioles).

monodichlamydeous. Having either one or both sets of floral envelopes.

monodynamous. Having one stamen much longer than the other.

Monoecia. A Linnaean class characterized by having flowers with sexes separate but on the same plant.

monoecious. 1. Having stamens and pistils in separate flowers on the same plant. 2. Having a gametophyte which bears both male and female organs. 3. With microspores and megaspores on the same plant. 4. Monoicous.

monoecious homogamy. Fertilization from another inflorescence of the same plant.

monoeciously polygamous. Having perfect and imperfect flowers on the same plant.

monoecism. The possession of monoecious flowers.

monoenergid. A protoplast possessing a single nucleus.

monoepigynia. Monocotyledons with epigynous stamens.

monofacial. With a folded leaf as that of *Iris*.

monofactorial. Controlled by a single gene (factor) in inheritance.

monogam. A plant with simple flowers but united anthers.

Monogamia. A Linnaean order in the *Compositae* with united anthers but flowers free on the same receptacle.

monogamous. Paired with a single mate.

monogenesis. 1. The development of organisms through sexual reproduction. 2. The origin of new forms at a single place or time. 3. The theory that all organisms develop from single cells.

monogenetic reproduction. Asexual reproduction.

monogenocentric. Reproductocentric.

monogenodifferent. Having hybrids in which the gametes differ from each other in a single point.

monogenous. Endogenous, asexual.

monogenus. Monocotyledonous, monotypic.

monogony. Nonsexual or asexual reproduction.

monograph. An exhaustive systematic account of a particular genus, order, or group.

monogyn. A plant having a single pistil in the flower.

Monogynia. A Linnaean group of plants with a solitary pistil or style.

monogynoecial. Having simple fruits which develop from the pistil of one flower.

monogynous. Having only one pistil, monogynian.

monohybrid. A hybrid offspring of parents differing in one character.

monohypogynia. Monocotyledonous plants with hypogenous stamens.

monoicodimorphic. Cleistogamic.

monoicous. Having antheridia and archegonia on the same plant (a term used by bryologists), monoecious.

monokaric. Having a single nucleus.

monokaryon. A nucleus with a single centriole, a centrosome, a monocaryon.

monokont. An organism having a single flagellum.

monolepidous. With one scale.

monolepsis. False hybridism, when the characters of only one parent are transmitted.

monolobous. With one lobe.

monolocular. One-celled, applied to anthers and ovaries.

monolophous. Said of spicules with one ray forked or branched like a crest.

monomastigate. Having one flagellum, as certain protista; a monokont.

monomeric. Not broken into segments.

monomeristele. A single outgrowing leaf trace.

monomerous. 1. Of one part. 2. Of flowers having a single organ (one pistil or one stamen). 3. With a fruit from one carpel.

monomial. A name or designation consisting of one term only.

monomitic. With one kind of hyphae.

monomorphic. Producing spores of one form or kind.

monomorphous species. Species in which all the flowers resemble one another in the relative position of the stamens and pistil.

monomycelial. Said of the culture obtained from a single mycelium, as from a single spore or a single hyphal tip.

monont. A single individual which reproduces without conjugation, a zygote.

mononucleus. A single nucleus.

Monopetalae. Sympetalae.

monopetalous. 1. Having only one petal. 2. With petals united all around. 3. Gamopetalous.

monopetaly. Gamopetaly.

monophagous. Limited to one host.

monophylesis. The origin from a single ancestral type.

monophyllous. 1. Having only one leaf, unifoliate. 2. Gamophyllous, with the calyx or corolla in one piece.

monophylogeny. Origination and evolution from a single ancestral stock.

monoplanetic. 1. Of one phase with no resting period. 2. Having one period of locomotion (of zoospores).

monoplast. 1. One nucleus with its associated protoplasm. 2. Protoplasm which is all of one form or type.

monoplastic. 1. With one monoplast. 2. With substance of one kind or form, uniform.

monopleuric cambium. The cambium which produces tissue on only one side.

monoploid. Haploid.

monopodial. 1. Having one continuous main stem or axis. 2. With growth at the apex in the direction of previous growth with the lateral structures of like kind produced beneath the apex in acropetal succession.

monopodial branching. Branching with the apical bud a persistent leader and new branches arising laterally below the apex.

monopodium. A single main or primary axis from which all main lateral branches develop below the apex, a monopode.

monopterous. With one wing.

monopyrenous. Containing a single stone, nutlet, or pyrene.

monosaccharide. Any sugar which cannot be split into simpler sugars.

monosepalous. With sepals united into one piece, gamosepalous.

monosiphonic. Of algae, having a filament on a single row of cells.

monosis. The isolation of one organ from the rest.

monosomatic. Pertaining to a nucleus or cell with the typical diploid number of chromosomes as contrasted with the disomatic, tetrasomatic, etc., condition; exhibiting monosomaty.

monosome. 1. An unpaired chromosome (accessory, sex, or X chromosome). 2. An abberant chromosome which passes undivided into the daughter nuclei. 3. A diploid nucleus with one chromosome of a pair missing, formula (2n-1).

monosomic. Pertaining to a monosome.

monosperm. A plant producing only one seed.

monospermous. Having only one seed or one spore.

monospermy. The normal fertilization in which only one sperm fuses with the egg.

monospirous. Consisting of a single spiralled elator, as in the *Hepaticae*.

monosporangiate. 1. Having only one sporangium. 2. Bearing only one spore. 3. Bearing flowers of only one sex.

monosporangium. A sporangium which produces simple spores, an organ producing monospores.

monospore. 1. A simple undivided spore. 2. The special spore in the alga *Ectocarpus* thought by some to be a gemma.

monosporous. Having only one spore.

monostachous. Arranged in one spike.

monostele. The axis stele when only one is the direct continuation of the plerome.

monostelic. Having a single stele or central cylinder running through the whole axis.

monostelous. Containing an unbranched solid stele occupying a central position.

monosterigmatic. Having one sterigma.

monosteromatic. Consisting of a single layer, as the leaves of mosses and certain algal thalli.

monostichous. Arranged in a single row or along one side.

monostigmatous. Having only one stigma.

monostylous. With a single style.

monosy. The separation of parts which are normally fused.

monosymmetric. Capable of bisection in only one plane, zygomorphic.

monothalamic. 1. Of fruits formed from single flowers having one gynoecium. 2. Applied to apothecia consisting of a single chamber. 3. Unilocular, monothalmic.

monothecal. Having a single loculus or cell.

monotocous. Fruiting once, as annuals or biennials; monocarpic.

monotopic. Originating from a single center of dispersal.

monotrichous. Having only one flagellum at one pole.

monotrophic. Confined to one host species.

monotropic. Visiting only one species of flower.

monotype. A genus having only one species.

monoverticillate. Having one whorl, applied to *Penicillium*, etc.

monoxenous. Restricted to one species of host plants, autoecious.

monoxylic. Said of vascular bundles in which the centrifugal part is primary xylem.

monozygotic. Originating from a single fertilized egg which gives rise to two or more individuals (twins or triplets) which are genetically identical.

monozygous. Linked.

monsoon forest. A tropical deciduous high forest with heavy rainfall and a long dry season, a forest in a monsoon area.

monspeliensis. Of Montpelier.

monspessulanus. Of Montpelier.

monster. A plant or animal having any marked abnormal development in form, an abnormality.

montane. Pertaining to mountains.

monte community. A bushland of thorny growth.

montevidensis. Of Montevideo, Uruguay.

monticolous. Living in the mountains.

montigenus. Mountain-born.

moor. An extensive marshy waste covered with patches of heath and abounding in peat.

mop-headed. Applied to trees with many small branches at the top.

mor. Matted humus, duff, litter, etc.; humus lying on top of the soil. Moder.

mor humus. Poorly decomposed matted humus formed on the surface of acid heaths. The decomposition is retarded by excess acid which hinders the growth of the decomposing microorganisms.

moraine. An accumulation of earth, stone, etc., deposited by glaciers.

morass. Swamp.

morbose. Diseased.

morchelloid. With a hymenium like that of *Morchella*, a helvellaceous fungus, a morel.

mordant. Solutions, usually basic hydroxides, used to fix dyes in tissues prepared for microscopic study.

morea. A hypothetical stage of *Volvox*.

mores. The reactions common to the dominants of a community which have the same habitat requirements and react similarly to the physical factors present. The organisms constituting the more are often of the same species.

mores index. The index of physiological conditions of the environment reflected in the life history of the organism.

mores ratio. The ratio between different life habits which characterize the dominants of a community, such as arboreal.

morgan. A unit of relative distance between genes in a chromosome equal to one percent of crossing over; see MENDEL.

morifolious. With leaves like *Morus*, mulberry.

moriform. With mulberry-like clusters.

morin. A substance derived from the yellow heartwood of fustic, *Maclura aurantiaca*, bois d'arc or mock orange.

morinus. Mulberry black, the deep purple of the ripe fruit of *Morus nigra*.

moroccanus. Of Morocco.

morozymase. An assumed enzyme in the mulberry now thought to be a mixture of diastase and zymase.

morphaestesia. The tendency to assume definite relations of symmetry.

morphallaxis. 1. The transformation of one part into another in the regeneration of parts. 2. The gradual growth or development into a particular form.

morphe. Form.

morphine. The best known of all the alkaloids contained in the opium poppy.

morphocytological. Based on evidence drawn from systematic and genetic sources.

morphogenesis. The origin and development of organs or parts of organisms.

morphogenous irritants. External factors necessary for the start of propagation.

morphogeny. The totality of the adaptations of the plant to its habitat from which its physiognomy results.

morphography. Anatomy and descriptive histology.

morphological alternation of generations. Alternation of generations in which the asexual (2n) generation does not structurally resemble the sexual (n) generation.

morphological species. Species based upon changed morphology in relation to varied environment.

morphology. The study of form and structure.

morphon. A morphological individual.

morphoplasm. Formative protoplasm, kinoplasm.

morphosis. The manner and order of development of a plant part or organism.

morphotic. Tissue-building.

-morphous. A suffix meaning shaped.

mortar fruits. 1. Seeds or fruits enclosed in a persistent calyx which are distributed by wind or animals. 2. Seed pods which eject the seeds.

morulit. A nucleolus or karyosome.

morulose. Purplish black.

mosaic. 1. A display of varying characters in patches in hybrids. 2. A disease of tobacco and other plants evidenced by light and dark green areas on the leaves.

mosaic complex. A phytocoenosis, a complex of comparatively small stands.

mosaic variability. Pattern variation within a habitat.

mosaicus. Parti-colored like a mosaic.

moschate. Musk-scented.

mose. A bog or marsh.

moss. 1. The common name for bryophytes. 2. A lowland moor.

moss carpet. Ground covered with moss.

moss moor. A moor usually higher in the center due to the growth of sphagnum.

Moss-schicht. A ground cover of mosses.

moss tundra. A flat undulating tract devoid of forest covered with mosses in arctic regions.

mossing. In *Cinchona* culture the process of covering decorticated trunks with moss to induce bark formation.

moth flowers. Flowers adapted for pollination by moths.

mother cells. Cells from which one or more new cells arise.

mother-of-coal. Charred wood found in coal.

mother-of-vinegar. A heavy membrane-like formation formed in alcoholic liquids which are being converted into vinegar through alcoholic fermentation.

mother plant. 1. The parent plant from which vegetative portions have been derived. 2. The female or seed-bearing plant of hybrids.

mother skein. A continuous ribbon-like figure of chromatin in the early stages of nuclear division.

mother star. A monaster, a stage of nuclear division.

motile phase. The stage in the life of an organism during which it is free swimming.

motile region. 1. The region of elongation in growing members. 2. An organ such as the pulvinus in *Mimosa pudica*, the sensitive plant.

motility of protoplasm. The contractility of protoplasm.

motion dicogamy. The condition in which the sexual organs vary in length or position during flowering.

motor cell. A cell which may cause movement in a plant member.

motor reflex. A negative chemotropism, a reactive motion.

motor system. A general name for the tissues and structures concerned in the movements of plant members.

motor zone. A motile region.

mountain meadow. A grassland at high altitudes often with shrubs dwarfed from grazing.

movement of variation. See ALLASOTONIC.

moxa. The woody leaves of *Artemisia Moxa*.

mucedin. A tough viscous body associated with gluten in vegetable gelatin.

mucedinous. White and cottony, moldy, musty.

mucic. Gummy.

mucid. Moldy or slimy.

muciform. Like or resembling mucous.

mucigen. The substance of certain granules in the cells of mucous membranes.

mucilage. 1. Dissolved vegetable jelly. 2. Any slimy vegetable product. 3. A gummy secretion. See GUM.

mucilage cell. A plant cell which secretes mucilage.

mucilage duct. A mucilage canal, a space caused by the breakdown of the cell walls.

mucilage glands. The secreting organs at the back of the leaf sheaths and axils in the *Plumbagineae*.

mucilage hairs. The trichomes in some phaeophyceaen alga and some liverworts.

mucilage slit. An opening (like a stomata but without guard cells) on the under surface of the thallus of hornworts (*Anthocerotae*) which lead to a cavity filled with gum.

mucin. A glucoproteid of mucus.

mucine. A water-soluble constituent of wheat gluten.

mucinogen. Any of a class of substances easily converted into mucins by the reaction with alkalis.

muciparous. Mucus-secreting.

muck. Any kind of impure or decayed peat or black swamp earth.

mucocellulose. A substance formed of cellulose mixed with mucus found chiefly in seeds and fruits.

mucocutaneous. Concerning the skin and mucus membrane.

mucoid. Like or caused by mucus.

mucoraceous. Of or pertaining to the *Mucoraceae*, a family of phycomycetous fungi.

mucorin. An albuminoid substance occurring in species of *Mucor*, a genus of mold fungi.

mucorine. Mucedinous, resembling the genus *Mucor*.

mucorini. The reduction of the sporangium to a unicellular conidium.

mucormycosis. A disease due to pathogenic molds of the genus *Mucor* or allied genera.

mucosa. Mucous membranes.

mucous. Slimy, mucilaginous, mucose.

mucro. A sharp terminal point or tip.

mucronate. With a broad apex ending abruptly in a sharp tip or spine.

mucronulate. Slightly or minutely mucronate.

muculent. Mucoid, containing mucous, mucilaginous or gelatinous.

mucus. 1. A gum-like substance which is water soluble. 2. A gelatinous covering. 3. Slime.

mudar. One of the milk weeds (*Asclepiadaceae*) which produces fibers from the bark and floss from the seeds, madar, wara.

mudarin. A substance used as a fiber from the bark of mudar, *Calotropis gigantea* and *C. procera*.

Mueller bodies. Metamorphosed glands found in some plants which form a velvety coating on the underside of the base of the petiole which are used by ants for food.

mulberry. 1. Attractive trees from many regions of the northern hemisphere, species *Morus*. 2. The aggregate fruit of *Morus*.

muld. Mull.

mule. A sterile seedless hybrid.

mulga. A thicket composed chiefly of *Acacia* forming an important feature of vegetation in Australia.

mull. A humus layer, mor, mold.

Müllerian mimicry. The possession of certain warning colors; see BATESIAN MIMICRY.

multi-. A prefix meaning many or much.

multiallelic. Having more than one allele occupying the same position on a chromosome.

multiarticulate. With many joints.

multiaxial. Having the main axis composed of a number of more or less parallel filaments.

multibracteatus. With many bracts.

multicamerate. Multilocular, with many chambers.

multicapsular. Having many capsules.

multicarinate. Having many keels.

multicaulis. With numerous stems.

multicavous. With many hollows.

multicellular. Consisting of more than one cell.

multicentral. Having more than one center of growth and development.

multiceps. With many heads or with many branches.

multiciliate. With many cilia.

multicipital. With many heads or branches arising from one point (usually applied to roots).

multicolor. Having several colors.

multicostate. With many ribs or veins.

multicuspidate. Having many cusps, points, or teeth.

multidentate. With many teeth or indentations.

multidigitate. With many fingers.

multidigitato-pinnatus. Having many secondary petioles with digitate pinnae.

multienzyme system. A situation in which several enzymes stimulate similar reactions at the same time and place without interference.

multifarious. Many ranked, arranged in many rows.

multiferous. Fruitful or producing fruit several times a season.

multifid. Cleft into many lobes or segments.

multifid-crisped. Cut into segments which are spread out and curly.

multiflagellate. Having many flagella.

multiflorous. With many flowers.

multifoliate. With many leaflets.

multiform. Having many shapes, forms, or appearances.

multifurcatus. With many forks or divisions.

multigenic. Pertaining to a character that is controlled by many genes, polygenic.

multiguttulate. With many oil drops.

multigyrate. With many turns.

multijugate. Having many pairs of leaflets.

multijugate types. Leaf arrangements in which the secondary spirals are divisible by a common factor.

multilaminate. Composed of several laminae.

multilateral. Having many sides.

multilateral symmetry. The symmetry of many radial parts.

multilayered. Consisting of several layers of cells.

multilineate. With many lines.

multilobate. Composed of many lobes.

multilobulate. Having many lobules.

multilocular. Having many cells, chambers, or locules; multiloculate.

multilocular spore. A sporadesm, a compound spore.

multiloculares. Compound spores.

multinervate. Having many nerves.

multinodal. With many nodes or internodes.

multinomial. Composed of several names or terms.

multinuclear. Multinucleate, having many nuclei.

multinucleolate. With more than one nucleolus.

multiovulate. With many ovules.

multiparous. Developing several lateral axes, pleiochasial.

multipartite. Finely divided into many parts.

multiple alleles or allelomorphs. A series of three of more alternative forms of a gene occupying a single locus on a chromosome, genes produced by a number of mutations of different natures at the same locus.

multiple chromosome. A chromosome produced by the fusion of two or more chromosomes.

multiple corolla. A corolla with two or more whorls of petals.

multiple division. The repeated division of a

protoplast to form many daughter protoplasts.

multiple factors. Two or more factors all of which are needed to produce a certain result in inheritance.

multiple fission. Repeated division or the division into a large number of parts or spores.

multiple fruit. A collective fruit; a fruit developed from a cluster of flowers, as the pineapple or mulberry.

multiple perforations. Two or more openings in a perforated plate.

multiple primary root. A root with several main divisions from the crown, as in dahlias.

multiple spiral. A system of two or more genetic spirals.

multiplex. Having many of the same parts occur together.

multiplicate flowers. Double flowers.

multiploid. Occurring in even multiples, applied to genera differing in the number of chromosomes.

multipolar. Having more than two poles.

multipolar diarch. A stage in spindle formation during nuclear division.

multipolar spindle. A star-shaped achromatic spindle between several nuclei.

multiradiate. Having many rays.

multiramose. Having many branches.

multisectus. Dissected or cut many times.

multiseptate. Having numerous septa.

multiserial. Arranged in many rows or series.

multisiliquous. Having many pods or seed vessels.

multispiral. With many coils or spirals.

multisporous. Having many spores.

multistaminate. Having many stamens.

multistelic. Polystelic, with many steles.

multisulcate. With many furrows or grooves.

multiternate. In multiples of three.

multituberculate. Having many tubercles.

multivalent. Having a value greater than one, said of a group of chromosomes which are held together at meiosis by mutual attraction or by chiasmata.

multivalve. Having many valves.

multivoltine. Producing several generations a year, each generation taking only a short time for its development.

multizonate. Having many zones.

mummification. The withering and dessication of fruits brought about by the digestion and replacement of the susceptible tissue by the sclerotial stroma of fungi, often by the genus *Ciboria*.

mumonian. Related to Munster, a province in Southwest Ireland.

mundulus. Trim, neat.

mung. A type of grass, the green gram of India, *Phaseolus Mungo*.

munientia folia. Protecting leaves which overhang or otherwise guard parts which need protection.

mural. Growing on walls.

murali-divided. Muriform.

muricate. Rough with minute, sharp points.

muricate-hispid. Covered with short, sharp points and rigid hairs or bristles.

muricate-scabrous. Rough with a short, stiff pubescence or scattered tubercules.

muriform. Having cells like bricks in a wall with both longitudinal and transverse septa.

murine. Mouse gray.

musaform. Resembling the large tropical herbs with perennial, epigeous evergreen stems of involute leaf sheaths, such as *Musa*, banana.

musaicus. Like *Musa*, the banana.

muscardine. A silk worm disease caused by *Botrytis bassiana*.

muscariform. 1. Having long hairs toward the tip like the ancient fly-flap or fly-whisk. 2. Resembling the styles of some *Compositae*.

muscarine. One of the toxic substances of *Amanita muscaria*, the fly agaric, and other poisonous mushrooms; muscarin.

muscarium. A loose, irregular corymb.

musci. Mosses.

muscicoline. Living or growing among mosses.

musciform. 1. Moss-like in appearance. 2. Shaped like a fly (*Muscidae*).

muscipula. 1. A mousetrap. 2. A flycatcher.

muscivorous. Fly-eating.

muscoid. Mossy, muscous, resembling or belonging to moss.

muscology. Bryology, the study of mosses.

muscose. Mossy.

mushroom. A fleshy agaric.

mushroom headed. Having a cylindric body topped by a convex head of larger diameter.

muskeg. A mossy bog of the Canadian forests.

must. Unfermented fruit juice.

mustard. A brassicaceous plant of the genus *Brassica*.

mutable. Capable of mutation.

mutant. An individual bearing a mutation, an individual with a genotypic constitution different from that of its parents and not obtained in the normal process of exchange of genes but by a change in the germ plasm.

mutation. The result of an abrupt change in the genotypic nature independent of normal segregation or crossing over, a sudden variation in an inherited character.

mutation atavism. A tendency to revert to an ancestral type, recessive mutation.

mutation, degressive. A change taking place in the partial latency of a character.

mutation hypothesis. The hypothesis that evolution is founded in mutation.

mutation, progressive. Mutation in which an entirely new character appears.

mutation, retrogressive. The mutation when an active character becomes latent.

mutation theory of evolution. DeVries' theory that new forms evolve suddenly by great mutations rather than by natural selection or by gradual accumulations of small variations.

mutic. Awnless, pointless.

muticate. Blunt, without a point, awnless.

mutilation. The loss of an essential part.

mutilus. Nearly or wholly lacking petals.

mutual parasitium. See SYMBIOSIS and MUTUALISM.

mutual translocation. The reciprocal transfer of parts of two homologous chromosomes.

mutualism. A form of symbiosis in which both parties derive advantage without sustaining injury, commensalism.

mutualistic symbiosis. A reciprocal advantage or mutual service.

mutuality. Mutual benefit or mutual dependence arising from the proximity of plants to one another.

myall. The Australian acacias having hard, fragrant wood.

myc-, mycet-, myceto-, myco-. A prefix meaning fungus.

mycelconidium. A stylospore.

mycele. A mycelium.

myceloid. Resembling a mycelium.

mycelial. Of or pertaining to the mycelium.

mycelial layer. The membranous mycelium.

mycelial strand. Fibrous mycelium.

myceliate. 1. Covered or overgrown with mycelium. 2. Resembling mycelium.

mycelioid. With the characteristics of mycelium.

mycelitha. Sclerotium.

mycelium. 1. A hypha. 2. The plant body of a fungus. 3. A mass of thread-like structures which constitute the thallus of a fungus.

mycelium, filamentous. The thread-like loose felting of hyphae.

mycetism. Poisoning by fungi.

mycetocyte. See MYCETOMA.

mycetodomatia. Fungus chambers which are formations of peculiar characters found on the roots of plants sometimes regarded as possessed with the power of attracting fungi and ingesting them.

mycetogenetic. Produced by fungi.

mycetogenetic metamorphosis. Deformation due to parasitic fungi.

mycetogenous. Producing fungi.

mycetogenous chloranthy. The development of green in organs normally of some other color due to a fungus parasite.

mycetogenous chlorisis. The condition in which the chlorophyll is bleached by the action of the hyphae of some fungi.

mycetoid. Fungoid, with the appearance of fungi.

mycetology. Mycology.

mycetoma. 1. Mycetocytes collectively. 2. A disease of the foot due to a fungus which produces sinuses throughout the member with gradual absorption of the bones.

mycetome. A cellular organ inside an aphid containing symbiotic yeasts.

mycetophagous. Feeding on fungi.

mycetozoa. Myxomycetes.

mychogamia. Self-fertilization of plants.

mycina. A stipitate globular apothecium in lichens.

mycocecidium. A gall caused by a fungus.

mycoclema. The fungus mantle in mycorrhiza.

mycocriny. The reduction of humus by fungi.

mycoderm. A bacterium of alcoholic fermentation.

mycodomatia. Mycetodomatia.

mycogenous. Arising from or growing on fungi.

mycologist. A student of fungi.

mycology. The study of fungi.

mycoma. The body of a fungus.

Mycomycetes. The higher fungi.

mycomycophytes. Fungi and certain lichens.

mycophagist. One who eats mushrooms.

mycophthorous. Said of a fungus parasitic on another fungus.

mycophytic. Belonging to the fungi.

mycophytophytes. Lichens other than mycomycophytes.

mycoplasm. 1. A latent symbiotic form of plant rust (*Puccinia*) which may exist in the seed and later develop into mycelium when the host develops into a plant (Eriksson's explanation of epidemics of plant rust.) 2. The bacterioid rhizobia found in the root nodules of legumes.

mycoprotein. A gelatinous albuminoid resembling protoplasm of which the putrefactive bacteria are composed.

mycorhiza. 1. The stunted rootlets of trees which are coated with or permeated by the mycelium of fungi. 2. The association of a fungus with the roots of a higher plant for mutual benefit.

mycorhizome. A mycorhiza-like structure in the roots of the orchids *Corallorhiza* and *Epipogum.*

mycose. The nitrogenous substances in the cell wall of fungi which corresponds to the chitin of insects.

mycosin. Mycose.

mycosis. A disease of plants or animals caused by parasitic fungi.

mycotic. Caused by fungi (disease).

mycotrophic. Living symbiotically with fungi.

mycrocyst. A microcyst.

mycroprotein. Micoprotein.

mycropyle. Micropyle.

mycrozyme. Microzyme.

myeloid. Like marrow in appearance or structure.

myiophilous plants. Plants with inconspicuous and often ill-smelling flowers pollinated by flies.

mykokleptic. Having hairs on the rhizome which seize the mycelium, as in the orchid *Corallorhiza innata.*

mylitta. A type of sclerotium, the large resting stage of certain polypores and agarics.

myochrous. Mouse-gray.

myonemes. Contractile thread-like structures in some protozoa.

myoporoid. Resembling *Myoporum*, Asiatic trees.

myr. A moor in Ireland and Iceland.

myrcioid. Like *Myrcia*, a genus of tropical trees.

myriacanthous. With many spines.

myriangiaceous. Resembling the fungus *Myriangium.*

myriaspored. Having many spores.

myricarietum. An association of *Myricaria germanica* in the *Tamaricaceae* family.

myricetum. An association of *Myrica*, a genus of aromatic shrubs (bayberries).

myriocarpous. With many fruits.

myriocladous. With many branches.

myriomere. A transition from mitosis to amitosis.

myriophylletum. An association of *Myriophyllum*, a genus of aquatic plants (water milfoil).

myriophylloid. Like *Myriophyllum.*

myriophyllous. With many leaves.

myriosporous. Having many spores.

myriostigmous. With many stigmas.

myrmecobromous. Furnishing food for ants.

myrmecochorous. Dispersed by ants.

myrmecodomatia. Shelters formed by plants in which ants live.

myrmecodomous. Affording shelter only for ants.

myrmecolous. Inhabiting galleries of ants.

myrmecophilous. 1. Pollinated by ants. 2. Said of plants which are inhabited by ants and offer specialized shelter or food for them. 3. Ant-loving.

myrmecophily. A symbiotic association between plants and ants, the plant being adapted for attracting ants.

myrmecophobic. Shunning ants, said of plants with hairs, glands, or other mechanisms to repel them.

myrmecophyte. A plant which affords shelter and food to certain species of ant which live in symbiotic relations with it.

myrmecosymbiosis. The mutual relations between the ants and their host plants.

myrmecotrophic. Furnishing food to ants.

myrmecoxenous. Supplying both food and shelter to ants.

myrobalans. Gall nuts, astringent fruits used for tanning and in medicine.

myromecophilism. The state of being pollinated by ants.

myrosin. An enzyme which occurs in seeds. In mustards it decomposes the glucoside into allyl mustard oil, glucose, and acid potassium sulfate.

myrrh. An aromatic gum resin from *Commiphora myrrha.*

myrsinoid. Resembling the dicotyledonous family *Myrsinaceae.*

myrtifolious. With leaves like the myrtle.

myrtiform. Shaped like myrtle.

myrtilletum. An association of *Vaccinium Myrtillus*, the whortle.

myrtillinus. Myrtle green.

myrtle. A variety of trees and shrubs with fragrant berries and fragrant evergreen leaves, including the spice-bearing trees as clove and all spice.

mystrin. A peculiar carbohydrate found in *Mystropetalon*, one of the tropical parasitic dicotyledons of the *Balanophoraceae.*

mytiliform. Shell-shaped.

myurous. Long and tapering like a mouse's tail.

myxamoeba. A developmental stage of a myxomycete when it is uninucleate and composed of naked protoplasm which creeps or flows like an amoeba. It may precede or follow the zoospore (myxoflagellate) aquatic stage in which it has flagellate; myxoamoeba.

myxobacteria. Bacteria which form colonies united by a gelatinous covering.

myxobia. A large group of simple organisms which exhibit characteristics which are common to both plants and animals, the protista.

myxchimaera. A myxomycetous organism with two genetically different sources, as the plasma of *Mucor* when parasitized by *Chaetocladium*.

myxochromosomes. Paired chromosomes.

myxoflagellate stage. The swimming spore stage of myxomycetes in contrast with the creeping myxamoebae stage.

myxogasters. Myxomycetes, the slime molds.

myxomonad. A swarm spore of myxomycetes.

myxomycetes. The slime molds.

myxon. A constituent of wheat gluten which is precipitated by alcohol.

myxophyceae. The schizophyceae, plants which reproduce by fission; the blue-green algae which show no sex differentiation and propagate vegetatively, the *Cyanophyceae*.

myxophycin. A form of carotin occurring in *Myxophyceae*.

Myxophyta. A proposed phylum name for myxomycetes.

myxophyte. Rhizopoda which are regarded as plants.

myxopod. The old term for the myxamoeboid stage of the myxomycetes as contrasted with the mastigopods.

myxopodium. A slimy pseudopodium.

myxosomes. Dyads.

myxospore. A spore produced in the midst of a gelatinous mass without a distinct ascus or basidium, a spore of the myxogasters.

myxothallophytae. Myxogasters.

myxotrophic. Feeding by the ingestion of solid particles, as of chlorophyll-bearing protista and algae containing animals that have two modes of nutrition in the same organism.

N

n. Used to denote the chromosome number. The n-generation has a nucleus with the haploid number of chromosomes; the 2n-generation has the diploid number.

N and P ions. Nitrogen and phosphorus in plankton and other plants.

nacreous. Yielding or resembling mother of pearl or nacre, with pearly luster.

nacrini. Mother-of-pearl color.

NAD. Nicotinamide adenine dinucleotide.

NADP. Nicotinamide adenine dinucleotide phosphate.

Nährlösung. A nutrient solution of horsedung used in laboratory cultures.

naiades, najades. Branching monocotyledonous aquatic plants.

nail-head rust. A rust due to *Cladosporium herbariorum* var. *citricola*.

naked. 1. Lacking a covering, such as a perianth, scales, pubescence, or ground cover. 2. Not enclosed in a pericarp.

naked buds. Buds without protective scales.

naked flower. A flower without a perianth.

naked seeded. Gymnospermous.

namatad. A brook plant.

namathophilous. Brook-loving.

namatium. A brook community.

namatophyta. Brook plants.

nana. Dwarfed.

nanandrium. Nannander.

nanandrous. Producing dwarf males.

nanellus. Very small or dwarfed.

nanism. Dwarfishness, the condition of being abnormally small in stature.

nannandrous. Dwarfed as the antheridia from small male plants attached to the female filaments near the oogonia of *Oedogonium*.

nannocyte. A dwarf spore-like cell produced by some myxomycetes.

nanophanerophytes. Plants not exceeding two meters in height.

nanophanerophytium. A community of nanophanerophytes.

nanophyll. A very small leaf.

nanoplankton. Floating organisms of extremely small size.

nanoplanktonts. The items comprising the nanoplankton.

napaceous. Turnip-shaped, napiform.

napiform. Turnip-shaped, napaceous.

nappy. Tomentose, downy.

narbonensis. Of Narbonne, in southern France.

narceine. An opium alkaloid forming silky, odorless, bitter crystals.

narcissiflorous. With flowers like *Narcissus*.

nardetum. An association of *Nardus stricta*, matgrass.

nardine. Resembling *Nardostachys Jatamansi*, which produces a very fragrant rhizome.

nariform. Shaped like the nostrils.

narinosus. Broad-nosed.

northex. An apiaceous plant of Afghanistan, the source of asafoetida.

nascent tissue. Meristem.

nastic movement. 1. Automatic curvature of a dorsiventral organ influenced by continued growth in length. 2. Plant movement caused by diffuse stimuli.

-nasty. A suffix indicating that a plant response is determined by inherent rather than external factors.

nasutus. Large-nosed.

natalensis. Of Natal, South Africa.

natto. A vegetable cheese made in Japan out of soybeans.

natural color. The maintenance of the population of a pest species by the action of natural factors at a certain numerical level whether this level is below the point where financially measurable loss to crops is produced or not.

natural family. An association or group of related genera or of plants which are closely related in their structure and important characters.

natural graft. Graft resulting when branches are naturally united by approach.

natural history. The study of animal and plant life.

natural order. A group of several allied families.

natural pasture. Uncultivated land wholly or mainly occupied by native or naturally introduced plants useful for grazing.

natural plant. A wild plant characteristic of relatively undisturbed areas.

natural pruning. The natural falling or dropping of branches and twigs of trees.

natural selection. The natural process tending to cause the survival of the fittest and the extinction of poorly adapted forms.

natural starters. Impure cultures of lactic-acid bacteria secured by allowing milk to turn sour spontaneously.

natural system. An arrangement according to the affinity of the plants and the sum of their characters as opposed to an artificial system.

natural tribe. A natural family.

naturalized. Introduced from another region and maintaining its position in competition with wild plants.

nature reserve. A nature sanctuary.

nature sanctuary. An area of natural vegetation containing the native fauna in which the constituent organisms are allowed free play to fluctuate.

naucum. 1. The fleshy part of a drupe. 2. A seed with a very large hilum.

naucus. A cruciferous fruit which has no valves.

nautiform. Spirally formed, like a nautilus shell, nautiloid.

navel. The point of attachment, as the blossom end of the navel orange.

nave-shaped. Round and depressed with a small opening.

naviculae. Free frustules of diatoms.

navicular. Boat-shaped, cymbiform.

naviculoid. 1. Navicular. 2. Like the diatom genus *Navicula*.

neapolitan. Of Naples.

neap tide. The tide at low ebb.

nearctic. The American arctic.

nearctic region. North America as far south as Mexico.

Nebenkern. The paranucleus.

Nebenstand. A coenosis, a society.

necessaria. Composite flowers in which the ray flowers are female and the disk florets are male.

neck cells. In the archegonium of bryophytes the drawn-out portion as distinct from the venter.

necrides. Certain cells in some *Cyanophyceae* which become gelatinous and disappear.

necridia. Dead cells in algae.

necrocoleopterophilous. Pollinated by carrion beetles.

necrogenic abortion. A speedy death of the tissues of a plant close under the point of attack of a parasite checking the spread of the latter.

necrogenous. 1. Living or developing in dead

bodies. 2. Hastening the decay of the host plants.

necron. Dead plants not yet turned to humus.

necrophage. An eater of dead animal and plant bodies, a saprophyte.

necrophagous. Saprophytic, feeding on dead bodies.

necroplasm. The homologue of protoplasm in a dead seed.

necroplast. A dead protoplast.

necrosis. 1. Canker in plants. 2. The death of part or all of an organism.

necrotypes. Fossils, extinct forms.

nectar. The honey secreted by glands or by any part of the corolla, a sweet secretion by flowers.

nectar flowers. Flowers lacking colored perianths or petals and producing sticky pollen, as *Salix*, the willow.

nectar glands. The secreting organs which produce the nectar, nectaries.

nectar guides. Lines of color leading to the nectary which may serve as guides to insects seeking nectar.

nectar marks. Nectar guides.

nectar spots. Nectar guides.

nectaria. Peloria with every petal or sepal spurred.

nectariferous. Producing nectar or honey.

nectarilyma. Appendages of a nectary as the long hairs in *Menyanthes*, a gentian.

nectarine. A smooth-skinned peach.

nectarivorous. Nectar-sipping.

nectarosema. Nectarostigma.

nectarostigma. A mark or depression indicating the presence of a nectariferous gland.

nectarotheca. The portion of a flower which immediately surrounds a nectariferous pore.

nectary. The nectar-secreting organ, a nectarium.

nectism. Swimming by means of cilia, as zoospores.

nectocalyx. 1. A swimming bell. 2. A modified medusiform individual adapted for swimming found as a part of a siphonophore colony.

necton. See NEKTON.

nectonic benthos. Small organisms floating at the bottom of the water.

nectosome. The upper or swimming part of a siphonophore.

nectriaceous. Like the fungus genus *Nectria*, with perithecia on an erumpent stroma.

needle. The stiff leaf of *Coniferae*, a needle-shaped leaf.

needle forest. Evergreen or coniferous forest.

negative geotropism. Growth upward in opposition to gravity, as the leafy growth of most stems.

negative heliotropism. Growing away from light or shunning light, aheliotropism.

negative pressure. Lower interior tension in plant tissue when the gases in the tissues are at a lower tension than the outside air (usually due to the withdrawal of water).

negative reaction. A tendency of an organism or an organ to grow away from rather than toward a stimulus or away from a stronger stimulus and toward a weaker stimulus.

negative rheotropism. The tendency of a plant or one of its organs (usually the roots) to grow against the current of water rather than with it.

negative tropism. The tendency to move away from the source of a stimulus.

neidioplankton. Plankton organisms possessing swimming apparatus.

neism. The origin of an organ on a given place, as the formation of roots in a cutting.

nekrophytophagous. Feeding on dead plant substances.

nekton. Actively swimming organisms at the surface of water as opposed to organisms which move with the current or wave action; see NEIDIOPLANKTON.

nelumbifolious. With lotus-like leaves.

nema. A filament.

nematablast. A nematoplast.

nematea. A flagellate consisting of a linear series of plastids.

nemathecoid. Resembling a nemathecium.

nemathece. A nemathecium.

nemathecium. A wart-like protuberance formed on the thallus of seaweeds which bear reproductive organs. Nematothecium.

nemathecium, medullary. A nemathecium of loosely packed threads in the interior of an algal thallus.

nematium. A plant formation at the water's edge.

nematodes. 1. Thread-like worms. 2. In botany, the filamentous algae.

nematogone. A thin-walled propagation cell in certain mosses, an asexually produced gemma on moss protonema.

nematoid. Thread-like, filamentous.

nematomyces. Hyphomycetes, *Fungi Imperfecti.*

nematoparenchymatous thallus. An algal thallus composed of united threads which are still recognizable as individuals.

nematoplast. A thread-like plastid in the cytoplasm of *Momordica Elaterium*, the squirting cucumber.

nematothecium. A structure found on some seaweeds which bear the reproductive organs. It is a cushion-like projection on the thallus.

nemeae. Cryptogams whose sporules elongate into a thread-like form in germination.

nemeous. Thread-like, filamentous.

nemoblastus. Mosses and ferns.

nemoral. Inhabiting open woods or groves, nemorose.

nemus. An open woodland or savannah.

nemus paludosum. Swampy open woodland.

Neo-Darwinism. A revival of Darwin's doctrine of natural selection: a chief factor in evolution depends on germinal variations and not on inheritance of acquired characters.

neogaean. Of the western world.

neogamous. Exhibiting precocious fertilization in the early stage of the gametocyte.

neogeic. Occurring on recent geological formations.

Neo-Lamarckism. A revival of the evolutionary theories of Lamarck which postulate that the differences between species arose by the inheritance of the effects of use and disuse of a character or were influenced by environmental changes.

Neolaurentian. The early Proterozoic Era which has the earliest known abundant fossils.

Neo-Mendelism. Modern developments of the Mendelian doctrine.

neomorph. A structural variation from type.

neomorphogenous. Causing a new growth in contrast to that existing.

neomorphosis. A regeneration where the new part is unlike the part replaced.

neophyte. A newly introduced plant.

neophytic. Referring to fossil plants of the Neozoic or Tertiary Periods.

neoplasm. Abnormal new tissue.

neoplast. A new individual arising from one or more previously existing protoplasts.

neoteinia. Arrested development which delays maturity.

neoteny. The retention of embryonic characters throughout life.

neotropical. In the tropics of the New World.

neotype. A specimen selected to replace the holotype in case all type material of a species is lost or destroyed.

Neozoic. From the Mesozoic to the present day.

nepalensis. Of Nepal.

nepenthin. A proteolytic enzyme occurring in the pitchers of *Nepenthes*, the pitcher plants.

neptoid. Like the genus *Nepeta*, the mints.

nephrodioid. Resembling or akin to the fern *Nephrodium.*

nephroid. Kidney-shaped, reniform.

nephrolepis. Kidney-scale.

nephrosta. The sporangia of *Lycopodium.*

nepionic leaves. The first leaves of a seedling developed immediately succeeding the embryonic stage of the cotyledons.

nereid community. A community composed largely of algae.

nereidion. An association of water plants.

nereids. Water-loving plants which grow on rocks and stones.

nereifolious. With leaves like *Nerium*, the oleander.

neritic. Of the coast or shore line in shallow water.

neritic plankton. The plankton which originates from the organisms of the bottoms, e.g., free-swimming parts such as spores, etc.

neroplankton. Neritic plankton.

nervalis. 1. Loculicidal with dehiscence along the midrib of the carpels. 2. Prolonging the midrib of a leaf, as a tendril.

nervate. Nerved, veined.

nervation. The system of venation of a leaf.

nervature. Venation.

nerve. A single simple or unbranched vein or slender rib in a sepal, petal, leaf, carpel, bract, or scale.

nerveless. Without veins.

nervicole. Growing on veins, nervicolous.

nervile. A fine nerve or vein of a leaf blade, a nerville.

nervimotility. The stimulating effect of the substratum on a growing organ.

nervimotion. The power of motion in leaves.

nervine. Composed of nerves.

nervisequent. Following the nerves or veins.

nervi-seguus. Following the veins.

nervose. Full of veins or prominently nerved.

nervuration. The arrangement of veins, the venation.

nervures. The principal veins of a leaf.

nest epiphyte. An epiphyte which develops a tangle of stems, roots, and leaves among which humus and water collect and are used by the plant.

nestepiphytic leaves. Dimorphous leaves of ferns with heart-shaped bases in which humus and water collect to nourish to plant.

nestepiphytic roots. Negatively geotropic roots of epiphytes which form nest-like masses in which humus and water accumulate.

net. The loose tissue of pseudoparenchyma.

net knots. A karyosome, a chromatin nucleolus formed as a local aggregation of basichromatin, often irregular in shape.

net plasmodium. The network of filaments and the cells of the aquatic slime mold *Labyrinthula*. The filaments or tracks are laid down by the cells and the other cells glide over them.

net veined. Furnished with branching veins which form a network.

Netherveld. A hilly district, a transition between the brush steppe and the tropical savannah.

netrum. The initial spindle of a dividing cell, the minute spindle within the centrosome during division of the centromere.

netted. Reticulated.

neurad. Dorsal.

Neuramphipetalae. The *Compositae*.

neuranthum. 1. Nerved flowers. 2. The outer netted glumes of a spikelet.

neuration. Nervation.

neuromotor apparatus. Tissue from which the flagella of the motile cells (gametes and zoospores) are developed. It is closely associated with the nuclei of the green algae.

neurose. Nervose.

neuston. Floating vegetation, minute organisms which float against the surface film, plankton.

neuter. Without stamens or pistils, without fertile sporophylls, sexless.

neuter flowers. Functionally asexual flowers.

neutral axis. The axis common to the several I-girders in stems.

neutral flowers. Flowers without stamens and pistils.

neutral lamina. The plane of zero tension in a stem or girder when subjected to a bending force.

neutral zone. The line or place where rotating streams of protoplasm flow beside each other in opposite directions, as in *Characeae*.

neutriflorous. Having neuter ray florets as *Compositae*.

nevadensis. Of the Sierra Nevada Mountains.

New Jersey tea. *Ceanothus*.

new place effect. The effect of the removal of a plant or seed to a new locality which produces a marked change in the plant.

new species. A species not hitherto described.

Newtonian curve. A graphic representation of variations plotted geometrically in two dimensions, the binomial or Galtonian curve.

nicked. Emarginate or notched.

nicotianus. Tobacco-colored, brown.

nicotine. A poisonous alkaloid found in tobacco leaves. It is used as an insecticide.

nicotinic acid. A substance found in plant and animal proteins. One of the vitamin B complex which is used in treating pellagra. Niacin, nicotinamide.

nictitans. Blinking, moving.

nidorose. Nidose.

nidose. Foul-smelling, having the odor of burnt or rotten meat or of rotten eggs.

nidulant. Partially encased or lying free in a cavity or nest-like structure, nidulate.

nidularium. The mycelium of some fungi (a little used term).

nidus. A nest or nest-like structure bearing spores.

Niederblätter. Cataphylla, the early leaves.

night position. The position assumed by leaves during darkness (the edges usually turned toward the zenith).

nigrescent. Turning black, approaching black in color.

nigricornis. With black horns.

nigrifactous. Blackened.

nigripes. With black feet or stalks.

nigrite. Blackened, or clothed in black.

nigrofructous. With black fruit.

nigrolimitate. Outlined in black or with black lines.

nigrophile. With black hairs.

nigropunctate. Marked with black dots.

nigropurpureous. Atropurpureous, purplish black.

nigrostrigose. With black bristles or hairs.

nilotica. Of the Nile.

nine digitate. With nine fingers.

nipetum. An association of *Nipa* palms.

nipho. Snow.

nipple. A papilla.

nipponicus. Of Japan.

Nissl bodies. Angular bodies of granular appearance occurring in the cell bodies of a neurocyte which stain deeply.

nitelinous. Dormouse-colored.

nitelletum. An association of the alga *Nitella*.

nitid. Glossy, lustrous, smooth and clear.

nitidous. Having a smooth or glossy surface.

nitrate. A salt or ester of nitric acid which is essential to plant growth.

nitrate bacteria. Soil-inhabiting bacteria which convert nitrites into nitrates.

nitrification. The oxidation of nitrogenous animal and vegetable substances to nitrates.

nitrifying bacteria. Soil bacteria which are able to bring atmospheric nitrogen into combination and use it in their nutrition.

nitrite. A salt or ester of nitrous acid.

nitrite bacteria. Soil bacteria which form nitrites from compounds of ammonia.

nitrobacteria. Bacteria which produce nitrification by their action, the nitrate and the nitrite bacteria.

nitrocellulose. Cellulose nitrates; see CELLULOSE.

nitrogen cycle. Transformations which take place to circulate nitrogen in nature. Decaying organic matter is converted into ammonium compounds, and then plants assimilate the nitrites during their growth and development. The nitrifying bacteria of the soil fix some nitrogens in the root nodules (of legumes). Denitrifying bacteria convert some nitrates to gaseous nitrogen which is released into the atmosphere to be used again.

nitrogen fixation. The fixation of nitrogen by bacteria and fungi.

nitrogenous. Containing nitrogen or pertaining to nitrogen.

nitrogen equilibrium. The equilibrium of income and output of nitrogen maintained by an organism.

nitrophilous. Thriving in nitrogenous soils, preferring alkaline soils.

nitrophytes. Plants thriving best on soils providing the most alkalis or potash.

nitrosation. The conversion of ammonium salts into nitrites by the action of bacteria, the second stage in nitrification in the soil.

Nitschia plankton. Floating masses of *Nitschia*, a diatom.

nival. 1. Living in or near snow. 2. Snowy white.

nivaflora. Flora growing above the snow line.

nixus. The affinity of one species to another of the same genus.

nocanamum. The sporangium of *Selaginella*.

noctiflorous. Night-flowering.

noctilucent. Phosphorescent, shining or glowing at night.

nodal cell. A cell at the base of the oogonium in *Chara* interposed between the egg cell and the stalk cell.

nodal diaphragm. Any septum which extends across the hollow of the stem at a node.

nodal plexus. The net or transverse girdle of bundles which sometimes exists at a node.

nodding. Hanging down, nutant, drooping, cernous.

node. 1. The joint of a culm. 2. The place on the stem where leaves ordinarily arise.

nodiferous. Bearing nodes.

nodiflorous. With flowers at the nodes.

nodose. Knotty, knobby, having prominent nodes.

nodose septum. See CLAMP.

nodular. Having nodules or knots.

nodular bodies. Rounded bodies composed of one or more closely compacted and intertwined hyphae.

nodule. A small hard knot or rounded body formed on roots by the nitrogen-fixing bacteria.

noduliferous. Bearing nodules or knots.

nodulose. Having little knots or knobs.

nomad. A pasture plant.

nomadic. Of certain steppe plants blown from their original stations.

nomenclature. The system of naming plants, animals, organs, etc.

nomium. A pasture formation, a nonwooded pasture community.

nomogenesis. The belief that evolution is due to chemical laws of development irrespective of environment.

nomologia. The laws which govern the variations of organs.

nomophilous. Dwelling in pasture land.

nomophyllous. Having leaves normal for the genus or group.

nomophyta. Pasture plants.

nomospermous. Having seeds normally occurring in the order, tribe, or genus.

nonamyloid. With spores which remain hyaline or become yellowish.

nonanalogous. Divergent.

nonarticulate. Not cut off by an absciss layer.

noncellular protista. Unicellular protista.

noncorprinus-type. See AEQUI-HYMENIIFEROUS.

noncrossover gamete. A gamete containing a chromosome which has not been affected by crossing over.

nondisjunction. The failure of paired (synapsed) chromosomes to separate at the reduction division of meiosis and both go to the same pole of the spindle.

nonporous. Said of wood which is homogenous, without large pores.

nonpyric subsere. A subsere created by conditions other than fire.

nonreducing sugar. A sugar which will not extract oxygen from substances.

nonreduction. Ameiosis.

nonsensibility. The ability of a plant to support the development of a parasite without showing marked signs of disease.

nonviable. 1. Incapable of developing normally. 2. Unable to live.

nonpinnatus. Not pinnate.

nonscriptus. Undescribed.

nontuple. With nine sets of chromosomes.

nootkatensis. Of Nootka Sound by Vancouver Island.

nori. See LAVER, PURPLE.

normal allelomorphs. The factors conditioning the characters of the wild or normal type of a species in contrast with the factors which condition mutant characters.

normal curve. A symmetrical curve of distribution of variations which are due to a multiplicity of independent causes acting equally in both directions.

normal dispersion. The distribution of individuals according to the law of probability.

normal distribution. The normal curve of errors.

normal specific assembly. The floristic bases of the concrete study of an association.

norvegicus. Norwegian.

nose bleed. Yarrow, *Achillea millefolium.*

nosology. The science and classification of diseases, plant pathology.

Nostoc-layer. The algal layer in lichens which consists of *Nostoc* or closely allied forms.

nostochaceous. Resembling *Nostoc* or allied to it.

notate. Marked with spots or lines.

notch flowers. Flowers with fringed or indented petals.

noterophile. A mesophyte.

nothogamy. The process of crossing varieties rather than crossing species, heteromorphic xenogamy.

nothus. False or bastard, usually apppplied to the false root of a parasite.

notorhizal. See INCUMBENT.

nototribal. Having flowers whose anthers and stigma touch the back of an insect as it enters the calyx (a device for assuring cross-fertilization).

Novae Angliae. Of New England.

Novae Caesareae. Of New Jersey.

Novae Zealandiae. Of New Zealand.

noveboracensis. Of New York.

Novi Belgii. Of New Belgium or New Netherlands (i.e., New York).

noviform. Of recent origin, a cultivated form.

NP. An abbreviation for nucleoprotein.

N. S. quotient (Niederschlag and Sättigungsdefizit). The relationship of precipitation to saturation deficit. The measure of the relative humidity of a climate.

nubicolous. Dwelling among clouds.

nubigenous. Cloud-borne.

nubilus. Greyish blue, cloudy.

nucamentaceous. Resembling a small nut.

nucamentum. An amentum, a catkin.

nucellar. Of or pertaining to the nucellus.

nucellar budding. The formation of an embryo from cells of the nucellus and not from the fertilized egg, nucellar embryony.

nucellus. The central mass of an ovule, the tissue within which the embryo sac is developed and which is subsequently absorbed or remains as a perisperm or albumen.

nuciferous. Bearing or producing nuts.

nuciform. Shaped like a nut.

nucivorous. Nut-eating.

nuclear association. An association caused by the fusion of protoplasts containing nuclei.

nuclear barrel. A stage in karyokinesis immediately preceding the nuclear spindle stage.

nuclear budding. The production of two daughter nuclei of unequal size by the constriction of the parent nucleus.

nuclear disc. 1. The mother-star stage in mitosis. 2. A star-like structure formed by fine threads in the cytoplasm surrounding the nucleus.

nuclear division. The entire sequence of events taking place as the nucleus divides: mitosis, meisois, amitosis.

nuclear fibrils. Chromosomes.

nuclear filament. The chromatin or chromatic filament of the nucleus.

nuclear fusion. The union of two nuclei, syngamy.

nuclear membrane. A delicate two-layered membrane bounding a nucleus formed by the surrounding cytoplasm. The outer layer is perforated by circular nuclear pores.

nuclear osmosis. The theory that the nucleus enlarges like a sap vacuole.

nuclear plate. The equatorial plate in cell division, the aggregation of chromosomes at the equatorial plane during cell division.

nuclear pores. Round holes in the outer nuclear membrane.

nuclear reduction. A reduction presumed to have taken place when a smaller number of segments occur than at a previous division of the paretn cell.

nuclear reticulum. A meshwork of delicate threads of chromatin seen in stained preparations of metabolic nuclei.

nuclear ring. The equatorial arrangement of chromosomes.

nuclear sap. The ground substance or enchylema of the nucleus; see KARYOLYMPH.

nuclear spindle. The fusiform structure composed of fine fibrils arranged longitudinally and converging at the poles. The fibrils appear in the cytoplasm of the cell surrounding the nucleus during mitosis and meiosis. It begins to appear in the skein stage and is completed in the mother-star stage.

nuclear stain. A stain which will bring out the nuclei in a prepared tissue section in different colors or shades.

nuclear star. The aster in cell division.

nuclear threads. The spindle fibers in cell division.

nucleases. Enzymes which activate the hydrolysis of nucleic acid.

nucleate. Having a nucleus of nuclei, guttate.

nucleation. The formation of nuclei.

nuclei, bladder. Nuclei found in latex which seem to increase by direct division.

nuclei, giant. Exceptionally large nuclei found in some species of *Aloe*.

nuclei, thread. Nuclei that are long and drawn out in the mucilage of the *Amaryllidaceae*.

nucleic acid. An acid found in the nucleus which is rich in phosphorus. It is the nonprotein constituent of nucleoprotein. In RNA (ribonucleic acid) the sugar is ribose, in DNA (deoxyribonucleic acid) it is 2-deoxyribose. The DNA and RNA play an important part in protein synthesis and in the transmission of hereditary characters.

nucleiferous. Bearing nuclei.

nucleiform. 1. Shaped like a nucleus or nuclei. 2. Tuberculate as the apothecia of some lichens.

nuclein. Chromatin, a chemical compound found in nuclei similar to protein but with the addition of phosphorus; see NUCLEIC ACID.

nucleo-. A prefix meaning nuclear.

nucleocentrosomes. Bodies found in *Psilotum triquitrum* (a primitive vascular plant) during nuclear division, secretion bodies.

nucleochylema. The fluid which fills the spaces in the linin, the ground substances of the cell nucleus, nuclear sap, karyolymph, karenchyma.

nucleo-cytoplasmic ratio. The relationship of the volume of the cell nucleus to that of the cytoplasm. A change in this ratio may contribute to cell division.

nucleohyaloplasm. Nuclear sap.

nucleoidioplasm. The formative part of the nuclear hyaloplasm or nuclear sap.

nucleolar body. The body at the periphery of the nucleolus of *Lathyrus*, the sweet pea, which is a darkly staining thread.

nucleolar organizer. A minor constriction of a spiral chromosome believed to influence the activity of the nucleolus.

nucleolate. Having one or more conspicuous oil drops in the spore, having a nucleolus.

nucleole. A small globular, deeply staining body found within a nucleus.

nucleoli. Fungus protoplasm which separates

itself from that of the host into special corpuscles.

nucleolini. Small, intranucleolar, deeply staining granules which do not disappear during mitosis and sometimes divide during mitosis.

nucleolocentrosome. A nuclear body which may act as a centrosome during mitosis.

nucleolonucleolus. An endonucleus.

nucleome. All of the nuclear substance in a protoplast.

nucleomicrosomes. Chromatin, nuclear chromatin granules.

nucleonema. A fiber-like network of the nucleolus.

nucleophyses. Tubular septate projections in certain fungi which correspond to the base of the perithecium and ultimately become ascophyses.

nucleoplasm. The dense protoplasm in the nucleus, a nuclear substance containing the different nuclear ingredients.

nucleoplasmic ratio. The ratio between the volume of the nucleus and the cytoplasm of a given cell, the karyoplasmic ratio.

nucleoplasmic tension. The tension exerted on the nucleus and the chromatin after cell division when the increase of the protoplasm and of the nucleus cannot proceed equally.

nucleoproteid. 1. Any of a class of proteids found in nearly all cell nuclei. 2. A nuclein with much albumin.

nucleoproteins. A group of compounds made up of a group of protein molecules and nucleic acids which are important constituents of cell nuclei but are also found in cytoplasm. Viruses appear to consist almost entirely of nucleoproteins.

nucleostatoliths. Nuclei which are more or less united to starch grains or starch-containing chloroplasts to form gravitational units.

nucleus. 1. A concentrated spherical mass of protoplasm which contains the chromosomes enclosed in a thin membrane and is surrounded by the cytoplasm of the cell. The nucleus stains deeply and appears to control the activities of the cell and determine the transmission of hereditary characters. 2. The kernel of an ovule or seed, the nucellus. 3. The central portion of a starch grain. 4. An oil drop. 5. A centrum.

nucleus barrel. See NUCLEAR BARREL.

nucleus, cell. A more or less spherical body surrounded by cell cytoplasm which is the center of activity and cell division. A membrane encloses and contains the nucleic acids which are important in metabolism, protein synthesis, cell growth, reproduction, and heredity. The cell nucleus is the most important body in all organic life.

nucleus, closed. The type of nucleus occurring in higher plants.

nucleus of the embryo sac. The secondary nucleus.

nucleus, generative. The active nucleus in karyokinesis.

nucleus, germ. A nucleus resulting from the fusion of a male and female pronucleus.

nucleus, incipient. The central body in cells of the *Myxophyceae*, the nucleus of diatoms.

nucleus of the oösphere. The female nucleus or pronucleus in the oösphere with which the male nucleus fuses to form a germ nucleus.

nucleus, open. The central body of phycochromaceous plants of much looser structure than higher plants and lacking a true nuclear membrane.

nucleus, rejection. A sister nucleus to the female nucleus which plays no part in fertilization.

nucleus spindle. The nuclear spindle.

nuculane. A drupaceous or baccate fruit containing more than one stone or stony seed; a superior stony-seeded berry, as the medlar or grape.

nucule. 1. The female sex organ (both the oogonium and the outer protective cells) of *Chara.* 2. A nutlet.

nuculosus. Containing hard, nut-like seeds.

nucumentaceous. Nucamentaceous.

nudation. The occurrence of bare areas due to various causes, denudation.

nudicaulous. Having stems without leaves.

nudiflorous. Having flowers without glands or hairs, having naked flowers, lacking a perianth.

nullinervis. Enervis, lacking veins.

nulliplex. Recessive, used in polyploids when all the genes for a given character are recessive, in the condition in which no determiners of a given character exist in a particular individual.

nulliplex factor or character. A factor or

character which is absent because its determiner is not found in either parent.

numerical hybrid. A hybrid produced from parents whose chromosome numbers differ.

numerical mutation. An alteration in the chromosome number, either balanced to give polyploidy, or unbalanced to produce aneuploidy.

numerical plan. The fundamental plan or number exhibited by the different whorls of the same flower. The numerical plan of monocotyledons is commonly three, that of dicotyledons is usually five.

numidicus. Of Numidia, an ancient country of North Africa.

nummularifolious. With coin-shaped leaves or seed pods.

nunataks. Areas of small unglaciated land in the arctic regions which support vegetation near the margins of great ice fields.

nupharetum. An association of *Nuphar*, the water lilies.

nurse. In horticulture, a shrub or tree which serves for the protection of a younger tree or plant.

nurse cells. Sterile nutritive cells.

nursery. A place in which plants are propagated and grown until later planting.

nursing foot. See HAUSTRUM.

nut. A hard, dry, indehiscent fruit derived from two or more carpels enclosed in a hard or leathery pericarp and usually containing one seed. The term is loosely used for any hard, dry, one-seeded fruit.

nut, baccate. A nut enclosed in a pulpy covering, as in the yew.

nut, spurious. A fruit which owes its hardness to something other than the pericarp.

nutant. Nodding, drooping.

nutation. The rotating or rhythmic movements in plants or plant organs due to growth or to a stimulus such as light.

nutation chorisis. The separation of parts due to the growth of a tissue.

nutation, revolving. Circumnutation.

nutlet. A small nut or a one-seeded portion of a fruit which fragments as it matures.

nutmeg. The seed of *Myristica fragrans*, a tropical tree, the source of the spices mace and nutmeg.

nutricism. A symbiotic relationship in which one organism is nourished or protected by the other without apparent reciprocal benefit, as in *Monotropa*, the Indian pipe.

nutrient solution. An artificially prepared solution containing some or all of the mineral substances in controlled laboratory studies.

nutrition. The process of absorption, digestion, and assimilation of food which makes growth and reproduction possible in living organisms.

nutritive jacket. A layer of nutritive tissue surrounding the embryo sac in the *Gamopetalae*.

nutrix. A host.

nux. A nut.

nux baccata. A nut enclosed in a pulpy covering.

nyctanthous. Flowering at night.

nycticalous. Night-blooming.

nyctigamous. With flowers which close during the day and open at night.

nyctinastic movements. Movements of plants associated with the alteration of day and night due to changes in temperatures and illumination, sleep movements.

nyctipelagic. Rising to the surface of the sea at night.

nyctitropism. The tendency of certain leaves to curve upward at night, the sleep movement.

nymphaeaceous. Resembling or kin to the water lilies, *Nymphaea*.

nymphaeetum. An association of *Nymphaea*.

nymphaeform. Having the shape of a nymph or chrysalis, as some spores in lichens.

nymphoid. Like *Nymphae*.

O

O. The symbol for the pycnial stage of the rusts.

oak. Any tree or shrub of the genus *Quercus*.

oakwood association. Woods in which oaks are dominant.

oangium. An apocytial oogonium which forms oospores by free cell formation, as in *Saprolegnia*, a slime mold.

oat. The seed of *Avena sativa*.

obclavate. A reversal of clavate, inverted club-shaped.

obcompressed. Flattened from front to back.

obconic. Cone-shaped but attached by the point.

obcordate. Inversely heart-shaped.

obcrenate. Denticulate.

obcurrent. Running together and adhering at the point of contact.

obdiplastemonous. Having a double row of stamens, the outer whorl of stamens being opposite the petals rather than alternate with them, the inner whorl of stamens being opposite the sepals. Obdiplostemonous.

obforms. Forms in *Rosa* with very glandular teeth and glands on the margin of the calyx.

obices. Biological or physical barriers or hindrances to plant distribution.

obimbricate. Having regularly overlapping scales with the overlapping ends downward.

oblanceolate. Long and narrow but broadening outward, lance-shaped with the tapering point downward.

oblate. Globose but flattened at the poles and broader than long.

obligate. Limited to a single form of life.

obligate gamete. A gamete which is not capable of further development without union with another gamete.

obligate parasite. A parasite which is incapable of free-living existence.

obligate saprophyte. An organism which lives on dead organic material and cannot attack a living host.

obligate symbiont. An organism which is dependent on another for its existence.

obligatory. Limited to a single life condition, e.g., parasitic, facultative, etc.

obligulate. Said of ligulate florets of *Compositae* extended on the inner side of the capitulum instead of the outside.

oblique division. The development of a septum which is neither parallel to the longitudinal axis of the cell nor across it at right angles.

oblique partition. A partition slanting in relation to the longitudinal axis.

oblique plane. Any plane of a flower other than the median and lateral planes.

obliteration. The crushing and closing of tubular elements within a plant by the pressure set up by new elements as they develop, suppression, abortion, erasure of parts or plants.

oblongifolious. With oblong leaves.

obovate. Inverted ovate, egg-shaped with the big end outward.

obovoid. Inverted oval, with the shape of an inverted egg.

obpyramidal. Inversely pyramidal.

obpyriform. Inversely pear-shaped.

obringent. Having a ringent floret of the *Compositae* with the lower lip composing four-fifths of the whole and appearing uppermost.

obrotund. Somewhat round.

obrute. Covered, buried.

obscure. Said of venation which is very little developed so that hardly more than the midrib can be seen.

obsolescent. Becoming rudimentary.

obsolete. Rudimentary, indistinct.

obsubulate. Very narrow, pointed at the base and widening toward the apex.

obsuturalis. See SEPTIFRAGAL.

obtectovenosus. With the principal and longest veins connected only by simple cross veins.

obtrite. Broken, crushed, rubbed.

obturaculum. An opening.

obturator. A structure which closes a cavity, as the small body accompanying the pollen masses of orchids and asclepiads which close the opening of the anthers; a caruncle.

obturbinate. Inversely top-shaped, swollen at the base and narrow at the tip.

obtuse. Blunt-pointed, rounded.

obtuse angled. With stem angles rounded.

obtusilobous. With blunt or obtuse lobes.

obvallate. Appearing as if surrounded by a wall.

obverse. With a base narrower than the apex (used when the point of a radicle in a seed approaches the hilum), inverse, reverse.

obversely. Contrary to the usual position.

obvolute. Wrapped or rolled up, with the margins of one structure overlapping those of another.

obvolvent. Bent downward and inward, enveloping.

occasional species. A species which is found from time to time in a given community but is not a constant member of that community.

occellate. With openings.

occlusion. 1. The process by which wounds in plants are healed by the growth of callus. 2. The blocking of a stoma by the ingrowth of parenchymatous cells into the substomatal cavity.

oceanad. An ocean plant.

oceanic. Living in the open sea.

oceanicus. Of Oceanica.

oceanid. A marine plant.

oceanium. An ocean community.

oceanophilous. Ocean-dwelling, of ocean-dwelling organisms.

oceanophyte. An ocean plant.

ocellate. Marked by a round patch different in color from the background, with openings.

ocellus. 1. An enlarged discolored cell in a leaf. 2. A swelling on the sporangiophore in some fungi. 3. An opening through which one can see light. 4. An eye-like spot of color.

ocher. Dull yellow, yellow tinged with brown, ochery, ochreous.

ochetium. A plant succession caused by artificial drainage.

ochnaceous. Like *Ochna*, a genus of African trees and shrubs.

ochraceous. Ocher-colored.

ochrea. See OCREA.

ochreate. See OCREATE.

ochreolae. Flowers having subtending ocrea, ocreolae.

ochroleucous. Whitish yellow, cream-colored, buff.

ochrophore. A cell bearing yellow pigment, an iridocyte.

ochrosporous. With yellow or yellow-brown spores.

ochtad. A bank plant.

ochthium. A bank community.

ochthopilous. Bank-loving.

ochthophyte. A plant of banks or dikes.

ocrea. 1. A nodal sheath formed by the fusion of two stipules, as in many *Polygonaceae*. 2. A type of armilla formed on the stipe of an agaric when the universal veil disintegrates.

ocreaceous. Resembling an ocrea.

ocreate. Having an ocrea.

octad. With eight nuclei.

octagynia. Plants with eight-styled flowers.

octamerous. With eight organs or parts.

octandrous. With eight stamens.

octant. One of the eight cells formed by the division of the fertilized ovule in plants.

octant division. The division of an embryonic

cell by walls at right angles giving eight cells, the division of an oospore.

octant wall. A septum which cuts the oospore into octants.

octarinus. Octandrous.

octinucleate. Having eight nuclei.

octodiploid. Formed by the fusion of eight diploid nuclei.

octofarious. In eight ranks or rows.

octogynous. With eight pistils.

octokont. Having eight equal flagella.

octolocular. With eight cells or compartments in a fruit or pericarp.

octopetalous. Having eight petals.

octophyllous. With eight leaves.

octoploid. Having eight sets of chromosomes or eight times the normal number.

octoradiate. With eight rays or arms.

octosepalous. With eight sepals.

octoseptate. With eight crosswalls.

octosome. With eight sets of chromosomes.

octospermous. Having eight seeds.

octospore. 1. An eight-celled spore. 2. Formerly applied to the oogonium of *Fucus vesiculosus*, which contains eight oospores.

octosporous. Having eight spores.

octostemonous. With eight fertile stamens.

octosterigmata. With eight sterigmata.

octostichous. Having leaves in eights or in eight vertical ranks.

octotriploid. Formed by the division of syntriploid nuclei and their subsequent fusion.

oculate. Ocellate, having oculi or eye-like spots.

oculus. 1. A leaf bud in a tuber. 2. A leaf bud when used as a cutting. 3. An eye.

ocymoid. Like *Ocimum*, sweet basil.

odd-pinnate. Having pinnate leaves with an odd number of divisions, pinnate with a single terminal leaflet, imparipinnate.

odessanus. Of Odessa in southern Russia.

odont-, odonto-. A prefix meaning tooth.

odontochilous. Having a toothed lip or margin.

odontoid. Tooth-like, dentate.

odoriferous. Having an odor, fragrant.

oecesis. Ecesis.

oecology. Ecology.

oedema. 1. A large mass of unhealthy parenchyma. 2. A swollen condition of plants due to reduced transpiration and excessive absorption of water. Edema.

oedematin. The microsomes of the ground substance of the nucleus.

oedocephaloid. With an enlarged or swollen head or tip as found in the conidiophores of *Cunninghamella* and other fungi.

oedogoniaceous. Of or pertaining to the alga *Oedogonium*.

oekiophyte. A native cultivated plant for ornament or use.

officinal. Medicinal.

officinarum. Officinal.

offset. A lateral shoot used for propagation, a short branch next to the ground which takes root, a stolon, an offshoot.

oidioid. Like the mildew genus *Oidium*.

oidiospores. Spores which develop in chains.

oidium. One of a number of spores formed in a chain by the development of transverse septa in a hypha and the subsequent separation across the septa, as in the genus *Oidium*, a mildew.

oil body. A rounded mass of oily material occurring in the cell content of many *Hepaticae*.

oil cell. A hyphal cell containing fat globules, a gum cell.

oil plastids. Elaioplasts.

oil tube. A vitta, one of the tubular oil receptacles in the fruit of umbellifers.

Okotype. Ecospecies, ecotype.

okra. The large, green, erect pods of *Hibiscus esculentus*.

old wood. Primary wood, cryptogamic wood.

oleaefolious. Olive-leaved.

oleaginous. Containing or producing oil.

oleic acid. A glyceride or fat occurring in plants.

oleiferous. Producing fat or bearing oil.

olein. A fat formed in animal and vegetable tissues which is liquid at ordinary temperatures.

olens. Odorous.

oleoid. 1. Olive-like. 2. Having leaves which are traversed by fibers.

oleoresin. The natural admixture of a resin and an essential oil forming a vegetable balsam or turpentine.

oleosolocular. Having cells which appear as drops of oil.

oleosome. A large fatty inclusion in the cytoplasm of a cell.

oleous. 1. Oily. 2. With oil drops.

oleraceous. Edible, esculent.

olibanum. A bitter substance and aromatic gum resin from several species of *Boswellia*, frankincense.

olid. Having a strong disagreeable smell, fetid, rancid.

oligacanthous. Having few spines.

oligahalile. Of upper estuarine areas in which the total salt content is one to five parts per thousand.

oligandrous. Bearing few stamens, oligostemonous.

oliganthous. With few flowers.

oligarch. A vascular cylinder which contains but few bundles, a stele which possesses few protoxylem elements.

oligastachyous. With few spikes.

oligo-. A prefix meaning few.

oligocarpous. Having few carpels, fruits, or spore cases.

Oligocene. The Tertiary Geological Period between the Eocene and the Miocene Periods.

oligodynamic. 1. Caused by small or minute forces. 2. Containing minute quantities. 3. Slightly poisonous.

oligomerous. Having one or more whorls with a smaller number than normal, of few members, with few parts.

oligonitrophilous. Occurring in nutritive media which lack nitrogenous compounds.

oligopelic. Preferring rocks which yield a small amount of clayey detritus, living in areas containing little clay.

oligopetric. Oligopelic.

oligophagous. Feeding on several definitely fixed food plants.

oligophylla. Bracts.

oligophyllous. Having few leaves or bracts.

oligopsammic. 1. Containing little sand. 2. Living on dolomite or granite soils.

oligopyrene. An abnormal form of spermatozoa, a sperm deficient in chromosomes.

oligorhizous. With few roots, as marsh plants.

oligosaprobia. Organisms which flourish in water that is only a little contaminated.

oligosaprobic. Living in water which is high in oxygen and low in dissolved organic matter with little decomposition of organic substances.

oligosaprobic zone. The zone of clear water.

oligospermous. With few seeds.

oligosporous. With few spores.

oligostemonous. With few stamens.

oligotaxis. With fewer whorls or fewer members in a whorl than normal.

oligotrophic. 1. Having little nourishment; living on poor soil or in areas low in nutrients, as on steep banks, rocky shores, or in lakes or swamps with few nutrients available. 2. Applied to bees with a restricted range of plants.

oligotrophic peat. Peat from swamps poor in nutrients, moor peat.

oligotropic. Oligotrophic.

oligotrophyte. A plant growing in soil or water with few available nutrients.

olisthium. A succession of plants on landslides.

olitorious. Pertaining to vegetable gardens or gardeners.

olivaceous. Dusky, olive green.

olivaeform. Shaped like an olive.

olivascent. Becoming olive-colored.

olive. The fruit of *Olea europaea*, the tree olive.

ologenesis. Hologenesis.

olopetalarious. Having floral envelopes which change partially or wholly (as stamens or pistils change into petaloid organs), holopetalarious.

olympicus. Of Olympus, or Mt. Olympus.

ombratropism. The tropic responses of organisms to the stimulus of rain.

ombrocleistogamy. The condition in which certain flowers are self-fertile while unexpanded because of rainy weather.

ombrometer. A rain gauge.

ombrophile. A rain-loving plant.

ombrophilous. Rain-loving or capable of withstanding much rain, as the plants of the humid tropic region.

ombrophobe. A plant disliking rain.

ombrophyte. A shade-loving plant.

ombrotiphic. In temporary pools left by melting snow and temporary rains.

omnicolous. Ubiquitous.

omoplephytum. A monadelphous flower in which the stamens are in one bundle.

omphalode. The place in a hilum through which the vessels pass to the chalaza.

omphaloid. Navel-like, umbilicate.

omphaloidium. The scar at the hilum of a seed or the hilum itself.

onagraceous. Pertaining to *Oenothera*, the evening primrose, whose pre-Linnean name was *Onagra*.

oncidioda hybrid. The orchid hybrid *Oncidium-Cochlioda*.

oncospore. A plant with hooked disseminules.

onisciform. Resembling a wood louse in shape, as some lichen spores.

oniscus. Lead-colored.

onobrychioid. Like the legume *Onobrychis*.

onomatologia. The rules to be followed in the construction of names.

ontocycle. The evolution which in its later stages tends to produce forms exactly like those in the early stages.

ontogenesis. The life history of a single individual, ontogeny.

ontogeny. The development of the individual as opposed to phylogeny.

ontoplastid. A cell in the process of division.

onychomycosis. A fungus disease of the nails.

ooapogamous. Producing parthenogenetically.

ooblast. A structure formed in the red algae which is a tubular outgrowth from the base of the carpogonium and connects with an auxiliary cell.

ooblastema. The egg after fertilization.

ooblastema filaments. Fertilizing tubes.

ooblastic filaments. Ooblastema filaments.

oocarp. An oospore.

oocenter. The division center of the egg; see OVOCENTER.

oocyst. The oogonium, a female organ or oogonium of doubtful nature, an oogone.

oocyte. An egg before maturation, a gametocyte.

oogametangium. A structure bearing female gametangia.

oogamete. An oosphere of *Sporozoa*, a female gamete.

oogamous. Having sexually differentiated gametes.

oogamy. The conjugation of two dissimilar gametes.

oogemma. An archegonium.

oogenesis. The formation, development, and maturation of the egg.

oogloea. Egg cement.

oogon. An oogonium.

oogone. An oogonium.

oogonial branch. A hypha on or in which an oogonium develops.

oogonial incept. The early stage of the oogonium of certain fungi.

oogonial tube. The neck canal.

oogonium. The female sex organ in the thallophytes and oomycetes containing one or more oospheres.

ooid. Egg-shaped, oval.

ookinesis. The mitotic happenings in the egg cell during maturation and fertilization.

ookinetic. Tending to produce the female element.

oolysis. Viridescence, especially in carpels and ovules.

oomycetes. Fungi producing oospores.

oon. An egg.

oonangium. The embryo sac.

ooneion. An archegonium.

oonucleus. The nucleus of an oosphere.

oonyle. An unfertilized female organ of any sort.

oophore. An oophyte of the archegoniates, the first or sexual generation in plants having an alternation of generations.

oophoridangia. The macrosporangia of *Marsilea*.

oophoridium. A macrosporangium.

oophyte. A gametophyte, the portion of the life cycle of a plant which produces the sexual organs.

ooplasm. The denser central portion of the oogonium; see PERIPLASM.

ooplast. The oosphere.

oosperm. A fertilized egg, an oospore.

oosphere. The unfertilized female gamete.

oosphere, compound. An oosphere which contains several or many functional sexual nuclei, as in *Albugo*, the white-rust fungus.

oosporangium. The sac or sporangia which produces oospores, an oogonium.

oospore. The final stage of development after the fusion of unlike gametes in the *Oomycetes*.

ootheca. A sporangium, as in ferns.

ootid. The mature egg.

ooze. The soft deposit found over large areas of the ocean floor.

open. 1. In aestivation, with leaves not meeting at their edges. 2. Loose, as of panicles.

open bundle. A fibrovascular bundle which contains cambium.

open collateral bundle. A bundle with phloem on the outside separated from the xylem by a cambium ring.

open communities. 1. Plant communities in which the plants are scattered due to poor soil, shifting soil, or changing soil conditions. 2. Communities in which competition is not severe and new plants are able to invade successfully.

open formation. A formation in which the plants are scattered.

open nucleus. The nucleus of *Cyanophyceae*.

open system of growth. A manner of growth typical of plants in which new cells are formed at the apices.

open vascular bundle. An open bundle.

open woodland. A woodland composed of trees in groups with a general herbaceous ground cover but without a closed canopy.

opening cells. Special cells by which the dehiscence of sporangia or pollen sacs take place.

opercle. 1. The persistent base of a style forming a prominent point of an ovary in an epigynous flower. 2. An operculum.

opercular. 1. Like an operculum. 2. Covered with a lid. 3. Operculate.

opercular cell. A lid cell by means of which some antheridia open.

opercule. 1. The lamina of the leaf of *Sarracenia*, the pitcher plant of bogs. 2. The lid of the flower in *Eucalyptus*. 3. The operculum of mosses.

operculiform. Shaped like a lid.

operculigenous. Producing or forming a lid.

operculum. A lid, the upper portion of a circumscissile capsule, the lid covering the capsule in mosses.

opertus. Covered, tectus.

ophio-. A prefix meaning snake.

ophiocarpous. With snake-like fruits.

ophiglossaceous. Akin to or resembling *Ophioglossum*, the adder-tongue fern.

ophioglossifolious. With leaves like *Ophioglossum*.

ophioglossoid. Like *Ophioglossum*.

ophiuroid. Like the grass *Ophiurus*.

ophrydeous. Resembling or allied to the orchid *Ophrys*.

opisthelium. The posterior border of a stoma.

opisthial aperture. The opening between the base of the stomatal pore and the substomatal cavity.

opisthocont. Having flagella or cilia at the posterior end, opisthocontous.

opisthodal. Posterior, opisthelial.

opistodromous. Growing or curving in back (of a flower), as a spiral stem passes on its shortest way from a bract to the first floral segment between the flower and the stem.

opium. 1. The juice from the opium poppy, *Papaver somniferum*. 2. A parasitic community or a parasitic plant formation.

oplarium. A scyphus, an open cup.

opophilus. Sap-loving.

opophyte. A parasite.

opplete. Filled.

opportunism. The direction of metamorphosis due to the factors potent at the moment.

opposite pinnatus. With leaflets on the same plant at right angles to the common petiole.

opposite pitting. The type of pitting in which the pits are in horizontal pairs or in short horizontal rows.

oppositely pinnate. With leaflets in pairs.

oppositiflorous. Having opposite peduncles and flowers.

oppositifolious. With opposite leaves.

oppositipetalous. Placed in front of a petal.

oppositisepalous. Situated in front of a sepal.

opseospermata. Tubercules on the surface of some algae which contain spores.

opsigony. The delayed production and development of preventitious buds.

-opsis-form. A suffix meaning having pycnia, aecia, and telia on the same host (in the *Uredinales*), i.e., with urediospores lacking.

optimal area. The most favorable area for the development of a species or variety.

optional parthenogenesis. Facultative parthenogenesis.

opulasteranum. A vegetational layer of ninebark (*Physocarpus*, formerly known as *Opulaster*).

opuliflorous. Like the flowers of *Opulus*, (*Viburnum*).

opulifolious. With leaves like *Opulus*.

orae radicum. A root tip or spongiole.

orange. The fruit of *Citrus aurantium*.

orbicular. Circular in outline, nearly round and flat, rotund, orbiculate, disk-shaped.

orbiculus. 1. The fleshy corona in the flower of *Stapelia*. 2. A round flat hymenium in fungi.

orbilla. The shield of certain lichens, as *Usnea*.

orchard country. A parkland with a typical orchard-like aspect with trees and often palms occurring singly and generally scattered throughout the grass.

orchella. 1. Lichens which yield dyes, as *Lecanora*, *Roccella*, etc. 2. Cask-shaped lichen spores.

orchidaceous. 1. Having two tubers at the roots, as species of the genus *Orchis* and its allies. 2. Pertaining to the orchids.

orchideous. Of or belonging to the *Orchideae*, orchidean.

orchidiflorous. With flowers like an orchid.

orchidology. The study of orchids.

orchil. A valuable dye obtained from the lichen *Lecanora tartarea* and some other lichens, cudbear and litmus dyes.

orchiod. Orchid-like.

orcin. The coloring substance from various tinctorial lichens.

orculiform spore. A two-celled spore with a thick median wall pierced by a connecting tube between the two cells, a cask-shaped lichen spore, a polarilocular spore, an orculaeform spore.

ordeal tree. A poisonous tree of Madagascar, the *Cerbera Tanghinia*. Persons suspected of crime are forced to eat the seeds. Criminals are put to death by being pricked with lances dipped in the juice of the seeds.

order. A group of families, the chief subdivision of a class.

ordinal names. The names of the natural orders, groups, or families of plants.

ordinary chloroplast. A chloroplastid containing small though sometimes numerous starch grains.

ordinate. Having markings or ornamentation arranged in rows.

ordinatopunctate. With dots in rows.

Ordovician. Of, pertaining to, or designating the period following the Cambrian.

ore. A pasture (Danish).

oread. A sun plant, a heliophyte.

oreganus. Of Oregon.

oreo-. A prefix meaning mountain.

oreophilous. Mountain-loving.

orgadad. An open woodland plant.

orgadium. An open woodland community.

orgadocolous. Dwelling in open woodland.

orgadophilous. Dwelling in open woodland.

orgadophyte. An open woodland plant.

organ. A part of an organism specialized to perform one or more functions.

organ center. The point or axis around which growth takes place. It may or may not be the structural center.

organ-forming substances. Differentiated

materials in spores or seeds which indicate the formation of definite organs of the embryo.

organ-genus. A genus name used for parts of fossil plants which may be classified in a family.

organel. A cell organ.

organellae. The various parts of a cell.

organelle. A little organ, an organoid or organ-like structure, the organs of unicellular plants or animals.

organic. 1. Of living beings. 2. Of organisms.

organic acids. Acids containing carbon although carbonic acid is usually not included.

organic axis. The main axis of a cell which passes through the centrosome and the nucleus in the resting cell.

organific. Producing an organ or organized structure.

organism. A living body whether simple or complex.

organization. Differentiation and integration, i.e., different parts united into a whole.

organogen. Any of the four elements (C, H, O, N) which are essential elements of organic compounds.

organogenesis. The formation and development of organs from their primitive condition.

organogeny. Organogenesis.

organography. 1. The study of organs and their relations. 2. The description of organs in a living organism.

organoid. Of apparently unknown function.

organology. The study of organs and their relationships.

organonomy. The laws which deal with life or living organisms.

organonymy. The phylogeny of organs, a study of the laws of life.

organophyly. The phylogeny of organs.

organophysiology. The study of the necessary modifications in structure to enable a species to settle in a given place.

organoplastic. Having the power to produce organs.

organotrophic. Forming and nourishing organs.

organs, conservative. The root, stem, leaf, and sporangium of a plant.

organs, reproductive. The organs concerned in the production of seeds or spores.

organs, vegetative. Organs connected with growth only.

organule. A cell or element of an organism.

orgya. Vegetation two meters in height.

orgyalis. Having a length or height of about two meters.

oriental. Eastern.

orientation. The alteration in position shown by organs or organisms under stimulus.

orientation, inverse. The inversion of the ovuliferous scale bundles in *Coniferae*.

orifice. An opening, a mouth, an aperture.

origanifolious. With leaves like the herb *Origanum*.

origanoid. Like the herb *Origanum*.

origoma. The cup of a *Marchantia* containing gemmae, orygoma.

ormogon. A hormogone.

ornitho-. A prefix meaning bird.

ornithocephalous. Resembling the head of a bird.

ornithocoprophilous. Feeding upon the excreta of birds, as some lichens.

ornithogaea. The New Zealand regions.

ornithogamous. Fertilized by birds.

ornithophilae. Plants habitually fertilized by pollen brought by birds.

ornithophilous. Adapted to pollination by birds.

ornithopodous. Like a bird's foot.

ornithorhynchus. Shaped like a bird's bill.

orobanchaceous. Like *Orobanche*, the parasitic broom-rape, a root parasite without green foliage.

oroboid. Like *Orobus*, a legume.

orogenic. Originating in the mountains.

orographic characters. Physiographic characters created or influenced by the configuration of the surface of the earth, particularly by mountains.

orophylile. Of subalpine forests.

orohylion. An alpine forest of *Picea* and *Abies*.

orolochmis. Subalpine thicket associes.

orophilous. Dwelling in subalpine regions.

orophyte. A subalpine plant.

orophytia. Subalpine plant communities or formations.

orothamnic. Of alpine heaths.

orthenchyma. Orthosenchyma, parenchyma with vertically arranged cells.

orthidium. A supposedly new type of fructification in lichens probably a cyphella.

ortho-. A prefix meaning upright, straight, or regular.

orthobiont. An organism of direct succession from one zygote to a following one.

orthoblast. A confervoid prothallus growing in an ascending direction.

orthobotrys. With straight clusters.

orthocarpous. With straight fruits.

orthochilous. With straight lips.

orthocladous. With straight branches.

orthoclema. With straight branches or leaves.

orthogamy. Self-fertilization (the normal relations of the male and the female in some plants).

orthogenesis. 1. The doctrine that evolution is definitely directed by intrinsic causes. 2. Evolution in a definite direction.

orthogeotropism. The growth of a stem vertically upward or of a root downward in response to gravity.

orthogonal arrangement. The manner of arrangement of four parts of a flower when two are median and two are lateral.

orthoheliotropic. With movement directed toward the source of light.

orthomorphous. With radial and erect arrangement.

orthophototaxy. The direct arrangement of such organisms as *Volvox* and *Spirogyra* under the stimulus of light.

orthophototropic. With movement due to the direct influence of light.

orthophyte. A plant from egg to egg, or the sporophytic plus the gametophytic stages.

orthoploceae. The *Cruciferae* which have conduplicate cotyledons.

orthoploceous. Having conduplicate cotyledons; with the incumbent cotyledons folded around the radicle, as in mustard.

orthoploid. Octoploid.

orthopterous. With straight wings.

orthosepalous. With straight sepals.

orthospermeae. Plants whose seeds have albumen flat on the inner face and are neither involute nor convolute.

orthospermous. With straight seeds, especially in the *Umbelliferae*.

orthostichy. Arrangement in a straight or vertical line; a vertical arrangement of leaves, scales, or flowers on a stem.

orthostomous. With a straight opening.

orthotactic. Normal.

orthotriaene. A trident-shaped spicule with the branches at right angles.

orthotropal. Orthotropous, orthotropic.

orthotropic. Having organs which show a definite positive or negative tropism to a given stimulus, as stems which are erect in contrast to leaves and horizontal branches, etc.; orthotropal, orthotropous.

orthotropous. 1. Erect with a micropyle at the apex, straight. 2. Showing a definite response to a given stimulus.

orthotropous ovule. An ovule with a straight axis, with the micropyle at the apex in a straight line with the hilum at the base; an ovule which is straight, not curved, so that the chalaza, hilum, and micropyle are in a straight line.

orthotype. A genus provided with a type by original designation.

orthotypic. Of or pertaining to orthotypes.

Ortstein. A layer of soil which stops downward growth of roots and is the result of the accumulation of humus at the contact of sand and a mineral salt solution.

orygoma. See ORIGOMA.

oryzoid. Like *Oryza*, rice.

os, oris. A mouth, an orifice.

os. See ESKER. (pl. osar).

os, ossis. A bone.

oscillanus. Oscillating.

oscillation. A swinging or moving back and forth like a pendulum.

oscillatoriaceous. Allied to the blue-green alga *Oscillatoria*.

oscular. Of or pertaining to an osculum.

osculate. Having characters in common with two groups.

oscule. A pore in rust spores.

osculum. An ostiole, a mouth.

osmanthus. With fragrant flowers.

osmometer. An instrument to measure osmosis.

osmoscope. An apparatus for the demonstration of osmosis.

osmosis. The diffusion of a liquid, gas, etc., through a semipermeable membrane, the denser solution absorbing from the more diffuse solution.

osmosis, nuclear. The increased size of a nucleus attributed to absorption of a fluid through the nuclear membrane.

osmospores. Certain uredineous spermagones characterized by their having a scent.

osmotaxis. The rearrangement of moving organisms in response to the influence of fluids.

osmotic. Of, pertaining to, or having the property of osmosis.

osmotic chamber. A chamber enclosed by a semipermeable membrane.

osmotic pressure. The pressure which develops within an osmotic chamber, the pressure which develops in diffusion in solutions of different concentration.

osmotropism. Tropism due to osmotic action.

osmundaceous. Akin to the fern *Osmunda*.

ossiculus. 1. The pyrene of a fruit, as a medlar or cherry stone. 2. A little stone.

ossified. Becoming hard as bone, as the stones of drupes such as the peach and plum.

ostariphytum. A plant which produces a drupe or drupe-like fruit.

osteosclereide. A thick-walled idioblast resembling a thigh bone in shape.

ostiate. Having an ostium.

ostiolate. Having an ostiole or mouth, ostiolar.

ostiole. An opening, pore, or mouth which permits spores, pollen, or gases to escape from a plant structure; an opening.

ostium. An opening, an entrance.

ostracodermatous. Resembling shells of molluscs, applied to certain lichens; astracodermatine.

ostruthietum. An association of *Peucedanum Ostruthium*, of the parsley family.

-osus. A suffix indicating enlargement, as radiosus (large-rooted).

oued. An Arabic term for a valley containing water in the rainy season, a wadi or wed.

outbreeding. The crossing of unrelated gametes.

outcross. A cross with an individual which is not closely related.

outer. Morphologically the lower surface of the leaf of sphagnum, exterior, abaxial.

outer aperture. The opening of the canal into the bordered pit chamber.

outer bark. The rough corky tissue developed from the cork cambium outside of the inner bark which is developed from the stellar cambium.

outer glumes. Glumes at the base of spikelets in grasses enclosing one or more flowers, barren or empty glumes.

outer peridium. External peridium.

outer space. Water-free space.

oval. Egg-shaped, broadly elliptical, widest at the middle.

ovalifolious. With oval leaves.

ovaricole. Growing in ovaries, ovaricolous.

ovariform. Egg-shaped.

ovariophylly. The descending metamorphosis of a carpel into a leaf.

ovary. The enlarged base part of the pistil or

carpel in which the ovules appear, the ovarium.

ovate. Shaped like the longitudinal section through a hen's egg, broadest below the middle with the broad end downward (applied to flat surfaces, ovoid applied to solids).

ovate-acuminate. Ovate but narrowed at the end into a slender point or sharp tip.

ovate-deltoid. Triangularly egg-shaped.

ovate-ellipsoidal. Ovate approaching ellipsoid.

ovate-falcate. Of a curved, oval, or egg-shaped form.

ovate-lanceolate. Intermediate between ovate and lanceolate.

ovatifolious. With ovate leaves.

ovate-oblong. Oblong with one end narrower than the other.

ovate-rhomboidal. Rhomboidal egg-shaped.

ovato-cylindraceous. Egg-shaped with a convolute cylindrical figure.

ovato-rotundate. Roundly egg-shaped.

ovellum. A young carpel bearing the same relation to a mature carpel as an ovule to a seed.

ovenchyma. Loose tissue of oval-shaped cells.

over-dominance. Greater than complete dominance due to the heterozygous (Aa) state yielding more or expressing more of a character than the homozygous (AA) state.

overgrazing. Grazing which when excessive reduces the forage crop or results in an undesirable change in the type of vegetation.

overstocked. The condition existing in a forest stand when more trees of a particular species or age are present than the site is able to support.

overtopped. Having the crowns shaded from above (there may be light from the sides).

overturn. The thorough circulation of water in deeper lakes brought about by wind which overcomes the stratification of the water due to differences in specific gravity of the water.

ovicel. An aecium.

oviferous. Bearing eggs.

oviform. Ovoid or egg-shaped.

ovigerous. Egg-bearing, oviferous.

ovinus. Of or pertaining to sheep.

ovocentrum. A central mass of fine-grained protoplasm surrounding the nucleus in the oogonium of the fungus *Achlya*.

ovoid. Solid like an egg in form and attached at the large end; see OVATE.

ovoid oblong. Lengthened ovoid.

ovular. Pertaining to or of the nature of an ovule.

ovulary. The ovule-bearing part of a closed carpel or set of carpels, the ovary.

ovulate. 1. Containing or bearing an egg or ovule. 2. Somewhat egg-shaped.

ovule. The unfertilized young seed in the ovary; the structure which, after fertilization, develops into a seed; the megasporangium of a seed plant which later develops into a seed; a rudimentary seed.

ovule tube. A thread-like extension of the amnios rising beyond the foramen.

ovuliferous. Bearing or containing ovules.

ovuliferous scales. The scales composing the fertile fructifications of the *Coniferae* which bear the ovules and the seeds.

ovum. The egg or oosphere, a female germ cell. *Ovum* is used in animals and *ovule* is usually used in plants.

oxalates. Substances occurring in certain fruits and vegetables due to the accumulation of oxalic acid.

oxalic. 1. Pertaining to the genus *Oxalis*, wood sorrel. 2. Pertaining to oxalic acid.

oxalic acid. An acid found in the genus *Oxalis* and some other plants.

oxalidaceous. Of or pertaining to the genus *Oxalis* or its allies.

oxaliferous. Producing oxalic acid or its salts.

oxalileucite. A vacuole which contains oxalic acid.

oxarch. An oxysere.

oxbow lake. A lake formed from an abandoned river channel which is filled at the ends with silt deposits.

oxidase. An enzyme which brings about oxidation.

oxidation. The addition of oxygen to a compound. The removal of positive ions or the addition of negative ions from a molecule.

oxodad. A plant of a humus marsh.

oxodic. Of a peat bog community.

oxodiion. An association on acid soil.

oxodium. A humus marsh plant community.

oxyacanthous. With many thorns or prickles.

oxycarpous. Having sharp-pointed fruit.

oxycelluloses. Any of the group of substances regarded as oxidized cellulose occurring in wood fiber or obtained artificially by the oxidation of cellulose.

oxychromatin. Granules in the linin thread which do not form the chromosomes and stain lightly with acid dyes as eosin. They contain little nucleic acid.

oxydase. An oxidizing enzyme.

oxygenotaxis, oxytaxis, oxygenotactic, oxytactic. A response or reaction of an organism to the stimulus of oxygen.

oxygeophilous. Dwelling in humus.

oxygeophyte. A humus plant.

oxygonous. Sharp-angled.

oxygyrous. Sharply twisted.

oxylepis. The sharp scale of the very acute or sharp-pointed glumes.

oxylic. Of sour or acid soil communities.

oxylium. A humus marsh plant community.

oxylophilous. Humus-loving.

oxylophyte. A plant inhabiting acid or humus soil.

oxyon. A heath climax community.

oxypetalous. With sharp petals.

oxypetrile. Of acid communities.

oxyphil. A structure or substance having a strong affinity for acidic stains.

oxyphilic. Of or pertaining to oxyphils.

oxyphyllous. With sharp-pointed leaves.

oxyphytes. Plants which indicate a lack of oxygen in the soil with low chresard (available water).

oxyrietum. An association of *Oxyria* plants, mountain sorrel.

oxysepalous. With sharp sepals.

oxysere. A hydrosere having its origin in acid aquatic media or acid soils.

oxytropism. Movement in response to an excess of acids.

ozonium. A bundle of cobwebby hyphae, the sterile mycelium of the basidiomycetous stage.

P

P. The parental generation, the parent or parents of the first (F_1) generation.

P_2, P_3, etc. The second, third, etc., parental generations.

pabularious. Of fodder or pasturage.

pachy-. A prefix meaning thick.

pachyanthrous. With thick flowers.

pachycarpous. With a thick pericarp.

pachycladous. With thick branches.

pachyclema. With stout branches.

pachydermaticous. With a thick skin or covering.

pachydermous. With a thick skin or walls.

pachygyrous. Coiled in thick whorls.

pachynema. The pachytene stage in meiosis, the period of the thick unsplit spireme in late synapsis.

pachyneurous. With thick nerves or veins.

pachynosis. Thickness in structural plant growth.

pachyphloeous. With thick bark.

pachypleurous. With thick walls.

pachyphyllous. With thick leaves.

pachypterous. With thick wings.

pachystichous. With thick-sided cells.

pachyte. The secondary region of the stem composed of secondary xylem with liber.

pachytene loops. The loops which are formed by the chromatin threads in the pachytene stage before they divide longitudinally.

pachytene stage. The stage in meiosis when the double threads of chromatin shorten and thicken and chiasmata take place.

pacificus. Of the Pacific Ocean or regions bordering it.

packet form. The association of bacteria in certain genera, as *Sarcina*, etc.

packing cells. Füllzellen, complementary cells.

pad. 1. A popular name for the floating leaves of water lilies. 2. A cushion-like growth.

paddy. 1. Unhusked rice. 2. A rice field.

paedogamous autogamy. The copulation of nuclei and gametes in place of the union of complete gametes.

paedogamy. The copulation of two gametes from the same gametangium.

paedogenesis. Extreme precocity, as when the seedling of a tree flowers when only a few inches high, pedogenesis.

pagina. The blade or surface of the leaf or other organ, the lamina.

pagium. A succession of plants on glacial soil.

pagophylous. Dwelling in foothills.

pagophyte. A foothill plant.

pagophytium. A foothill plant formation.

painted. Having colored streaks of unequal density.

pairing cell. A gamete.

pairing of chromosomes. The coming together of chromosomes at the zygotene stage or the continuance of their association at the first division metaphase.

pairing, secondary. The pairing of chromosomes among bivalents at meiosis.

pairing segment. A segment or short portion of a chromosome which undergoes pairing with a corresponding segment in another chromosome.

pairing, somatic. The lying close together of homologous chromosomes at the metaphase of mitosis.

pajonales. Reed thickets at the edge of pampas streams.

palaceous. With the edges of an organ decurrent or adherent to the support or stem.

palachila. A spade lip.

palaeaceous. Chaffy, chaff-like.

palaearctic region. Europe, Africa, and Asia north of the Tropic of Cancer.

palaeobiologist. A student of fossil life-forms.

palaeobotanist. A student of fossil botany.

palaeobotany. The study of fossil botany.

Palaeocene. The early Tertiary Period.

palaeogaea. The regions including arctic Europe and the Ethiopian, Indian, and Australian zoological regions.

palaegeic. Applied to soils derived from the older geological formations.

palaeogenetic. With primitive features fully developed, usually characteristically embryonic.

Palaeolaurentian. The Archezoic Era.

palaeontology. The science of past organic life based on fossils and fossil impressions.

palaeophytology. Palaeobotany.

palaeotropic. Paleotropic.

palaeotropic flora. The tropical flora of the Old World.

Palaeozoic. The geological era before the Mesozoic, the age of fishes and amphibia.

palaestinus. Of Palestine.

palar. With the root continuous with the stems.

palari-ramosus. With a palar root which has many branches.

palate. The projecting part of the lower lip of a corolla which closes the throat (as in snapdragons), the mouth of a ringent flower, a projecting lip of a personate flower.

pale, palea (pl. paleae), or palet. 1. The inner bracteole, thin and membranous, which, with the flowering glume, encloses the grass flower. 2. A general term for the glumes associated with the grass flower. 3. The scales which form the ramentum in ferns. 4. The chaffy scales on the receptacle of *Compositae*.

paleaceous. Chaffy, with chaffy scales furnished with paleae or chaff.

paleaeform. Resembling paleae, paleform, upright.

palecology. Paleoecology.

paleic. Past or fossil.

paleobotanist. A student of paleobotany or fossil botany.

paleoecology. The ecology of geological periods.

paleola. A diminutive of palea, or the lodicules or squamellae of grasses.

paleolate. Having a lodicule or paleola.

paleoliferous. Bearing paleae.

paleontology. The science dealing with the fossil remains of animals and plants.

paleophytes. The vegetation of the Paleozoic Period characterized by pteridophytes.

paleophytology. The study of fossil botany.

paleosere. The eosere or plant succession in the Paleozoic Age, a pterosere.

paleostrate. A definitely paleophytic eostrate.

paleotropic. Belonging to the tropics of the Old World, Asia, Africa, and North Australia.

paleous. Chaffy.

Paleozoic. The geological period in which the oldest fossils occur.

palescent. Inclined to paleness, becoming pallid.

palet. Chaff, the inner bract or glume of the flower in grasses, the pales of English botanists, palea.

paliform. Like an upright stake, paleaeform.

palingenesis. 1. That phase in the development of an individual organism which repeats the evolutionary history of the groups to which it belongs. 2. The abrupt metamorphosis or rebirth of ancestral characters. The opposite of cenogenesis.

palingenetic. Of remote or ancient origin.

palisade cells. 1. A layer of elongated cells set at right angles to the surface of a leaf underlying the upper epidermis containing numerous chloroplasts and concerned with photosynthesis. 2. The terminal cells of the hyphae of a fastigiate cortex in lichens.

palisade chlorenchyma. The palisade tissue consisting of cells which contain chloroplasts.

palisade epithelium. The palisade tissue consisting of glandular cells.

palisade fungi. The basidiomycetes.

palisade layer. The layer of palisade cells.

palisade parenchyma. The layer or layers of palisade cells in a leaf just below the upper epidermis and extending downward to the spongy parenchyma.

palisade sclerenchyma. The palisade tissue consisting of thick-walled cells.

palisade stereide. A rod-shaped thick-walled cell in the testa which is elongated and at right angles to the surface of the seed.

palisade tissue. The layer or layers of palisade cells beneath the epidermis.

palisadic. Of or pertaining to palisade cells.

pallescent. Becoming light in color, turning pale.

palliate. Having a mantle or similar structure.

pallidiflorous. With pale flowers.

pallidifolious. With pale leaves.

pallidispinous. With pale spines.

palliflavens. A pale yellow color.

pallium. A gelatinous envelope of diatoms.

pallustre. Paluster.

palmaris. Palmate, about three inches long.

palmate. With lobes or divisions spread from a common center like the radiating fingers of a hand, with veins or leaflets radiating like fingers.

palmately cleft. Having the divisions in a palmate leaf reach about halfway to the base.

palmately compound. Having leaflets all jointed to the petiole at its summit.

palmately lobed. Having the lobes directed toward the apex of the petiole, palmatilobate.

palmately parted. Cleft nearly to the base in a palmate manner, palmatipartite.

palmately veined. Having the veins palmately arranged.

palmatifid. Palmate; with the lobes extending to the middle of the leaf; palmately cleft, lobed, or divided.

palmatiform. Having venation arranged in a palmate manner.

palmatilobate. Palmately lobed with rounded lobes and divisions halfway to the base.

palmatim. In a palmate manner.

palmatinervis. Palmately veined.

palmatipartite. Palmate with divisions more than halfway to base.

palmatisect. Palmate with the divisions extending to the bottom of the leaf.

palmella phase. A nonmotile resting stage of some unicellular algae during which division takes place. The flagella are withdrawn, and the algae are embedded in a gelatinous sheath.

palmellin. A red coloring matter obtained from some algae during the palmella phase.

palmelloid. Having the characteristics of the palmella stage.

palmicolous. Growing on palms.

palmids. Palms, cycads, and tree ferns of palm-like aspect.

palmiferous. Producing palm trees.

palmifid. Palmatifid.

palmifolous. With palm-like leaves.

palmiform. Shaped like a palm.

palminerve. With palmate veins.

palmitic acid. A fatty acid derived from vegetable fats and oils.

palmitin. A glyceride in vegetable fats and oils.

palmogloeon. Resembling the once proposed algal genus *Palmogloes*, now included in the genus *Mesotaenium*.

palmographer. A specialist or monographer of palms.

paludal. Living in marshes.

paludicolous. Living in ponds, streams, or a palus.

paludine. Growing in marshes or swamps.

paludophilae. 1. Algae with thin filaments. 2. Unicellular green algae.

paludose. Growing in marshy places.

palule. A small palus.

palumbine. A dull grayish blue, dove-colored.

palus. A swamp or low ground near rivers.

paluster. A plant inhabiting boggy ground or the marginal zone of a lake.

palustrine. Of or inhabiting swamps or marshes, paludose.

palustris. Marsh-loving, swampy.

palynology. The study of pollen grains and spores.

pamir. Alluvial mountain meadows, high mountain meadows like those in the Pamir Mountains between China and Russia.

pampas. The grassy plains of temperate South America.

pampas grass. *Cortaderia argentea*, a handsome, tall, coarse grass which grows in large clumps. It is a native of South America but is used widely as an ornamental plant.

pampiniform. Resembling the tendril of a vine.

pampinody. The change of foliar parts into tendrils.

pan. 1. A compact layer or substratum of earth cemented by organic material or other compounds which is impermeable to water and impervious to roots. 2. A depression in a salt marsh in which salt water stands for lengthy periods and affects plant growth. 3. Hardpan.

panaposporous. Having prothalli developed aposporously over the entire surface of a fern frond.

panary. Pertaining to bread-making or the cereals used in bread-making.

Panaschiering. A variation in leaf coloration produced by an enzyme.

panche. Having pale faint stripes.

panclimaxes. 1. Related climax plant formations with similar climatic requirements, similar life forms, and common dominants. 2. Climax formations which have developed from a common origin or from the same geological periods.

pandurate. Fiddle-shaped, constricted about the middle.

panduriform. Fiddle-shaped.

panformation. A coenosis composed of several independent and stable formations in which one layer (the higher if not otherwise noted) is dominated by a species of a distinct genus or family.

panformion. A stable synusium of one or more formions dominated by species of distinct genera or families but only exceptionally with the same species present in different formations.

pangamic. Mating indiscriminately.

pangen. The hypothetical particle (which might be likened to a "floating gene") suggested by Darwin as an explanation of inheritance and modification of characters in his pangenesis hypothesis.

pangenesis. The hypothesis that every cell of the body throws off minute granules (pangens or gemmules) which collect in the sex cells where they initiate the corresponding organs or parts in the offspring.

pangenosomes. A complex of pangens.

panicle. 1. A branched or compound raceme with each branch bearing a raceme. 2. In more casual meaning, an irregular compound inflorescence with pedicellate flowers.

panicled. Having a panicle or panicles.

paniculate. With flowers arranged in panicles.

paniculiform. Panicle-shaped.

paniculigerous. Panicle-bearing.

panicula. A panicle.

panification. The fermentation changes by which dough is converted into bread.

panmerism. The doctrine that all particles of protoplasm are capable of assimilation, growth, division, and adaptation.

panmictic. Of or pertaining to panmixis.

panmixis. Random mating or crossing in the absence of selection, panmixia, panmixy.

pannary. Panary.

panne. A lagoon in the Danish West Indies separated from the sea the edges of which bear luxuriant mangrove vegetation.

pannexterna. An epicarpium.

panniform. Having the appearance or texture of felt or woollen cloth.

panninterna. An endocarpium.

pannonicus. Of Pannonia on the Danube.

pannose. Felt-like, ragged, tattered.

panphotometric. Oriented to avoid maximum direct sunlight, said of narrow leaves which stand nearly erect.

panspermia. The theory that cases of spontaneous generation arise from the widespread and universal distribution of germs and spores.

panspermism. The universal diffusion of germs, seeds, and spores throughout the atmosphere.

pantachobryous. 1. Growing in a circular or irregular manner. 2. Growing everywhere.

pantanos. The blackish or freshwater marshes of Argentina.

pantogenous. Growing everywhere and not confined to a single host.

pantophagous. Eating a great variety of food, omnivorous.

pantotactic. Having the sori arise at the tip of the leaf vein, as in the fern *Trichomanes reniforme*

pantothenic acid. A vitamin found in yeasts and some grains. It plays a vital role in cell metabolism.

papain. A protein-digesting enzyme present in the fruit and leaves of the papaya, *Carica Papaya*, used as a meat tenderizer.

papaveraceous. Belonging to or resembling the poppy, papaverous.

papaw. See PAWPAW.

papayotin. The dried leaves of *Carica Papaya*, which contain a digestive enzyme.

papilionaceous. Butterfly-like, as the corollas of the pea flowers and most other legumes; having a flower with a banner, wings, and a keel.

papilionaceous flower. Shaped like a butterfly or like the pea flower.

papilla. A soft superficial protuberance; a small, nipple-like elevation.

papilla, receptive. A structure in *Phytopthora*, the downy mildews.

papillar. Papillate, nipple-shaped.

papillate. Papillar, much the same as granular with the granules more elevated, papillose.

papillately hairy. Having short thick hair or hairs from papillae.

papilliferous. Producing papillae.

papilliform. Shaped like a papilla.

papillose. Having minute nipple-shaped projections, having papillae, papilloid.

papillose-pilose. With stiff hairs arising from papillae.

pappiferous. Bearing a pappus.

pappiform. Resembling a pappus.

pappo. The down of thistles.

pappose. Downy or covered with feathery hairs, having a pappus.

pappus. The downy or feathery bristles or scales on an achene representing the calyx, the modified calyx of the *Compositae*, a tuft of hairs as on the achene of the dandelion seed which serves in seed dispersal by wind.

papule. A pimple or small pustule.

papuliferous. Bearing pustules.

papulose. Having small glands like nipples.

papulospore. A close hyphal coil of short somewhat enlarged cells, each of which germinates and acts as a spore, as in the fungus genus *Papulospora*.

papyraceous ferns. The filmy ferns which have very thin, paper-like leaves one cell thick, as the *Hymenophyllaceae*.

papyriferous. Paper-bearing.

para-. A prefix meaning alongside, beyond, or against.

parabasal body. A cytoplasmic body connected with the basal apparatus of the flagellum in many flagellates presumed to be an accessory part, a kinetic reservoir of the motor apparatus.

parabolic. Having a broad base and gradually narrowing by curved sides to a blunt apex, ovate-oblong or ovate-obtuse and contracted below the apex.

parabuxine. An alkaloid occurring in *Buxus sempervirens*, the box tree or shrub.

parabuxinidine. Parabuxine.

paracallus. A substance which resembles the callus of sieve tubes but differs in reaction and chemical constitution.

paracarpium. 1. An abortive pistil or carpel. 2. The persistent portion of some styles or stigmas.

paracarpous. Having ovaries whose carpels are joined together by the margins only.

paracellulose. The cellulose which forms the epidermal cells of plants.

paracentral. Lying near a center or central part.

parachromatin. The achromatic nuclear substance giving rise to spindle fibers, linin.

parachromatophorous. 1. Having pigment chiefly in the cell wall. 2. Excreting coloring matter which adheres to the organism, as in some bacteria. 3. Parachromatophoric.

parachute. 1. A special structure of seeds as aril, caruncle, wing, etc., which assists in dispersal. 2. A seed or fruit, as the achene of a dandelion, fitted for wind dispersal by a parachute-like pappus, coma, or other appendage.

parachute disseminule. A fruit or seed provided with a pappus, a tuft of hairs, or any device which facilitates dispersal by the wind.

paracme. The decline of a species or race after reaching the highest point of its development, decadence.

paracorolla. An appendage to a corolla, the corona of a flower.

paracotyledonary. The development of an axis derived from the anterior inferior segment (quadrant) of the oosphere of the fern *Marsilea*.

paracycadales. Proangiosperms.

paracyst. 1. The antheridium of the fungus *Pyronema*. 2. A gamete in *Peziza*.

paradesmose. A slender filament of stainable material which connects the centers of two dividing halves of a blepharoplast.

paradiphyllum. A double leaf resulting from the dichotomy of the lamina.

paradisiacus. Of a park or garden.

paraffin. A waxy substance produced by distilling wood, lignite, coal, etc., and occurring also in the earth as a constituent of petroleum or as a solid deposit.

paraffinic acid. An acid found in humus.

paraffinoid. Having the scent of paraffin, as the rose, lime, elder, etc.

paragalactin. A reserve substance in the seeds of lupines.

paragamic. Having vegetative or gametic nuclei lying in a continuous mass of cytoplasm which fuse to form a zygote nucleus.

paragamy, apocytial. The fusion of the vegetative nuclei of an apocyte to form an oospore in *Saprolegniaceae*.

paragenesia. The fertility of hybrids with parent species but not between themselves.

paragenesis. All modes of reproduction resulting in a body which simulates a zygote in the same or allied forms.

paragynous. With lateral antheridia, i.e., with antheridia which penetrate the side of the oogonia with the fertilization tube. They may grow on the side or grow up the side of the oogonia.

paraheliode. A parasol or protective set of spines in *Cactaceae*.

paraheliotropism. The tendency of plants to turn the edges of leaves and other organs toward intense sunlight to protect them from excess light, diurnal sleep.

parahormone. A substance which acts like a hormone but is only a product of ordinary metabolism of cells.

paralinum. The ground substance of the nucleus, the substance composing the nucleohyaloplasm.

parallel chorisis. A lateral separation into two or more members.

parallel descent. The descent which results in similar structure though the plants are not descended from an immediate common ancestor.

parallel geotropism. The tropic response of an organism directing itself axially toward the force of gravity.

parallel spires. Spirals in phyllotaxy.

parallel type. A paratype.

parallel-veined. Having venation in which all the veins are parallel, straight-nerved or -veined.

parallelinervate. With parallel leaves with veins or nerves.

parallelism. The evolution along similar lines in unrelated groups of plants.

parallelodrome. A plant having veins parallel to each other.

parallelotropism. A movement toward the source of light parallel to its rays.

paralysers. Enzymes which inhibit action or growth.

paramstigate. Having a single principal flagellum and a short accessory flagellum.

paramere. Half of a bilaterally symmetrical structure or organ.

parameridian. A plane in a diatom frustule which is parallel to the meridian.

paramitome. The ground substance or interfilar substance of protoplasm as opposed to mitome or reticulum.

paramo. The alpine region of the North Andes.

paramutualism. Parasaprophytism, facultative symbiosis.

paramylum. A starch-like substance found in the cytoplasm of some algae (brown and red), paramyl.

paranasty. Continued longitudinal growth of lateral parts.

paranemata. The paraphyses in some algae, slender sterile hairs.

paranematal filaments. Paranemata.

parang. The second growth vegetation, as a repeated cutting of bamboo.

paranuclein. Parachromatin, the substance of a nucleolus which does not yield nitrogenous matter on decomposition.

paranucleolus. A secondary or additional nucleolus when more than one is present with the nucleus.

paranucleus. 1. An additional nucleus near the tree nucleus, a spherical mass of mitochondria destined to form an axial filament envelope. 2. A general term used to indicate any structure lying beside the true nucleus. 3. A micronucleus.

parapectic acid. An acid derived from pectin by the action of alkalis.

parapectin. Hydrolyzed pectin.

parapetalous. Having stamens on each side of a petal.

parapetalum. An appendage to a corolla consisting of several pieces.

paraphototropic. Diaphototropic.

paraphototropism. The movement of leaves or other organs to be at right angles to the incidence of light, diaphototropism.

paraphyll. A very small leaf-like or much branched structure found among the leaves of mosses, a stipule.

paraphysagone. The initial element which gives rise to the branching terminated by paraphyses.

paraphysiate. With paraphyses.

paraphyses. 1. Sterile filaments occurring in the fructification of many lower plants.

2. Slender thread-like bodies growing with the asci. 3. Sterile capilliform hyphal branches accompanying spore mother cells in a hymenium.

paraphyses envelope. The peridium of the *Uredineae.*

paraphysoids. Plates of cellular tissue sometimes found between asci, more or less like paraphyses.

paraplasm. The vegetative or inactive part of cytoplasm, the more liquid interfilar portions of protoplasm.

paraplectenchyma. A modification of the hyphal tissue.

parapodic. 1. On the ground. 2. With very short stems.

parasaprophytism. Endosaprophytism.

parasite. A plant or animal requiring a living plant upon which to live and from which sustenance is derived.

parasite, partial. A parasite, usually with chlorophyll, which is only partially dependent on its host for nutrition.

parasite, total. A parasite which derives all its nourishment from its host, i.e., completely dependent upon the host.

parasitic saprophyte. A parasite which kills a host and then continues to feed on it.

parasitic castration. Sterility induced by a parasite which damages the reproductive organs.

parasitism, spurious. An epiphytic or false parasitism.

parasitology. The study of plant and animal parasites.

parasol. A paraheliode.

paraspermatia. Small reproductive bodies resembling spores found in some algae.

paraspore. The carpospore of the red algae.

parastades. The coronal rays of *Passiflora,* the passion flower.

parastamen. An abortive stamen, a staminodium.

parastemon. A sterile stamen, a parastamen.

parastemonal. Having structures which arise from or are close to the insertion of the filaments with the corolla.

parastichy. A spiral line passing once around a stem through the bases of successive leaves, a secondary spiral in *Phyllotaxy.*

parastrophe. The arrangement of chloroplasts along the cell walls rather than at the surface during intense sunlight.

parastyle. An abortive syle.

parasymbiont. One of the members in parasymbiosis.

parasymbiosis. The condition in which two organisms are in harmless association but not mutually useful.

parasynapsis. The side-by-side union of the elements of a pair of chromosomes, syndesis when the homologous chromosomes conjugate lengthwise, parasyndesis.

parasynaptist. One who regards the parallel threads of the heterotypic prophase as the pairing of entire chromosomes.

parasyndesis. Reduction by chromosomes paired in parallel positions, parasynapsis.

parataxis. The location of sori on an abortive vein which does not prolong the axis.

paratagma. A mass of micellae.

parately. Superficial resemblance of organisms which have evolved from unrelated sources.

parathecium. The hyphal layer around the apothecium of a lichen.

parathermotropism. The response to temperature and light by movement of leaves and other organs as exhibited by *Drosera*, *Oxalis*, *Mimosa*, etc.; paraheliotropism.

paratomy. Asexual reproduction in which a special zone or division is prepared in advance of the actual division.

paratonic. Depressing, retarding growth.

paratracheal parenchyma. The xylem parenchyma occurring at the edge of the annual ring and around the vessels but not elsewhere.

paratracheal wood parenchyma. The xylem parenchyma arranged in groups around the vessels.

paratransapical. Having sections parallel to the straight transapical axis or plane in diatoms.

paratransversan. With the planes parallel to the transverse plane.

paratroph. A parasite.

paratrophic. Obligately parasitic, as pathogenic bacteria.

paratropism. Parallelatropism.

paratype. A specimen other than the holotype cited with the original description of a new species. An allotype.

paravalvar. Having planes which are parallel to the valvar plane of a diatom, either epithecal or hypothecal.

paraxial. Alongside the axis.

pardalinus. Leopard-like, spotted, pardinus.

pardochoren. Organisms which are motile at one stage in their life history and sessile at another period.

pareira root, white. *Abuta rufescens*, the root of a South American vine used as a diuretic and tonic. Also pareira brava.

parellinus. Litmus violet.

parenchymatous. Resembling parenchyma.

parenchym. Parenchyma.

parenchyma. The soft green undifferentiated cellular tissue made up of large, blunt-ended cells with thin cellulose walls found in many plant organs, particularly in the pulp of leaves and fruit and the pith of stems. The tissue is involved primarily with the distribution and storage of carbohydrates.

parenchyma elements. The cells or units composing the parenchyma.

parenchyma tracheids. The short-pithed spiral ducts or vessels.

parenchymatic class or system of elements. Cells occurring only in secondary xylem or phloem whose contents are living protoplasm and which have all the characteristics of parenchyma.

parenchymatose. 1. Of parenchyma. 2. Having a pulpy mass of cells with vacuoles. 3. Spongy or porous.

parent material. The source material which after weathering and the addition of organic matter becomes soil.

parental generation. P_1 or F_1, the first parental generation.

parhomology. The apparent similarity of structure.

parichnos. A pair of scars, one on each side of the leaf base (in certain lower vascular plants). Each scar marks the end of a strand of parenchyma passing into the stem.

paries. The outer wall or enclosing wall of an organ.

parietal. Attached to or lying near and more or less parallel with a wall. Applied to the placenta when it arises from the peripheral wall of a carpel and to chloroplasts of algae lying close to the cell wall.

parietal cells. 1. Cells which form the inner wall of the pollen sac. 2. Any of the oval secreting cells lying between the central cells and the basal membrane.

parietal cytoplasm. The layer of cytoplasm

lining the cell wall in cells which contain one or more sap cavities.

parietal placenta. A placenta borne on the wall of an ovary instead of on the axis.

parietal utricle. The layer of protoplasm next to the cell wall.

parietin. The coloring matter found in the lichen *Physcia parietina*.

paripinnate. Having a pinnately compound leaf which has no terminal leaflet.

parkland. An area with isolated trees or with trees in small groups with the ground cover continuous or of interrupted herbaceous cover, usually without lianas.

parkland savannah. Open grassy country with patches of forest or copse.

parmeleine. Like the lichen *Parmelia*.

parmelietum. An association of *Parmelia*.

parnassifolious. With leaves like the bag plant *Parnassia*.

paroicous, paroecious. Having the male and female reproductive organs borne on the same branch but not mixed. In the bryophytes the antheridia are borne lower on the stem than the archegonia; in flowering plants the staminate and pistillate flowers may be borne on the same cluster but are not mixed.

paronychietum. An association of the herb *Paronychia*.

parothotropism. The movement of leaves which places them with the lamina vertical but not necessarily meridional.

parque. A parkland of *Acacia* and narrow-leaf grassland.

part spore. A single-celled spore which was originally part of a several-celled ascospore.

parted. Cleft nearly to the base, deeply cleft.

parthembryosperm. A parthenosperm with a parthenogenetic embryo and endosperm resulting from fertilization.

parthenapogamy. The fusion of the nuclei of vegetable cells.

parthendosperm. A plant whose endosperm is parthenogenetic and the embryo the result of fertilization.

parthenocarpy. The production of fruit without true fertilization and therefore without fertile seeds.

parthenocarpy, aitionomic. The production of fruit with the aid of an outside stimulus, as pollination by insects, etc.

parthenocarpy, autonomic or vegetative. The production of sterile fruit without any outside stimulation. The fruit lacks seeds, as the navel orange.

parthenogamete. A gamete which develops without pairing.

parthenogamy. 1. The preliminary stage of fertilization exhibited by macrogametes or macrosporangia. 2. Fertilization between two female cells. 3. Parthenomixis.

parthenogenesis. The occasional production of true spores or seeds without fertilization, the development without fertilization of male or female gametes into spores.

parthenogenesis, diploid. The development of spores by parthenogenesis when meiosis has failed, parthenapogamy.

parthenogenesis, generative. Haploid parthenogenesis.

parthenogenesis, haploid. The development of an oosphere with a reduced number of chromosomes.

parthenogenesis, male. The process in which the male nucleus develops into the embryo.

parthenogenesis, somatic. Parthenapogamy.

parthenogenetic. Developing without fertilization.

parthenogeny. Parthenogenesis.

parthenogonidia. Zooids of a protozoan colony with the capability of asexual reproduction.

parthenomixis. Parthenogamy.

parthenosperm. 1. A body resembling a zygospore but not resulting from the coalescence of two sexually different cells. 2. A plant having parthenogenetic embryos. 3. A sperm produced without fertilization.

parthenospore. The spore in certain algae which resembles a zygospore but which is produced without conjugation, a spore produced without fertilization.

parthenote. An individual developed from an egg with one haploid nucleus.

partial. Of secondary rank, subordinate, not complete or general.

partial habitat. A habitat used by a plant for part of its life cycle.

partial parasite. A plant that manufactures some of its own food by photosynthesis but depends on its host for some materials (as water, minerals, salts, etc.).

partial umbel. One of the minor umbels which make up a compound umbel.

partial veil. The inner veil of an agaric which

extends from the margin of the pileus to the stem and which leaves an annulus or cortina on the stem when it breaks away.

partible. Ultimately separating, easily separable.

particulate inheritance. The inheritance in one organism of distinctive paternal and maternal characteristics, Mendelian inheritance.

partridge-wood. Oak wood destroyed by the *Stereum.*

parturital. Sexual.

parviflorous. Having small flowers.

parvifoliate. With a dominant stem, long internodes, and small or few leaves.

parvigrade evolution. Continuous evolution.

parvocariceta. Communities of small species of the sedge *Carex.*

paryphodrome. A vein which closely follows the margin.

pascual. Growing in pastures or grassy commons.

paspalum. Millet.

passage cells. Thin-walled nonsuberized cells in the endodermis or exodermis in roots through which solutions can diffuse in a transverse direction.

passelus. A gamosepalous calyx.

passive absorption. Entirely physical absorption of substances into a cell.

passive protoplasm. Gynoplasm in a female gamete.

pasteurization. A method devised by Pasteur to arrest the growth of bacteria and other fermenting organisms found in milk and other liquids. The liquids are heated to 142-145° F. for thirty minutes and sealed to prevent contamination.

patagonicus. Of Patagonia.

patana. 1. A xerophytic grassy slope somewhat similar to a savannah. 2. A treeless area resulting from the burning of a forest.

patavinus. Of Padua.

patella. A rounded apothecium in some lichens; an orbicular, sessile apothecium with a marginal rim distinct from the thallus.

patellar. Circular or disk-shaped.

patellate. Shaped like a patella.

patenti-reflexed. Spread out and turned back.

pateriform. Saucer-shaped.

pathfinder pointers. Defensive protection such as prickles, etc., against undesirable insect visitors.

pathfinders. Honey guides or lines of color leading to the nectary.

pathogen. A disease-producing organism, a pathogene.

pathogenic. Disease-producing.

pathological. Diseased.

pathology. The study of disease.

patriclinous. Inclined hereditarily toward the male side.

patrogenesis. The development from a male nucleus because the female nucleus has been dispossessed.

patromorphic. Resembling the father.

patulent. Spreading open, expanded. Patulous.

patulin. An antibiotic obtained from *Penicillium.* Clavacin, clavatin, or claviformin.

pauciflorous. With few flowers.

paucifolious. With few leaves.

paucijugatous. Having only a few pairs of leaflets on a pinnate leaf.

paucilocular. With few cells or locules.

paucinervis. With few nerves or veins.

paulospore. A chlamydospore.

pauperculae. The depauperate generation, as the dwarf males of the alga *Oedogonium.*

pausiaceous. Olive green, olivaceous.

pavonine. Peacock blue.

pawpaw. 1. The fruit of *Asimina triloba,* the North American pawpaw. 2. The tropical papaya, *Carica papaya,* papaw.

peach. The sweet, juicy fruit of the tree *Amygdalus Persica.*

pear. The fleshy pome fruit of the genus *Pyrus,* especially *P. communis.*

pearl glands. Structures in *Pterospermum Javanicum* contained in cups serving as food bodies for ants. The cups are broadly metamorphosed stipules.

pearl grey. A very pale blue-grey.

peat. A carbonaceous substance formed by the partial decomposition in water of various plants, especially mosses of the genus *Sphagnum.*

peat, eutrophic. Fen-peat.

peat, mesotrophic. Peat from transitional moors.

peat, oligotrophic. Moor-peat.

pebrine. A bacterial disease of the silkworm, gattine.

pecan. One of the hickory nuts, *Carya (Hicoria).*

pecopteroid. Resembling the fossil fern *Pecopteris*.

pectase. An enzyme of plants which forms a vegetable jelly, an enzyme which transforms pectin into pectic acid.

pecten. A comb-like structure, a sterigma.

pectic sheath. A covering of pectin outside the cell wall of green algae.

pectin. A mixture of noncrystalline carbohydrates found in the cell walls of fruits and vegetables especially in the middle lamella of unlignified tissue. The mixture is soluble in water and can form jellies when proper proportions of acids are present.

pectin substances. Distinct chemical substances occurring in all layers of the cell wall and especially conspicuous in the middle lamella. They promote the formation of intercellular spaces by passing into a state of solution.

pectinaceous. Resembling pectin, gelatinous.

pectinase. A cytolytic enzyme.

pectinate. Split into narrow, close, even segments like a comb; pectiniform.

pectinate hyphae. Hyphae which end in a comb-shaped structure, i.e., somewhat inflated at the tip and bearing a short process on one side.

pectinatory. Having two series of vascular bundles whose members alternate with each other, as the teeth of two combs.

pecine. The fringe constituting a corona on the corolla of some gentians.

pectiniferous. 1. Bearing comb-like structures. 2. Bearing the characteristic brown-coated spores of *Albugo* in which pectin is the chief constituent.

pectocellulose. Cellulose and pectin mixed, as in fleshy roots and fruits.

pectose. The carbohydrate-like constituent of cell walls.

pectosic acid. An acid associated with pectic acid in fruit jelly.

pedalfer. A type of soil developed in moist conditions.

pedalineous. Allied to the order *Pedalineae*, tropical herbs with mucilaginous seeds.

pedate. In a fan-like arrangement with divided leaves.

pedate leaf. A leaf divided nearly to the petiole into narrow segments with the lateral segments diverging.

pedate-lobed. Pedate with rounded divisions or lobes.

pedately cleft. Cut in a pedate manner, pedatifid.

pedately veined. Having no midvein but with two strong lateral veins from each of which others originate and extend toward the apex.

pedatifid. Divided nearly to the base in a pedate manner. Pedafid.

pedatiform. Pedatifid.

pedatilobed. Palmate with supplementary lobes at the base.

pedatinerved. Having the midrib stop short and two strong lateral nerves proceeding from the base giving rise to others which extend only to the apex.

pedatipartite. Pedately veined and lobed with the sinuses reaching nearly to the principal veins; having pedate venation with lobes nearly free.

pedatisectus. Pedatipartite.

pedemontanus. Of Piedmont, northern Italy.

pedestal. An enlarged petiole base which remains on the stem after the leaf falls.

pedical. 1. A slender stalk or stem. 2. The stalk of a single flower in a flower cluster, a peduncle.

pedicel cell. A stem-like single cell in the antheridial globule of the stonewort (*Chara*) which supports the other structures of the globule.

pedicellate. Having a pedicel or stem.

pedicellulus. A filiform support to the ovary in certain *Compositae*.

pedicle. A pedicel.

pedicularius. Resembling a louse.

pediculate. Pedicellate.

pediculus. 1. A pedical or stalk. 2. The filament of an anther.

pediferous. Having a stalk or support.

pedigree culture. Cultivation of a group of individuals whose pedigrees are known.

pedilatous. Furnished with a pedilis.

pedilis. The contracted upper portion of the calyx tube in the florets of *Compositae* which have a stipitate pappus.

pediophilous. Dwelling in uplands or foothills of mountains.

pediophyta. Upland plants.

pediophytia. Upland communities.

pedocals. Soils which are well drained with a layer of calcium carbonate, usually found in drier climates.

pedogamy. The pseudomictic copulation between mature and immature vegetative cells, as in yeasts.

pedogenesis. Reproduction by young or immature individuals.

pedology. Soil science, the study of the quality and the ability of various soils.

peduncle. A primary flower stalk supporting an inflorescence or a solitary flower.

peduncle, partial. A branch of a peduncle.

peduncular. Pertaining to or serving as a peduncle.

pedunculate. Having a peduncle or stalk.

pedunculeanus. With a modified peduncle.

pedunculicolous. Growing on peduncles.

pedunculosus. With many peduncles.

peg. An outgrowth from the hypocotyl of seedlings of cucumbers and related plants. It plays a part in assisting the seedling to emerge from the testa.

pekinensis. Of Peking, China.

pelagad. A plant of the sea surface.

pelage. A skin or covering.

pelagic. Ocean-inhabiting.

pelagium. A surface community of the deep seas.

pelagophilous. Living at the sea surface.

pelagophyta. Surface sea plants.

pelious. Livid, black-and-blue.

pellicle. 1. A very thin covering or film of the matrix of a chromosome. 2. The thin skin of the kernel of a nut. 3. The outer layer of the upper surface of a pileus when it can be stripped off as a delicate membrane. 4. A cuticle that is viscid and peels easily.

pelliculate. Having a pellicle.

pellitus. Skinned, deprived of skin.

pellucid-dotted. Applied to leaves which contain internal oil glands which are translucent, punctate, or glandular.

pellucid-punctate. Having punctures to permit light to pass through.

pellucid-striate. Visible through a translucent pileus, as in the genus *Coprinus*, etc.

pelochthium. A mudbank formation.

pelochthophilous. Living on mudbanks.

pelochthophyta. Plants of mudbanks.

pelochthophytia. A mudbank formation.

pelophile. A plant occurring on clay, a pelophyte.

pelopsammagenous. Growing on clayey sand.

pelopsammic. Composed of mixed clay and sand.

peloria. An abnormal condition in which

flowers normally irregular produce regular flowers, pelory.

peloria, irregular. A condition in flowers in which there is symmetric multiplication of irregular parts.

peloria, regular. The suppression of irregular parts.

peloric flowers. Regular flowers borne on plants which normally have irregular flowers.

pelorisation. The process of conversion of a flower to a regular form from its normally irregular form.

pelosammic. Containing both clay and sand.

peloton. A tuft of tangled hyphae of some endotrophic mycorrhiza.

pelta. The shield-like apothecium of certain lichens.

peltafid. Having a peltate leaflet cut into segments.

peltate. 1. Having a rounded leaf blade with the petiole attached at or near the middle of the lower surface. 2. Fixed to the stalk by the center. 3. Shield-shaped.

peltately veined. With veins radiating from the central point of attachment.

peltate-digitate. Having a divided shield-shaped leaf with the petiole enlarged at the base at the insertion of the leaflets.

peltid. Orbicular, buckler-shaped.

peltifolious. With peltate leaves.

peltiform. Shield-shaped.

peltinerved. Having ribs or veins arranged as in a peltate leaf, radiately nerved or ribbed all around.

pelviform. Basin-shaped, formed like a shallow cup.

pen. A leaf midrib.

pencilled. Marked with fine distinct lines.

penduliflorae. Wind-fertilized pendulous flowers.

pendulinous. Pendulous.

pendulous. Hanging down, drooping.

pendulous ovule. An ovule that hangs from the side of the cell.

peneplain. A land surface reduced by erosion almost to base level so that most of it is approximately a plain, a peneplane.

penetrance. The frequency with which a particular gene is able to exert its influence on the heredity of the progeny.

penicillate. Like a little brush, penicilliform.

penicilliform. With the form of a little brush or artist's pencil.

penicillin. An antibiotic obtained from species of *Penicillium*.

penicillium. A tuft of hairs.

penicillus. The complex system of branches bearing conidia-producing organs in the mold *Penicillium*.

pennaceous. Pinniform, like a plume or feather.

pennate. Pinnate.

pennaticisus. Having incisions of the leaf in a pinnate manner.

pennatus. Feathered, pinnatus.

penniform. In the form of a feather or plume.

penninerved. Having the veins of a leaf radiate obliquely and regularly from the midrib as in a feather, pinnately veined.

pennisetum. A feather-like awn.

penniveined. Pinnately veined.

pennsylvanicus. Of Pennsylvania.

pensilis. Pensile, hanging.

penta-. A prefix meaning five.

pentacamarous. Having five loculi.

pentacapsular. With five capsules.

pentacarpellary. Having five carpels.

pentachenium. A cremocarp with five carpels instead of two.

pentacoccous. Having five seeds or carpels.

pentacotyl. With cotyledons so divided as to appear to possess five seed leaves.

pentactinal. With five rays or five branches.

pentacyclic. 1. Having five cycles. 2. Arranged in five whorls.

pentadactylous. With five fingers, having five finger-like divisions.

pentadelphous. 1. Having five clusters of more or less united filaments. 2. With stamens in five clusters. 3. With five pistils or styles.

pentadenius. With five teeth.

pentafid. In five divisions or lobes.

pentagonal. With five sides.

Pentagynia. A Linnaean order of plants having five pistils.

pentagynous. Having five pistils or styles.

pentakenium. Pentachenium.

pentalophous. With five wings or five tufts.

pentamerous. With flower parts in fives or multiple of fives.

pentander. Having five stamens.

Pentandria. The Linnaean class of plants having five stamens.

pentandrous. Having five stamens.

pentangular. With five angles and five flat or concave faces.

pentanthous. With five flowers.

pentapetaloid. Like five petals.

pentapetalous. Having five petals.

pentaphyletic. Composed of five strains, five species, or five forms in hybrids.

pentaphyllous. Having five leaves or five floral parts.

pentaploid. With five sets of chromosomes.

pentapterous. With five wings.

pentarch. A root with five strands of xylem and phloem.

pentarinus. Pentandrous.

pentasepalous. Having five sepals.

pentasome. Pentaploid.

pentaspermous. With five seeds.

pentasterigmatic. With basidia having five sterigmata.

pentastichous. Arranged in five vertical rows or in five ranks.

pentosan. A polysaccharide sugar.

pentoses. A group of monosaccharide sugars.

penultimate cell. The last cell but one at the tip of an ascogenous hypha which is commonly binucleate and later becomes an ascus.

peonidin. A magenta-colored anthoxanthin pigment.

pepo. A gourd fruit; an inferior, one-celled, many-seeded, pulpy fruit with a rind; a fruit like a melon, squash, cucumber, etc.

peponidium. A gourd fruit, a peponium.

pepper. 1. The small fruit or berry of *Piper nigrum*. 2. The condiment of that name.

pepsin. The enzyme which changes proteins into peptones.

peptase. A fibrin-digesting enzyme.

peptic. Relating to or promoting digestion.

peptic ferments. Enzymes which convert proteids into peptones.

peptones. Substances akin to albuminoses derived from the decomposition of proteids.

peptonization. The process of converting proteids into peptones.

peptonizing bacteria. Bacteria which produce enzymes which break down proteids and lead to the formation of albuminoses, peptones, amides, and ammonia.

per-. A prefix meaning through or thoroughly.

peranosis. A change in the permeability of protoplasm.

perapetalum. Parapetalum.

peraphyllum. Paraphyll.

percnosomes. Small deeply-staining granules of obscure nature found in the cytoplasm of sperm mother cells of mosses; perknosomes.

percurrent. Extending throughout length or from base to apex, as in leaves or trees.

percurrent costa. 1. A main vein running to the apex of the leaf. 2. The main trunk continuing to the top of a tree.

perdigon. A soil concretion markedly sesquioxidal in character but containing some silica. Characteristic of Cuba.

perdominant. A dominant species which is present in all or nearly all of the associations of a formation.

perembryum. The part of a monocotyledonous embryo which invests the plumule and radicle but which is not externally distinguishable, a perembryo.

perenchyma. Cellular tissue containing starch material.

perennate. Perennial, living more than two years.

perennation. Survival for a number of years.

perennial. A plant which lives for more than two years. The top may die to the ground or become dormant in adverse seasons but the roots persist. Evergreens have persistent foliage.

perennial herb. A plant which dies to the ground level in adverse seasons and grows from the root in favorable seasons.

perennial monocarp. A plant which lives long but dies after flowering once.

perfect flower. 1. A flower having all organs in a functional condition; 2. A flower having both pistils and stamens. 3. A bisexual, hermaphroditic, or monoclinous flower.

perfect stage. The stage or state of pleomorphic fungi in which spores (oospores, zygospores, ascospores, or basidiospores) are produced as the result of some sort of sexual process, or morphologically similar spores are formed parthenogenetically.

perfect succession. A sere passing in the usual succession from initial to ultimate conditions without interruption or omission.

perfoliate. 1. Having leaves through which the stem appears to pass. 2. Having leaves which grow around the stem.

perforate. 1. With pierced holes. 2. Containing rounded transparent dots which appear as holes.

perforation. An interruption in the continuity of a stele brought about by some other cause than a leaf gap.

perforation pits. In xylem vessels, pits which are caused by the disappearance of their closing membranes.

perforation plate. The area of the wall, originally imperforate, involved in coalescence of two members of a vessel.

perforation rim. The remnant of perforation plate forming a border around a simple perforation, an annular ridge.

performs. Forms with double serrated leaves and glabrous calyxes, as in the genus *Rosa*.

perfossate. Hollowed out.

perfuse. Completely covered.

pergameneous. Of the texture of parchment, pergamentaceous.

peri-. A prefix meaning around.

periachene. An achene arising from a partially superior flower.

periandra. The bracts of the male inflorescences in mosses.

periandricous. Having a nectary arranged around the stamens.

perianth. 1. The calyx and corolla collectively, particularly if they are of the same color. 2. The outer envelope of a flower. 3. The cup-shaped or tubular sheath surrounding the archegonia of some liverworts.

perianthial. Relating to the perianth.

perianthomania. An abnormal multiplication of perianth segments or bracts.

periaxial wood. The outer wood, as in stems of the *Bignoniaceae*, the catalpa family.

periblem. The portion of an apical meristem from which the cortex is ultimately formed, the layers of ground or fundamental tissue between the dermatogen and the plerome of the growing points.

pericalycious. Peristamineus.

pericambium. Thin-walled cells of the central fibrovascular cylinder in contact with the inner face of the endodermis, the pericycle.

pericambium sheath. A rhizogenous tissue within the endodermal sheath.

pericarp. The mature ovary wall, the wall of the fruit or seed vessel developed from the wall of the mature ovary.

pericaryoplasm. Perikaryoplasm.

pericaulome. The outer portion of the stem including the leaf-trace bundles derived theoretically from the fused bases of the leaves.

pericentral. Around the center.

pericentral cell. A cell cut off in a radial plane, as some found in the red algae.

pericentral siphon. One of the tubular elements surrounding the central siphon in the thallus of certain red algae.

pericentric. Having perigynous stamens arranged concentrically with the calyx.

perichaeth. A cluster of bracts (an involucre) surrounding the fruiting structures in bryophytes, the perichaetium.

perichaetial bracts. The leaf-like structures composing the perichaetium in mosses.

perichaetial leaves. Perichaetial bracts.

perichaetium. 1. A cup-like structure surrounding the archegonia in some liverworts. 2. The group of involucral bracts around the archegonia of mosses.

perichyle. A plant whose water-storing tissue is between the epidermis and the chlorenchyma.

perichladium. The sheathing base of a leaf petiole which surrounds the supporting branch.

periclinal. 1. Having a system of cells parallel to the surface of the apex of a growing point. 2. Curved in the same direction as the surface or circumference of an organ.

periclinal chimaera. A chimaera in which one or more layers of tissue derived from one graft member enclose the central tissue derived from the other member of the graft, a graft-hybrid.

periclinal planes. Planes which conform to the exterior structures.

periclinal wall. A cell wall which is parallel to the surface of an apical meristem or other part of a plant.

pericline. A periclinium, a periclinal wall.

pericliniod. Having a false involucre.

periclinium. The involucre composed of scales or bracts which surrounds the elevated receptacle of the flower in *Compositae*.

pericoecium. The protoplasm surrounding the nucleus.

pericolium. A perichaetium, a sheath.

pericorollate. Having a gamopetalus perigynous corolla, as in dicotyledons.

pericycle. A layer of nonconducting cells one or more layers thick at the periphery of a stele. It is usually composed of parenchy-matous cells in roots but is often modified into fibers in the stems. The pericambium.

pericycle fiber. A twisted rope of sclerenchyma in the pericycle.

pericycle, internal. The procambium retained on the inner side of the vascular bundle.

pericycle sectors. Interruptions in the pericycle caused by thick-walled cells in the roots of some mosses.

pericyclic fiber. A strand of sclerenchyma in the pericycle.

periderm. A protective outer cylinder of tissues formed in woody stems which consists of cork, cork cambium, and phellogen.

periderm cells. Cells in periderm which have a suberin layer and usually lack intercellular spaces.

peridermioid. More or less like a peridermium.

peridermium. An operculate or peridermioid aecium of the *Uredinales* with a blister-like, tongue-shaped, or cylindric peridium.

peridesm. The layer of cells which surrounds each vascular bundle beneath the special endoderm in astelic stems.

peridial. Of a peridium.

peridial cells. The outer cells of a peridium which are coherent.

Perediniales. *Dinoflagellata.*

peridinin. A coloring matter found in some algae.

peridiole. 1. A membrane which covers some algae spores. 2. A chamber of the gleba which forms a nest of spores (seedlike bodies free or attached by a funicle) within the peridium of the sporophore, as in *Nidulariales*, the bird's nest fungi. 3. The peridiolum.

peridium. A general term for the outer wall of a fruit body of certain fungi when the wall is organized as a distinct layer or envelope partially or completely surrounding the spore-bearing organs.

peridium externum. The outer of the two layers of a peridium, the exoperidium.

peridium internum. The endoperidium, the inner layer directly enclosing the gleba.

peridium mitriforme. The receptacle of certain fungi.

peridroma. The rachis of ferns.

perienchyma. The irregular cellular tissue chiefly in glands and spheroidal masses, perenchyma.

perifoliary. Around the margin of a leaf.

periforium. Periphorium.

perigamium. A portion of a fertile reduced branchlet of a moss which contains the archegonia.

perigloea. The entire gelatinous covering of a diatom.

perigone. A perianth which is not clearly differentiated into calyx and corolla, a perigonium, a perichaeth.

perigonial bract. One leaf of the perigonium in mosses.

perigonial leaves. The perichaetal leaves (excluding bryophytes).

perigoniarius. 1. With the character of a perigone. 2. Having double flowers resulting from the transformation or multiplication of the floral organs assuming the characters of perianth segments.

perigonium. 1. A group of leaves, often forming a flat rosette, surrounding the antheridium in mosses. 2. The floral envelope or perianth. 3. A perichaeth, a perigone.

perigynandra. The involucre of composites.

perigynandra, interior. The corolla of a composite floret.

perigynandra, exterior. The involucre.

perigynium. The modified leaf-like structure that surrounds the ovary in plants, as the inflated sac (utricle) in *Carex* and the membranous scales of the perichaeth in mosses.

perigyynous. 1. With floral parts adnate to the perianth and therefore around the ovary instead of at its base. 2. Of stamens, adherent to the calyx and free from the ovary.

perigynous flowers. Flowers intermediate in structure between hypogynous and epigynous; flowers with the sepals, petals, and stamens borne at the top of a tubular or cup-shaped structure (the floral cup or hypanthium) which surrounds the ovary.

perihadromatic. Surrounding the hadrome.

perikaryoplasm. A zone of granular protoplasm seen in the vine *Coboea scandens* in the cytoplasm of the resting pollen mother cell on its approaching division.

perileptomatic. Surrounding the leptome.

perimedullary. In the peripheral region of the pith outwardly bounded by the protoxylem.

perimelitae. Plants having honey glands placed in the lower portion of the perianth, as in certain species of the *Gentianaceae*.

perimeristem. Tissues consisting of several layers of cells which at first divide in every direction but subsequently divide tangentially in the external region.

perimicropylar. Situated near or around the micropyle.

perine. The outermost layer of sculpturing on pollen.

perinectarial. Surrounding the area of the nectar glands.

perinium. The outermost of the three layers of a fern spore, the epispore.

perinuclear. Surrounding the nucleus.

perinucleolar vacuole. A clear zone surrounding each nucleolus in prophase of pollen mother cells.

periodic movement. The opening and closing of flowers or the nyctotropic movement of leaves, etc., when occurring habitually or with some regularity.

peripetalous. Around the petals.

periphaericus. Peripheric, circumferential.

peripheral cytoplasm. The cytoplasm just inside the cell membranes.

peripheral hybrid. A hybrid with lethal factors which prevent the development of variation. The hybrid breeds true for successive generations.

peripheral steles. The four long curved steles in the fossil fern *Psaronius* from which adventitious roots take their origin.

peripheral tissue. In roots, the piliferous layer furnished with root hairs.

periphericoterminal. 1. Belonging to the circumference and apex of a body. 2. Of stems which grow both in length and breadth.

periphialoporous. Around the phialospore.

periphloem. The phloem sheath or pericambium.

periphloematic. Having concentric bundles, as in ferns.

periphoranthium. The involucre of *Compositae*, the periclinum.

periphorium. A fleshy elongated support of the ovary to which the stamens and corolla are attached.

periphragm. The pericycle of a stem.

periphyllia. The hypogynous scales or lodicules of grasses.

periphyllogeny. The presence of numerous leaflets around the edge of a leaf blade.

periphyllum. A lodicule.

periphysis. A sterile filament in the ostiolar canal of the *Pyrenomycetes*.

periplasm. The protoplasm in the oogonium and the antheridium which does not share in conjugation, protoplasm surrounding the egg in the oogonium of the *Peronosporeae*.

periplasmodium. The material produced by the breakdown of the tapetum in the sporangia of pteridophytes and phanerogams. It helps in the nutrition of the developing spore.

periplast. A hyaline structure enveloping the cell nucleus.

periplastid. A periplast.

peripodium. The perichaetium.

peripterous. Surrounded by a wing or border, alate.

periscyphe. The perichaetium.

perisoploid. In uneven multiples.

perisperm. The albumen of the seed, the tissue of the megasporangium which persists and is present in the seed stage as a nutritive tissue.

perisporangium. The indusium of ferns, a membranous covering of the spores.

perispore. A covering of one or more spores, as the cell or sac in which tetraspores are formed; the membrane surrounding a spore; an epispore.

perisporinium. The outermost membrane of pollen in angiosperms.

perisporium. The perithecium.

peristachyum. The glume of grasses.

peristaminia. Petalous dicotyledons with perigynous stamens.

peristem. The young cortex in a nascent condition.

peristemones. Peristaminia.

peristomatic. With perigynous stamens attached around the mouth of the calyx tube.

peristome. The single or double row of hygroscopic teeth in the opening of the spore case or capsule of mosses which assist in ejecting the spores.

peristromium. The lining of the membrane of a chloroplast.

peristylicus. Having epigynous stamens inserted between the styles and the limb of the calyx.

perithallium. The upper layer of calcareous algae.

perithece. Perithecium.

perithecial wall. The exciple of the angiocarpic lichens enclosing the hymenium except for the apical ostiole.

peritheciocole. A parasite on perithecia.

perithecigerous. Bearing perithecia.

perithecioid glands. The glands on the pitcher of *Nepenthes* resembling the perithecium of a *Sphaeria*.

peritheciophorous. Bearing perithecia.

perithecium. A globose or flask-shaped fruiting body characteristic of the pyrenomycetes and lichens which contains asci and paraphyses. A true perithecium has an opening at the top, but the term is also applied to a cleistocarp which has no opening. A pyrenocarp.

peritrichiate. Having hairs or flagella over the entire surface, peritrichous.

peritrochium. A ciliary band.

peritropous. With the axis of the seed perpendicular to that of the pericarp, peritropal.

perivasal. Vasicentric.

perixylematic. Having concentric bundles, as in the roots of *Acorus*, *Cyperaceae*, etc.

perixylic. Developing both inwardly and outwardly, applied to growth of stems and roots.

perizonium. A thin membrane which encloses the young auxospore in diatoms.

perlarious. Shining with a pearly lustre, perlate.

perlatent. A permanently fixed character.

permanent collenchyma. Functional collenchyma present in petioles and in the stems of herbaceous plants.

permanent communities. The communities of plants which remain unchanged for a long time and maintain their social individuality without corresponding to the climax of the region.

permanent hybrid. A peripheral hybrid.

permanent pasture. Grazing land occupied by perennial pasture plants or by self-seeding annuals (usually both).

permanent quadrat. A square of one meter marked so as to permit a study from year to year.

permanent tissue. Fully matured tissue as distinct from meristematic or generative tissue.

permanent wilting. Wilting from which a plant does not recover.

permeability. The power of allowing the passage of certain substances out of or into the vacuole.

permease. An enzyme presumed to increase the translocation of ions across a membrane.

Permian. The Permian Period.

permutation. An enlargement of the floral envelopes with the abortion of sex organs.

perniciasm. The killing of host cells by a parasitic fungus.

perocidium. A perichaetum.

peronate. 1. Having the stipe, particularly the base, covered by thick, felted hair. 2. Sheathed by a volva or universal veil. 3. Covered with woolly hairs.

peroral. Formed by the concrescence of rows of cilia.

perovulatae. Phanerogams having true seeds.

perpelic. Yielding or thriving on pure clay.

perpendicular system. The fibrovascular system.

perpetuating structure. A structure which by its resistance to cold, drought, etc., can carry an organism through unfavorable conditions and thus maintain the existence of the species.

perpsammic. Yielding or growing on sandy detritus.

perquadrat. A quadrat of 16 meters or more.

perrumpent. Breaking through abruptly.

persicaefolious. Peach-leaved.

persicicolor. Persicine, peach-colored.

persicus. 1. Of Persia. 2. Of the peach.

persimmon. 1. An ebonaceous tree of warm climates, the source of ebony wood in the tropics. 2. In North America, *Diospyros virginiana* produces a small, sweet fruit and also hard wood.

persistent. Retaining its place, shape, or structure; remaining attached after the growing period; not deciduous; evergreen.

persistent perianth. A perianth which remains unwithered and often enlarged around the fruits.

personate. A bilabiate corolla with a projection or palate in the throat.

perspermal. Producing numerous seeds from each flower.

perthophyte. A pathogenic fungus that kills tissue of its host by secretions and then enters the dead cells and is saprophytic on them.

perthophytic. Destructive of plant life.

pertusarioid. Resembling the lichen genus *Pertusaria*.

pertusate. Pierced at the apex, having pits or holes, perforated, pertuse.

perulate. Having perules or scales.

perule. The scale of a leaf bud.

Peruvian bark. The chief source of quinine, *Cinchona*.

Peruvian nutmeg. *Laurelia aromatica*, an aromatic forest tree, the fruits used as a spice. Not the true nutmeg (*Myristica*).

peruvianus. Of Peru.

pervalvar. Dividing a valve longitudinally.

pervalvar axis. The main longitudinal axis of a diatom frustule. The line which forms the center of the dividing plane penetrates the cell cavity, extends from one end to the other at the same distance from the enclosing walls, and unites the center of the valves.

perverted. Turned from the right or upside down, as in some diatoms.

pervious. 1. Having an open passageway. 2. Capable of being penetrated.

petal. One of the modified, usually colored leaves of the corolla.

petalate. Having petals or a corolla.

petaliferous. Bearing petals.

petalification. Petalody.

petaliform. Petal-shaped.

petaline. Petal-like or relating to petals.

petalode. An organ simulating a petal, a false petal.

petalodic. Having a tendency to form double flowers.

petalody. The metamorphosis of other organs into petals.

petaloid. 1. Shaped like the petal of a flower. 2. Colored like and resembling a petal.

petaloid anther. An anther borne on a petal with the filament resembling a petal.

petalomania. An abnormal multiplication of petals.

petalostemones. Plants with flowers whose stamens are adherent to the corolla.

petalous. Having petals.

petasospore. A seed with parachute-like appendages.

petiolaceous. Referring to the petiole (attachment, transformation, and appearance).

petiolaneous. Consisting of the petiole or some modification of it.

petiolar. Having or growing on a small stalk, borne on or pertaining to a petiole.

petiolate. Having a petiole.

petiole. The leaf stalk.

petiole gutter. The leaf stalk grooved and leading down to hairy buds or grooves on the stem.

petiole, sensitive. See CLIMBING PLANTS.

petiole, partial. A division of a petiole, a petiolule.

petiole trace. The characteristic scar left by

the strand of vascular tissue connecting the leaf petiole to the stem.

petiolous. Producing petals.

petiolular. Pertaining to the petiole of a leaflet.

petiolulate. Having a petiolule.

petiolule. A small petiole, the petiole of a leaflet in a compound leaf.

petrad. A rock plant.

petraceous. Growing among stones.

petran. Of Rocky Mountain vegetation.

Petri dish. A covered shallow circular glass dish used for cultures.

petrifaction. Fossilization through a saturation by mineral matter in solution subsequently turned to solid form.

petrium. A rock formation.

petrochthium. A rockbank formation.

petrochthopilous. Living on rocky banks.

petrochthophyte. A rockbank plant.

petrodad. A plant of a boulder field.

petrodium. A boulder-field formation.

petrodophilous. Dwelling in boulder fields.

petrodophyte. A boulder-field plant.

petrophilous. Rockdwelling.

petrophyte. A rock plant.

petrose. Growing among stones.

petrous. 1. Growing on rocks. 2. Hard, stony.

Pe tsai. Chinese cabbage, celery cabbage.

peucedanetum. An association of the herb *Peucedametum astruthium.*

Peyer's patches. Oval patches of aggregated lymph follicles on intestine walls appearing in certain bacterial diseases.

pezizaxanthine. A special orange coloring matter from species of the fungi *Pezizaceae.*

pezizin. An orange-colored pigment in *Peziza aurantia.*

pezizoid. *Peziza-* or cup-shaped, cyathiform or nearly so.

pF. A symbol indicating the availability of water in soil. pF7 is oven-dry, pF4 is at wilting point, pF2 soil is well drained soil.

pH. The measure of acidity or alkalinity of substances. pH7 is neutral, less than 7 is acid, more than 7 is alkaline.

phacidioid. Like the fungus *Phacidium*, black and disk-like.

phacoid. Lenticular, with lens-shaped seeds.

phaeism. Duskiness.

phaenantherous. With stamens exserted.

phaeniceus. Of Phoencia.

phaenobiotic. From the geologic period when plants made their appearance as evidenced by their fossil remains.

phaenocarpous. Having a distinct fruit with no adhesion to surrounding parts.

phaeno-ecological spectrum. A diagram combining the seasonal aspect, duration, and life-form features of a plant community.

phaenogam. A phanerogam or spermatophyte.

phaenogamous. Phanerogamous, bearing true flowers.

phaenological. Phenological.

phaenology. Phenology.

phaenos-. A prefix meaning showy.

phaenotype. Phenotype.

phaeocarpous. With dark fruit.

phaeochrome. A chromaphil.

phaeochrous. Of dusky color.

phaeocyst. The cell nucleus.

phaeodictyae. Dictyospores with dark or opaque spores.

phaeodictyosporous. Having dictyospores with dark muriform spores.

phaeodidymae. Didymosporae with brown or dark spores.

phaeophore. The chlorophyll granule when it is dark brown, as in the *Phaeophyceae*, the brown algae.

phaeophragmae. Fungi which have muriform spores of a dark color.

phaeophragmious. Having dark spores with cross walls.

phaeophragmosporous. Having dark spores with cross walls.

Phaeophyceae. The brown algae. A large group of chiefly marine algae, brown in color, varying in size and complexity.

phaeophycean. Relating to the phaeospores, a group of olive or brown marine algae.

phaeophyll. The brown or olive green pigment in *Phaeophyceae.*

phaeophytes. The brown sea weeds, the *Phaeophyceae.*

phaeophytin. A gray pigment in chlorophyll.

phaeoplast. The chromatophores of the brown algae *Fucoideae.*

phaeosporae. Fungi with dark colored spores.

phaeospore. A member of the brown algae.

phaeosporeae. Brown algae which produce asexual swarm spores.

phaeosporous. With dark one-celled spores.

phaeus. Fuscous, swarthy, dusky.

phagedenic. Corroding.

phagocyte. A cell which ingests other cells.

phagocytosis. The ingestion or destruction of invading bacteria by phagocytes.

phagolysis. Dissolution by phagocytes.

phagophyte. A plant which can use organic food either as a parasite or saprophyte.

phagoplankton. Autotrophic algae. An individual is called a phagont.

phagotrophic. Feeding on assimilated foods, as protoplasm. Holozoic.

phaiophyll. Coloring matter of various tints of brown in the leaves of plants.

phalange. A fascicle of coherent stamens united by broad filaments as found in diadelphous and polyadelphous flowers, a phalanx.

phalarsiphytous. Polyadelphous.

phallin. A poisonous substance in many fungi; a toxalbumin, the chief poison in some *Amanita* mushrooms; phalline.

phalloid. Resembling the fungus genus *Phallus*.

phallus. The peridium of certain fungi resembling the genus *Phallus* or *Ithyphallus*.

phanerantherous. Having the anthers protrude beyond the perianth.

phaneranthous. With the flower manifest.

phaneri. Organisms which are visible under the microscope without the use of reagents.

phanerocotyledoneae. Dicotyledons.

phanerogam. A flowering plant with stamens and pistils which develop seeds, a seed plant, a spermatophyte, a phaenogam.

Phanerogamia. The highest division of plants, those with flowers which produce seeds.

phanerogamian. Of the phanerogams or flowering plants.

phanerogamic wood. Secondary or centrifugal wood.

phanerogamous. Having flowers which produce seeds.

phanerophyte. A tree or shrub with the dormant buds exposed to the air, i.e., the branches above the surface of the soil.

phanerophytion. A main isocies of phanerogamous plants.

phaneropore. A stoma or superficial opening in the same plane as the epidermis.

phaneroporous stoma. A stoma lying in the level of the epidermis.

phaopelagile. Of the upper pelagic area of the ocean (the surface to thirty meters down).

pharmacognosy. The knowledge of the distinctive features of vegetable drugs.

pharyngeal rod. A rod-like structure lining the gullet in some of the algae *Euglenophyta*.

phase. 1. Any one of different and varying appearances of an object. 2. A stage in the development of an association.

phaseoliform. Bean-shaped.

phaseolin. A reserve proteid occurring in *Phaseolus* (bean) seeds forming their main proteid store.

phaseolunatin. A glucoside in linseed and in some other legumes.

pheasant's eye pink. A ring-necked variety of the common garden pink.

phellad. A rock-field plant.

phellandrene. A terpene found in *Eucalyptus* spp.

phellem. Tissue formed in the initial celled secondary cork on the outside of the phellogen, the outermost layer of the periderm consisting of true cork, phellema.

phellium. A rocky field community.

phelloderm. A layer or layers of parenchymatous (often green) tissue developed inwardly from the cork cambium or phellogen, a kind of secondary cortex.

phellogen. A layer of meristematic cells lying a little inside the surface of a root or stem which forms cork on its outer surface and phelloderm on the inner surface, the cork cambium.

phelloid tissue. A crust of nonsuberized or weakly suberized cells present in the surface of some plants replacing true cork.

phellophilous. Dwelling in stony fields.

phellophyte. A plant growing among loose stones.

phellos. Cork.

phenhybrid. An obvious hybrid.

pheniceous. Phoeniceous, phenicine.

phenocopy. An organism so changed by external conditions that it physically resembles another phenotype.

phenogam. Phanerogam.

phenogamous. Phanerogamic.

phenological inversion. An abnormal inversion of various phenomena, as leafing and blossoming of plants, caused by meteorological conditions.

phenological isolation. Isolation from similar species brought about by a marked change in the usual time of flowering and fruiting of a particular species.

phenology. The science of the interrelations

of climate and periodic biological phenomena of plants and animals. It consists largely of dates of budding, flowering, fruit ripening, etc., of shrubs and trees.

phenomenology. Phenology.

phenospermy. An abortive seed condition.

phenotype. A group of individuals similar in appearance but not in genetical constitution.

phenotypic variation. Variation produced by changes in environment.

phialea. A hollow sphere in *Volvox*.

phialide. A short, flask-shaped sterigma from the apex of which thin-walled conidia (phialospores) are abstricted.

phialiform. Saucer-shaped, cup-shaped.

phialo-meristem spore. See MERISTEM SPORE.

phialocelian. Of or pertaining to the phialocoele.

phialocoele. The young internal bud of *Volvox*.

phialoderm. The coat of the young buds of *Volvox*.

phialopore. A small hole in the cynobium of the *Volvocaceae*, found at the posterior end.

phialospores. Spores formed successively (endogenously or exogenously) to produce chains or spore heads on phialides. They may be exposed or enclosed in pycnia or pycnidia.

phialula. A colonial stage of sixteen plastids formed by successive bipartition into hollow spheres.

philadelphicus. Of the Philadelphia region.

-phile, -philous. A suffix meaning loving.

phillilesia. Leaf curl or blister.

philotherm. A plant requiring warmth to complete the life cycle.

phleboidal. Spiral annular or porous moniliform bundles.

phlebomorpha. The vein-like mycelium of fungi.

phleiod. Like *Phleum*, timothy grass.

phleumetum. A plant association of *Phleum pratense*, etc.

phlobaphenes. An amorphous brown coloring matter of the bark.

phlocoterma. The endodermis.

phloem. The part of a vascular bundle consisting of sieve tubes, their companion cells, and adjacent parenchyma; the portion of the vascular bundle which is largely concerned in the transportation of food material; the inner part of the bark of a tree; the bast portion of a vascular bundle.

phloem arch of cambium. The part of the cambium on the inside of a phloem bundle in roots.

phloem bundles. Vascular bundles composed of sieve tubes and parenchyma called cambiform; vascular bundles composed of secondary phloem and some parenchymatic tissue of primary phloem (exclusive of companion cells).

phloem commissure. The union of phloem tissues as the beginning of a central strand.

phloem fiber. A sclerenchymatous element or a strand of such elements present in phloem affording support to the delicate sieve tube.

phloem island. A group of phloem cells surrounded by secondary wood, groups of bast strands surrounded by xylem.

phloem parenchyma. Thin-walled cells in the phloem whose primary function is the translocation of sugars from the leaves down; see BAST PARENCHYMA.

phloem, primary. Phloem formed from procambium tissue.

phloem ray. The part of a ray outside the cambium, the portion of a vascular ray which traverses the phloem.

phloem, secondary. Phloem formed from cambium tissue.

phloem sheath. A layer of thin-walled cells surrounding the vascular tissue just within the cortex (best seen in roots).

phloem vessels. Sieve tubes.

phloeodic. Bark-like in appearance.

phloeoterma. The innermost layer of the primary cortex, the heavily suberized endodermis.

phloeotracheides. The vascular elements of the haustorium of parasitic *Santalaceae*.

phloeum. The cortical tissues.

phlogiflorous. Flame-flowered, phlox-flowered.

phlogifolious. Phlox-leaved.

phloridzin. A white crystalline substance which gives the bitter taste to the bark of the root of the apple, pear, cherry, and plum trees.

phloroglucin. A substance of frequent occurrence in the bark of trees derived from glucosides.

phlox. Annual and perennial herbs of the *Polemoniaceae*.

phlyktioplankton. Organisms supported by hydrostatic means.

-phobe. A suffix meaning hating.

phobism. The repulsion of plants.

phobochemotactic. Repelling by chemical influence, as in swarm spores of myxomycetes.

phobochemotaxis. A chemical influence which repels growth, a reaction of plants to a nocuous stimulant which causes a change in the direction of growth or repels growth.

phobophototropism. Movements induced by shunning light, phobophototaxis.

phoeniceous. Scarlet.

phoenicolasius. With purple hair.

phoenocin. A scarlet dye produced by some species of *Penicillium*.

phoenogamous. Phanerogamous.

phoeosporous. Phaeosporous.

phoma stage. The perithecial stage of beetroot rot caused by *Phoma Betae*. The ascigerous stage is caused by *Sphaerella*.

phomatoid. Like *Phoma*, a parasitic fungus.

phoranthium. The receptacle of the capitulum in *Compositae*.

-phore. A suffix meaning carrying, supporting, bearing.

phosphorescent. Shining with a faint light or luninosity like that of phosphorus.

photeolic. Exhibiting the characteristics of sleeping plants.

photic. Influenced by or adapted to the action of light.

photic region. The region of aquatic environments in which the intensity of light is sufficient for the normal development of macrophytes.

photic zone. The area of bodies of water (extending as far down as 1000 meters) which is penetrated by sunlight.

photism. The emission of light under stimulus.

photoaesthesia. The power of an organ to respond to the stimulus of light.

photobacteria. Bacteria that cause phosphorescence in the media in which they are growing.

photobia. Ectoparasitic fungi.

photoblast. A shoot developed above the soil and adapted to live in light and air.

photocleistogamia. Flowers which fail to open because of the rapid growth of the outer side of the petals due to photohyponasty.

photocleistogamic. Having flowers remain closed because of light deficiency.

photocliny. The response due to the direction of the incident rays of light.

photodynamics. The study of the effects of light stimulation on plants.

photoepinasty. Epinasty, the downward curvature due to the presence of light.

photogenic. Light-producing, phosphorescent, luninescent, producing or generating light.

photoharmose. The response to a light stimulus.

photohyponasty. Hyponasty, the upward curvature due to increased illumination.

photokinesis. Movement induced by light.

photolepsy. The catching of light.

photolysis. 1. Breaking up by the activity of light. 2. The arrangement of chlorophyll granules under stimulus of light, including both apostrophe and epistrophe.

photometer. An instrument for measuring the amount of light.

photometry. The measurement of the intensity of light.

photomorphosis. Morphosis depending upon light as the cause.

photonasty. One-sided growth in the length of an organ due to unrestricted action of light, a response to light the nature of which is determined by factors inherent in the organism.

photopathy. The response to light stimulus, phototaxis.

photoperceptor. The part of an eye-spot which is sensitive to light.

photoperiodic. Reacting to the relative length of day.

photoperiodism. The response of a plant to the amount of light received by it which affects the vegetative and reproductive processes. Plants often exhibit a definite response to their particular optimum day-lengths.

photophilous. Seeking and thriving in strong light.

photophobism. The avoidance of light.

photophore. A light-emitting plant, a phosphorescent plant.

photophygous. Avoiding strong light, shade-loving.

photoplagiotropy. A tendency to be arranged obliquely toward incident light.

photoreceptor. The terminal organ receiving light stimuli.

photospheres. Spheres of light, luminous areas.

photostage. An early stage in the development of a seedling during which it needs a supply of light.

photosyntax. The formation of complex carbon compounds from simple ones under the influence of light.

photosynthate. The carbohydrate product of photosynthesis.

photosynthesis. The process of constructive metabolism in the green cells of a plant by which carbohydrates are formed in the presence of sunlight from carbon dioxide and water in the air with chlorophyll acting as an energy transformer.

photosynthetic capacity. The efficiency of a plant, a cell, or a chloroplast in carrying out the process of photosynthesis.

photosynthetic number. The ratio between the number of grams of carbon dioxide absorbed per hour by a unit of leaf to the number of grams of chlorophyll which that unit contains. 2,500 molecules of chlorophyll reduce one molecule of carbon dioxide.

photosynthetic quotient. The ratio between the volume of carbon dioxide absorbed to the volume of oxygen set free during a given time by plant material occupied in photosynthesis.

photosynthetic ratio. The ratio between the volume of carbon dioxide absorbed to the volume of oxygen set free during a given time by plant material occupied in photosynthesis.

photosynthetic unit. The photosynthetic number.

phototactic. Taking up a definite position with reference to the direction of incident rays of light.

phototaxis. 1. The response or reaction of an organism to the stimulus of light. 2. The placement or arrangement of organisms with reference to light.

phototaxy. A change in position in response to light.

phototonus. 1. The state of being responsive to or irritated by exposure to light. 2. The condition resulting from the alteration of day and night.

phototrophy. The unequal increase on one side of an organ due to the incidence of light in relation to the parent shoot.

phototropic. Exhibiting phototropism.

phototropic conduction. The conduction of growth-promoting substances (auxins) along the side of a plant most exposed to light which results in growth toward light.

phototropic induction. The influence of the exposure of the tip of a plant to light which affects the growth of the plant lower on the stem or the entire plant.

phototropism. The tendency shown by most plants to turn their aerial growing parts toward the greater light, tropistic response to light, heliotropism, phototaxis.

phototype. A photograph of a type specimen, a photographotype.

photrum. The whole scale of illumination affecting photolysis.

phragma. A horizontal false dissepiment in a pericarp, a septum.

phragmatospore. A multicellular spore capable of germinating from more than one point.

phragmifer. A plant divided by partitions, a phragmiger.

phragmites. A hedge.

phragmitetum. An association of reeds, *Phragmites.*

phragmabasid. A septate basidium in basidiomycetes.

phragmobasidiate. Having septate basidia, as in most of the *Heterobasidiomycetes.*

phragmobasidium. A basidium in which septation follows directly after the first and second division of the primary basidial nucleus so that the mature basidium is divided into four cells.

phragmoid. Septate at right angles to the long axis, as in the conidia of various fungi.

phragmoplast. The barrel-shaped stage of the spindle in mitosis; the enlarged connecting spindle, barrel-shaped or greatly broadened in the later phases of an astral plant mitosis within which the cell plate is formed.

phragmosphere. The spindle fibers and associated cytoplasm becoming transformed into a large hollow space.

phragmospore. A septate spore, a spore of several cells.

phragmosporous. With septate spores.

phreatophyte. A plant which derives its water supply from ground water and is more or less independent of rainfall, a well plant a desert plant which is very deep rooted.

phretad. A tank plant.

phretium. A formation or community in a tank.

phretophilous. Dwelling in tanks.

phretophyte. A tank plant.

phrygana. Prickly and stiff undershrubs.

phrygius. Of Phrygia in Asia Minor.

phthiriasis. A plant disease produced by aphids or plant lice.

phyad. A vegetation or growth form, as a tree, shrub, etc.

phycoblastema. The modified soredium in lichens.

phycoblastus. A lichen which has a flat, leaf-like expansion of the thallus.

phycobrya. *Characeae*, phycobryophytes.

phycocecidia. Galls due to the attacks of algae.

phycochromaceous. Having gonidia which are not chlorophyll green.

phycochromacetum. A community of blue-green algae and diatoms.

phycochrome. 1. A characteristic coloring matter of the blue-green algae, a mixture of chlorophyll and phycocyanin. 2. The coloring matter of the brown algae.

phycochrysin. A golden-brown pigment phycochrome in *Chrysophyceae*.

phycocyanin. Seaweed blue, a bluish coloring matter found in certain marine algae, phycocyanine.

phycodomatia. Plant shelters inhabited by other plants.

phycoerythrin. A red pigment formed by the red and blue-green algae, phycoerithrin, phycoerythrine.

phycohaematin. A special type of red coloring matter found in certain algae as *Rhytiphloea tinctoria.*

phycolichen. A lichen in which the gonidia are blue-green algae.

phycology. Algology, the study of algae.

phycoma. The entire mass of an alga including thallus and reproductive organs.

phycomater. The hymenial jelly in which some spores germinate.

phycomycete. A group of the lower fungi which approach the algae in some characters, the algae-fungi.

phycomycetous. Of or pertaining to phycomycetes.

phycophaein. Fucoxanthin, the brown pigment in algae.

phycophyta. The *Characeae*.

phycoporphyrin. A purple pigment from several species of the alga *Zygnema*, viola xanthin.

phycopyrrhine. A pigment found in the *Peridineae*, the pigment in the algae of the red tide caused by dinoflagellates.

phycoscope. A tube to view sea weeds in situ under water.

phycostemones. Hypogynous or other scales adhering to the disk.

phycoxanthin. A buff-colored pigment in diatoms and certain other algae, diatomine.

phygoblastema. A modified form of soredia in lichens.

phykenchyma. The elementary tissues of algae.

phykocyan. Phycocyanin.

phykoerythrin. Phycoerythrin.

phylesis. The assumed succession of development.

phyletic. Of or pertaining to a phylum or line of descent.

phyletic margin. The true indusium of the fern *Blechnum.*

phylktioplankton. Plankton organisms supported by hydrostatic means.

phyll-, -phyll. A suffix or prefix meaning leaf.

phylla. The verticillate leaves which form the calyx.

phyllachoroid. Like *Phyllachora*, having the stroma fused with the epidermis.

phyllade. A reduced scale like a leaf, a cataphyllary leaf, a bladeless petiole or rachis.

phyllanthoid. Like *Phyllanthus*, a spurge with flowers borne on phylloclades very much like leaves.

phyllaries. The bracts forming the involucre of the flower head in *Compositae*.

phyllid. A flat leaf-like structure in bryophytes which lacks vascular tissue.

phyllilesia. The leaf curl or blister, phillilesia.

phyllite. A fossilized leaf.

phyllo-. A prefix meaning leaf.

phyllobiology. The biology of the leaf.

phylloblastus. A lichen which has a flat leaf-like expansion of the thallus.

phyllobranchia. A gill consisting of numbers of lamellae or thin plates.

phyllobryon. The contracted pedicel of an ovary, as in some peppers.

phyllocarpic movement. A curvature of the fruit stalk bringing the young fruit under the shelter of the leaves.

phyllochlorin. A pigment found in chloroplasts which contains chromo-protein carotinoids and some lipoid molecules.

phylloclade. A flattened stem or branch functioning as a leaf in some cacti and other plants.

phyllocally. The production of new leaflets from the leaf surface.

phyllocyanin. The bluish pigment which with phylloxanthine forms the green coloring matter of chlorophyll, cyanophyll.

phyllode. An expanded petiole modified in form and functioning as a leaf.

phyllodineous. Having flattened leaf-like twigs or leaf stalks instead of true leaves.

phyllody. The metamorphosis of an organ into a foliage leaf.

phyllogen. Any leaf-bearing organ, a phyllophore.

phyllogenetic. Producing or developing leaves.

phyllogenous. Growing or borne on leaves, epiphyllous.

phylloid. Leaf-like.

phylloid cladode. A phylloclade.

phylloid shoots. The foliage of pines.

phylloideous. Foliaceous.

phyllolobeae. Plants having green and leaf-like cotyledons.

phyllomania. An unusual or abnormal production of leaves.

phyllomaniacus. Leafy, running wildly to leaves.

phyllome. 1. A group of leaves or their primordia in a bud. 2. A general term for all organs which are morphologically leaves-- as bracts, scales, petals, etc.

phyllome, epipeltate. Leaves with an expanded base resulting from the growth of the upper surface of the primordial leaf.

phyllome, hypopeltate. Leaves with the growth from the undersurface, as in the sepals of *Viola*.

phyllomorph. A dorsiventral frondose system resembling compound leaves and deciduous by cladoptosis in three or four years.

phyllomorphosis. The variation of leaves at various seasons, phyllody.

phyllomorphy. The transformation or metamorphosis of floral organs into leaves, phyllody.

phyllonecrosis. Decay or death in leaves or leaf-like organs.

phyllophagic. Deriving sustenance from leaves, phyllophagistic, phyllophagous.

phyllophore. 1. The terminal bud or growing point of palms. 2. The leaf-bearing organ.

phyllophorous. Bearing or producing leaves.

phyllophyte. A plant which draws its nourishment mainly from the leaves, a cormophyte.

phyllopode. A dead sheathing leaf of *Isoetes*.

phyllopodic. 1. Of or pertaining to phyllopodes. 2. With a leafy base.

phyllopodium. 1. The petiole and rachis of the leaf of a fern. 2. Any structure as an axis, stipe, rachis, petiole, etc., which serves as a support for the expanded portion of a leaf. 3. A phyllode.

phyllopodous. Said of the genus *Hieracium* when the radical leaves are in full vigor at the period of flowering.

phylloporphyrin. A byproduct of chlorophyll in dark red-violet crystals.

phylloptosis. The unnatural fall of leaves.

phyllorhize. 1. An organ intermediate between the leaf and the root, as the capillary leaves of many water plants. 2. An entire primitive plant.

phyllosiphonic. Having a tubular central cylinder in the higher plants where leaf gaps are constantly present.

phyllosperm. A leaf-borne seed, as in the *Cycadales* and *Pteridospermophyta*.

phyllostictoid. Like the fungus *Phyllosticta*.

phyllotaonin. A product of chlorophyll resembling phyllocyan but dull green in tint.

phyllotaxis. The system of leaf arrangement on an axis or stem.

phyllotaxy, discontinuous. A leaf system having a definite break of ratios.

phyllotaxy, falling. A leaf system passing into a lower series.

phyllotaxy, rising. A leaf system passing into a higher series.

phylloxanthin. The yellow coloring matter of leaves, xanthophyll.

phyllula. 1. The scar left on a branch when a leaf falls. 2. The embryo stage of vascular plants when the first leaf and roots appear.

phyllule. The free portion of the pulvinus at the leaf base, as in *Pinus*.

phyllum. A leaf.

phylogenic. Pertaining to phylogeny, the development of the race; concerning real and hypothetical ancestral organisms.

phylogeny. The history of the evolution of the group or race to which a species belongs rather than of individuals.

phylon. A group of animals or plants constructed on a similar general plan, a tribe, a race, a genetically related group.

phylum. A major plant group, one of the primary divisions of the animal or plant kingdom.

phymatochilous. With long lips.

phymatodeous. Warted, verrucose.

physaroid. Like the slime mold *Physarum.*

physcion. An acid produced by some molds and lichens.

physema. The frond of an aquatic alga, as a branch of *Chara.*

physical drought. The condition in which the soil contains very little available water.

physiogeny. The development of vital activities.

physiognomic dominance. A condition where certain species provide the characteristic facies. In this sense dominance has no necessary connection with frequency.

physiognomic dominants. Species which dominate physiognomically in a given piece of vegetation and are frequently dominants.

physiognomy. The external morphology of a community, the general appearance or aspect of a plant community.

physiognomy, botanic. 1. The habit of a plant or plant community. 2. The general aspect of a plant.

physiographic climax. A plant community maintained at a certain stage of development by some natural feature of the habitat such as active erosion or slow but persistent movement of ground.

physiographic conditions. Conditions which are associated with the form, structure, and behaviour, of the earth's surface; edaphic conditions.

physiographic factors. Factors such as altitude, exposure, slope, surface features, etc.

physiographic formation. A complex of associations which are geographically linked with one another by physiography.

physiography. The study of the surface of the lithosphere primarily and the relation of the air and water to it. Its field is the zone of contact of air and water with the land, and of air and water.

physiologic drought. The condition in which soil contains a considerable amount of water but little available for plant use, as when water is frozen or the concentration of chemicals is too high for use by the plant.

physiologic form. Physiologic race.

physiologic species. Plants differing in physiologic type or behaviour but not in morphological form and therefore not named taxonomically, physiological races.

physiological. Relating to the functions of a plant or animal as a living organism.

physiological anatomy. A study of the effect or relation of the structure of a plant to its life processes or functions.

physiological balance. The balance of nutrients in a culture solution so that no particular nutrient may exert a detrimental effect on the growth of a plant.

physiological basis of classification of communities. The use of physiological characters as criteria in ranking communities.

physiological botany. The science which studies how plants live, grow, and perform their various functions; plant physiology.

physiological drought. A lack of available water for plant use because of physical barriers (as frozen water) or physiological factors (as excess salts or nutrients).

physiological heterothallism. Heterothallism of a physiological sort, as in fungi which are haplo-synoecious, as distinguished from sexual heterothallism.

physiological life history. The sequence of physiological states through which an organism passes from the sexually mature adult to the same stage of the next generation.

physiological pilosism. Hairiness occasioned by circumstances, as growth in a dry soil.

physiological race. A subdivision of a species which shows a variation in physiological traits buit not in morphological form, as certain pathogenic fungi which show preferences for particular hosts.

physiological response. Physiological changes due to a stimulus.

physiological speciation. See PHYSIOLOGICAL RACE.

physiological units. The ultimate particles of living matter that determine characters, such as ids, biophores, and determinants.

physiological variety. See BIOLOGIC FORM.

physiological zero. The threshold of temperature below which the metabolism of a cell, organ, or organism ceases to function.

physiology. The study of life processes of organisms.

physodes. Vesicles in algae filled with liquid containing structures formerly called microsomes.

phyta-, -phyte. A prefix or suffix meaning plant.

phytalbumose. A proteid found in seeds.

phytal zone. The littoral area along lake shores which supports vegetation.

phytentoscope. An instrument to ascertain the depth light rays penetrate into plant tissues, a a phytoendoscope.

phyteris. Plant migration and competition.

phytin. A substance found in the outer layers of some seeds, especially grains, which forms insoluable salts with calcium, magnesium, and iron which inhibit their absorption by animals.

-phytium. A suffix meaning formation.

phytoalbumin. Plant albumin.

phytobenthon. Vegetation of the depths.

phytobenthos. The portion of the bottom of the ocean which is covered with vegetation.

phytobiology. The life history of plants, the study of vital functions of plants.

phytobiotic factors. Ecological factors of the nonanthropeic environment such as: climate (shade, windshelter, change in humidity), edaphic (factors of the lithosphere and hydrosphere), vegetational (humus formation, changes in soil moisture), and changes caused by fire.

phytoblast. A cell in its first stage of development.

phytoblastea. A spherical coenogenetic alga, as *Volvox*.

phytocecidia. Galls produced by other plants.

phytochemy. The chemistry of vegetation and its products.

phytochlore. Chlorophyll.

phytochrome. A pigment which is light-sensitive.

phytocoenose. Phytocoenosis.

phytocoenosis. The total plant population of a given habitat usually separable into two or more synusia which are more or less distinct and which may or may not be spatially divided into subcommunities.

phytocoenosis complex. A vegetational unit consisting of phytocoenoses with little or no relationship to each other but more or less alternating.

phytocoenosium. A plant community, the vegetation of a unitary habitat, an association.

phytocoenostics. Phytosociology.

phytocyst. A cell with its walls.

phytoderma. Any fungus parasite growing on the skin.

phytodichogamy. Plant dichogamy.

phytodomatia. Shelters in which other plants live.

phytodynamics. The movements and processes of plants.

phytodytes. Inhabitants of habitats above the ground (divided into gramnicolous, compositicolous, thamnocolous, and hylacolous).

phytoecology. The relation of a plant to its environment.

phytoedaphon. Microscopic soil flora.

phytoflagellata. Unicellular ciliate algae.

phytogamy. Cross-fertilization in flowers.

phytogelin. The gelatin of algae.

phytogen. A vital center.

phytogenesis. The origin and development of a plant.

phytogenic soil. A soil which contains a quantity of plant humus. It is found widely distributed in the temperate zones where it supports rich vegetation.

phytogenous. Growing on plants, arising from plants.

phytogeogenesis. The origins of plants in geologic time.

phytogeographical formation. A vegetative or plant formation.

phytogeography. The geographical distribution of plants.

phytognosis. Botany.

phytogonidium. An immobile gonidium capable of independent germination.

phytograph. A graph which shows the role a tree plays in the structure of a plant community. The graph gives data on the dominant trees (10" D.B.H. or over) showing: the percentage of abundance, the percentage of frequency, the size classes in which the species occurs, and the percentage of basal area.

phytography. Descriptive botany including both the describing and naming of plants, taxonomic or descriptive botany.

phytohormone. A hormone produced by

plants or one used to stimulate plant growth.

phytol. A constituent of chlorophyll.

phytolphytohaematins. Colorless chromogens becoming pigments under the action of oxygen in the presence of oxydases.

phytoid. Plant-like.

phytolaccoid. Like *Phytolacca*, tropical herbs with fleshy roots.

phytolite. A phytolith.

phytolith. A petrified fossil plant.

phytolithology. 1. Palaeobotany. 2. The science of plant distribution as affected by soil or rock.

phytology. Botany, the study of plants.

phytolysis. Photolysis.

phytomastigopod. See MASTIGOPOD.

phytome. The vegetative body or substance of all plants, phytomer.

phytomelane. The black structureless layer found in the pericarp of many *Compositae*.

phytomer. 1. A plant part, unit, or rudimentary plant. 2. A portion of a vascular plant which, when removed and treated as a graft or cutting, may produce a new plant. 3. A phyton, a phytome.

phytometer. A plant or group of plants grown under controlled conditions and used as a measure of the physiological response to various environmental factors.

phytometry. The measurement of the physiological responses of a plant or group of plants to various environmental factors.

phytomitogens. Plant products which stimulate cell division. They are suspected of being a factor in cancer growth. See MITOGENIC RAYS.

phytomonadina. Phytoflagellata.

phytomorphology. The science of plant form and structure.

phytomorphosis. Any change induced by plants.

phytomyxaceae. Myxomycetes.

phyton. A hypothetical plant unit composed of bud, leaf, blade, and stalk which repeated many times makes up a plant; a phytomer.

phytonomy. The laws of origin and development of plants.

phytonymia. Plant organography.

phytopalaeontology. Palaeobotany.

phytopathology. The study of plant diseases.

phytophagous. Feeding on plants, herbivorous.

phytophenology. The observation and recording of dates in the leafing or flowering of plants.

phytophilous. Feeding or growing on plants, phytophagous.

phytophysiology. Plant physiology.

phytoplankton. Floating pelagic plant organisms, floating microscopic plants.

phytoplasm. Plant protoplasm.

phytopleuston. Plants which are lighter than the surrounding water and consequently float on the surface.

phytopolitus. A plant which is or seems to be parasitic.

phytoproterandry. The maturing of the stamens before the styles are receptive.

phytoproterogyny. The maturing of the styles before the stamens have ripe pollen.

phytoptocecidia. Galls caused by fungi.

phytoptosis. A hypertrophic disease of plants due to gall mites.

phytosociology. A branch of ecology devoted to the consideration of vegetation rather than habitat factors.

phytostatics. The various causes which tend to produce equilibrium in the energies of a plant.

phytosterol. A product derived from plants resembling cholesterol in animals.

phytostrote. A plant or species that moves or migrates by means of the movement of the entire body, as surface phytoplankton which move with a current, etc.

phytosuccivorous. Feeding on plant saps.

phytotaxonomy. The systematic study of plants.

phytoteratology. The study of monstrous growths in plants.

phytoterosia. Plant pathology.

phytothallea. The presumed source of the plant kingdom.

phytotomy. Plant anatomy or histology.

phytotopography. Descriptive local botany.

phytotoxin. A soluble toxin of certain plants and some pollens.

phytotrophia. Plant culture.

phytozoa. Flagellata.

phytozoid. Antherozoid.

phytozooflagellum. The initial organism.

phytozoon. A zoophyte, an antherozoid or mobile fertilizing body formed in antheridia.

piceous. 1. Of or like pitch. 2. Pitchy black.

picnidium. Pycnidium.

picotee. A variation in flower in which the petals are of a uniform color (white or yellow) and have a marginal band of another color (often red).

picroerythrin. A pungent red coloring matter found in lichens.

picrotoxin. A bitter white crystalline substance found in the herb *Cocculus indicus* and in the roots of *Stephania*.

picturatus. Variegated, colored.

pietra fungaia. Fungus stone, the sclerotium of *Polyporous tuberaster*

piezatropism. Movement by compression acting as a stimulus.

pigment cell. A chromatophore or cell containing coloring matter.

pigment spot. 1. A specialized mass of cytoplasm permeated by a red coloring matter present in the motile cells of many algae. 2. An eye spot.

pigmentosa. The pigmented part of an eye spot.

pignons. Edible seed of *Pinus pinea*, the piñon pine.

pilaris. Having small hairs, pilose.

pileate. Having a cap, like a pileus, crested.

pileiform. Pileus-shaped, cap-shaped.

pileogenous. Giving rise to a pileus.

pileola. 1. A small cap or cap-like body which encloses the bud. 2. The diminutive of pileus. 3. The plumule in grasses. 4. A coleoptile.

pileorhiza. A root covering, a root cap.

pileus. The cap of an agaric which bears the gills on its underside, the umbrella-shaped fruiting structure of a mushroom.

pilidium. An orbicular, hemispherical shield in lichens, the outside changing into a powdery substance, as in *Calicium*

piliferous. Bearing or producing hair, applied to the outermost layer of root or epiblema which gives rise to root hairs.

piliferous layer. The young superficial tissue of roots producing the root hairs.

piliform. Hair-like, filamentous.

piligerous. Bearing hairs.

pillar. A stipe.

pillar roots. Aerial roots.

pillosellous. Somewhat hairy.

pilocarpine. An active substance in the shrub *Pelocarpus*, a genus of the *Rutaceae*

pilocystidium. A cystidium or cystidium-like cell on the surface of a pileus.

piloglandulose. Having glandular hairs.

pilose. Covered with long, soft, hairy filaments; having long, soft hairs.

pilosism. Abnormal hairiness in plants.

pilosism, deforming. Excessive hairiness which completely disfigures the species.

pilosism, teratological. Excessive hairiness which becomes a deforming disease.

pilosity. Hairiness.

pilous. Pilose.

pilula. A spherical inflorescence, a cone like a galbulus.

pilularis. With globular fruit.

piluliferous. Bearing globules.

pilus. A hair.

pimeleoid. Like *Pimelea*, Australian shrubs.

pimelic acid. A growth-promoting substance effective on some bacteria.

pimpinellifolious. Leaved like *Pimpinella*, the saxifrage.

pimpinelloid. Resembling the umbelliferous genus *Pimpinella*

pinkenchyma. The muriform tissue of medullary rays whose component cells are tubular, pinechyma.

pinares. Forest of *Pinus canariensis* with xerophytic undergrowth in the Canary Islands.

pinching bodies. The pair of horny clips at the junction of the pollinia in asclepiads which cling to the leg of insect visitors, the corpuscula.

pinching traps. Pinching bodies.

pinch trap flowers. Flowers adapted for insect visitors able to draw out the pollinia.

pinder. The ground nut.

pine barrens. Pine forests on the dry, sandy, gravelly soil of the low indented coastal shelf of the eastern United States.

pinenchyma. Pinakenchyma.

pinetum. 1. A study devoted to *Coniferae*. 2. An association of pines. 3. A plantation of pine trees.

pinetum cladinosum. A pinetum with the soil covered with the lichen *Cladonia*.

pinetum herbidum. A pinetum with grasses covering the soil.

pinetum hylocomiosum. A pinetum with the mosses *Hylocomium* and *Dicranum*.

pin eyed. 1. With the styles more conspicuous than the stamens. 2. With a stigma on a level with the throat of the corolla and the anthers lower down enclosed within the tube.

pinguifolious. With thick leaves.

pinheiros. A forest composed of *Araucaria brasiliensis*.

pinifolious. Pine-leaved.

pinite. A sweet and crystalline glucoside derived from *Pinus lambertiana*.

pinna. A leaflet or a branch of a pinnately compound leaf.

pinna trace. The vascular bundle connecting a pinna with the stem or principal petiole.

pinna trace bar. An arc of xylem formed by the fusion of two entering pinna traces of diplolabis.

pinnabar. A pinna trace bar.

pinnae, alternate. Pinnae not arranged opposite each other.

pinnate. With leaflets or veins on each side of a common stem or vein in a feather-like arrangement.

pinnate-pinnatifid. Once pinnate then pinnatifid, feather-like.

pinnately cleft. Pinnately veined with marginal divisions reaching about halfway to the midrib, pinnatifid.

pinnately compound. Having leaves which have leaflets arranged on each side of a common axis of a compound leaf.

pinnately decompound. Bipinnate or further divided in a pinnate manner.

pinnately lobed. Having several lobes of about the same size on each side of an elongated leaf, pinnatilobate, pinnatipartite.

pinnately nerved. Penninerved.

pinnately parted. Pinnatepartite, having marginal divisions in a pinnate leaf reaching nearly to the base.

pinnately ternate. Pinnately trifoliate.

pinnately trifoliate. Trifoliate with the terminal leaflet stalked.

pinnately veined. Having one primary vein or midrib from which secondary veins run parallel toward the margin, feather-veined.

pinnatifid. Pinnately cleft to the middle or beyond, deeply cut into segments nearly to the midrib, pinnately notched, pinnatisect, pinnately cleft and pinnately parted, remaining confluent at the base.

pinnatifolious. With pinnate leaves.

pinnatifrons. With pinnate fronds or foliage.

pinnatilobate. Having leaves pinnately lobed.

pinnatinervis. Pinnate-nerved.

pinnatipartite. Pinnate with the divisions acute and almost free, with leaves lobed three-fourths of the way to the midrib, pinnately parted.

pinnatisect. Pinnate with the divisions reaching nearly to the midrib, as the leaves of water cress; having the lobes of a pinnate leaf divided to the midrib but not petioled.

pinnatodentate. Pinnate with toothed lobes.

pinnatopectinate. Pinnate with pectinate lobes.

pinniform. Feather-shaped.

pinninervate. Having veins like parts of a feather.

pinniveined. Pinnately veined with a prominent midrib and secondary veins.

pinnulate. Having pinnules.

pinnule. A secondary pinna of a decompound or tripinnate leaf.

pinnulets. Secondary pinnules.

pinocytosis. The presence of vesicles or small vacuoles in the cytoplasm.

pinoid. 1. Like a pine needle. 2. With characteristic dry cones and wind dispersed seeds.

pinometer. An instrument for observing the transpiration stream in plants.

piñon. Pinym, *Pinus cembroides*, *P. Parryona*, *P. Pinea*; pines with edible seeds.

pinulus. A spicule resembling a fir tree owing to the development of small spines from one ray.

pinyon. The piñon, *Pinus cembroides*, etc.

pioneer. A plant or animal which invades a primary bare area and persists upon it.

pioneer community. The first plant community to become prominent on a piece of ground which has been stripped of its vegetation and is being reoccupied by plants.

pioneer species. 1. A species among the first to occupy bare ground. 2. Species which are intolerant of shade and competition.

pioneer stage. The extreme condition of a primary area with reference to a climax, as lichens in rock seres and submerged plants in hydroseres.

pionnotal. Having a continuous spore layer, as the fungus genus *Pionnotes*.

pionnote. A slimy or gelatinous mass in which conidiophores and conidia are embedded.

P-ions. Phosphorous ions.

pip. 1. The popular name for the seeds of an apple or pear. 2. A florist's term for a single flower of a truss. 3. A perpendicular or upright small rootstock used in propagation, a flowering rootstalk.

piperate. Peppery, pungent.

piperine. An inactive alkaloid found in pepper, *Piper nigrum.*

piperitonal. Scented like heliotrope.

piperitus. Peppery, having a hot biting taste.

pipette. A small piece of apparatus usually graduated in milliliters or fractions thereof used in transferrring fluids in experiments.

piriform. Pear-shaped, pyriform.

piriniversiform. Reverse pear-shaped, obpyriform.

pisaceus. Pea green.

piscicolous. Living in fishes, as some parasites.

pisciform. Fish-shaped.

piscine. A pond or pool community.

pisiferous. Pea-bearing.

pisiform. Pea-shaped.

pisocarpous. Pea-fruited.

pistietum. An association of *Pistia*, a floating water plant.

pistil. 1. The seed-bearing organ of a flower normally consisting of an ovary, style, and stigma. 2. The seed-bearing organ composed of one or more carpels. 3. The megasporophyll or the gynoecium.

pistil, compound. A pistil consisting of two, three, or more carpels united into one body.

pistil, simple. A pistil composed of one carpel.

pistillaceous. Growing on the pistil.

pistillar. Club-shaped.

pistillaribacillar. Oblong and slightly thicker at the ends, as some spermatia.

pistillary cord. The channel which passes from the stigma through the style into the ovary.

pistillate. With pistils but not stamens, female, having pistils only, producing functional ovules only, bearing the gynaecium.

pistillate flowers. Flowers with pistils but no stamens.

pistillidia. The mother cells produced on the germ frond of ferns which gives rise to the embryo and axis of growth, the archegonia.

pistilliferous. Bearing pistils only.

pistilline. Pertaining to or consisting of a pistil.

pistillode. A rudimentary pistil in the male flowers of such genera as the water plant *Elatostema.*

pistillody. The conversion of any floral organ into a carpel, carpellody.

pistillum. The columnar body situated in the center of a flower consisting commonly of three parts--the ovary, style, and stigma.

piston mechanism. A device found in some flowers in which the pollen is shed into a tube from which it is pushed by the style to come into contact with an insect visitor.

pit. 1. A thin localized area in the wall of a cell or other plant structure. 2. The two opposite thin areas in the walls of two cells or structures in contact. 3. A thin spot in the wall of the oogonium of some *Oomycetes.*

pit annulus. The outer thicker rim of a bordered pit membrane.

pit aperture. The opening or mouth of a pit.

pit border. The over-arching part of the secondary wall.

pit canal. The passage from the cell lumen to the chamber of any bordered pit.

pit cavity. The entire space within a pit from the membrane to the lumen.

pit chamber. The space between the pit membrane and over-arching border.

pit chamber of the bordered pit. The much widened outer part of the pit canal.

pit field. The thin-walled area of a pit in plant cells.

pit membrane. The thin sheet of unbroken wall between two opposite pit cavities.

pit pair. Two complementary pits of adjacent cells.

pit, primordial. Oval patches in the wood of *Pinus* within which only bordered pits arise, a primary pit area.

pitch. A resinous exudation from spruce, *Picea alba.*

pitcher. An urn-shaped or vase-shaped modified leaf which contains secreted digestive fluids. It serves to catch and digest insect visitors.

pitcher plant. Any of the *Nepenthes, Sarracenia,* or *Darlingtonia Californica.*

pitcher-shaped. Tubular with a contracted throat.

pitchers. Hollow leaves.

pitfall flowers. Transitional flowers, such as *Asarum*, which catch small flies.

pitch. The soft tissue in the interior which often disappears so that the stem becomes hollow, a central core of parenchymatous cells in stems and roots, the medulla or central region of a dicotyledonous stem.

pith fleck. Dark marks in timber due to cavities made by the larvae of some insects working in the cambium but later filled by cellular tissue.

pith ray. A vascular ray.

pith ray fleck. A dark spot in timber composed of cells which have filled a cavity resulting from the attacks of insects on the cambium.

pithioid. Jug-shaped, spherical to oval with a well-defined open neck at the top.

pits. Locally thin parts in cell walls corresponding with similar places in neighboring cells.

pits, air. Pits which have no counterpart on the side of the air space.

pitted. Lacunose, with little depressions, punctate, marked with fine indentation.

pitted cell walls. Walls marked with small apertures or depressions.

pitted vessels. Dotted ducts, vessels with secondary thickenings leaving thinner spots, xylem vessels with pitted walls, bordered pits.

pityriasis versicolor. A disease of the skin caused by *Microsporon furfur*, a disease of the skin characterized by irregular patches of thin scales.

place-constant. An invariable factor in a given locality.

place-mode. The prevalent condition of size, number, color, etc., of organs of a plant in a given locality.

placenta. The part of the ovary to which the ovules are attached, usually the margin of the carpels; the ovule-bearing part of the ovary.

placental cell. A cell found in some red algae which supplies food for the developing gonimoblast (carposporophyte).

placental scale. An ovuliferous scale.

placentarium. The placenta.

placentary. 1. A placenta which is long and narrow and bears many ovules. 2. Relating to the placenta.

placentate. Having a placenta.

placentation. The method by which ovules are attached, the disposition of the placenta.

placentation, axile. The attachment of the ovules to a central axis.

placentation, free central. Ovules attached to a central placenta in the center of the ovary.

placentation, parietal. The placentation in which the ovules are attached to the wall of the ovary.

placentiferous. Having or bearing a placenta.

placentiform. Quoit-shaped, disc-shaped.

placentiformis. Placentiform.

placentoid. Occurring in the anthers to assist in the dispersion of pollen.

placochromation. A plate-like arrangement of chromatophores.

placode. A lichen resembling a rounded plate.

placodioid. With an orbicular thallus depressed and lobed, with a thallus having a squamulose determinate outline generally orbicular.

placodiomorphous. Polarilocular.

placodium. The horny sclerotic rind or layer surrounding the perithecial mount, the primordial layer producing the ascocarp.

placophytes. The *Peridineae*, *Diatomaceae*, and *Desmideae*.

placoplast. The elaioplast attached to the inner surface of the margin of the chromophores in certain diatoms.

placula. A stage of *Volvox* with four plastids in a plane, a type of blastula in which the animal or vegetative halves are somewhat compressed toward each other.

pladabole. A plant whose seeds are scattered by propulsion due to moisture.

pladopetric. Of rocks moistened by dripping water.

plagiodromous. Said of tertiary leaf veins when at right angles to the secondary veins.

plagiogeotropic. Growing at an oblique angle in response to gravity.

plagioheliotropic. Turning obliquely to the sun.

plagiophototaxy. The oblique arrangement of chlorophyll granules with regard to incident light.

plagiophototropic. Assuming an oblique position to the rays of light, as the leaflets of *Robinia tropaeolum* etc.

plagiotropic. Obliquely inclined, having the direction of growth oblique or horizontal.

plagiotropism. The tendency to incline from a vertical line to the oblique or horizontal.

plaguliform. Spot-like.

plain. Applied to a margin which is not undulate although it may be sinuate.

plakea. A flat colony of phytoflagellates in a single layer.

planation. The process by which a stream develops its flood plain by erosion and deposition, stream erosion.

plancton. Plankton.

plane of insertion. A plane which passes through the point of insertion of a lateral organ and coincides with the main axis and that of the organ.

plane of section. The direction in which a plant member is cut or assumed to be cut for the purpose of revealing its structure.

plane of symmetry. The plane which divides an object into symmetrical halves.

plane, principal. The plane of the longer axis in transverse section.

plane, secondary. The plane of the shorter axis.

planetism. The condition of having swarm spores.

planetons. Migratory species.

planetus. A migratory species.

planiflorous. With flat flowers.

planifolious. With flat leaves.

planiform. With a surface nearly flat.

planipes. With flat feet.

planiusculus. Nearly flat.

plank buttresses. The flat roots arising from the bases of certain trees, as *Bombax*, the kapok tree.

plank root. A flattened modified root which supports the stem. It grows with its broad side against the stem and also against the ground. A particular kind of prop root.

plankt(er). The individual organisms comprising plankton.

planktology. The study of the floating organisms of the ocean.

plankton. The free-swimming or floating oceanic life, passively floating or weakly swimming organisms of bodies of water.

plankton formation. A community of free-floating plants.

plankton, freshwater. The plankton of lakes and rivers.

plankton, neritic. The plankton found near the coast.

plankton pulses. The fluctuation in total population of plankton which assumes rhythmic cycles.

plankton, tycholimnetic. A false plankton algae at first but afterward buoyed by gas and floating.

planktonology. Planktology.

planktont. A constituent of plankton.

planktophyte. A plant forming an integral part of plankton.

planoblast. A free-swimming hydroid individual, the medusa form of a hydroid.

plano-compressed. Compressed to a flattened surface.

plano-convex. Plane on one side and convex on the other.

planocyte. A motile cell.

planogamete. A ciliated gamete, a ciliated or otherwise motile coalescing zoogamete.

planogamic. Having motile gametes.

planomenon. A wandering type of vegetation which includes these life-form classes: plankton (passive movement in open water), pleuston (passive movement on the water surface), kryo-plankton (passive movement, preponderantly in and on snow and ice), edaphon (living in soil water, passive movement), tracheron (active movement in water, air, and on land).

planont. A wandering organism.

plano-plastid. A flagellate cell.

planose. Plane.

planosome. A supernumerary chromosome due to nondisjunction of mates in meiosis.

planospore. A ciliated spore-zoospore, a motile zoospore.

planozygote. A motile zygote.

plant. 1. A vegetable organism which gets its food from gases or liquids and not by ingesting solid particles of food except in the plasmodial stage of myxogasters. 2. A young tree, shrub, or herb planted or ready to plant.

plant association. A group or community of plants which occupies a common habitat.

plant bullions. Coal balls.

plant cane. The first-year growth of the sugar cane from seed; a sugar cane produced directly from seed as distinct from ratoon, a root shoot.

plant casein. A substance produced in some plants which is akin to animal casein.

plant commune. Plants which are usually found in the same formation.

plant communities. Plants of a locality subjected to and adapted for life under common conditions.

plant community. See COMMUNITY.

plant cover. Vegetation cover.

plant formation. An assemblage of plants living together in a community under the same environment.

plant mass. The usually shapeless mass of individual plants remaining in close proximity to each other after their formation either because nothing occurs to separate them or because they are definitely held together by a gelatinous excretion.

plant pathology. The study of plant diseases.

plant plankton. Phytoplankton.

plant sociology. Phytosociology.

plantae tristes. Plants flowering in the evening.

plantagineus. Plantain-like.

Plantesamfund. An association (Danish).

planticle. The embryo in a seed.

plantulatio. Germination.

plantule. The plumule.

plaque. A sterile or clear area in a bacterial culture caused by the action of a bacteriophage.

plasma. Protoplasm.

plasmagene. A small particle in the cytoplasm of the cell, separate from the nucleus, which affects the cell characteristics. It is usually found in the female gamete.

plasmalemma. A very thin layer of specialized protoplasm forming the outer boundary of the protoplast that is in contact with the cell wall.

plasma membrane. The ectoplasm or the outer layer of the cytoplasm, the limiting membrane of a protoplast. The plasmagel.

plasmamoeba. Amoebiform masses of protoplasm.

plasmosol. The endoplasm.

plasmosome. A plasmatosome, a protoplasmic corpuscle, a plasome.

plasmatic. Protoplasmic, pertaining to or of the nature of plasma.

plasmative. During the creation of a species.

plasmatogennylicae. Angiosperms and gymnosperms.

plasmatoogosis. Of *Pythiaceae*, a plasmatic outgrowth or bud-like outgrowth of the mycelium in the tissue of the host similar to a prosporangium and serving as a storage organ or producing vegetative growths.

plasmatoparous. Germinating directly into a protoplasmic rounded mass which becomes invested in a membrane and then puts out a germ tube as the grape mildew, *Plasmopara*.

plasmatosome. A plasmosome.

plasmochym. The thick albuminous fluid substance of the cell body.

plasmocyte. A leucocyte.

plasmode. Plasmodium.

plasmoderma. Ectoplasm.

plasmodesm. An extremely delicate strand of protoplasm passing through a fine perforation in a cell wall which provides a connection between contiguous cells.

plasmodiae. The myxogasters.

plasmodial granules. Minute, strongly refractive granules in certain myxogasters.

plasmodial stage. A stage in the development of some lower plants which moves in an amoeboid fashion. See PLASMODIUM.

plasmodiation. The assumed softening of the wall of a spore on its germination.

plasmodic granules. Microscopic, dark-colored granules scattered, clustered, or in lines on the outside of the peridium or net and often on the spores of the myxomycete *Cribrariaceae*.

plasmodieresis. The akinetic or karyokinetic division of protoplasm.

plasmodiocarp. An asymmetrical sporangium of the myxogasters, a fructification in certain slime moulds consisting of an elongated and sometimes branched body in which spores develop.

plasmodiogen. The protoplasmic units of a plasmodium.

plasmodiophorous. Producing a true plasmodium.

plasmodium. The plant body of a slime mold, a body of plurinucleated protoplasm exhibiting amoeboid motion in myxomycetes, a collection of amoeboid masses without nuclear fusion.

plasmodium, aggregated. The myxamoebae conjugated without fusion each cell giving rise to a spore or foot cell.

plasmodium, fused. The union of myxamoebae and subsequent fructification.

plasmogamy. In protozoa, the fusion of several individuals into a multinucleate mass without nuclear fusion.

plasmogenesis. The origin of protoplasm.

plasmolization. Plasmolysis.

plasmolysis. The removal of water from a cell causing death, the contraction of the protoblast of a living cell by the addition of a solution which cause exosmosis of water from the protoplast.

plasmolyte. The substance causing plasmolysis.

plasmomites. 1. Minute fibrillae forming with plasmosomes. 2. The intergranular substance of a cell.

plasmonema. The conducting threads of protoplasm connecting with the plastids.

plasmophagous. Absorbing the living organic matter of the host plant without selection.

plasmoptyse. A mycorrhiza infection of *Asclepias* and *Apocynaceae* in the exodermis of the root.

plasmoptysis. The extrusion of protoplasm from bacteria with subsequent envelopment by a membrane.

plasmorgan. A rudimentary organ.

plasmosome. The true nucleolus, a karysome, a minute cytoplasmic granule, a bioblast.

plasmosphere. The perisphere.

plasmosynagy. The accumulation of protoplasts of the polioplasm and of the plastids included in it due to plasmolytic irritation.

plasmotomy. The division of a plasmodium by cleavage into multinucleate parts.

plasm sac. In diatoms, a colorless layer of protoplasm forming a lining to the frustule and enclosing the cell contents.

plasome. Plasmosome.

plasometric. Measuring the osmotic pressure of individual cells.

plasson. The formative substances which may give rise to cellular elements.

plastic equivalent. Consumed carbon in a body, the amount contained in the substance of the organism. Cf. respiratory equivalent.

plastic material. Any substance used up in growth processes.

plastic products. The products of katabolism which remain an integral part of the organism.

plastic substances. Substances employed in metabolism, as cellulose, starch grains, proteids, etc.

plastid. Small variously shaped portions of the protoplasm of a cell differentiated as a center of chemical activity; see CHLOROPLAST, LEUCOPLAST, CHROMOPLAST, etc.

plastid colors. Colors due to plastids in the cell as distinct from colored sap.

plastid inheritance. The inheritance through plastids carried in the cytoplasm of the ovule. The variegation in several plants is known to be inherited in this manner.

plastid mutation. A variation in the production of chlorophyll due to a change in the chloroplast.

plastid primordia. The large mitachondria-like structures which produce leucoplastids.

plastidome. The sum total of plastid contents in a cell.

plastidplasm. A theoretical substance differing from other forms of protoplasm by morphological characters.

plastidule. The smallest mass of protoplasm which can exist as such, the hypothetical unit of protoplasm.

plastin. The basic substance of the nucleus less highly colored by staining than the rest, linin.

plastochondria. Mitachondria.

plastochrone. The period of time elapsing between the formation of one leaf primordium and the next on the growing point of a shoot in which there is a stable spiral phyllotaxis.

plastocont. A chondriocont.

plastodynamia. The plastic or formative power.

plastogamy. Cytoplasmic fusion as opposed to nuclear fusion, the fusion of cytoplasts into a plasmodium with the nuclei remaining distinct.

plastogeny. The condition when cytoplastic elements undergo reorganization by fusion.

plastoid. A needle-shaped body found in the stalk cells of the tentacles of *Drosera* (sundew) which becomes rounded under stimulus, a rhabdoid.

plastomere. The part of a sperm containing the chondriosomes, a chondriomere.

plastonema. The deeply staining peripheral cytoplasm in the sporogenous tissue in mosses.

plastosome. A chondriosome, threads or granules in the cytoplasm which are colored by certain dyes.

plastotype. A cast from an original type as of a fossil plant.

platenoid. Like the plane tree, *Platanus*.

platanthous. With broad flowers.

plate. See SIEVE PLATE.

plate method. A method of isolating bacteria from colonies on gelatin, agar, or similar materials that can be melted, poured, and solidified.

plate ringer. The external concentric strands of vascular tissue in medulosa.

plateation. The physiological variation caused by external influences such as locality, climate, soils, and so forth; place variation.

plateau. 1. The very short stem which bears the scales in a bulb. 2. A tract of land of large summit area which is high or above the adjacent land on at least one side, a table land.

plates. The exterior parts of *Peridinaceae*, as apical plates, antapical plates, intercalary plates, postcingular plates, precingular plates, ventral plates, etc.

plating. The process of pouring Petri dishes.

platycanthous. With broad spines.

platycarpic. With broad fruit.

platycaulous. With broad stems.

platycenter. A broad center.

platycladous. With broad branches.

platyglossous. With a broad tongue.

platygonidia. Gonidia in broad spreading groups.

platylobate. With broad lobes.

platylobeae. The crucifers with flat cotyledons.

platyneurus. With broad nerves.

platyopuntia. An *Opuntia* with flattened stems.

platypetalous. With broad petals.

platyphyllous. With broad leaves.

platypodous. With broad feet or stalks.

platys-patchus. With broad spots.

platysperm. A seed which is flattened in transverse section.

platystachys. With broad spikes.

playa. Sea coast or beach.

plecolepis. The involucre of *Compositae* when the bracts are united into a cup.

plectascaceous. With the characteristics of the *Plectascales*.

plectascalian. Plectascaceous.

plectenchyma. A tissue of woven hyphae or the pseudoparenchyma of fungi.

plectenchymatous. Composed of plectenchyma.

plectenchymic. Like plectenchyma, woven or fibrous.

plectenchymoid. Like plectenchyma.

plectomycetes. A group of fungi sparsely septate and lacking detached spermatia.

plectostelic. Having a number of entwined longitudinal plates of xylem in the star-shaped protostele.

pleiandrous. Having a large indefinite number of stamens.

pleio-, pleo-. A prefix meaning several, full of, or many.

pleioblastous. Germinating at several points, as in some lichen spores.

pleiochasium. The axis of a cymose inflorescence which has more than two lateral branches, a multibranched cyme.

pleiocyclic. Living through more than one cycle of activity, perennial.

pleiogeny. An increase from that of the parental unit, as by branching or interpolation of members.

pleiohalile. Lower estuarine, in the portion of the estuary in which the total salt content is from 6-15 ppm.

pleiomerous. With more than the usual or normal number of parts.

pleiomorphism. The occurrence of more than one independent form in the life cycle of a species.

pleiomorphy. Pleiomorphism.

pleion. A period of abundance the presence of which is determined by climatic factors which usually recur in cycles of 2-5 years.

pleioneurus. With many nerves.

pleiontism. Polymorphy.

pleiopetaly. The duplication of petals to produce double flowers.

pleiophyllous. Having more than the normal number of leaves or leaflets.

pleiopyrenium. A small apothecium in one verruca in lichens.

pleiospermous. With an unusually large number of seeds.

pleiosporous. With many spores.

pleiotaxy. A multiplication of whorls, as in double flowers; an increase in the number of whorls in a flower.

pleiotomy. Multiple dichotomy or fission.

pleiotracheae. Membranous tubes or tracheae containing a compound spiral fiber.

pleiotropistic. Having one factor affect simultaneously more than one character in the offspring.

pleioxeny. The condition in which one kind of parasite can attack several species of host plants.

pleiozygous. Unlinked.

Pleistocene. Of the geological period following the Tertiary.

pleistomere. The chromatin divided only by granules.

pleniflorous. With double flowers.

pleobiotic. Having many life-forms.

pleochroicistic. Having various colors in the cell wall.

pleogamy. Pollination varying in time, the

maturation of the sex organs at various times.

pleogamy, female. Gynodioecism, gynomonoecism.

pleogamy, male. Androdioecism, andromonoecism.

pleogeny. Mutability of function.

pleomorphic. With more than one form in the life cycle, polymorphic.

pleomorphism. Mutability of shape, polymorphism.

pleon. An aggregate of molecules smaller than a micella, a pleuston.

pleonasm. Redundancy in any part.

pleophagous. Not restricted to one host.

pleophyletic. Descended from numerous lines, polyphyletic.

pleotrophic. Feeding on more than one substance.

plerome. A shaft of nascent fascicles, the central portion of the primary meristem at the growing points of stems and roots. It is in periblem and dermatogen, and gives rise to the stele.

plerome sheath. A bundle sheath, the phloem sheath in its nascent state.

plerotic. Having spores fill the oogonium.

plesiasony. Abnormal shortenings of the stem so that the leaves arise from nearly the same point.

plesiomorphous. 1. Having nearly the same form. 2. Crystallizing in closely similar forms while unlike in chemical composition.

plesiotype. A specimen compared with a species and newly described and figured.

plethen. The merism of a sporadic swarm with its later transformation.

pletheoblasteas. The alternation of plethea and blastea resulting in the formation of planospores.

pleur-. A prefix meaning to a side.

pleura. The girdle or hoop of diatoms.

pleuracrogenous. Borne at the tip and at the sides.

pleuranthous. Having the inflorescences borne on lateral axes, the main axis not ending in an inflorescence but simply stopping growth.

pleurenchyma. The elongated or woody tissue of plants.

pleuriloculate. With many locules or cells.

pleuroacrogenous. Borne at the tip and at the sides.

pleuroblastic. Producing vesicular lateral

outgrowths serving as haustoria, arising from a lateral bud.

pleurocarpi. Mosses which have axillary "flowers" and fruit bodies lateral upon the stems or branches.

pleurocarpous. 1. Having axillary flowers and lateral fruit. 2. In bryology, having the archegonia and sporogonia on short lateral branches. 3. Pleurocarpic.

pleurocystidia. Lateral cystidia.

pleurodiscous. Attached to the sides of a disc.

pleurogenous. Growing from the sides, borne laterally on hyphal cells.

pleurogynia. Glandular or tubercular elevations arising close to or parallel with the ovary.

pleurogyrate. Having the annulus in ferns placed laterally, with the annulus horizontal in fern sporangia.

pleuroplastic. Having the central portion of a leaf first attain permanency, the meristem being marginal.

pleuropodal. Having more than one stem arising from the branching of the main stem.

pleurorhizal. With the radicle of the embryo against one edge of the cotyledons which are then accumbent; lying upon or against another body, as the edge of the cotyledons against the caulicle in some *Cruciferae*.

pleurosperm. An angiosperm which begins with chalazogamy but becomes porogamous.

pleurosporangium. A sporangium which produces pleurospores.

pleurospore. A spore formed on the sides of a basidium in the basidiomycetes.

pleurosporous. With the sterigmata and spores on the vertical sides of the basidia.

pleurostachys. With spikes on the side.

pleurotribal. Having flowers whose stamens are adapted to deposit their pollen upon the sides of insect visitors.

pleurotribe. A pleurotribal flower.

pleuston. 1. Plants which float by reason of relative lightness. 2. Rootless, free-floating, submerged spermatophytes.

pleuroblastus. A condition when cotyledons rise above ground in germination but do not assume the appearance of leaves.

plexiform. Like a network.

plexus. A network, especially an intricate or interwoven combination of elements.

plica. 1. A plait or fold. 2. The lamellae in

fungi. 3. A disease of entangled twigs, the buds producing abnormally short shoots. 4. An abnormally great development of twigs or branches.

plicate. Plaited.

plicate aestivation. Valvate aestivation in which the perianth segments are plicate.

plication. A fold or folding.

pliciform. Resembling a fold, plait-like.

plinth. 1. The tapering free end of the nucellus of certain fossil seeds. 2. The lowest member of a base.

plinth jacket. The epidermis of the soft integument surrounding the plinth.

Pliocene. The latest Tertiary Period.

ploadostadion. Aquatic plants with upper parts above the water.

plococarpium. A fruit which is composed of follicles arranged around an axis.

plotophytes. Floating plants with their functional stomata on the upper surface of their leaves, floating leaved vegetation.

plug. A growth of protoplasm which closes the pore openings in the cells of certain algae.

plum pocket. A plum aborted to make a hollow swollen bag and finally a more or less mummified sac caused by the fungus *Taphrina*, a bag plum.

plumarious. Plumed, feathered.

plumate. Plume-like, plumose.

plumbagene. The crystalline principle in the roots of *Plumbago*.

plumbaginoid. Resembling *Plumbago*.

plumbago blue. Light olive gray.

plumbeous. Lead-colored.

plumed disseminule. A fruit or seed bearing a plume.

plumicone. A spicule with plume-like tufts.

plumigerous. Feathered.

plumose. Resembling a plume or feather.

plumular axis. The primary axis.

plumulate. Downy, having a downy covering, plumulaceous.

plumule. The embryonic shoot or bud in the seed located between the cotyledons which develops into the stem and leaves of the plant.

plumule bulb. A bulb which is produced directly from the germination of the seed.

plur-. A prefix meaning several or many.

plurannual. A plant with tender leaves and stems which are killed by frost at the end of each growing season but which grows anew from the perennial and persistent roots each spring.

pluri-articulate. With many cells or joints.

pluriaxial. Having flowers developed on secondary shoots.

pluricellular. Composed of two or more cells.

pluricepts. Having more than one head, as many roots.

plurichromosomal. With one chromosome complex taking one or more chromosomes of the other in the reduction division.

pluriciliate. Having many cilia.

pluriflorous. Having many flowers.

plurifoliate. Having many leaflets.

plurifurcate. With many forks.

plurigametic. Consisting of many gametes.

pluriguttulate. With many spots.

plurijugate. In several pairs.

plurilocellate. Having many hollows.

plurilocular. Having two or more loculi, having several or many cavities.

pluripartite. With many lobes or partitions, deeply divided into several nearly distinct portions.

pluriperforate. Having several openings.

pluripetalous. Polypetalous.

pluriploid. With multiple chromosomes.

pluriseptate. With more than one septum, with transverse septa, with several partitions.

pluriserial. Arranged in two or more rows, pluriseriate.

plurispermous. Having two or more seeds.

plurisporangiate. With many sporangia.

plurisporous. Having two or more spores.

pluristratose. Having many layers.

plurivalent. Used of nuclear divisions in which each element is composed of two normal elements; applied to chromosomes that are multiples, i.e., have the value of more than one univalent (unpaired) chromosome.

plurivalvis. Having many valves.

plurivorous. Living on many hosts or substrates, not confined to one species.

plus strain. One of the two strains of a heterothallic mold often distinguished from the minus strain by a stronger growth.

pluteal. Pertaining to *Pluteus*, the mushroom.

pluviifruticeta. Rain scrub, low tropic rain vegetation as mangrove swamp, dwarf palm, and bamboo communities.

pluviilignosa. The rain scrub and rain forest combined, woody vegetation in the rain tropics.

pluviisilvae. Rain forest.

pluvio-viscid. Viscid only in wet weather as a result of rain or heavy dew.

pluvo-fluvial erosion. Erosion by running water and wave action.

P.M.C. The pollen mother cell.

pneumatatactic. Showing an irritability caused by dissolved gases caused by respiration of the zoospores in the sporangium.

pneumathode. 1. An outlet, usually composed of loosely packed cells on the surface of a plant, through which an exchange of gases between the air and the interior of the plant is facilitated. 2. An aerating root as in *Taxodium*, swamp cypress.

pneumatic tissue. Open tissue filled with air.

pneumatized. Furnished with air cavities.

pneumato-chymifera vasa. Air vessels; see CHYMIFERA VASA.

pneumatocyst. An air sac used as a float to provide buoyancy in water plants; an air cavity in a pneumatophore.

pneumatode. 1. Any opening of the nature of a lenticel or stoma. 2. Certain upward growth from the roots of palms and some other plants which are in aeration.

pneumatoferous. Having air spaces, as the external membranous tube of the spiral vessels.

pneumatophore. An aerial structure which grows vertically upward from roots embedded in mud, composed of spongy tissue (aerenchyma), presumed to function as respiratory organs, as the knees of the bald cypress; the air bladder of water plants.

pneumotactic. Depending on the presence of dissolved gases, as some zoospores respond to the presence of the products of respiration of the zoospores in the sporangium; pneumatotactic.

pneumataxy, negative. The type of irritability which determines the development of certain spores, as in *Achlya*.

pneumotaxis. 1. The response or reaction of an organism to the stimulus of carbon dioxide in solution. 2. The response to the stimulus of gases generally. 3. Pneumatotaxy, pneumotropism.

pnoium. A plant succession on drifting (aeolian) soils, as blown sand.

po flowers. Flowers which offer pollen only to visitors.

poad. A meadow plant.

pocillus. The widened podetium of the lichen *Cladonia*.

pocket. The hollow in the leaf of *Lemna*, the duckweed, from which a new leaf arises.

pocket leaves. Mantle leaves, certain specialized leaves which collect humus.

pocket plums. See PLUM POCKETS.

pocketing. An intrusion of cortex.

poculiform. Shaped like a goblet or drinking cup; deep cup-shaped, like a pocillus.

pod. A dry, multiseeded, unicarpellate, elongated fruit dehiscent along both dorsal and ventral sutures; a legume.

podagricous. With swollen stalks.

podal. Pertaining to the foot.

podalyriaefolious. With leaves like the legume *Podalyria*.

podeta. A podetium.

podetiiform. Resembling a podetium.

podetium. A stalk-like, cup-like, or much-branched erect structure arising from the thallus of some lichens which supports an apothecium.

podicellate. Having stalks, as applied to lichens.

podicellum. A very short podetium.

podium. A foot or foot-like structure; a support for another part; the base of an organ; a foot stalk, stipe, or other such support.

podo-. A prefix meaning a foot, stalk, or base.

podocarp. A stipitate fruit, a fruit having the ovary borne by a gynophore.

podocarpineous. Resembling or allied to a podocarp.

podocarpous. Having a gynophore, with stipitate fruit.

podocephalous. Having a head of flowers on long stalks, with a pedunculate head, having a head of flowers supported on a distinct peduncle or pedicel.

podogynium. A stipe supporting the gynaecium, an elevation in the center of a flower which carries the ovary, a gynophore.

podolicus. Of Podolia in southwestern Russia.

podophyllous. With stalked leaves.

podopterous. Having winged peduncles.

podosperm. The stalk of a seed, the funicle.

podosyncarpy. The condition of a double

moss capsule when one half is fully developed and the other half is abortive.

podsol. Well drained soil in a cool temperate climate with sufficient rainfall. A layer of humus is on top of a grayish, leached soil with a darker layer of soil beneath where the salts have accumulated. Podzol.

podus. Podium, a foot.

poecilothermic. Poikilothermic.

poetum. An association of *Poa*, grasses.

pogon. A collection of long hairs, a beard.

poic. Of grassland.

poikilodynamic hybrids. Hybrids when the character of one parent is practically absent.

pointal. A pistil.

poion. A meadow association, a poium.

poium. A plant association in which *Poa* is a dominant genus, a meadow formation or community.

pol. The pole nearest the centrosome in a resting nucleus.

polachena. A fruit like a cremocarp which has five carpels.

polar body. A portion of a gamete sometimes budded off prior to fertilization, one of the two small cells detached from the ovum during maturation divisions, a polar globule, a polocyte.

polar bilocular. Having cells at the opposite apices of lichen spores, etc.

polar cap. A group of fine plasmatic threads formed early in division at the pole of a dividing nucleus and contributing to the formation of the spindle.

polar cell. A polar body.

polar corpuscle. The central mass in each aster of a dividing nucleus.

polar fusion nucleus. The nucleus formed in the embryo sac by the union of the two polar nuclei. Later it unites with the male nucleus and forms the primary endosperm nucleus.

polar lakes. Lakes whose temperature is never above 40° C.

polar nodules. 1. Spherical swellings at each end of the raphe or groove in diatoms. 2. Highly refractive granules which surround an inner swelling at the end walls of a heterocyst in the blue-green algae.

polar nuclei. Two nuclei in the embryo sac which unite to produce the polar fusion nucleus, the fourth nucleus in each end of the embryo sacs prior to fertilization.

polar plates. The achromatic spheres at the poles of the spindle in mitosis.

polar pyrenoid. A pyrenoid which is not entirely enveloped in a sheath of starch grains.

polar radiations. The radiations which surround the poles of the spindle during karyokinesis and later, near the end of nuclear division, the daughter nuclei.

polar rays. Astral rays; a term sometimes applied to all of the astral rays as opposed to the spindle fibers, the group of astral rays opposite the spindle fibers.

polar rings. Two ring-shaped cytoplasmic masses near the ovum poles formed after the union of germ nuclei.

polarilocular. Having two-celled spores with a thick median wall traversed by a connecting tube, polaribilocular.

polarinucleate. Having an oil drop (nucleus) at each end of a spore.

polarity. The assumption of a direction pointing to the poles, as the compass plant, *Silphium laciniatum.*

polarization. 1. The attraction of the split chromosomes to the poles of the nucleus during the telophase of mitosis. 2. The movement of the ends of chromosomes toward the centrosomes at the zygotene stage. 3. The proper arrangement of matching kinetochores during the metaphase of mitosis.

pole. One end of an elongated spore.

pole plasm. Polar discs.

pole plates. Polar plates, condensed plate-like bodies at the ends of the spindle in certain forms of mitosis.

polembryony. Polyembryony.

polemonietum. A plant association of *Polemonium*, Greek valerian.

poles, anterior. The apex of the axis in vascular plants.

poles, posterior. The base of the sporogonium in bryophytes, the tip of the suspensor in vascular bryophytes.

polexostylus. A carcerule.

poliaxial. Having the flowers of an inflorescence borne on secondary, tertiary, etc., branches.

polichoris. See ETAERIO.

polifolious. With white leaves like *Polium*, the wood sage.

polioplasm. The granular plasma of plants,

the circulating portion of cytoplasm, spongioplasm.

politropism. Polytropism.

pollacanthic. Flowering more than once, pollachantic.

pollachigenous. Polycarpic.

pollaplasy. The condition of a normally simple organ when it is divided into several of like shape.

pollard. The tree dwarfed by frequent cutting of its boughs a few feet from the ground and the subsequent thick growth of shoots.

pollen. The dusty or sticky material produced in the stamens of flowers. It is composed of microspores each of which contains two male nuclei and upon contact with a suitable stigma fertilizes the ovules to produce seed.

pollen carrier. The retinaculum of asclepiads, the gland to which the pollen masses are attached either directly or by caulicles, the anther, the stamen.

pollen cells. The cavities of the anther in which pollen is formed.

pollen chamber. A small cavity formed in the apex of the nucellus in gymnosperms in which the pollen grains lodge after pollination. It is here that the pollen slowly develops and ultimately brings about fertilization.

pollen flower. A flower which offers pollen but no nectar to insect visitors.

pollen grain. A pollen granule, the male gametophyte of seed plants, an individual microspore.

pollen mass. Pollen grains cohering by a waxy texture or fine threads into a single body, a coherent mass of pollen, a pollinium.

pollen mother cells. Cells which give rise to pollen.

pollen prepotency. The greater potency of one kind of pollen than another in fertilization.

pollen sac. The microsporangium in phanerogams, the cavity of an anther containing the pollen.

pollen spore. A pollen grain.

pollen, stalked. Pollen with a spiny surface and three or more pores.

pollen tetrad. A group of four cells resulting from the tetrad division of a pollen mother cell.

pollen tetrahedron. A structure of certain groups of four grains cohering in a pyramid, as in *Oenothera*.

pollen tube. A tubular process which develops from pollen grains after the attachment to the stigma, the slender tube sent down from the pollen grain through the style of the pistil to the ovule in the ovary.

pollen tube, ectotropic. The pollen tube in acrogamy proceeding along the conducting tissue of the style to the micropyle.

pollenation adaptions. The changes leading to pollination.

polleniferous. Pollen-bearing.

pollenine. The contents of pollen grains.

pollenody. The development of sporogenous tissue of the nucellus into pollen in place of an embryo sac.

pollenoid. A pollinoid, an antherogoid.

pollinarium. The male organ in higher cryptogams, the androecium, the cystidium.

pollinarious. Like fine flour.

pollination. The process of the bringing of pollen from the anther to the stigma.

pollination, lateral. See PLEUROTRIBAL.

pollination, over. See NOTOTRIBAL.

pollination presentation. The sensitive action of the styles during pollination.

pollination, self-. Pollination from the same flower, but in the cultivator's sense it may be affected by any flower of the same variety in its vicinity.

pollination, under-. See STERNOTRIBAL.

pollination, wind. The spread of pollen from the anther to the stigma by the agency of the wind.

pollinia. A coherent mass of pollen grains in certain plants such as the orchids and the milkweeds.

pollinic chamber. The pollen chamber.

pollinide. A single antheridial corpuscle.

pollinicus. Composed of or bearing some relation to pollen.

polliniferous. Bearing or producing pollen.

pollinium. See POLLINIA.

pollinizer. A plant used to furnish pollen in crossbreeding.

pollinodium. A club-shaped branch of mycelium, the antheridium of certain fungi; the cell which plays the part of a male organ and fertilizes the carpogonium.

pollinoid. A male gamete or spermatium.

pollinosus. As though dusted with pollen.

pollution carpet. A mat of slimy organic material found on the bottom of stagnant pools. It consists of masses of bacteria, protozoa, fungi, etc.

pollutional zone. See MESOSAPROBIA.

polocytes. Polar bodies.

poloicous. Having both fertile and sterile flowers.

polotropism. The tendency to direct proximal or distal extremities to the same point or pole.

polverine. The calcined ash of a soda-yielding plant.

poly-. A prefix meaning numerous or many.

polyacanthous. With many spines.

polyadelphia. A Linnaean artificial order with polyadelphous stamens or in several phalanges or brotherhoods.

polyadelphous. Having stamens united by filaments into more than two bundles, with stamens in many bundles or fascicles.

polyadenous. Having many glands.

polyam. A phylogenetic transition form.

polyandria. A Linnaean class of plants possessing many stamens in each flower.

polyandrian. Having an indefinite number of stamens.

polyandrous. Having twenty or more stamens, with numerous stamens.

polyandry. The condition of having many stamens, the state of being polyandrous.

polyanthous. Having many flowers, particularly if within the same involucre; multiflorous.

polyarch. Having many arcs of xylem and phloem, having many xylem bundles in wood tissue, having many protoxylem groups in a stele.

polyarinus. Polyandrous.

polyarthro-dactylous. With ultimate rays or dactyls each of more than two cells, as in some species of *Nitella*.

polyascous. Having many asci in a single hymenium not separated by sterile bands.

polyaster. The structure formed when several centers exist in a cell and are united by spindles.

polyaxon. A type of spicule formed among numerous axes.

polyblastic. Having multiseptate spores.

polybotrya. With many clusters.

polybulbon. Having many bulbs.

polycamarous. Polycarpic.

polycarpellate. Consisting of many carpels, as in a compound ovary.

polycarpic. 1. Fruiting many times, applied to perennials. 2. Having many carpels. 3. Forming two or more distinct ovaries. 4. Forming many spore cases. 5. Pollacanthic, pollachanthic.

polycarpicous. Polycarpic.

polycarpous. 1. Polycarpic. 2. Said of a flower in which the gynoecium forms two or more distinct ovaries. 3. Consisting of many spore cases. 4. With many fruits.

polycaryon. Having many centrioles or centrosomes in the nucleus.

polycentric. Having many centers of growth and development, as in *Cladochytrium*.

polycephalous. Having many heads or capitula.

polychasium. A cymose branch septum when more than two branches arise about the same point.

polychlamydeous chimaera. See CHIMAERA.

polychorion. See ETAERIO.

polychorionid. See ETAERIO.

polychroite. The yellow coloring matter of saffron.

polychromasy. Multiple and differential tinting with one staining mixture.

polychromatic. With various colors in the same organ.

polychromatism. The variation of colors or tints in the same corolla.

polychrome. A substance in the bark of the horse chestnut which gives rise to varying colors.

polychromosomic. Having many chromosomes.

polychromy. Polychromatism.

polychronic. Arising at two or more times.

polyciliate. Having numerous cilia.

polycladia. A supernumerary development of branches and leaves.

polycladous. Having abnormally numerous branches.

polyclady. An excessive development of twigs or branches.

polyclinal chimaera. A graft hybrid or natural mutation involving two or more genetic types.

polyclonal. 1. Developed from two male clones, as in the liverwort *Sphaerocarpus*. 2. Comprising a group of plants developed by asexual means by clones from one common ancestor.

polycoccous. Having many cocci.

polycormic. Having a number of erect vertical trunks.

polycotyledon. A plant having more than two cotyledons, a polycot.

polycotyledonous. With more than two cotyledons.

polycotylous. With more than two cotyledons.

polycyclic. 1. Having the members of a series, such as calyx, corolla, etc., in several circles. 2. Having many whorls. 3. Having accessory vascular strands in addition to the principal cylinder.

polycysted. Septate, with partitions.

polycystic. Multicellular, with several cysts.

polycystin. A pigment allied to carotin from *Polycystus flos-aquae.*

polydactylous. With many fingers.

polydelphous. Polyadelphous.

polydemic. Living in several regions.

polydemics. Sun and shade plants of the same species.

polyderm. A tissue which is composed of endodermal and parenchymatous cells which forms the endodermous layers of the central cylinders.

polyedricous. Polyhedral.

polyembryony. The production of two or more embryos within an ovule.

polyembryony, cleavage. The formation of several embryos resulting from the splitting of a basal tier of cells in the proembryo.

polyembryony, simple. The formation of multiple embryos in a seed resulting from fertilization of more than one egg.

polyembryonate. Having more than one embryo in a seed.

polyenergid. With many nuclear centers, with several centrioles, coenocytic.

polyergic. Having many vascular bundles, polyergidic.

polyflorous. Multiflorous, polyanthous.

polygalinae. Plants in which the stipules are double the number of petals.

polygamia. Plants with polygamous flowers.

polygamian. Polygamous.

polygamo-dioecious. Polygamous but with a tendency to be dioecious.

polygamo-monoecious. Polygamous but with a tendency to be monoecious.

polygamous. Having unisexual and bisexual flowers on the same plant, with hermaphroditic and diclinous flowers variously mixed on the same plant, having antheridia and archegonia on the same plant.

polygamy. The condition of being polygamous.

polygenesis. Polyphylesis, multiple origin, the origin of a new form at two or more places or times, sexual production, diverse lineage.

polygeny. Polyphylesis.

polygerm. The masses of embryonic nuclei and surrounding cytoplasm which follow the stages of the parasitic body in polyembryonic *Hymenoptera* and give rise to definite embryos.

polygoma-dioecious. Having perfect and imperfect flowers on different plants.

polygonaceous. Of, pertaining to, or resembling the knotweed genus *Polygonium.*

polygonatous. Having many knots in the stem.

polygonetum. An association of *Polygonum,* the knotweed.

polygonifloral. With flowers like *Polygonum,* the knotweed.

polygonous. Having many angles, knots, or nodes.

polygynia. 1. Plants with polygynous flowers. 2. Containing many carpels.

polygynicous. Having many distinct styles.

polygynoecial. Having multiple fruits formed by the united pistils of many flowers.

polygynous. Having many styles or an indefinite number of pistils.

polygyny. Polygamy.

polygyrous. Arranged in several whorls or circles.

polyhaploid. Haplopolyploid.

polyhedron. A stage in the growth of *Hydrodictyon* in which the hypnospores or resting spores break up into several megazoospores which have horn-like appendages. These polyhedra break up into zoospores.

polyhybrid. The offspring of parents which differ in more than three characters.

polykaric. Multinucleate.

polykarion. A polyenergid nucleus, a nucleus with more than one centriole.

polykont. A flagellate having many flagella.

polylepidetum. An association in which *Polylepis* predominates.

polylepidous. With many scales.

polylophous. With many crests.

polymastigate. Having a tuft of flagella.

polymeric. Producing the same quality or

character in the offspring with several nonallelomorphic genes.

polymerous. Consisting of many parts or members in each series.

polymery. 1. The production of a given character by the action of two or more independent factors or genes each of which when separate is able to produce the same character. 2. The condition when a whorl consists of many members.

polymery, cumulative. The cumulative action of several genes.

polymery, noncumulative. The condition in which one single gene can produce as much as many.

polymitosis. Excessive cell division of spores immediately after meiosis.

polymorphic. With various forms.

polymorphic colony. A heteromorphic colony.

polymorphism. The condition of having many shapes or structures, the capacity for assuming different forms.

polymorphous. Having many forms.

polymorphy. The existence of more than one form of the same organ on a plant.

polyneuris. Having numerous veins, especially secondary veins.

polynucleate. Containing many nuclei.

polyoecism. The condition in plants whose flowers differ in sex.

polyoicous. Having a combination of autoicous, heteroicous, or synoicous mosses with dioecious mosses.

polyovulate. Having many ovules.

polyoxybiontic. Depending on an abundant supply of oxygen.

polyparium. The common base and connecting tissue of a colony of polyps, a polypary.

polypeptides. Protein derivatives produced by the condensation of amino acids.

Polypetalae. Dicotyledons in which the corolla consists of separate petals.

polypetalous. Having separate and distinct petals.

polyphagous. 1. Subsisting on many kinds of foods. 2. Living on several hosts. 3. With the mycelium occupying many host cells.

polyphore. A common receptacle for many distinct carpels, a torus with many pistils.

polyphylesis. The origin of a form, species, or genus from two or more ancestral types, from diverse lineage.

polyphyletic. Derived from diverse ancestors, having several lines of descent.

polyphyll. An increase in the number of organs in a whorl.

polyphyllode. A polymeric individual with each component merid having produced a leaf.

polyphyllous. Having many leaves.

polyphyllomania. A large increase in the usual number of floral organs in a whorl.

polyphylogeny. The history of a race or group of genera or species which indicates possible descent from several sources or shows diverse evolution.

polyphyly. Origin from several stocks.

polyplanetic. Having several motile phases with resting periods between.

polyplanetism. A succession of different phases of the swarm period which are separated by resting periods.

polyplast. 1. A group of monoplasts which are the organic elements of protoplasm. 2. The multicellular stage of the embryo before the differentiation of cell layers or organs in mosses, ferns, etc.

polyplastic. Capable of assuming many forms.

polyploid. A cell, tissue, or organism having three, four, or more times the normal number of chromosomes in its nuclei (triploid, tetraploid, hexaploid, etc.); having complete sets of chromosomes.

polyploid, secondary. A homozygous allopolyploid in which some of the chromosomes in the basic set are reproduced more frequently than others.

polypodiaceous. Of or pertaining to the fern genus *Polypodium*.

polypodioid. Resembling *Polypodium*, the fern.

polyporoid. Relating to the fungus genus *Polyporus*.

polyporous. Like the fungus genus *Polyporus*, with many pores.

polyrhizoid. With many roots or rhizoids.

polyrihizal. Having numerous rootlets, polyrhizous, polyrhizic.

polysaccharide. A carbohydrate decomposable by hydrolysis into three or more molecules of simpler carbohydrates.

polysaprobe. An organism able to live in contaminated water.

polysaprobic. Thriving upon many kinds of dead organic material.

polysarca. An unnatural growth due to excess nutriment.

polysecus. An etaerio.

polysepalous. With many separate sepals.

polysiphonous. Consisting of a central row of elongated cells surrounded by one or more layers of peripheral cells, as in the thallus of some algae.

polysoma. Polyploid.

polysomic. Having more than two chromosomes of one type with the remainder of the chromosome complex usually diploid.

polysomitic. Having many body segments which are formed from the fusion of primitive body segments.

polysomy. A condition in which one or more chromosomes but not the entire set are present in the polyploid state.

polysperm. A plant producing many seeds in each flower.

polyspermatous. With numerous seeds in a pericarp.

polyspermous. Having many seeds.

polyspermy. The fertilization of a female cell by more than one male cell.

polysporangiate. Having many sporangia.

polyspore. A multicellular spore composed of merispores.

polysporous. Containing many spores.

polyspory. The formation of more than the usual number of spores.

polystachyous. Having many spikes.

polystelous. Having more than one plerome strand at the growing point so that the stem has more than one stele.

polystemous. Having the number of stamens more than double the number of petals and sepals.

polystichous. In several rows or layers.

polysticti. With many dots.

polystigmous. Having many carpels.

polystomatic. Having many stomata.

polystomatous. Having many pores, mouths, or openings.

polystromatic. Having many stromata.

polystylar. With many styles.

polysymmetrical. Having bilateral symmetry in more than one plane, actinomorphic.

polytaxic. Varying in a discontinuous manner.

polythalamic. 1. Having more than one female flower in the involucre. 2. Derived from more than one flower like a collective fruit.

polythallea. A thallus having several merids.

polythelous. Containing distinct ovaries.

polytocous. Prolific year after year.

polytomous. Having more than two second-ary branches, having several branches arising at the same level.

polytomy. Multiple branching of an inflorescence, a false pinnation.

polytopic. Of independent origin in more than one place.

polytopism. Polygenesis, multiple origin.

polytrichaceous. Resembling or akin to the moss *Polytrichum*.

polytrichetum. A formation of the moss genus *Polytrichum*.

polytrichosus. Having the ground under heather carpeted with mosses.

polytrichous. Having many hairs, covered with an even coat of cilia.

polytrophic. Obtaining food from several sources, nourished by more than one substance, visiting a variety of flowers, omnivorous.

polytropism. The ability of leaves to turn in several directions.

polytypic. Having several species.

polyvalent. Composed of many strains of the same organism.

polyxeny. Pleioxeny.

polyzygosis. The conjugation of more than two gametes or cells.

pomaceous. 1. Like a pome. 2. Belonging to the *Pomaceae*. 3. Apple green.

pomarium. An orchard.

pome. A fleshy, many-seeded fruit derived from a compound inferior ovary. The fleshy portion is derived from the enlarged base of the perianth tube with the central part composing the pericarp; both the exocarp and mesocarp are fleshy while the endocarp (the core) is stony or cartilagenous, as in the apple, pear, etc.

pomegranate. *Punica Granatum*.

pomelo. See PUMMELO

pomeridian. Blooming after noon.

pomiferous. Pome-bearing.

pomiform. Shaped like an apple.

pomologic. Pertaining to pomology.

pomology. The science of fruit cultivation.

pomona. An account of the fruits cultivated in any given district.

pompion. Pumpkin.

pompon. 1. A tuft or topknot. 2. A headed inflorescence, as in the dahlia and the chrysanthemum.

pontederietum. An association of *Pontederia*, pickerelweed.

ponticus. Of Pontus, Asia Minor.

pontium. A deep sea community.

pontohalicolous. Inhabiting a salt marsh.

pontophilous. Dwelling in the deep sea.

pontophyte. A deep sea plant.

poocola. A grass meadow.

poophile. A meadow-loving plant which grows with grasses.

poophyte. A plant inhabiting moist meadows.

popcorn. A variety of maize whose kernels expand and pop open when heated, *Zea Mays* var. *everta.*

population intensity. The degree to which a species occupies the available territory.

populeus. The blackish green of poplar leaves, *Populus nigra.*

populifolious. Poplar-leaved.

populin. The crystallizable substance from the bark of the aspen.

populineus. Pertaining to poplars.

poral axis. The long axis of a pore.

poral ring. Four to six epidermal cells surrounding the pore in fossil species of *Sequoia.*

porandrous. Having anthers which open by pores.

porcatus. Ridged.

porcelaneous. Like porcelain.

porcinus. Pertaining to swine.

pore. 1. The aperture of a stoma. 2. The ostiole in *Pyrenomycetes.* 3. One of the tubular cavities lined by basidia in pore-bearing fungi.

pore canal. The passage through a pit between neighboring cells.

pore capsule. A capsule from which the seeds or spores escape through a pore or pores.

pore chain. A series or line of adjacent pores that retain their separate identities.

pore circle. The zone in the annual rings of certain trees such as the oak which has numerous tracheids.

pore cluster. An isolated, rounded, or irregular aggregation of pores surrounded by other elements.

pore, multiple. A group of two or more pores crowded together and flattened along the lines of contact so as to appear as subdivisions of a single pore.

pore mushroom. Any mushroom which is distinguished by having the spore-bearing surface within tubes or pores, a polyporous mushroom.

pore organs. A part of the cell wall in desmids, each pore being surrounded by a cylindrical tube-like structure.

pore passage. The stomatic passage between the inner and the outer cavities.

pore space. Pore volume, the sum of the spaces in soils not taken up by solid particles.

pore volume. Pore space.

porecork. Strips of a few layers of compact brownish cells in lenticels, the cork cells in lenticels with intercellular spaces between them.

porenchyma. Tissue composed of elongated cells apparently pierced by pores, pitted tissue.

pores, air. Stomata, pneumathodes.

pores, apical. Hydathodes.

pores, bordered. In *Sphagnum*, the openings surrounded by a distinct thickened ring.

pores, cortical. Lenticels.

poricidal. Dehiscing by valves or pores, as in the poppies; porandruous.

poriferous. Having pores.

poriform. Shaped like a pore.

porogam. A plant in which the pollen tube enters the ovule through the micropyle.

porogamy. The entrance of the pollen tube into the ovule through the micropyle to insure fertilization.

poroid. Resembling pores, having small circular dots in the cell wall of diatoms which resemble pores, having pores.

porometer. An instrument to measure the dimensions of stomata.

porophyllous. Having leaves with large numbers of transparent spots.

porophyrophore. A cell bearing a reddish purple pigment.

porose. Containing pores, pitted, porous.

porous dehiscence. The liberation of pollen or seeds from the containing structure by means of pores.

porous vessels. Pitted or dotted vessels.

porphyreous. Porphyry red.

porphyroleucous. Light purple.

porphyroneurus. Purple-nerved.

porphyrostelic. With purple steles.

porraceous. Leek green.

porrect. Extended.

porrifolious. *Porrum* or leek-leaved, porrophyllous.

portoricensis. Of Porto Rico.

portulaceus. Like portulaca.

positive geotropism. Growth toward the center of the earth.

positive heliotropism. Heliotropism, the positive response to light.

positive reaction. The tendency of a plant or plant organ to move or to grow away from a region where the stimulus is weaker to one where it is stronger.

positive tropism. The tendency to move toward the source of a stimulus.

positively rheotropic. Having the direction of growth in a rheotropic organ coincide with that of the stream in which it is placed, pointed downstream.

post cingular. Having fewer and sometimes larger plates behind the girdle in the *Peridineae*.

post clisere. A sere proceeding from lower to higher climaxes succeeding a clisere.

post floral movement. A change in position of the flower stalk or inflorescence stalk after fertilization has occurred bringing the young fruits into a more favorable position for development or placing the seeds in good condition for germination.

post reduction, postreduction. The chromosome reduction in the second meiotic division, a reduction occurring in the metaphase of the second mitosis.

postcarpotropic. Having the peduncle inclined at the maturation of the fruit to help in dissemination.

postcotyledonary. After the development of the seed leaves.

postembryonic. After the embryonic period.

posteriform. The late derivative of an ancestral form.

posteriolateral. Placed posteriorly and toward the side.

postfloration. The persistence of the floral envelopes after flowering.

postical. Back of, under, or lower, used in reference to leaves, stems and other organs.

postnotum. Postscuttellum, the plate behind the scutellum.

postphyllome. Leaf.

postsynapsis. The processes of nuclear division succeeding the synapsis.

postrophosporophyll, postrophophyll. Sporophyll.

postventitious. Arising subsequent to their normal time of growth.

potamad. A river plant.

potamic. Of a stream community.

potamicolous. River-dwelling.

potamium. A river community.

potamogetonetum. A formation of pond-weeds, genus *Potamogeton*.

potamophilous. River-loving.

potamophyta. River plants.

potamoplankton. The floating vegetation of inland waters.

potential climax. The actual climax of the adjacent area which will replace the climax of the region concerned whenever the climate is changed.

potential gametophyte. A gametophyte which is functionally asexual.

potential parasite. A saprophyte which can live as a parasite.

potential saprophyte. A parasite capable of existing as a saprophyte.

potetometer. An apparatus to measure the amount of water given off by leaves of plants.

potherbs. Edible plant products.

potomato. A combination potato-tomato plant produced by grafting one on the other.

potometer. An instrument for measuring absorption.

pottiaceous. Allied to the moss *Pottia*, pottioid.

pouch. 1. A little sack or bag at the base of some petals or sepals. 2. The silicle or short pod, as in shepherd's purse; a kind of a saccate pod.

pouch, digestive. The root cap of the lateral roots of *Leguminosae* and *Cucurbitaceae*.

-pous, -podo. A suffix meaning foot or stalk.

poussieroid. Having the chromatin distributed in fine granules (dust-like), as prior to the prophase in mitosis.

powder seed. Minute seeds or spores, pollen.

powdery. Covered with a fine bloom, as the leaves of *Primula farinosa*.

powdery mildew. A series of plant diseases by that name.

prae-, pre-. A prefix meaning before.

praeangiospermous. Existing before the angiosperms came into being.

praeaxial. On the anterior border or surface.

praecox. Appearing or developing early, precocious, abundant, premature.

praeform. An early form, the original ancestral strain.

praemorse. Premorse.

praemutation. The inner preparation of a plant for outward manifestation, mutation.

praenomen. The generic name of a plant.

praeuste. Looking as if scorched.

prairie. The grassland area dominated by the tall prairie grasses as distinguished from the short grass plains, the grass country east of the Rocky Mountains.

prairie opening. A break or opening of prairie.

prairie pond. See BUFFALO WALLOW.

prasinatus. Greenish.

prasine. Leek green, grass green.

pratal. Growing in meadows.

pratense. Growing in meadows, pratensis.

pre-Linnaean. Prior to 1753, the date of the first edition of Linnaeaus' *Species Plantarum.*

preaecidiospore. A trichogyne.

preaecidium. A young caeoma, a fruiting structure which precedes the aecidium in rust fungi.

preangiosperms. Early forms of plants previous to the evolution of plants with closed ovaries.

preaxial. In front of the axis.

prebracteole. The subsporal bract in *Chara* which may be only a thick swollen cell.

precatorius. Like a necklace, as the seeds of the tropical legume *Abrus.*

precatorius-contextus. Necklace-shaped.

precession. The passage of the undivided X chromosome in the heterokinesis to one pole in advance of the other chromosomes.

precingular. Having plates under and usually larger than the apical plates as found in some genera of the algae *Peridinium.*

precipitation rose. A radical diagram giving the monthly precipitation in percentages.

precipitin. An antibody which precipitates its antigen.

precius. Flowering or fruiting early.

preclepsydroid trace. The early state of the leaf trace in the ferns *Ophioglossaceae.*

preclimax. The state of vegetation preceding the full development of a climax.

preclisere. A sere which proceeds from higher to lower climaxes preceding a clisere.

precocious flowers. Flowers which appear before the leaves.

precocity, differential. The habit of some nuclei of beginning the prophase of meiosis before the division of the chromosome.

precommunity. A community in which the individuals are not regulated through mutual effects.

predominant. Of outstanding abundance or obvious importance, having the ascendency over others.

preferential species. Species preferring one given community to others though growing more or less abundantly in all.

prefertilization. The early state of an ovule as far as completed pollination.

prefloration. The arrangement of floral leaves in a flower bud, praefloration, aestivation.

prefoliation. The arrangement of foliage leaves in the bud stage, praefoliation, vernation.

preformation theory. The theory that a germ cell contains the young organism in miniature.

preformed. With definite shape or structure, as leaves within the bud.

pregametospore. An early stage of *Volvox.*

prehaustorium. A rudimentary root-like sucker, papillate epidermal cells by which nutriment is obtained before haustoria are formed.

prehensile flowers. Flowers whose insect visitors grasp the style and stamens so as to cover their venters (breasts) with pollen and so effect pollination.

preheterokinesis. The segregation of the sex chromosomes in the first meiotic division.

preinduction. A modification of the second filial generation caused by the action of environment on the germ cells of the parental generation.

preinheritance. The transmission of characters developed in a previous generation.

prelamellar chamber. A structure in developing agarics in which the gills and hymenium develop on the under surface of the pileus.

prelocalization. The theory that certain portions of the ovum are predestined to develop into certain organs or parts.

premedian. In front of the middle of the body.

premeiotic. Previous to the reducing division in karyokinesis.

premorse. Appearing as if bitten or broken off abruptly, irregularly notched, premorous, praemorse.

premutation. The inner preparation of a plant for outward manifestation of changes, preparation for mutation.

preoral. In front of the mouth.

prepotent. Able to impress individual characteristics upon offspring to a marked degree.

prereduction. A reduction occurring in the metaphase of the first mitosis.

presence. The more or less persistent occurrence of a species in all the stands of a certain plant community.

presence classes. Dominance classes.

presence and absence hypothesis. The hypothesis that any simple Mendelian difference between individuals results solely from the presence of a factor in the genotype of one individual which is absent from that of another.

presentation. Pollen presentation.

presentation time. The minimum time required for a stimulus to call forth a response on the part of a plant.

presociation. A morphological part of an association characterized by the presence of one or more predominants of animals or parasitic plants on land.

presocies. A subordinate group of plants living among the dominant plants of an associes.

pressure, root. The pressure which exists in the tissues of a root and has a tendency to cause the rise of liquid in a stem.

presynapsis. The condition of nuclear division before synapsis.

presynaptic. Previous to synapsis.

preventitious buds. Dormant eyes on any portion of the stem from which epicormic branches arise.

prevernal. Early spring flowering.

prevernal aspect. The condition of the vegetation of a community very early in the year.

prickle. A stiff, sharp-pointed outgrowth from the epidermis; a needle-like outgrowth from the bark. A thorn is an outgrowth from the wood.

prickle cells. The cells of a prickle or the cells from which prickles arise.

prim. Privet, *Ligustrum vulgaris.*

primary root. The root formed by an extension of the radicle of the embryo.

primary association. An aggregation which arises through sexual or asexual reproduction or when individuals from the same parent(s) remain near the place of origin.

primary axis. The main stem.

primary bast. Bast consisting of sieve tissues and parenchyma.

primary body. The part of the plant body formed directly from cells cut off from apical meristems.

primary cell wall. The cell wall that surrounds the protoplast until it is mature. The thin, usually nonstratified wall contains

much pectin and little cellulose, and persists as the middle lamella.

primary colonies. Aggregations which have arisen from the same mother.

primary community. A natural community not caused by man.

primary constriction. The place where a chromosome is attached to the spindle.

primary cortex. The outer portion of the stem (including the starch sheath or endoderm) to the epidermis, the periblem.

primary cycle. The succession of developments in a life history of a fungus which takes place over a period of twelve or more months caused by structures arising after the overwintering stage.

primary desmogen. Procambium.

primary increase. The increase in the size of a stem or root not brought about by the addition of cells from a cambium.

primary lamella of a spore. The outermost layer of a spore coat representing the original wall.

primary layer. See PRIMARY TAPETAL CELLS.

primary leaves. The primordial leaves.

primary medullary ray. A vascular ray passing radially from the pith to the cortex.

primary megaspore. The megaspore mother cell, the early stage of the embryo sac.

primary members. The primary shoot and root, the first developments from the seed embryo.

primary membrane. The first or original cell wall.

primary meristem. The embryonic tissues of a young organ, the persisting part of primitive meristem which gives rise to cells which build up the primary body of a plant.

primary mycelium. The uninucleate haploid mycelium formed from the germinating basidiospore. It is sexually differentiated but does not form sex organs.

primary node. The node at which the cotyledons are inserted.

primary peridium. An enclosing membrane or veil that does not arise from the parts of a fruit body enclosed by it but arises from the original mycelium and surrounds the young fruit body primordia before any differentiation of the fruit body primordium has taken place.

primary permanent tissue. The tissue formed from primary meristem which does not ordinarily divide further.

primary petiole. The main rachis of a compound leaf.

primary phloem. The first year's phloem which developed from the procambium. It consists of protophloem and metaphloem.

primary pit field. A thinner area of the intercellular layer and primary walls within the limits of which one or more pit-pairs usually develop.

primary sere. A plant succession beginning on land which has not borne vegetation in recent geological time.

primary shoot. The main shoot developed from the plumule.

primary stem. The stem produced from the seed.

primary structure. A nascent organ, as root or shoot; the early structure of a plant or organ after all its distinctive tissues are formed and before any further growth or modification takes place.

primary succession. A succession starting from bare soil or upon soil surfaces exposed for the first time.

primary suspensor. The filamentous row of cells preceding the actual embryological divisions, the early stage being the proembryo.

primary tapetal cells. The cells or layer of cells surrounding a spore mass which develops into spore-producing tissue, the layer of cells in a stem which gives rise to the periblem which ultimately produces the cortex.

primary thickening. The first layer of wall material to be laid down in the very young cell wall, often rich in pectin.

primary tissue. A tissue which arises from an apical or intercalary meristem, the tissue first formed or formed during the first season's growth.

primary trisomic. Having one chromosome present in triplicate and the others present in duplicate.

primary universal veil. The loose flocculent layer covering the teleblem of *Amanita*, *Amanitopsis*, etc.; the protoblem.

primary uredinium (uredium). A stylosporic or uredinioid aecium usually without a peridium or paraphyses resembling a uredium but from its place in the life cycle and its mode or origin being a true aecium, a true uredium which arises from an aeciosporic infection. The uredia from urediosporic infections are secondary uredia.

primary vascular bundle. A vascular bundle formed from a procambial strand.

primary wall. The wall of a meristematic cell which is modified during differentiation. It is not to be confused with the thin, anisotropic, first-formed part of the secondary wall.

primary wood. Primary xylem, the wood developed from the procambium, the first-formed xylem developed from apical meristem.

primary xylem. Primary wood formed without cambial activity.

primeval forest. A virgin forest which has kept its original character undisturbed by man.

primine. The outer coat of an ovule, the outer integument of an ovule called the testa in the seed.

primitive. Applied to the first developed specific types in contrast to varieties and hybrids, primordial.

primitive sex cells. The earliest recognizable progenitors of the sex cells in development.

primitive spindle. An embryo with polarity.

primitive wall. A boundary between the ooplasm and the periplasm of the oosphere in *Cystopus Bliti*.

primofilices. A group of fern-like plants presumed to be the progenitors of the true ferns.

primordial. Of the first order, basic, analogous to Mendelian unit characters, in the earliest condition of a member or organ.

primordial cell. A naked cell without a cell wall.

primordial covering. The outer layer of very young carpophores, the primordial cuticle, the blematogen.

primordial epidermis. The epidermis when first formed.

primordial germ cells. The cells set apart during the early development of the embryo from which the definite germ cells of the future organism are to be derived.

primordial hypha. The very intensely colored hypha in *Russulaceae* which differs from other hyphae of the epicutis, the velum hypha.

primordial leaf. The first leaf to succeed the cotyledons.

primordial meristem. A tissue composed of thin-walled, undifferentiated cells located at the extremity of a root or shoot which produces elongation and other growth in this area.

primordial shaft. The initial monaxial conical state of the developing fruit body, especially in the *Clavariaceae*.

primordial tissue. Ground tissue.

primordial utricle. The outer layer of cell protoplasm which lines the inner surface of a vacuolated cell, ectoplasm.

primordial veil. The protoblem in angiocarpic and gymnocarpic species; a light, flocculose, delicate and fungacious layer of the primordium of the carpophore which arises from the mycelium. It is often confused with the universal veil.

primordium. The earliest development of any structure or organ. A rudiment, an Anlage.

primospore. A spore little differentiated from the ordinary cells of the organism.

primrose. Any plant or flower of the genus *Primula*.

primuletum. An association of *Primula*.

primulifolious. Primrose-leaved.

primulinous. Primrose-like, primrose yellow.

primuloid. Primrose-like.

prisere. A primary sere, the previous development of a succession.

prismatic layer. A layer of cells in *Isoetes* surrounding the xylem cylinder.

prismatocarpous. With prism-shaped fruit.

prismenchyma. Prismatic cellular tissue.

prison flowers. Flowers which imprison their insect visitors until fertilization is effected.

pro-. A prefix meaning before in time or place.

proanthostrobilus. The flower of the hypothetical ancestors of the angiosperms.

proangiosperm. A fossil type of angiosperm.

proanthesis. Flowering before the normal period as in the case of spring flowers blossoming in autumn.

probasid. An organ intermediate between a basidium and a sporophore in basidiomycetes bearing a teleutospore.

probasidiomycetes. The basidiomycetes producing probasidia, i.e., the heterobasidiomycetes (frequently including all of the basidiomycetes except the hymenomycetes and the gasteromycetes).

probasidium. The primary vesiculose body in the heterobasidiomycetes.

proboscideus. 1. Having a large terminal horn, as the fruit of *Martynia*. 2. Proboscis-like.

procambial strand. The primordium of the vascular tissues.

procambium. A group of elongated apical meristematic cells arranged in strands from which the xylem and phloem in the vascular bundles develop. When some cambium remains between the xylem and phloem, the bundle is open and continues to develop. A closed bundle is one which has no remaining cambium.

procarp. The female reproductive organ of the gametophyte in certain red algae, an archicarp with a special receptive apparatus, the trichogyne.

procerous. Tall and slim.

process. A protuberance, outgrowth, or projection from a surface.

prochondriomes. Chromatic granules more or less globular in shape and probably derived from the nucleolus, prochondriosomes.

prochosium. A succession in an alluvial soil.

prochromatin. The plasmosome substance, the substance of nucleoli, the chromatic substance in diffused and modified condition.

prochromogen. A colorless substance in some plants which in the presence of an enzyme becomes a chromogen which in turn can produce color in certain chemical combinations.

prochromosomes. Specific segments of chromosomes which appear as dense, deeply staining bodies during interphase and are thought to be tightly coiled chromosome regions; chromocenters.

proclimax areas. Relics of original climaxes somewhat modified by human agencies and introductions.

procormophyta. The flora of the *Devonian Period*.

procryptic. Having coloration adapted for concealment.

procumbent. Prostrate but not taking root at the nodes, lying on the ground, trailing.

procumbent cells. Medullary ray cells with their largest diameter radially directed.

procumbent ray cell. A ray cell with its longest axis radial.

procurrent. Running through but not projecting.

prodophytium. An initial community, a pioneer community.

prodromous. Pioneering, as an exploratory

botanic study intended to be followed by a more complete treatise.

productum. A calcar, a spur.

proembryo. An embryonic structure preceding the true embryo.

proembryonic branch. In *Chara*, a propagative body having the structure of a proembryo arising from a node of the stem.

proenzyme. An incompletely developed enzyme, a precursor of an enzyme.

proferment. A substance from which an enzyme is formed or a substance which is necessary for its action, a zymogen.

profile chart. The diagrammatic record of vertical relations of the vegetation.

profile position. The position assumed by leaves when the edge of the structure is turned toward the brightest light.

progametal. Having the nature of a progamete.

progametange. A resting body in *Protomyces macrosporus*, a lateral branch which forms a gametangium and a suspensor cell.

progametangium. A hypha from which a gametangium is subsequently cut off by a transverse septum.

progametation. The act of synkaryons becoming progametes.

progamete. A cell which gives rise to gametes, usually by division.

progametophyte. A plant which produces progametes.

progamic. Before fertilization.

progamic cell. A cell which is formed in the pollen grain which has the sperm nucleus.

progemmation. The process in which stylospores are given off from basidia, new terminal cells being developed from older or basal cells.

progeoesthetic. Applied to the root tip when it extends downward.

progeotropism. Positive geotropism.

prognathous. With anthers projecting forward at the base.

progonotaxis. The scheme of ancestral development.

progrediens. Growing at one part and dying at the rear.

progression. The evolution of an inflorescence by progressive expansion in the sequence of development.

progressive inflorescence. An indeterminate inflorescence in which the whorls are widely separated.

progressive metamorphosis. The change resulting when organs appear in an ascending scale, as petals replaced by stamens, etc.

progymnosperms. Prototypic gymnosperms, as *Bennettites*.

prohepatic. In a hypothetical original thalloid state of the higher plants.

prohybrid. A mycelium whose nuclear content has been increased by hyphal fusions and nuclear migrations.

prohydrotropism. Positive hydrotropism, the turning toward a source of moisture.

prolycopod. A hypothetical ancestor of vascular plants itself derived from the prohepatic form.

proiospory. Prospory.

projectura. A small longitudinal projection of a stem where the leaf originates.

prokaryogamete. The nucleus of a primary progamete.

prokaryogametisation. A quantitative reduction.

prokinesis. The early stage of nuclear division up to the aster.

prolate. Drawn out towards the poles, elongated in a polar direction.

prole. Progeny, race, species, or subspecies.

prolepsis. Accelerated development, as in the disease known as peach yellows where axillary buds develop into branches the first year.

prolepticus. Precocious.

proletarian. A plant having only a small reserve of material and which is self-fertilized, a proletariat.

proletariat. Proletarian.

proliferous. Producing offshoots, bearing abnormal supernumerary parts.

prolific cells. Disjointed cells of the thallus of *Pithophora* which serve as a means of vegetation propagation, reproductive cells.

prolification. 1. The production of terminal or lateral leaf buds in a flower. 2. The development in a prolific and proliferous manner.

proligerous. Proliferous, bearing reproductive bodies of any kind.

promeristem. The meristem of the growing point and embryonic rudiments.

prometetropic. Fertilizing an ovary with pollen from a different plant, interchanging pollen between plants.

prometaphase. The phase in somatic mitosis when the chromosomes thicken and begin to uncoil, the spindle begins to appear, and the membrane disrupts.

promitosis. A primitive type of mitosis in protista in which the whole process is intranuclear, asters are absent, and a large karyosome is present.

promunturium. A rocky sea shore.

promycete. A promycelium, the short-lived product of tube germination of a spore which abjoints a few spores unlike the mother spore and then perishes.

promycelial spore. A spore produced from a promycelium, a spore generated in an ascus.

promycelium. A short germ tube put out by some fungus spores on which are produced a few spores (unlike the mother spore) which are soon abstricted. The tube then dies.

prong cells. Parenchymatous cells of a special form containing silica bodies.

pronucleus. The nucleus of a gamete, one of the gametic nuclei within the egg after the entrance of the sperm but before cleavage.

proodophytia. An initial plant formation or a pioneer initial community.

proophioglossum. An assumed ancestral form of the fern *Ophioglossum*.

prop. A stipule, a part from the stem above ground entering the soil for mechanical support.

prop root. A root which serves as a prop or support to the plant, as in the mangrove.

propaculum. A shoot for propagation.

propaculiferous. Bearing offsets.

propagation. The asexual reproduction or multiplication of plants.

propagines. A bulblet, a branch bent down for layering.

propogule. 1. A bud, bulblet, gemmule, stolon, etc., of a plant capable of asexual propagation. 2. One of the powdery organs of lichens that constitute the soredia. 3. One of the three-pronged reproductive bodies of the *Atichiaceae*.

proper exciple. An exciple with an upward continuation of the hypothecium devoid of algal cells.

proper juice. Characteristic fluid of a plant, as the milk of lettuce, as distinct from sap.

proper margin. The hyphal margin surrounding the apothecium.

proper valves. Spathe valves.

properimeristem. Permeristem, the young cortex in a nascent condition.

prophase. The preliminary stages in mitosis or meiosis leading to the formation of the asteroid, the stage in cell division prior to the metaphase during which the chromosomes appear in the nucleus after the resting stage, the first stage in karyokinesis.

prophasis. A term for the stages in cell division including the prophase and the metaphase.

prophloem. 1. Protophloem, the first-formed elements of phloem in a fibrovascular bundle. 2. The cylinder of elongated cells with thickened walls occurring in the seta of some mosses around the protoxylem.

prophototaxis. The turning toward the light.

prophototropism. Positive phototropism, motion toward the center of the radiating light.

prophylaxis. The prevention of infection.

prophyll. A bracteole.

prophyllatous. Having prophylla.

prophylloid. Like prophylla.

prophyllum. A primary leaf of an axis or branch, a small bract, or the bracteole at the base of an individual flower.

prophysis. Prosphysis.

prophytogams. Cryptogams.

proplastid. 1. A young plant as it occurs in meristematic cells. 2. A minute granule in cytoplasm definitely concerned with the formation of chloroplasts.

propolis. A resinous material collected by the hive bees from the opening buds of various trees.

propositus. An individual through which a pedigree is established.

propteridophyta. Procormophyta.

pros. Positive phenomena.

prosaerotaxis. The stimulus of oxygen on the movement of zoospores and other motile organisms.

proschemotaxis. The attraction to certain substances shown by bacteria, antherozoids, etc.

proscolla. The retinaculum in orchids.

prosembryum. The perispermium.

prosenchyma. The tissue composed of elongated cells with tapering dovetailing ends which usually fit together closely without intercellular spaces. The cell walls are thick and afford mechanical support for the stems of higher plants. They are the wood cells.

prosenchymatic elements. Spindle-shaped elements with two or more pointed ends.

prosenthesis. The arrangement of whorled flowers with a gap between two successive whorls. Generally the divergence of the gap is greater than that of the whorl.

prosere. A formation composed of ephemeral communities that are not essential parts of the true successional series which is to follow (the autogenic main sere).

prosgalvanotaxis. Galvanotaxis.

prosgeotropism. Positive geotropism.

prosheliotropism. The turning of a plant or organ to the source of light.

proshydrotaxis. Negative osmotaxis.

prosoplasm. Pathologic tissues caused by parasites, as in galls.

prosoplasy. Hypertrophy, new histological characteristics and functional activities associated with hyperplasia.

prosoplectenchyma. A modified hyphal tissue.

prosorus. A body developed from a zoospore in a cell of *Synchytrium* into nucleus cytoplasm and outer membrane.

prososmotaxis. The movement of motile organisms because of the influence of fluids.

prospective significance. The actual destiny of a cell or organ in the development processes regardless of the potentialities.

prosphototaxis. A definite arrangement as the result of the action of light on organisms capable of response.

prosphysis. The abortion of pistillidia in the mosses.

prosporangium. 1. The initial cell which forms the vesicle which functions as a sporangium. 2. In *Chytridiales*, the vesicular cell the protoplasm of which passes into an outgrowth of itself (the sporangium) and becomes divided into swarm spores.

prospory. The precocious development of spores in certain algae.

prostady. The early fruiting in certain algae.

prostelic. Having an axis consisting of a single concentric bundle.

prosthermotaxis. The movement of bacteria or zoospores toward heat.

prosthigmotaxis. Thigmotaxis.

prostypus. A raphe.

protalbumose. One of the primary albumoses which is soluble in hot or cold water.

protandrism. The maturation of the anthers

before the pistils in the same flower, protandry.

protanthesis. The normal initial flowering of an inflorescence.

protase. The hypothetical first enzyme of the archebiotic process.

protaxis. The innate tendency of one organism or cell to react in a definite manner to another organism or cell.

proteaceous. Relating to or resembling the *Proteaceae*.

protease. A proteolytic enzyme.

protecting organs. The calyx and corolla (the perianth).

protective layer. The layer of suberized cells composing the leaf scar.

protective potential. The ability of an organism to protect itself against the dynamic forces of the environment.

protective sheath. The endodermis.

proteid. The nitrogenous material of plant cells.

proteid basis. The portion of protoplasm which is not composed of granules.

proteid granules. Reserve materials such as aleurone granules.

proteid vacuoles. The nuclei of cells of the tapetal layer in gymnosperms.

protein. A complex compound of oxygen, hydrogen, carbon, and nitrogen with traces of other elements; an albuminous substance which is an essential constituent of the living cell for food and growth.

protein crystal. Protein bodies in the form of crystals.

protein grain. An aleurone grain.

proteinaceous. Pertaining to or composed of protein.

proteine. Protein.

proteism. The ability of lower organisms to change shape, as in the flagellate myxomycetes.

proteolytic enzyme. An enzyme active in breaking down protein.

proton. Protenchyma, all tissue not of the fibrovascular system.

protenchyma. Fundamental or ground tissue.

protenema. The green filamentous phase of the gametophyte in mosses.

proteobacteria. Bacteria which are able to transform nitrogen compounds into protein.

proteochemotropic. Attracted by protease.

proteoclastic. Breaking down proteins.

proteofication. The breaking down of protein.

proteohydrolysis. The hydrolysis of proteids.

proteoid. Having sclerous cells as in the leaves of *Protea*.

proteolysis. The breaking up of proteids by enzymes.

proteoses. Protein derivatives found in gluten which are soluble in water but not coagulated by heat.

proteosomes. Granular precipitations in the cells which are caused by the action of certain alkaloids such as caffeine.

proteosynthesis. The formation of proteids.

proterandrous. Having the anther ripen before the pistil in the same flower.

proteranthous. Forming flowers before foliage leaves appear.

proterocladous. Having a rudimentary branch division.

proterogynous. Having the pistils receptive before the anthers contain ripe pollen.

proteropetalous. Having obdiplostemonous flowers in which the epipetalous whorl of stamen is the inner one.

proterosepalous. Proteropetalous.

proterotype. A primary type.

Proterozoic. The geological era before Paleozoid, the age of primitive invertebrates.

prothallatae. The mosses and vascular cryptogams.

prothallial cells. The two cells in *Cycads* one of which gives rise to the antheridial cell.

prothallial tubes. Embryo sac tubes.

prothalliform. Resembling a prothallus.

prothalline. Prothalloid.

prothallium. The prothallus, the gametophyte in ferns, a thalloid oophyte or its homologue, the protoneme.

prothallium, bulbous. A fleshy or tuberous prothallium.

prothallium, flattened. A filamentous or flattened prothallus.

prothallogamia. Vascular cryptogams.

prothallogams. Vascular cryptogams.

prothalloid. Pertaining to or resembling a prothallus.

prothallus. A prothallium.

prothecium. A primitive or rudimentary perithecium.

protista. The group of primitive organisms from which plants and animals arose, the protobionta.

protoaecium. A haploid structure in rusts which develops into an aecium after the fusion of the flexuous hyphae with pycniospores or spermatia.

protistoid. Like the protista.

protistology. The study of the protista.

protists. Protista.

proto-. A prefix meaning first, earliest, or primordial.

protobasidiomycetes. Fungi with septate basidia, as the *Uredinales* and *Tremellales*.

protobasidium. A basidium which is divided by transverse septa into four cells from each of which a sporidium develops by abstriction.

protobenthos. The earliest ocean bottom vegetation, protobenthon.

protobiont. A primitive being, a protophyte.

protoblast. A naked cell without a membrane.

protoblem. A loose flocculent layer covering the teleblem of *Amanita* and *Amanitopsis*, sometimes called the primary universal veil.

protobroch. The resting nuclei of gones in the resting stage.

protocaulome. The first axis of a plant which is frequently evanescent.

protochlorophyll. A pigment found in etiolated leaves with carotin and xanthophyll.

protochlorophylline. A product resulting from the reduction of the green substance of chlorophyll.

protochromosome. A variable number of chromatophile granulations which at the end of the prophase unite into two chromosomes.

protococcaceus. Of *Protococcus*.

protococcoid. Resembling the alga *Protococcus*.

protocollenchyma. The earliest formed elements of collenchyma.

protoconidium. A spherical, globose-to-clavate cell at the apex of a filament which later divides to form several hemispores or deuteroconidia.

protocorm. A tuber of *Phylloglossum* and other lycopods.

protoderm. Dermatogen, the primary meristem which develops into the epidermis, the rudimentary dermal tissue.

protoderma state. A culture state of *Protococcus* which resembles *Protoderma*.

protodoche. A primary association of plants, a prisere.

protoepiphytes. Strictly epiphytic plants, species which must acquire food from the surface of the supporting structure and directly from the atmosphere.

protogamy. The union of gametes without fusion of their nuclei.

protogene. The dominant or *A* element in inheritance.

protogenesis. Reproduction by budding.

protogenic. Persistent from the beginning of development, formed in the beginning.

protogonidium. The first generation in a succession of gonidia.

protograph. The original specimen of a species or variety.

protogynous. With receptive stigmas before the anthers open.

protohadrome. The protoxylem.

protohemicryptophytes. Plants whose aerial shoots have scales or undeveloped leaves at the base and fully developed leaves toward the middle of the stem.

protohymenial. Having a primitive type of hymenium in which the new basidia arise directly on the secondary mycelium and gradually force their basic tissue between the older basidia.

protokaryon. A simple nucleus which consists of chromatin suspended in the nuclear sap.

protoleptome. The protophloem.

protolog. The original description of a genus, species, or variety.

protolysis. The splitting or decomposition of proteins.

protomeristem. The meristem of the growing point which forms the foundation of an organ or organism.

protomerite. Primite.

protomonostelic. Having a stem or root which has a protostele or central cylinder.

protomorphic. Primordial.

protomycelium. A formative protoplasmic mass formed as mycelial filaments between the cells of parasitic fungi or in the intercellular spaces.

protonema. The green filamentous gametophyte in mosses which produce leafy sexual branches.

protonematoid. Like a protonema.

protonta. Ultramicroscopic organisms differing fundamentally from bacteria.

protophloem. The part of the phloem bundle which is developed earliest and differentiated during longitudinal growth, the first phloem tissue produced from the procambium.

protophyll. A leaf borne by a protocorm, a primary leaf of a cryptogam.

protophylline. Protochlorophylline.

protophyt. A plant of the sexual generation.

protophyte. A unicellular organism or primitive plant, a protophyton.

protophytia. The initial stages of succession in plant growths.

protophytology. 1. The study of unicellular plants. 2. The study of primitive plants, paleobotany. 3. The study of prototypes.

protoplasm. The physical basis of life, the living jelly-like contents of plant cells, a chemical compound or probably an emulsion of numerous compounds providing the basis of the vital processes in living cells.

protoplasm, active. The androplasm of male gametes.

protoplasm, passive. The protoplasm of the female gamete, gynoplasm.

protoplasmic respiration. Respiration at the expense of protein materials in a starved plant.

protoplast. The protoplasmic contents of a cell, a unit of protoplasm which is capable of individual action, the cytoplasm and nucleus of a cell.

protoplastid. An individual of presumably primitive type.

protoplastin. A hypothetic substance, the ultimate source of vital movement and chemical combination.

protopteridophyta. The primitive group of pteridophytes from which the known orders may have been derived.

protos-. A prefix meaning first.

protosclerenchyma. Collenchyma which resembles true hard bast, provisional collenchyma.

protosiphonogamic. Having the pollen of certain gymnosperms germinate on the ligule or cone scale before passing to the micropyle.

protosome. An assumed central structure in a gene (which is also a hypothetical body).

protospore. 1. A spore of the first generation. 2. A spore which develops a promycelium.

protosporophyte. A cryptogam not otherwise defined.

protostele. A solid stele, a stele with a solid xylem core.

protostely. The possession of a protostele.

protostrophe. A secondary spiral in the development of leaves.

protothallogamae. Angiosperms, gymnosperms, and vascular cryptogams.

protothallus. A hypothallus, the first-formed stratum of a lichen.

prototroph. A symbiont in *Lecidia intumescens* which eventually gets its nourishment by means of another symbiont in a different lichen.

prototrophic. Requiring no organic compounds for nourishment.

prototrophism. The peculiar state of commensalism in prototrophs, sometimes called the "wet nurse" relationship; prototrophy; protrophy.

prototype. An original type of species, an ancestral form, an archetype.

protoxylem. The first-formed xylem with tracheary elements characterized by annular or spiral thickening.

protozoophilous. Fertilized by the protozoa which carry the pollen to certain water plants.

protozygote. A homozygote possessing the dominant AA- elements in inheritance.

protrophy. Prototrophy.

protropic. With movement toward the stimulus.

provaccine. A preparation of dead bacteria for immunization purposes.

provascular. Primordial to the fibrovascular tissue.

provenance. The geographical source or place of origin of a seed or plant.

province. 1. A subdivision of a region characterized by at least one climax community and by various edaphic communities. 2. An area in which climate tends to dominance, as of woodland or moorland.

provincialis. Of Provence, southern France.

provine. To layer a vine.

provirus. A particle in the cytoplasm which may develop into a virus.

proximal. Nearest the axis, nearest the point of attachment.

proxylar. Capable of forming wood.

proxylem. The first-formed xylem in a bundle, proxyle, protoxylem.

prozymogen. The precursor of zymogen activated by secretin.

pruina seminalis. The spores of certain fungi.

pruinate. Pruinose, covered with a bloom or powder.

prunase. An enzyme present in many species of *Prunus*.

prunasin. A glucose associated with prunase.

prunelloid. Like *Prunella*.

prunetum. An association of various shrubby forms of *Prunus spinosa*.

pruniferous. Bearing plums.

prunifolious. Plum-leaved.

pruniform. Plum-shaped.

pruninus. Plum color.

psamathad. A strand plant.

psamathium. A strand formation on the sand of a seashore.

psamathophilous. Strand-loving.

psamathophyte. A strand plant.

psammarch. An adsere starting on sand.

psammetum. A grass association of *Psamma arenaria* on sand dunes.

psammic. Growing on sand or gravel.

psammogenity. The percentage of sand in the soil affecting the plants growing in it.

psammogenous. Producing a sandy soil.

psammophile. A plant of light sandy soil, a plant preferring sandy soils for its growth.

psammophilous. Living on sand.

psammophyte. A plant growing in dry sandy ground.

psammophytia. A sand or sandstone plant formation.

psammosere. A loose sandy adsere, a sere having its origin on sand.

pseud-, pseuda-, pseudo-. A prefix meaning false.

pseudacranthic. Having apparent terminal flowers from dichasial shoots.

pseudannual. A plant which completes its growth within a single season but survives winter by means of bulbs, corms, tubers, etc.

pseudannulus. An apparent annulus of specialized cells exterior to the peristome in mosses.

pseudanthic. Simulating a simple flower but composed of more than a single axis with subsidiary flowers.

pseudanthis. The condition of being pseudanthic.

pseudapogamy. A replacement of a normal fusion of sexual nuclei by a fusion of two female nuclei or of a female nucleus and a vegetative nucleus or by two vegetative nuclei.

pseudapogamy, facultative. Pseudapogamy which occurs occasionally.

pseudapogamy, obligate. Essential pseudopogamy.

pseudaposematic. Having mimetic and attracting coloration.

pseudapospore. A diploid spore formed without meiosis.

pseudaxillary. The condition in which the terminal bud apparently becomes axillary by the growth of lateral buds.

pseudaxis. The apparent main axis, the sympodium, the monochasium.

pseudembryo. A group of cells cut off in the endosperm of *Balanophora.*

pseudhomonymic. With partial homonymy.

pseudinulin. A subordinate constituent of inulin from roots and tubers.

pseudoadventice. Arrested at a very early age.

pseudoaethalium. A cluster of separate and distinct sporangia in myxomycetes which simulates an aethalium.

pseudoalveolar. Containing starch grains, as deutoplasm spheres.

pseudoamitosis. An unusual nuclear division induced in cells by treating them with poison.

pseudoangiocarps. Gymnocarpic species in which the hymenium is at first gymnocarpic and then continues its development covered by a pseudoveil of secondary origin which disappears later.

pseudoannual. An herb which lives over winter as a tuber or bulb.

pseudoaquatic. Thriving in moist ground.

pseudoautoiceous. Dioicous but occasionally autoicous, as some mosses.

pseudoberry. A fleshy fruit which looks like a berry but in which some of the succulent material is derived from the enlarged persistent perianth.

pseudobiatorine. Without a conspicuous thalline margin and therefore falsely biatorine.

pseudobulb. The fleshy base or corm in many epiphytic orchids, the aerial corm in epiphytic orchids.

pseudobulbil. An outgrowth from the base or roots of certain plants, especially ferns, which replaces the sporangium in apospory.

pseudobulbous. Adapted to xerophytic conditions by the development of pseudobulbs.

pseudocalcareous. Growing on clay, slate, etc.

pseudocambium. A meristematic tissue which resembles cambium.

pseudocapillitium. A plate, tube, or thread-like body in the fructification of myxomycetes which is not developed in direct connection with the sporogenous protoplasm but represents the outer region of the plasmodial veins or the walls of the constituent sporangia in a pseudoaethalium.

pseudocarp. A false fruit, a fruit derived from parts other than the ovary.

pseudocellulose. See CELLULOSE.

pseudocephalodium. A growth formed in the prothallus by a germinating hypha investing an algal colony of some type other than the normal gonidia of the lichen.

pseudochromatin. Prochromatin.

pseudochromosomes. Amalgamations of chromatin into filaments which pass into a spireme stage and then segment into chromosomes.

pseudocilium. Motionless whip-like bodies occurring in pairs from each cell of *Apiocystis Brauniana.*

pseudocleistogamy. The condition in which flowers remain closed but the genitalia are normal in size and function.

pseudocolumella. A mass of limeknots in certain myxomycetes which are confluent in the center of the sporangium and resemble a columella yet remain free from the stalk.

pseudoconchoid. A curve in phyllotaxis.

pseudocormophytes. Mosses.

pseudocortex. A cortex devoid of cellular structure commonly showing well defined and more or less gelatinized hyphae.

pseudocostate. With marginal nervation where the veins are united in an outer vein parallel to the margin.

pseudocotyledon. A proembryo.

pseudocotyledoneae. The vascular cryptogams.

pseudocyphella. A pit-like structure similar to a cyphella on the underside of some lichens; a pulverulent, sparingly sorediate, excavated point in the undersurface of lichens.

pseudocyst. A green protoplasmic body

which has no cell walls in the *Protococcoideae*.

pseudodichotomy. The monopodial production of lateral axes from the segments of a dominant three-sided apical cell, fake division.

pseudodystrophy. The condition of gaining access to nectar by secondary means, as when bees bore into the nectaries instead of entering by the opening of the flower.

pseudoelaters. The sterile cells in the spore capsule of *Anthoceros* which form a netted tissue and later break up into a more or less connected chain.

pseudoephemer. A flower which lasts a little over a day and then closes.

pseudoepinasty. Geotropism.

pseudoepiphyte. A plant whose stems die away at the base, the upper part then deriving its nourishment from its aerial roots.

pseudofecundation. The process in which two of the four nuclei combine to form the egg and the other two form the albumen.

pseudofertility. The condition in self-sterile plants of a mere environmental fluctuation having nothing to do with heredity.

pseudofoliaceous. Having expansions resembling leaves.

pseudogametange. A swelling in ascomycetes from which gametophores develop.

pseudogamy. The union of two vegetative cells which are not closely related; parthenogenetic fruiting, as pollination without impregnation of ovules; pseudosexual copulation of cells not differentiated for reproduction.

pseudogenus. A form-genus, a so-called genus constituted of similar form-species.

pseudogeogenous. Intermediate between dysgeogenous and eugeogenous rocks, Yoredale limestone.

pseudogranular. Simulating granulation.

pseudogymnosperm. A cycadeoid plant.

pseudogyratous. Falsely ringed, as when the annulus is confined to the apex of the sporangium in ferns.

pseudohaustorium. An immature or rudimentary organ seen in the seedlings of *Cuscuta*, dodder.

pseudohermaphrodite. A flower which has become unisexual functionally because of the suppression of either stamens or pistils.

pseudohermaphroditism. The condition

when spermatogenous filaments are found in the oogonium, as in *Nitella*.

pseudohybridation. The production of hybrids which are practically the same as either parent and show no signs of crossing.

pseudohymenium. A covering of sporidia resembling the hymenium of fungi.

pseudoidia. Disarticulated cells which may germinate.

pseudoimpregnation. The coalescence of the two nuclei of the cells of a teleutospore.

pseudolamina. 1. The expanded apical portion of a phyllode. 2. The leaf blade of the monocotyledons regarded as a petiolar phyllome.

pseudolatex. An abundant gummy juice, white or colorless, which is found in some species of vanilla.

pseudoleucodermis. A periclinal chimaera in *Arabis* and *Glechoma*, in which the seedlings have a white subepidermal layer.

pseudoliber. Libriform tissue which is derived from secondary meristem without genetic affinity with the cambium or vascular bundles.

pseudolichen. A lichen which does not possess an algal layer of its own but is parasitic on another lichen thallus.

pseudolobes. Palm leaf segments which were torn during development.

pseudomacchia. Xerophilous evergreen scrub formation with juniper and evergreen oak predominating.

pseudomaqui. A xerophytic evergreen bush formation capable of withstanding a more severe winter than maqui, pseudomacchia.

pseudomeiosis. Pseudoreduction.

pseudomitosis. Showing one longitudinal and one seemingly or false transverse division of the tetrad, falsely or seemingly diaschistic.

pseudomitosis. Nuclear division in which the chromatin in the spireme stage becomes granular instead of forming chromosomes, nuclear division intermediate between mitosis and amitosis.

pseudomitotic. Pseudomeiotic.

pseudomixis. The fusion of two vegetative cells or two gametes that are not differentiated as gametes.

pseudomonocarpy. In cycads, the occurrence of mature cones embedded in the trunk, the seeds not being shed until the death of the tree.

pseudomonocotyledon. A dicotyledon, as *Capsella*, in which one cotyledon aborts.

pseudomonocotyledonous embryo. An embryo in which one embryo develops although two were originally started.

pseudomorph. An individual which has an unusual or altered form.

pseudomorphytus. A capitate inflorescence which affects the form of the capitulum in the *Compositae*.

pseudomucelium. Loosely united chains of cells (as in yeasts) which resemble mycelium which is composed of hyphae.

pseudomycorrhiza. False mycorrhiza in which the fungus is decidedly parasitic.

pseudonemathecium. A medullary nemathecium in algae believed to be parasitic.

pseudonodule. A space on a diatom valve resembling a nodule but not thickened and devoid of markings.

pseudonuclein. Paranuclein.

paeudonucleole. A cyanophilous nucleole.

pseudonucleolus. A knot or granule in the nuclear reticulum which is not a true nucleolus.

pseudonucleus. A cavity containing chromatin masses surrounded by a definite membrane during cytomixis.

pseudoostiole. A false ostiole not formed in the characteristic manner but lysigenously.

pseudoparaphysis. An organ growing in association with paraphyses but of much greater development.

pseudoparasite. A false parasite, either a saprophyte or an epiphyte.

pseudoparemchyma. 1. False parenchyma, tissue which resembles parenchyma. 2. Hyphae of fungi which are divided into short cells and resemble parenchyma in arrangement.

pseudoperculum. A structure which resembles an operculum or closing membrane.

pseudoperianth. The cup-shaped envelope covering the archegonium which develops after fertilization in some *Hepaticae*.

pseudoperidium. 1. A false peridium. 2. The cup or container of an aecidium.

pseudoperithecium. A false perithecium.

pseudopetal. One of the numerous petal-like constituents of the corolla in *Mesembryanthemum*.

pseudophelloid. Cork-like.

pseudophotometric. Not conforming to the action of light.

pseudophyll. The sheathing bract of certain bamboos which falls off when the leaves develop.

pseudophyllodic. Having semioverlapping leaves as *Phormium*, the New Zealand flax.

pseudophyllopodous. With the lower leaves of a normally aphyllopodous species more or less oppressed to the ground.

pseudophysis. A paraphysoid structure of the *Cyphellaceae* which is thin-walled, smooth, swollen at the top, and moniliform.

pseudopinnate. Falsely or imperfectly pinnate, with the leaflets not articulated at the base.

pseudoplankton. Organisms accidentally floating.

pseudoplasmodium. A mass of closely associated myxamoeba which have not united to form a true plasmodium, a false plasmodium.

pseudopleuston. The pollen of conifers floating in quantity.

pseudopod. 1. A protrusion of protoplasm in the slime molds which may be drawn in or into which the whole mass may move. 2. A false foot. 3. The elongation of the false pedicel of the vaginule of the capsule of *Sphagnum*.

pseudopodetium. A stalk-like assimilative structure bearing the apothecia in some lichens which is derived from the thaline tissue. (A true podetium differs in being derived from the basal tissue of the ascocarp).

pseudopodia. False feet like the temporary projections of the protoplasm of the myxamoeba.

pseudopodiospore. An amoebula or amoeboid swarm-spore which moves by means of pseudopodia.

pseudopodium. 1. A projection of protoplasm used by protozoans for locomotion. 2. A false foot or pedicel, a false seta.

pseudopolyembryony. The occurrence of either (a) coalescence of ovules, (b) division of the nucellus, or (c) development of several embryo sacs in one nucellus.

pseudopores. In *Sphagnum*, thickened rings without perforations.

pseudoposematic colors. Protective mimicry.

pseudoprosenchyma. Tissue of fine elongated hyphae somewhat resembling the prosenchyma of higher plants.

pseudopycnidial. Plectenchymatous.

pseudopycnium. A more or less pycnidiod structure formed of hyphal tissue in the *Fungi Imperfecti.*

pseudopyrenium. The perithecium of certain fungi.

pseudoramose. Having false branches.

pseudoramulus. A spurious branch in certain algae.

pseudoraphe. An apparent raphe in diatoms before its disappearance.

pseudoreduction. The apparent reduction or halving of chromosome number by pairing or fusion of homologous chromosomes during the later prophase of nuclear division which precedes actual reduction.

pseudoreticulate. Falsely reticulate.

pseudorhiza. 1. A root shaped like a turnip or carrot in bulbous monocotyledons. 2. A rooting base as in the fungus *Collybia radicata.*

pseudosematic colors. False warning and signal coloration.

pseudoseptate. Falsely septate, not morphologically septate.

pseudoseptum. A septum which is perforated by one or more pores.

pseudoshrub. A growth-form resulting from the growth of suckers after cutting back.

pseudosperm. A false seed or carpel.

pseudospermic. Having a single seed so closely invested by the pericarp that the whole appears like a seed.

pseudospermium. A one-seeded fruit which is indehiscent and resembles a seed, such as an achene.

pseudospore. 1. A teliospore or winter spore of rusts. 2. A gemma or asexual vegetative bud. 3. A false or barren spore.

pseudostauros. A broadening of the stauros in some diatoms.

pseudostele. A petiole which assumes the conditions of a stem with a similar arrangement of tissues.

pseudostereous. Partly grown together, as bud scales in the crown imperial.

pseudostiole. A false ostiole.

pseudostipules. Lowermost leaflets in *Crataegus*, *Cineraria*, etc., the true stipules being parts of the leaf sheath.

pseudostoma. A temporary mouth or mouth-like opening of a pseudoosculum.

pseudostroma. A false stroma.

pseudostrophiole. A part of the floral axis which remains attached to the nutlets in *Labiatae.*

pseudosynaptic. Shrunk together, as in the synapsis of the nuclear filament in mitosis.

pseudosyncarp. A collective fruit.

pseudoterminal. Having intercalary inflorescence cease and a false terminal flower appear.

pseudothallus. 1. A false thallus. 2. The axis of a crowded inflorescence, as a glomerule or umbel.

pseudothecium. The globose perithecium-like fruit body possessed by most of the *Pseudosphaeriales* instead of an apothecium-like structure.

pseudotrichophore. A vegetative filament of algae which simulates a trichophore.

pseudotype. An erroneous indication of a type.

pseudounicellular. Apocytial.

pseudovacuoles. Dark reddish granules in the cytoplasm of certain *Cyanophyceae*, suspensory bodies.

pseudovascular. Apparently made up of vessels.

pseudovalve. A semisolid carpel splitting at maturity between the two vascular bundles of the midrib.

pseudovessels. The components of tissue containing vessels.

pseudovivipary. The condition in which leafy rooting shoots are produced in the floral region side by side with flowers.

pseudoxerophilous. Of a subxerophilous condition where the plants show less sensitiveness to moisture.

pseudoyeast. Any yeast which does not produce fermentation.

pseudozoogloeae. Clumps of bacteria not having the degree of compactness and gelatinization of *Zoogloeae.*

pseudozygospore. An azygospore.

psilad. A prairie plant.

psilic. Of savannah communities.

psilicolous. Prairie-dwelling.

psilile. Of a prairie.

psilium. A prairie community.

psilo-. A prefix meaning slender but more correctly used for bare or naked.

psilocolous. Psilophilous, inhabiting treeless prairies.

psilophilous. Prairie-loving.

psilophyte. A prairie plant.

psilostemon. A slender or naked stamen.

psilostachyous. With bare spikes.

psilotaceous. Resembling *Psilotum*.

psoriasiform. Scaly.

psorosperma. Parasitic organisms generally.

psychopilae. A group of plants pollinated by diurnal lepidoptera and possessing brightly colored flowers with nectar in the flower tube.

psychric. Of cold soil communities.

psychro-. A prefix meaning frost.

psychrocleistogamy. Cleistogamy resulting from lack of warmth.

psychrograph. A self-recording psychrometer giving simultaneous readings of the dry-bulb and the wet-bulb thermometer.

psychrokliny. The behavior of growing parts under the influence of low temperature.

psychrometer. An instrument for measuring humidity by the fall of temperature.

psychrophilic. Cold-loving.

psychrophyte. An alpine plant on soil which hinders root action by its temperature.

psycodes. Fragrant.

psydomorphytus. Pseudomorphytus.

ptarmicaefolius. *Ptarmica*-leaved.

ptarmicoid. *Ptarmica*-like.

ptenophyllium. A deciduous forest formation.

ptenophyllophilous. Dwelling in deciduous forests.

ptenophyllophyte. A deciduous forest plant.

ptenophytium. An intermediate community.

ptenothalium. A deciduous thicket community.

ptenothalophilous. Dwelling in deciduous thickets.

ptenothalophyte. A deciduous thicket plant.

ptenphyllium. A ptenophyllium.

pter-. A prefix meaning wing, feather, or fern.

pterampelid. A climbing fern.

pteranthous. Having winged flowers.

pterate. Winged.

ptereosere. A sere characterized by fossil *Pteridophyta*, a paleosere.

pterid. Allied to *Pteris*, the bracken fern.

pteriditum. An association of ferns.

pteridium. A winged fruit like that of the ash, elm, or maple, a key fruit or samara.

pteridographia. A treatise on ferns.

pteroid. Fern-like.

pteride. A samara.

pteridoid. *Pteris*-like.

pteridology. The study of ferns.

pteridoma. The body or substance of a fern.

Pteridophyta. One of the four major divisions of plants including the ferns and fern allies.

pteridophytic. Fern-like.

pteriosperm. A plant with obligatory and pterophytic seeds and monomorphic embryos, as the *Lepidostrobus*.

pteridospermaphyta. Pteridophytic seed-bearing fossil plants.

pteridum. A samara.

pterigynous. Winged.

pterocarpous. With winged fruits.

pterocaulous. Having stems with winged appendages.

pterodium. A samara.

pterogonous. Fern-like.

pteroid. Fern-like.

pteroneurous. With winged nerves.

pteropodous. Wing-footed, with winged petioles.

pteropsida. The ferns, gymnosperms, and angiosperms which have leaf-gaps in the stele.

pterosere. The eosere of the Paleozoic Period, a paleosere.

pterospermous. With winged seeds.

pterospore. A spore with winged disseminules.

pterygium. A wing.

pterygonous. Having winged expansions on the angles of the stem.

pterygopous. With a winged peduncle.

pterygospermous. Pterospermous.

pterygynous. With winged seeds.

ptomaine. A type of poisoning due to a nitrogenous base of substances formed in putrefaction, broadly used for any alkaloid produced by the activity of pathogenic bacteria.

ptyalin. The enzyme diastase of saliva which breaks down starch into sugar by fermentation.

ptychode. The primordial utricle.

ptychoid. With an outer surface of the primordial utricle.

ptyxis. The form in which young leaves are folded or rolled on themselves in the bud, vernation.

pubescent. Hairy or downy.

pubiflorous. With pubescent flowers.

pubinervis. With pubescent veins.

pucciniacous. Having the characteristics of the rust family *Pucciniaceae*.

puccinioid. Like *Puccinia*.

puccoon. A plant yielding a red pigment.

puff balls. The common name of globose

basidiomycetes with the property of discharging the ripe spores in a smoke-like cloud when struck or pressed, the *Lycoperdales*.

puffin. A puff ball.

puffing. The emission of spores in a cloud.

puffs. Pilidia in lichens.

pugioniform. Dagger-shaped.

pull root. A special form of root whose function is to contact and draw the plant deeper into the soil.

pullate. A blackish chestnut color.

pullulate. To bud, to germinate.

pulp. The soft fleshy mass of fruit.

pulpose. Pulpy, fleshy.

pulpwood. Soft wood used in making pulp.

pulsating vacuole. A contractile vacuole.

pulse. The edible seeds of various leguminous crops as peas, beans, etc.

pulsellum. A posterior flagellum of a zoospore.

pulsule. A large vacuole found in the *Dinophyceae* which has two canals leading to the outside that do not pulsate but do change in size.

pulvereo delitescent. Covered with a layer of powdery granules.

pulverulent. Covered as if with powder.

pulvilliform. Like a small cushion.

pulvillum. A hot bed in a botanic garden.

pulvinate. 1. In the form of a cushion. 2. Having a pulvinus.

pulvinulus. A simple or branched soredium on the surface of some lichens, a diminutive of pulvinus.

pulvinus. A swelling at the base of a petiole which frequently acts as a center of sensitivity or irritability in the leaf, a cushion.

pulviplume. A powder-down feather.

pulvisculus. The powder contained in the spore cases of some fungi.

pumilus. Dwarfed, short and dense in habit.

pummelo. *Citrus maximas* or *grandis*, grapefruit.

pump-form. Having concealed anthers, such as *Lotus*, *Coronilla*, and *Ononis*.

pumpkin. *Cucurbita pepo*.

puna. Rock and salt waste plateaus between the Cordilleras of the Andes; a cold, arid, tableland in the Andes in Peru.

puncta. The markings on the valves of diatoms.

punctate. Dotted as if by punctures, having translucent dots or glands.

punctation. A minute spot or depression.

puncticulate. Having very minute punctures or indented points, minutely punctate.

punctiflorous. With dotted flowers.

punctiform. In the form of a point or dot.

punctilobulous. With dotted lobes.

punctum vegetationis. The growing point.

puniceous. Crimson, carmine red, reddish purple.

purebred. A plant whose ancestry is registered on both sides.

pure breeding. Mating only plants of known pedigree.

pure culture. A culture of microorganisms consisting of members of one species.

pure forest. A forest of which more than 80% are of one species.

pure line. A population consisting of the individuals produced by strictly autogamous reproduction of one homozygous individual, a group of individuals derived solely from a common homozygous ancestor.

purpureous. Purple.

purpurescent. Becoming purple.

purpurine. A color principally in madder.

pusillaejuncetum. An association of small species of *Carex*.

pustular. Blister-like, covered with pustule-like prominences.

pustule. A small elevation or spot resembling a blister.

pusule. A small vacuole present in the protoplast of some lower plants which is able to expand and contract, a pusula.

pusule apparatus. The peculiar vacuole in the protoplast of certain *Peridiniae*.

pusule, collecting. A small specimen with a duct leading to the flagellar pore.

puszta. The grass steppes of Hungary.

putamen. The shell of a nut, the bony part of a stone fruit.

putaminaceous. With the texture of a stone or drupe.

putrescible. Fleshy and likely to decay.

pycnacanthous. Densely spined.

pycnanthous. Densely flowered.

pycnial lesion. A diseased area bearing pycnia or pycnidia.

pycnicole. An organism living on a pycnium or pycnidium.

pycnid. A cavity resembling a pyrenocarp in lichens, etc., containing gonidia (pycnogonidia).

pycnide. A pycnidium.

pycnidiophore. A compound sporophore bearing pycnidia.

pycnidiospore. The spore borne in a pycnidium or conidium.

pycnidium. A roundish fructification formed by many species of fungi, usually with an opening, and having a general resemblance to a perithecium. It contains fertile hyphae and pycnidiospores but no asci and has no apparent connection with any sex act.

pycniospores. A term applied, chiefly in America, to the spermatium in *Uredinales.*

pycnium. A term applied, chiefly in America, to the spermagonium of the *Uredinales.*

pycnocephalous. Thick-headed, as in the case when composite flower heads are clustered closely; with flowers densely crowded in an inflorescence.

pycnoconidium. A conidium produced in a pycnidium, a pycnidiospore, a stylospore.

pycnogonidium. A pycnoconidium.

pycnophytium. A closed formation or community.

pycnos-. A prefix meaning thick.

pycnosclerotia. Sclerotia bearing pycnidia.

pycnosis. 1. The formation of a perithecium under the cover of the tissue of a stroma. 2. The shrinkage of the stainable material of a nucleus into a deeply staining knot.

pycnospore. A spore formed inside a pycnidium, a spermatium, a stylospore.

pycnostachous. In thick or compact spikes.

pycnothecium. The fructification formed by pycnosis.

pycnoxylic wood. The compact wood characteristic of pine trees with little or no parenchyma.

pygmaeous. Dwarfed.

pyocyanase. The enzyme produced by *Bacillus pyocyaneus.*

pyogenic. Generating pus.

pyracanth. The evergreen fire-thorn shrub, *Cotoneaster Pyracantha.*

pyracanthous. With red or yellow spines.

pyrena. A nutlet, or the stone of a small drupe.

pyrenaicus. Of the Pyrenees.

pyrenarium. A pear fruit, a pome fruit which tapers, a nucule.

pyrene. A small, hard, stone-like seed in a fruit, as the stone in a cherry or the seed in huckleberry; a kernel, a piren.

pyreniform. Nut-shaped.

pyrenin. The substance or contents of a true nucleolus, the paranuclein.

pyrenium. The sporocarp of the fungus *Sphaeriales.*

pyrenocarp. 1. A cup-shaped ascocarp with an incurved margin so as to form a narrow-mouthed cavity, a perithecium. 2. Any drupaceous fruit.

pyrenodeous. Like a pyrenoid, wart-like.

pyrenodine. Globular and nuclear.

pyrenoid. 1. A small mass of refractive protein occurring in or on the chlorophyll structures in some lower plants which are concerned with the formation of carbohydrates. 2. A center of starch formation or storage in a chloroplast.

pyrenolichens. Lichens having perithecia.

pyrenomycetes. One of the major subdivisions of the *Ascomycetes,* mostly the small fungi. The characteristic fructification is a perithecium formed on the hyphae or developed in groups in a mass of hyphae known as stromas, which are dark brown or brightly colored; the *Sphaeriales.*

pyrenopsidian. Similar to the fungus genus *Pyrenopsis.*

pyrenous. Having pyrenes.

pyridion. The fruit of the pear, a tapering pome.

pyridium. A pome, a fruit like an apple or pear.

pyriferous. Pear-bearing.

pyrifolious. With pear-shaped leaves.

pyriform. Pear-shaped.

pyrium. A burn succession.

pyrophilous. Growing on burnt earth.

pyrophobe. A plant liable to destruction in forest fires and incapable of being replaced under the changed conditions.

pyrophyte. A tree having a thick, fire-resistant bark, thus escaping permanent damage from forest fires.

pyroxylophilous. Growing upon burnt wood.

pyrrhophyll. The coloring matter contained in the *Peridineae.*

pythmic. Of lake bottoms.

pyxidate. 1. Resembling or bearing a pyxidium. 2. Furnished with a lid. 3. Box-like or having the character of a pyxis (box).

pyxidium. A seed pod or capsule opening horizontally by means of a lid, a pyxis or capsular fruit which dehisces by a transverse circular ring.

pyxis. 1. A capsule having a circumscissile

dehiscence, the upper portion acting as a lid. 2. The theca of a moss. 3. A pyxidium. 4. A scyphus.

Q

quadrant. The quarter of an oospore which is divided by the quadrant wall.

quadrat. A square marked out for study of the vegetation contained in it.

quadrat chart. A diagram of a quadrat with the position of each plant marked.

quadrat, denuded. A quadrat with the original plants cleared away.

quadrat, major. A sample area of four square meters.

quadrat method. A method of enumerating or charting the individuals of a community within a circumscribed area registering the changes in population structure which are the record of development.

quadrat, permanent. A quadrat intended for study from year to year.

quadrate. Square or nearly square.

quadriauritus. With four ears.

quadricapsular. Having four capsules.

quadriciliated. Having four cilia.

quadricoccus. Of four round cells.

quadricolor. Of four colors.

quadricotyledonous. Having four cotyledons, each normal cotyledon divided at the base.

quadricrural. With four supports.

quadridentate. With four teeth.

quadridigitate. In four digitate divisions.

quadridigitatopinnatus. With four digitate divisions each of which is pinnate.

quadrieremus. A colony of independent organisms united by a common investment, as *Volvox*, a coenobium.

quadrifarious. In four ranks or rows.

quadrifid. 1. Deeply cleft into four parts. 2. Having four pairs of leaflets on the same axis.

quadrifid organ. The four long terminal cells arising from a collar at the apex of a pear-shaped cell in the bladder of *Utricularia*.

quadrifoliate. Having four leaflets diverging from the same point.

quadrifurcate. Dividing into four branches.

quadrigeminate. Growing in fours.

quadriglandular. Having four glands.

quadrihilatus. Having four apertures, as some pollen grains.

quadrijugate. Having four pairs of pinnate leaflets.

quadrilobate. With four lobes.

quadrilocular. Having four loculi or chambers, having four cells in the ovary.

quadrimaculate. Having four spots.

quadrinate. Quadrifoliate, with four leaflets at the end of a petiole in a digitate arrangement.

quadrinucleate. With four nuclei from the division of a binucleate cell.

quadripartite. Consisting of or divided into four parts.

quadripartition. Division into four parts, as the division of a spore mother cell into four spores.

quadriphyllous. Quadrifoliate.

quadripinnate. Four times pinnate.

quadripinnatifid. Four times pinnatifid.

quadriplex. Having four dominant genes.

quadripolar. With four daughter nuclei arising at the same time in nuclear division.

quadripolar spindle. An achromatic spindle with four poles seen in preparation of spore mother cells in the course of nuclear division.

quadriserial. Having all four flower parts: pistil, stamens, corolla, and calyx.

quadrisporous. Four-spored.

quadritubercular. With four tubercles.

quadrivalent. 1. A nucleus having two pairs of homologous chromosomes. 2. A plant containing two pairs of homologous nuclei.

quadrivalent chromosome. Having four chromosomes in one, theoretically.

quadrivalvular. With four valves.

quadruple hybrids. Hybrids which split into four types in the first generation.

qualitative composition. The species composition and the adaptation to the environment of those species, adaptation or life form.

quantitative composition. The total and proportional amounts of the constituent species of a community.

quaquaversal. Bending in every direction.

quartering. Having petals with a space between them.

quartet. A group of four related nuclei or cells formed as a result of meiosis, four cells or nuclei which arise from the two usual maturation divisions.

quartine. A fourth interior integument in an ovule.

quartospore. A spore enclosing protective and more or less vegetative cells as in the liverwort *Riccia*.

quasiradiatus. Slightly radiant, as when the florets of the ray in some *Compositae* are small and not conspicuous.

quasi-circle. The ovoid curve in a log-spiral quasi-square mesh in phyllotaxis.

quasi-climax. A pseudoclimax in an aquatic sere which is a true climax in the sense that it is relatively stable and not determined primarily by climate.

quassine. A bitter substance in quassia wood.

quaternate. Consisting of four, in fours, growing in fours.

quaternate-pinnate. Pinnate, the pinnae being arranged in fours.

quaternous. Growing four together.

quercetum. An association of oaks.

quercetum roburi. An association of *Quercus Robur*.

quercifolious. Quercus-leaved, oak-leaved.

queriform. Shaped like an oak leaf.

quercine. Oaken.

quercion. An association of *Quercus Ilex*.

quercite. A glucoside derived from acorns which is sweet like sugar but does not ferment with yeast.

quercitophilous. Living in oak woods or on oak trees.

quercitrin. A glucoside in oak bark used as a commercial dyestuff.

Quetlet-Galton curve. See NEWTONIAN CURVE.

Quetlet's law. Individuals of a species represented by the mean measurements survive in the struggle for existence while those individuals which depart somewhat radically from type as represented by the maximum and minimum are eliminated in the struggle for existence.

quill wort. Any plant of the genus *Isoetes*.

quilled. Having normally ligulate florets which have become tubular; having a quill-like, or nearly tubular, corolla or florets, as the flowers of the cactus, dahlias, or certain garden asters.

quinary. Consisting of five.

quinate. Growing together in fives, as leaflets from the same plant.

quince. The fruit of the plant of that name.

quincuncial. Having the petals arranged in a five-leaved whorl in which two petals are interior, two are exterior, and the fifth has one edge covered by one of the exterior petals and the other edge covering one of the interior petals; in a quincunx.

quincuncial aestivation. A particular type of imbricate aestivation in a five-petalled corolla; see QUINCUNCIAL.

quincunx. An arrangement (∴) of the petals in a five-petaled flower.

quinia. Quinine, quinin.

quinicine. Alkaloids from *Cinchona* bark.

quinidine. An alkaloid isomeric with and resembling quinine found in some species of *Cinchona*.

quinine. An alkaloid occurring in the bark of *Cinchona*, *Remijia*, etc.

quinquangular. With five angles.

quinquecapsular. Having five capsules.

quinquecolor. With five colors.

quinquecostate. Having five ribs on leaves.

quinquedentate. With five teeth.

quinquefarious. In five directions or parts, in five ranks.

quinquefid. In five segments reaching about halfway to the base or margin.

quinqueflorous. With five flowers.

quinquefoliate. With five leaves.

quinquefoliolate. With five leaflets.

quinquejugate. In five pairs.

quinquelobate. With five lobes.

quinquelocular. Having five cells in a pericarp.

quinquenerved. With the midrib divided into five--that is, with the main rib and a pair on each side.

quinquepartite. Divided into five parts.

quinquepunctatus. With five spots.

quinqueremus. A five-celled gynobasic fruit, as *Gomphia*, a tropical shrub.

quinqueseptate. With five partitions.

quinquevalvate. With five valves.

quinqueveined. With five veins.

quinquevulnerous. With five wounds or marks.

quintate. Having five leaflets, applied to pines whose needle-like leaves grow in bundles of five.

quintine. An integument of an ovule, the fifth from the outside (the skin of the nucellus).

quintospore. A spore which has attained sexual potentiality, as in vascular cryptogams and phanerogams.

quintuple nerved. With five veins.

quintuple ribbed. Quinquecostate, when of five ribs the four lateral ones arise at the base of the midrib.

quintuplinerved. Having five main veins or ribs in the leaf.

quisquilicolous. Living on rubbish or trash.

R

R_1, R_2, etc. Signs for successive root-like organs.

R_2 **generation.** The offspring of a backcross.

rabdoid. Rhabdoid.

race. A variety of a species which may be propagated by its seeds which produce plants with similar physiological and morphological characters. Races may be geographic, climatic, edaphic, physiologic, etc.

race, adaptive. A physiological race.

race, between. A half race which shows a small number of plants with racial differences but the majority follow the original species; a midrace, with about one half showing differences from the original species.

race, biological. A physiological race.

race, geographic. A subspecies or race geographically isolated from other races of the species which have either physiological or morphological differences due to geographic differences.

race, physiological. A race or subspecies which has physiological differences such as food preferences in parasitism but shows no morphological differences or changes.

racemation. A cluster or bunch, as of grapes.

raceme. An inflorescence composed of pedicelled flowers arranged along the axis which elongates for an indefinite period. The lower flower blooms first and eventually the terminal bud forms the last flower (e.g., the lily-of-the-valley).

raceme, compound. A panicle.

racemiferous. Bearing racemes.

racemiflorous. With flowers borne in a raceme.

racemiform. In the form of a raceme.

racemose. With stalked flowers on a single

axis, resembling a raceme, racemed, racemous, like a bunch of grapes.

racemule. A small raceme.

racemulose. In small clusters.

rachemorphus. Rachimorphus.

racheole. The prolongation of the secondary axis of the spikelets of sedges within the perigynium, the rachilla.

rachiform. Reduced to the form of a rib or rachis.

rachilla. A stem-like structure to which a spikelet is attached, the axis of a spikelet in grasses, a secondary rachis.

rachilla flaps. The upward outgrowths from the internodes of the spikelets of grasses.

rachimorphus. The small zigzag flowering axis of some grasses.

rachion. The breaker line in lakes marking the place where wave action and undertow cause the greatest turmoil.

rachis. 1. The main flower stem to which the outer parts are attached. 2. The axis of a compound leaf, spike, or raceme. 3. The main ribs of a frond.

rachis spine. A spine which is a metamorphosed leaf rachis.

rachitis. A disease causing abortion in the fruit or seed.

rachitism. Hypertrophy of floral envelopes, especially in grasses and sedges.

racket cells. Cells in the hyphae of which the apical portion is swollen and thus more or less resembles a tennis racket with a long handle.

radial. Belonging to the ray as in the flowers of *Compositae*; see ACTINOMORPHIC.

radial bundle. A vascular bundle in which the xylem and phloem occur as separate radial strands, as in most roots.

radial dot. A Casperian dot.

radial longitudinal section. A longitudinal section which is cut parallel to the radius of a cylindrical organ.

radial plane. Any plane which passes through the axis of growth and cuts the surface at right angles.

radial section. The radial longitudinal section.

radial strand. A wedge-shaped mass of tissue formed of large cells and the hypodermal strand in the stem of bryophytes.

radial symmetry. The symmetry of a plant body, organ, or tissue which may be divided into two equal parts in any number of planes.

radial vascular bundle. A radial bundle.

radial wall. An anticlinal wall placed in or across a radius of an organ.

radiant. With marginal flowers enlarged and ray-like, with ray flowers.

radiant umbel. An umbel in which the flowers on the outside are larger than those in the rest of the umbel.

radiar. With branches extending uniformly on all sides.

radiate. 1. Having ray flowers at the circumference. 2. Spreading like a ray from the periphery of any densely packed inflorescence. 3. Having a stigma in which the receptive surfaces radiate outward from a center.

radiate-lineate. Having radiating lines.

radiate thallus. A thallus in which the tissues radiate from the center.

radiate-veined. Palmately veined.

radiatiform. The shape of ligulate florets of composites which increase in length outward with radiating marginal florets.

radiatropism. The effect of radioactive minerals on plants, negative or positive, inhibiting or stimulating growth.

radical. 1. Arising directly from a root, as basal leaves. 2. Concerning or pertaining to roots.

radical leaves. Leaves which arise immediately from the root stock in the form of a rosette.

radicant. Having roots developing from stems.

radicantia. Sessile organisms.

radicating stem. A stem assuming the functions of a root.

radication. 1. The arrangement or disposition of roots in the soil. 2. The act of taking roots. 3. The root system of a plant, its disposition and branching.

radicel. A rootlet.

radicellulose. Bearing rhizoids.

radicicolous. 1. Situated directly upon roots. 2. Growing upon or living in roots, as a parasite.

radiciferous. Bearing roots or rooting.

radiciflorous. Having flowers arising at the extreme base of the stem directly from the root.

radiciform. Root-shaped.

radicine. Root-like.

radicivorous. Root-eating.

radicle. The embryonic root, the portion of the embryo below the cotyledons, the canticle.

radicolous. Inhabiting roots.

radicose. With many or large roots.

radicula byssoidea. The mycelium of fungi.

radicule. A rootlet, a radicle.

radiculoda. The apex of the radicle in grasses.

radiculose. Covered with radicles or rhizoids, having many rootlets.

radiosperm. 1. A seed which is approximately circular in cross-section. 2. A plant bearing such seeds (especially fossil plants).

radiosymmetric. Displaying symmetry from the center as opposed to bilateral symmetry, divisible into equal symmetrical portions by any one of three or more longitudinal planes passing through the axis.

radish. *Raphanus sativus.*

radius. The group of ray flowers in a capitulum, the outermost florets when distinct from those comprising the disk in composite flowers, the ligulate corolla.

radius medullaris. A medullary ray.

radix. The root, the descending axis.

radula. A structure, as a hypha, conodiophore, or ascospore which is roughened by the development of sterigmata along the sides with no relation to the growing points.

radula spore. A spore borne on a radula.

raduliform. Like a radula or flexible file, rasp-like.

raffia. The fibre-like material obtained from the leaves of *Raphia pedunculata* and *R. vinifera*, used in weaving, etc.

raffinase. An enzyme which decomposes raffinose, the sugar occurring in beets and germinating cereals.

raffinose. A sugar occurring in beets and germinating cereals.

rag. The white stringy core and fibrous membrane investing the pulp of an orange, shaddock, or other citrus fruit.

rain forest. A low-lying, tropical woodland in which the annual rainfall exceeds forty inches. It is characterized by lofty evergreen trees, lianas, and herbaceous and woody epiphytes.

rain forest, high. A rain forest having more than 72 inches of rainfall annually.

rain forest, hot. An equatorial evergreen

forest zone of the Amazon and Congo basins.

rain forest, tropical. A hot rain forest.

rain forest, subtropical. A high rain forest.

rain leaves. Generally acuminate leaves which are adapted to shed rain from their surfaces.

ramal. Pertaining to a branch, rameal.

ramilia. Branches or twigs which carry out the greater part of metabolic activity.

ramalia, cortical. Twigs near the cortex.

ramastrum. A secondary petiole or petiolule of compound leaves.

ramate. Branched.

rambler. 1. A weak-stemmed plant which leans and scrambles over other plants or objects for support. 2. One of a group of roses of which the crimson rambler is the type and original variety.

rameal. Ramal, ramous, twiggy.

ramearius. An aerial root which rises from a branch.

ramellus. A side branch in algae.

ramelose. Having small branches.

ramentacous. 1. Covered by a rament. 2. Having a hair-like scaly covering.

ramentiferous. Bearing ramenta.

raments. Thin chaffy scales of the epidermis, as the scales of many ferns; chaffy loose scales, one cell-layer thick; scaly trichomes of ferns.

rameous. 1. Branched. 2. Belonging to a branch.

rami. Branches.

ramicole. Growing on branches or twigs.

ramie. The fibres of rhea, *Boehmeria tenacissima*, used in making fine cloth.

ramiferous. Having branches.

ramification. 1. Branching or separation into branches. 2. A branch, division, or offshoot.

ramiflorous. Having flowers on branches.

ramiform. Shaped like a branch.

ramiform pits. Simple pits with coalescent, canal-like cavities, as in stone cells.

ramigerous. Bearing branches.

ramillary buds. Buds of climbers which develop into short branches, fruits, or leaves.

ramiparous. Producing branches, ramose.

ramoconidium. A part or branch of a conidiophore which functions as a spore, as in *Cladosporium*.

ramondioid. Like *Ramondia*, an ornamental rock plant with reddish villouslanate hairs.

ramose. Branched.

ramular. Pertaining to a branchlet.

ramule. A small branch or twig.

ramulet. The vascular strands in the shell of a nut.

ramuliferous. Having small branches.

ramuline. On the branches, ramulose.

ramulus. A small branch.

ramunculus. A twig, the ultimate division of a branch.

ramus. 1. A branch or a branch-like structure. 2. A shoot.

ramusculum. 1. A ramulus or branchlet. 2. The mycelium of certain fungi.

ranalian. Resembling or akin to *Ranales*, a group including *Ranunculaceae*.

rand. The latest formed layer of a starch grain.

range. The area over which a species grows and reproduces itself in the wild state or grows naturally.

rangiferoid. Branched and pronged like a reindeer horn, as polyporoid sporophores under certain conditions.

ranunculaceous. 1. Buttercup yellow. 2. Allied to the genus *Ranunculus*.

ranunculetum. An association of *Ranunculus*, the buttercup.

ranunculoid. Resembling the genus *Ranunculus*.

rapaceous. Fusiform, turnip-shaped.

rape. *Brassica napa*.

raphe. 1. The continuation of the seed stalk along the side of an anatropous ovule or seed, an elongated mass of tissue or vascular strand lying on the side of an anatropous ovule between the chalaza and the attachment to the placenta. 2. A longitudinal suture on the valve of a diatom indicating the narrow slit in the wall bearing a nodule at each end and one in the middle. 3. A suture, a rhaphe.

raphia. Raffia.

raphide. A needle-shaped crystal of calcium oxalate found in many plant cells generally massed.

raphidiferous. Cells containing raphides.

raphidines. Free needle-shaped cells with partly lignified cellulose walls occurring among phloem islands in some *Acanthaceae*.

raphidoplankton. Floating needle- or spindle-shaped organisms.

raphioid fibres. Raphidines.

raquet cells. Racket cells.

rariflorous. With few or scattered flowers.

raroform. Said of a new form having imperfect connections with its surroundings.

Rasenserien. Herbaceous seres.

raspberry. The collective fruit of various *Rubus* species.

Rasse, geographische. Subspecies.

rath ripe. Ripening or maturing early in season, rare-ripe.

ratoon. A shoot from the root of a plant which has been cut down, as a sugar cane stalk or shoot, especially one of the second year's growth from the root or lata.

rattan canes. The stripped stems of climbing palms.

Raumparasit. An *Aulophyte.*

ravidous. Gray, tawny, ravous.

raw humus. Mor.

ray. 1. One of the branches of an umbel. 2. A ligulate flower in *Compositae.* 3. A vascular ray.

ray, aggregate. A secondary ray.

ray cell. A cell of the medullary ray.

ray, compound. A secondary ray.

ray floret. One of the small flowers radiating from the margin of a capitulum or other dense inflorescence.

ray flower. A marginal flower in a composite head; an outer floret, ligulate or tubular, of *Compositae.*

ray fungi. The *Actinomycetes*, so-called because of the ray-shaped bodies in lesions.

ray, initial. One of the cells of the cambium which takes part in the formation of a vascular or medullary ray.

ray, medullary. 1. Ribbon-like tissue formed by the cambium and extending radially from the pith to the bark, a pith ray, a vascular ray. 2. The limb of a branchlet in *Nitella.*

ray, multiseriate. A secondary ray.

ray, parenchyma. The horizontal or radial parenchyma cells partially disjoined during the process of differentiation, thick-walled cells elongated radially.

ray, tracheid. A somewhat thickened cell which with many similar cells occurs in the vascular rays of pine trees. It has bordered pits and conducts aqueous solutions horizontally.

ray, wood. A medullary ray.

rays, diffuse. Rays scattered in the woody tissue, diverging rays.

rays, distended. Lines of ray-tracheids of peculiar shape.

rays, fusiform. Rays walled by a flattened epithelium and further surrounded by thin-walled parenchyma arranged radially.

rays, primary. The tissue between the vascular bundles passing radially outward, uniseriate rays.

rays, secondary. Rays derived from fascicular cambium, their extremities being bast and wood; multiseriate rays.

rays, ultimate. Finger-like rays.

rays, uniseriate. Ray parenchyma, vertical cells placed singly one over another, primary rays.

reaction level. A space bisected by the soil surface including a few inches above and below.

reaction time. The period required for an organism to respond to a stimulus.

reaction type. A phenotype.

rebalsa. Palm forests of the Amazon basin periodically flooded which have trees feebly rooted, supported by each other and tied together by lianas; caa-gapu, iga-qu.

recapitulation. The repetition in development of an individual organism of its phylogenetic history.

recapitulation hypothesis. A hypothesis that every organism in its life history recapitulates the various stages through which its ancestors have passed in the course of evolution; the theory that ontogeny recapitulates phyllogeny.

recaulescence. The adhesion of attached leaves to the stem.

recept. A receptacle, especially in *Euphorbiaceae.*

receptacle. 1. In fungi, a spore-bearing structure, usually more or less concave. 2. In algae, a swollen end of a branch containing reproductive organs. 3. In liverworts, a cup containing gemmae. 4. In mosses, a group of sexual organs surrounded by bracts. 5. In ferns, the tissue bearing the sporangia. 6. In flowering plants, the more or less enlarged end of the flower stalk (the torus or thalamus) or the enlarged end of the peduncle which bears the flowers of a composite flower.

receptacle of flowers. The end of the axis to which floral organs are attached.

receptacle of oil. A cyst containing an oily secretion, as in the rind of an orange.

receptacle of secretion. Any interior cavity containing special products.

receptacle tube. The calyx tube.

receptacula accidentalia. Indeterminate passages filled with secretion.

receptacula caeciformia. The aromatic oil tubes of the *Umbelliferae*, the vittae.

receptacula Succi proprii. Receptacles for sap.

receptacula tubulosa. Latex-bearing vessels, cinenchyma.

receptacula vesiculosa. Receptacles of oil.

receptive papilla. A small outgrowth from the oogonium into the antheridium to which the antheridium becomes attached in some of the lower plants.

receptive spot. A clear area in the egg cell of some fungi, algae, and ferns through which the sperm enters.

receptiveness. The condition of the stigma when effective pollination may take place.

receptor. An organ which is very sensitive to stimuli, as the stigma of the pistil.

recessive. Of characters, those not appearing in a hybrid owing to the domination of the other character; a character which disappears in crosses.

reciprocal. Mutual; of crosses involving the same type of individuals but with the sexes reversed.

reciprocal autophagy. Sexuality in primitive forms of algae in which the gametes act mutually.

reciprocal cross. A cross between plants in which each plant receives pollen from the other (e.g., ma x fb and mb x fa).

reciprocal hybrids. Hybrid offspring derived from reciprocal crosses of the parents.

reciprocal matings. Two matings between unlike individuals within each mating one sex having the same characteristics as the opposite sex in the other mating.

reciprocal translocation. Mutual translocation.

reclinate. Curved downwards from apex to base, bent over so that the apex is lower than the base, turned or bent downward.

recolonisation. The re-establishment of vegetation in an area which has been stripped of plants.

recombination. The uniting of parental factors in individuals of the second or later generations after a cross.

rectiflorous. With the axes of the florets parallel to the main axis of the inflorescence, as in some *Compositae*.

rectigradation. A qualitative change or the genesis of a new character, an adaptive evolutionary tendency from the beginning.

rectinerved. With nerves or veins parallel.

rectipetality. The tendency to grow in a straight line.

rectipetive. Continuing a formative impulse by certain stimuli.

rectirostral. Straight-beaked.

rectiserial. Arranged in vertical or straight rows.

rectivenous. Having straight veins.

recurrent. In venation, when the veinlets return toward the main rib; returning or reascending towards origin.

recurvate. Curved backward or downward, bent back.

recurvifolious. Having recurved leaves.

recurvo-patent. Bent back and spreading.

recutite. Apparently bare of epidermis.

red algae. *Rhodophyceae*.

red brown. Porphyreus.

red mold. A mold caused by species of *Fusisporium*.

red rust. A rust of the tea plant caused by *Cephaleurus mycoidea*.

red snow. The discoloration of snow by *Haematococcus nivalis*.

redivive. An herbaceous perennial which dies down each year and grows the following year from an underground bud.

reduced apogamy. The development of a sporophyte from a cell or cells of a gametophyte without fusion of gametes resulting in a plant whose nuclei have the gametic number of chromosomes.

reduced fertilization. Fertilization which takes place in the absence of normal male cells in which situation the female cell fuses with a vegetative cell or another female cell.

reduced members. Parts which have retrograded and no longer act normally (e.g., potato tubers which were originally shoots).

reduced vessels. 1. Simple pits which replace bordered pits. 2. An incomplete development of the thickening bands and their looser arrangement.

reducing sugar. A sugar which can extract oxygen from certain substances.

reductase. A reducing enzyme.

reduction. The halving of the number of chromosomes during nuclear division from the diploid number to the haploid number, the division which precedes the formation of gametes, meiosis.

reduction division. Meiosis.

reduction, double. The occurrence of a reductional division at both divisions in regard to particular parts of chromosomes (possible in some hybrids and polyploids).

reduction, gametic. Meiosis immediately before fertilization.

reduction series. Changes brought about by arrest.

reduction, zygotic. Meiosis immediately after fertilization.

reductional split. Meiosis.

reduplicate. Folded and projected outward, doubled back (a term in aestivation when the edges are valvate and reflexed).

reduplicate aestivation. Valvate aestivation in which the micropyle is protected by a pouch-like structure.

reduplication. 1. An increase of parts by the insertion of additions on the same plane, as whorls, etc.. 2. The act of doubling or state of being doubled.

redwood. *Sequoia sempervirens*.

reeds. Various tall, bamboo- or grass-like plants with jointed, hollow stems, usually found in wet ground.

reed swamp. A formation of tall, usually monocotyledonous plants which grow in standing water.

reflected. Turned or folded back on itself, turned backward or outward abruptly.

reflex. 1. Abruptly bent or turned downward. 2. A simple automatic response to a stimulus.

reflex movements. Responses to stimuli which are usually classed reactions.

reflexed recesses. The sinuses of leaves which are bent backward from the usual direction of the surface of a leaf.

reflexion. A teratological change of position.

reflorescence. A second blossoming.

refracted. Bent sharply backward from the base.

refringent. Refracted.

reg desert. Portions of the Sahara which have a clay or pebble-stone surface, an alluvial desert, a reg.

regermination. The continuation of germination after complete interruption.

regional climax. See CLIMAX.

regional succession. A succession due to a secular change.

regional types of vegetation. The characteristic types of vegetation (as to layer, structure, dominant species, etc.) which predominate through the developmental series of the same general region.

registered seed. Seed derived by genetically controlled methods of reproduction from foundation stock which complies with standards for purity and quality.

regma. A form of schizocarp of three or more carpels which when ripe splits into one-seeded portions which burst open elastically.

regmacarp. A regma.

regression. The tendency of offspring of parents which have a below- or above-average characteristic to revert to the general average of the race.

regular. Having the flower parts alike in size and shape, having the parts so arranged that it can be divided into equal halves by several longitudinal planes passing through the center, symmetrical, actinomorphic.

regulariflorous. Composed entirely of disk or tubular flowers, lacking ray flowers in a composite flower head.

regulariform. Regularly formed.

regulation. The ability to preserve the normal state and function in spite of unfavorable conditions.

regulation, auto-. The power of an organism to adjust itself.

regur. A black soil in India which is clayey, cracks when dry, and is low in organic content. It is the soil of grass steppes, used as cotton-soil.

reinforced. Having various petal-like or calyx-like bracts or leaves attached to the flowers and fruits.

reinforced fruit. Fruit having other parts grown to the pericarp.

rejection nuclei. Nuclei which do not become part of the functional oospheres, the nuclei of abortive oospheres.

rejuvenescence. Regeneration, the transformation of the whole of a protoplast of a previously existing cell into a cell of different character.

relationship. A numerical statement of the average extent to which two individuals resemble each other because of genes inherited from common ancestors.

relative sexuality. The occurrence of strains in a species producing gametes which are able to fuse with those produced by either of the normal strains.

relative velocity of development. The reciprocal of the time to complete a definite process.

relic. What is left of a former but now suppressed vegetative organ.

relict. A species which properly belongs to an earlier type than that in which it is found.

reliquiae. See INDUVIAE.

remote. 1. Of gills, free and at some distance from the stems. 2. Of the annulus, at some distance from apex of the stem. 3. Separated by greater intervals than usual.

remotiflorous. With flowers spaced far apart.

renarious. Reniform.

reniform. Kidney-shaped.

reniform-cordatus. Combined heart- and kidney-shaped, as the leaves of *Asarum europaeum.*

rennet, vegetable. An enzyme found in the flowers of *Galium verum* and other plants which curdles milk.

R-enzyme. An enzyme which is active in breaking down starch.

reorientation. The alteration of relative positions of organs.

repand. Bent or turned up or back with a slightly undulating or sinuous margin, wrinkled.

repando-dentate. Repand and toothed, varying between undulated and toothed.

reparative steles. Four bands corresponding to the four orthostichies of leaves in *Psaronius.*

repeated emergence. A condition in fungi in which the zoospores, after swimming for a time, encyst and then emerge from the cysts without any change in morphology.

repens. Creeping, prostrate.

repertorium. An inventory, a catalogue.

repium. A succession of plants on soils which have subsided.

replacement. A theory of fertilization which assumes that the female cell gets rid of certain elements which leaves it an imperfect cell until fusion with the male cell replaces them.

repletum. A fruit with the valves connected by threads (persistent after dehiscence) as in orchids, *Aristolochia*, and some *Papaveraceae.*

replicate septum. A septum in some algae which bears a collar-like appendage projecting into the cavity of the cell.

replication. Systematic repetition used in field work to designate the systematic distribution of plots of each strain or variety to overcome soil heterogeneity.

replum. A thin wall dividing a fruit into two chambers. It is formed by an ingrowth from the placenta and is not a true part of the carpellary walls.

reponsi-creeping. Prostrate and rooting.

reproduction by division. The simplest form of reproduction by fission.

reproductive cells. Gametes.

reproductive potential. The number of females of a species which are able to reproduce in a given period multiplied by the number of offspring which each female will produce.

reproductocentric. (Of the organization of the thallus in *Myxochytridiineae* and *Rhizidiaceae*) with the center of gravity of the thallus at once or soon transformed into a reproductive structure, genocentric.

reprogression. When in an inflorescence the primordial flower at the summit opens first and is followed by others in succession from the bottom upward.

reptant. Creeping on the ground and rooting.

repulsion. A mutual avoidance by organisms or allelomorphs.

res herbacia. Botany.

research preserve. A natural sanctuary which is isolated and controlled.

reserve cellulose. A special thickening in the cells of seeds, such as the date, which can be turned into food in germination.

reserve materials. Plant products of metabolism which are stored and may be used later.

reserve proteid. Nitrogenous substances stored in the plant, as proteids, amides, etc.

reserve tracheids. Tracheid-like cells from the parenchyma sheath for the storage of water.

reservoir. An intercellular space often containing resin, essential oil, or some product of metabolism.

residual strand. The smaller trees left behind after lumbering or the trees available for a second logging.

resin. An excretion product of certain plants; any of various solids or semisolid organic substances, chiefly of vegetable origin, yellowish to brown, transparent and translucent, and soluble in ether.

resin cell. A cell which secretes resin.

resin cyst. A sack or cavity filled with resin.

resin ducts. Tubes containing and excreting resin, canals which contain fluid resin.

resin flux. An unnatural and abundant flow of resin caused by the attack of *Armillaria mella* on conifers.

resin gland. A group of cells which form resin.

resin glut. Resin flux.

resin passage. An intercellular space or continuous gland in or into which resin is secreted, a resin duct, a resin passage.

resin plates. Tissue found in conifers most frequently in contact with the medullary rays.

resin tube. An intercellular passage containing resin.

resin warts. Glands that secrete resin.

resiniferous. Producing resin.

resinocysts. Hemispheric structures in the cell wall of the hairs of the stems or leaves of *Begonia*.

resinogenetic. Giving rise to resin.

resinosis. A resin flux.

resinous. 1. With copious resin. 2. Having the odor of resin.

resolution. The division of a coenocyte into uninucleated cells.

resolvent. Having the power of dissolving or resolving.

resorptus. Absorbed.

respiration. The oxidation of oxydizable material with release of energy, the fusing of carbon dioxide and water; the gaseous exchange of an organism with its environment and the release of energy.

respiration, aerobic. Respiration in the presence of free oxygen.

respiration, anaerobic. Respiration in the absence of free oxygen and in the presence of combined oxygen.

respiration, fermentative. Respiration due to an enzyme action, possibly an exaggerated anaerobic function.

respiration, insulation. The release of oxygen in the decomposition of vegetable acids.

respiration, vinculation. Respiration in which oxygen is absorbed but no carbon dioxide is lost. It occurs in the early stages of germination of oily seeds.

respiratory cavity. The intercellular space below a stoma corresponding with its pores.

respiratory chamber. The stomatal chamber.

respiratory chromogen. A colorless substance which gives rise to a colored substance on oxidation or reduction and may play a part in respiration.

respiratory equivalent. The percentage of carbon which has reappeared in a given body as carbon dioxide.

respiratory index. The number of milligrams of carbon dioxide freed from one gram of plant material (dry weight) when the temperature is 10°C when the amount of respirable material is unlimited and when oxygen is present in the same proportion as in the ordinary atmosphere.

respiratory quotient. The ratio between the volume of carbon dioxide given off and that of oxygen taken in during a given time.

respiratory ratio. The respiratory quotient.

respirometer. An instrument to measure gaseous exchange in respiring material.

restant. Persistent.

restible. Perennial.

restiform. Having the appearance of a rope.

resting cell. A cell which has passed into a quiescent state.

resting nucleus. A nucleus not in the act of division.

resting period. A period of dormancy or quiescence.

resting sporange. Certain sporangia occasionally formed on old mycelia in *Saprolegnia*, their contents being zoospores.

resting spore. A spore not capable of immediate germination but remaining inactive for a period of time.

resting stage. The stage of dormancy or quiescence, the rest period.

resting swarm cell. Naked masses of protoplasm with amoeboid motion in *Confervaceae*.

restinga. A Brazilian forest forming the transition from the littoral to the xerophytic forest.

restitution nucleus. A single nucleus formed through the failure of the first division.

resupinate. 1. Of a pileus, with the upper surface reclining on the substratum with gills, pores, etc., facing outward. 2. Of a flower, with a rotation through a half circle so that the posterior side appears anterior.

resupinate-reflexed. Of a pileus, attached for some distance by the back surface, the other portion extending out like a shelf.

resupination. Inversion, turning or twisting to an inverted or apparently upside-down position, a resupinate condition.

resurrection plants. Plants which are dessicated and appear dead but which can be revived with the application of water. Many are desert plants. The most common are found in the mustard family and some club mosses, including the rose of Jericho and the bird's-nest moss (a *Selaginella*), some composites, etc.

retama bushland. A shrub steppe in the south of Spain.

retainer. A double sheet of thin paper containing a specimen throughout the drying process.

retarded phase. The third phase in the growth of a yeast.

rete. A net, network, or plexus resembling a network.

retecious. In the form of a network.

reticle. A reticulum, a reticule, a small net.

reticular. Net-like.

reticulate cells. Cells having reticulate thickenings of the walls.

reticulate perforation plate. A plate which has a small group of bordered circular openings.

reticulate-veined. With netted veins.

reticulate vessels. Xylem vessels with reticulate wall thickenings.

reticulum. 1. A network consisting of linin threads and chromatin granules found in resting nuclei. 2. A delicate network of all protoplasm. 3. The fibrous network found at the base of the petiole in certain palms.

reticuloplasm. Alveolar plasm.

retiform. Reticulate, net-like.

retinaculum. 1. A small, viscid, gland-like body at the base of the stalk of a pollinium; a horny elastic body to which pollen masses are attached. 2. A funicle which is curved like a hook and retains the seed until maturity.

retinerved. Net-veined, reticulate veined.

retinispora. A chamaecyparis.

retort cells. Cuticular cells of *Sphagnum* having an outward curved apex.

retractous. Having the radicle completely hidden by the enlargement and prolongation of the base of the cotyledon.

retroculture. The re-isolation of a pathogen from an inoculated host.

retrogression. The reversion to or development towards simpler organization, the passing from a higher to a lower state, assumption characters of a lower type.

retrogressive metamorphosis. A change from a more complex to a simpler place or position.

retrogressive mutation. The change of an active character which becomes latent.

retromorphosis. Development with a degenerating tendency, catabolism.

retrorse. Turned or directed back or downward.

retrorsely aculeate. Having prickles which turn back or down.

retroserrate. Saw-toothed, runcinate.

retroverse. Retrorse.

retting. The steeping of flax or hemp in water to free the fibrovascular portion from the cellular tissue.

retuse. Having a bluntly rounded apex with a central notch, as found in some leaves.

reversed shoots. Sprouts which show young or embryonic forms of foliage in mature plants.

reversion. Atavism, a return in greater or lesser degree to some ancestral type, the reappearance of an ancestral character not exhibited by the immediate parent.

revert. To exhibit ancestral features, to return to some ancestral type.

revoluble. Capable of being rolled back; curling off, as in the case of the annulus of many mosses.

revolute. Rolled back or up.

revolutivus. In aestivation, with the edges rolled back spirally on each side, as in rosemary.

revolving nutation. Circumnutation.

rh-. See R-.

rhabarbarine. Yellow or rhubarb color, near flavous.

rhabdocarpous. With long or rod-shaped fruits.

rhabdoid. Rod-shaped as the cells of *Drosera*, the sundew, and as the cells in the mesophyll of *Dionaea*, Venus'-flytrap.

rhabdolith. A detached portion of a rhabdosphere.

rhabdosphere. A pelagic alga, *Rhabdosphaera tubifer* and *R. claviger*.

rhabdus. 1. A rod-like spicule. 2. The stipe of some fungi.

rhachis. See RACHIS.

rhacimorphous. Racimorphous.

rhacomitrietum. An association of *Rhacomitrium lanuginosum*.

rhagadiose. Cracked, fissured.

rhamnaceous. Resembling or belonging to *Rhamnaceae*.

rhamnase. An enzyme acting upon glucosides which occurs in the berries of *Rhamnus infectoria*.

rhamnifolious. *Rhamnus*-leaved, buckthorn-leaved.

rhamnin. The coloring matter in the berries of *Rhamnus infectoria*.

rhamnoid. Like *Rhamnus*, the buckthorn.

rhamphoid. Beak-shaped.

rhaphe. A raphe.

rheine. A medicinal substance of rhubarb, *Rheum officinal*.

rheophilae. Algae inhabiting rapidly running water.

rheotaxis. Rheotropism, the tendency of certain organisms, as the plasmodia of myxomycetes, to respond to the stimulus of a water current by definite movement.

rheotropism. Rheotaxis.

rhexifolious. With leaves like *Rhexia*, meadow-beauty.

rhexigenesis. The origin of tissues where formed by mechanical rupture.

rhexolytic. Having gemmae detached by the rupture of a cell and the disorganization of its contents.

rhipidate. Fan-shaped.

rhipidium. A fan-shaped cyme in which the branches of the dichasium lie in the same plane and are suppressed alternately on each side.

rhipsalioid. Like the cactus *Rhipsalis*.

rhiz-. A prefix meaning root.

rhiza. A root.

rhizamorphoid. Root-like.

rhizanthous. 1. Producing a root and a flower apparently straight from it. 2. Parasitic upon the roots of another plant and producing flowers with little or no green foliage of its own.

rhizanths. Rhizanthous plants, rhizogens.

rhizautoicous. Having antheridial and archegonial branches coherent.

rhize. The root element in succession, R_1, R_2, etc., as primary, secondary, etc.

rhizel. The base of the root, i.e., the root apart from the radicles.

rhizidium. A rhizoid in the oophore condition.

rhizine. Rhizoid, a root-like organ in many cryptogams.

rhizinophylla. The posterior bracts of *Hepaticae* which bear rhizoids.

rhiziophysis. An expansion of the radicle, as in *Nelumbium*, the lotus.

rhizobia. The organisms which cause tubercles on the roots of *Leguminosae*.

rhizoblast. The definite strand which connects the blepharoplast at the base of the cilium with the nucleus.

rhizocaline. A substance which promotes root growth.

rhizocarpic. Root-fruited, producing subterranean sporangia or flowers and fruits in addition to the aerial ones, with a perennial root and an herbaceous stem.

rhizocaul. The root-like horizontal portion of a zoophyte.

rhizocollesy. The union of the axes of two individuals of the same species solely by the roots.

rhizocorm. The large fleshy rhizome of *Iris*, *Acorus*, etc.; an underground stem like a single-jointed rhizome.

rhizoctonia. 1. Hyphae twisted into strands like twine which fasten on the roots of trees. 2. A genus of *Phycomycetes*.

rhizoctoniose. A disease caused by *Rhizoctonia*.

rhizoderm. The outermost cortical layer.

rhizoflora. The bacteria, actinomycetes, and other fungi usually found near roots and mycorrhiza.

rhizogen. 1. A plant which produces a root and flower only. 2. Any organ which gives rise to roots or rhizoids. 3. A plant which is parasitic upon the roots of another.

rhizogenetic. Root-producing.

rhizogenic. Root-producing from the endodermal cells and not from the pericycle.

rhizogenic cells. The mother cells of the peripheral layer of the central cylinder which frequently give rise to all the tissues of the rootlet.

rhizogenum. The dilated base in the fronds of some algae from which holdfasts develop.

rhizoid. 1. A root-like structure or outgrowth of many mosses and thallophytes. 2. Radiating hyphae extending into the substratum from the base of the stem.

rhizoidal cell. A small cell in the antheridium of *Isoetes*.

rhizolithophytes. Lichens.

rhizoma. A subterranean stem, especially if thickened uniformly for food storage; a root stock.

rhizomastigoid. A whip-like flagellum or pseudopodium.

rhizomaticae. Plants having root stocks.

rhizomatiform. Shaped like a rhizome.

rhizomatose. Like a rhizome.

rhizome. A thickish, prostrate, more or less subterranean stem producing roots and leafy shoots; see ROOTSTALK.

rhizome geophyte. A perennial herb with horizontal underground shoots which give rise to leaves and flowers.

rhizomorph. 1. A root-like hypha of certain fungi. 2. A root-like organ in agarics and some other fungi composed of many united strands of hyphae.

rhizomorphous. Having a delicate branching form like rootlets, resembling a rhizomorph.

rhizomycelium. The thallus of the *Cladochytriaceae* as distinguished from the mycelium of the higher fungi and the rhizoidal system of the *Rhizidiaceae*.

rhizophagist. A plant which is nourished by its own roots, an autophyte, a rhizophyte.

rhizophagous. Living or feeding on roots.

rhizophilous. Growing attached to roots.

rhizophore. 1. A naked branch which grows down into the soil and develops roots from the apex. 2. A leafless branch in some club mosses from which roots arise.

rhizophoretum. An association of mangroves, *Rhizophora sp.*

rhizophorous. Bearing or giving rise to roots.

rhizophyll. A compound pigment in certain algae which consists of phycoerythrin and floridean green.

rhyzophyllaceous. Having fronds arising directly from the roots or rhizomes, as the ferns in the *Rhizophyllaceae*.

rhizophyllous. Forming roots from leaves.

rhizophysis. Rhiziophysis.

rhizophyte. A rhizophagist, a vascular plant.

rhizopin. A substance which stimulates the production of carbon dioxide by yeasts.

rhizoplane. The area where roots and soil meet.

rhizoplasts. Chromatic threads which start from the blepharoplast toward the interior of the cell, the intermediate fiber of *Gymnodinium*.

rhizopod. The mycelium of fungi.

rhizopodous. Amoeboid, rhizopodal.

rhizosphere. The region in the soil surrounding the root system of a plant which is affected by its excretions.

rhizotaxis. The system or order of arrangement of roots.

rhizothamnion. Tubercles on roots of the tropical tree *Casuarina*.

rhizula. The protonema of mosses.

rhizumenon. Sessile organisms.

rhoad. A creek plant.

rhodanthous. With red flowers.

rhodellus. Rosy pink.

rhodo-. A prefix meaning red.

rhodochilus. With red lips or margins.

rhodochrous. Rose-colored, pink.

rhodocinctus. With a red band.

rhododendretum. An association of *Rhododendron*.

rhodogen. The red substance in beets which is easily oxidizable.

rhodoleucus. Reddish-white.

rhodology. The study of roses.

rhodoneurus. Red-nerved.

rhodophyll. The compound pigment which is the coloring matter of red algae, the *Florideae*.

rhodophyta. Red algae.

rhodoplast. The chromatophore of the red algae.

rhodoplastid. A rhodoplast.

rhodoretum. An association of *Rhododendrum Rhodora*.

rhodospermin. Crystalloids of proteids found in the *Florideae* containing the rhodophyll, the red coloring matter.

rhodosporous. With rose-colored spores.

rhoeadales. Herbs having flowers in racemes.

rhoifolious. With leaves like *Rhoeo* or *Tradescantia*, a tropical or greenhouse plant with striking leaves.

rhoium. A creek formation.

rhombifolious. With rhomboidal leaves.

rhomboid. Lozenge-shaped, diamond-shaped.

rhomboid-ovate. Between rhomboid and oval in shape.

rhoophilous. Creek-dwelling, creek-loving.

rhoophyta. Creek plants.

rhoptometer. An instrument used to measure absorption of water by the soil.

rhubarb. *Rheum rhaponticum.*

rhubarb-yellow. Rhabarbine, near flavous; the color of the rhubarb root.

rhyacad. A torrent plant.

rhyacium. A torrent community.

rhyacophilous. Torrent-loving.

rhyacophyta. Torrent plants.

rhynchodont. Having a toothed beak.

rhynchophorous. Beaked, ending in a beak.

rhynchosporetum. An association of *Rhyncospora alba.*

rhyncosporous. Having beaked spores or fruits.

rhysion. A plant succession on volcanic soil.

rhytidome. 1. A plate of cellular tissue within the liber. 2. An external covering of a plant member made up of alternating sheets of cork and dead cortex or dead phloem.

rhytidophyllous. With wrinkled leaves.

rhytismoid. Like *Rhytisma*, with a flat, compound, apothecoid fruiting structure splitting open along several lines.

rib. A primary or prominent vein of a leaf, the central vein.

ribitol. A sugar alcohol found in plant cells.

riboflavin. Vitamin B_2 which is found in all plant cells. It is abundant in green leaves and essential for tissue repair in animals. It is a constituent of some flavoproteins which act as coenzymes in cellular oxidation.

ribonuclease. An enzyme active in the disintegration of RNA.

ribonucleic acid (RNA). A constituent of the cytoplasm and nucleoli of plants and animals, a minor constituent of chromosomes.

ricciform. Like the liverwort *Riccia.*

ricinifolious. With leaves like *Ricinus*, the castor plant.

ricinolein. The glyceride of ricinoleic acid in seeds of *Ricinus.*

rickettsia. Bacteria-like bodies found in lice and ticks and in bodies of persons suffering from typhus and similar diseases.

rictus. The mouth or gorge of a bilabiate corolla, the throat of a personate corolla.

rigor. The rigid state of plants when not sensitive to stimuli.

rima. A narrow and elongated aperture.

rimate. Having fissures.

rimiform. In the shape of a narrow fissure.

rimose. Fissured.

rimose-areolate. Cracked or chinked in such a way as to mark out the surface in patches, definitely marked areas, or almost in scales.

rimose-diffract. Widely cracked or chinked.

Rims-of-Sanio. Markings on the radial walls of tracheids, especially the spring wood in *Pinus.*

rind. The cortex in a fungus body, the outer skin.

ring. The annulus, the growth ring, an elastic band surrounding the spore case.

ring bark. The outer bark when disengaged in strips or layers.

ring cells. Thick-walled cells which form an annulus in the sporangium of a fern.

ring chromosome. A chromosome in which the two ends have fused together so that it forms a continuous circle.

ring fasciation. The apical division of a stem or flower by the formation of a central, circular, inversely-orientated set of tissues corresponding to the normal set.

ring porous wood. Wood in which the pores of one part of a growth ring are in distinct contrast in size or number to those of the other part.

ring scale. A disease caused by the fungus *Trametes pini.*

ring wood. The innermost part of the wood.

ring worm. A contagious infection of the skin in man and domestic animals due to a parasite which forms a ring-shaped discolored patch covered with vesicles or powdery scales, a disease of the skin caused by the fungus *Trichophyton.*

ringed. Annulated.

ringed bark. The bark of a tree with cylindrical formations of phellogen.

ringed cells. The cells in *Oedogonium* which divide.

ringed rhytidoma. Secondary annual cork layers.

ringent. Gaping, having the lips of a bilabiate corolla widely separated.

ringentiflorous. Having ringent florets.

ringentiform. Gaping.

ringless. Without an annulus.

ringporous. Having the vessels in the spring growth of wood larger than those of later growth.

riparian. Growing by rivers or streams.

rivalis. Growing by a brook side.

rivose. Having irregularly winding furrows or channels.

rivulariaceous. Resembling the algae *Rivulariaceae.*

rivularioid. Resembling *Rivularia.*

rivularis. Growing by water courses.

rivulose. Marked with sinuate narrow lines, furrows, or channels.

RNA. Ribonucleic acid.

roborinus. The grey color of last year's oak twigs.

rod fructification. Fructification occurring in basidiomycetes by means of rod-like gonidia from the hyphal branch, unbranched gonidiophores in basidiomycetes.

rod, golden. *Solidago sp.*

rod organ. A pharyngeal rod.

rodlets. Straight rigid bacteria.

roestelia. An aecium with a cornute peridium thin at the sides with a pointed and thickened apex which usually ruptures by longitudinal slits. It is composed of characteristically marked and imbricated cells. The name is derived from the form genus *Roestelia*, one of the *Uredinales.*

roestelial stage. A stage in the development of the rust fungi in which the peridium is elongated and fimbriate resembling the genus *Roestelia.*

roestelioid. Like the genus *Roestelia*, hornlike.

roffia. Raffia.

rogue. 1. A sport or variation from type. 2. An inferior sport or variation, i.e., a plant which deviates in an undesirable manner from the type of the species or variety. 3. A gardener's name for a plant which does not come true from seed.

roguing. The act of removing undesirable individuals from a varietal mixture in the field by hand selection.

Romanus. Roman.

root. The underground part of a plant which supplies it with nourishment; the absorptive, anchoring and storage organ in plants.

root, adventitious. 1. A root which develops from a plant organ other than the root, usually from a stem or a leaf. 2. A root which is not developed from the primary root.

root, aerating. A root with aerenchyma tissue.

root, aerial. Adventitious roots arising from above-ground structures forming but-

tresses, pillars, clasping or climbing organs, water-absorbing organs, thorns, or parasitic suckers, etc.

root, bacillus. A bacillus which lives on roots, like the nitrifying bacteria.

root, bitter. *Lewisia*, a portulaca.

root, buttress. A root, usually adventitious, which assists in the support of the stem of a plant; a prop root.

root cap. A cushion of constantly renewed epidermal cells covering the growing tip of the root which serves to protect the meristematic tissue from damage as it pushes through the soil, a cone of tissue derived from the calyptrogen which protects the root, a calyptra, a pileorhiza.

root cell. The clear colorless base of an alga attaching the thallus to the substratum; a rhizoid.

root climber. A plant which climbs or clings by means of aerial roots.

root hair. A tubular outgrowth from the epidermis of a young root which serves to absorb water and mineral salts from the soil. It arises above the root cap and growing point, and its cavity is continuous with the cell from which the root hair has developed.

root knobs. Orchid tubers.

root knot. A disease of cucumbers and tomatoes due to eelworms, the nematodes.

root leaf. A basal leaf, a leaf springing from the base of the stem or directly from the root.

root nodule. An enlargement on a root caused by nitrogen-fixing bacteria, found chiefly on legumes. A root tubule.

root, paint. *Lachnanthes*, a plant with rhizomes and long stolons with red juice used in dyeing.

root parasitism. The condition of plants partially parasitic their roots penetrating the roots of other plants.

root, pareira. See PAREIRA ROOT.

root pocket. 1. A sheath containing a root, especially in aquatic plants. 2. The false rootcap in *Lemna* roots.

root pole. The basal or distal end of a shoot or cutting from which roots are produced.

root pressure. The force by which fluids are made to rise into the xylem by osmotic pressure in the roots, the pressure demonstrable in roots shown by the exudation of fluid when the stem is cut just above the ground, exudation pressure.

root, primary. The main descending axis of the plant, the root developed from the radicle in the embryo of the seed.

root process. A branched structure fixing an alga thallus to its substratum.

root rot. A disease in roots usually caused by fungi.

root rot, black. A root rot caused by *Thielavia basicola*.

root rot, white. A root rot caused by *Rosellinia necaterix*.

root rubber. The latex of *Carpodinus* and *Clitandra*.

root sheath. A many-layered epidermal sheath surrounding certain aerial roots, as the velamen in epiphytic orchids; a coleorhiza.

root sucker. A sprout from an adventitious bud on a root.

root tendrils. Aerial roots which are contorted and act as tendrils to help support the vine, as *Vanilla*.

root thorns. Thorns which develop on aerial roots, acanthoriza.

root, true. A root which develops from the radicle of the seed and embryo, a primary root.

root tuber. A swollen modified stem containing reserve food material.

root tubule. A root nodule.

rooting. An attenuated prolongation of the stem into the soil or substratum which sends out lateral roots.

rootlet. An ultimate branch of a root, a small root, or a root fiber.

roots as thorns. Adventitious roots which develop into thorns, as in *Acanthorhiza*.

roots as tubers. Modified underground stems from which roots grow, as in *Dahlias*, *Bravoa*, etc.; tuberous roots.

roots, apogeotropic. Roots which exhibit growth negative to the force of gravity, as the roots of the cycad *Bowenia*, which has branched roots above ground.

roots, double. Lateral roots in monocotyledons in the area between two protoxylem clusters.

roots, fibrous. Roots which lack a main axis and have many roots of almost uniform size and length.

roots, parasitic. Special organs of parasites which penetrate the tissue of the host and derive nourishment from it, suckers, haustoria.

rootstalk. A horizontal underground stem with leaf scales which gives rise to shoots and adventitious roots.

rootstock. 1. An erect rhizome, as in ferns. 2. A root used as a stock in propagation of plants through grafting.

rootstock tubercle. A small swelling on a legume root caused by bacteria.

roridous. Like dew, covered with transparent elevations resembling drops of dew.

rosaceous. 1. Having an affinity or likeness to *Rubus rosaceus*. 2. Arranged like the five petals of a normal rose. 3. Rose-colored.

rosaeflorous. With rose-like flowers.

roseate. Rosy, fringed with rose color.

roseform. The shape of a rose in flower.

rosella. A rosette.

rosella, double. A dyaster.

rosella, peach. A disease attacking peach trees developing short rosette-like growths of leaves in spring, peach rosette.

rosella plants. Plants with short internodes and closely set leaves, usually epigeous and evergreen.

rosella shoot. A cluster of leaves on a branch from the same plant.

rosella, umbilical. Of diatoms, a central star-shaped projection or depression of a few larger cells, as in *Coscinodiscus*.

rosellate. 1. Arranged like rosettes. 2. Having a small beak.

roselle. An annual hibiscus.

roseolate. Rosy, pinkish.

roseopicta. Rose-painted.

rosette. 1. A dense, flat, imbricated cluster of leaves growing from a short stem at the base of a plant, as a dandelion. 2. A collection of leaves growing close together and radiating from the main stem. 3. A cluster of four cells which lie above the suspensor in the embryo of the pine seed.

rosette organ. An organ in certain ascidians which is a ventral complex stolon from which buds are constricted.

rosetum. A rose garden.

rosile. A society of *Rosa*.

rosin. A crude resin; the hard commonly amber-colored resin left after distilling off the volatile oil of turpentine.

rosmarinifolious. With leaves like rosemary.

rostellate. Rostrate, beaked.

rostellum. 1. A small rostrum or projecting

structure developed from the stigmatic surface of an orchid flower; a little beak, especially the process upon the column in orchids containing the disk (retinaculum) of the pollinia. 2. The caulicle, a radicle. 3. The projecting free end of perithecia in certain fungi.

rostrate. Beaked or spurred.

rostriform. Beak-shaped.

rostrulate. Like a rostrum.

rostrum. Any beak-like extension, such as the inner segment of the coronal lobes in asclepiads.

rosulaceous. 1. Pertaining to a rosule, a rose-like tuft of leaves. 2. Having the form of an umbel.

rosular. Arranged in rosettes, rosulate.

rosule. A rosette, a rosula.

rosuliferous. Bearing rosettes.

rot. Decay, decomposition; disease caused by fungi or bacteria.

rotaceous. Wheel-shaped.

rotang. Rattan.

rotate. Wheel-shaped with flat and spreading parts.

rotate corolla. A corolla which is flat and circular in outline.

rotate-plane. Gamopetalous with a flat border and no tube.

rotation. The movement of the protoplasm in a cell in a constant direction, the movement around the wall of a cell, cyclosis.

rotation of gyration. The peculiar rotation in *Characeae*.

rotation pasture. A field for grazing which is seeded to perennials and/or self-seeding annuals but which forms a unit in the crop rotation plan and is plowed within a five-year interval.

rotation of protoplasm. The movement around and within the cell.

rotatoplane. A rotate plane.

rotiform. Wheel-shaped.

rotuliform. Shaped like a small wheel.

rotundifolious. With rounded leaves.

rotundo-ovate. Roundly egg-shaped.

rough leaves. A gardener's term for the first true leaves of a seedling.

rozelle. Roselle.

rubber. The coagulated latex of caoutchouc.

rubedo. Rubor, redness of any kind.

rubefacient. Any substance which reddens the skin or raises slight cutaneous inflammation.

rubellous. Reddish, rubellinus.

rubescent. Turning red.

rubiaceous. Belonging to or resembling the chiefly tropical madder family, *Rubiaceae*.

rubiaefolious. Bramble-leaved like *Rubus*.

rubicolous. Parasitic on brambles.

rubidous. True red.

rubigenous. Rust-colored, rufous.

rubioid. Like *Rubia*, the madder.

rubologist. A student of brambles or batology.

rubricalyx. A red calyx.

rubricaulis. Red-stemmed.

rubrifolious. With red leaves.

rubrofructous. With red fruit.

rubronervis. With red veins.

ruderal. Growing among rubbish or debris or in waste places.

rudiment. 1. The earliest recognizable stage of a member or organ. 2. An imperfectly developed, vestigial, or aborted part of a plant.

rudimentary. Incompletely or imperfectly developed, in an early stage of development, stationary at a stage of development which is too immature to function, vestigial.

rudis. Wild, not tilled.

rufescent. Becoming reddish or rufous, fulvous.

ruffle. The volva.

ruffling. A faint crumpling of a leaf attacked by a virus disease.

rufinervis. Red-nerved.

rufous. Reddish, dull red, rusty.

ruga. A fold or wrinkle.

rugged. Rough with short stiff hairs or points, asperate.

rugose. Coarsely wrinkled, uneven, rough.

rugula. A longitudinal groove in the upper lip of the flower which encloses the style of the tropical plant *Justicia*.

rugulate. Wrinkled or wormy, usually applied to the spore wall markings.

ruminate. 1. Having a mottled or wrinkled appearance through the unfolding of the tegmen. 2. Having mottled albumen penetrated with irregular channels or portions filled with softer matter. 3. Looking as if chewed.

ruminate endosperm. Endosperm or albumen which appears as if chewed or composed of a mixture of several colors due to the wrinkling of the endosperm and the folding of the seed coat into wrinkles. Sometimes the cotyledons have holes or channels which are penetrated by the darker seed coat, as in nutmeg, annona fruits, pawpaw, etc.

ruminated. Mottled and wrinkled as if chewed.

runcinate. Sharply pinnatifid or incised with the lobes or segments turned backward; coarsely toothed or cut, the pointed teeth turned toward the base of the leaf; lyrate but with lobes directed backward.

runcinato-dentate. Hooked back and toothed.

rundle. An umbel.

rundlet. A partial or secondary umbel.

runner. A prostrate, slender stem, such as in the strawberry; a slender shoot producing roots and leaves at the end only and at that point giving rise to another plant; a filiform or very slender stolon.

runner bulb. A bulb formed by a stolon as distinct from the main axis.

running. Repent, reptant, prostrate upon or beneath the surface but not rooting.

runt. 1. An old or decayed tree stump. 2. The hardened stem of a cabbage or other plant. 3. A stunted, undersized or dwarfish plant.

rupescent. Growing on walls and rocks.

rupestrine. Growing or living in rock or in rocky places.

rupicolous. Living on, inhabiting, or growing on rocks.

rupifragous. Rock-breaking.

ruptile. Bursting in an irregular manner.

ruptinervis. Havings ribs interrupted and swollen at intervals on a straight ribbed leaf.

ruscifolious. Leaved like *Ruscus*, a lily whose dried leaf-like cladodia are used for decoration.

rusciform. Having leaflets which resemble the shape of the phyllodes of *Ruscus aculeatus*.

russatus. Reddish, russet.

rust. A disease caused by parasitic fungi *Uredinales*, whose mycelium lives in the intercellular spaces of higher plants.

rust fungi. The *Uredinales*.

rusticanus. Rustic.

rutabaga. The Swedish or Russian turnip, a turnip which has a large elongated yellowish root.

rutaceous. Of or pertaining to the *Rutaceae*.

ruthenicus. Ruthenian (Russian).

rutidobulbon. Rough-bulbed.

rutifolious. With leaves like *Ruta*, the common rue.

rutilant. 1. Brilliant red or reddish with a mixture of orange or yellow, deep red with a metallic luster. 2. With glowing flowers.

rytidocarp. A fruit with the surface covered by wrinkles.

S

sabal. A type of dwarf palms.

Sabalian life zone. The U.S. Gulf strip.

sabulicole. A plant growing on sandy places.

sabuline. Sandy, sabulose, growing in sandy places.

sac. A sack, pouch, or deep or closed receptacle.

sac, air. An empty cavity in the pollen of *Pinus* and in certain other plants.

sac, tannin. A cell secreting or containing tannin.

sac, water. A peculiar bowl-shaped leaf-like organ in *Hepaticae*.

saccal. Relating to the sac.

saccaratus. Containing sugar.

saccate. Sac-shaped, pouched.

saccate fruit. A fruit with a bag-like envelope around it.

saccharate. A sucrate.

sacchariferous. Bearing or producing sugar.

saccharification. Changing to sugar, as starch to sugar.

saccharine. With shining grains on the surface so as to appear sprinkled with sugar.

saccharobiose. Sucrose.

saccharochemotropic. Attracted to sugar, as pollen tubes.

saccharoid. Like sugar.

saccharolytic. Applied to bacteria which depend on simple carbohydrates and starches as sources of energy.

saccharomycetes. Yeasts.

saccharophylly. The production of sugar leaves.

saccharose. Cane sugar.

saccharum. Sugar.

sacciferous. Bag-shaped, pouch-shaped.

saccoderm. Having the cell wall consisting of one piece, as in certain desmids.

saccophytes. All plants which are not placophytes.

saccospore. 1. A plant with sac-like disseminules. 2. A fruit enveloped by a membrane.

sacculate. Having sacculi, having a sac
within sacs, with a series of sac-like expansions.

sacculiform. Like a little sac.

sacculus. 1. A small sac or ascus. 2. A peridium or wall enclosing spores, i.e., forming
a sac.

sacellus. A one-seeded indehiscent pericarp
enclosed within a hardened calyx in such
fruits as *Chemopodium* which burst irregularly.

Sachilinensis. Of Sakhalin Island, off Japan.

Sach's curvature. A curved growth of the
root due to a difference in the rate of
growth of the two sides of the organ.

Sach's rule. A cell wall always tends to set itself at right angles to another cell wall.

Sach's law. The nucleus of a blastomere
tends to be in the center of the protoplasmic mass, and the axis of the mitotic
spindle tends to be in the longest axis of the
protoplasmic mass.

sack-pusule. A pusule.

sadd. Sudd.

saerhadd. Elevated summer pastures in Persia.

saffron. 1. The dried stigmas of *Crocus Sativus* which yield a yellow dye. 2. Yellow,
crocate, croceous.

sagittate. Like an arrowhead.

sagittifolious. With arrow-like leaves.

sagittiform. Arrow-shaped.

sago. A granulated starch obtained from the
pith of certain palms.

sails. Bamboos.

Saint-Valery apple. A stamenless monstrosity having sepaloid petals and a double row
of carpels.

sal. A fire subclimax, an area which is prevented from developing to the usual climax
for the region because of frequent fires.

salep. The dried tubers of some species of
Orchis, salop, saloop.

salicariaefolious. Willow-leaved.

salicetum. A plant association of *Salix*, willows.

salicifolious. Willow-leaved.

salicin. A glucoside in the bark of willows.

salicinase. An enzyme derived from almond
which decomposes salicin.

salicine. Of the willows.

salicologist. A student of *Salix*.

salicornetum. A salt marsh association of
Salicornia, saltwort.

salicornioid. Of or pertaining to *Salicornia*,
saltwort.

salicylous acid. An acid occurring in many
flowers, especially spiraea, probably due to
oxidation of the alcohol saligenin.

saligenin. The orthohydroxy derivative of
benzyl alcohol obtained by the decomposition of salicin.

salignus. Of willow.

saline. Growing in places impregnated with
salt, salsuginous, salty.

saline matters. Chemical salts occurring in
plants the result of the union of acids and
bases.

salitrales. Argentine salt steppes, esteros.

salitrates. Salitrales.

sallow. *Salix*.

salmoneous. Salmon-colored.

saloop. Salep, salop.

salpiganthy. The transformation of the ligulate or disk-florets of composites into conspicuous tabular florets.

salsola. 1. A spiny halophyte. 2. The generic
name of glasswort and Russian thistle.

salsoletum. An association of *Salsola*.

salsuginosus. Growing in salt water or brackish soil.

salsus. Growing in places inundated by salt
or brackish water, as saltings.

salt bushland. An area of the Mediterranean
region.

salt area communities. The various communities occurring in salt areas.

salt desert. A desert in Persia which has no
plant or grass.

salt glands. Certain glands in leaves which
excrete salt.

salt marsh. A marsh similar to a fresh marsh
but covered wholly or in part by salt water.

salt panne. A lagoon in the Danish West
Indies separated from the sea. The edges
are luxuriant mangrove swamps.

salt steppe. A steppe in which the plants are
usually gray with scales, hairs, or wax.

salt swamp. A swamp occurring in still maritime inlets with *Phragmites* and *Scirpus*.

saltant. A variable form or mutant from the
normal.

saltated. Varied.

saltation. Mutation, a mutation within an isolate known to be a pure genotype.

saltatory evolution. Evolution showing discontinuous advance with long strides.

saltings. Salt marshes in which the grass is covered at high water and has numerous muddy channels at low water.

salver-form. A corolla composed of a slender tube abruptly expanding into a flat top, the form of an antique salver, hypocrateriform.

salviaefolious. With leaves like *Salvia*.

saman. A leguminose tree of the American tropics, a handsome tree widely planted for shade whose pods are eaten by cattle; the rain tree, the monkey-pod tree, the zaman.

samara. A dry, one-seeded, winged achene called a key, as the seed of the maple, elm, ash, etc.

samarideous. Key-shaped.

samariform. Key-shaped.

samaroid. Samariform, winged like a samara.

sambucene. A terpene derived from *Sambucus nigra*.

sambucifolious. Leaved like the elder.

samphire. Common fleshy plants along the seacoast; sea oxeye, glasswort, etc., of the *Chenopodiaceae* family, genus *Crithmum* or *Salicornia*.

sample area. A portion of a sample plot.

sample plot. An accurately measured area used for the purpose of experiment or mensuration either permanently or temporarily,

sandbar. An extensive ridge of sand formed by currents in the water, usually submerged but sometimes exposed by receding water.

sand binder. A plant which forms a mat of rhizomes and roots, and holds sand down so that it is not readily moved by the wind.

sand community. A community of plants growing on sandy soil.

sand culture. An experimental method of determining the mineral requirements of plants which are grown in purified sand to which various solutions are added.

sand drift. A tract of drifting sand.

sandus wood. Sandalwood.

sandivicensis. Of the Sandwich or Hawaiian Islands.

sanguicolous. Living in the blood of animals, as certain parasites.

sanicle. Any plant of the herb genus *Sanicula*, formerly reputed to have healing power.

Sanio's band (bar or beam). A rod stretching across from one tracheid to another in coniferous wood, a trabecula.

Sanio's law. The order of cell division of the cambium.

Sanio's rims (rings). Markings on the radial walls of tracheids, especially in the springwood of *Pinus*.

Sanio's trabecula. Ligneous processes crossing the cavity of the tracheids, possibly due to parasitic fungi.

sansouires. Moist alluvial soils covered with *Salicornia* and *Atriplex*.

santalin. A resinous substance from red sandalwood, *Santalum*.

santonin. A bitter substance from wormwood, *Artemisia*.

sap. The watery contents of a plant, an indefinite and undescriptive term for the so-called juice of a plant.

sap cavity. A vacuole.

sap color. Flower tints due to coloration of the sap, not to plastids.

sap particles. Vesicular bodies present in cell sap.

sap periderm. A periderm which may be distinguished from ordinary periderm by its cell wall and contents being in living condition and serving as absorption tissue.

sap pressure. The force exerted by the soil fluid entering the plant and by the sap in passing upward within the stem, root pressure.

sap rot. A disease of *Liquidambar* caused by the fungus *Polyporous adustus* attacking the sapwood.

sap vesicle. A vacuole surrounded by a thin skin of protoplasm.

sap vessel. A duct or continuous vessel.

sap warting. Ruptures and corky outgrowths in the bark of stems and branches when grown under glass.

sapid. 1. With a pleasant or savory taste. 2. Filled with sap.

sapling. A young tree.

saponaceous. Soapy, slippery to the touch.

saponarious. Having scouring qualities like soap.

saponin. Any of a group of glucosides occurring in many plants, as in soapwort, etc., characterized by their producing a soapy lather.

sapor. That quality in a plant which produces taste or flavor, savor.

sapotaceous. Relating to or resembling the *Sapotaceae.*

saprium. A saprophytic plant formation or community.

saprobe. A saprophyte.

saprobia. Organisms growing in polluted water.

saprogenous. Growing on decaying substances or in decayed matter.

saprogeophytes. Saprophytic fungi and flowering plants.

saprolegniaceous. Of or resembling the water mold *Saprolegnia.*

sapromyiophilae. Flowers which are fertilized by carrion or dung flies. The flowers smell putrid.

sapropel. Sedimental remains of plants in water.

saprophile. A plant growing on humus.

saprophyte. A plant which lives upon dead animal or vegetable matter.

saprophyte, symbiotic. A phanerogam which subsists by means of a mycorrhiza or felting of hyphal tissue on the roots.

saprophytophagous. Feeding on decaying plants.

saproplankton. Foul-water plankton.

saproxylobios. Inhabitants of dead wood.

sapwood. The living outer portion of the trunk of a tree between the heartwood and the bark, the young outer wood, the alburnum.

sarcenchyma. Parenchyma tissue whose limited ground substance is granular.

sarcina. A cubical packet of spherical bacteria.

sarciniform. Packet-like, having the cubicle form of the spherical bacteria *Sarcina.*

sarcobasis. 1. A fleshy carcerule. 2. Gynobase when very fleshy.

sarcocarp. The fleshy or pulpy part of a fruit or drupe, a baccate fruit.

sarcocaul. A fleshy-stemmed plant, as cacti and many euphorbias.

sarcocyte. The middle layer of gregarine ectoplasm.

sarcode. Protoplasm.

sarcoderm. The fleshy layer between a seed and its external covering.

sarcodic. Resembling protoplasm.

sarcody. The possession of a fleshy consistency.

sarcogenic. Flesh-producing.

sarcoid. Fleshy, as sponge tissue.

sarcollin. A glucoside from sarcolla gum, an exudation from *Astragalus fasciculifolia.*

sarcoma. 1. A fleshy excrescence. 2. A fleshy disk.

sarcophagous. Living on flesh.

sarcosoma. The fleshy part of the body.

sarcosperm. Sarcoderm.

sarcospore. A plant with fleshy disseminules.

sarcotesta. The fleshy part of a seed coat.

sarmaticus. Of Sarmatia, an ancient territory in southern Russia and Poland.

sarment. 1. A long, slender runner, stolon or twig. 2. A flagellum.

sarmentaceous. Having slender prostrate stems or runners.

sarmentary. The buds of climbing plants which develop into long slender branches and tendrils.

sarmentidium. A group of cymes or spikes arranged centrifugally as those in the cyme itself.

sarmentiferous. Bearing sarments.

sarnian. Of the Channel Islands (Sarnia-Jersey).

sassafras. A lauraceaeous, deciduous, aromatic tree of North America.

satinwood. Smooth wood used for furniture, often East Indian mahogany.

sathrophylia. Saprophytic communities.

sathrophyta. Humus plants.

sathropilous. Feeding on offal.

saties. A subdivision of a seasonal society.

satiform. A noviform which is produced by seed.

sation. A subdivision of a seasonal society.

sativa. Cultivated.

saturate virens. Green as grass, a full deep green.

saturation deficit. The difference expressed in percentage of total saturation between the amount of moisture present in a given medium and the amount of moisture it can hold when saturated at the same temperature.

saturatus. Saturated.

saturnine stage. The equatorial-ring stage of promitosis during which the nucleole lies in the center of a ring of chromatin.

satus. Arising from sown seed.

saurocephalous. Lizard-headed.

saurochore. A plant disseminated by lizards and snakes.

saurophilous. Of or pertaining to saurophily, adapted to dissemination by lizards and snakes.

sautellus. A bulbil, such as those of *Lilium tigrinum.*

savanna(h). A treeless plain or relatively open region; xerophylous grassland with isolated trees; parkland, campo, lalang, psilic.

savanna forest. A more or less leafless forest during the dry season, rarely evergreen, xerophilous, usually less than 20 m. high, park-like, very poor in undergrowth, lianas, and epiphytes but rich in terrestrial herbs, especially grass.

savory. 1. Smelling like thyme. 2. Pleasing to taste or smell.

saxatile. Rupestrine, growing among rocks.

saxicole. A rockdweller.

saxifragous. Rock breaking, growing in crevices.

saxosus. Full of rocks.

scab. A type of disease due to various fungi, usually indicated by dark, colored, crust-like spots.

scaber. Rough to the touch.

scabiosaefolious. Leaved like *Scabiosa.*

scabrate. Rough with a covering of stiff hairs, scales, or points; scabrous.

scalariform. Ladder-shaped; having transverse thickenings like rungs of a ladder; of xylem, with ladder-like secondary wall thickenings.

scalariform bordered pits. Pits strongly slit-like, transversely directed, and arranged in a longitudinal row.

scalariform conjugation. Conjugation involving two neighboring filaments which are connected by conjugating tubes arranged in a ladder-like sequence.

scalariform duct. A scalariform vessel; a vessel having scalariform markings, as in many ferns.

scalariform marking. An elongated pit of a scalariform vessel.

scalariform perforation plate. A plate with multiple perforations which are elongated and parallel.

scalariform perforation of xylem vessels. The numerous perforations that are arranged in rows in xylem elements.

scalariform pitting. A type of pitting in which elongated or linear pits are arranged in a ladder-like series.

scalariform vessel. 1. A vessel having scalariform marking, as in many ferns. 2. A xylem vessel with scalariform pits.

scale. 1. A small, thin, semitransparent bract or leaf-like structure, usually appressed, found on winter leaf buds, bulbs, at the base of shoots and flowers, on rhizomes and other organs. 2. A hardened, usually nongreen bract of a catkin or cone.

scale bark, scaly bark. Bark which becomes detached in irregular patches; rhytidome.

scale hairs. Multicellular flattened hairs, frequently resembling leaves, which cover fern rhizomes.

scale leaf. 1. A leaf usually reduced in size, membranous, of tough texture, and ordinarily protective in function. 2. The protective cover on leaf buds, rhizomes, etc.

scale trace. The strand connecting the scale with the stem in bryophytes.

scales, interseminal. The scales of a cone-like fruit which are between successive seeds or ovules.

scallion. A small or imperfect onion, particularly the shallot.

scallop budding. A mode of budding by peeling off a strip of bark from the stock and applying the bud with its wood directly to the surface thus formed.

scalloped. Crenate, with rounded teeth on the edge.

scalpelliform. Shaped like a scalpel or lancet.

scalpriform. Chisel-shaped, as incisor teeth.

scaly bark. The bark which is thrown off in patches, as in the plane tree.

scaly buds. Buds covered with scale-like leaves.

scaly bulb. A bulb with overlapping swollen leaf bases which do not form complete circles in cross section, as the onion, lily, etc.

scaly rhytidoma. A structure having scale-like secondary cork layers.

scandent. Climbing by stems, roots, or tendrils.

scansorial. Formed or adapted for climbing.

scantentes. Climbers and twiners.

scapaceous. With a scape.

scape. 1. A naked or leafless flower stalk arising at or under the ground. 2. A radical peduncle, as the hyacinth.

scapellus. The neck or caulicle of a germinating embryo.

scaphidium. The sporangium of algae.

scaphium. The keel of papilionaceous flowers.

scaphobrya. The *Marattiaceae* ferns in

which the frond rises between two stipular appendages forming a socket.

scaphoid. Shaped like a boat, scaphyform.

scapitflorous. Having the flowers on scapes.

scapiform. Scape-like, resembling a scape, scapoid.

scapigerous. Scape-bearing.

scar. The mark left by the natural separation of a leaf or other organ.

scarfskin. The cuticle or epidermis.

scarify. 1. To stir or loosen the surface soil. 2. To scratch or puncture the skin of seeds.

scariose. Thin, dry, and membranous, as of certain bracts in the involucre of some *Compositae*.

scarrose. Squarrose.

scendesmetum. An association of *Scendesmus*, an alga.

Schamm. The muck or gyttja found on lake bottoms, ooze, slime.

Schar. A community with several dominants, a cenosis.

Schichtenaufbau. Stratification.

schidigera. Spine-bearing plants.

Schimper Braun. See FIBONACCI SERIES.

schinetum. An association in which the tropical tree *Schinus* is predominant.

schinopsidetum. An association of *Schinopsis* trees.

schistaceous. Slate gray.

schistogams. The *Characeae*.

schistose. Slate colored.

schistous. Rocky, formed of schist or resembling schist.

schizaeoid. Like the fern *Schizaea*.

schizo-. A prefix meaning divided or cleft.

schizobolites. Products of catabolism due to the decomposition of a body of definite composition.

schizocarp. A dry compound fruit which splits apart into single-seeded segments at maturity, each of which is called a mericarp; a carcerule.

schizocotyly. The division of a cotyledon either by forking or by complete separation into two parts.

schizogenesis. Reproduction by fission.

schizogenetic. Formed by separation of tissue elements owing to the splitting of the common wall of cells, schizogenic, schizogenous.

schizogenetic intercellular spaces. Spaces formed by the separation of tissue or dissolution of the cell wall separating the cells.

schizogenic. Schizogenetic, formed by the separation of parts, schizogenous.

schizogenic development. Development due to division.

schizogenous glands. Internal glands with a cavity arising as an intercellular space but enlarging by disorganization of the surrounding cells, schizolysigenous glands.

schizogone. The characteristic structure of the schizont stage, the multinucleate amoeboid cell which develops from the original myxamoebae.

schizogonous. Schizoorgonous.

schizogony. 1. The reproduction by the formation of endospores. 2. The splitting off without a sexual process.

schizolysigenous cavity. An intercellular space formed in part by the separation of cells and in part by the dissolution of the cell walls.

schizolytic. Having gemmae which are detached by splitting through the middle lamellae of the cells.

schizomerous. Splitting into portions.

schizomycetes. Fission fungi, bacteria.

schizoneurus. Split-nerved.

schizont. 1. A nucleus which divides or splits in a distinctive manner. 2. A multinucleate stage obtained by marked and repeated protomitotic nuclear division of one myxoamoeba.

schizoogenous. Not breeding true, isogonous.

schizopetalous. With split petals.

schizophyceae. Schizophytes.

schizophyllous. With split leaves.

schizophytae. *Schizomycetes*.

schizophytes. Plants which reproduce by fission. They lack a well defined nucleus and do not appear to have sexual reproduction.

schizosomes. Reduced chromosomes.

schizosporeae. *Schizomycetes*.

schizostele. One of the vascular strands or partial steles to which the plerome gives rise in the stems of certain plants.

schizostelous part. A part containing a branched and sometimes a hollow stele with the branches often showing an incomplete structure.

schizostely. The condition of a stem in which the plerome gives rise to a number of strands each composed of one vascular bundle.

schizotracheal. With dividing tracheae.

Schwendenerian theory. The theory that lichens are not distinct organisms but are composed of a fungus and an alga growing symbiotically.

sciad. A shade plant or sciophyte.

scias. A shade form of any plant.

scientific name. The Latin genus and species name of a plant.

scilloid. Squill-like or like the genus *Scilla*.

scimitar. A leaf presenting an edge to incident light.

scion. A portion of a plant, usually a piece of young stem, which is inserted into a rooted stem for grafting; a young plant formed at the end of, or along the course of, a runner; a stolon.

sciophilous. Shade-loving.

sciophyll. The leaf of a shade plant.

sciophyllous. Having leaves which can endure shading.

sciophyte. A shade plant.

sciophytium. A shade plant formation.

scirpetum. An association of *Scirpus* plants, bulrushes.

scissile. Splitting into horizontal layers, capable of being pulled or cut smoothly into horizontal layers.

scission layer. An absciss layer.

scissiparous. Fissiparous.

scitamineous. Of or referring to the *Scitamineae*, an order of the monocots.

sciuroid. Curved and bushy, like a squirrel's tail.

scler-. A prefix meaning hard.

scleranthium. An achene which is enclosed in an indurated portion of the calyx tube, as in *Mirabilis*.

sclere. A skeletal structure, any small skeletal element.

sclereid. A general term for a short cell with a thick lignified wall, any sclerenchymatous cell, a thick-walled cell mixed with the chlorenchyma in a leaf providing support, a stone cell, a sclerite or sclerid.

sclerenchyma. Rigid or strengthening tissue composed of thick-walled cells often having the shape of fibers, stone cells in tissue, hard tissue, mechanical supporting tissue.

sclerenchyma cells. Thick-walled cells which retain their protoplasm.

sclerenchyma sheath. A sheath consisting of sclereids or sclerenchyma fibers.

sclerenchymatous cell walls. Hard and lignified cell walls strongly thickened over a considerable area.

sclerenchymatous elements. Elements with sclerenchymatous thickening of the walls.

sclerenchymatous tissue. Tissue composed of thick-walled cells.

scleric. Of communities of bush and forest.

sclerid. A sclerotic or stone cell, a sclereid.

sclerite. A large, thick-walled idioblast with the walls of its numerous arms thickly set with small crystals, a calcareous plate or spicule, a sclerid or sclereid.

sclerization. The process of becoming hardened.

sclerobasidium. A thick, encysted, gemma-like hypobasidium, a sort of resting cell very resistant to external conditions found in the *Uredinales*, the *Ustilaginales*, and the *Auriculariales*.

scleroblast. A stone cell, a sclereid.

scleroblastic. Forming skeletal tissue.

sclerocarpous. With hard fruit.

sclerocaulous. With a hard stem.

sclerocauly. The condition of excessive skeletal structure in a stem; the possession of dry hard stems, as in *Ephedra*; an excessive development of sclerenchyma in a stem, as in certain desert plants.

sclerodermatous. Having an external skeletal structure.

sclerogen. 1. Woody tissue in plants. 2. The lignified deposits in nut shells or the grit cells of pears.

sclerogenia. The induration of parts amounting to a disease.

sclerogenic. Secreting lignin.

sclerogonidial. Having loose, yellowish, or colorless gonidia of uncertain functions.

scleroid. Hard, skeletal, woody, bony in texture.

sclerophellous. Having lens-shaped groups of compact cells in the lenticels.

sclerophyll. A hard, stiff, and tough leaf with a strongly cutinized epidermis.

sclerophyll vegetation. Woody plants with hard, tough, and generally small leaves.

sclerophyllous. 1. With leaves resistant to drought through the possession of much sclerenchymatous tissue and reduced intercellular spaces. 2. Having hard, stiff leaves.

sclerophyllous forest scrub. See DURIFRUTICETA.

sclerophylly. Excessive skeletal structure in leaves or a great development of sclerenchyma in leaves.

sclerophyte. A shrub or bush having sclerophyllous leaves, usually evergreen and resistant to summer drought.

scleropodous. With hard and thorny persistent peduncles.

sclerosed. Hardened, lignified.

sclerosis. The induration of a tissue or a cell wall either by thickening of the membranes or by their liquefaction, hardening by increase of connective tissue or lignin.

sclerote. A consolidated and hardened mass of hyphae in a resting condition, a sclerotium.

sclerotesta. The hard lignified inner layer of a testa, the woody layer of a seed coat.

sclerotin. Hard storage masses of fungal tissue.

sclerotic cells. Grit cells, sclereids.

sclerotic cell walls. See SCLERENCHYMATOUS CELL WALLS.

sclerotic nests. Characteristic groups of dark colored tissue of uncertain origin seen in sections of the fossil *Lyginodendron*.

sclerotic parenchyma. The parenchyma containing stone cells, as in the grit cells in pears.

sclerotiet. A small sclerotium, a small concretion of lime.

sclerotiniose. A disease of lettuce caused by *Sclerotinia libertiana*.

sclerotioid. Resembling a sclerotium.

sclerotium. 1. A resting body of small size composed of a hardened mass of hyphae from which fruit bodies may develop. 2. A hard, compact, tuber-like body containing stored food.

sclerotized. 1. Having a thickened wall. 2. In a resting condition.

scobicular. Resembling sawdust, in fine grains.

scobiform. Scobicular, resembling sawdust.

scobina. The zigzag or flexuous rachis in the spikelet of some grasses.

scobinate. Roughened.

scolecite. A vermiform body branching from the mycelium of discomycetes, a Woronin hypha, an ascogonium, an archicarp.

scolecosporae. Plants having spores with a long, worm-like shape.

scolecospore. A long filiform or vermicular spore.

scolecosporous. With thread-like or acicular spores.

scolopendrioid. Resembling the fern *Scolopendrium*.

scopa. A pollen brush.

scoparious. Broom-like.

scopate. With a tuft of hairs like a brush.

scopiform. Brush-like.

scopulate. Broom-like, brush-like.

scopuliferous. Having a small brush-like structure.

scorpioid. Coiled like a scorpion's tail, circinate.

scorpioid cyme. A determinate inflorescence with seemingly lateral flowers borne alternately on opposite sides of a pseudoaxis and sometimes appearing racemose, a circinate cyme.

scorpioid uniparous cyme. A cymose branching when the right and left forks are alternately the larger.

scorpioid dichotomy. The development of alternate branches in the successive bifurcations, circinal dichotomy.

scorpioidal. Curved or circinate at the end like the tail of a scorpion.

scorzoneroid. Resembling black salsify, *Scorzonera*, a vegetable.

scotica. Of Scotland.

scoticaplankton. Floating mosses of *Ceratium*.

scotophilous. Dwelling in darkness.

scotophyte. A plant which lives in the dark.

scotophytia. Darkness plant formations.

scrambler. A plant which grows over other plants or any support by means of long shoots, sometimes helped by short, strong hairs or spines, but lacks aerial roots and tendrils and does not twine around the support.

screefing. Weeding or thinning a forest.

screw lines. Spirals in phyllotaxis.

scrinaceous. Of or pertaining to a scrinium.

scrinium. An unusual seed pod of the tropical plant *Lecythis*, also called monkey pod because of its use to catch monkeys. The pod is baited with sugar and when the monkey tries to extricate its hand, the opening is too small for it to escape because of the small woody lid.

scrobiculate. Marked with small pits or depressions, pitted, hollowed, roughened, furrowed.

scroll gall. Malformations caused by insects or leaves which curl up on the side when attacked.

scrotiform. Pouch-shaped.

scrotum. The pouch or volva of some fungi.

scrub. Stunted or densely packed bushes.

scrub forest. A forest occurring in clumps on plains and on ridges with little shade, little litter, and two strata: the arboreal and the ground.

scrupose. Jagged, rough.

scullion. A misshapen scallion.

sculptured. Having peculiar markings.

scum. 1. Surface growth. 2. Floating islands of bacteria. 3. An interrupted pellicle or bacterial membrane.

scurf. 1. An epidermal covering of some leaves. 2. Bran-like scales.

scurfiness. The appearance produced by membranous scales.

scurfy. Rough with short woolly hairs, covered with scales or hairs.

scutate. Shield-shaped, having horny plates.

scutate pile. Scales.

Scutellar. Pertaining to scutellum.

scutellar epithelium. A layer of elongated cells covering the surface of the scutellum lying against the endosperm and producing enzymes which assist in the utilization of the latter.

scutellum. 1. The single massive cotyledon lying next to the starchy endosperm in the seed of maize. 2. The shield-shaped cotyledon of grasses. 3. The conical cap in the endosperm in *Cycadeae*. 4. In lichens, an apothecium as in *Parmelia* with an elevated rim derived from the thallus.

scutiform. Scutate, shield-shaped.

scutiform leaf. The first-formed leaf in *Salvinia* differing in form from the succeeding leaves.

scutigerous. Bearing a shield-shaped structure.

scutiped. Having a foot or part of it covered by scutella.

scutum. 1. A shield. 2. A large, circular disklike part or organ, as the dilated stigma of *Stapelia*. 3. The broad dilated apex of the style in *Asclepias*. 4. The eight shield-like plates which unite to form the outside of the antheridium of *Chara*.

scyphiferous. Bearing scyphi, as some lichens.

scyphiform. Shaped like a cup or scyphus.

scyphiphorous. Bearing cups or scyphi.

scyphogeny. The production of scyphi or (sometimes) ascidia, pitcher-shaped organs.

scyphose. Cup-shaped, having scyphi.

scyphus. A goblet- or cup-shaped part of a plant as the cup-shaped podetium of some lichens or the corona of a narcissus, a scypha.

scytinum. An indehiscent pulpy pod.

scytonematous. Of or pertaining to the alga *Scytonema*.

scytonemin. A brown pigment peculiar to the *Scytonema*.

seabeans. Any of the various beans or bean-like seeds of tropical origin often carried by ocean currents to remote shores.

sea-green. Glaucous, peculiar greenish gray which is the most common color of lichen thalli.

sea grape. 1. A polygonaceous tree or shrub of the sandy shores of Florida and tropical America. 2. A gnetaceous shrub of southeastern Europe. 3. Gulf-weed or glasswort.

sea kale. A fleshy mustard plant, *Crambe maritima*, which grows near the coast. Its shoots are used like asparagus.

seam. A group of peculiarly thickened cells found in the leaves of conifers on both sides of the vascular bundle and formerly regarded as part of the transfusion tissue; see SUTURE and TRACHEID SEAM.

seam cells. Flat cells with thickened walls which direct the line of rupture in the stomium of fern sporangia.

seam nodules. Coal balls.

season, biotic. The period of duration of a seasonal society.

seasonal amphichromatism. The production of two differently colored flowers on the same stock because of seasonal changes.

seasonal heterochromatism. Different colors in the flowers of the same inflorescence due to season.

seasonal predominant. A predominant effective during the active open season only, as summer or winter residents, etc.

seaweed. Any plant or plants growing in the sea, any alga.

sebaceous. 1. Wax-like. 2. Producing wax.

sebakh. A depression holding salt water in the rainy season, dry in summer, and covered by salt incrustation when dry.

sebiferous. Producing wax.

sebiparous. Secreting fatty matter.

sebum. The secretion of sebaceous glands.

secalinus. Rye-like.

seceding. Separating from the stem after having been attached.

secernibilis. Separable.

sechellarum. Of the Seychelles Islands in the Indian Ocean.

secondary. Arising from primary branches,

arising from other tissue but not from the growing point.

secondary association. 1. The juxtaposition of bivalent chromosomes at meiosis. 2. An aggregation resulting from the coming together of free individuals rather than their merely remaining together.

secondary bast. The formation of bast of the same essential character as the primary bast but not forming a part of the original bundle.

secondary bud. An axillary bud accessory to the normal one, a bud additional to the usual bud when more than one occurs in or near the axil.

secondary capitula. Six small cells rising from each capitulum of *Chara*.

secondary cell wall. The layers of wall material (usually high in cellulose and low in pectin and often pitted) developed from the inside of an aging wall.

secondary colony. A society developing by concrescence.

secondary communities. Communities arising through human interference.

secondary contraction. The contraction which takes place in the diplotene stage of meiosis when the chromosomes tend to thicken and clump together.

secondary cortex. A collective term for the successive formations of liber or bast within the cortical sheath and primary cortex; phelloderm.

secondary cycle. The succession of events in the life history of a fungus which is instituted by summer spores and is completed during the growing season.

secondary desmogen. Desmogen formed from the cambium and destined to become secondary permanent tissue.

secondary edaphic communities. Edaphic communities arising through human agencies, such as lumbering, cultivation, etc.

secondary embryo sac. The secondary utricles of *Welwitschia* which correspond to the corpuscula of *Coniferae*.

secondary formations. The formations which have arisen through human interference.

secondary fungus. A saprophytic or parasitic fungus which attacks a plant after it has been killed or injured by another fungus.

secondary growth. 1. The development of secondary meristem or cambium producing new tissues on both sides, as in woody dicotyledons; growth in addition or sub-

sequent to primary growth. 2. Forest growth which comes up naturally after cutting, fire, or other disturbing causes.

secondary hybrid. A hybrid one or both of whose parents were also hybrids.

secondary liber. Secondary bast.

secondary medullary rays. Rays which are intermediate between the primary rays and do not extend to the pith.

secondary members. Parts of a plant developed from a primary or permanent part. Primary parts develop from the primary meristem (cambium) or other developmental tissues.

secondary meristem. Meristem (cambium) formed from permanent tissue by means of which further growth is possible, the growth tissue responsible for the increase in thickness in a stem through the development of secondary permanent tissue.

secondary mycelium. Rhizoid attachments developed from the base of the sporophore which are somewhat like the normal mycelium of the species.

secondary nucleus. The nucleus of the embryo sac which results from the union of the two polar nuclei.

secondary peduncle. A branch of the many-flowered inflorescence having more than one flower.

secondary permanent tissue. Permanent tissue formed from the secondary meristem.

secondary petiole. The stalk of a leaflet, a partial petiole.

secondary phloem. The part of the bark formed by the cambium, permanent tissue developed from the fascicular cambium.

secondary polyploid. A polyploid in which some of the diploid sets of chromosomes have been reduplicated.

secondary prothallium. A tissue developed by the megospore of *Selaginella* subsequent to the formation of the true prothallium.

secondary root. A root branching from other roots or growing from stems.

secondary sclerenchyma. Sclerenchyma which consists of elongated prosenchymatous cells with lignified walls marked with narrow, oblique, bordered pits.

secondary sexual characters. Sexual characters which depend on hormones from the male or female gonads but not necessarily having any direct reproductive function.

secondary shoots. Shoots arising from primary shoots or after primary shoots have been formed.

secondary spore. A small abjointed spore formed on promycelium, vegetative mycelium, or on the hyphae of a fruit body (not borne on a basidium); a chlamydospore, a conidiospore, etc.

secondary succession. 1. Any succession formed by human agency. 2. A succession on denuded soils.

secondary thickening layers of cell walls. Layers adjoining the middle lamella on both sides mostly forming the bulk of the cell walls.

secondary tissue. Tissue formed by the activity of secondary meristem.

secondary uredium. The true uredium which arises from urediosporic infections as contrasted with the primary uredium which arises from aeciosporic infections.

secondary wall. The wall formed inside the primary wall.

secondary wall layer. The secondary cell wall.

secondary wood. Permanent wood derived from fascicular cambium which is formed behind the cambium while the phloem is formed toward the outside of the stem. It differs from primary wood by lacking spiral or annular vessels like those on the protoxylem. Secondary xylem.

secondary xylem. Secondary wood.

secondine. The inner coat of the ovule, the coat inside the primine, the secundine.

secretion bodies. Secretory sacs.

secretory. Secreting.

secretory cell. A cell in which oils, resins, nectar, etc., are formed.

secretory duct. An elongated intercellular space in which secretions accumulate.

secretory sac. A unicellular or aggregated sac containing excreta such as gum, resin, oil, etc.

secretory space. An intercellular space containing similar products of secretion, as gum, resin, oil, etc.

secretory tissue. A tissue forming a storehouse for the waste products of the plant.

sect. Divided.

sectile. Cut, divided into separated parts.

section. 1. A thin slice usually made for microscopic examination. 2. A natural subdivision of a classification group, genus, family, etc.

sector. 1. An area without any peculiar climax of high rank. 2. A mycelial growth on a Petri dish in the shape of a geometrical sector.

sector, pericyclic. An interruption of the continuity of the central cylinder of the subterranean portion of *Polytrichum* as seen in cross section.

sectorial chimaera. See CHIMAERA, SECTORIAL.

sectoring. A noticeable change brought about by mutations, in the growth pattern of a plate-culture of organisms.

seculate. Sickle-shaped.

secund. All turned toward one side, arranged along one side.

secundiflorous. Having flowers on only one side of stem with the flowers all turned in the same direction, secund-flowered.

secundine. 1. The inner coat of an ovule. 2. An old term for the albumen of a seed.

secundospore. A spore which can also act as a gamete, as in *Ulothrix*.

sedes floris. The torus of a flower.

sedetum. An association of *Sedum*, stonecrop.

sedge. Any cyperaceous plant of the genus *Carex*.

sedges. Marsh plants.

sedile. A society of *Sedum*.

seed. A multicellular structure of higher plants developed after fertilization. It contains the embryo and stored food protected by a seed coat or testa.

seed bed. A placenta.

seed bud. An ovule or ovary.

seed coat. The seed covering, the testa.

seed genus. Any fossil genus of which the seed or fruit is the only part known.

seed leaves. Cotyledons, the first leaves formed in the embryo.

seed lobe. A cotyledon.

seed pedicel. The strand supporting each seed in *Bennettites*.

seed sport. A seminal variation.

seed stage. The formation of cones in gymnosperms.

seed stalk. A funicle.

seed stems. The seminiferous spadix of *Bennettites*.

seed variation. A variation derived from seeds instead of buds.

seed variety. A variety resulting from seed variation.

seed vessel. A structure containing seed, as a pod; a pericarp.

seed year. The year in which a given species bears seeds more or less abundantly.

seedling. A plant newly formed from a seed as distinct from one propagated by layers, buds, or other vegetative methods.

segetal. Growing in fields of grain.

segetum. Of grain fields.

segment. 1. A multinucleate portion of a hypha or filament delimited by transverse walls. 2. A daughter cell cut off by the division of a single apical cell. 3. A portion of a blade of a leaf when deeply lobed but not divided into two leaflets. 4. To divide or separate into pairs.

segment cell. The basal portion which is successively cut off from the apical cell in growth.

segment halves. The two external cells in apical cell division in *Hepaticae*, the remaining cell being internal.

segmental allopolyploid. An allopolyploid in which two genomes from different parental ancestors have some chromosomal segments in common (but other segments differ), preventing free interchange in meiosis and resulting in partial or complete sterility in the diploid offspring.

segmentation cavity. The central cavity of a blastula.

segmentation nucleus. The body formed by the union of male and female pronuclei, the segmental nucleus.

segregant. An individual of a segregating generation (of the second or later generations of a cross).

segregation. 1. The process by which a pair of allelomorphic characters becomes separated into pure dominants and pure recessives of the second and subsequent generations of a cross. 2. The separation of hereditary factors from one another during spore formation.

segregation, secondary. The segregation in an allopolyploid of the chromosomes derived from the diploid parents.

segregation, transgressive. The appearance in the segregating generations of a cross of one or more individuals showing a more extreme development of a character than the parents showed, probably due to cumulative and complementary genes contributed by both parents.

seirolytic. Separating hereditary characters.

seirospore. A spore produced in a branched row resulting from the division of terminal cells of particular algal branches in *Ceramiaceae*.

seismonastic. Moving as a result of the stimulus of mechanical shock or vibration.

seismonic. Sensitive to vibration.

seismotropism. The power to react to the stimulus of vibration.

sejugous. With six pairs of leaflets.

selaginoid. Like *Selago*, an old name for clubmosses.

selago type. A plant which resembles *Lycopodium Selago* in having alternate fertile and sterile zones.

selagraph. An instrument for the automatic recording of light values.

selection. The limiting of reproduction to certain favored individuals either by nature or man.

selection, natural. The selection determined by the environment.

selection, methodical. The selective process as carried on by man in order to accomplish changes.

selectionist. One who believes that natural selection is an especially important factor in evolution.

selective absorption. The power attributed to a plant to absorb some substances and reject others.

selective fertilization. The union between some types of gametes but not by all types of a species.

selective hybrid. A hybrid in which certain factors selected from the parents are fully developed.

selective species. Species which are mostly found in a certain community but also, though rarely, in other communities.

selenoid. Crescent-shaped.

selenotropism. The tendency of an organism to turn toward the moon's rays.

self. A florist's term for a flower or plant which is wholly of one color.

self-bred. Self-fertilized.

self-colored. With a uniform tint or color.

self-compatible. Self-fertile.

self-differentiation. Self-regulation.

self-fertile. Capable of being fertilized by its own male elements, fertile by means of its own pollen, hermaphroditic.

self-fertilization. The union of the egg cell of

an individual with the sperm cell of the same individual, close fertilization.

self-incompatible. Self-sterile.

self-parasitic. Parasitic on its own species.

self-pollination. Fertilization by pollen of same flower.

self-pruning. The process by which living buds or twigs are naturally separated from the plant.

self-purification. The natural decomposition and disappearance of organic substances in streams or other bodies of water.

self-regulation. The innate regulatory activities in an organism, especially those extremely remotely related to external factors.

self-sterility. The inability of a plant to set viable seed from self-pollination because of defective pollen, defective ovules, or other aberrations.

selfed. Fertilized by its own pollen, self-pollinated.

selfing. The pollination of a stigma from the anthers of the same flower or plant.

sellaeform. Saddle-shaped.

selva. A low, frequently flooded plain of the Amazon subject to heavy equatorial rains and high humidity.

sematic. Functioning as a danger signal with warning colors or odors.

semen. Seed of flowering plants.

semen-corniculatum. The receptacle of certain fungi.

semen multiplex. The sporidesm.

semester ring. The ring produced in the wood of many tropical trees as a consequence of two periods of growth and rest in one year.

semet. An anther.

semi-. A prefix meaning half, partial or somewhat.

semi-adherent. Half or partially adherent, as the lower part of a leaf which is partially clasping the stem, or a calyx which adheres to the lower part of the ovary.

semialatus. Half or somewhat winged.

semiamplectus. Equitant.

semiamplexicaul. Partially surrounding or clasping the stem.

semianatropous. With a half inverted ovule.

semiapogamy. A reduced form of fertilization as in the rust fungus *Phragmidium*.

semiaquatic plants. Water plants which root in soil beneath the water but produce aquatic leaves, otherwise living as land plants.

semibivalvular. Almost divided into two valves.

semibordered pit. A unilateral bordered pit.

semicalyciform. Half cup-shaped.

semicapsula. A cupule.

semicaudate. In the shape of the lateral half of a cordate body.

semicell. One half of a desmid.

semicolumnar. Semiterete.

semicomplete. Incomplete.

semiconnate. Half united.

semicordate. Half heart-shaped.

semicordiformis. Somewhat cordate.

semi-cultivated communities. Communities which have been somewhat affected by civilization but have not been affected in appearance.

semicylindraceous. Semiterete or semicylindrical.

semidecandrous. With about five stamens.

semidesert. A transition between desert and wood or grassland.

semidigynus. Having two carpels cohere only near the base.

semidouble flowers. 1. Flowers which have only part of the stamens replaced by petals. 2. Flowers with the inner stamens perfect, the outer stamens becoming petaloid, being half double flowers.

semiectotrophic. Having an intermediate type of micorrhizal infection in conifers.

semielliptic. Half elliptic, the division being longitudinal.

semiexertus. Half extended.

semifloret. A floret in the *Compositae* which has a strap-shaped corolla, a ligulate floret.

semifloscular. With the corolla split and turned to one side as in the ligulate florets of *Compositae*.

semifloscule. A semifloret.

semifrutex. An undershrub.

semihaustatus. Hastate in one side only.

semiheterotypic division. A first division which gives rise to a restitution nucleus following defective pairing.

semilanceolate. Half lanceolate, half divided longitudinally.

semilatent. Having the progeny of an abnormal individual repeat its marked departure in only a few individuals.

semilenticular. Sublenticular.

semilianes. The scrambling plants in hedges and margins of forests.

semilichens. 1. Lichens which when destitute of their appropriate algae can subsist as saprophytes. 2. Fungi which can combine with some algae to form a lichen.

semilocular. With incomplete loculi, having the dissepiments incomplete and the pericarp unilocular.

semilunar. Half moon-shaped.

semimesophytic. Intermediate between xerophytic and mesophytic.

semimetamorphosis. Partial or semicomplete metamorphosis.

seminal. Pertaining to seed.

seminal cavity. The cavity in which seeds are borne.

seminal leaf. A cotyledon.

seminal sport. A seed sport.

seminase. An enzyme occurring in *Trigonella* and *Medicago*.

seminatae. Plants which have true seed coats.

semination. The natural dispersal of seeds.

seminatural vegetation. Vegetation which is influenced in its occurrence and persistence by human agency though not planted by man.

semine. The anther or anther and filament.

seminicolous. Growing on seeds.

seminiferous. Bearing seed.

seminiferous scale. The scale in *Coniferae* above the bract scale on which the ovules are situated and the seeds borne.

seminific. Forming or producing seed.

seminification. Propagation from seed.

seminiform. Having reproductive bodies which are not part of the fructification, as in cryptogams.

seminin. A sinistrose carbohydrate occurring in reserve cellulose in the endosperm of some seeds.

seminose. A dextrose from ordinary cellulose belonging to the grape sugars.

seminude. Having ovules or seeds exposed.

seminule. A spore.

seminuliferous. Bearing spores or sporophores, bearing unfertilized ovules in the cavity of the ovule.

semiorbicular. Hemispherical.

semiparasite. A partial parasite, such as a plant which derives only part of its nutriment from its host.

semipenniform. Bearing some resemblance to a feather.

semipermeable membrane. A membrane which permits the passage of the solvent of a solution and at the same time will not allow the solute to pass, a differentially permeable membrane.

semipetaloid. Of the shape or texture of a petal.

semipinnate. Half or imperfectly pinnate.

semiradiate. With only a portion of the outer florest of a composite radiant and different from those of the disk, semiradians.

semireniform. Uniform with one lobe lacking, kidney-shaped on one side only.

semireticulate. The condition in which one of several layers is netted and the others are membranous.

semirevectus. A partition or dissepiment; see SEPTUM.

semisagittate. Arrow-shaped on one side of the longitudinal axis.

semisaprophyte. A plant that is partially saprophytic, a facultative parasite or facultative symbiont.

semiseptate. Half partitioned, the dissepiment not projecting far enough to divide it into two cells.

semistaminate. With part of the stamens changed into petals.

semisymphiostemonis. A condition in which some stamens cohere and the rest remain free.

semiterete. Half terete or half cylindrical.

semitrigynous. Having two of the three styles united halfway and the third free in the ovary.

semituberous. Having a somewhat tuberous root.

semivalvate. With the valves only partially dehiscent.

semixerophytic. Showing a tendency to a xerophytic condition.

semolina. Granules of endosperm of wheat sifted out in milling.

semperflorens. Ever-flowering.

sempervervivoid. Resembling the house-leek, *Sempervivum*.

sempervirent. Evergreen.

sempervirentiherbosa. Grasses and herbs, mostly evergreen, which depend on cell turgor rather than mechanical tissue to maintain an upright position.

sempervirentiprata. Meadow associations

dominated by species mostly evergreen in temperate climates when frequent rain enables them to grow during most of the year.

semperviretum. An association of *Carex sempervirens.*

senary. In sixes.

senecioid. Like *Senecio.*

senecionetum. An association of *Senecio cineraria.*

sense triplet. The three nucleotides of the RNA molecule which are needed for the production of amino acids.

sensibility. The condition of a plant liable to parasitic attack.

sensitive plant. *Mimosa pudica,* a plant with leaves which droop, recoil, or close at a touch.

sensitiveness. The power of movement in a definite manner under the influence of external stimuli, irritability.

sepal. Each part of the calyx, a segment of the calyx, one of the modified leaves making up the calyx.

sepaline. Sepaloid.

sepalody. The conversion of petals or other parts of a flower into sepals.

sepaloid. Sepal-like, resembling a sepal.

sepalous. Having sepals.

separate flowers. Diclinous flowers, flowers of distinct sexes.

separated flowers. Flowers having stamens or pistils but not both.

separating layer. The absciss layer; a layer of cells which separates organs, tissues, or parts.

separation. 1. A form of division of bulbs. 2. Multiplication by means of naturally detachable asexual bodies or organs.

separation cultures. Pure cultures which have been obtained by repeated innoculations in successive media after selection of the surviving species or forms from the chosen cultures.

separation disc. A substance in the *Myxophyceae* secreted by two adjoining cells appearing like a ring.

separation layer. The absciss layer in defoliation where the leaf is ultimately detached.

sepiaceous. Sepia-colored, dark brown.

sepiarius. Pertaining to hedges.

sepicolous. Living in hedges.

sepiment. A partition.

septal. Pertaining to a septum.

septamerous. With seven parts.

septangularis. With seven angles.

septate. Having septa.

septate fiber. A fiber in which the lumen is divided into several compartments by transverse septa.

septate fiber-tracheid. A fiber-tracheid with thin transverse walls across the lumen.

septate libriform fibers. 1. Fibers divided into cells by very thin, unpitted cross walls. 2. Fibers having side walls with simple pits.

septate parenchyma cell. A wood or ray parenchyma cell with thin transverse cells across the lumen.

septate spore. A spore with cross walls, a sporidesm.

septate wood fiber. A libriform wood fiber with thin transverse walls across the lumen.

septation. The division into parts by a septum.

septemfid. Cut into seven divisions.

septemlobus. With seven lobes.

septempartite. With seven divisions extending nearly to the base.

septempunctatus. With seven spots.

septenatal pinnate. Having seven pinnules in each leaf.

septenate. Having parts in sevens, like seven leaflets arising from the same point.

septentrional. Northern.

septet. A set of seven.

septic. Polluted, poisonous.

septic tank. A tank used for the anaerobic decomposition of the solid matter in sewage. Some decomposition may also be aerobic.

septicemia. Blood poisoning, a diseased condition caused by pathogenic bacteria in the blood.

septicidal. Dehiscing along the partitions, dividing through the middle of the ovary septa.

septiferous. Having septa.

septifolious. With seven leaves.

septiform. In the form of a septum.

septifragal. With valves breaking from the partitions in dehiscing or falling away from the partition.

septilis. Of or belonging to dissepiments.

septio praecox. A cell wall formed early in development.

septio procrastinata. A cell wall delayed in progress.

septulate. 1. Having spurious septa. 2. Sparsely septate.

septum. A wall, any kind of partition.

septum provectum. A cell wall advanced into a branch of *Cladophora.*

septum revectum. A cell wall formed across the stem of *Cladophora.*

septum semirevectum. The cell wall which forms an angle of 45°.

septuple. In a set of seven.

septuplinervis. With seven nerves or veins.

sequence hypothesis. A theory that the particular arrangement of nucleotides of the RNA molecule determines the sequence of protein production from amino acids.

sequence theory of parasite control. The theory that it is necessary to use different parasites at different stages to effect complete control of an insect infestation.

seral community. A plant community which is not established but represents a stage in a succession.

seral plant units. Associes, consocies, socies, colonies, or families.

seral stages. The development stages of a climax community other than the mature stage, which is termed an associes.

serclimax. An interrupted stage in the normal development of a plant association brought about by some condition, such as flooding or standing water, etc., which causes it to remain a subclimax for a period of time.

sereh. A disease of sugar cane probably caused by *Hypocrea Sacchari.*

seres. The series of developing plant communities which follow one another in an area to reach a climax association. They are classified according to the climatic or edaphic conditions in which they originate or the type of vegetation which they can support.

serial. In series, as branch buds one above the other at the same node; in rows or regular succession.

serial bud. A supernumerary bud lying at the side of the axillary bud.

seriate. In a series or row.

seriation. A series of communities produced by a graduated compensation across a valley and operating within a formation or an ecotone.

sericanthous. Silky-flowered.

sericate. Covered with fine, closely-pressed silky hairs.

sericeous. Silky, with a satiny pubescence.

sericiferous. Silk-bearing.

series. 1. A group of communities based on physiographic aspects and development. 2. A group of sister plants from the same parent or the same cross in any one season.

serodiagnosis. Diagnosis with the aid of serum.

serology. The science of disease diagnosis and treatment with serum.

serotinal. Blooming later in the season than customary for the species.

serous. Thin and watery like a serum.

serpens. Creeping.

serpiform. In the form of a serpent, sinuous.

serpyllifolious. Thyme-leaved, serpyllum-leaved.

serra. Any saw-like structure, as the tooth of a serrate leaf.

serrados. Savannahs strewn with clumps of scattered trees.

serraefolious. Serratifolious.

serrate. With teeth pointing toward the apex, saw-toothed.

serrate-ciliate. Having hairs fringing toothed edges, toothed and with a marginal series of hairs.

serrate-dentate. Having the serrate edges toothed.

serratifolious. With toothed leaves.

serratiform. With a saw-like edge.

serrato-denticulate. With many saw-toothed serrations.

serratulate. Having small teeth pointed upward.

serrature. A saw-like notch, a serration, the teeth or sharp segments of a serrate margin.

serriferous. Having a saw-like organ or part.

serrulation. A small notch like the tooth of a saw.

sertao. A half desert covered with white woods or caatingas.

sertulum. 1. A selection of plants described or figured. 2. A simple umbel.

sertum. An account of a collection of plants.

serum. The clear portion of any animal liquid separated from solid elements, especially of the blood.

sesamoid. Granular like the seeds of *Sesamum.*

seslerietum. An association of the grass *Sesleria.*

seslerioid. Like *Sesleria.*

sesquireciprocation. Reciprocation in the hybrid between an F_1 individual and one of its parents.

sessiflorous. Without pedicels.

sessifolious. Without petioles.

sessile. Without a stalk, sitting directly on the base.

sessile benthos. Plants attached to the bottom of a body of water.

seston. Tiny plankton material which is retained by very fine meshed sieves.

sestonology. The study of seston.

set. A vegetable part used in propagation, as offsets, layers, root-cuttings, etc.

set of chromosomes. A minimum group of chromosomes derived from the gametic complement of an ancestor.

seta. 1. The multicellular stalk which bears the capsule of mosses and liverworts. 2. A hollow outgrowth from a cell, a slender straight prickle or bristle. 3. A thick-walled unicellular structure found among the asci in some ascomycetes. 4. A single elongated cell or row of cells with scanty colorless contents found in some algae. 5. An arista or awn of grasses.

setaceo-rostrate. Having a beak tipped in a bristle.

setaceo-serratus. With the serratures ending in a bristle-like point.

setaceous. Bristle-like.

setria. A bristle.

setiferous. Bristle-bearing.

setifolious. Having leaves with bristles.

setiform. Bristle-shaped.

setigerous. Bristle-bearing.

setipodus. Bristle-footed.

setispinus. Bristle-spined.

setose. Having many bristles.

settlement. Any small combination of individual plants without regard to taxonomic value or sociological status; see COLONY, FAMILY, etc.

settling basins. Tanks, pits, or depressions in the ground in which suspended solids in sewage or water gradually settle out.

setula. The stipe of some fungi, a setule or diminutive seta.

setuliform. Like a fine bristle or thread.

sex-. A prefix meaning six.

sex. The sum total of the characteristic structures and functions by which animals and plants are classed as male or female.

sex cell. A gamete.

sex chromosomes. The chromosomes that are particularly connected with the determination of sex and which are distinguished by shape and function from other chromosomes, the X and Y chromosomes.

sex-controlled inheritance. The characters which can only be manifested in one or the other sex, the genes producing them being carried either in the sex chromosomes or in the autosomes.

sex determination. The circumstances which take place before and during the development of an organism which establishes its sex.

sex intergradation. The presence of male characters in female flowers and vice versa, polygamy.

sex-intergrade. A plant bearing staminate and pistillate flowers but belonging to a species of which members are normally dioecious.

sex-limited. Restricted to sex intergrades or found in one sex only.

sex linkage. The association of an hereditary character with sex in such a way that in the case of a recessive character it crosses from one sex to the other in successive generations (crisscross inheritance) due to the fact that its chromosome is the mate of an empty (dummy) chromosome for the gene in question.

sex-linked characters. Hereditary characters borne by the sex chromosome.

sex-linked inheritance. The association of the determiner for any unit character with a sex determiner in such a way that the two determiners are either generally included in the same gamete or are generally included in different gametes.

sex mosaic. An intersexual individual with characters of both sexes.

sex organ. A gametangium.

sex ratio. The proportion of males to females, usually expressed as the number of males per 100 females.

sex reversal. A change from one sex to the other naturally, pathologically, or artificially induced.

sexangular. Having six angles.

sexfarious. Having six rows or six faces.

sexfoil. 1. A group of six leaves or leaflets around one axis. 2. A flower with six leaves.

sexifid. In six divisions.

sexilocular. With six cells or locules.

sexpartite. In six parts.

sexsporous. With six spores.

sexsulcatus. With six furrows.

sextant. A radial cell division of segments into three series, a sixth part of the original.

sextuplex. Six-fold.

sexual cell. A sperm or an egg.

sexual dimorphism. Strongly marked differences in size, color, etc., between male and female of one species.

sexual generation. The generation or stage which bears the sexual organs.

sexual reproduction. Reproduction resulting from the fusion of two germ cells of different sexes.

sexual spore. A spore formed by the union of sexually differentiated gametes.

sexual system. Linnaeus' artificial arrangement by the number and position of the sexual organs.

sexuality. The quality or state of being distinguished by sex.

sexually heterocaryotic. Having bisexual mycelia the cells of which contain a mixture of nuclei of both sexes not arranged in conjugate pairs.

shade chomophyte. A plant which inhabits shaded rock crevices, a shade chromophore.

shade leaves. Leaves adapted to modified light, ombrophiles.

shade plant. 1. A plant which flourishes only or grows best in shade. 2. A quick-growing plant which is grown to afford shade to crops and removed when the protection is no longer needed.

shadow cell. A degenerate, senescent, or dead cell of yeast which is devoid of contents and does not stain.

shaft. 1. The trunk, stem, or stalk of a plant. 2. The style of a flower.

shaggy. Rough with long compact fibrils, villous or hirsute with long hairs.

shagreen. Roughly pebbled or minutely cobble-stoned in appearance, papilliate.

shake. A defect in timber due to attack of *Trametes pini*, also known as bark-, heart-, or ring-shake.

shaling. Scaly, in large flakes.

shallot. An onion-like plant (*Allium ascolonicum*) producing small clustered bulbs used like garlic for flavoring, a small onion.

shallow sea. The zone extending from the low-water mark of spring tides to the edge of the continental shelf.

shearing. Displacement of the particles of a body by lateral strain.

sheath. 1. A gelatinous envelope surrounding a plant. 2. The base of a leaf when it is a sheath. 3. A tubular envelope. 4. A cylindrical tube surrounding organs or cells.

sheath cells. Upright ray cells tending to form a sheath about the smaller cells of a multiseriate ray.

shelf, conducting. A ledge within the ascidium of *Cephalotus follicularis*.

shell. The hard outer covering of a fruit, the hard envelope of a nut.

shell bark. Rhytidome.

shelter parasite. See DOMATIA, SYMBIOSIS, RAUMPARASIT, AUTOPHYTE.

sherds. The fragments of potting employed by gardeners to drain flower pots.

shield. 1. A broad table-like process in the flower of *Stapelia* and its allies. 2. An apothecium or disc arising from a lichen thallus containing asci.

shift. The displacement of a segment of a chromosome from one location to another location in the same chromosome, the segregation of factors causing variation in the offspring.

shifting. Gliding growth.

shingle. Banks which arise on coasts when material such as flints are drifted together by littoral currents. Recognized types include fringing, spit, bar, and apposition.

shoot. Any portion of a plant which has been formed by one growing point, the part of the plant coming from the plumule, a sprout.

shoot, long. A leader.

shoot, pole. The point where new shoot growth begins.

shoot, thalloid. An unsegmented shoot.

short plant. A plant in which the onset of flowering is hastened by giving the plant alternating periods of relatively short illumination and relatively long darkness.

short rods. Short bacteria.

short shoot. A spur, a dwarfed fertile branch.

short-shoot styled. With styles shorter than the anthers.

shoshun. The suction response of plants.

shoshungraph. An apparatus to record suctional response in plants.

shot. A hollow in a desert which accumulates water which leaves a salt spot when dry, a chott.

shot hole. A disease resulting in small holes being formed in the leaves of various plants due to certain fungi.

shoulder. The part in *Lagenostoma* which curves inward toward the apex of the seed.

shrub. A woody perennial smaller than a tree, usually with several stems.

shrub layer. A growth of short woody perennial plants which form an understory in a forest.

shrub steppe. A community where vegetation is very scanty but nevertheless regular.

shrub stratum. Mixed woodland from three to fifteen feet in height.

shrub wood. Woodland in which the shrubs constitute the chief feature.

shrubbage. The vegetation which composes the shrub stratum or layer taken collectively.

shrubbery. A growth, group, or collection of shrubs.

shrubby. 1. Woody, with more than one trunk. 2. Full of shrubs. 3. Resembling a shrub.

shrublet. An undershrub.

siamens. Of Siam.

sibiricus. Of Siberia.

siblings. Plants from the ovaries or the pollen of the same plant, offspring of same parents but not at the same birth.

sibljak. 1. A transitional layer between a steppe and a forest composed of species which tolerate more light and warmth than forest species. 2. A transitional open shrubby forest community which develops on cutover land.

sibship. The relationship of siblings.

siccans. Drying.

siccideserta. Steppe formations, dry areas with open vegetation.

siccissimideserta. Deserts on which less than half of the substratum is covered with vegetation.

siccitate. In the dry state, as herbarium specimens.

siccocolous. Xerophilous.

siccous. Dry, juiceless.

sickle stage. A crescent-shaped body at one margin of the nucleus supposed to represent a stage in the disappearance of the nucleolus, a paranucleus.

siculiform. Sickle-shaped.

siculus. Of Sicily.

sicyoid. Gourd-shaped, elongate pyriform.

side-chain theory. A theory of the phenomena of immunity: that toxins unite with living protoplasm by possessing the same property as that by which nutritive proteins are normally assimilated.

siderophil. Staining deeply with stains containing iron.

siderophiles. Iron-loving plants.

siderophloius. Iron bark.

siderophobes. Iron-hating plants.

sideroplasts. Plants whose shapes vary with the iron in the soil.

siderotrophic water. Water with large amounts of dissolved iron compounds.

sierra. A ridge of rugged mountains.

sieve area. A limited area on the longitudinal wall of a sieve tube perforated by numerous free fine pores through which material may pass.

sieve cells. Cells of the phloem characterized by the presence of perforated plates in the wall.

sieve disk. The end wall of sieve cells thickened and modified, the perforated septum between the ends of adjoining sieve tubes, a sieve plate.

sieve field. Thin perforated areas in the walls of sieve tubes.

sieve pit. A perforation of sieve plates.

sieve pitting. The arrangement of small pits in cribriform clusters.

sieve plate. 1. A thin perforated end wall of a sieve tube. 2. A perforated area in the lateral wall of a sieve tube, as in ferns. 3. A sieve disk.

sieve pores. The perforations in a sieve disk.

sieve structure. The finely dotted closing membrane of bilateral and unilateral bordered pits.

sieve tissue. The conducting tissue of the phloem usually in the vascular bundle but occasionally found in the pith or cortex. It consists of the sieve tubes and some companion cells.

sieve tubes. An element of the phloem with lateral or terminal sieve plates.

sieve xylem. Groups of sieve cells in the wood of *Dicella*.

sieversetum. A plant association in which *Sieversia* is the predominant factor.

sigillarian. Resembling or allied to *Sigillaria*, a fossil plant.

sigillate. Having seal-like markings on certain roots, adorned with figures resembling the impression of a seal.

sigmatoid. Doubly curved in opposite directions like the Greek sigma (Z), sigmoid.

signature. Any outward mark by which internal characteristics are supposed to be indicated.

sikkimensis. Of Sikkim in North India (Sikhim).

sikyotic. Parasitic by fusion of the plasma of host and parasite, as *Chaetocladium* on *Mucor*.

silage. Fodder, usually finely cut, preserved by compressing and covering it while green in a silo, pit, or stack.

silaifolious. With leaves like *Silaus*, one of the *Umbelliferae*.

silenetum. An association of *Silene*, the pink.

silica. The mineral of which quartz, sand, flint, etc., are composed and which occurs in many rough (to the touch) plants.

siliceous. Showing a preference for flinty or sandy soils.

silicicole. A plant showing a preference for siliceous soils.

silicification. The deposition of silica in plant tissue.

silicion. Sand-flinty soils.

silicle. A short capsule containing many seeds derived from two united carpels divided by a replum, a short silique which is broader than long, a silicule or silicula.

silico-cellulose. Having silica intimately blended in tissue, as in *Equisetum hyemale*.

silicole. A plant thriving in siliceous soil.

silicular. Like or having a silicle.

silicule. A silicle.

siliculosus. Bearing silicles.

siliculous. See SILICULOSE.

silique. A special long, slender capsule of two carpels found in the mustard family; an elongate two-valved capsular fruit with two parietal placentae, usually dehiscent.

siliquella. A subordinate part of a fruit, such as the poppy, consisting of a carpel with two extended placentae.

Siliquosa. An order of the *Tetrodynamia* having siliques.

siliquose. Bearing or resembling siliques.

silk. The style of the corn; a coat of fine, soft, closely-appressed straight hairs.

silk-bark oak. The silky oak of Australia, *Grevillea robusta*.

silk-cotton. The cottony substance enveloping the seeds of various bombacaceous trees.

silk-cotton tree. The tree which yields kapok fiber, *Ceiba pentandra*.

silky. Having shiny, close-fitting fibrils or a coating of soft, appressed, fine hairs.

Silurian. The earlier middle Paleozoic geological period.

silva. A forest, the forest trees of a region or country considered collectively.

silva paludosa. A swamp forest.

silver grain. Plates of medullary rays which appear as glimmering spots on the surface of wood when it is split radially, the medullary rays.

silver leaf. A disease of plum leaves caused by *Stereum purpureum*.

silvester zone. The extramarginal zone of a lake.

similary parts. Elementary organs or tissues.

similiflorous. Having the flowers in an umbel all alike.

similisymmetry. Consimilarity, when the two halves of a diatom valve are similar.

simple. 1. Not branched. 2. One-celled. 3. In one piece.

simple frond. An entire undivided frond.

simple fruit. A fruit composed of a single ripened ovary.

simple gland. A single cell containing a special secretion.

simple gonidiophore. A single hypha, as in *Penicillium*.

simple hairs. Hairs which are not compound or branched. Formed by the simple proliferation of one epidermal cell.

simple inflorescence. A flower cluster having one axis, such as a spike, spadix, or catkin; an inflorescence in which only the main flower stem branches.

simple leaf. A leaf with the blade in one piece.

simple medullary ray. A medullary ray not composed of vertically alternating different parts.

simple nutation. Nutation in one direction only.

simple pistil. A unicarpellate pistil.

simple perforation. A single and usually large and more or less rounded opening in the perforation plate.

simple pit. A pit in which the canal is equally wide throughout or widens toward the cell cavity.

simple pore. A pore with only a slight enlargement at the center where it meets the neighboring cell.

simple primary root. A tap root.

simple sorus. A sorus made up of a single sporangium.

simple sporophore. A sporophore consisting of a single hypha or branch of a hypha.

simple starch grain. A starch grain with a single hilum.

simple stem. An unbranched stem.

simple tissue. A tissue composed of cells all of the same kind.

simple umbel. An umbel in which each ray terminates in a single flower.

simple vascular bundle. A bundle which does not contain medullary rays.

simple veins. Single unbranched veins.

simple venation. Venation in which only the midrib is clearly visible.

simplex. 1. Simple, unbranched. 2. Having one dominant gene.

simplex character. A simplex factor.

simplex factor. A determiner for a character which is derived from one parent only.

simplex group. The haploid complement of chromosomes.

simplices. Homosporous ferns in which the sporangia are produced simultaneously, especially those occurring in primary rocks, as the *Marattiaceae*.

simplicicaule. Simple-stemmed.

simplicifolious. Simple-leaved.

simulation. The assumption of features or structures intended to deceive enemies, as form of leaf and all varieties of protective coloration.

simultaneous whorl. A whorl in which the members are of the same age and develop at the same time.

sinagrin. A glucoside occurring in the seeds of *Brassica sinapoides*.

sinalbin. Mustard oil from *Brassica alba*, a white crystalline basic glucoside in white mustard seed.

sinapisin. Sinapin; an alkaloid from the seeds of mustard, *Brassica*.

sinensis. Chinese.

single flower. A flower with one set of petals and no indication of doubling.

singuliform. Having variation in one organ which is independent of variation in another.

sinicus. Chinese.

sinigrin. Sinagrin.

sinistral. Turned to the left, sinistrorse, sinistrad.

sinistrin. A carbohydrate from the lily *Urginea* and certain other bulbs.

sinistrorse. Turning toward the left.

sinistrostylous. With the styles bent to the left.

sink holes. Surface depressions resulting from the dissolving of certain substances underground and the resulting lowering of the surface.

sink lakes. Lakes whose basins are produced by the dissolution of the limestone strata and the descent of the overlying soil.

sinkers. The secondary roots of mistletoe forming laterals which strike perpendicularly downward into the wood of the host.

sinuate. 1. Of gills, having a concave indentation of the edge near the stem. 2. Having strongly waved margins. 3. Winding.

sinuate-dentate. Having teeth with the clefts or openings rounded at the bottom, wavy.

sinuate-serrate. Having serratures with the clefts or openings rounded at the bottom.

sinuated. Deeply waved.

sinuately pinnatifid. Unevenly pinnatifid alternately with deep concavities and convexities.

sinuato-dentate. Sinuate and toothed.

sinuolate. Faintly or minutely sinuate.

sinus. 1. A pore in some fungi. 2. The recess between the half cells of *Desmidiae*. 3. The bay or recess formed by leaf lobes. 4. The gap in a fimbriated micropyle in *Lagenostoma*.

siotropism. The response to shaking.

siphon. A siphon-like structure of various organisms, e.g., a large, long, tubular cell in *Chara* and some other algae.

siphonea. A stage in *Volvox* when the blastopore is drawn out and the archenteron has become tubular.

siphonein. A pigment found in the algae in *Siphonales*.

siphoniphyton. A composite with all its florets tubular.

siphonogam. A plant which is fertilized by means of a pollen tube, as a phanerogam.

siphonostele. 1. A hollow cylindrical stele with or without pith. 2. A vascular cylinder surrounding a central pith. 3. The central vascular cylinder when complete as a tube.

Sippe. A theoretical typical plant instead of an actual specimen plant.

siraplankton. Floating marine vegetation mainly composed of *Thalassosira*.

sirenin. A hormone produced by the female gametes of some algae which attracts the male gametes.

sirosiphoid. Like the genus *Sirosiphon* in which the cells occur in two or more rows.

sirosiphonaceous. Like the alga *Sirosiphon*.

sisal hemp. A fibrous material used extensively for cordage and binder twine obtained chiefly from *Agave sisalana*.

sister cell. A cell with the same origin as another.

sisymbrifolious. Leaved like *Sisymbrium*, a mustard.

sitchensis. Of Sitka, Alaska.

sitotropism. The tendency to turn in the direction of food.

site index. The average height of the dominant trees in a stand at 50 years or the height which would be reached by the dominant trees at 50 years.

situs. 1. The position occupied by an organ. 2. The mycelium of some fungi.

skaphoplankton. Boat-shaped organisms floating as a mass.

skatobios. The inhabitants of detritus.

skein. The condition of the chromation of the nucleus in the first and last stages of karyokinesis when the nucleus filament is emerging from or passing into its reticulated condition in the resting nucleus, the spireme.

skeletogenous. Embryonic and later becoming part of the skeleton.

skeleton. Hard or bony framework, internal or external, which supports and protects the softer parts of plants and animals.

skeletoplasm. The formative material destined to form supporting structures.

skew curve. An asymmetrical variation curve in contrast to the symmetrical Gaussian curve.

skinny. 1. Scariose. 2. Consisting chiefly of skin.

skiophyte. A plant which is not adapted to full exposure but prefers shade.

skittle-shaped. Shaped like a ninepin.

skoliotropic. Curved.

skotopelagile. Below the limit of light in the ocean or lakes, in the deeper areas of lakes or oceans.

skotophilous. Geophilous.

skotropism. The response of a plant seeking darkness.

sky light. The diffuse light falling on a plant from the sky in contrast to direct sunlight.

slacks. Shallow valleys due to glacial lakes in the Pleistocene Age.

slashed. Deeply cut into narrow incisions more irregular and larger than fimbriate.

slean. The smut of oats caused by *Ustilago Avenae*.

sleep. The repose of plants with changes in position of organs such as leaves due to absence of light, nyctitropism.

sleep movement. Changes in position of some plant parts (usually due to absence of light) as leaflets which fold at night or flowers which close at night, etc.

sleeping. A disease of tomatoes due to *Fusarium lycopersici*.

Slette. Danish for plain.

sliding growth. The gradual change in the relative position of vessels, fibers, etc., due to their development in a longitudinal direction.

slime flux. A flow of liquid from diseased fruit and forest trees due to the attacks of various fungi producing a fermentation of the cortical elements down to the cambium zone.

slime fungi. *Myxomycetes*.

slime molds. *Myxomycetes*.

slime plug. A mass of shiny material filling the pores in a sieve tube.

slime strings. Metabolized material in a state of flux which passes by the pores of the sieve plates from one sieve tube to another.

sling fruit. Any fruit which by possessing contractile tissue projects its seeds some distance.

slip. A softwood cutting used for propagation.

slit. The narrowest portion of pores in stomata.

slit-like bordered pits. A bordered pit with a slit-like opening.

slit-like simple pit canal. A pit canal (or part of it toward the cavity) more or less elongated in surface view.

slooting. Erosion by water in narrow channels which form gulleys.

slough. A swamp, bog, marsh, or a sluggish channel.

sludge. The material which settles out of sewage or is precipitated by means of chemicals.

small fruits. A horticultural term for certain low-growing perennial fruit-bearing plants and their products, including strawberry, raspberry, and other berries.

smaller secondary medullary rays. Secondary medullary rays which do not reach to the pith or pericycle.

smaragdine. Emerald green.

smilaceous. Like *Smilax*.

smilacine. A crystalline body occurring in the roots of the officinal sarsparilla, *Smilax*.

smooth margins of perforations. Simple perforation pits in xylem vessels.

smut. A destructive disease of various plant species which is caused by parasitic fungi of the *Ustilaginales*.

smut fungus. *Ustilaginales*.

smut spores. Reproductive bodies of the *Ustilaginales*.

snail plants. Plants which are fertilized by snails and slugs, malacophilous plants.

snipt. Incised.

snow flushes. The dark patches of soil due to accumulated deposit from melting snow. The vegetation is known as anthelietum.

snow leaves. Thin or leathery leaves folded in the bud and having no pulvinus, winter leaves.

snow patch flora. Snow flushes.

sobole. A creeping underground stem which develops leaf buds and roots at intervals.

soboliferous. Producing young plants from the roots, having shoots near the ground, bearing soboles.

sobriniform. A versiform which belongs to a subgregiform, as *Rubus moluccanus*.

socia. A society.

sociability. The manner in which the individuals of the same species are disposed in relation to one another, the predetermined degree of aggregation of individuals or shoots based on the manner of growth.

social. 1. Growing in clumps or masses. 2. Permitting the entrance of other individuals.

social, competitive. Having roots compete at the same level.

social, complementary. Having component plant roots at different levels.

social, exclusive. Having a pure group of plants with no other species present.

social flowers. *Compositae* or flowers with florets grouped in a head.

social habits. Formations of homogenous forests of one or more species as pine, birch, beech-maple, etc.

social, inclusive. Permitting the entrance of other species into a plant group.

social plants. Plants which grow well in the presence of other species and occupy wide areas.

socialis. Sociable, companionable.

socials. Dominant species as an expression of frequency.

sociation. 1. A stable phytocoenosis of essentially uniform composition with uniform dominants in every layer. 2. The elementary unit of a plant community. 3. A seasonal society.

socies. A seral community with one or more subdominants.

société. A community.

societies, plant. Descending grades of communities of plants found associated together on land with similar ecological characters.

society. A plant community of minor rank forming part of a consociation, a climax community with one or more subdominants.

society, layer. A plant community within an association which develops at more or less definite levels.

sociological affinity. The tendency of two or more plant species to compose a mixed community.

sociological relevé. A floristic enumeration accompanied by coefficients or numbers corresponding with analytical or synthetical characters such as abundance and density, dominance frequency, sociability, vitality, periodicity, and stratification.

sociology, plant. Plants living together in relation to one another, plant ecology, economic botany.

socion. A synusium which is limited to a definite sociation and so exhibits at least the homogeneity of a consocion.

sociule. A seasonal socies of a microcommunity.

socotranus. Of the island of Socotra (south of Arabia).

sodomeum. Of Sodom.

soft bast. The part of phloem made up thin-walled cells, namely sieve tube companion cells and phloem parenchyma; the sieve tubes together with any other unlignified portion of the phloem.

soft wood. Technically the lumber derived from conifers; any wood light in texture, nonresistant, and easily worked.

soft-wooded. Suffruiticose, not fully lignified.

soil flora. Plants, chiefly fungi, living in the soil.

sol. A colloidal solution.

solanaceous. Of or pertaining to *Solanum*.

solanin. A poisonous crystallizable alkaloid in many species of *Solanum*, especially in the potato and the tomato.

solar. Having branches or filaments like rays of sun.

solar cycle. Equivalent to the sunspot cycle.

solar plants. Plants which twine with the sun, that is, dextrorsely.

solarisation. The temporary stoppage of photosynthesis in a leaf when it is exposed for a long time to bright light.

solarium. A place for exposing plants to the full rays of the sun.

soldanelloid. Like *Soldanella*, an alpine flower which blooms in the snow.

sole. The end farthest from the apex in a carpel.

soleaeform. Slipper-shaped, almost resembling an hour glass.

solenaidy. The conversion of the genitals into barren tubes.

soleniaplankton. Floating neritic vegetation characterized by an abundance of *Rhizosolenia*.

solenostele. 1. A siphonostele in which there is an endodermis both inside and outside the vascular tube. 2. An amphiphloic vascular tube with widely separated leaf gaps.

solenostele, perforated. A solenostele in which gaps other than leaf gaps occur.

solenostelic. Having internal and external phloem in a tubular stele.

solfataras. Hot sulphur springs around which a special xerophilous vegetation grows.

solid bulb. A corm.

solitary gregarious. In a single clump of one species.

solitary pore. A pore completely surrounded by other elements.

solod. A saline soil after it has been leached.

solopathogenic. Having a single-spored strain of a smut.

soluble starch. A product of the hydrolysis of starch obtained by treating starch with dilute acids or boiling in glycerin or by the action of a diastase.

solum. Soil.

solution. 1. The abnormal separation of parts usually united, as the detachment of various whorls normally adherent. 2. A homogenous mixture of two or more substances one of which is usually liquid.

somacules. 1. Hypothetical units, the ultimate component parts of protoplasm. 2. The ultracellular units ranking between the molecule and the cell, such as physiological units, genes, primordia, gemmules, etc.

somaplasm. Somata.

somata. Granules of any kind.

somatarchous. Having cell division in which one portion continues the reproductive function and the other transmits the somatic function.

somatella. Usually a transient stage in development in which the nucleus has divided several times while the cell body remains undivided.

somatia. Starch-like structures found in the fovilla of pollen grains.

somatic. Pertaining to the body as contrasted with germinal; referring to body tissues, not germ cells.

somatic apogamy. The condition in the cell which gives rise to the sporophyte possessing the haploid chromosomes.

somatic budding. The separation of the buds from the soma or plant body.

somatic cell. A body cell as distinguished from a germ cell.

somatic mitosis. An equational division of the nucleus as it occurs in the process of growth.

somatic mutation. A mutation taking place in body cells instead of in the cells forming the gametes.

somatic parthenogenesis. A condition in which an embryo is formed without fertilization from a diploid egg.

somatic segregation. Segregation during somatic division.

somatocyst. An air cavity in the pneumatophore of siphonophores.

somatogen. A somatogenic variation.

somatogenesis. See DEVELOPMENT.

somatogenic. Originating in the soma, developing from somatic cells.

somatome. A somite or body segment.

somatophyte. A plant whose cells develop mainly into adult body tissue, a higher plant possessing adult parts and organs.

somatoplasm. The substance of the somatic cells, the body plasm as contrasted to germ plasm.

somatotropism. An influence which the substratum exerts on the direction of growth of certain plants and organs, somatropism.

somniferous. Causing sleep.

sonchifolious. With leaves like *Sonchus*, the sow-thistle.

sonoran. Of Sonora in the region of the Gulf of Lower California, a very dry area.

sonoran life zone. The plants in Sonora.

sooty mold. Sooty patches on fruit and leaves of plants, chiefly citrus.

soral. Relating to a sorus.

soralium. A group of soredia surrounded by a definite margin.

sorbifolious. With leaves like *Sorbus*, the mountain ash.

sorbin. A glucose occurring in *Pyrus*.

sordid. Dirty, dingy, dirty white, muddy.

sorede. A soredium.

soredial branch. A branch produced by the development of a soredium into a new thallus while still on the mother thallus.

sorediate. Bearing soredia, having patches on the surface.

sorediferous. Bearing a soredium.

soredium. A single algal cell or group of algal cells wrapped in hyphal tissue which, when set free from the thallus, is able to grow into a new thallus at once; a broad bud.

soredium-heap. A sorus.

sorema. A cluster of carpels belonging to one flower.

soreuma. A soredium.

sorghin. The product of the transformation of sorghorubin.

sorghorubin. The natural pigment of *Sorghum vulgare*.

soridium. A soredium.

soriferous. Bearing sori.

sorocarp. The undifferentiated fruiting structure of the *Acrasieae*, often irregularly shaped, without membrane or containing wall.

soroma. The sporangial apparatus of the vascular plant with its receptacle or stalk.

sorophore. 1. A gelatinous cushion on the neutral edge of the sporocarp of *Marsilea* and ferns. 2. The stalk or the supporting structure of the sorus in *Acrasieae*.

sorores. A physiological species.

sorosis. A multiple fruit like a pineapple, mulberry, etc.

sorosphere. A hollow sphere of cells each of which becomes a spore, as in *Sorosphaera*.

sorrowful flowers. Flowers which lose their odor only at certain hours of the day.

sorus. 1. A powdery mass of soredia on the surface of a lichen thallus. 2. In ferns, fungi, etc., a cluster of sporangia with a cover. 3. A group of antheridia on male fronds of marine algae.

sorus canals. Cavities in the young sporangia of certain pteridophytes.

sorus fusion. Several sori which have run together without apparent distinction.

sorus gametangia. Reproductive bodies in *Giraudia* on the assimilating cells.

sorus sporangia. Reproductive bodies crowded into groups on the branches of the alga *Kjellmania*.

space parasite. A plant receiving shelter but possibly taking nothing else which inhabits intercellular spaces in another plant.

spadiceous. 1. Date brown. 2. Bearing a spadix.

spadiciflorae. Spadix-forming plants.

spadix. An inflorescence consisting of a fleshy central column bearing many stamens below and many pistils above, surrounded by a large bract or spathe usually showy, giving the whole the effect of a single flower.

spanandary. The disappearance or extreme rarity of males in normal bisexual lines of descent.

spananthous. Having few flowers.

spangles. Patellulae.

sparganiaceous. Related to *Sparganium*, an aquatic herb.

sparganietum. An association of *Sparganium*.

sparganium cortex. Fossil stems with a vertical system of fibrous strands which do not anastomose, as *Medullosa*.

sparganium type. The cortex having short radiating bands of fibrous sclerenchyma running vertically without anastomoses.

sparganum. A type of cortex of parenchymatous tissue with vertical groups of thick-walled fibers.

sparsae. Species having only isolated individuals.

sparsiflorous. With few flowers.

sparsifolious. With few leaves.

sparsioplasts. Elaioplasts variable in position and numbers.

sparteous. Pertaining to the broom genus *Spartina*.

spartinetum. An association of *Spartina*, cord or marsh grass, broom.

spartoid. With persistent corticated mycelium.

spathe. The leaf-like colored bract investing the inflorescence of aroids and palms, a large bract or pair of bracts subtending a spadix or flower cluster.

spathe valves. The bract-like envelopes beneath the flowers in certain monocotyledons as *Allium* and *Narcissus*.

spathella. 1. A small spathe surrounding divisions of a palm spadix. 2. A glume in grasses.

spathellula. A palea of a grass.

spathiflorae. Herbs or woody plants, sometimes climbing, rarely forming an erect stem, usually sympodial.

spathilla. A secondary spathe as in the inflorescence of palms.

spathulate. Spatula-shaped, oblong with an attenuated base.

spawn. The commercial term for a mixture of organic matter containing mycelium of a mushroom.

specialization. Modifications of structure or habit enabling an organism to live in particular conditions or to perform particular functions.

specialized. Adapted by modifications or evolution to particular environments or functions.

specialized form. A biological race.

speciation. The evolutionary process by which species are formed.

specient. A term used to emphasize the fact that each individual possesses a dual nature: as an individual and as a member of a species or genus.

species. A term used in classification to denote a group of closely allied, mutually fertile individuals which show constant differences from allied groups; the second name of plants or animals in binomial nomenclature which distinguishes the species from other species in the same genus.

species centre. The particular spot where the species is supposed to have originated.

species character. The criterion which separates one species from another.

species, constant. The characteristic species of a social unit.

species, elementary. A true unit, not a collective species.

species guild. An invading community.

species, hybrid. A hybrid between two species of the same genus.

species, Jordan's. A group of organisms believed to have arisen by a mutation.

species, Linnaean. A group of organisms of closely similar appearance.

species, morphologic. A species based on form and structure.

species, name. See SPECIES.

species, physiological. See PHYSIOLOGIC RACES.

species, sorores. Any two species of *Uredineae* which inhabit two distinct hosts but show no morphological differences.

specific. Referring to characteristics which are used in designating or distinguishing species.

specific character. See SPECIFIC.

specific conductivity of woods. The rate at which water flows through a piece of wood of standard area and length in a given time.

specific name. The name of the species.

specificity. The restriction of parasites to particular hosts.

specimen. A part or an entire plant prepared and preserved for study, a sample or example intended to show the kind and quality of the whole.

speciology. The study of species.

speciosus. Handsome.

spectabilis. Visually striking or remarkable.

spectans. Opposite.

spectrophore. An instrument to determine the action of the different rays of light on the elimination of oxygen by plants.

speiranthy. The assumption of a twisted form by a flower.

speirema. A gonidium in lichens.

speirogonimium. A twisted gonimium; an algal cell which occurs in a lichen, either singly or scattered; the asexual reproductive body in lichens; a gonidium.

speirostichies. A spiral series.

spergulin. A florescent substance occurring in the seeds of *Spergula*, spurry.

sperm. The male element or elements in sexual reproduction, the male gamete, a spermatazoon, a spermatozoid, a pollen grain.

sperm cell. A male reproductive cell.

sperm centrosome. The small body at the apex of the head of a spermatazoon.

sperm chromatin. The part of the male nucleus which is receptive to stains.

sperm mother cell. The cell which develops into sperms.

sperm nucleus. The nucleus in the sperm which fuses with the nucleus of the egg to form a germ nucleus.

spermaduct. The duct for conveying spermatozoa.

spermagone. A cell or receptacle in which spermatia are produced, a pycnidium-like structure, pycnium.

spermamoebae. Certain specialized portions of the antheridial protoplasm of *Saprolegniae* which fertilize the oosphere.

spermangium. The sporangium of an alga.

spermaphore. The placenta.

spermaphyte. One of the *Spermatophyta*, one of the great divisions of the plant kingdom including all seed-producing plants.

spermapodium. A branched gynophore in the *Umbelliferae*.

spermapodophorum. A spermapodium.

spermarium. An antheridium.

spermary. An organ in which sperms arise, a pollen tube, a gamete.

spermatange. A spermagonium, an antheridium.

spermatic. Pertaining to a spermary.

spermatid. A mature male germ cell which has not undergone final transformation into a spermatozoon.

spermatiferous. Bearing spermatia.

spermatiform. Like or resembling a spermatium.

spermatigerous. Bearing spermatia.

spermatioid. Like a spermatium.

spermatiophore. A structure bearing a spermatium.

spermatium. 1. A nonmotile gamete carried to the tricogyne by water. 2. A spore-like structure which is formed by some lichens and some fungi which may perform sexual functions.

spermatization. The application of macroconidia or spermatia to receive mycelial structures of the opposite sex or polarity with the result that ascocarps and basidiocarps are produced.

spermatize. To impregnate.

spermatoconidium. A spermatium.

spermatocyst. A seminal sac; the mother cell of antheridia, especially in mosses.

spermatocyte. A spermatocyst, the sperm mother cell, a gametocyte.

spermatocytium. A single sporangium containing spermatozoids.

spermatogamete. A male gamete.

spermatogenesis. A sperm formation, the development of a spermatozoon from a primitive sex cell.

spermatogonidium. A spermatozoid.

spermatogonium. A primordial sperm cell.

spermatoid. Like a sperm.

spermatoidium. One of the small cells containing gonidia in algae.

spermatokalium. The perithecium in *Verrucaria*.

spermatokinetic. Tending to produce the male elements in plants.

spermatomerites. Chromatin granules formed from the sperm nucleus.

spermatophore. A structure bearing a spermatium, a capsule of albuminous matter containing a number of sperms.

spermatophytes. The seed plants (the highest plants).

spermatoplasm. The protoplasm of sperms.

spermatoplast. A male sexual cell.

spermatosome. A spermatozoon.

spermatosphaeria. Presumed male bodies in *Spirogyra*.

spermatostrote. A plant migrating by means of seeds.

spermatothamnia. The antheridial filaments of *Rhodophyceae*.

spermatoxin. Antibodies causing sterility.

spermatozoid. A motile fertile body produced in an antheridium, the male gamete ready for fertilization, an antherozoid.

spermatozoon. A male reproductive cell.

spermatum. Spermatium.

spermidium. An achene.

spermiogenesis. Spermatogenesis.

spermioteleosis. Spermiogenesis, the metamorphosis of the spermatid into the sperm, spermateleosis.

spermism. Animalculism, the theory that the sperm or spermatozoon contains the germ of the future embryo.

spermocarp. 1. An oogonium after fertilization. 2. The fruit of the *Characeae*.

spermocarpous. Phanerogamous.

spermocentre. The male centrosome during fertilization.

spermoderm. The outer covering of a seed, the seed coat.

spermodophorum. The gynophore in *Umbelliferae*.

spermogemma. The archegonium.

spermagone. A cup-shaped receptacle in

which spermatia are abjointed, differing from a pycnidium by the smaller spores.

spermogonia. Flask-shaped bodies containing spermatia.

spermogoniferous. Bearing spermogonia.

spermogonium. A capsule containing spermatia in the fungi and lichens.

spermology. The study of seeds.

spermophore. The funiculus and the placenta, a modified shoot of the thallus of certain algae which produces male organs.

spermophyte. A phanerogam, a flowering plant.

spermotheca. A spermatheca, a pericarp.

spermotype. A specimen cut from a seedling raised from the original type.

sphacela. The apical cell mechanism.

sphacelate. Dead, decayed, withered, dark and shrunken.

sphacelia. The conidial stage of ergot, *Claviceps purpurea*.

sphacelic acid. An acid derived from ergot.

sphaer-. A prefix meaning round; see also SPHER-.

sphaeraphides. Spherocrystals.

sphaeraplankton. The floating spherical algae chiefly composed of *Halosphaera viridis*.

sphaerenchyma. Spherical cells making up tissue, as the pulp of fruit.

sphaeriaceous. Resembling or allied to the ascomycetous order *Sphaeriales* some of which have globose perithecia.

sphaerioid. Resembling or allied to the order *Sphaeriales*.

sphaerite. A spherocrystal.

sphaerobacteria. Bacteria with extremely small rounded cells which become detached.

sphaeroblastus. A cotyledon which arises above ground and bears a rounded tumor at its apex.

sphaerocarpon. A round fruit.

sphaerocarpous. Having round fruit.

sphaerocephalous. Having flowers crowded into a spherical head, as a globular flower.

sphaerochorisis. The division of an axis in all directions, as in a witch's broom.

sphaerocrystal. A spherocrystal.

sphaerocyst. 1. A globular cell in the flesh of some fungi. 2. Two-nucleated bloated cells in fungi with fragmented nuclei.

sphaeroid. Spherical, globular.

sphaeroid cell. A swollen hyphal cell containing fat globules.

sphaerome. Composed of microsomes alone or in chains, not enclosed in a vacuole.

sphaerophytum. A fern with globular sporangia.

sphaeroplast. A bioplast, a cytomicrosome.

sphaerosirian. Having small, ciliated, ellipsoid, yellow-green sperms, as is typical of the genus *Volvox*.

sphaerosome. The envelope of the stratosphere of idiozome formed by the Golgi bodies.

sphaerospore. A tetraspore.

sphaerostachys. With spherical spikes.

sphaerraphide. A spherocrystal.

sphaerula. A globose peridium emitting sporidia buried in pulp, a sphere.

sphaerula ascigera. The receptacle of certain fungi.

sphagnetum. A plant society of *Sphagnum* moss.

sphagnicolous. Inhabiting peat moss.

sphagniherbosa. Communities characterized by the abundance of *Sphagnum* by acid substrata and by the formation of peat.

sphagnion. A *Sphagnum* moor.

sphagniopratum. A moss moor dependent upon rain rather than underground water.

sphagnodyt. An inhabitant of water-saturated moss.

sphagnology. The study of the genus *Sphagnum*.

sphagnophilous. Growing in *Sphagnum*.

sphagnophytes. Plants which prefer to grow on *Sphagnum* cushions.

sphagnosus. Having *Sphagnum* growing under a heath.

sphagnous. Resembling or allied to *Sphagnum*.

sphalerocarpium. An accessory fruit, as an achene in a baccate calyx tube.

sphenoid. Wedge-shaped, cuneate.

sphenophyllaceous. Resembling or allied to the extinct order *Sphenophyllales*.

sphenopsida. A group of plants allied to *Lycopsida* consisting of *Equisetales* and other articulate vascular cryptogams.

sphenopterid. Like the fossil genus *Sphenopteris*.

spher-. A prefix meaning round; see also SPHAER-.

spheraster. A multi-rayed globular spicule.

spherecrystal. A spherocrystal.

sphere yeast. A growth form of *Mucor* which resembles yeast.

spheridium. A capitulum.

spheroblast. A wood ball on the beech and other trees from a dormant eye disconnected from the vascular bundles.

spherocrystal. A rounded crystalline mass of calcium oxalate needles forming a radiating structure found in some plant cells.

spherogenic. Self-rounding, as an amoeboid organism.

spheroid cell. A reserve receptacle in some calcareous lichens.

spherome. A cell inclusion which gives rise to globules of fats and oils.

spheroplast. A chondriosome, a bioblast, a body found among granulations of protoplasm.

spherulate. Covered with small spheres.

spherule. 1. A small spherical body. 2. A spherical body occurring in the sporangioles of *Selaginella*. 3. A comparatively large, thin-walled, spherical pathogenic structure formed in the host tissue which in its later stage of development is a sporangium-producing endospore.

sphinctriform. With an apothecium which is almost sessile, as in the fungus *Sphinctrina*.

sphingophile. A plant whose flowers are pollinated by hawk moths and nocturnal *Lepidoptera*.

sphrigosis. Rankness.

sphyric. Of rock slides.

sphyrion. A plant succession in a talus soil.

spica. A spike.

spicate. Spiked or spike-like.

spiciferous. Bearing or producing spikes.

spiciflorous. With spike-like flowers.

spiciform. Shaped like a spike.

spicigerous. Bearing flower spikes.

spicose. With spikes, spiculate.

spicular cell. A hard, thick-walled cell, spindle-shaped or branched, occurring in soft, thin-walled tissue.

spiculate. Set with spicules, divided into small spikes, having a surface covered with fine points.

spiculation. An attenuated constriction of the hypha in the formation of spores.

spicule. A small pointed appendage somewhat soft and fleshy, the point of the basidium in fungi, a sterigma, a diminutive spike or prickle.

spiculiferous. Having spicules, protected by spicules.

spiculifolious. With spiked leaves.

spiculiform. Spicule-shaped.

spike. A type of inflorescence in which the flowers are sessile on the sides of a long common peduncle or rachis.

spike, compound. An inflorescence consisting of spikes.

spike stalk. The rachis.

spiladophilous. Dwelling in clay.

spiladophyte. A clay plant.

spiladophytia. Clay plant communities.

spilus. The hilum in grasses.

spinaceous. Pertaining to or resembling spinach.

spinate. 1. Spine-shaped. 2. Spine-bearing.

spindle. 1. The nuclear division figure, a mechanism consisting of delicate fibrils concerned with the distribution of the chromosomes during mitosis. 2. A rachis.

spindle, achromatic. The thread-like protoplasmic figures in nuclear division between the poles.

spindle attachment. The point in a chromatid which moves first to the pole at anaphase.

spindle elements. The elements of which the spindle is probably composed and which usually correspond in number to the chromosomes.

spindle fiber. A fine, thread-like structure which forms a spindle and extends from pole to pole or from pole to equator.

spindle hairs. Hairs which resemble malpigheaceous hairs attached centrally and with the ends hooked.

spindle, nuclear. The thread-like protoplasmic figures in nuclear division between the poles.

spindle pole. An extremity of the nuclear spindle.

spindle, primitive. An embryo with polarity.

spindle-shaped. Terete and tapering toward each end.

spine. A thorn, a sharp process originating in the wood, a pointed abortive branch, any pointed rigid process which lacks vascular tissue.

spine-arm. The barren stigma in the genus *Najas*.

spine cells. 1. Transitional spine-arms. 2. In *Chara*, cells of the cortex on the internodes ending in a spine.

spines of the leaves. Hardened extremities of the lobes or spiny elevations, as in holly.

spinicarpous. Having spiny fruit.

spiniferous. Bearing spines, thorny.

spinifolious. With spiny leaves.

spiniform. Shaped like a spine or thorn.

spinigerous. Bearing or producing thorns.

spinulate. Covered with small spines.

spinuliferous. Having small spines.

spinuligerous. Spine-bearing.

spiracle. An air hole, an aperture.

spiraculate. Having spiracles.

spiraculiform. Shaped like a spiracle.

spiral cells. Five cylindrical cells which clasp the egg cell in *Characeae*.

spiral cells and fibers. Cells and/or fibers with spiral thickenings of the walls.

spiral cleavage. Cleavage in which the direction of the spindle axis is shifted obliquely from the vertical direction with regard to the egg axis. In an eight-celled stage the upper quartet of cells usually appears turned in a clockwise spiral.

spiral duct. A spiral vessel.

spiral flower. A flower in which the members are arranged in spirals in place of in whorls.

spiral hyphae. Hyphae which terminate in either a flat or helical coil.

spiral marking. 1. The spiral fibrous thickening characteristic of spirals. 2. A secondary deposit in tracheids.

spiral, oblique. Cleavage into unequal parts, arranged in a mosaic fashion and interlocking with upper cells rotating to the right to alternate with the lower.

spiral phyllotaxy. See PHYLLOTAXY.

spiral thickenings. Helical ridges on the inner face of and a part of the secondary wall.

spiral torsion. See TORSION.

spiral tracheae. Tubes in which the thickening is continuous and passes spirally around the cell.

spiral tracheid. A tracheid in which the secondary wall is laid down in the form of spirally arranged thickenings.

spiral vessel. A duct or vessel which has fibrous thickenings upon the wall in the form of a spiral, a xylem vessel with spiral wall thickenings.

spiralism. The monstrosity of a flower due to torsion.

spirals. The spiral thickenings of tracheids and vessels.

spiranthy. The displacement of flower parts through twisting.

spire. 1. A young leaf or shoot of grass. 2. The continuation of the trunk in excurrent trees like pines.

spireme. The preliminary stage in nuclear division in which the nucleus assumes an involved filamentous condition or ribbon from which the chromosomes are formed.

spireme state. The stage in nuclear division in which the chromosomes are disengaged.

spiricle. 1. A minute spiral thread or filament. 2. A delicate coiled thread in the surface cells of some seeds and achenes which uncoils when moistened, as in *Collomia*.

spiriferous. Having a spiral structure.

spirilla. Spiral bacteria.

spirilliferous. Bearing or having spiricles.

spirillum. A bacterium with a strongly spiral shape, any helicoidal bacterial cell.

spirobacteria. Bacteria which form spirally curved filaments, as the genus *Spirillum*.

spirofibrillae. The spirally twisted hollow threads which constitute all living protoplasm.

spirogyretum. An association of *Spirogyra*.

spiroid. 1. Having spiral thickenings as in the cells of the tentacles of *Drosera*. 2. Like a screw or spiral.

spiroism. The coiling of an organism in development.

spirolobeae. The *Cruciferae* which have cotyledons folded transversely and the radicle dorsally.

spirolobous. With the cotyledons spirally rolled.

spirophase. The spiral or spireme stage in synapsis.

spirophototropous. Having leaves turn so that the light falls on all the leaves around the axis.

spirospart. The finest spirals of hyaloplasm which constitute the spirofibrillae.

spirulate. Coiled.

splash cup, splashing cup. An open cup-like fructification of some fungi and lichens from which the spores are disseminated by falling drops of water.

splashed. Having broken stripes of various sizes.

splint. Alburnum, sapwood.

splintwood. Softwood.

split fruit. A cremocarp.

split layer. The loose felt-like layer of hyphae in *Geaster* connected with the inner peridium and torn into flakes at maturity.

spodogram. A record of the ash content of a portion of a plant (particularly a woody portion) used to determine or investigate structure.

spokes. Pedicels of *Umbelliferae*.

spondioid. Like *Spondias* (*Anacardiaceae*).

spondochrous. With a grayish tint.

spongelet. A spongiole, a young root-tip

which was once supposed to be a peculiar organ.

spongicolous. Living in sponges.

spongilliform. Having the form of a sponge.

spongiola pistillaris. The extremity of the pistil, the stigma.

spongiola radicalis. The root cap.

spongiola seminaris. The caruncle of certain seeds.

spongiole. The extreme apex of growing roots which was thought to be a special absorbing organ, the epiblema.

spongioplasm. The cytoplasmic threadwork of a cell, the cytoreticulum, the cytoplasmic framework.

spongophyll. A leaf with abundant spongy tissue, as a shade leaf.

spongy cortex. The cortical tissue with air-bearing intercellular spaces frequent in water plants.

spongy layer. A layer of irregularly shaped cells separated by large intercellular spaces just above the lower epidermis in a dorsiventral leaf which contains many chloroplasts.

spongy mesophyll. A spongy layer.

spongy parenchyma. Leaf tissue with conspicuous intercellular air spaces, a spongy layer.

spongy stuffed. Having a spongy pith, as a mushroom stem.

spongy tissue. Parenchyma with many intercellular spaces.

sponsalia plantarum. Anthesis, the fertilization period.

spontaneous generation. Abiogenesis, the assumed origin of living organism from non-living matter.

spontaneous movements. Movements without external stimulation.

spoonform. With the inner surface concave or disk-shaped, as the outer leaves of a cabbage head.

spora-. A prefix meaning seed.

spora cellulosa. A sporidesm or spore.

spora composita. A sporidesm.

spora multilocularis. A sporidesm.

sporabola. The curve described by a basidiospore in its course after being ejected from its sterigma.

sporadophytia. Open communities.

sporal. Relating to a spore.

sporal arrest. The partial or complete arrest of the development of a spore and the consequent loss of reproductive function.

sporange. A sporangium.

sporangial sac. The very thin-walled and often evanescent outgrowth from the sporangium in lower fungi in which zoospores complete their development and from which they are freed.

sporangial vesicle. A sporangial sac.

sporangidium. 1. The columella of mosses. 2. The capsule of mosses. 3. The spore case of fungi.

sporangiocyst. The sporangium in the *Woroninaceae* surrounded by a strong membrane adapted to withstand unfavorable conditions.

sporangiody. The conversion of sterile tissue into sporangia, as in *Botrychium*.

sporangiogenic. Giving rise to sporangia.

sporangiole. A secondary or small sporangium with few spores, an ascus, a reduced sporangium in *Mucorales*.

sporangioliferous head. A rounded head composed of a group of sporangioles.

sporangioliferum. The axis upon which the thecae of ferns are borne.

sporangiophore. The stalk supporting the sporangium.

sporangiophorous. Bearing sporangiophores.

sporangiospore. A spore produced in a sporangium.

sporangium. A spore case, a sac producing spores endogenously.

spore. A simple reproductive body of the lower plants. A spore is analagous to the seed of higher plants but lacks an embryo. It usually consists of one cell but sometimes several spores are enclosed by a protective covering. The single cells are protected from destruction by a thick cell wall. See MACROSPORE, MEGASPORE, MICROSPORE, etc.

spore ball. 1. A globular mass of spores, either solid or hollow. 2. A spore bulbil.

spore bed. The layer of cells parallel to the surface in uredineous fungi.

spore bulbils. Abortive apothecia in certain lichens.

spore case. A sporangium.

spore cell. 1. A spore. 2. A cell which gives rise to a spore.

spore, cellular. A sporidesm.

spore forms. The divisions of a genus according to the characters of the spores as in *Puccinia*.

spore group. A sporidesm, a spore consisting of more than one cell.

spore horn. A tendril-like agglomeration of more or less sticky spores which have been exuded through an orifice which may be either the ostiole of a pycnidium or a rupture in the bark above an acervolus; a cirrhus.

spore hybrid. A hybrid arising in the gametophytic stage.

spore initials. Small processes borne by the fertile hyphae of *Graphiola* which produce spores by one or more bipartitions of their contents.

spore layer. A layer of mother cells of the spores of *Phascum*.

spore mother cells. The cells which give rise to spores.

spore, multilocular. A sporidesm.

spore plasm. The protoplasm of a sporangium devoted to the formation of spores.

spore, plurilocular. A sporidesm.

spore print. The spore mass obtained by placing the cap of a mushroom flat on a piece of paper, glass slide, etc.

spore sac. 1. A moss capsule. 2. A structure in which spores are produced.

spore, septate. A sporidesm.

spore sport. A variation which may arise from the act of sexual reproduction.

spore tetrad. The four spores resulting from the two divisions before their separation.

sporeling. A young plant or embryo developing from a spore on the ground, not in the seed.

sporeocarp. A sporocarp.

sporeophyll. A sporophyll.

sporeophyte. A sporophyte.

sporetia. Idiochromidia, chromidia of generative chromatin.

sporid. A spore formed upon a promycelium.

sporidesm. A multicellular spore each cell of which is capable of independent growth, a spore group, a compound spore, a spora composita, a septate spore, a semen multiplex, a multilocular spore, a cellular spore, a plurilocular spore.

sporidiferous. Sporidia-bearing.

sporidiform. Shaped like a sporidium.

sporidiole. A sporidium.

sporidium. 1. A diminutive spore. 2. A granule resembling a spore. 3. A spore abjointed from a promycelium. 4. An ascospore.

sporidochia. The receptacles or the stipes of certain fungi.

sporiparity. Reproduction by spore formation.

sporoantheridic. Having spores and antheridia borne on distinct individuals.

sporoantheridic-hermaphroditic. Having some spores produced asexually and others borne hermaphroditically.

sporoantheridic-oogonous. Bearing spores in one individual and oogonia in another.

sporoblast. A merispore or a spore mother cell.

sporobola. The trajectory of a spore shot out horizontally.

sporocarp. A many-celled body serving for the formation of spores, a spore-producing body, the spore-containing structure of water ferns.

sporocide. An agent which destroys the vitality of spores.

sporocladium. A spore-bearing branch, as a stichidium in the *Florideae*; a branch upon which the reproductive bodies of some algae are found.

sporoconidium. An acrospore.

sporocyst. The mother cell of a spore, a unicellular structure producing asexual spores, a sporocyte.

sporocyte. A spore mother cell, a simple sporangium containing spores.

sporoderm. The integument of a spore.

sporodochium. The sporiferous apparatus in fungi belonging to the *Tuberculariales*, a compact conidial body or a mass of sporophores.

sporoduct. A special apparatus for dissemination of spores of sporozoa and of some fungi.

sporogamia. The heterosporous cryptogams.

sporogamy. The production of spores after gametic fusion.

sporogemma. The oogonium (nucule) of *Chara*.

sporogen. A plant which produces spores.

sporogenesis. The production and development of spores.

sporogenous cells. Cells which give rise to pollen grains or other spores.

sporogenous filaments. Outgrowths of the fertilized carpogonium of *Dudresnaya*, the ooblastema filaments.

sporogenous layer. The hymenium.

sporogenous nucleus. The nucleus resulting from the fusion of the nuclei of the spermatium and the carpogonium of *Florideae*.

sporogenous tissue. Tissue from which spore mother cells are formed.

sporogone. A sporogonium; an egg which germinates immediately to form a sporangium, as in an ascus or an agglomeration of spores in a synascus.

sporogonium. 1. The spore-bearing plant in the bryophytes which develops from the fertilized egg and lives almost as a parasite on the gametophyte, the capsule of mosses. 2. The product of sexual reproduction in the higher cryptogams.

sporoid. Like a spore.

sporokinete. A motile spore from the oocyst of certain *Haemosporidia.*

sporomorphic. Spore-shaped.

sporomycetes. Spore-bearing plants including myco-, sipho-, theca-, and basidiomycetes.

sporont. The gametocyte stage in the life history of sporozoa, the sporogenous stage of *Plasmodiophora* giving rise to gametes.

sporophas. Sporophydium.

sporophase. The production of a fruit body giving rise to spores.

sporophore. A mycelial structure which bears a spore, a spore-bearing branch or organ, a fruit body, the reproductive body in fleshy fungi.

sporophorum. The hymenium of fungi.

sporophullody. The change of vegetative leaves into sporangiferous organs.

sporophydium. 1. The sporangium of certain thallophytes. 2. The nucule of *Characeae* while still unfertilized.

sporophyll. A spore-bearing leaf.

sporophyllary leaves. Stamens and pistils.

sporophyllum. A leaf-like lobe of the thallus in algae bearing tetraspores.

sporophyte. The nonsexual generation of plants, the asexual spore-producing plant or generation in plants having an alternation of generations.

sporophytic budding. The formation of vegetative buds on the sporophyte which form new sporophytes.

sporoplasm. The dense and chromophilous cytoplasm in a sporangium or ascus which gives rise to the spores and is surrounded by nourishing epiplasm.

sporosac. One of the simple, degenerate gonophores of certain hydroids, often little more than a gonad and never medusoid.

sporosome. The body which actually serves for reproduction.

sporostegium. The oosporangium or fruit of the *Characeae,* the cellular envelope of the nucule in *Chara.*

sporotamium. The cellular layer immediately beneath the disk of the shield of a lichen.

sporothalamia. Compound or branched sporophores as of fruticose lichens or agarics.

sporotrote. A plant disseminated by means of spores.

sporozoid. A zoospore.

sport. A mutation, a suddenly appearing marked deviation from type, a bud or seed variation.

sporula. A small spore, a sporule.

sporulation. The act of forming spores.

sporule. 1. A spore. 2. A small spore. 3. In mycology, a spore borne within a perithecium. 4. The structure in cryptogams that corresponds to the seeds in higher plants.

spot. 1. A disease of orchids apparently caused by chill. 2. Patches of discoloration produced upon leaves, fruits, etc., by various fungi.

spot bound. Stationary, sedentary.

sprawls. Small branches or twigs.

spray. The aggregate of smaller branches and branchlets, the ultimate division of a branch.

spring wood. The early wood of an annual ring, the wood produced early in the year characterized by larger ducts and cells than later growth.

sprout. 1. Any quickly grown part. 2. A vigorous branch arising from the root or stem. 3. A shoot or germinated seed.

sprout cell. A cell produced by sprouting.

sprout chain. 1. A chain of cells produced by sprouting. 2. A row of united cells in fungi formed by budding.

sprout gemmae. Chain gemmae.

sprout germination. The germination of a spore in which a small process (germ cell) with a narrow base protrudes at one end or at points on the surface of the spore, assumes an elongated spherical form, and finally is abjointed as a sprout cell.

sprouting fungus. A growth form in which the thallus consists of a sprouting cell or chain of sprouts.

spur. 1. A tubular elongation of the base of a petal or of a gamopetalous corolla. 2. An extension of the base of the leaf beyond its point of attachment. 3. A short branch in many trees on which flowers and fruit are borne. 4. A short branch borne in the axil of a scale leaf and bearing the true foliage leaves of the plant.

spur, foliar. A short branch having only leaves.

spur, fruit. A short branch which bears blossom buds, as in the peach.

spur pelory. An abnormal condition in which all the petals of an irregular flower develop spurs so that the flowers become regular.

spur scar. The scar from which a dwarf shoot has fallen.

spur shoot. A short, stubby branch bearing leaves or fruit.

spur top. An upland salient.

spurious branch. A false branch found in certain *Nostocaceae* consisting of a younger filament agglutinated for a portion of its length to the older one.

spurious chloroplast. Plastids containing few large starch grains which do not disappear after a short time in the darkness.

spurious dissepiment. A false septum.

spurious fruit. A pseudocarp; a collective, aggregate, or accessory fruit.

spurious tissue. Hyphal tissue in which the filamentous cells are not regularly united, as in phanerogams, but cross one another irregularly and are often more or less grown together; see FELTED TISSUE.

spurious whorl. A whorl which is formed by displacement and unequal growth of the axis.

spurred corolla. A corolla composed of spurred petals or segments.

squama. A scale or part arranged like a scale.

squama-fructifera. A seminiferous scale.

squamate. Scaly.

squamatio. The unnatural formation of rosettes of scale-like leaves, as in the rose willow.

squamation. Scale arrangement.

squamella. A small scale or bract, a squamula.

squamellula. A subdivision of the pappus lip in *Compositae*.

squamiferous. Bearing scales, squamigerous.

squamiflorous. 1. Having flowers which resemble scales or are borne upon scales. 2. With a perianth of scale-like bracts but not disposed around an axis as in *Coniferae*.

squamiform. Squamoid, scale-like.

squamigerous. Scale-bearing, squamose.

squamody. The change of foliar organs into scale-leaves.

squamosis. A disease of the orange tree in which the bark scales off (thought to be a form of gummosis).

squamous bulb. A bulb with narrow and somewhat separate scales, as the lily.

squamous epithelium. Epithelium which consists of small scale-like cells in the outer layer.

squamulae intervaginales. The axillary scales of the marine monocot *Halophila*.

squamule. The hypogynous scale of grasses, the lodicule.

squarrose. 1. Having its parts or processes (such as the tips of the involucral scales) spreading or recurved at the ends. 2. Jagged; rough, or with prominent reflexed scales.

squarroso-dentatus. Having teeth which do not lie in the plane of the leaf but at an angle.

squarrosus. Roughly scurfy with spreading processes.

squinancy. A European perennial herb which formerly was thought to cure quincy.

stabilization. The tendency of a succession in which each stage becomes more stable; and increase of dominance culminating in a stable climax; an equilibrium in plant growth, the final adult stage of development.

stabiloplasts. Elaioplasts which are fixed in number and position.

stable community. A plant community which remains unaltered in its general characters for a long time.

stable formation. As opposed to a migratory formation, a formation occurring on palaeogeic or past geological processes.

stachy-. A prefix meaning spike.

stachyoid. Spike-like.

stachyosperms. Plants which bear seeds on their stems, as *Cordaites*, *Ginkgoales*, and *Coniferales*.

staddle. Seed-trees left standing in a forest when logging.

stade. A stage, a phase.

stadium. Stade, a period or a stage in the development or life history of a plant or animal.

stagheaded. A forestry term for a tree which is dying at the top.

staghorn. 1. A plant or part having the shape of a staghorn. 2. An orchid by that name.

stagnicolous. Growing in stagnant water.

stagnophile. A species which occurs only in stagnant water.

stagnoplankton. The floating vegetation of stagnant water.

staircase response. The response when successive stimuli greatly enhance responses by increasing molecular mobility.

stalagmoid. Elongate, drop-shaped, tear-shaped.

stale. Botanically, when growth ceases in cultures.

staling. Becoming unfit for the growth of organisms due to the accumulation of organic wastes in the substratum.

stalk. The lengthened above-ground support to which organs are attached, as the petiole of a leaf or the peduncle of a flower, etc.

stalk cell. The barren cell of the two into which the antheridial cell of pine divides, the cell between the antheridial mother cell and the vegetative cell.

stalk nucleus. A nucleus delimited from the male prothallus of *Pinus*.

stalked gland. A glandular hair, an epidermal appendage of one or more cells of which the apex is enlarged and contains the secretion.

stalklet. A secondary or very small stalk, a secondary petiole, the stalk of leaflets.

stamen. The pollen-bearing organ in a flower, a microsporophyll found in the flower and producing pollen grains.

stamen lodicules. Organs having characters of both stamen and lodicules.

staminal column. The androphore.

staminal leaves. The stamens regarded as metamorphosed leaves.

staminalpode. The organs in the androecium of *Malvaceae* which produce stamens on their margins.

staminate. Having, producing, or consisting of stamens.

staminate flowers. Flowers having stamens but no pistils.

stamineal. Formed of or attached to stamens.

stamineal column. A column of united filaments supporting the anthers; see ANDROPHORE.

staminidium. An antheridium.

staminode. An abortive stamen, usually the filament only, which may be reduced to a scale or tiny projection; a vestigial stamen.

staminodia. Imperfect organs occupying the position of and resembling stamens, the transition between petals and stamens.

staminody. The metamorphosis of flower organs into stamens.

staminoid. Resembling a stamen.

staminose. Having unusually large or numerous stamens.

stand. A pure association.

standard. 1. The upper dilated (broad) petal of a papilionaceous corolla; the upper or posterior petal of a pea flower which is outside the others in the bud. 2. In horticulture, a small tree commonly produced by grafting a weeping or dwarf form on a trunk of the desired height.

standard climate. The climate recorded at a meteorological station by standard methods of exposure.

standard theoretical time. The length of time of a given developmental stage in hours or days as calculated for average organisms from developmental units which takes into account temperature and humidity only.

standardized fertility. The crude birthrate corrected by a statistical method intended to make allowance for changes in age composition in the population.

standels. The standards in a coppice.

Standort. The habitat of a plant or plant community; a stand, in a forester's sense.

starch. The common carbohydrate formed by plants and stored in seeds, stems, roots, etc.

starch builder. A plastid, generally a leucoplast, in which a starch grain originates.

starch cellulose. The framework of starch grains remaining after the soluble parts have been removed.

starch crescent. A strand of cells crescentric in cross section containing starch grains which are presumed to act as statoliths.

starch generators. Leucoplasts, starch builders.

starch grain. A rounded, irregularly shaped inclusion in a cell consisting of a series of layers of starch giving a stratified appearance surrounding the hilum.

starch granule. A body of definite shape varying according to the plant which produces it and having the appearance of parallel layers around a hilum.

starch layer. A bundle sheath serving as a starch layer.

starch plant. A plant in which the carbohydrate formed in excess of immediate requirements is stored in the cells of the leaf as temporary starch.

starch producer. A leucoplast.

starch sheath. 1. A one-layered cylinder of cells having prominent starch grains which develops on the inner boundary of the primary cortex of a young stem. It is homologous to an endodermis. 2. A layer of starch grains around a pyrenoid in algal cells.

starch stars. Stellate nodules or internodes on the roots of *Chara stelligera* filled with starch.

starch substance. The pure starch material apart from any associated or transformed matters which may also be present.

starrings. The small central steles in the fossil *Medulloseae*.

starters. Pure or impure cultures of lactic acid bacteria used in considerable proportion to ripen cream and cheese.

stasad. A plant growing in stagnant water.

stase. A fossil plant deposit in which the plant residue stays in the place, a definite series of layers formed by the remains of the associes and climax of a sere, a fossil deposit in stagnant water.

stasimorphy. A deviation in form due to arrested development.

stasis. An arrested growth.

stasium. A stagnant pool formation or community.

stasophilous. Dwelling in stagnant water.

stasophyta. Stagnant water plants.

state. A most trivial variation from the type.

statenchyma. Tissue formed of statocysts.

staticetium. An association of *Statice*.

station. The exact place of occurrence of a species or individual within a given habitat.

statoblasts. Internal masses of cells which are morphologically buds from which new individuals develop.

statocyst. A cell containing starch grains or other solid inclusions which act as statoliths. The contents of the cell are fluid so that the statoliths readily move to the lower face of cell if the position of the cell is changed by the displacement of the plant or plant part.

statocytes. Statocysts.

statolith. A solid inclusion in a cell, such as a starch grain, which moves readily in the fluid contents of the cell, comes to rest on the portion of the protoplast lining the lower wall of the cell, and is presumed to play some part in the perception of gravity by plants; starch grains regarded as causing curvature in plants.

statoplasts. Movable starch grains.

statospermous. Having a straight or erect seed within the pericarp.

statosphere. The idiozome or centrotheca.

statospore. A spore furnished with thick walls able to retain its vitality for considerable time, a resting spore.

stauracanthous. Having cross-shaped spines.

staurigamia. Cross-fertilization, staurogamia.

stauromatic. Resembling the genus *Stauroma*, isidioid.

staurophyll. A leaf consisting of palisade cells.

staurophyllous. Having cross-shaped leaves or petals, cruciate.

stauros. In diatoms: 1. The central nodule of the valve. 2. A transverse band without markings.

staurosomes. Tetrads, four-parted chromosomes.

staurospore. A spore made up of several stellately grouped cells.

stearin. The solid part of fat, an abundant ingredient of animal and vegetable fats.

stearinolipoids. Fatty compounds occurring in plants.

stearoptene. A solid crystallizable matter allied to camphor found in many essential oils.

steganochamaephytium. A dwarf-shrub community under trees.

steganocryptophytium. A community of hemicryptophytes and geophytes under an upper layer.

stegium. The thread-like appendages sometimes found covering the styles of *Asclepias*.

stegma. 1. A small elongated cell nearly filled with silica. 2. A horizontally flattened cell in some ferns, etc., containing silica. 3. A covering plate.

stegmatomycosis. An injury to fruits apparently sound but damaged by punctures of plant-feeding bugs.

stegocarpic. With capsules having a distinct operculum.

stegocarpous. Having a capsule with operculum and peristome, with an operculate capsule.

stelar system. The vascular and associative conjunctive tissue of plants.

stele. The axial cylinder of tissues in roots and stems of vascular plants which includes the vascular tissue, the central or vascular cylinder of an axis.

stelidium. The teeth of the column in *Bulbophyllum*.

stellate pubescence. Star-like hairs or scales radiating around a center.

stellate scales. Disks attached by their edges or at the center.

stellate-scurfy. Scurfy with star-shaped hairs or scales.

stellato-pilosus. Covered with stellate hairs.

stellinervius. Star-ribbed, as the leaves of *Hydrocotyle vulgaris*.

stellipilous. With stellate hairs.

stellula. A whorl of perigonial leaves in mosses, a small rosette.

stellular pubescence. Compound or fasciculate hairs with the branches spreading like rays.

stelolemma. A sheath of thickened peridesmic or stelar tissue in angiospermous petioles.

stem. The main ascending axis of a plant bearing leaves or flowers or both.

stem body. The equatorial part of the spindle which elongates at anaphase and telophase forming a long strand between the two resulting nuclei.

stem bud. The plumule.

stem cell. A primordial germ cell.

stem form (Stamm form). The ancestral form.

stem history. Phylogeny, the history of the species or larger group.

stem leaf. A leaf growing from the stem above the ground.

stem parasite. A parasite plant which lives on the stem of its host.

stem, subterranean. A rhizome or a stem beneath the surface of the ground.

stem, succulent. A juicy stem with very small leaves which are often reduced to spines.

stem tendril. A tendril which is morphologically a stem structure, a transformed stem.

stem xerophyte. A plant characteristic of very dry places with ephemeral or much reduced leaves and with the photosynthetic tissue located in the peripheral cells of the stem.

stemonitoid. Like *Stemonitis*, a myxomycete.

stenocarpous. With narrow fruit.

stenocephalous. With a narrow head.

stenochoric. With a range of distribution over a narrow area of constant climate and confined to one or very few plant formations.

stenocoenose. Restricted in distribution.

stenocysts. Auxiliary cells in the leaves of certain mosses.

stenoecic. Limited to a narrow range of environmental conditions.

stenogynous. Having a narrow stigma.

stenohaline. Enduring only three to four per cent of salt in solution.

stenomorph. A diminutive form caused by a cramped habitat.

stenopetalous. Having narrow petals.

stenophotic. Requiring a constant amount of light within narrow variation.

stenophyllous. With linear or narrow leaves.

stenopterous. Narrow-winged.

stenos-. A prefix meaning narrow.

stenosepalous. Having narrow sepals.

stenosis. Cell formation in which there is a direct constriction of the walls of the original cells, as budding.

stenostachys. Narrow-spiked.

stenostomatous. Narrow-mouthed.

stenosynusis. Restricted in distribution.

stenothermal. Restricted to limited temperatures or uniform temperatures.

stenotherms. Species which can tolerate only a very narrow range of temperature and are limited in distribution to areas where this limit is not exceeded.

stenotribal. Having anthers so arranged that their pollen is dusted on the under part of the thorax of their insect visitors.

stenotropic. Having narrow limits of adaptation to varied conditions.

stenotype. An organism restricted to a single habit.

stentor. A ciliated protozoan.

step allelomorphism. The overlapping effect of a series of multiple allelomorphs which are presumed to be determined by their linear order in the distribution of units within the gene.

stephanocarpous. Having the fruit arranged so as to resemble a crown.

stephanodophytum. A plant which produces an inferior achene.

stephanokont. Having an anterior circlet or flagella.

stephanokontan. Bearing a crown of cilia,

resembling the green algae (*Stephanokontae*) whose zoospores are characterized by a crown of cilia around the anterior end.

stephanoum. Cremocarp.

steppe. A wide, treeless plain or grassland.

steppe period. A period following the tundra period in Switzerland when steppe plants were dominant.

steps. Portions between scalariform perforations in xylem cells.

stercorate. Manured.

stereid. A lignified cell from the stereome, a stone cell.

stereid bundles. Bands or bundles of sclerenchymatous fibers.

stereide. A stone cell.

stereodontaceous. Of or pertaining to the moss genus *Stereodon*.

stereogennylae. Bryophytes.

stereomatic. Resembling or composed of stereome.

stereome. Sclerenchymatous and collenchymatous masses along with hardened parts of vascular bundles forming the supporting tissues in plants, strengthening tissue, mechanical tissue.

stereome cylinder. A cylinder of strengthening tissue lying in a stem, usually just outside the phloem.

stereonemata. The solid threads which make up the capillitium in the myxomycete *Fuligo*.

stereoplasm. The solid portions of protoplasm.

stereospermous. Having solid seeds.

stereotaxis. Thigmotaxis.

stereotaxy. The mechanical reaction to continuous contact with a solid.

stereotropic. Capable of reacting to contact with solid objects.

stereotropism. The tendency of organisms to attach themselves to solid objects or to live in crannies or tunnels in total contact with solids, thigmotaxis, reaction to contact.

sterigma. 1. A tiny spicule-like stalk at the apex of a basidium on which the spore is developed. 2. A small woody peg-like projection at the base of needles of evergreens. 3. The foliaceous downward prolongation on the stem of a decurrent leaf. 4. A carcerule.

sterigmate. Borne on sterigmata.

sterigmate-deciduous. Borne on sterigmata but shed, not violently discharged.

sterile basidium. A structure in a hymenium like a basidium but nonsporiferous and possibly a paraphysis.

sterile flowers. 1. Flowers without pistils or stamens. 2. Flowers having only stamens or entirely neutral, staminate flowers.

sterile glume. One of the glumes at the base of the spikelet of a grass which does not subtend a flower.

sterile stamen. A body resembling a stamen but without pollen.

sterile vein. A strand or sheet of interwoven hyphae occurring with the spore-bearing hyphae in the fruit bodies of some fungi.

sternotribal. With anthers so arranged that their pollen is deposited on the under part of the thorax of insect visitors.

sternotribe. A flower which is sternotribal.

sterom. Strengthening tissue.

sterrhad. A moor plant.

sterrhium. A moor community.

sterrhophilous. Moor-loving.

sterric. Of a heath or an upland community characterized by ericaceous shrubs, xerophytic grasses, and lichens.

sterrophyte. A moor plant.

stesomy. The arrest of metamorphosis; see STASIS.

stichidium. A branch of the thallus in red algae containing tetraspores, a stichid.

stichobasidium. A type of holobasidium which is nearly cylindrical and elongates during its further development projecting above the hymenium at maturity with nuclear spindles longitudinal or oblique and at different levels.

stichocarpicous. With the fruit arranged along a spiral line.

-stichous. A suffix meaning row.

sticktights. Stickseed, *Bidens*.

stictopetalous. With petals covered with glandular points.

stigma. The tip of a pistil which is receptive to the pollen grains and upon which they germinate.

stigma disk. A disk forming the seat of a stigma; the part of the flower in which the stigma is seated, as in asclepiads.

stigmarhize. The part of the fossil Stigmaria considered a root.

stigmarhizome. The part of the fossil Stigmaria considered a modified stem or rhizome.

Stigmaria. The enormous, spreading, root-like underground stem of the fossil genera *Lepidodendron* and *Sigillaria*.

stigmarian. Resembling Stigmaria in structure or outward appearance.

stigmatae. The phanerogams which have stigmata.

stigmatastemon. A body formed by the union of anthers to the stigma.

stigmatic cells of the archeogonium. Lid cells, terminal cells in the necks of some archegonia which for a while serve to close the canal.

stigmatic chambers. The part of the rostellum in orchids in which the viscid disk or retinaculum is developed.

stigmatic fluid. A viscid substance secreted by a mature stigma which holds the pollen.

stigmatic papillae. Papilla-like structures covering stigmata.

stigmatic secretion. The stigmatic fluid.

stigmatic surface. The pollen-catching surface.

stigmaticae. The wind-pollinated flowers which have conspicuous stigmas.

stigmatiferous. Having stigmas.

stigmatiform. Resembling a stigma, stigmatoid.

stigmatocyst. The terminal cell of the stigmatopod of the *Englerulaceae* and *Hemisphaeriales* which develops into the perithecium.

stigmatomycosis. A condition in fruits where they are apparently sound but are really unsound within because of the punctures by plant-feeding bugs.

stigmatophorus. The part of the style of a composite which bears the stigmas.

stigmatopodium. In the *Englerulaceae* and *Hemisphaeriales*, a capitate hyphopodium, generally dark in color and usually consisting of two cells (a stalk cell and a terminal cell or stigmocyst) possibly related to haustoria.

stigmatospore. An osmospore.

stigmocyst. A stigmatocyst.

stigmonose. A plant disease characterized by pellucid spots or dots in the leaves, in the skin of the fruit, etc.

stigmopodium. A stigmatopodium.

stigmosus. Marked.

stigmula. A division of divided stigmas.

stignopodium. Stigmatopodium.

stilbeus. Like the fungus *Stilbum*, mallet-like.

stilbiform. Having a long stalk and head.

stilboid. With a stalked head, like *Stilbum*.

stilbum. A type of sporogenous structure in which the spores are borne in a head on a stalk, as in the genus *Stilbum*.

stilidium. A canal-like portion of the archegonium of a moss.

stiliplankton. Floating marine vegetation chiefly of *Rhizoselenia*.

still spore. A resting spore.

stilogonidia. Stylogonidia.

stilogonidium. A stalked spore, sometimes septate, produced in a pycnidium.

stilt roots. Oblique adventitious roots of the mangrove and similar forms.

stimulators. Tactile hairs or bristles which transmit stimuli to the sensitive motor tissue.

stimulose. Covered with stinging hairs.

stimulous. Stinging.

stinging hair. A stiff glandular hair whose swollen base secretes an acrid or irritating fluid, as in nettles.

stinking smut. A disease of wheat caused by *Tilletia tritici*.

stipate. Crowded, pressed together.

stipation. An accumulation in the tissues or cavities.

stipe. The stalk of a sporophore, the stem of a mushroom, the stalk of a carpel or pistil, the leaf stalk in ferns, an apothecial stalk.

stipel. The stipule of a leaflet, the appendage of leaflets analogous to the stipule of a leaf, a stipellum.

stipellate. Bearing stipels.

stipetum. An association of *Stipa tenacissima*.

stipiferous. Having small flower stalks, as the receptacles of some compositae.

stipiform. 1. Resembling a stalk or stem. 2. Having the appearance of an endogenous tree, as the pawpaw.

stipitate. Having a stem or stipe, stalked.

stipitiform. Stalk-like, stipiform.

stipticus. Astringent.

stipulaceous. Near or upon stipules, belonging to a stipule, having appendages called stipuli.

stipular. Having stipules, formed of stipules, pertaining to or derived from stipules.

stipular scar. The scar made by deciduous stipules on the bark.

stipular spine. A spine representing a stipule or having the position of a stipule.

stipular trace. Vascular tissue running into a stipule.

stipulation. The situation or arrangement of the stipules.

stipule. A leafy appendage at the base of the petiole, usually one on each side; a basal appendage of a petiole (the three parts of a complete leaf are blade, petiole, and stipule).

stipule scar. The scar left by the fall of the stipule.

stipule spines. Spines which are metamorphosed stipules.

stipulode. A stipular organ of one cell in one or more rows subtending the branchlets in *Chara*.

stipulose. With very large stipules.

stirpalis. Growing upon a stem.

stirps. 1. The germo or germ plasm, as contrasted with body soma. 2. A race, a permanent variety, or a species. 3. A stem or root.

stirps cirrhosa. A tendril-bearing stem.

stirps clathrans. A lattice-forming stem.

stirps fluctuans. A floating stem.

stirps humifusa. A prostrate stem.

stirps palaris. An erect unbranched stem.

stirps plectens. A weaving stem.

stirps radicans. A stem which climbs by means of roots.

stirps volubilis. A climbing stem.

stock. 1. The main or persistent stem of an herbaceous perennial. 2. The rooted stem upon which the scion is grafted. 3. The parentage of a particular strain or variety, a race or source.

Stoke's law. The fall of spherical particles in a medium varies directly as the square of their radius.

stolon. A modified propagating stem above ground creeping and rooting or curved over and rooting at the tip; a basal branch rooting at the nodes; a rooting shoot, runner, or stole.

stolonate. Having stolons.

stoloniferous. Producing stolons.

stoloniferous stem. A slender creeping stem with minute leaves.

stoma. An opening surrounded by guard cells which opens into internal air cavities, the breathing apparatus in the epidermis of leaves, a breathing pore in the epidermis of young leaves or stems.

stomal. Stomatal.

stomatal. Pertaining to or of the nature of a stoma.

stomatal aperture. The pore of a stoma.

stomatal opening. The pore of a stoma.

stomatal transpiration. The loss of water vapor through a stoma.

stomate. Having a stoma or stomata.

stomatic cells. The guard cells.

stomatic chamber. The intercellular space beneath a stoma.

stomatic cleft. A stoma without guard cells.

stomatiferous. Bearing stomata.

stomatograph. A recording instrument for measuring the variations in the stomatal apertures in a leaf.

stomatopodium, stomopodium. A hyphal branch or stem which plugs or clogs a stoma.

stomatose. Bearing stomata.

stomium. The thin-walled cells in a fern sporangium where the cleavage of the capsule takes place, the point of rupture in a fern sporangium.

stone. The hard endocarp of a drupe, the pit of a stone fruit.

stone cell. A lignified mechanical cell which is about the same diameter in every direction; see SCLEREID.

stone cork. Tissue with thick, sclerosed, and pitted walls in conifers.

stone fruit. A fruit with a stony endocarp, as the drupe in peach, plum, or cherry.

stone pine. The Swiss pine.

stool. 1. A plant from which offsets may be taken or with several stems arising together. 2. A clump of roots or root stocks that may be used in propagation. 3. To tiller, as the production of suckers by grains.

stooling. 1. The production of secondary branches from the lowest nodes, as in grasses. 2. Tillering.

stopper. The callus plates in algae.

stopper of pollen. Hyaline protoplasmic deposits in pollen tubes.

stopples. The projections or lids in pollen grains which fall away to permit the passage of the pollen tube.

storage pith. Pith in which starch or water is stored by the plant.

storage tracheid. A thick-walled cell resembling a tracheid without living contents in which water is stored.

storax. A resin derived from various styraceous trees, as from *Styrax officinalis*.

storied cambium. Cambium characterized by a horizontal seriation of the initials.

storied growth. Cells destined to form a tissue which do not divide simultaneously but show a limited number of divisions one after another.

storied layer of secondary xylem and phloem. The arrangement of secondary xylem and phloem due to the arrangement of the cambial fibers in transverse rows.

storied secondary cork. Cork formed by storied growth.

stove plants. Hothouse plants or tropical plants which need high temperatures and humidity.

stragulum. The paleae of grasses.

straight ribbed or veined. With the ribs running in a straight line, as in the leaves of many monocotyledons.

strain. A group of plants differing from the race to which it belongs by no apparent morphological characters but by some enhanced or improved physiological tendency, a group of individuals related by descent and differing in some respects from the other members of the variety.

stramen. Straw.

straminellus. Straw-colored.

stramineofructus. Having straw-colored fruit.

stramineous. Straw-colored.

strand. 1. A thread of chromatin in cell division. 2. Fibrous mycelium. 3. A bundle of vascular tissue in stems. 4. The area of bare beach above high water subject to the action of wind and sand blasts.

strand lakes. Extremely temporary lakes which are present only after heavy rains and vanish completely between rainy seasons.

strand plants. Shore plants.

strand tracheid. A tracheid of a vertical series (strand) of tracheids (or of mixed tracheids and parenchyma cells), each series arising from a single cambial strand.

strand vegetation. Open herbaceous vegetation occurring where the ground water is brackish under maritime influence.

strange species. Species which are rare and accidental intruders from another plant community or relicts from a previous community.

strangers. Species accidentally introduced into any given community.

strangury. A swelling or other disease in a plant caused by a ligature fastened tightly about it.

strap. The ligule of a ray floret in *Compositae*.

strata. 1. Layers of tissues. 2. Groups of organisms which occupy a recognizable vertical division of a unit area. 3. The difference in vegetation at different vertical levels. 4. Groups of consocies.

stratal. Of or pertaining to a stratum.

strates. Scattered fossil deposits.

stratification. An arrangement in layers, the thickening of a cell wall by the depositing of successive layers of material, the difference in vegetation at different vertical levels, growth by apposition.

stratification of cell walls. Concentric layers with thicker dense layers alternating with thinner less dense ones.

stratification of starch grain. The concentric layers which surround the hilum.

stratified cambium. A cambium in which the cells seen in tangential sections appear arranged in fairly regular horizontal rows.

stratified thallus. A lichen thallus in which the gonidia occupy more than one layer.

stratiform. Formed in a layer.

stratobios. Inhabitants of the litter layer of a community.

stratose. In distinct layers.

stratose thallus. Said of a thallus in which the tissues are in horizontal layers.

stratum cellulosum. The bark layer just within the epidermis.

stratum corticale. Any bast layer or rind.

stratum gonidiale. The algal layer of lichens.

stratum gonimon. The algal layer in lichens.

stratum ligneum. A layer of wood.

stratum medullose. The medulla or pith.

stratum society. A plant society which occurs as a well-defined layer in a plant community, as shrubs in a woods.

stratum sporidiiferum. The flesh of agarics.

stratum sporophorum. The hymenium of fungi.

Strauchschicht. A shrub stratum.

Strauchserien. A phanerogamic series.

straw. The stems of various edible grains, as wheat and oats, especially after being threshed (also extended to miscellaneous other plants); the hollow jointed culms of edible grains.

strawberry. The plant or fruit of *Fragaria sp.* grown for the large red fruit.

streak. A disease in *Lathyrus odoratus* caused by *Thielavia basicola*.

streaming. The flow of protoplasm as in *Myxomycetes* and other plants.

strengthening cells. Thick-walled cells present in the leaves of certain pines.

strepsinema. Delicate parallel threads twisted about each other in the nucleus in a stage of synapsis.

strepsitene. The stage in meiosis during which the diplotene thread seems to be more or less twisted, the stage in the meiotic prophase during which crossingover takes place.

streptocarpous. 1. With twisted fruit. 2. With spiral markings on fruit.

streptococcus. 1. A gram positive bacterium which tends to group in chains. Many are pathogenic and normally found in the mouth, throat, and intestines. 2. A genus of bacteria.

streptomycin. An antibiotic derived from the soil fungus Streptomyces which is effective in control of some bacteria.

streptopetalous. With twisted petals.

streptophyllous. With twisted leaves.

streptosepalous. With twisted sepals.

streptothrycin. An antibiotic effective against some bacteria and fungi.

streptotrichial. Relating to the fungus genus *Streptothrix*.

stria. A narrow line, streak, groove, or channel.

striate. Having minute radiating furrows.

striate-sulcate. Marked with slender longitudinal grooves or channels.

striation, cell-wall. Markings due to the manner of formation in bands by the protoplasm sometimes resulting in a latticework appearance.

striatulate. Faintly striped.

strict. Very straight and upright, close and narrow.

strictetum. An association of *Carex stricta*.

strictiflorous. With stiff flowers.

striga. A sharp-pointed, rigid, appressed bristle or hair-like scale.

strigose. Covered with sharp, straight, and stiff hairs which tend to lie flat.

striiform. Line-like.

strike. To take root.

string. A fiber, strand, or little fibrous root.

strings of protoplasm. See BANDS OF PROTOPLASM.

string wood. An extinct euphorbiaceous tree of the island of St. Helena.

stringy bark. Any of several Australian eucalyptuses which have inner fibrous bark.

striole. A fine narrow line or streak.

strobilaceous. Resembling or bearing a strobile, cone-shaped.

strobile. An inflorescence marked by imbricated scales or bracts, as in the hop or pine cone; a small cone or cone-like cluster of sporophylls.

strobiliferous. Producing strobili or cones.

strobiliform. Cone-shaped.

strobiloid. Having a convex or flat receptacle to which the other floral organs are united, strobiliform, cone-like.

strobiloid theory. The assumed origin of pteridophytes in those forms whose sporophytes are the most primitive, as *Lycopodium* and *Equisetum*.

strobilus. A strobile.

stroma. 1. A dense mass of interwoven hyphae, fleshy to thorny in texture, cushionlike, columnar, club-shaped or branched in form, on which or in which fructifications develop. 2. A dense, colorless part of a chloroplast.

stroma starch. The fine starch deposited throughout the chlorophyll body of some algae, as *Hydrodictyon*.

stromatous. Producing stromata.

strombuliferous. Bearing spirally coiled organs or structures, having twisted pods.

strombuliform. Spirally twisted, snail-shaped.

strombus. A spirally coiled fruit, as the legume of *Medicago*.

strongbark. A boraginaceous tree of south Florida and the West Indies.

strophanthine. A bitter, white, crystalline and very poisonous glucoside extract from species of *Strophanthus* used as a cardiac stimulant.

strophe. A leaf spiral.

strophic. 1. With a twisting movement in chemotaxis and phototaxis as contrasted with repulsive movements. 2. Pertaining to or consisting of strophes.

strophiolate. Having a strophiole or appendage at the hilum.

strophiole. An excrescence or appendage at or about the hilum of a seed, the caruncle.

strophism. A tendency to twist in response to some external stimulus.

strophogenesis. The differentiation of a single

original generation into the phases regarded as alternation of generations.

strophomania. Special torsion, as in the stems of some monstrosities.

strophotaxis. Arrangement due to a twisting movement.

strophular cleft. A tortuous opening in a seed coat through which water can enter before germination of the seed.

strophular plug. A suberized mass of cells which closes a strophular cleft and which must be removed before water can enter the seed.

strophy. Strophism.

-strote. A suffix meaning migratory.

structural botany. Morphology.

structural deviation. Any departure from the usual structure of a plant.

structural hybrid. A hybrid in which the parental chromosomes differ in structure, as an inversion, translocation, deficiency, or duplication of the genes.

structural mutation. A physical change in the location of genes in a chromosome.

structure. 1. The peculiar organization of plants with characteristic modifications. 2. The partially permanent arrangement of the chromosomes or genes in the chromosomes. 3. An expression of the life forms of a community together with their spatial relationship; see ECOLOGICAL ANATOMY.

struma. 1. A swelling on a plant organ. 2. The apophysis at the base of the capsule in some mosses. 3. The pulvinus at the base of some leaves.

strumarius. Of tumors or ulcers.

strumose. Having small cushion-like swellings.

strut roots. Buttress roots.

strychnia. Strychnine, a powerfully poisonous alkaloid from *Strychnos nux vomica.*

study set. The principal set of a collector's plants with his notes.

Stufe. See VEGETATION STUFE.

stump rooted. With a long tap root of which the upper fleshy edible portion terminates abruptly, as certain varieties of radishes, carrots, etc.

stupa, stuppa. A tuft of matted hairs resembling tow.

stupeous. Like tow, with loose scales or matted filaments, woolly.

stupulose. Covered with short filaments.

stygius. Growing in foul water.

stylans. With the gradual enlargement of the style into the ovary.

stylar. Of or pertaining to the style.

stylar brush. The collecting hairs of flowers.

stylar canal. The tube or loose tissue through which the pollen tubes pass.

stylar column. The column in orchids.

stylar foot. The stylopodium.

stylate. With a style.

style. The narrowed neck above the ovary which is surmounted by the stigma.

style of Hepaticae. Interlobule.

style of mosses. An old term for the neck of the archegonium.

style table. The flattened apex of the style in asclepiads.

stylet. A small, pointed, bristle-like appendage.

stylidium. The upper portion of an archegonium.

styliferous. Having bristly appendages.

styliform. Bristle-shaped.

styliplankton. Floating neritic vegetation composed of *Rhizosolenia stylifermis.*

styliscus. The stylar canal.

stylodeus. Furnished with a style.

stylodium. 1. A style-like stigma as in grasses and *Compositae.* 2. A false style as the appendage to the anthers of *Cynomorium.*

stylogonidium. A stalked spore, sometimes septate, produced in a pycnidium.

styloids. Columnar crystals occurring in plant cells.

stylopod. The enlarged bases of the styles in *Umbelliferae.*

stylose. With the styles long, numerous, and persistent.

stylospore. 1. A spore borne on a filament or pedicel. 2. A stalked spore borne inside a pycnidium.

stylosporic. (of aecia) Having spores borne on pedicels and usually lacking a peridium and paraphyses, uredinoid.

stylostegium. The peculiar orbicular corona, called a scutum or shield, which terminates the style in *Stapelia* and similar asclepiads.

stylostemis. Hermaphroditic.

stylostemon. An epigynous stamen.

stylosous. Having a prominent style.

stylotegium. A stylostegium.

stylus. A simple pointed spicule.

styphelioid. Like *Styphelia,* an Australian plant resembling the *Ericaceae.*

styraciflous. Flowing with storax or gum.

styrax. Storax, a solid resin from *Styrax officinale.*

styridophytous. With cruciform petals.

suaedetum. An association of *Suaeda.*

sub-. A prefix meaning under, nearly, almost, about, etc.

subacaulis. With stems barely apparent.

subacuminate. Somewhat tapering.

subacute. Moderately acute.

subaduncate. Somewhat crooked.

subaerial. Growing just above the surface.

subalbous. Nearly white.

subalpine. Just below the timber line, growing in the subalpine zone.

subalternate. Alternate but with a tendency to become opposite.

subalutaceous. Somewhat tan in color.

subapical. Nearly at the apex.

subapicularis. When the stem is prolonged beyond an inflorescence without a branch or leaf.

subapiculate. Having a small or poorly defined apiculus or point.

subarborscent. Somewhat like a tree.

subarcheporial pad. A cushion-like group of cells below the archesporium in *Lycopodium.*

subarctic. Beyond the limits of arboreal vegetation, above the timberline.

subaristate. Nearly or somewhat awned.

subassociation. A minor association.

subastomous. More or less mouthless.

subauriculate. Nearly eared.

subaxile. Nearly subaxillary.

subaxillary. Situated below the axil.

subbacteria. Bacteria which can pass through filters and are ultramicroscopic.

subbasal. 1. Situated near the base. 2. Below the basal cells in angiosperms.

subBellaradian. Slightly resembling *Rubus Bellardi.*

subbiatorine. Resembling the lichen genus *Biatora.*

subbifido-rumpens. Bursting into two divisions.

subbilocularis. Having partitions which do not quite join but leave a small interval.

subbipinnate. Nearly twice pinnate.

subbulbosus. Somewhat bulbous.

subbyssoid. Somewhat cobwebby.

subcaeruleus. Slightly blue.

subcaespitose. In small tufts, subcespitose.

subcalcareous. Somewhat limy.

subcampanulate. Somewhat bell-shaped.

subcanus. Somewhat hoary.

subcapsular. Inside a capsule.

subcarbonaceous. Slightly carbonaceous.

subcarinate. Somewhat keel-shaped.

subcarnosus. Nearly or rather fleshy.

subcaudal. Situated under a tail, as a shield or plate.

subcaudate. Having a tail-like process.

subcaulescent. 1. With a very short stem, nearly acaulescent. 2. Borne on very short stem.

subcentral. Nearly central.

subcentric oosphere. An oosphere in fungi having the protoplasm surrounded by one layer of fatty globules and with two or three additional layers on one side only.

subcespitose. Somewhat inclined to grow in bunches, somewhat tufted.

subciliate. Slightly ciliate.

subclass. A category below a class and above an order.

subclavate. Somewhat club-shaped.

subclimax. An edaphic minor climax.

subclypeate. Somewhat shield-shaped.

subcolumelliform. Somewhat like a columella.

subconcatenate. Growing in short or imperfect rows or chains.

subconical. Slightly conical.

subconoid. Slightly conical.

subcontinuous. Rarely or imperfectly septate, seldom or slightly constricted.

subconvolute. Partially convolute.

subcopious. Scattered somewhat loosely.

subcordate. Slightly cordate, somewhat heart-shaped.

subcoriaceous. Approaching a leathery texture.

subcorneous. Under a horny layer.

subcortical. Beneath the cortex.

subcrenate. Tending to have rounded scallops, as a leaf margin.

subcrustose. More or less crusted, crust-like.

subcuboid. Somewhat cubical.

subcultrate. Slightly cultrate.

subculture. A culture of bacteria or other organisms prepared from a pre-existing culture.

subcuticular. Under the cuticle, epidermis, or outer skin.

subcylindric. Somewhat cylindric.

subdecurrent. With the attachment of gills extending slightly farther down the stem than when adnate.

subdendroid. Somewhat tree-like.

subdentate. Slightly toothed or notched.

subdenticulate. Having small, imperfect marginal teeth.

subdermal. Beneath the skin.

subdeterminate. Limited.

subdifformis. Having some amount of irregularity.

subdioecism. A tendency to be dioecious.

subdiscoid. Somewhat disk-shaped.

subdivaricatus. Slightly divaricate.

subdominant. Prominent but falling short of dominance, applied to characters of inheritance or species in an association.

subdorsal. Situated almost on the dorsal surface.

subdumi. Dwarf shrubs.

subedentatus. Nearly toothless.

subeffuse. Slightly spreading.

subelevated. Somewhat raised.

subentire. Having only slight incisions.

subephedroid. Like the genus *Ephedra*, one of the *Gnetales*.

subepidermal. Below the epidermis.

subequal. Nearly equal.

suber. Cork or phellogen.

suberculatous. Corky.

suberect. Nearly erect but nodding at the top.

subereous. Of corky texture.

suberiferous. Cork-producing.

suberification. Suberization, conversion into cork tissue.

suberin. A complex fatty or waxy substance found in cell walls of corky tissues which makes them waterproof and resistant to decay.

suberin lamella. A layer of wall material impregnated with suberin in the cortex.

suberin membrane. Cell walls turned into cork.

suberization. Conversion into cork.

suberogenic. Forming suberin.

subex. The part of the axis which bears cataphyllary leaves.

subfamily. A group of genera subordinate to a family, a category below a family and above a genus.

subflexuose. Slightly wavy.

subformation. A plant formation of lesser grade, a local difference in littoral communities due to differences in the substratum.

subformion. A salient regional facies, Hauptteile, or the geographical race of a formion.

subforms. In *Rosa*, forms with irregular serrations and glandular calyx segments.

subfulcate. Somewhat scythe-shaped.

subfuscous. Dark, dusky.

subfusiform. More or less fusiform and with a somewhat rounded point at one end.

subgeniculate. Somewhat bent.

subgenital. Below the reproductive organs.

subgenus. A primary subdivision of genus.

subgeocolous. Living underground.

subgleba. A portion beneath the gleba or spore-bearing part, usually in a more or less well defined stalk of the *Phallales*.

subglobose. Almost spherical.

subglumaceous. Somewhat glumaceous.

subgregarious. Arranged in loose groups.

subgregiform. A versiform which has varied in different localities or countries.

subhastate. Nearly halberd-shaped.

subhirtellus. Somewhat hairy.

subhymenial. Below or beneath the hymenium.

subhymenial layer. The hypothecium.

subhymenium. The hypothecium, a layer of tissue beneath the hymenium.

subicle. A felty or cottony cushion beneath the fruit bodies of fungi made up of modified tissue of the host and hyphae of the attacking fungus, the subiculum.

subimbricate. Somewhat overlapping.

subimmersed. Slightly immersed.

subinferior. Not wholly inferior, as an ovary.

subinfluents. Organisms of lesser effect or shorter periods of influence than an influent.

subinsipidus. Almost devoid of taste.

subitane development. Active development as distinguished from latent.

subjacent. Lying under or below.

subkingdom. The highest subdivision of a kingdom.

sublanceolate. Tending to be narrow and to taper at both ends.

sublatus. Having support, real or apparent.

sublenticular. Somewhat lens-shaped.

subligneous. Partially or somewhat woody.

sublittoral. Near the seashore, growing between the low tidemark and in water to forty meters in depth.

sublobular. 1. Somewhat lobular. 2. With veins at the base of the lobules.

sublocular. Somewhat locular or cellular.

sublunate. Somewhat crescent-shaped.

submalleate. Somewhat hammer-shaped.

submarginal. Near the margin.

submarginate. Bordering a margin.

submaritime. Characteristic of the sea but also occurring inland.

submerged zone. All of the beach below low tide but exposed by the lowest spring tides.

submersibilis. Capable of existing when submerged.

submersiherbosa. Submerged aquatic communities of fresh and salt water.

submersiprata. Formations of macrophytic aquatic plants with submerged or floating leafy shoots.

submicron. An element seen as a separate disk with the aid of an ultramicroscope although not visible with an ordinary microscope.

subnascent. Originating or growing beneath.

subnude. Nearly destitute of covering.

subnullus. Scant.

subobtuse. Slightly obtuse or blunt.

suboral. Below or near the mouth.

suborbicular. Nearly circular.

suborbital. Below the orbit.

suborder. A group of genera within an order.

subordinate association. Associations other than the chief association in any area.

suboval. Nearly oval.

subovate. Somewhat oval or egg-shaped.

subovoid. Subovate.

subpalisade. Lying below the palisade tissue.

subpalmate. Tending toward palmate.

subpectinate. Comb-like in structure, as the margin of certain leaves.

subpedunculate. Resting on a very short stalk, subsessile.

subperennis. Imperfectly or nearly perennial.

subperiphaericous. Nearly peripheral, as the embryo of *Atriplex*.

subpetiolar. Situated under or within the base of the petiole, as the leaf buds of the sycamore.

subpetiolate. Nearly sessile.

subpotency. Lessened potency in the transmission of hereditary characters.

subpruinose. Slightly powdered.

subquadrat. A quadrat 1-8 decimeters square.

subradicating. With a slight prolongation of a stipe but hardly enough to be called a root-like extension.

subramealis. Growing on a branch below a leaf.

subramose. Having a tendency to branch but having few branches.

subregion. One of the primary divisions of a region.

subreniform. Slightly kidney-shaped.

subrhomboidal. Almost rhomboid.

subrigid. Slightly rigid.

subroseus. Pinkish.

subrotund. Nearly circular.

subscandens. Partially climbing.

subscyphiform. Somewhat boat-shaped.

subsection. The division of a genus below a section, a subdivision of a section.

subsere. A sere beginning in an area secondarily bare as a result of the removal of biotic cover, the partial development of a climax vegetation.

subserous. Having areolar tissue.

subserrate. Sparsely or obscurely serrate.

subsessile. Nearly sessile with almost no stalk.

subshrub. An undershrub or small shrub which may have partially herbaceous stems.

subsidiary cells. Accessory cells, additional modified epidermal cells lying outside guard cells, epidermal cells taking part in the formation of a stoma.

subsigillarian. *Sigillaria* stems without ribs, a part of fossil trees.

subsimple. Having few subdivisions or branches.

subsinuate. Somewhat sinuate or wavy-margined.

subsociation. A morphological part of the association characterized by the conspicuous presence of one or more subdominants under the general influence of the dominants, a society.

subsocies. A subsociation of an associes.

subsoil. The stratum of soil lying between the upper soil and bedrock occupied by few or no roots and practically unmodified by plants.

subspatulate. Somewhat spoon-shaped.

subspecies. A marked variety which is nearly equal in rank to a species.

subspicatum. Somewhat spiked.

subspinous. Tending to become spiny, somewhat spinous.

subspontaneous plant. A plant which has been introduced but which maintains itself fairly successfully by its ordinary means of reproduction.

subsporal cells. Certain colorless cells in *Pithophora* found in spore-bearing individuals.

subsporangial vesicle. The vesicular swelling just below the sporangium.

substantive variation. Changes of actual constitution or substance.

substipitate. Barely stipitate but with a very short attachment.

substitute association. Secondary formation.

substitute community. A community due to man or cattle, such as farmland and tree plantations.

substitute fiber. A prosenchymatous cell larger in diameter than a libriform cell and without its attenuated ends.

substitute parenchyma fibers. Nonseptate wood or bast parenchyma fibers.

substitution. Healing processes by the formation of new growth from secondary meristem.

substitution quotient. The sum total of modified and corrected temperature at the time of completion of a stage.

substomal. Below the stoma.

substomatic chamber. The intercellular space beneath a stoma, the stomatic chamber.

substrate. The material upon which an enzyme or fermenting agent acts, the material in or upon which a fungus grows or to which it is attached, the matrix.

substratose. Slightly or indistinctly stratified.

subsuccession. A sere beginning on rock surfaces or crevices and ending in mat growths.

subtegminal. Under the tegmen or inner coat of a seed.

subtend. 1. To enclose in its axil. 2. To be under or opposite to.

subtending leaf. The leaf in whose axil a bud or peduncle arises.

subterete. Nearly cylindrical and tapering.

subterminal. Near the extremity.

subtomentose. Slightly pubescent.

subtraction. The loss of an hereditary factor.

subtrapezoidal. Somewhat trapezoidal in shape.

subtremelloid. Gelatinous, resembling *Tremella*.

subtribe. A division between a tribe and a genus.

subtrilobate. Nearly divided into three lobes.

subtropic. 1. Nearly tropical but between the tropical and the temperate zone. 2. Thriving only in the summer in temperate regions.

subtropical. Inhabiting regions bordering the tropics.

subtruncate. Terminating rather abruptly.

subtypical. Deviating somewhat from a type.

subulate. Awl-shaped, tapering from a broad or thick base to a sharp point.

subule. 1. A delicate, sharp-pointed prolongation of an organ. 2. The terminal point of the awn of grasses.

subuli. The aciculae or sharp processes formed by certain fungi.

subuliferous. Having awl-shaped spines, bearing sharp points.

subumbellate. Tending to an umbellate arrangement with peduncles arising from a common center.

subumbonate. Slightly and usually broadly raised.

subuncinate. Somewhat hook-shaped.

subungual. Under a nail, claw, or hoof.

subuniversal veil. The primary universal veil or protoblem.

subvariety. A subordinate variety, a variety within a variety.

subventricose. Somewhat inflated, somewhat swollen.

subversatile. Somewhat versatile.

subverticillate. In imperfect or irregular whorls.

subvillosus. Pubescent with soft but not matted hairs.

sub vitro. Under the lens.

subvolubilis. Somewhat twining.

subxerophilous. Growing on fairly dry soil but not confined to it.

subzonal. Imperfectly zonal.

subzonate. Marked with obscure, indefinite zones.

succate. With milk or juice.

succession. The sequence of plant formations.

succession, deflected. A normal succession turned to one side by an external factor which may result in a temporary subclimax.

successional habitat. The changing habitat occupied by an allied group of plant communities which as a rule comprise the stages of a normal succession or sere associes.

successive whorl. A whorl whose members did not originate simultaneously but in succession.

succiferous. Producing or conveying sap.

succinctus. Encircled.

succineous. Amber yellow.

succinite. The commonest and best known form of amber resin exuded by *Pinus succinifera*.

succinosis. The abnormal occurrence of resin in fossil amber trees.

succise. Abrupt, appearing as if a part were cut off at the lower end.

succose. Soft, fleshy, juicy, sappy.

succotrinus. Of Socotra, an island off Arabia.

succous. Succate.

succubous. Having the lower margin of a leaf covering the upper margin of the leaf directly below it on the same side of the stem, as in the liverworts *Jungermaniales*.

succulents. The succulent plants, such as cacti and other xerophytes.

succulose. 1. Bearing suckers. 2. Succulent, juicy.

succus. The juice of a plant, any juice that can be expressed from a plant, a sap or sap tissue.

sucker. A shoot arising from a subterranean part of a plant, any shoot at first subterranean then aerial which may ultimately form an independent plant; see HAUSTORIUM.

sucker of parasites. The modified root by which parasites absorb from hosts.

sucking disk. A disk assisting in attachment.

sucrase. Invertase.

sucrose. Cane sugar, saccharose.

suction pressure. The avidity with which the cells take in water.

suctor. The haustoria of *Bartsia* and other root parasites.

suctorial. Adapted for sucking, having suctors.

sudanensis. Of the Sudan.

sudation. The exudation of water containing a small amount of substances in solution as opposed to secretion.

sudd. A dense mass of floating vegetation growing into a stream from the banks of a river often clogging the channel, as in the White Nile; sadd.

sudorific. Causing perspiration.

suffrutescent. Slightly shrubby.

suffrutescent stem. A stem which is woody at the base, the upper portion dying back at the end of the season leaving a persistent base.

suffrutex. An undershrub, a subshrub, a suffrutice.

suffruticose. Suffrutescent.

suffruticous. Shrubby at the base, trailing.

suffultus. 1. Supported or propped. 2. A plate or disk forming the base of a bulb.

sugar, beet. Sugar extracted from special selected strains of *Beta vulgaris*.

sugar, fruit. Levulose.

sugar, grape. Glucose, dextrose.

sugar, inverted. A sugar which occurs in some ripe fruits and honey dew.

sugar, maple. Sugar from *Acer saccharinum*.

sugar plant. A plant which forms little or no temporary starch, the carbohydrates formed in photosynthesis remaining as sugar.

sulcate. Grooved more extreme than striate but less so than plicate, furrowed.

sulciform. Sulcate.

sulcule. A little furrow or sulcus.

sulfobacteria. Bacteria which reduce sulfur out of its solutions.

sulfofication. The production of sulfur by bacteria.

sulfur bacteria. Bacteria which liberate sulfur.

sulfur rain. Pollen from pines brought by currents of air.

sulfur springs. Salfataras, hot sulfur springs with xerophytic vegetation.

sulfuraria. Algae which reduce sulfates from waters containing sulfur salts.

sulfureous. A very pale yellow.

sulfurescent. Becoming sulfur-yellow in color.

sulfuretum. A natural ecological community of sulfur bacteria.

sumatranus. Of or pertaining to Sumatra.

summer annual. A plant which lives for a short period in summer, sets seed at the end of its growth, and then dies.

summer spore. Any spore or gonidium which retains its vitality but a short time and is intended for the propagation of the plant during the summer, as the uredospores or rust fungi.

summer stage. The uredial or red-rust stage of the rusts of grasses.

summer wood. The late wood of an annual ring, the wood formed during the middle of the growing season.

sun leaves. Leaves which develop in full sunlight.

sun plants. Plants which prefer full sunlight.

sundarban. Food plants at the mouth of the Ganges River.

sunscald. An injury caused by brilliant sunlight.

sunscorch. The burning of foliage when the soil is parched.

super-. A prefix meaning over, above, or more than.

superagrarian. Above the limits of cultivation.

superarctic. Confined to the highest zone in Great Britain as the most alpine of the flora of the islands.

superaxillary. Situated above the axil.

superclass. A category of classification equivalent to a subphylum and above the class.

supercrescent. Growing on or in another growing thing.

superdecompound. Three or more times compounded, a supradecompound.

superfamily. A classification above a family, a group of families.

superfecundation. The union of more than two gametes.

superfemale. An individual with exaggerated female characters resulting from a preponderance of x chromosomes (sex chromosomes) over autosomes (xxx instead of xx chromosomes). They are usually sterile.

superfetation. The fertilization of an ovary by two or more kinds of pollen so that the seeds or offspring are not identical.

superficiales. Leptosporangiate ferns with sori arising from the surface of the frond.

superficies corporis. The hymenium of certain fungi.

superficies placentaris. The hymenium of certain fungi.

superfoliaceous. Superaxillary, suprafoliaceous.

superforms. In the genus *Rosa*, those with doubly serrated leaves and glandular calyx segments.

supergene. A group of genes performing as a unit.

super order. A series in plant classification above the order of class.

superior annulus. An annulus which is attached above the middle of the stem.

superior calyx. A calyx developed above the ovary whether free from the ovary or adnate to it.

superior corolla. A corolla growing above the ovary or adnate to it.

superior ovary. An ovary developed on top of a receptacle with the petals and stamens inserted hypogynously or perigynously, an ovary free from the calyx to its base.

superior radicle. A radicle which points toward the apex of a fruit.

supermale. An individual with exaggerated male characters resulting from a preponderance of autosomes over sex chromosomes. It is usually sterile.

supernatant. Floating on the surface.

supernumerary buds. Accessory buds.

supernumeraries. Chromosomes found in cells which are in addition to those usually found. They are usually smaller and often stain deeply.

superparasite. A hyperparasite, a parasite on a parasite.

superparasitism. The condition of any individual being attacked by two or more species of primary parasites or by one species more than once.

superplant. A plant which grows upon another plant either as an epiphyte or a parasite.

superposed buds. Accessory lateral buds borne above an axillary bud.

supersex. The ratio of chromosomes (2x : 2 = female, x : 2 = male; 2x : 3, an intermediate, the intersex).

supersociety. A presociety.

superspecies. A group of subspecies or new species regarded as an entity.

supertuberation. An abnormal production of secondary tubers directly upon those produced in the ordinary manner.

supervacuus. Redundant.

supervolute. With a plaited and rolled arrangement in the bud, convolute.

supinate. Inclining or leaning backward.

supporting fibers. Fibers which run from pole to pole of the spindle in nuclear division.

supporting plant. A host plant, a plant in or on which another plant lives.

suppressed forms. Organisms not included in the dominant groups, those which are dominated.

suppression. 1. The nondevelopment of organ or part. 2. Complete abortion.

supra. See SUPER.

supra-axillary. Borne above the axil.

supracanus. Gray pubescent above.

supracomposite. Excessively subdivided.

supracutaneous. Above the epidermis.

supradecompound. Several times compound, doubly compound.

suprafoliaceous. Situated above the axil instead of within it, situated above the petiole or growing above a leaf.

suprafoliar. Growing upon a leaf.

supralineate. With an excurrent rib-like projection or growth on the upper surface.

supralittoral. Above the highwater mark.

supranodal. Above a node.

supraseptal. With two plates diverging from an interorbital septum.

suprasoriferous. With sori on the upper surface.

suprastigmal. Above the stigma.

supraterraneous. Above the ground.

supravasal. Situated opposite the xylem groups in the wood.

surculate. Having the form of a sucker.

surculigerous. Having or bearing suckers.

surculose. Producing suckers, stoloniferous.

surculus. An underground shoot ultimately aerial and independent, a sucker, a rhizome.

surcurrent. With winged expansions from the base of the leaf prolonged up the stem.

surface sectioned. Cut parallel to and near the surface.

surface yeast. High yeast.

surfoyl. Outer scales.

surinamensis. Of Surinam.

sursum hamulosus. Bordered with hooks pointing to the apex.

survival characters. Characters which do not become merged or lost in transmission.

survival potential. The degree of environmental resistance which an organism can endure.

susianus. Of the province of Susiana (Persia), of Susa, a city of ancient Persia.

suspensor. 1. A hypha which forms a club-shaped or conical stalk of a gametangium in mucors, a cell which supports the conjugating cells, a zygosporophore. 2. A stalk-like structure of the embryo in seed plants and club mosses which appears soon after fertilization and grows into the nutritive tissue (the endosperm or gametophyte).

suspensor, primary. The row of cells preceding the actual embryological divisions.

sustentacular. Supporting.

suturarius. Possessing a suture.

suture. 1. A line of fusion. 2. A line along which dehiscence may occur.

suture, dorsal. In fruits, the mid-rib of a carpel.

suture, ventral. The inner line of junction along the enfolded edges of the carpel.

swamp. A flat wet area usually covered by standing water and supporting a growth of trees, shrubs, and grasses.

swang. Moorland bogs, particularly those in hollows; low, wet, grassy land.

swarm. A number of spores or unicellular individuals of common origin which remain together without being united in any way.

swarm cell. A motile naked protoplasmic body, a zoospore.

swarm sporangium. A zoosporangium.

swarmspore. A zoospore.

swarm stage. A stage of motile zoospores or swarmspores.

swarmer. A zoospore, a swarmspore.

sweet herbs. Fragrant herbs cultivated for culinary purposes.

swimming apparatus. In *Azolla*, three apical episporic spongy masses of tissue surrounding a central conical body with an array of fine filaments.

switch plants. Plants whose leaves are lacking or reduced with green shoots acting in the place of leaves.

sychnocarpous. Fruiting successively without dying.

sycolliphytum. A plant in which the perianth becomes combined with the pericarp.

syconium. A multiple fruit in which the seeds are surrounded by a fleshy thick mass formed from the much enlarged hollow common receptacle like the fruit of the fig, a syconus.

sycosis. A disease of the skin caused by a species of *Microsporon*.

sygolliphytum. A sycolliphytum.

sylva. Silva.

sylvaticus. Inhabiting woods, growing among trees, sylvestris.

sylvestral. Growing in woods or shady places.

sylvestrine. Growing in woods.

sylvicolous. Growing in woods.

sylvula. A plantation, a small sylva.

sym-, syn-. A prefix meaning with.

symbasic. Based on several types.

symbasis. The condition of having several independent types or free intercrossing lines of descent.

symbion. A symbiont.

symbiont. An organism which lives in a state of symbiosis, a symbiote.

symbiophiles. Free mycorrhiza of hymenomycetous fungi neither parasites nor saprophytes.

symbiosis. The living together of dissimilar organisms in a state of mutualism.

symbiosis, antagonistic. The symbiosis in which there is a struggle between the two organisms.

symbiosis, conjunctive. Symbiosis in which the symbionts are so intimately blended as to form an apparently single body.

symbiosis, contingent. A condition when one plant lives in the interior of another for shelter, not parasitism; Raum parasitismus.

symbiosis, disjunctive. The condition in which the symbiotic association is only temporary.

symbiosis, mutualistic. Symbiosis in which there is reciprocal advantage.

symbiote. A symbiont.

symbiotic. Living in beneficial partnership, of or pertaining to symbiosis.

symbiotic saprophyte. A phanerogam which subsists by means of a mycorrhiza or by felting the hyphae on roots.

symbiotropic. Deriving nourishment by a symbiotic relationship.

symedia. Primary associations or aggregations in which the offspring from the same mother form the aggregation without the presence of either parent.

symmetranthous. Divisible into equal perianth parts along several planes of division.

symmetricarp. A fruit which is symmetric.

symmetry, major. Symmetry applied to the organism as a whole.

symmetry, minor. Symmetry of a part of an organism.

symmetry, multilateral. Radial symmetry.

symmetry, radial. The equal division in more than one direction through the center.

symmixis. Chromosome pairing in which there is actual interchange of chromosome parts.

sympathy. 1. The faculty of ready union in grafting. 2. The capacity to hybridize and to receive foreign pollen.

sympeda. Symmetry by an intersecting plane.

sympedae. Diatoms having superficial symmetry.

sympetalae. Gamopetalae.

sympetalicous. With the stamens cohering to the petals.

sympetalous. Gamopetalous, with corollas whose petals are more or less united.

symphagia. Secondary associations created by a favorable food supply.

symphiantherous. Synantherous, syngenesious, synandrous.

symphicarpous. With confluent fruits.

symphily. Commensalism with mutual benefit or affection.

symphogenesis. The development of a part by the union of two separate parts.

symphogenetic. Arising by the intertwining and coiling of hyphal branches of different origin to form a network that becomes compact and knot-like, symphyogenous, symphiogenetic.

symphotia. Secondary associations collected around a given source of light.

symphyantherous. Having the stamens united by their anthers, symphiantherous, synantherous, synandrous.

symphycarpous. Having the parts confluent, as the apothecia in certain lichens.

symphyllode. The cone scales in the *Abietineae*.

symphyllodium. The combined ovuliferous scales in the flower of certain *Coniferae*.

symphyllous. Gamophyllous.

symphyogenesis. Symphiogenesis, symphogenesis.

symphyostemonous. Having the stamens united.

symphysia. Symphysis.

symphysiology. The science of correlation.

symphysis. The union of like parts with each other in the process of formation, as of petals; coalescence.

symphystemonous. With stamens united, monadelphous, synantherous.

symphytantherous. Symphiantherous, synandrous.

symphytic. Formed by the fusion of several nuclei, as a gameto-nucleus (oogamete) of *Peronosporeae* or an isogamete of *Dasycladus*.

symphytogynous. With the calyx and pistil more or less adherent, the ovary being inferior.

symphytothelous. Symphytogynous.

symplast. 1. A multinucleate body formed by nuclear fragmentation of a single energid. 2. An assemblage of energids, as in *Caulerpa prolifera*.

symplocium. 1. The sporangium of a fern. 2. The annulus of a fern sporangium.

symplokium. Symplocium.

sympode. A sympodium.

sympodial branching. A series of branches in

which the main axis of branching is made up of a series of lateral branches because of the self-pruning and withering of the terminal bud.

sympodial dichotomy. A dichotomy in which one branch of each successive bifurcation continues to develop and the other remains subordinate or aborts.

sympodice. Sympodially.

sympodium. A stem made up of a series of branches growing on each other giving the effect of a single stem, as a grape vine; a branch system in which the main axis ceases to elongate and one of the lateral branches grows on, which in turn ceases to grow and gives laterals which repeat the process.

sympolymorphism. The occurrence of various forms in a given organ in the same individual.

synacme. Synanthesis.

synandrium. A mass of stamens (including the anthers), the cohesion of the anthers of each male flower in certain *Aroideae.*

synandrodium. A concrescence of staminodes (sterile stamens).

synandrous. With united stamens.

synange. A synangium.

synangium. A compound sporangium in which sporangia are coherent, as in some ferns; a concrescence of sporangia.

synantherae. *Compositae.*

synanthericous. Having the anthers growing together, as in composites; syngenesious.

synantherology. The study of the *Compositae.*

synantherous. With stamens united by anthers, symphiantherous, syngenesious, synandrous.

synanthesis. 1. Synacme, synacmy, the ripening of the stamens and pistils at the same time. 2. The condition where seeds germinate near the parent instead of being dispersed at maturity.

synanthody. The lateral adhesion of two flowerbuds on the same stalk or on two peduncles which have become fasciated.

synanthous. 1. Having flowers and leaves appearing simultaneously. 2. With flowers united.

synanthrophytum. A plant having a fruit compounded of many carpels.

synanthrose. A sugar found in the roots and tubercles of certain *Compositae.*

synanthy. The abnormal coalescence of two or more flowers.

synaphosis. A change in the cohesion of plasma.

synaposematic. Capable of mimicry of a more powerful species as a means of defense.

synapsis. Syndesis, the conjugation of maternal and paternal chromosomes preceding maturation divisions, chromosome pairing at zygotene, the entire period from the contraction of the nucleus until the spireme segments into chromosomes.

synaptase. Emulsin.

synaptene. The zygotene stage in meiosis, the synaptic stage in meiosis while the chromosomes are conjugating two by two.

synaptic knot. Synapsis.

synapticula. One of the small rods connecting septa of mushroom coral or like structures.

synaptospermy. The condition in plants whose seeds germinate near the parent plant instead of being dispersed at maturity.

synaptotene. Synaptene.

synarch. The fusion of two sexual cells.

synarmophytous. Gynandrous.

synascomycetes. A group of fungi including *Pericystis apis.*

synascus. In *Pericystis apis,* an oogonium in which a sporogonium or ascus of uninucleate spores is organized around each diploid nucleus.

synatene. The zygotene stage in meiosis, synaptene.

syncarp. A fleshy aggregate or multiple fruit, an aethalium.

syncarpous. 1. Composed of united carpels. 2. Bearing a collective fruit.

syncaryophyte. A sporophyte.

synchoria. Secondary associations which are locality aggregations formed primarily because of a limited expanse of particularly favorable locations for living.

synchorion. A carcerule.

synchorology. 1. The geographic distribution of communities. 2. Plant distribution in time as fossil species and their duration during geological periods.

synchronogamy. The simultaneous maturity of male and female flowers on the same stalk.

synchronology. Plant distribution in time, i.e., fossil species and their duration during geological periods.

synchronous mitosis. The occurrence of a number of cell divisions which take place at exactly the same time in a group of neighboring cells.

syncladous. Growing in tufts from the same point.

synconium. A syconium.

syncotyl. A syncotyledon.

syncotyledon. A seedling in which the cotyledons are united.

syncotyledonous. Having coherent or coalesced cotyledons.

syncotylous. Having united cotyledons.

syncytium. A multinucleate mass of protoplasm without differentiation into cells, a plasmodium, a coenocyte.

syndesis. The conjugation or fusion of homologous chromosomes in meiosis, synapsis.

syndetocheilic. Having stomatal development in which subsidiary cells and guard cells originate from the same primordial tissue.

syndimorphism. The possession of different forms of a given organ on the same individual.

syndinal mitosis. Mitosis in the peridinial genus *Syndinium* which takes place without an achromatic spindle being formed, the chromosomes breaking apart.

syndiploid. With two or more diploid nuclei fusing.

syndiploidy. 1. Meiosis without syngamy. 2. The results from doubling of the chromosome number immediately prior to meiosis.

synechorology. Synchorology, the geographic distribution of communities.

synecology. 1. The study of plant communities. 2. The relation between a community and its habitat.

synecology, dynamic. The study of plant communities as the result of biotic factors.

synecology, geographic. The distribution of plant communities influenced by factors of environment.

synecology, morphological and physiololgical. Physiognomy, ecologic structure, and floristic communities as related to factors of environment.

synedral. Growing on the angles of a stem.

synema. A column of united filaments in a monadelphous flower.

synenchyma. Fungus tissue which arises by cell division in several places.

synergetic. Operating together.

synergid. A nucleus or cell adjacent to the megagamete at the micropylar end of the megagametophyte which appears to attract the tip of the pollen tube toward the egg-nucleus.

synergidae. Two cells or nuclei in the upper end of the embryo sac which together with the oosphere form the egg apparatus.

synergism. The ability of two or more species of microorganisms to accomplish a change that neither can bring about alone.

synergy. The combined and simultaneous action of several organs.

synfolium. The foliage layer in a stratified forest community.

syngame. Sex as determined by fertilization.

syngameons. Pairing communities or superspecies, a group of individuals which resemble each other more than they do any others, a linneon or linnaeon.

syngamete. The cell which arises from the fusion of two gametes, a zygote.

syngamy. Fertilization, the fusion of gametes to form a zygote, the fusion of a male and female gamete.

syngamy, binary. Syngenesis.

Syngenesia. A Linnaean class including the *Compositae* having flowers with united anthers.

syngenesious. In a ring, as the anthers in *Compositae*; having stamens united by their anthers.

syngenesis. 1. The natural development of communities toward the climax community. 2. Sexual reproduction, the sexual formation of an embryo. 3. The current theory that offspring are formed in part from one of the producing cells and part from the other, not from one cell alone, as presumed in some old theories.

syngenetic geobotany. The ecologic investigation of plant communities, ecology.

syngenetics. The development of plant communities, successional ecology.

syngonimia. Gonimia united in clumps.

syngrammae. Diatoms with linear symmetry.

syngynous. Epigynous.

syngyny. Epigyny.

synhaploid. Formed by the union of two or more haploid nuclei.

synizesis. The attraction figure associated with syndesis, synapsis.

synkaryon. A nucleus arising from the union of two nuclei.

synnema. A columnar bundle of closely united conidiophores; an erect fascicle of hyphae, as in *Stilbaceae.*

synocreate. Having the stipules united on the opposite sides of a stem enclosing it in a sheath, synochreate.

synoecious. Having antheridia and archegonia on the same receptacle or having the stamen and pistil in the same flower, having male and female organs in the same cluster, synoicous.

synonym. A Latin or scientific name which has been superseded or is by rules of nomenclature not acceptable.

synophtalmy. The adhesion of embryos or buds.

synophthy. Synophthalmy.

synophty. Synophthy.

synorhizous. Having a radicle whose point is united to the albumen.

synpetalous. Gamopetalous.

synphyllodium. The cone scale.

synplast. Symplast.

synsepalous. Having a calyx composed of fused or united sepals.

synspermous. Having several seeds united.

synsperms. Plants with seeds integrated with the placenta.

synspermy. The union of several seeds.

synsporous. Propagating by cell conjugation, as in algae.

synstigmaticus. Having a pollen mass furnished with a retinaculum by which it adheres to the stigma, as in orchids.

syntactic. Having irregularity which is zygomorphic.

syntagmata. Bodies built up of tagmata which are themselves aggregations of molecules.

syntepalous. Having tepals united.

synthease. A soluble enzyme effecting the union of sugar and phosphates.

syntriploid. Uniting triploid nuclei.

syntrophic. Epiphytic.

syntrophism. The antogonistic symbiosis of lichen with lichen.

syntrophs. Lodgers in lichens.

syntrophy. Syntrophism.

syntropia. An aggregation resulting from mass response to a given environmental factor.

syntype. Cotype, one of several specimens of equal rank upon which a species is based.

synusia. Life forms associated in growth and habitat but distinct as to affinity.

synusiologic. Ecologic.

synusium. A stratal society, a natural community of species belonging to the same life form groups with uniform ecological requirements.

synzoic. Of intentional dispersal by means of animals.

synzoospores. Large solitary zoogonidia in *Vaucheria.*

synzygia. The point of contact of opposite cotyledons.

syphon. A siphon, a large tubular cell in *Chara* and various algae.

syphoneous. Possessing a tubular structure.

syriacus. Syrian.

syringa. A lilac.

syringanthous. *Syringa*-flowered.

syringifolious. *Syringa*-leaved.

syringin. A substance occurring in *Syringa,* the lilac.

syringinous. A light purple.

syringodendron. Old or partially decorticated sigillarian stems.

syrphetobios. Organisms of mull or compost heaps.

syrtidad. A plant of a dry sandbar.

syrtidium. A dry sandbar formation.

syrtidophilous. Dwelling on dry sandbars.

syrtidophyte. A dry sandbar plant.

syrtis. A dry sandbar community.

systasis. A community which exhibits a difference constant but insufficient to rank as a separate community.

systellophytum. A plant with a persistent calyx which appears to form part of the fruit.

system. 1. A scheme of classification, an arrangement of natural objects according to some rule. 2. The sum of parts of an organism which are of the same morphological nature or perform to similar function, as the fibrovascular or intercellular system.

systematic botany. The study of plants in their mutual relationships and taxonomic arrangement.

systematic invasion. A type of invasion in which the infectious material invades all ▸portions of plant.

systematist. One who studies systematic botany.

systematy. Classification by academic systems, systematic or taxonomic botany.

systemic infection. A disease caused by a parasitic fungus which lives in the perennial parts of the host and passes from them into the new shoots developed during each season of growth.

systilius. A systylius.

systole. 1. The rhythmic contraction of any contractile cavity; the contraction of the contractile vesicles in certain algae, plasmodia, and zoospores. 2. The collapse of the nucleus and the outflow of nuclear material into the cytoplasm during mitosis due to dissolution of the nuclear membrane.

systrophe. The massing of the chlorophyll bodies of a cell under intense light.

systrophic interval. The portion of the photrium in which systrophe can take place, systrophion.

systylius. The lid affixed to the columella in mosses which is elevated above the capsule when it dries.

systylous. 1. Having coherent styles. 2. Having a fixed columella lid or stylius.

sysympaedia. Symphagia, secondary associations or aggregations.

T

T. A designation for terminal.

T^1. A second series.

tabacine. Tobacco-colored.

tabashir, tabasheer. A mass of silica found in the joints of bamboo, the sugar of bamboo.

tabashir. Of bamboo.

tabes. A disease with the loss of the power of growth and consequent wasting away.

tabescent. Withering, wasting away.

tabid. Dissolving, decaying.

tablet. 1. The frustule of diatoms when quadrangular. 2. The rectangular colony of *Gonium*.

tabula. The pileus of certain fungi.

tabulaeform. Table-shaped.

tabular roots. Buttress-like roots of certain tropical trees.

tabularis. Table-like.

tabulatus. Layer on layer.

tabuliform. Table-shaped.

tachydromile. Of swift flowing streams.

tachygenesis. Embryonic acceleration by shortening or omitting embryonic stages.

tachyspore. A plant which quickly disperses its seeds.

tachysporous. Quickly dispersing seeds.

tactic. Reacting to a stimulus by internal change.

tactile bristles. Stimulators.

tactile hairs. Stimulators.

tactile papilla. A mechanical sense organ such as a projecting cell on a tendril.

tactile pit. An unthickened area on the outer wall of a superficial sensory cell.

taedigerous. 1. Torch-bearing. 2. Resin-bearing.

taemopterid. A fern resembling *Taemopteris* in structure.

taenianus. Long, cylindric, and contracted in places (like a tapeworm).

taeniate. 1. Longitudinally striped. 2. Ribbon-like in shape. 3. Having band-like markings.

taeniole. A little band.

taeniopteroid. In fossil botany, resembling the genus *Taeniopteris*.

tagma. An aggregation of molecules including pleon, micella, and micellar aggregates.

tagmatic complex. A higher molecular system.

taiga. Flat marshy forests, the area between the tundra and the steppe, the Siberian primeval forest.

tailed. Having anthers with prolongations from the loculus which lack pollen.

take-all. An Australian name for the ravages of *Ophiobolus graminis* on wheat, the strawblight in England.

talara. The wing or ala of a papilionaceous corolla.

talea. A cutting or small branch for propagating.

talus. An accumulation of loose fragments at the base of rocks.

tamaricetum. An association of *Tamarix*.

tame pasture. Land once cultivated which has been seeded with and is now occupied by domestic pasture plants and used chiefly or entirely for grazing livestock.

tan bark. Any bark rich in tannin used in tanning.

tanacetifolious. Tansey-leaved.

tangential section. A section cut parallel to the longitudinal axis and at right angles to the medullary rays.

tangerine. A citrus fruit much like the mandarin orange but of deeper color and higher flavor.

tanghin. The poison occurring in the ordeal tree of Madagascar, *Cerbera Tanghin*; see ORDEAL TREE.

tangle. 1. Any large blackish seaweed. 2. A

mat of irregularly intertwined branches, roots, hyphae, etc.; see SKEIN.

tank epiphytes. Epiphytes in which the roots are reduced to anchoring appendages.

tankard-shaped. Thickened, about twice as long as broad, gradually enlarged downward, and then suddenly contracted or terminated.

tannase. An enzyme which occurs in *Aspergillus*.

tannin. An important group of astringents especially abundant in some barks, as that of the oaks.

tannin, aplastic. An excretion, as in the germinating date seed.

tannin, physiological. A waste product.

tannin, plastic. Tannin that can be modified and is presumably connected with nutrition.

tannin sacs. Strongly refractive globular bodies in cells which contain tannin.

tannin vesicles. Tannin sacs.

tanniniferous. Yielding tannin.

tapering base. The blade extending downward along the petiole.

tapesium. Dense and wefted superficial mycelium with ascophores on it.

tapestry. Forest growth on steep slopes forming an unbroken arboreal mantle.

tapestry forest. Groves which maintain themselves on precipitous slopes, as in Hawaii.

tapetal. Of or pertaining to the tapetum.

tapetal cell layer. The layer below the intermediate layer in anthers.

tapetal layer. The tapetum.

tapetal plasmodium. A multinucleate mass formed by the breakdown of the cell walls between the cells of a tapetum.

tapetal septum. The wall between the megaspore cavity and the nucellus in Palaeozoic seeds.

tapete. The tapetum.

tapetum. A layer of cells occurring in various plant structures such as sporangia, etc., which serves in a nutritive capacity.

taphrad. A ditch plant.

taphrenchyma. Bothrenchyma.

taphrium. A ditch community.

taphrophilous. Ditch-dwelling.

taphrophyte. A ditch plant.

tapioca. A granular preparation made from the roots of cassava, *Manihot*.

taproot. A central or leading root which penetrates deeply into the ground without dividing.

taraxacine. A bitter crystalline substance found in the dandelion, *Taraxacum officinale*.

taraxicifolious. Dandelion-leaved.

tardiflorous. Late-flowered.

targets. Peltae.

tarn. A small mountain lake or pool.

tartareous. 1. Having a rough crumbling surface. 2. Consisting of tartar.

tartaricus. Of Tartary.

tassel. A drooping spike or long cluster of flowers, as the staminate inflorescence of maize (corn).

tassement polaire. The formation of a dense mass by the chromosomes at the poles of the spindles as telephase approaches.

taungya. Deserted cleared areas of Burma which return slowly, if at all, to the native forest.

tauricus. Taurian, Crimean.

taurinus. Bull-like, ox-like.

tautonym. A name in which the specific name merely repeats the generic.

taxaceous. Relating to the *Taxaceae*, the yew family; taxineous.

taxadineous. Related to *Taxodium*, the swamp cypress.

taxetum. An association of yew trees, *Taxus baccata*.

taxifolious. Yew-leaved.

taxiform. Arranged distichously like the leaves of yew.

taxignomic. Taxonomic.

taxineous. Relating to the *Taxaceae*, the yews; taxaceous.

taxinomic. Taxonomic.

taxis. The tendency of an organism to move towards (positive) or away from (negative) a source of stimulus, the reaction of free organisms in response to external stimuli by movement.

taxism. The tendency of unicellular organisms to arrange themselves according to lines of force or stimulation.

taxitery. A modification which is so slight as to permit comparison with the normal form.

taxoid. Resembling or allied to *Taxus*, the yew.

taxoids. Seeds of conifers more or less succulent, solitary, and dispersed by birds.

taxology. Taxonomy.

taxon. Arrangement, order, classification.

taxonomic. Of or pertaining to taxonomy.

taxonomy. The mode of arrangement, the branch of biology which deals with the classification of the species of plants and animals.

taxy. The distinguishing constituent of a variation.

TDP. Thermal death point.

tea. A white-flowered evergreen plant grown in the tropics and subtropics whose leaves are dried and steeped to provide the drink. There are several varieties of plants used but the most common one is *Thea sinensis*.

tea, crystal. *Ledum palustre.*

tea, Jersey. *Ceanothus americanus.*

tea, Labrador. *Ledum groenlandicum.*

tea, Mexican. *Ephedra* or *Chenopodium ambrosiodes.*

tea, Oswego. *Monarda didyma.*

tea, phillipine. *Ehretia microphylla.*

tea-tree, Australian. *Leptospernum laevigatum* or *Melaleuca.*

tectology. Morphology in which an organism is considered as a group of morphological, as distinct from physiological, units or individuals.

tectonetum. An association of *Tectona*, teak.

tectoparatype. A specimen selected to show the microscopic structure of the original type of a species or genus.

tectoplesiotype. A tectoparatype but with subsequently described specimens.

tectorial. Covering.

tectotype. A fragment for microscopic investigation.

teen suda. A soil found in a zone between a desert and the equatorial humid area which is well drained and has a layer of calcium carbonate.

tegmen. The inner seed coat, the inner coat of the testa, an endopleura, a secundine, a covering.

tegment. The scale of a leaf bud.

tegmenta foliacea. Modifications of leaves.

tegmenta fulcracea. Modifications of leaves, stipules, and petioles.

tegminatus. Invested by a covering.

tegular. Consisting of a tile-like structure.

tegule. The sepal-like involucral bracts of a composite flower head.

tegulicolous. Living on tiles.

tegument. The outer protective covering scales of a leaf bud, the integument.

tegumentary system. The layer or layers of cells which cover the surface of a plant.

tegumentum. 1. The indusium of a fern. 2. The spermoderm. 3. The outer covering of scales upon a leaf bud.

teichosome. One of the droplets or spherules composing the cell wall.

teknospore. A spore produced directly from male or female organs of *Equisitaceae* and many ferns.

tela. 1. An elementary tissue such as meristem. 2. A web-like tissue. 3. A choroid membrane.

tela contexta. A weft of distinct hyphae, felted tissue.

teleblem. Teleoblema, a distinct universal veil, the volva; see BLEMATOGEN.

telebolites. The products of enzyme action.

telegony. An unfounded belief that if a mother has offspring by two mates, the offspring of the second cross will exhibit characteristics of the first; the supposed influence of a male parent on offspring subsequent to his own from the same female parent.

teleianthous. Having both gynoecium and androecium.

teleianthus. An hermaphrodite, a perfect flower.

telemorphosis. A situation where one hypha brings about a change in another hypha by sending out an opposing fusion hypha.

telemorphotic. Stimulating growth that brings about the fusion of hyphae or other structures.

teleoblem. The teleblem.

teleocentric. Telocentric.

teleology. The doctrine of final causes: a belief, as that of vitalism, that natural phenomena are determined not only by mechanical causes but by an overall design in nature as opposed to mechanism.

teleomitosis. Karyokinesis.

teleorganic. Vital to an organism.

teleplastids. Reproductive cells.

teleplasts. Products of division forming a merism.

telescopiform. Having joints that telescope into each other.

teleutostage. The stage producing a teleutospore, a telium.

teleutoconidium. Teleutospore.

teleutoform. The last or final fruit form in the alternating generations of *Uredineae.*

teleutogonidium. A teleutospore, a teliospore.

teleutosorus. An aggregation of teleuto-spores.

teleutospore. The thick-walled resting spore of the *Uredineae*, the winter spore in *Uredinales*, a spore formed in the fall which germinates in the spring.

teleutosporiferous. Bearing a teleutospore.

teleutostage. The stage in the life history of a rust fungus when teleutospores are formed.

telial stage. The teleuto stage.

telianthous. Hermaphroditic.

teliosorus. A teliosorus, a teleutosorus.

teliospore. A thick-walled rust spore which produces a promycelium when it germi-nates, a teleutospore.

teliostage. The teleutoform stage, the final or late summer stage of the rust spores.

telium. A teleutosorus, the sorus of the last summer stage of certain rust fungi.

tellimoid. Like *Tellima*, a saxifrage.

telluric. From the earth.

telmatad. A wet meadow plant.

telmathium. A wet meadow community, a wet marsh community, a telmatium.

telmatology. The study of moors.

telmatophilous. Dwelling in wet meadows.

telmatophyte. A wet meadow plant.

telmicolous. Dwelling in freshwater marshes, telmacolous.

teloblast. One of the large cells which pro-duce lines of smaller cells at the end of many embryos.

teloblastic band. A band of cells originally derived from two teloblasts which later produce the mesoblastic somites.

telocentric. Having a terminal kinetochore in a chromosome.

telogamae. The *Florideae* algae.

telogonidium. A gonidium arising from suc-cessive generations in the same cell.

telokinesis. 1. The last stage of mitosis when daughter nuclei are re-formed. 2. The changes in the cells after the telophase.

telome. A single terminal segment of a branching axis.

telome theory. A theory concerning plant evolution that states that plants evolved through the formation of vascular tissue, stomata, and terminal sporangia from an undifferentiated axis.

telomitic. Having chromosomes attached endwise to a spindle fiber.

telophase. The final phase in karyokinesis, the last phase of nuclear division, the clos-ing phase of mitosis and meiosis.

telosynapsis. Telosyndesis, metasyndesis, the end-to-end union of the chromosomes (synaptic mates) in synapsis.

telosynaptist. One who regards each parallel thread of the heterotype prophase as half of a somatic chromosome which separated in the preceding telophase.

telosyndesis. Telosynapsis.

telotaxis. Topotaxis.

temperate lakes. Lakes whose temperatures vary somewhat above and below 4°C.

temperate phage. A bacteriophage which does not destroy its host. A lysogenic phage.

temperature coefficient. The ratio of the rate of progress of any reaction or process in a plant at a given temperature to the rate at a temperature 10°C lower.

temperature summing. See ALIQUOTE.

temporary collenchyma. Collenchyma present in a young organ disappearing as secondary thickening progresses.

temporary starch. Starch which is stored for a time in the chloroplasts when the plant is forming carbohydrates more rapidly than they are being used or removed from a leaf.

temulin. An active substance occurring in rye grass, *Lolium temulentum*.

tenacle. A stalk of a plant, an organ of attach-ment, an adhesive structure of attachment as a haptera or holdfast of algae and other plants.

tender. Unable to endure winter cold.

tendril. A lateral climbing organ, sometimes a stem and sometimes a leaf; a filiform organ used for climbing representing a modified leaflet, leaf, stipule, or branch.

tendrillar. 1. Pertaining to or functioning as a tendril. 2. Twining or having tendrils.

tenebrosus. Of dark or shaded places.

tension flange. A mechanical tissue devel-oped on the concave side of a coiled tendril.

tension form. A papilionaceous flower with concealed anthers.

tent pole. A raised central portion of the apex of the prothallus.

tentacle. One of the sensitive glandular hairs on the leaf of *Drosera*, an irritable hair.

tentaculiferous. Bearing tentacles.

tentaculiform. Tentacle-shaped.

tentaculoid. Like a tentacle, as the long processes which pass through mammiform protuberances of the perigloea of diatoms.

tenuicaulis. Slender-stemmed.

tenuiflorous. Slender-flowered.

tenuifolious. Having thin narrow leaves.

tenuilobus. Slender-lobed.

tenuinucellatae. Plants with true seeds in which the nucellus is reduced to a layer of cells or wholly absorbed by the endosperm.

tenuipetalous. Slender-petaled.

tenuistylous. Slender-styled.

tepal. A segment of an undifferentiated perianth.

tepaloid. With the character of a tepal.

tephreous. Ash-colored.

tepidarium. A warm room.

ter-. A prefix meaning triple.

teratogeny. The production of monsters.

teratology. The science which deals with monstrosities or abnormal forms.

teratoma. An abnormal growth of leaf tissue in crown galls due to bacteria.

tercine. The third coat of an ovule or a layer of the second coat.,

terebene. A terpene which holds resin in solution, as turpentine.

terebinthaceous. Of turpentine.

terebinthifolious. Leaved like *Terebinthus*, tropical balsamaceous trees.

terebinthinate. Consisting of turpentine.

terebinthine. Pertaining to or consisting of turpentine.

terebrate. Having scattered perforations.

terebrator. The trichogyne in *Gyrophora*, a boring apparatus.

terebratorhypha. A tereborator.

terebriform. Screw-like.

teredo. A disease caused by the boring of insects.

teres. Terete, circular in cross section.

terete. Cylindrical and tapering.

tereticorn. With terete or cylindrical horns.

teretifolious. With terete leaves.

teretiusculus. Round cylindric.

tergal. Situated at the back.

tergeminal. Having three pairs of leaflets or other organs attached by secondary petioles or otherwise to the apex of a common support, tergeminate.

tergeminate. 1. Thrice-forked with twin leaflets. 2. With three pairs of organs.

tergiferous. Dorsiferous, bearing fruit upon the back, having dorsal sporangia.

tergispermous. Having dorsal sporangia, as ferns.

terminal affinity. The property by which chromosomes are held together end to end from diplotene until metaphase or brought together in this way at metaphase.

terminal bud. The bud at the end of the shoot.

terminal chiasma. See CHIASMA.

terminal parenchyma. Aggregated wood parenchyma forming a more or less continuous layer of variable width at the close of a season's growth.

terminal style. A style attached to the top of the ovary.

terminales. The fine end branches of the veins of a leaf.

terminalisation. The expansion of the association of the two pairs of chromatids on one side of a chiasma at the expense of that on the other side.

terminalisation, arrest of. Stoppage of the movement of the chiasma because the opposite segments distal to it are nonhomologous.

terminus phialospore. A phialospore which is formed at the apex of a phialide.

terminus spore. A terminus phialospore.

ternary. Arranged in threes.

ternary hybrid. The result of crossing a hybrid with a species different from either of its parents.

ternate. In threes, in three segments, branching in threes.

ternate pinnate. With secondary petioles proceeding in threes from the summit of the main petiole.

ternate rachis. A ternate stalk.

ternatea. Of the island of Ternate in the Moluccas.

ternately trifoliate. Having three leaflets attached at one point, as in clover.

ternatisect. Cut into three lobes or segments, as a leaf.

ternatopinnate. Having three pinnate leaflets to each compound leaf.

ternifolious. With leaves in threes.

terpenes. A group of hydrocarbons present in turpentine, liquid resin, or essential oils.

terpenoid. Having scents produced by terpenes, as orange flowers, gardenia, thyme.

terpinnate. Tripinnate, three times pinnate.

terra roxa. The red soil found in Brazil, the red earth.

terrace. A level plain usually with an abrupt front bordering a river, lake, or sea.

terraneous. Growing on land.

terreous. Earth-colored, brownish.

terrestrial. Growing on the ground.

terricole. Living on the ground.

terricolous. Living in the soil.

terrigenous. Earth-borne, produced by the earth.

terriherbosa. Herbaceous communities of dry land.

terripetal. Leaning toward the ground.

terriprata. A class of plant formations developed upon substrata not influenced by ground water and consisting of grasses, herbs, and bryophytes; the covering of meadows, grasses, etc.

tersiforms. Forms of the genus *Rosa* which have hairy leaf ribs.

tertial. Of the Tertiary Period or earlier two-thirds of the Cenozoic Period.

tertiary. 1. Of the third order, rank, formation, etc. 2. The Tertiary Period during which flowering plants developed and insects and mammals were dominant, the early Cenozoic Period.

tertiary cell wall. A deposit of wall thickening on the inner surface of the secondary wall of a cell, tracheid, or vessel, usually in the form of rings or of a loose spiral band.

tertiary layer. The tertiary cell wall.

tertiary mycelium. The mycelium differentiated from the secondary mycelium for the purpose of forming fructifications.

tertiary thickening. See TERTIARY LAYER.

tertiary tissue. Tissue due to the renewed action of secondary tissue.

tertiospore. 1. A fertilized egg which undergoes rejuvenescence and segments, usually into four motile spores similar to the spores of a gametophyte generation. 2. The result of sporophytic segmentation, as in *Oedogonium*.

tessellate. Checkered, formed into squares or checkers.

tesselately rimose. Cracked in a checkered or mosaic pattern.

tessellate, checker-worked. Checkered in little squares.

tessularis. Cubic.

test. A shell or hard outer covering, the testa.

test cross. A back cross of a diheterozygote to a double recessive to test linkage.

testa. The outer integument, the seed coat.

testaceous. Brick-red, the color of unglazed common pottery.

testicular. 1. With two oblong tubercles, as in

some orchids. 2. Testicle-shaped. 3. Testiculate.

testiculus. An anther.

testudinarius. Like a tortoise shell.

testule. A frustule.

tetaniform. Like tetanus, tetanoid.

tetanus. A rigid state of plant tissue caused by continued stimulus, a disease caused by *Clostridium tetanum*.

teter. A foul smell.

tetra-. A prefix meaning four.

tetrablastus. A lichen spore which consists of four cells.

tetracamarous. Tetracoccus, of four closed carpels.

tetracanthous. With four spines.

tetracarotin. A lipochrome pigment resembling carotin.

tetracarpillary. Of four carpels.

tetracerous. With four horns.

tetrachenium. A fruit composed of four adherent achenes.

tetrachocarpium. A tetraspore.

tetrachotomous. Divided into fours.

tetrachotomy. The fission of a stem into four branches of equal rank.

tetracoccus. 1. Of four cocci. 2. Having four carpels. 3. Composed of a tetrad of spheres.

tetracotyl. A seedling having both cotyledons deeply bifid.

tetract. A four-rayed spicule.

tetractine. A spicule of four equal and similar rays meeting at equal angles, a tetraxon.

tetracyclic. Having four cycles or whorls.

tetracyte. One of the four cells formed after a meiotic division.

tetrad. 1. A cluster of four spores which have arisen by division from a common spore mother cell. 2. A group of four pollen grains, cells, etc. which remain together until they are mature. 3. A bivalent chromosome formed during the latter part of the meiotic prophase which shows signs of division into four longitudinal threads.

tetradactyl. Having four digits or divisions.

tetradelphous. In four bundles.

tetradidymous. Eight-fold, with four pairs.

tetradiploid. Fusing four nuclei.

tetradogenesis. The formation of a tetrad of spores including all of the phenomena of meiosis.

tetradsporangium. A tetrad mother cell.

tetradymous. 1. Four-fold, having four parts,

as four-celled spores. 2. Having the lamellae of agarics alternate in length with one complete lamella branching into a set of four pairs, short and long.

tetradynamia. A Linnaean class which is characterized by tetradynamous stamens.

tetradynamous. Having four long and two shorter stamens.

tetrafoliatus. With four leaves.

tetrafolious. Having bijugate leaves (leaves with two pairs of leaflets).

tetragonidangium. A sexual reproductive organ in Floridean algae producing tetragonidia.

tetragonidium. A tetraspore, a gonidium or asexually produced spore in *Florideae*.

tetragonolobous. With a four-angled pod.

tetragonous. Four-angled.

tetragynia. A Linnaean order in which the flowers have four pistils.

tetragynous. Having four pistils, with four carpels to a gynoecium.

tetrahedral. Having or made up of four faces.

tetrakont. Having four equal flagella.

tetralophous. With four rays branched or crested.

tetrameristelic. Composed of four meristeles.

tetramerous. With parts or members in fours.

tetramorphic. 1. In four forms, as in variations in length of styles, anthers, stigmas, etc. 2. Having four sets of basidiospores in four different generations on basidia of four different heights above the general level of the basidioles, as in *Coprinus micaceus*.

tetramous. Four-parted.

tetrander. With four stamens.

tetrandria. A Linnaean class of tetrandous plants.

tetrandous. With four stamens.

tetranthous. With four flowers.

tetranucleate. Having four nuclei.

tetrapetalous. Having four petals.

tetraphyletic. With four strains in descent in a hybrid.

tetraphyllous. With four leaves.

tetraplocaulous. 1. With quaternary axes. 2. With four-parted intertwined stems.

tetraploid. With four haploid (monoploid) sets of chromosomes, with twice the normal number of chromosomes.

tetrapolarity. The condition of sexuality in basidiomycetes in which the sexual factors are segregated into four groups and in which matings between monosporous my-

celia are possible only between mycelia bearing complimentary pairs of these factors.

tetrapterous. With four wings.

tetrapyrenous. Having a four-stoned fruit.

tetraquetrous. Having four sharp angles.

tetrarch. A root with a stele with four protoxylem groups.

tetrarinus. Tetrandrous.

tetraschistic. Dividing into four.

tetrasepalous. Having four sepals.

tetrasome. 1. An organism having four chromosomes of one type, the remainder of the chromosome complex usually being diploid. 2. The association of four chromosomes of a kind at meiosis.

tetrasomic. Relating to four homologous chromosomes or genes.

tetraspermous. Having four seeds.

tetrasporaceous. Tetrasporic, tetrasporine, producing tetraspores.

tetrasporangium. A sporangium containing or producing tetraspores.

tetraspore. One of the four spores formed by the division of a mother cell into four parts.

tetrasporophyte. A plant bearing tetraspores.

tetrasporous. With four spores.

tetraster. A spindle of four centers in nuclear divisions.

tetrasterigmatic. Having four sterigmata to each basidium.

tetrastichous. Arranged in four rows.

tetrathecal. Having four loculi.

tetratriploid. With fusion of ditriploid nuclei.

tetravalent. Appearing to have four chromosomes in each nuclear reduction division.

tetraxon. Tetractine.

teucrioid. Like *Teucrium*, the woodsage.

texanus. Of or belonging to Texas.

texenus. Texanus.

texture epidermoidea. The walls of hyphae which are more or less confluent.

texture globosa. The cells which are nearly isodiametric and the separate hyphae not distinguishable.

texture intricata. The hyphae which run in various directions with walls not coalescent.

texture oblita. Hyphae nearly parallel and having small cavities with thickened walls.

texture porrecta. Hyphae with large cavities and no thickened walls.

texture prismatica. Cells not isodiametric, with hyphae not distinguishable.

thalamiflorae. A group of phanerogams which are thalamifloral, flowers having the stamens inserted upon the receptacle.

thalamifloral. Having the floral organs distinct from each other on the receptacle with the parts of a flower hypogynous.

thalamium. The hollow case containing spores in algae, fungi, and lichens.

thalamus. The receptacle or torus of a flower.

thalassad. A sea plant.

thalassic. Sea green.

thalassin. A toxin of the tentacles of the sea anemone.

thalassine. Sea green.

thalassium. A sea formation or community.

thalassophilous. Sea-loving.

thalassophyte. A marine or sea alga or plant.

thalassoplankton. Oceanic plankton.

thalictroid. Like *Thalictrum*, meadow-rue.

thallea. A mass of several layers of plastids formed by the division of one original plastid.

thalleosere. A proteosere.

thallicolous. Growing on a thallus.

thallidium. 1. The young medullary layer in lichens. 2. A vegetative reproductive body, especially in thallophytes and mosses.

thalliform. Like a thallus.

thalline. Resembling or pertaining to a thallus.

thalline exciple. In lichens, an exciple which contains algae.

thalline margin. An apothecial margin formed of and usually colored like the thallus.

thallochlore. The green coloring matter in lichens.

thallodal. Of or pertaining to a thallus.

thallogamae. Algae.

thallogams. Vascular cryptogams.

thallogen. A thallophyte.

thalloid. Like a thallus.

thalloid climax. A climax of the Pre-Devonian Period of bryophytes.

thalloid shoot. A shoot which develops only thallus-like branches and no leaf structures in certain hepatics.

thallome. A thallus.

thallophyte. Plants having thalli and lacking differentiation into root, stems, leaves, flowers, fruit, and seeds.

thallose. Thalloid.

thallospore. A spore formed internally or in an intercalary manner on or in thalli.

thallostrote. A species migrating by means of offshoots.

thallus. 1. A plant body without differentiation into root, stem, and leaf characteristic of thallophytes. 2. The entire body of a fungus or an alga.

thallus gonidia. The gonidia in the thallus of a lichen.

thallus lepodes. A crustaceous thallus, as in certain lichens.

thallus placodes. A foliaceous thallus.

thallus thamnodes. A fruticose thallus.

thamnium. The bush thallus of certain lichens, as *Cladonia rangiferina*.

thamnoblastus. A fruticose lichen.

thamnocolous. Inhabiting shrubs.

thebaicus. Of Thebes.

thebaine. One of the crystalline alkaloids occurring in small quantities in the opium poppy (from Thebes, where opium was widely used).

theca. A spore case, an ascus, a sporangium, an anther cell.

thecaphore. A structure on which a theca is borne, a petiole, the stipe of a carpel, a gynophore.

thecaspore. An ascospore or sporidium.

thecasporous. With enclosed spores.

thecate. Covered or protected by theca, theciferous, thecigerous.

thecial. Possessing thecae or pertaining to them.

thecial algae. The hymenial gonidia of lichens.

thecidion. An achene.

theciferous. Bearing asci or other thecae, thecigerous.

thecigerous. Theca-bearing, applied to the hymenium of fungi and branches of mosses which bear setae.

thecium. The part of a fungus or lichen which bears the sporules, a layer of tissue in the apothecium consisting of asci and paraphyses.

thein. An alkaloid in the leaves of *Thea*, the tea plant.

theke. The theca or ascus of lichens.

thelephoroid. Like the fungus genus *Thelephora*, with the hymenium slightly wrinkled.

thelephorous. Covered with nipple-like prominences.

thelotremoid. With tubercular apothecia like those of the lichen *Thelotrema*.

thelyblast. A mature female germ cell, a female genoblast.

thelygenous, castration. The production of pistils in the male flowers of a host by *Ustilago*.

thelykaryon. A maternal gamete nucleus or its descendant.

thelyotoky. Parthenogenesis where females only are produced.

thelyplasm. Female plasm.

thelytonic. Parthenogenetic, gynecogenic.

theobromine. The active substance in the cacao bean, *Theobroma cacao*.

theobrominus. The deep chocolate brown of the seed of *Theobroma cacao*.

theoretic diagram. A floral diagram of the theoretic components.

therion. A plant succession due to an animal agency, a therium.

thermad. A hot-spring plant.

thermal death point. The degree of heat at which a given organism dies, TDP.

thermal emissivity. The loss of heat from a leaf by radiation, conduction, and convection.

thermesotherm. Having summer heat of 12–20°C.

thermic constant. The sum of the mean temperatures of the days of active vegetation up to some definite phase in the plant's life minus a certain initial temperature determined by several years observation and varying for the species.

thermium. A warm- or hot-spring plant formation.

thermocleistogamy. The self-pollination of unexpanded flowers due to low temperature.

thermocline. A temperature gradient.

thermogenesis. The production of body heat by oxidation.

thermogenic. Heat-producing.

thermolabile. Susceptible to heat.

thermolysis. The loss of body heat.

thermonastic. With close appression of an organ due to heat.

thermonasty. Nastic responses to variations in temperature.

thermophile. A heat-loving organism.

thermophilic. Thriving in heat.

thermophilic bacteria. Bacteria which need a temperature of 45°–65°C for their development.

thermophyte. 1. A plant which prefers situations of more than average heat. 2. A plant which lives through unfavorable situations in the form of seed.

thermosis. A change in an organism due to heat.

thermostable. Able to resist heat.

thermostage. A stage in the life history of a flowering plant when at the outset of development from the embryo in the seed low temperatures are needed to insure further normal development.

thermotactic. Responding to heat.

thermotaxis. The response or reaction of an organism to the stimulus of heat.

thermotolerant. Able to endure high temperatures but not growing well in them.

thermotonous. Showing the relation between temperature and the manifestation of irritability.

thermotoxy. Death due to excess of heat, especially when plant is short of water.

thermotropism. The tendency to curve or turn in response to the heat stimulus.

therodrymium. A leafy forest community.

theromegatherm. Having a high summer temperature of 20°C or above.

theromesotherm. With summer heat of 12°–20°C.

therophyllous. Producing leaves in summer, deciduous.

therophyte. An annual plant.

therophyte climate. The climate of regions of the subtropical zone with winter rain.

thiamin. Vitamin B_1, found in plants, particularly the yeasts, wheat germ, and the legumes. It is important for the metabolism of carbohydrates and fats in humans.

thickening fiber. One of the spiral bands of thickening on the wall of a cell, tracheid, or vessel.

thickening layer. An apparent layer of cellulose on the inner face of a cell wall.

thickening ring. The cambium ring or any other ring or layer of meristematic tissue.

thigmomorphosis. A change in the original structure due to contact, as the adhering disk in *Amphelopsis*.

thigmotaxis. The reaction to the touch stimulus, the tendency of small organisms to attach themselves to objects on contact.

thigmotropism. Curvature induced by contact.

thinad. A dune plant.

thinic. Of a dune community.

thinicolous. Dwelling on shifting sand dunes.

thinium. A dune formation.

thinophilous. Dune-loving.

thinophyte. A dune plant.

thiobacteria. Bacteria which oxidize sulfur.

thiogenic. Producing sulfur.

thiorhodaceous. Belonging to the bacteria *Thiorhodaceae.*

thiourea. A thiocarbamide used to terminate dormancy in seeds.

thioxidans. Bacteria oxidizing sulfur compounds to sulfates.

thixotrophy. The conversion of a gel to a solution by shaking it.

thlaspietum. An association of *Thlaspi*, pennycress or candytuft.

thorn apple. *Crataegus* species.

thorn apple Datura. Any plant of the thorny genus *Datura.*

thorn country. Parkland of low thorn-bearing trees or thickets with spiny shrubs.

thorn forests. The Caatinga forests of Brazil which lose their leaves in dry seasons.

thread. A filament, a longitudinal half of an entire univalent spireme or chromosome.

thread blight. The destructive fungus *Stilbum nanum* which attacks tea plants.

thread hypha. A hypha with walls so strongly thickened that the lumen appears as only a fine line or disappears altogether.

thread indicator. A form of apparatus for measuring the rate of growth.

thread ring. A spireme half in karyokinesis.

thremmatology. The science of breeding animals and plants under domestic conditions.

threshold. The point of a series of graded stimulations above which response begins to be perceptible.

thrice compound. Thrice-pinnate.

thrombin. The ferment of fibrinogen which enables it to form fibrin.

throwback. A reversion.

thrum. 1. A stamen. 2. The filament of a stamen. 3. The anthers in composite flowers.

thrum-eyed. 1. Having the throat of the corolla more or less closed by anthers, as in the primrose in which the stamens alone are visible in the throat. 2. Being short-styled with long stamens or filaments.

thrush. A disease of the mucous membranes of mouth, throat, and esophagus caused by the fungus *Saccharomyces albicans.*

thryptophyte, thriptogen. A pathogenic fungus which weakens the host tissue but does not kill it. The weakened host is then susceptible to other attacks by different pathogens or to physical damage (as droughts or frost, etc.).

thujoid. Like *Thuja*, arbor vitae.

thunderbroom. Witches' broom.

thuriferous. Incense-bearing.

thyll. Tylosis, a protrusion from an adjoining cell into the cavity of a vessel sometimes showing repeated cell division within the vessel, tylose.

thylose. Thyll.

thymetum. An association of *Thymus*, thyme.

thymifolius. Thyme-leaved.

thymoid. Thyme-like.

thymol. A white crystalline substance of a pleasant aromatic odor and strong antiseptic properties found in oil of thyme.

thyriothecium. A shield-shaped fructification which conforms with its host's form rather than with the mycelium. The generative tissue is pendulant with the morphological base at the top.

thyroid. Shield-shaped.

thyrse. A mixed inflorescence or a contracted or ovate panicle with the main axis indeterminate but the secondary and ultimate axes cymose, a compact panicle like the lilac and grape.

thyrsiferous. Bearing a thyrse.

thyrsiflorous. With the flower in a thyrse.

thyrsiform. Shaped like a thyrse.

thyrsoid. Resembling a thyrse.

thyrsoid cyme. A compact, elongated cyme.

thyrsoidal. Relating to or having the form of a thyrsus.

thyrsula. The little cyme borne by most labiates in the axil of the leaves.

tibeticus. Of Tibet.

tidal forest. See MANGROVE.

tidal zone. The narrow strip of territory between high and low watermarks of spring tides, a strand zone.

tide pools. Pools of water left by tides.

tier-like cambium. Storied cambium.

tige. A stem.

tigel. A miniature or initial stem used for a caulicle, a hypocotyle, a plumule.

tigellatous. Having a short stalk, as the plumule of the bean.

tigelle. A caulicle, the first internode, the beginning of the true root.

tigellula. A short filament or stalk in the truffle.

tigellularis. Vascular.

tigellum. The central embryonic axis consisting of radicle and plumule, a miniature or initial stem.

tigline. The acrid substance in the seeds of *Croton tiglium.*

tigrine. Marked like a tiger.

tigrinus. Like a tiger, tiger-striped.

tile cell. Special apparently empty upright square cells occurring in indeterminate horizontal series usually intermingled with the procumbent cells.

tiled. Imbricate, overlapping.

tiles. See BAMBOO.

tilia. Linden, basswood.

tiliaceus. Like *Tilea.*

tiliaefolious. With leaves like *Tilea,* the linden.

till. The product of glaciation, a ground moraine, a soil of mixed clay and pebbles.

tiller. 1. A sucker or branch from the base of the stem. 2. To put forth suckers or new shoots.

tillow. Tiller.

tilth. The depth of the soil to which cultivation may be carried and to which the surface roots may penetrate.

timber line. The upper limit of tree vegetation on mountains.

tinctorial. Used for dyeing, imprinting colors, etc.

tinctus. Tinged, dyed.

tinder fungus. *Fomes fomentarius.*

tinea tonsurans. Ringworm.

tingitanus. Of Tangiers.

tinoleucite. A directing sphere, a centrosome.

tinsel flagella. Flagella with many fine hairs (mastigonemes) along the length of the flagella.

tip. 1. The plant arising at the end of a stolon, as in the black raspberry. 2. An anther.

tiphad. A pond plant.

tiphic. Of a pond community.

tiphicolous. Pond-dwelling.

tiphium. A pond formation or community.

tiphophilous. Pond-loving.

tiphophyte. A pond plant.

tipton. Detritus taken in plankton samples.

tipuliformis. In the shape of a daddy-long-legs.

tirad. A badland plant.

tirium. A badland community.

tissue. An aggregate of similar cells or hy-phae, an aggregate of cells alike in structure or function.

tissue, aqueous. A form of hypoderma which consists of thin-walled parenchyma and lacks chloroplasts but contains much watery sap.

tissue, conjunctive. Ground tissue which arises from the plerome or young stele.

tissue cord. A central cord; a cord or bundle of elongated thin-walled cells at the center of the stems, leaves, fruit, or stalks of many mosses which serve for the transfer of water.

tissue, culture. The growth of detached pieces of tissue in nutritive fluids under conditions which exclude bacteria and fungi.

tissue, cuticularized. Modified cell walls, as epidermis and periderm.

tissue, embryonic. Meristem.

tissue, extrastelar. Ground tissue.

tissue, false. Spurious tissue.

tissue, glandular. Tissue composed of secreting cells or glands.

tissue, ground. Fundamental tissue (neither vascular nor epidermal) either inside or outside of the stele.

tissue, heterogeneous. Tissue composed of various kinds of cells.

tissue, homogeneous. Tissue of uniform cells.

tissue, intrastelar. Conjunctive tissue.

tissue, limitary. Epidermal tissue.

tissue, parenchymatous. Thin-walled pith cells or thick-walled collenchyma cells.

tissue, permanent. Mature or adult tissue.

tissue, primary. First-formed tissue.

tissue, prosenchymatous. Woody tissue.

tissue, sclerenchymatous. Thickened or hardened tissue, as fibers or sclereids.

tissue, secondary. Tissue resulting from growth from continuous meristematic activity.

tissue, sieve. Long articulated tubes with sieve plates in the walls.

tissue, spurious. An approach to a tissue by hyphae massing into a felt or their apices forming a collective apical growing point.

tissue system. A particular tissue through the entire plant body.

tissue, tegumentary. The external epidermal layer.

tissue, tension. The mutual compressions and stretchings exerted by the tissues of a living plant.

tissue, tracheal. Composed of tracheids especially adapted for the conveyance of liquids.

tissue, vascular. The components of the vascular system in plants.

titanous. Clipt or sheared.

tjemoro. An aphyllous forest formed chiefly of *Casuarina* in Java and the Sunda Islands.

tmema. A cell ruptured in freeing a moss gemma.

toadstool. A fleshy unbrella-shaped fungus; a mushroom; in popular usage, a poisonous mushroom.

tofaceous. 1. Buffy drab or argillaceous in color. 2. With a gritty surface.

toleration, law of. The geographic or local range of any species is limited by the fluctuation of a single factor or factors beyond the limit tolerated by that species.

tolu. A resinous exudate from *Myroxylon toluiforum.*

tolypotrichetum. An association of the alga *Tolypothrix.*

tombolo. A bar which connects islands with a mainland.

tomentose. Woolly, hairy.

tomiange. The organ which produces tomies.

tomies. Asexual reproductive bodies which are neither spores nor diodes but living cells which do not arise from an adult stage but produce an adult individual directly.

tomillares. A sclerophyllous vegetation with little rainfall and dry air, sclerophytic subfrutescent vegetation of regions where the air is very dry and the rainfall short.

tomiogone. A tomiange.

tomiparous. Producing spores by division, reproducing by fission.

tonesis. The ability of an organism to exhibit a strain.

tongue. 1. A ligule. 2. A strap-shaped corolla in *Compositae*, such as those on the outer margin of the head in most sunflowers. 3. A membranous appendage on the inner side of the leaf in many grasses and some other endogens at the top of the sheath.

tonic. 1. Bracing. 2. Corroborative.

tonisis. A change in turgescence due to intercellular osmotic forces.

tonobole. A plant whose seeds or spores are scattered by ejection due to tension in the carpels or sporophores.

tonoplasm. The surface of the cytoplasm which lines the vacuoles.

tonoplast. The cytoplasmic membrane surrounding a vacuole in the protoplast, a vacuolar living membrane controlling the pressure of the cell sap.

tonosis. Tonisis.

tonotaxis. The response to osmotic variation.

tonotropism. The response to osmotic stimulus.

top yeast. The yeast which vegetates at the surface of a fluid in which fermentation is taking place.

tophaceous. See TOFACEOUS.

topiary. Formal ornamental gardening, especially trees or shrubs clipped into formal or unnatural shapes as animals, ships, etc.

topical. Confined to a limited area.

topochemotactic. Of or pertaining to chemotaxis.

topochemotaxis. Strophic chemotaxis.

topogalvanotaxis. The attraction towards the stimulus by galvanic action.

topographic. Referring to place changes due to water, wind, gravity, etc.; said of stable plant formations where the prevailing factors are physiographic and edaphic.

topophotaxis. Movement toward the source of light.

topotactic. Of or pertaining to topotaxis.

topotaxis. The response or reaction of an organism to a stimulus in which the organism orients itself in relation to the stimulus and moves toward or away from it.

topotropism. The turning towards a stimulus.

topotype. A specimen from the locality of the original type.

torals. *Thalamiflorae.*

Torf. Acid humus.

torfaceous. Growing in bogs.

Torfschlamm. Dy.

toriloid. Resembling the umbellifer *Torilis.*

toriod. Rounded, protuberant.

tornate. With blunt extremities, rounded off.

torose. Contracted or constricted at intervals along its length, knobby, moniliform.

torsion. The spiral twisting of an organ or part of a plant.

torsion. antidromous. Torsion against the direction of twining as may be caused by the friction of the support.

torsion, apical. Lateral displacement of the apical cell in certain mosses resulting in the twisting of the resultant stem.

torsion, homodromous. Torsion in the same direction as climbing with the internode gyrating in the same way.

torsion symmetry. The symmetrical twisting of the paired valves in a diatom or of other paired parts.

torsional response. The response when a stimulus is applied laterally to an organ.

torsivus. Spirally twisted, not quite as in contorted, there being no obliquity in the insertion, as in the petals of *Orchis*.

tortifolious. With leaves twisted.

tortism. Tropism.

torula condition. Yeast-like isolated cells from the growth of blue mold conidia in a sugar solution.

torulaceous. Resembling the yeast *Torula*, bead-like, moniloid.

toruloid. Torulaceous, chain-like.

torulose. Knobby, with a cylindrical body swollen at intervals, much twisted, moniliform.

torus. 1. The receptacle of a flower. 2. The tiny thickening on the middle of the closing membrane of a bordered pit.

totipotent. Bisexual, capable of producing a fructification.

tototype. A specimen collected at the same place as the type specimen, a topotype.

touchwood. Decayed wood caused by fungus mycelium formerly used as tinder.

touradon. Hillocks in sand areas around which sand and humus collect.

toxaspire. A spiral spicule of more than one revolution.

toxicarious. Poisonous.

toxicology. The science treating of poisons, their effects, antidotes, and recognition.

toxiferous. Producing poison.

toxin. A complex poisonous substance formed by bacteria and other forms of living organisms.

toxon. 1. A bow-shaped spicule, as in sponges. 2. An altered toxin of lessened activity.

toxophore. The portion of a toxin which carries the poisoning power, the poison substance in toxin molecules.

trabant. A segment of a chromosome which is separated from the main body of the chromosome by a long constriction.

trabant, intercalary. A trabant with full-size chromosome limbs on both sides.

trabant, lateral. A trabant which is a branch of a chromosome.

trabecula. 1. A little beam, a small band of tissue joining others together often transverse in direction. 2. A row of cells bridging an intercellular space. 3. One of the thickenings on the inner face of the peristome teeth in mosses. 4. The plates of sterile cells across a sporangium in pteridophytes. See BARS OF SANIO.

trabecular duct. A vessel with crossbar markings.

trabecular vessel. A vessel whose cavity is crossed by ligneous threads or bands.

trabeculate. With trabeculae, crossbarred, having horizontal crossbars on the inner surface.

trace. A strand of vascular tissue which connects a leaf with the stem.

trace element. An element essential for healthy growth and development of organisms but needed in such small amounts that it is almost immeasurable.

trace gap. A gap in the wood caused by the passage of a leaf trace bundle in the stele.

tracer. A radioactive element added to other compounds of importance whose path can be followed as it passes through the plant during the physiological processes.

trachea. A conducting tube or duct located in the xylem, a xylem element made up of a linear series of cells which form a continuous tube by the disintegration of their end walls, a vessel.

tracheal cells. Tracheids.

tracheal class or system of elements. The longitudinal trachea in secondary xylem which serves to conduct water and air. They have a large cavity without septa, and the outer walls have bordered pits and spiral bands.

tracheal tissue. Vascular tissue composed of lignified cells which have lost their protoplasmic contents and serve in a conducting capacity.

tracheary elements. The principal water-conducting elements of the xylem, mostly vessel members and tracheids.

tracheid fibers. The strengthening tissue in the xylem of the stem. They are elongated, thickened cells generally tapered at the ends and lack crosswalls.

tracheid seam. A group of peculiarly thickened cells found in the leaves of conifers on both sides of the vascular bundle formerly regarded as part of the transfusion tissue.

tracheidal medullary ray cells. Ray tracheids.

tracheide. Tracheid.,

tracheids. The woody, sieve-like conducting cells in secondary xylem; the pitted conducting cells which are elongated cylindrical cells with tapered ends and no crosswalls. They are derived from a single cell and lose their living contents to serve as conducting tissue for water and dissolved nutrients.

tracheids, autumn. Later tracheids which have thicker walls and smaller lumina than spring tracheids.

tracheids, spring. Tracheids produced early in annual growth.

trachenchyma. Tissue made up of tracheids or spiral vessels.

tracheoma. The tracheal or hydral system of the bundle or hydrome.

tracheophytes. Plants which have a vascular system, i.e., xylem and phloem.

trachycarpous. Having rough fruits.

trachypleurous. Rough-ribbed or nerved.

trachys-. A prefix meaning rough.

trachyspermous. With rough seeds.

tractellum. The anterior flagellum of the zoospore of *Saprolegnieae*.

tractor fibers. Fibers which are attached to the chromosomes in the mitotic spindle, tractile fibers.

tragacanth. A gum from *Astragalus tragacanth* and from other species of that genus.

tragacanthin. Bassorin.

tragophyllous. Leaved like the grass *Tragus*.

trailing. Having elongated stems spreading on the ground, prostrate but not rooting.

traject. A reconnaissance or trip through a region.

trajectile. Widely separated, with the connective tissue completely separating from the anther cells.

trama. The interior portion of gills or a pileus which is composed of closely associated hyphae, the middle layer of the gill.

trama contexta. The hyphae composing the trama which are normally aparallel or slightly oblique.

trama inversa. The hyphae of the trama when they are derived from the subhymenium.

trama permixta. Trama hyphae without apparent order.

trametoid. Like the fungus *Trametes*.

transapical. At right angles to the apical axis or plane.

transapical axis. An axis at right angles to the apical axis passing through the center of the pervalvular axis of a diatom.

transapical plane. The plane which is at right angles to both valvular and apical planes passing through the pervalvular and transapical axis.

transduction. The transfer of hereditary material from one bacterial cell to another by bacterial viruses (bacteriophages).

transect. 1. A cross section or belt of vegetation. 2. To cut across or to cut transversely.

transect, belt. A band or transect varying in width from a decimeter to a meter.

transect, line. An enumeration of species found in a direct line between two points.

transection. A transverse section.

transeptate. Having all cross walls transverse, crosswalled.

transformed branch. A branch which is modified into a tendril or thorn, etc.

transformed cell. The final shape of the cell, as a fiber, tracheid, etc.

transformed organ. An organ which shows a distinct phase in the individual from one type of the normal structure to another, any morphologic modification of an organ.

transfusion cells. Thin-walled cells in the endodermis of the root, passage cells.

transfusion strand. A strand consisting of parenchymatous or slightly thickened cells at the junction of phloem and xylem bundle elements where a ring of sclerenchyma is formed.

transfusion tissue. A group of short tracheids lying by the side of the xylem in a leaf of a coniferous plant by means of which material passes to or from the vascular strand and the rest of the leaf.

transgressive segregation. The appearance in the F_2 or a later generation of a cross of individuals which show a more extreme development of a character than either parent. It is assumed to be due to cumulative and complementary effects of genes contributed by the parents of the original hybrid.

transgressive strata. Inferior strata of some communities which are also found in other communities.

transilient. A mutation.

transition cell. A thin-walled cell at the end of a vein in a leaf representing the last of the phloem, a cell which is the continuation of a sieve tube where the longitudinal division into sieve tubes and companion cells stops and the transition tissue is formed.

transition, high. The hypocotyl structure hardly distinguishable from the root.

transition. intermediate. The region of the collar up to the hypocotyl.

transition, level of. The area in seedlings where the root and stem systems meet.

transition, low. The transition begun below the collar and completed in that region.

transition region. The portion of the axis of a young plant in which the change from root structure to shoot structure occurs.

transition tissue. Tissue formed of transition cells where the longitudinal division into sieve tubes and companion cells stops.

transitory starch. Starch formed temporarily in a leaf in which photosynthesis is proceeding faster than the removal or consumption of carbohydrates.

translator. 1. The retinaculum of asclepiads. 2. A pollen-transferring organ in orchids.

translocase. Permease.

translocation. 1. The transference of any reserve material from one part to another. 2. A change in position of a segment of a chromosome to another part of the same chromosome or of a different chromosome.

translucent. Capable of transmitting light without being transparent.

transmedian. Crossing the median plane.

transmission cells. Transfusion tissue.

transmutation. 1. The conversion of one element into another, either spontaneously or artificially. 2. Organic reconstruction by addition or reconstruction of composition without complete resolution into its elements.

transmutation of host. Lipoxeny.

transmutation theory. The theory that one species can evolve from another.

transovulate. Having transitory ovules.

transpiration. The loss of water vapor by plants either through the stomata or cuticle.

transpiration current. The ascending sap or current of water in plants through the xylem vessels or woody portion of the vascular bundles.

transpiration, cuticular. The small amount of water transpired through the cuticle.

transpiration, stomatal. The loss of water through the stomata.

transpirometer. An instrument for measuring the amount of transpiration.

transvection. The condition in *Cladophora* when the basis of the initial branch cell is partly in contact with the mother cell and partly against the succeeding cell.

transversal axis. The axis of diatoms which lies in the transversal plane cutting the pervalvular (main longitudinal) axis.

transversal wall. The wall which divides the basal and median walls of the proembryo of *Archegoniatae* at right angles into upper and lower halves.

transversan plane. The plane which passes through the center of a diatom frustule vertical to the pervalvular axis.

transverse chorisis. The condition in which two or more organs stand above or within another.

transverse geotropism. Diageotropism; a kind of geotropic irritability in certain organs, as root stalks, which causes them to assume a horizontal position.

transverse heliotropism. Diaheliotropism; the tendency of organs to place their surfaces at right angles to the sun's rays, as most leaves.

transverse planes. The planes which cut the axis of growth and the surface at right angles.

transverse section. A cross section.

transverse septum. A crosswall or partition.

transverse tropism. Diatropism.

transversely joined leaf scars. Scars of a pair or whorl of leaves connected by a ridge or line running around the twig.

transylvanicus. Of Transylvania.

trap flower. A prison flower which confines insect visitors until pollination has taken place.

trap hairs. The special hairs which confine insects in certain flowers until pollination has taken place.

trapeziform. Trapezium-shaped in the form of an unsymmetric four-sided figure.

trapezio-oblong. With a lengthened trapezoidal form.

trapezoid. With four unequal sides.

traps. Prison flowers which keep insect visitors confined during and after pollination, as *Aristolochia*.

Traube's cells. Certain artificial cells formed by solutions of gelatin and other colloids which have been used to explain the phenomenon of intussusception (growth).

traumatism. An abnormal growth resulting from an injury.

traumatonasty. The curvature response to the stimulus of wounding.

traumatotaxis. The response caused by a wound.

traumatotropic. Curving away from a wound.

traumatropism. Sensitivity to wounds.

traumotaxis. The reaction after wounding, as in nuclei and protoplasts.

traumotropism. The development of curvatures after wounding.

trechometer. An instrument to measure water run-off.

tree. A woody plant with one main trunk and a more or less distinctly elevated head.

tree fern. Any fern with an arborescent habit having a woody trunk or caudex, the *Cyatheaceae*.

tree grass steppe. A tree savannah chiefly of various species of *Acacia*.

tree moss. Lichens of several genera, *Usnea*, *Physcia*, etc., spanish moss.

tree stratum. In woodlands, the tallest stratum composed of developed trees.

trees, canopy. A canopy formed of the well-branched crowns of trees.

trees, tuft. Trees whose trunks are usually unbranched, such as palms, cycads, etc.

trefoil. With three lobes.

trehalase. An enzyme which hydrolyzes trehalose.

trehalose. A white crystalline sugar obtained from trehala, the ergot of rye, and certain fungi. The only disaccharide found in fungi.

tremalith. With a hole through the structure.

tremellaceous. Of, pertaining to, or resembling the fungus *Tremella*.

tremelliform. Gelatinous in texture like *Tremella*.

tremelline. Jelly-like.

tremelloid. Resembling *Tremella*, jelly-like in substance and appearance.

tremuloid. 1. Tremulous like the trembling poplar or quaking aspen. 2. Like the gelatinous fungi of the *Tremellaceae*.

trephones. Nutritive substances secreted by lymphocytes.

treue. Exclusive species.

tri-. A prefix meaning three.

triacanthophorous. Bearing three spines.

triacanthous. With three spines.

triachenium. A dry fruit which splits into three one-seeded parts.

triacrorhizae. Plants whose roots arise from

three initial cells or groups at the apex, as the phanerogams.

triactinal. Having three rays.

triadelphia. Plants with their stamens in three sets.

triadelphous. Having the stamens united into three bundles by their filaments.

triaene. A somewhat trident-shaped spicule.

triander. Having three stamens.

triandria. A Linnaean class of three-stamened plants.

triangularly elongate. A lengthened triangular form.

trianthous. Having three flowers.

triarch. Having three strands of xylem in the stele.

triarinus. Triandrous.

triarticulate. With three joints.

Triassic. A division of the early Mesozoic Period.

triaster. A mitotic figure resulting from tripolar (usually abnormal) division of a nucleus.

triaxon. A spicule having three axes, as a sponge.

tribe. A group superior to a genus but less than an order, a group of genera, related plants intermediate between orders and genera.

tribium. A succession of plants on eroded soils.

triblastus. A lichen spore which is trilocular with each cell viable.

tribracteate. Having three bracts.

tribuloid. Like the fruit of *Tribulus*, beset with sharp bristles, echinate.

trica. A lichen apothecium with a ridged spherical surface, the button-shaped apothecium of the genus *Gyrophora*.

tricamarous. Composed of three loculi.

tricarinate. Having three keels or angles as certain diatoms.

tricarpellary. Having three carpels in a flower or pistil, trigynous.

tricarpellate. With three carpels.

tricarpous. Of three carpels.

tricaudatus. With three tails.

tricellular. Having three cells.

tricephalous. Three-headed, with three heads of flowers.

tricephalus. Tricephalous.

trich-. A prefix meaning hair.

trichasium. A cymose inflorescence with three branches.

trichidium. A sterigma.

trichiferous. Producing or bearing hairs.

trichiform. Bristle-shaped.

trichite. A needle-shaped crystal of amylose in starch grains in plants.

trichobacteria. An order of bacteria comprising the higher filamentous forms, bacteria which have flagella.

trichoblast. 1. An internal hair like those which project into the intercellular spaces of some water lilies. 2. A specialized cell which gives rise to a root hair.

trichocalyx. A hairy calyx.

trichocarpous. With hairy fruit, having a reproductive structure covered with a pubescence.

trichocephalous. Collected into heads and surrounded by hair-like appendages.

trichodes. Hair-like structures.

trichodragmata. Straight, fine, hair-like spicules in bundles.

trichogonium. A trichogyne.

trichogyne. 1. A thread-like extension of the carpogonium in red algae to receive the male cell. 2. A thread-like filament in lichens and other ascomyetes which is impregnated above and gives rise to the carpogonium or perithecium below.

trichogynial. Of or related to the trichogyne.

trichome. A hair-like outgrowth of the epidermis, as a hair or bristle.

trichome hydathodes. Hair-like organs secreting moisture in *Agaricales*.

trichomanefolious. With leaves like *Trichomanes*, the bristle fern.

trichomanoid. Like the genus *Trichomanes* in habit.

trichophore. A group of cells bearing a trichogyne, the row of cells of a procarp which bears the trichogyne in *Florideae*.

trichophoretum. An association of *Trichophorus*.

trichorphoric cell. The central cell in the procarp of the fungus *Laboulbenia* after becoming fused with the carpogenic cell.

trichophorum. The stipe of a fungus.

trichophyllous. Having the young stems and leaves protected from dessication by a thick coating of hair.

trichoplankton. Floating marine vegetation composed of *Thalassiothrix*.

trichosanthous. With hairy flowers.

trichosis. 1. The arrangement or distribution of hair. 2. A disease of the hair.

trichospermous. With hairy seeds.

trichosporange. A trichosporangium, the multilocular sporangium of fucoid algae, a sporangium which is morphologically a hair, the multilocular sporangium of the *Phaeosporeae* which is apparently formed of jointed hairs.

trichospore. A conidium.

trichothallic. Having a filamentous thallus.

trichothallic gemmation. The origin of young plants of *Asperococcus* from the hairs scattered on the thallus.

trichothallic growth. A filiform thallus with the tips bearing tufts of hairs.

trichothecin. An antibiotic which is toxic to plants, fungi, and animals. It is obtained from the fungus *Trichothecium roseum*.

trichotomous. Divided into three branches arising from the same part of the stem.

trichromosomal. With three chromosomes.

tricoccous. With a three-carpelled fruit, of three cocci, of three roundish carpels.

tricornute. With three horns.

tricostate. Having three ribs.

tricotyledonous. Having three cotyledons, tricotylous.

tricotyledony. The condition of having three cotyledons, one or two so deeply divided as to seem double.

tricrural. With three branches.

tricuspid. Three-pointed, tricuspidate.

tricussate. Having whorls each of three leaves, the leaves of each whorl alternating with those above and below.

tricyclic. With three whorls, with the members of a series in three whorls.

tridactyle. Having three digits or three movable parts attached to a common base.

trident. Having three teeth or points.

tridigitate. Ternate, having three finger-like lobes.

tridymous. Having the middle of three gills of an agaric larger and longer than the two beside it.

tridynamous. Having three long and three short stamens.

trieder. Triangular.

triennial. A plant which fruits the third year and then dies, lasting three years.

trifariam. 1. In three vertical ranks. 2. Facing three ways.

trifarious. 1. In groups of three. 2. In three rows. 3. Facing three ways.

trifasciatus. With three bands.

trifid. Divided about halfway down into three parts, cleft to form three lobes, in three parts.

triflagellate. Having three flagella.

triflorous. With three flowers.

trifoliate. With three leaflets, with leaves arranged in threes.

triform. Having flowers of three different kinds, as in certain *Compositae*; trimorphic.

trifoveolate. With three hollows.

trifurcate. With three forks or branches, trichotomous.

trigamous. With staminate, pistillate, and hermaphroditic flowers in one flower head.

trigeminous. Tergeminate and trijugate, with three pairs of leaflets.

trigener. The product from three genera.

trigenic. Controlled by three pairs of genes for one character.

triglandular. Having three nutlets in one involucre.

triglochidiatous. Having three barbed bristles.

trigonal. Trigonous.

trigone. A thickened angle of a cell, as in the leaves of certain hepatics or as in collenchyma cells.

trigonocarpous. With fruit having three evident angles.

trigonophyllous. Having leaves with three corners.

trigonous. Having three angles and three convex faces, three-cornered, three-angled with plane faces.

trigynia. A Linnaean order of plants with three styles.

trigynous. Having three styles, carpels, or pistils.

trihilatous. Having three apertures, as in some grains of pollen.

trihybrid. The offspring derived from parents differing in three characteristics, a hybrid heterozygous with respect to three pairs of genes.

trijugate. Having three pairs of leaflets, with three pairs of pinnae.

trilabiate. Having three lips.

trilamellar. Having three divisions flattened like bands in a compound stigma.

trilateral. With three sides.

trilineate. With three lines.

trilobate. Divided into three lobes.

trilocular. Having three cells or loculi.

trilophous. With three rays branched or ridged in a spicule.

trimeristele. A stele formed of three members.

trimerous. 1. With three parts. 2. Composed of multiples of three, as parts of a flower.

trimestris. Lasting for three months and maturing in that time.

trimodal. In three forms or modes.

trimonoecious. With male, female, and hermaphroditic flowers on one individual.

trimonoecium. A plant with male, female, and perfect flowers.

trimorphic. 1. Having three forms, trimorphous. 2. Having three kinds of flowers in the same species which differ in the relative length and placement of the filaments, anthers, and stigmas.

trimus. Lasting or maturing in three years.

trinacriform. With three prongs.

trinervate. Having three veins or ribs.

trinervulatus. Having three nerve-like strands in the placenta.

trinodal. Having three nodes.

trinomial. Consisting of three terms in the scientific names.

trinotatus. With three marks or spots.

trioecia. A Linnaean order of plants with trioecious flowers.

trioecious. Having staminate, pistillate, and hermaphroditic flowers on three distinct plants.

trioeciously hermaphroditic. Trimorphic.

trioicous. Trioecious.

trioperculate. Having three lids.

triovulate. Having three ovules.

tripaleolatus. Consisting of three paleae, as the flowers of bamboos.

tripalmate. Thrice palmate, thrice palmately compound.

tripalmatin. Palmatin.

tripartite. Deeply divided into three parts nearly to the base, more than trifid; divided into three lobes, as a leaf.

tripennate. Tripinnate.

tripetaloid. Appearing to have three petals.

tripetalous. Having three petals.

triphyletic. Containing the blended strains of three species.

triphyllome. Hypothetically three segments to form a carpel—two hypophylls superior and fertile, the third sterile and inferior.

triphyllous. Having three leaves or leaf-like bodies in a whorl or otherwise associated, three-leaved.

tripinnate. Thrice pinnate, divided pinnately three times.

tripinnatifid. Divided three times in a pinnatifid manner.

tripinnatisect. Three times lobed with divisions nearly to the midrib, tripinnatifid.

triplasy. The division of an organ into three analogous structures.

triple fusion. Double fertilization.

triple nerved. With three prominent veins, having a midrib dividing into three or sending off a strong branch on each side above the base of the blade.

triple ribbed. Triple nerved.

triplets. Individuals resulting from the division of the ovum into three parts, each then developing.

triplex. 1. Triple. 2. Having three dominant genes for a given character.

triplicate-geminate. Having three pairs of leaflets or other organs attached by secondary petioles or otherwise to the apex of a common support.

triplicate-pinnate. Having three pairs of veins, tripinnate.

triplicate-ternate. Having three pairs of organs, triternate.

triplicato-geminatus. Tergeminate.

triplicato-nervatus. Triplinerved.

triplicato-pinnatus. Tripinnate.

triplicostate. Having three ribs.

tripliform. Triple-leaved.

triplinerved. Triple-nerved, triple-ribbed.

triploblastic. Having three primary germ layers.

triplocaulous. Possessing ternary axes.

triplocauscent. Having axes of a third order, having a third system of axes.

triploid. Having three times the normal number of chromosomes in the nucleus, i.e., three times the haploid number for the species.

triplostichous. With three rows of cortical cells to each branchlet or bract cell in charads.

tripolar. Having three poles (applied to the division of chromatin into three poles in diseased cells instead of the normal two poles in mitosis).

triposplankton. Floating marine vegetation made up chiefly of *Ceratium tripos*.

tripterous. With three wings.

tripunctatus. With three spots.

triquadripinnate. Three times quadripinnate.

triqueter. With three edges, with three salient angles.

triquetral. Three-sided, three-angled.

triquetrous. Having three concave sides meeting in three angles, as some stems.

triquinate. Divided into three, with each lobe divided again into five; ternate with the divisions quinate.

trisepalous. Having three sepals.

triseptate. Having three partitions or septa, as in fruit.

triserial. Arranged in three rows, having three whorls, in three horizontal ranks or series, trifarious.

triseriate. In three rows under each other.

trisomic. Pertaining to a cell or organism having one of the chromosomes present in triplicate (2n + 1), the other chromosomes being normally diploid (2n); having an extra chromosome in a normally diploid chromosome.

trisomic, secondary. Having the extra chromosome made up of two identical halves.

trisomic, tertiary. Having the extra chromosome made up of halves corresponding with the halves of different chromosomes in the normal set.

trispermous. With three seeds.

trisporous. Having three spores.

tristachyous. With three spikes.

tristearin. Stearin.

tristerigmatic. Having three sterigmata on each basidium.

tristes plantae. Evening flowering plants.

tristichous. With leaves or branches arranged one above another in three rows.

tristigmatic. Having three stigmas.

tristylous. Having three styles.

trisulcate. Having three grooves or furrows.

trisyncotyledonous. Tricotyledonous.

trisyncotylous. With three cotyledons fused for half their length.

triternate. Thrice ternately divided; thrice ternate, as a compound leaf whose primary petiole divides into three secondary petioles, each of which again divides into three, each division having three leaflets.

triticetum. An association of *Triticum junceum* and other congeneric species.

triticin. The proteid found in the gluten of wheat, *Triticum vulgare*.

tritozooid. A zooid of the third generation in asexual reproduction.

triturated. Reduced to powder by grinding or pounding.

triundulate. Having three undulations on the dorsal side of the valve in diatoms.

trivalent. A multivalent composed of three chromosomes, apparently having three chromosomes in each single one in nuclear divisions.

trivalvular. Having three valves or dehiscent portions of pericarp.

triverted. Asymmetric, applied to diatoms.

trivial name. The specific name.

trixeny. The condition of a parasite which passes its career in three hosts.

trizygous. Dependent on three pairs of chromosomes.

trochal. Wheel-shaped.

trochate. Trochal.

trochiferous. Trochate, trochal, trochiform.

trochlear. Shaped like a pulley, trochleariform.

trochoid. 1. Wheel-shaped. 2. Capable of rotating motion.

troglocolous. Cave-dwelling.

trolein. Olein.

trolliifolious. With leaves like *Trolius*, the globe flower.

tropaxis. A hypothetical plane between the epicotyl and hypocotyl from which growth proceeds in opposite directions.

tropeic. Keel-shaped.

tropelagic. Collecting food material for the plant.

trophic. Pertaining to nutrition.

trophilegic. Collecting food material for the plant, as the shell-like barren fronds of *Platycerium* are supposed to do.

trophime. The result of the fusion of the central nucleus of the embryo sac (the mesocyst) with the second antherozoid.

trophobia. The condition existing when one species feeds on the excretion or wastes of another species and in turn furnishes protection for the weaker species.

trophochondrion. Protoplasmic inclusions which produce enzymes concerned with nutrition.

trophochromatin. Vegetative chromatin or that which regulates metabolism and functions, vegetative chromidia.

trophochromidia. Chromidia which arise from trophochromatin and of predominantly vegetative or nutritive functions, indiochromidia, vegetative chromidia.

trophocyst. A structure in *Pilobolus* from which the sporangium develops.

trophocyte. A zygote or fusion cell.

trophogone. An antheridium which fulfills a physiological function of nutrition only.

trophology. The science of nutrition.

trophonema. Plasmonema.

trophonucleus. The larger nucleus of binuclear protozoa which regulates metabolism and growth.

trophophyll. A vegetative leaf or frond as distinct from one which produces fructification.

trophophyte. The fusion-product in *Welwitschia* and angiosperms to distinguish it from the prothallus of the lower crptogams. It has been incorrectly applied to the endosperm of cycads. See TROPOPHYTE.

trophoplasm. The nutritive or vegetative substance of the cell as distinguished from the idioplasm, the active substance of the cytoplasm other than the kinoplasm or archiplasm.

trophoplast. A plastid.

trophopollen. The partition of an antherloculus or its remains.

troposome. Any organ which is concerned with supplying nourishment only.

trophosperm. The placenta.

trophosphere. The upper layer of high temperature in the ocean where plants and nutrition are plentiful.

trophospore. A spore of diatoms, desmids, *Bulbochaete*, and *Coleochaete*.

trophosporosome. An organ which is engaged in nourishing and also in reproducing the plant.

trophotaxis. Trophotropism, a form of chemotaxis in which the stimulating agent may serve as food to the organism.

trophotropism. The tendency of an organism to turn toward a food supply.

trophy. An unequal lateral growth of tissue or organ.

tropic. Reacting to a positive or negative stimulus by internal change in an orgainsm.

tropic curvature. A curvature of a plant organ caused by one-sided growth under the influence of a stimulus falling on the plant from one side.

tropic movement. A response to stimulation.

tropical. 1. Growing in the tropics. 2. Expanding in the morning and closing at night during several successive days.

tropical lakes. Lakes in which the temperatures are always above 4°C.

tropical life zone. The zone on both sides of the equator where the day and night are of about equal length and the temperature is rather uniform throughout the year with the mean daily temperature about 43°F.

tropis. The keel of a papilionaceous flower.

tropism. A growth response in plants, the tendency of a organism or part to turn in response to an external stimulus either by attraction or repulsion.

tropistic. Moving in response to a stimulus.

tropo-. A prefix to denote climate alternating between torrential rain and sunny drought.

tropodrymium. A savannah forest community.

tropophilous. Having the ability to respond to an outside stimulus of heat or cold, dryness or moisture, etc., as the seasonal changes in plants.

tropophylls. Deciduous leaves of shrubs and trees.

tropophyte. A plant which is mesophytic part of the year and xerophytic during the remaining part, as deciduous trees; a plant which can survive in a climate that is damp or dry and warm or cold in different seasons of the year.

troposphere. The atmosphere below the stratosphere where clouds form and convective disturbances develop, the lower part of the earth's atmosphere.

tropotaxis. Topotaxis.

true. Conforming to parental type.

true fruit. A fruit produced from the ovary only.

true parasite. An obligate parasite.

true reproduction. Reproduction which takes place by special cells.

truffle. An edible subterranean fruit body of the fungi *Tuberales*.

trullifer. In the shape of a bricklayer's trowel.

trumpet hyphae. Tubes in the laminarieae having swollen portions and transverse septa.

trumpet-shaped. Tubular with an enlargement at or towards the summit, as the corolla of trumpet creeper.

truncate. Blunt, as if cut off; cut off abruptly; having a square termination.

truncate-dimidiate. Imperfectly truncate, cut off abruptly.

truncicolous. Growing on trunks.

truncus. 1. The main stem or trunk of a tree. 2. In lichens, the thallus.

truss. A popular name for a rather compact, moderate-sized terminal flower cluster of any kind, as an umbel, spike, or raceme.

tryma. A drupaceous nut which decays and finally dehisces or separates from the surrounding matrix, such as the walnut, hickory nut, etc.

trypsin. A group of proteolytic enzymes found in various animal or plant juices.

trypsinogen. Trypsin.

tryptase. Any enzyme of the trypsin type.

tryptic. Relating to trypsin or a similar enzyme.

tuba. A tube, a style.

tubaeform. Trumpet-shaped, said of some podetia and corollas.

tubar. Consisting of an arrangement of tubes, forming a tube.

tubat. Tubaeform, trumpet-shaped.

tube. The concrescent part of a calyx or corolla, a pipe or hollow cylinder, the united portion of a gamosepalous calyx or monodelphous androecium, the cylindrical perforations in the *Polyporaceae* which bear the hymenium.

tube cell. The special cell which gives rise to the pollen tube.

tube germination. The germination of a spore in which the first product is a germ tube.

tube nucleus. The nucleus nearest the end of the pollen tube.

tuber. A relatively short, thickened rhizome with numerous buds as in the potato; a subterranean stem which is shorter and thicker than the root stock.

tubercle. 1. A wart-like or knob-like excrescence. 2. A nodule. 3. The persistent base of the style in some *Cyperaceae*. 4. The bulbil of charads.

tubercle bacteria. 1. The organisms in the nodules on roots of legumes. 2. The organism causing tuberculosis.

tubercle, primary. The ovoid body formed by the germination of *Lycopodium* spores.

tubercorm. A fleshy root such as beet, yam, turnip, etc.

tubercular-striate. With striae roughened by small tubercles as on an agaric pileus.

tubercularine. Like the fungus *Tubercularia*.

tuberculate. Having tubercules or rounded projections, warty.

tuberculate-striate. With the striae of a pileus roughened by small tubercles.

tuberculiform. Wart-like.

tuberculization. The formation of tubers, assumed to be due to the attack of a fungus.

tuberidium. The pseudobulb of an orchid.

tuberiferous. Bearing or producing tubers.

tuberiform. Resembling or shaped like a tuber.

tuberogemma. A bud-like tuber which occurs in the axil of the leaves or as a root tubercle and propagates the plant asexually.

tuberous. 1. Having the appearance of a tuber. 2. Covered with or having tubers.

tubes, prothalline. Embryo sac tubes.

tubicolous. Inhabiting a tube.

tubicorn. With hollow horns.

tubiferous. Bearing tubes.

tubiflorous. With tubular florets, as many *Compositae*; with tube or trumpet flowers.

tubiform. Tube-shaped.

tubiliferous. Having a tubule.

tubillus. 1. An elongated cell in tissue. 2. The tube of the filaments in *Compositae*.

tubispathus. Tube-spathed.

tubular. With sepals united except at the toothed margins.

tubular floret. A disk flower in *Compositae*.

tubulate. Tubiform.

tubule. Any small cylindrical structure.

tubuliflorous. Having florets with only tubular corollas.

tubuliform. Tube-shaped.

tubulose. Tubular.

tubulus. 1. A hymenial pore. 2. In *Pyrenomycetes*, the neck. 3. One of the cells surrounding the central siphon in *Chara*. 4. A tubule.

tubus. One of the hymenial tubes of such fungi as *Polyporus*.

tufa. Drab sandy colored and textured.

tuft. A bunch or fascicle growing from the same root or originating at nearly the same point.

tufted hairs. A modification of stellate hairs but branched from the base upward.

tufted trees. Trees having unbranched stems, as palms and arborescent *Liliaceae* such as Yucca, etc.

tuitant. Appearing to guard, as leaves in the sleep position appearing to guard the stem.

tulasnellaceous. Having the characteristics of the order *Tulasnellaceae*: having a nonseptate heterobasidium with a more or less pyriform hypobasidium; with two, four, or eight thick ventricose epibasidia separated from the hypobasidium by crosswalls; having hypobasidial meiosis.

tulipiferous. Tulip-bearing.

Tulle. Tylose.

tumble weeds. Weeds which break adrift when dry and are blown about scattering their seeds as they go.

tumid. Swollen, inflated, turgid.

tumor strands. Strands conveying infection into healthy tissue and inducing the growth of galls.

tumulus. Of a dune.

tundra. Cold northern treeless desert which is flat or gently undulating.

tundra period. The period which succeeded the Ice Age in Switzerland.

tunic. 1. The skin of a seed, the spermoderm. 2. Any loose membranous skin not formed from the epidermis. 3. The coat of a bulb. 4. The peridium in certain fungi. 5. The utricle of *Carex*. 6. The exospore, particularly the gelatinous membrane covering the epispore.

tunic grasses. Grasses whose leaf sheaths remain attached after their upper parts have died.

tunica. 1. A coating. 2. The thin white membrane surrounding the peridiole in most species of *Nidulariaceae*. 3. The peripheral layer or layers of the apex of a shoot.

tunicate. 1. Having numerous concentric layers. 2. Enveloped in a leathery testa or mantle.

tunicate bulb. A bulb composed of a number of swollen leaf bases each of which completely encloses all parts of the bulb inside it, as in the onion.

tunicle. A natural covering, an integument.

turbarian. The stage in the formation of peat characterized by the presence of dwarf willows.

turbinal. Spirally coiled or rolled.

turbinate. Conical.

turf. An association in which *Gramineae* dominate, the grassy sod.

turfaceous. Pertaining to bogs.

turfophile. A bog plant.

turfosous. Growing in bogs.

turgor. The distention and resiliency of living cells, the balance between the osmotic pressure of the cell sap and the elasticity of the cell wall.

turgor pressure. The hydrostatic pressure set up within a cell by the liquid acting against the elasticity of the cell wall.

turion. 1. A young scaly sucker or shoot from an underground stem. 2. A swollen perennating bud of water plants which contains food and is separated from the parent. It remains inert during winter and gives rise to a new plant in the spring. 3. A winter bud. 4. A turio.

turioniferous. Bearing turions, like the shoots of *Asparagus*.

turmeric. The powdered rhizome of *Curcuma longa* from which a yellow dye is obtained.

turning cells. Three small cells at the base of the oogonium of *Nitella* derived from one at the base of the oosphere.

turning in. Commencing to head.

turpentine. The balsams or fluid resin of the *Coniferae, Burseraceae,* etc., which distill oil of turpentine and leave resin, the solution of resins in terebene.

turpentine vessels. Tubes in the wood in which the turpentine collects during growth, common in conifers.

turriform. Shaped like a tower.

turritus. Turreted, tower-like.

tussock. A dense tuft or bunch formed at the root, as in some species of *Carex*, grasses, etc.

tussock formation. A formation found in New Zealand and the Falkland Islands composed of thick tufts of certain grasses.

twig climbers. Brazilian lianas, the young leafy lateral branches being sensitive when in contact with their supports.

twig gall. A morbid growth attributed to the action of certain bacteria.

twig spine. A spine metamorphosed from a twig.

twin bundle. The double leaf trace in *Lyginodendron*.

twin communities. Consociations, biocoenoses which conform only in one or two of the communities (synusiae, layers) composing them while others change.

twin crystals. Double styloids.

twiner. A plant which climbs by twisting its stem around a support.

twinned fruit. Fruit formed from connate ovaries surmounted by separate calyxes and corollas.

twinned hairs. A form of pubescence with only two rays in a straight line.

twisted aestivation. Contorted aestivation.

two-factor inheritance. The inheritance of two hereditary elements or factors.

two-ranked. In two vertical rows on opposite sides of the stem, distichous.

tycholimnetic. At first fixed but later breaking loose and floating, said of floating fresh water vegetation which at times is at the surface and at other times is attached to rocks or plants at the bottom.

tychopelagic. Tycholimnetic.

tychopotamic plankton. 1. The floating organisms of pools and overflows of rivers. 2. Plankton found in a river but derived from a pond.

tylhexactine. A hexactine spicule with the rays ending in knobs.

tylicolor. Slate, dark gray.

tylosis. A bladder-like growth of a parenchymatous cell into the lumen of a neighboring vessel or tracheid which is then blocked by the intrusion and ceases to function as a conducting element, a tylose.

tylosoid. With the proliferation of a thin-walled epithelial cell into an intercellular canal, like a tylosis except it does not pass through the cavity of a pit.

tylostyle. A spicule pointed at one end and knobbed at the other.

tylotate. With a knob at each end.

tylote. A slender dumbell-shaped spicule.

tympaniform. Drum-shaped.

tympanoid. Resembling the head of a drum.

tympanum. The epiphragm or membrane across the mouth of the capsule in some mosses.

Tyndall effect. A milky effect in a colloidal solution brought about by shining light, scattered by a Tyndall cone, through the fluid. The fluid appears clear to the naked eye.

type. The original specimen or specimens from which the species was first described and named, the ideal representative of a group, a model or form, the ideal pattern.

type genus. The genus upon which a family is based.

type, primary. Proterotype.

type, secondary. A plesiotype, a neotype.

type specimen. The specimen from which the original description of a species was drawn.

type, supplementary. A plesiotype, a neotype.

typhaceous. Akin to or resembling *Typha*, the bulrush.

typhetum. An association of *Typha*.

typhinus. Smoky, dull.

typhoid. Like *Typha*, the bulrush.

typical cells. Fundamental cells.

typical diagram. The resultant form from several empiric diagrams.

typical specimens. Icotypes.

typiform. A constant form arising either by natural selection or by animal adaptations.

Its existence is frequently dependent on animals.

typonym. A name which has been rejected because an older name was based upon the same type.

tyrosin. An amino acid formed in fungi which upon oxidation by tyrosinase yields dark-colored substances, an amide similar to asparagin.

tyrosinase. An oxidizing enzyme which acts upon tyrosin in certain fungi and produces a dark-colored substance.

U

ubiquist. A plant which can grow on any type of soil.

ubiquitous associates. Species which reoccur constantly in many communities.

Uferflucht. A mass of fresh-water plankton which has been blown away from the shore-line toward the center of the lake.

-ule. A suffix meaning socies.

ulicetum. An association of *Ulex* (gorse or furze).

ulicinus. Resembling *Ulex*.

uliginous. Growing in swamps or marshes; uliginal, uliginose.

ulmic acid. An acid found in humus.

ulmifolious. Elm-leaved.

ulmin. A substance derived from ulmic acid.

ulmoid. Resembling *Ulmus*, the elm.

ulodendroid. Like the former fossil genus *Ulodendron*, applied to branches of *Lepidodendron* and *Sigillaria*, bearing two opposite rows of large, cup-shaped scars.

ulotrichaceous. Resembling or allied to the algal genus *Ulothrix*.

ulotrichous. Having woolly or curly hair.

ulterior pith. Cellular structures formed in the axis of the root after separation of the stele.

ultimate strength. The minimum load on a tissue which causes its rupture.

ultonian. Relating to the province of Ulster.

ultramicrobe. A substance too small to be seen with a usual microscope but able to cause disease.

ultrasetaceous. Very long and drawn out.

-ulus. A suffix meaning small.

ulvaceous. Resembling the parenchymatous lichen *Ulva*.

umbel. 1. A flat-topped inflorescence in which the pedicels are of equal length and arise from a common point. 2. The pileus of certain fungi.

umbel, cymose. An inflorescence with the pedicels arising at a common point but with the main axis bearing a flower (determinate or definite) with the outer flowers blooming later than the inner flowers.

umbel, partial. An umbellule or umbellet, a secondary umbel of a compound umbel.

umbel, simple. An umbel in which each of the rays bears a single flower.

umbellate. Arranged in an umbel, having the inflorescence in an umbel, borne in umbels.

umbellate cyme. A cyme having a centrifugal inflorescence.

umbellet. A secondary umbel, a small or simple umbel, a partial or secondary umbel.

umbellifer. A plant bearing umbels.

umbelliferous. Having umbellate flowers.

umbelliform. In the shape of an umbel, umbrella-shaped.

umbelligerous. Bearing flowers or polyps in umbellate clusters.

umbelloid. Similar to an umbel.

umbellulate. 1. In the form of a small or a partial umbel. 2. Having partial or secondary umbels.

umbellule. A small or secondary umbel, an umbellet, a division of an umbel.

umber. Olive brown, dark brown.

umbilical cord. The stalk of an ovule or seed by which it is attached to the placenta, the funiculus.

umbilicate. With a central navel-like depression, with a central depression or umbilicus but not funnel-shaped.

umbilicus. A navel-like depression, a hilum, any depression resembling a navel.

umbo. A raised conical-to-convex knob or mound on the center of a pileus, a small central elevation on the pileus.

umbonulate. Slightly umbonate, having or ending in a small swelling or nipple.

umbraculifera. Umbrella-bearing, shade-producing.

umbraculiferous. Like an expanded umbrella in shape.

umbraculiform. Shaped like an expanded umbrella.

umbraculum. Any umbrella-like structure, as the fruit-cap of *Marchantia*.

umbraticolous. Growing in shady places.

umbrinaceous. Raw umber, umber-brown.

umbrosous. Growing in shade places.

unangulate. One-angled.

unarmed. Having no spines or prickles.

unbalanced polyploid. An aneuploid.

uncate. Hooked or bent at the tip in the form of a hook.

unciferous. Bearing hooks or hook-like processes.

unciform. Shaped like a barb or hook.

uncinate. Provided with a narrow decurrent extension of gills on the stem, hooked, unciform.

uncorticated. Without cortex.

unctuous. Having a greasy appearance.

uncus. 1. A hook or claw. 2. An uncinate hair.

undate. Wavy, undulate.

undecimpunctatus. With eleven spots.

undecuple. Eleven sets of chromosomes.

underground roots. Roots which arise from the stem below the ground.

undergrowth. Underbrush, seedlings, shoots, small saplings, and all herbaceous growth in a forest which grow under the trees.

underleaf. One row of leaves on the underside of the stem of a liverwort.

undershrub. A low-growing woody plant, a low shrub less than 3 feet high, a partially shrubby or a very low shrub.

undose. Wavy, undulate.

undulatifolious. With undulate leaves.

undulato-rugose. Rugged and wavy.

undulifolious. With wavy leaves.

unequally pinnate. Odd pinnate with a single terminal leaflet, imparipinnate.

unessential element. A chemical element sometimes found in plants which appears to play no part in nutrition and seems not to be necessary to the welfare of the plant.

unguiculate. Clawed, said of a petal which is contracted at the base into a claw-like structure.

unguiculus. The length of the nail of the little finger.

unguiform. Like the claws of a petal.

unguipetalous. Having claw-shaped petals.

unguis. A nail or claw; a narrow stalk-like portion of some petals, as in *Dianthus*; the tapered base of a petal.

unguispinus. Having a claw-like spine.

ungulate. Hoof-shaped, clawed.

unguliform. Shaped like a claw or hoof.

uni-. A prefix meaning one.

unialate. With one wing or decurrent ridge.

uniarticulate. With one joint.

uniaxial. 1. With one main unbranched stem. 2. In algae, having one main unbranched filament with small filaments clinging to it; monoaxial.

unicalcarate. With one spur.

unicapsular. Having only one seed case, having all carpels united to form one capsule.

unicarinate. Having one carina or keel, as in leguminose flowers.

unicarpellate. Composed of only one carpel, having a one-celled fruit.

unicell. A plant consisting of only one cell.

unicellular. One-celled.

uniciliate. With one cilium.

unicolor. Of one color.

unicorn. Having one horn-like spine.

unicostate. Having one prominent midrib.

unicotyledonous. Monocotyledonous, having only one cotyledon.

unicuspid. Having one tapering point.

unidentate. With one tooth.

uniembryonate. Having one embryo.

unifacial. With one face or principal surface.

unifarious. In one rank or row.

uniferous. Bearing once a year.

uniflagellate. With one flagellum.

uniflorous. Having one flower.

unifoliate. With one leaf.

unigemmius. Giving rise to only one bud.

unigenous. Leafing annually.

uniidusiate. Having one indusium.

unijugate. With one pair of leaflets.

unilabiate. With one lip, as the corolla of *Acanthus*.

unilaminate. With one layer.

unilateral. Arranged on one side only.

unilateral bordered pit. A combination of a simple pit and a bordered pit belonging to two adjacent elements and corresponding in place to one another.

unilateral segregation. Segregation confined to one sex.

unilaterally compound pitting. A type of pitting in which one or more pits subtend two or more smaller pits in the cell adjacent.

unilocular. With one loculus or cell.

unimodal. Confined to one shape or mode.

unimucronate. With a single sharp point or tip.

uninervate. With one nerve, vein, or rib.

uninodal. With one node.

uninuclear. Having one nucleus.

uninucleate. Uninuclear.

unioculate. Having one vegetative point.

unioloid. Like *Uniola*, spike grass or spangle grass.

unionized. With molecules not divided.

uniovulate. Having one ovule.

unipalmate. Divided once.

unipared. Bearing one, as a cyme giving forth one axis at each branching.

uniparous. Having a cymose inflorescence with one axis at each branching, monochasial, unipared.

uniparous cyme. A cyme with one main axis.

unipetalous. Having one petal.

unipinnate. Divided only once.

unipolar. Having only one pole.

uniporatous. Opening by one pore.

uniprophyllate. Having one prophyllum.

uniseptate. With one septum or dividing partition.

uniserial. 1. In one horizontal row or series. 2. Having only the gynoecium.

uniseriate. Having only one row of seriations on the edge.

uniseriate hairs. Hairs consisting of a single row of cells.

uniseriate sorus. A sorus with a single series of sporangia forming a rosette around a central cushion.

uniserrulate. Having one row of small serrations on the edge.

unisetose. With one bristle.

unisexual. Of only one sex, bearing only stamens or only pistils.

unisexual crosses. Individuals one of which bears a particular character entirely lacking in the other; see BISEXUAL.

unisexual heredity. The heredity in which the qualities of only one parent are transmitted.

unisoriferous. Having or bearing one sorus.

unisorous. Consisting of one sorus.

unispiral. Having only one spiral.

unistrate. With one persistent kind of indumentum.

unistratose. Having one layer of cells.

unit character. A character which is inherited as a whole and cannot be subdivided.

unit factor. A unit character; see FACTOR.

unit of vegetation. See COMMUNITY.

unitegminatae. The phanerogams which have only one covering on their ovules.

unitegminous. With one coat on the ovule.

unitegminy. The state or condition of having one coat on the ovule.

unitypic. Monotypic.

univalent. 1. Having chromosomes of a simple character. 2. A single unpaired chromosome in the first division of meiosis.

univalved. Of one piece or valve, as a pod of only one piece after dehiscence.

univalvular. Dehiscing along one suture only so that the pericarp has only one valve.

universal involucre. A general involucre.

universal umbel. A general or compound umbel.

universal veil. The veil which completely covers the sporophore in *Agaricaceae*.

univerted. Having mirror-like symmetry.

univesicular. Unicellular.

univittatus. With one stipe.

univorous. Restricted to a single host, monophagous.

unorganized ferment. An enzyme.

unseptate. Without septa, undivided.

unseptate fibers. Libriform cells.

unstratified. Nonlayered, not showing distinct layers of hyphae and gonidia in lichens.

uovoli. Gnaurs of the olive tree which are used for propagation.

upland salient. The tops of spurs of small upland areas consisting of ends and corners which are too small or narrow for cultivation.

upper beach. The area reached only by extreme high tides.

upright cells. Erect cells.

upright ray cells. A ray cell with its longest axis vertical.

uracil. A pyrimidine base.

urbanus. City-loving.

urcaulome. The primitive stem.

urceolar. Pitcher-like.

urceolate. Like a pitcher or contracted at the mouth, as the flowers of many heaths; urceolar.

ureaceus. A charred black color.

urease. An enzyme from the soybeans which acts on urea, an enzyme produced by certain bacteria which transforms urea into ammonium carbonate.

uredial stage. The summer stage of rust fungi.

uredicolous. Growing parasitically on rust fungi.

uredineous. Of or pertaining to *Uredinales*, the rust fungi.

uredinicolous. Growing on rusts.

urediniosorus. The sorus in which the urediniospores are formed.

urediniospore. A red rust pore produced in *Uredinia*, a uredospore, urediospore.

uredinium. Uredosorus.

uredinology. The study of rusts, *Uredinales*.

uredinosis. A disease produced by rust fungi.

urediospore. A urediniospore.

uredium. Uredinium.

uredo. 1. The hymenium which produces uredospores only. 2. A form genus for the summer stage of rust fungi.

uredoconidium. A uredospore.

uredoform. Resembling uredo in appearance.

uredofruit. A sorus or group of uredospores.

uredogonidium. A uredospore.

uredosorus. A group of uredospores.

uredospore. A one-celled summer stage of the rusts, a urediospore.

uredostage. The summer stage of *Uredineae* when uredospores only are produced.

urens. Stinging, as in the manner of nettles.

urn. The theca of mosses, the base of a pyxidium.

urniform. Urn-shaped.

urnigerous. Pitcher-bearing.

uro-bacteria. Bacteria prominent in the decomposition of urine.

uromorphous. Uromorphic, tail-like.

urophile. A plant growing on soil containing ammonia.

urophyllous. Tail-leaved.

urostachyous. Tail-spiked.

urticaceous. Of or pertaining to the nettles, *Urticaceae*.

urticant. The stinging thread cells found on nettles and other organisms, a stinging substance.

urticial. Urticaceous.

urticifolious. Nettle-leaved.

urticoid. Nettle-like.

use and disuse. The effect of use and disuse upon the development of an hereditary character and its consequent retention or loss by the individual race.

use inheritance. The transmission of acquired characters.

useneoid. Like the lichen *Usnea*.

ustal. Charred, brownish black.

usterophyte. One of the ustilagineous fungi.

ustilaginosis. A disease caused by *Ustilago*, a genus of fungi which produces smut in corn. The contents of each cariopsis is replaced by a black powdery mass of spores.

ustilaginous. Like or allied to *Ustilago*.

ustulate. Blackened as though burnt or charred.

uterus. The peridium in gasteromycetes.

utricle. 1. A more or less inflated membranous, bladder-like envelope surrounding some fruits and fructifications of fungi. 2. An achene with a loose involucral covering. 3. A parenchymatous cell 4. A large hyaline cell of the leaves of *Sphagnum*.

utricle, primordial. A utricle in its earliest stage of formation.

utricular. 1. Containing small bag-like vessels. 2. Bladder-like, inflated.

utricularform. Like a bladder in appearance.

utriculi seminales. Spores of certain fungi.

utriculiform. Bladder-shaped.

utriculose. 1. Having utricles. 2. Having a bladder-like appearance.

utriform. Bag-shaped.

utrigerous. Bearing utricles.

utrimque. On both sides, in both directions.

uva. A berry formed from a superior ovary.

uvarius. Like a bunch of grapes.

uveous. Like a bunch of grapes.

uviferous. Grape-bearing.

uviform. Grape-shaped.

V

vaccine. 1. A preparation of any microorganism or virus, either killed or treated so as to lose its virulence, for introduction into the body in order to stimulate the production of antibodies to the microorganisms. It is introduced in order to confer immunity against subsequent infection by the same type of micro-organism. 2. Of or pertaining to vaccinia, the cowpox, or the lymph (containing virus) taken from a cow-pox vesicle.

vaccinictum. An association of *Vaccinium*.

vaccinifolious. *Vaccinium*-leaved.

vaccinoid. *Vaccinium*-like.

vacuolar. Of, pertaining to, or describing vacuoles.

vacuolar membrane. The limiting membrane separating the cytoplasm from an enclosed vacuole.

vacuolar wall. The boundary of the vacuole.

vacuolate. Possessing vacuoles.

vacuole. A cavity surrounded by cytoplasm and filled with cell sap.

vacuole, contractile. A vacuole found in protoplasm of many unicellular organisms which gradually increases in size and then suddenly collapses, often making regular pulsations.

vacuolization. The regular formation of vacuoles.

vacuome. An area composed of metachromatic corpuscles in vacuoles of *Selaginella*.

vadal. Floating near the shore.

vage. Indifferent to the limitations of habitat.

vagiform. Having no definite figure.

vagil benthon. Wandering organisms of the ocean bottom.

vagin. The brown coloring substance in certain ferns, a form of phlebotannin.

vagina. A sheath, a part which invests another.

vaginaefolius. Sheath-flowering.

vaginant. Sheathing.

vaginate. Sheathed, surrounded by a sheath, having a long volva or sheath at the lower end.

vaginella. A small vagina, a ramentum.

vaginervose. With the small veins in no apparent order.

vaginiferous. Invested by a sheath.

vaginula. A small sheath, the sheath surrounding the basal portion of a moss sporophyte.

vaginule. A small sheath, the modified remains of the lower part of an archegonium at the base of the seta.

vaginuliferi Flores. The tubular florets of an anthodium.

valdivianus. Of the province of Valdivia in Chile.

valency. The degree of frequency index.

valentinus. Of Valencia, Spain.

vallecula. A depression, a groove.

vallecular canal. One of the canals in the cortical tissue of the stem of horsetails, a large intercellular passage alternating with the fibrovascular bundles in the stem of *Equisetum*.

valsoid. Resembling the genus *Valsa*, the sphere fungi.

valsous. Having the perithecia in a circle in the stroma.

valvaceus. Having visible valves.

valvae seminium. Cotyledons.

valvar. 1. Opening by doors or valves.

2. With parts of a flower-bud meeting exactly without overlapping.

valvar plane. The plane which passes through the apical and transapical axes of a diatom.

valvate. 1. Hinged at the margin. 2. Meeting at the edges. 3. Opening by or furnished with valves.

valvate dehiscence. The liberation of pollen or of seed by means of little flaps of upraised wall material.

valve. One of the segments in which the walls of a fruit separate by dehiscence; one of the parts of a dehiscent pericarp; in diatoms, a part of a dehiscent pericarp or one-half of the silicified membrane in side view.

valve view. The diatom frustule seen from the side, the girdle being then marginal.

valvelet. 1. A diminutive valve. 2. A flowering glume of grasses or a bract in *Cyperaceae*. 3. A small fold.

valvula. A valvelet.

vanilla. *Vanilla planifolia*.

vanillin. A substance deposited in cell walls on lignification, a fragrant compound of vanilla. With coniferin it gives a wood reaction.

Vant Hoff's formula. The velocity of a reaction increases with the temperature and coefficient Q_{10} (expressing the rate of increase per 10°C) which has a value between two and three for each 10° interval.

vaporarium. A bark stove in botanic gardens.

var., varietas. A variety or modification of a species.

variad. A variant.

variant. An individual or species deviating in some character or characters from type, a form arising from a variation.

variate. The variable quantity in variation, a single magnitude determination of a character.

variation. Divergence from type in certain characteristics, a filial departure founded on a germinal change from the parental type, the occurrence of differences among the individuals of the same species.

variation, acquired. A digression from type acquired during the development of the individual.

variation, analagous. A similar variation in allied species.

variation, correlated. A change in one organism which causes a change in another although the changes are seemingly not connected.

variation discontinuous. A variation arising by distinct steps.

variation, genetic. A variation whose origin is in the germ cells.

variation, homologous. A variation in related species arising from mutation in homologous genes, a morphological variation in distinct species.

variation, meristic. A change in symmetry and numbers of parts.

variation, substantive. A change in the actual constitution or substance of the parts themselves.

varicose. Appearing abnormally enlarged in places.

varietal differences. Differences between varieties.

varietum. An association of various species of fescue, *Festuca*.

variety. 1. An indefinite subdivision of a species usually applicable to a morphological variant or variant group, a form which is not typical but is not sufficiently recognizable to be designated by a specific name, a variant in color or in habitat. 2. A plant subordinate to a species.

variety group. A complex of varieties which resemble each other more than varieties belonging to different groups.

variety hybrid. A cross between varieties of the same species.

variifolious. Possessing leaves of various forms.

variiform. Of variable or many forms.

variola. A pustular shield occurring on the thallus of the lichen genus *Variolaria*.

variolarioid. With granular tubercles like the fructification of *Variolaria*.

variolate. Marked as if by the pustules or pitting of smallpox.

variolose. Variolarioid.

varnish. The gummy substance of many buds.

varzea. A partially submerged forest of Brazil.

vas. A vessel or duct.

vasa exhalantia. Stomata.

vasa propria. The portion of phloem containing the sieve tubes and other thin-walled tubular cells.

vasal. Vascular.

vasal bundles. Vascular bundles.

vascular. Furnished with vessels or ducts through which fluid is conveyed.

vascular anastomosis. A small transversely directed vascular bundle acting as a link between the main vascular bundles of a stem or root.

vascular bundle. One of the groups of connecting and supporting tissue characteristic of vascular plants; a strand of conductive tissue composed of a strand of xylem and a strand of phloem, sometimes separated by cambium and sometimes containing sclerenchymatous supporting tissue.

vascular bundle sheath. A layer of cells between the phloem and cortex or surrounding a fibrovascular bundle, as an entire fibrovascular cylinder.

vascular cryptogam. A nonflowering plant that has vascular tissue, as ferns.

vascular cylinder. The central cord of vascular tissue.

vascular plant. A plant having vascular bundles, such as phanerogams and *Filicales*.

vascular ray. A sheet of cells (usually parenchymatous) lying radially in a stem or root appearing in cross section as a narrow radial streak or in radial longitudinal section as a plate of cells. The ray lies partly in the xylem and partly in phloem and serves to conduct solutions horizontally in the stem or root. A medullary ray.

vascular ray, initial. A cell of the cambium which divides to give daughter cells which are converted into cells forming a vascular ray.

vascular strand. A strand of conducting tissue consisting of xylem and phloem sometimes separated by cambium. Sclerenchymatous supporting tissue may also be present.

vascular system. The fibrovascular tissues of a plant considered collectively, the interior parts in which the vessels occur.

vascular tissue. Specially modified plant cells, usually consisting of either tracheal or sieve cells, for the movement of sap.

vascular tracheids. Perforated cells resembling in form and position the members of a small vessel, degenerate or imperfect vessel elements; see VESSEL TRACHEIDS.

vasculares. Plants which have vessels, as phanerogams and *Filicales*.

vasculiferous. Producing vessels.

vasculiform. Shaped like a little pot.

vasculose. A component of the vegetative skeleton of the cellulose group.

vasculum. 1. A botanist's collecting case. 2. An ascidium.

vasicentric. With parenchyma around the vessel.

vasicentric parenchyma. Paratracheal parenchyma forming a vascular sheath of variable width circular or oval in cross sections.

vasicentric tracheids. Short, irregularly formed tracheids in the immediate proximity of vessels not forming definite longitudinal rows or series.

vasiduct. A raphe.

vasiform. Functioning as or resembling a duct.

vasiform elements. Tissue, ducts, or tubes with spiral markings.

vasiform tracheid. A wide tracheid capable of conducting water.

vasiform wood-cell. A tracheid.

vasodilation. A product of protein disintegration corresponding in properties to histamine.

Vaucheria gall. A hypertrophied formation on *Vaucheria* caused by the attack of some animal, as a rotifer.

vector. Any agent which transmits a virus disease from one host plant to another, as an insect vector.

vedomin. A small domin, the role of minute planktons; see DOMIN.

vefluent. A microscopic influent of little significance in a community.

vegetable. Belonging to or consisting of plant parts.

vegetable acids. Acids occurring in plants.

vegetable albumen. A substance resembling animal albumen not the albumen of seeds.

vegetable anatomy. The study of the form and the arrangement of the parts of plants.

vegetable casein. Legumin, plant casein.

vegetable cell. The cell of a plant.

vegetable fibrin. Gluten.

vegetable globulin. See GLOBULIN.

vegetable ivory. The seeds of *Phytelephas macrocarpa*.

vegetable mucilage. See MUCILAGE.

vegetable mucus. See MUCILAGE.

vegetable nosology. The classification and diagnosis of plant disease.

vegetable parchment. Paper after treatment with acid, parchment made from plants.

vegetable pathology. The science of plant diseases and treatments.

vegetable taxonomy. The orderly and systematic classification of plants.

vegetable wax. 1. Any waxy product secreted by various plants, as palm wax, Chinese wax, etc. 2. The bloom of plant parts.

vegetal. Vegetable, vegetative.

vegetation. Plants in general, the total aggregation of plants, the process of plant growth.

vegetation belt. Vegetational regions homologous in their altitudinal position.

vegetation form. A characteristic plant form, as a tree, shrub, rosette, etc.; a characteristic growth form usually divided as monocarpic or polycarpic, or wood plants, perennials, and annual herbs.

vegetation, lines of. The boundary lines of the distribution of a given species.

vegetation region. A phytocoenosis extending over a large area composed for the most part of an extremely variable mosaic, often of large stands of definite phytocoeroses.

vegetation stage. An associes, vegetation Stufe.

vegetation Stufe. A vegetation belt, a phytocoenosis consisting of a series of vegetation regions of whatever rank homologous in altitude and mostly showing a clearly recognizable floristic relationship.

vegetation types. The primary divisions of the ecologists.

vegetational type. A plant community of any size, rank, or stage of development.

vegetationsfleck. A small area of vegetation.

vegetative. Concerned with growth and development as distinguished from reproduction, growing or causing to grow.

vegetative apogamy. The apogamous production of growing shoots in the place of seeds or spores.

vegetative cell. A cell which vegetates and does not reproduce the plant of which it is a part.

vegetative cone. The apical point; see APICAL MERISTEM.

vegetative division. The heterotypic nuclear division.

vegetative multiplication. The increase in number of plants by the production of portions of the plant which root and become detached from the parent.

vegetative mutation. A mutation occurring in any somatic cell.

vegetative nucleus. Any nucleus in a pollen tube which takes no direct part in fertilization.

vegetative organs. Organs concerned with the growth and function of the plant and not with reproduction.

vegetative pole. A vegetal pole.

vegetative propagation. The increase in number by detachment of a part of a vegetative plant body.

vegetative propagative cells. Brutzellen, gonidia.

vegetative reproduction. Reproduction by vegetable parts such as buds, gemmae, etc.; nonsexual reproduction.

vegetatus. Full of growth, vigorous.

vegetistic. Having the nature of plants.

vegetometer, electro-. An apparatus for applying electric currents to growing crops.

vegetus. Vigorous, fresh, vegetating.

vehiculum. The stigmatic secretion.

veil. 1. A velum. 2. An evanescent membrane over an apothecium. 3. A sheath of hyphae forming a complete membrane over the developing fruit body of an agaric. 4. The calyptra of a moss. 5. The membranous indusium of Isoetes.

vein. A thread or branch of fibrovascular tissue in a leaf which forms the framework, a strand of conducting tissue in the leaf.

vein, costal. A vein which springs from the midrib of a leaf, a primary vein.

vein, external. A vein close to the margin of the leaf.

vein, islets. The small islands of photosynthetic tissue enclosed by the veinlets.

vein, primary. A vein which arises from the midrib, a costal vein.

veines aeriferes. Venae internae.

veines aquiferes. Venae externae.

veining. The general arrangement of veins.

veinulet. Veinlet.

velamen. A multilayered sheath of dead empty cells occurring on the surfaces of some aerial roots which give a silvery appearance.

velamenaris. Having an anther which dehisces by rolling up one side of a cell from base to apex.

velaminous. Having a velamen.

velar. Pertaining to or near a velum.

velate. Having a veil or velum, veiled.

veld. A velt, the tree steppe or African savannah in South Africa.

veldt. A veld.

vellus. 1. The stipe of some fungi. 2. Fleece, wool.

velocity of development. The number of developmental units per hour under any combination of conditions.

velum. A veil.

velum partiale. A partial veil, the marginal veil.

velum universale. The universal veil which covers the entire sporophore as it grows and is ruptured by the unfolding pileus, the remains of which form the volva.

velumen. A covering of close, soft, short hairs.

velutinous. Velutinate, velvety due to a covering of silky hairs.

venae externae. The white, sterile, air-filled veins in the fruit bodies of truffles (*Tuberales*) which are found between the venae internae; the veines aeriferes.

venae internae. The dark fertile veins in the fruit bodies of truffles (*Tuberales*), venae lymphaticae, veines aquiferes.

venae lymphaticae. Venae internae.

venate. Veined, venose, venous, having veins.

venation. The arrangement or the distribution of veins.

venation, circinate. Venation in which veins are rolled inward from the summit towards the base.

venenate. Poisonous.

veneniferous. Bearing or containing poison.

veniform. Vein-like.

venose. Veined.

venose nervosus. With primary veins branched and united irregularly.

venter. The enlarged part of the archegonium which contains the egg, the ovary.

ventilating pits. Pits in certain ferns resembling lenticels and probably pneumatodes.

ventilating tissue. The spongy parenchyma of the leaf.

ventilatorius. Fan-shaped.

ventral. 1. On the anterior or inner face of an organ. 2. On the upper surface of a leaf. 3. On the front part nearest the axis of an organ.

ventral canal cell. A nonfunctional unwalled

cell which lies in the venter of an archegonium above the egg of which it is the sister cell.

ventral plate. The cover of the ventral area in *Peridineae*.

ventral surface. The surface of the leaf next to the stem.

ventral suture. The ventral seam or line of dehiscence in a carpel.

ventral trace. One of the two laterally placed vascular strands often present in the wall of the carpel.

ventricose. Swelling in the middle, strongly inflated, bellied out.

ventricose rostrate. Ventricose with a tip, beak, or narrowed prolongation.

ventricumbent. Prone, face-downward.

ventriodorsal. Extending from the ventral to the dorsal surface.

ventrolateral. On the side of the ventral region.

venulae communes. Veinlets which proceed from anastomoses of the venulae propriae.

venulae propriae. The veinlets which first leave the costal or primary veins.

venule. A small vein, a veinlet.

venulose. Thickly veined.

venuloso-hinoideous. Having parallel equally curved veins which originate at the midrib and do not lose themselves in the passage.

venuloso-nervosus. Having straight parallel veins connected by cross veinlets.

veratrine. An alkaloid derived from the lily, *Veratrum*.

verbascifolious. With leaves like *Verbascum*, the mullein.

verbenaceous. Allied to or resembling *Verbena*.

Verein. A synusium.

vermian. Worm-like.

vermicular. Worm-shaped, vermiculate.

vermiculate. 1. Marked with numerous fine lines or bands of color or by irregularly depressed lines. 2. Vermicular. 3. Bearing worm-like processes.

vermicule. A small worm-like structure.

vermiform. Shaped like a worm.

vermiform body. The ascogonium or archicarp in certain *Ascomycetes*, a scolecite.

vermuth steppe. Extensive plains of which the dominant plants are species of *Artemisia*.

vernalization. The process of shortening the

vegetative period of plants by treating the seeds.

vernation. The arrangement of leaves in the bud.

verniciferous. Varnish-bearing.

vernicose. Shiny as if varnished.

verruca. 1. A wart-like projection. 2. A sessile apothecium as in the lichen *Verrucaria*. 3. The perithecia of some fungi.

verrucarioid. Resembling *Verrucaria* as to verrucae or apothecia.

verrucate. Warty.

verrucose. Warty.

versatile anther. An anther attached near the middle and turning freely on its support.

versicolorous. Changing color.

versiform. 1. Varying in form. 2. Altering in shape as it matures.

versipalm. With a palmate arrangement in which the divisions are not all in the same plane.

verspecies. A true species.

vertex. 1. The uppermost point. 2. The apex of an organ. 3. The pileus of an agaric.

vertical anther. A normal anther, one which is attached at the apex of the filament.

vertical chorisis. Transverse chorisis.

vertical leaves. Leaves as those of the *Iris* which have no distinct or obvious dorsal or ventral surfaces.

vertical system. The fibrovascular system.

verticel. A whorl.

verticil. A whorl or circular arrangement of similar parts around an axis.

verticillaster. A cluster which resembles a whorl but is composed of two opposite cymes, a false whorl formed by a pair of opposite cymes.

verticillastrate. Having false whorls, arranged in verticillasters.

verticilliflorous. A spicate arrangement of whorls.

verticillus spurius. A false whorl.

vertilinear. Rectilinear, in a straight line.

veruculate. Cylindrical and somewhat pointed.

vervain. *Verbena*.

vesicatorious. Blistering.

vesicle. A small blister, bladder, or air cavity.

vesicle, multinucleated. Peculiar bodies found in hyphae of the endophytic fungus of the prothallium of *Lycopodium clavatum*.

vesicula amnios. The embryo sac.

vesicula colliquamenti. The embryo sac.

vesicula sporophora. The sporophore of a fungus.

vesiculaeform. Bladder-shaped.

vesicular. Composed of or covered with vesicles, inflated like a bladder.

vesicular gland. A gland below the epidermis in plants containing essential oils.

vesicular vessels. Lactiferous cells.

vesiculate. Composed of or like vessels.

vesicule. A bladder-like cyst or sac.

vesiculose. Vesiculate, as if composed of little bladders.

vesiculose trama. Bladdery, formed of vesicles or small air cavities.

vesperal. Blooming just after sunset.

vespertine flowers. Flowers which expand in the evening.

vessel. A water-conducting tube made up of comparatively long cylindrical cells in the xylem most of which have the horizontal ends disintegrated. The side walls of mature cells are thickened in a variety of ways, as by lignified rings or spirals or are pitted in various shapes. A trachea, a tracheide.

vessel element. One of the cellular components of a vessel.

vessel member. A vessel element.

vessel segment. A vessel element.

vessel tracheides. Articulation of xylem vessels without perforations or perforated only at one end.

vestibular. Of or pertaining to the vestibule of a stoma, bulb, or gland, etc.

vestibulate. Resembling a vestibule, in the form of a passage between two channels.

vestibule. 1. A cavity leading into another cavity or passage. 2. An opening or chamber above the stomata in certain plants, as in *Cycas.*

vestigial remains. Parts which are imperfectly formed but which mark the place where normally a fully developed part would be.

vestured pit. A bordered pit with a cavity wholly or partly lined with projections from a secondary wall.

veteran. In forestry, a very old tree, at least 24 inches D.B.H.

vexillary. Having the vexillum folded over the other organs in the aestivation peculiar to papilionaceous flowers.

vexillum. The upper petal in a papilionaceous flower.

viatical. Growing by the roadside or path.

vibrinogen. Longitudinal bands of active tissue in the cortex of tendrils which is supposed to cause their movement of circummutation.

vibrio. Any bacterium having a comma shape.

vibrioid. Like a vibrio.

vibrioid body. A slender cylindrical body found in the superficial layer of cytoplasm of many algae and fungi.

vibrissa. Sensitive hairs as in *Dionaea.*

viburnifolious. *Viburnum*-leaved.

vicarial species. An elementary or microspecies.

vicifolious. Vetch-leaved.

vicine. Derived from adjacent regions, invading from adjacent communities.

vicinin. A substance from *Lathyrus sativus.*

vicinism. The effect on a plant or group of plants of other types or varieties growing nearby, the unexpected pollination of a plant (more or less under control by a grower) by related plants growing in the vicinity.

vicinist. A plant derived by vicinism.

viduae. Unisexual plants or flowers.

vigiliae florum. Periods during which certain plants open and close their flowers; see PHOTOPERIODISM.

villiferous. Bearing villi.

villiform. 1. Having the form or appearance of velvet. 2. Resembling villi.

villose. Covered with long, soft, weak hairs; shaggy.

villous. Having long soft hairs.

villus. A fine straight hair.

vimen. A long slender shoot or branch.

vimineous. With long flexible twigs.

vinacea. Grape stones.

vinaceous. Of the color of red wine.

vinealis. Growing in vineyards.

vinegar. Fermented juices of various fruits and the ultimate formation of acetic acid.

vinegar plant. The mother of vinegar.

vineus. Of or belonging to wine.

vinicolor. The color of wine, dark or purple red.

vinose. Wine-colored, vinous.

violaceous. 1. Violet-colored. 2. Of the violet family.

violine. A poisonous substance in *Viola odorata.*

virellous. Greenish.

virent. Green, not withered.

virescence. The production of green coloring matter in petals rather than the usual color.

virgate. 1. Streaked usually by different colored fibrils. 2. Wand-shaped. 3. Slender, straight , and erect.

virgatum. Twig-like.

virgin forest. Mature or overmature forest essentially uninfluenced by human activity.

virginicus. Of Virginia.

virgulata. A thicket or coppice.

virgulate. Shaped like a little twig or rod.

virgultum. 1. A vigorous twig or shoot. 2. A bush. 3. A copse.

viridarium. A greenhouse.

viridetum. An association of *Alnus viridis*.

viridicarinatous. Green-keeled.

viridiflorous. Green-flowered.

viridifolious. Green-leaved.

viridifuscous. Greenish brown.

viridina. Chlorophyll.

viridous. Greenish.

virose. 1. Poisonous. 2. Malodorous.

virosis. A virus disease.

virulence. 1. The power of bacteria to produce a disease in pathogenic species. 2. The power to produce tubercles in certain tubercle-forming species.

virulent. 1. Active. 2. Poisonous. 3. Able to produce disease.

virus. Ultramicroscopic disease-causing agents which can multiply in a living cell but not in artificial media. They are the cause of many infectious diseases of plants and animals.

viscid disk. The retinaculum of an orchid.

viscid disseminule. A spore or seed with a sticky surface or sticky hairs.

viscid pubescent. With a clammy pubescence.

viscin. 1. A substance intermediate between resin and caoutchouc. 2. The sticky substance forming threads uniting pollen grains.

visco-saccharose. An enzyme producing a viscous mass from cane sugar.

visual purple. Rhodopsin.

vitaceus. Vitis, vine-like.

vital force. The form of energy manifested in living phenomena when considered distinct from chemical, physical, and mechanical forces.

vital stain. A stain which can be used on living cells without killing them.

vitalism. The doctrine that life in living organisms is caused and sustained by a vital principle that is distinct from all physical and chemical forces and that life is, in part, self-determining and self-evolving; the opposite of mechanism.

vitalist theory. A theory of fermentation as an effect with vegetation as a cause.

vitality. 1. The power of germination. 2. An expression of vigor attained by different species. 3. The principle of life.

vitamin. Substances in foods necessary for the vital processes, basic nitrogenous substances occurring in varying amounts in different foods.

vitellin. 1. The phospho-protein of egg yolk and similar related substances in seeds. 2. A reserve protein found in crystals in potato tubers, vegetable vitellin.

vitelline. Yellowish.

vitellose. A substance formed in the digestion and hydrolysis of vitellin.

vitellus. 1. The embryo sac as it appears in the seed. 2. The peculiar albumen which is sometimes deposited in the embryo sac. 3. An oily substance which adheres to the spores of *Lycopodium*.

viticole. A parasite on the grapevine.

viticolous. Living on or in vines.

viticula. 1. A trailing stem like that of cucumber. 2. A little vine.

viticulose. Bearing or resembling viticulae, sarmentaceous, producing vine-like twigs or suckers.

vitifolious. Grape-leaved.

vitis. The vine (grape).

vitricole. Growing on glass bottles, etc.

vitricous. Having a glassy appearance.

vitta. An oil tube such as is found in the *Umbelliferae*.

vittae of diatoms. The longitudinal ribs.

vittate. Striped or ridged lengthwise.

vittigerous. Bearing stripes.

vittin. A substance found in the more watery vittae of *Umbelliferae*, a corky cell wall substance containing no phellonic acid occurring in the vittae of *Umbelliferae*.

vivacious. Living over winter or from year to year.

vivification. One of the series of changes in assimilation by which proteid material which has been taken up by a cell is able to exhibit phenomena of living protoplasm.

viviparity. 1. The condition of bringing forth living young. 2. Multiplying by means of shoots or bulbils.

viviparous. Bearing young plants, sprouting

or germinating while attached to the parent plant.

viviparous germination. Viviparity.

vixgregarious. Sparse vegetation.

vlei soils. A soil found in Africa in depressions subjected to wetness during some seasons. It resembles gley soil.

volatile oil. Oil which is readily vaporizable.

volgaricus. Of the Volga River region.

volubile. Ascending spirally or climbing by embracing another object, twining, voluble.

volunteer. A crop or a plant which has come from self-sown seeds.

volute. Spirally twisted, rolled up in any direction.

volutin. Metachromatic granules in the yeast cell occurring in the nuclear vacuole.

volutin grains. Grains forming in cytoplasm representing a food material which is absorbed by the nucleus in growth and the formation of chromatin.

volution. A spiral turn, wreath, or twist.

volutus. Rolled up.

volva. The remains of the universal veil found at the base of the stipe of an agaric or of the peridium of some *Phallales*. It is often cup-shaped.

volvaceus. Having a volva.

volvate. Having a volva.

volvocaceous. Constituted like the genus *Volvox*.

volvocine. Volvocaceous.

Von Baer's law. The recapitulation theory.

vulcanicus. Of Vulcan, of a volcano.

vulnerary. Useful in the care and healing of wounds.

vulva vegetabilium. The stigma.

vulviform. Having a cleft with projecting edges, shaped like a vulva.

W

W. A flower class, flowers fertilized by wind.

W chromosome. See SEX CHROMOSOMES.

waahoo (American). *Euonymus atropurpureus*, the spindle tree.

wadi. See WED.

Waldserriesm. Tree seres.

Wallace's life zones. The Californian, Rocky Mountain, Allegheny, and Canadian.

Wallace's line. An imaginary line separating Australian and Oriental regions between Bali and Lombok, between the Celebes and Borneo, and eastward to the Philippines.

walling over. The growth of a callus over a cut or injured surface.

wampee. 1. An Asiatic rutaceous tree. 2. The fruit of the tree.

Wandering Jew. Tradescantia, a trailing plant of universal distribution.

wara. Mudar.

waratah. An Australian proteaceous plant of the genus *Telopea*.

wasp flowers. Flowers adapted for wasp visitors.

waste products. The final products of tissue metabolism.

water balance. The ratio between the water taken in by a plant and the water lost by it.

water bladders. Hairs acting as water reservoirs.

water bloom. Large masses of algae, chiefly *Myxophyceae*, which sometimes develop very suddenly in bodies of fresh water, water flowers, breaking of the meres.

water calyx. A calyx in the form of a closed sac into which hydathodes secrete so much water that the outer parts of the flower continue their development without risk of damage from dryness.

water cells. Large suberized cells in the palisade tissue of succulent plants.

water content, physical. The total amount of soil water.

water content, physiological. The amount of water available to plant life.

water core. An abnormal condition of a part or the whole of the flesh of the apple in which the cells usually appear as if water-soaked.

water culture. An experimental method of growing plants in distilled water to which nutritive salts in certain definite proportions are added.

water flower. A water bloom.

water gland. A structure in the mesophyll of leaves regulating water excretion through stomata.

water leaf. In *Salvinia*, a submersed and finely divided leaf which simulates a root.

water parasite. A parasite for which the host serves only as a root and provides absorption, conduction, and mechanical support.

water plants. Hydrophytes, plants growing in water immersed wholly or in part.

water pollinated. Pollinated by means of water, either under water or on the surface.

water pores. Hydathodes, enlarged stomata whose guard cells no longer function.

water sacs. In *Hepaticae*, lobes of the leaves which retain moisture.

water sprout. A strong, rapid-growing adventitious shoot upon the body of a tree where older limbs have been removed.

water stoma. A water pore, a pore on the surface of a leaf which excretes water.

water storage tissue. Cells which are used to store excess water in a plant. They are usually large, thin-walled cells.

water table. The level of the saturation of soil by ground water.

water tissue. Parenchyma filled with clear sap and some mucilage.

water vesicle. A much-enlarged epidermal cell which serves for the storage of water.

watten. The shallows separating certain of the Friesian Islands.

wax. A fatty waste product of plants, any wax-like product secreted by plants.

wax, vegetable. A fatty body occurring as a waste product, either superficially as bloom or leaves, or in quantity in fruits and stems.

waxy. Resembling beeswax in texture or appearance.

waxy coating. A thin epidermal layer of rods or grains forming a glaucous bloom on fruits and leaves.

waxy substances. Cell-wall substances in micrography chiefly characterized by a melting point beneath 100°C and by being soluble in several of the same reagents as beeswax.

waxy yellow. An impure yellow, the color of natural beeswax.

web. The cluster of slender soft hairs at the base of the floret in certain species of *Poa*.

wed. A wady, a oued, an arroyo, an oasis.

wedge. A lip which broadens strongly outward.

weed. A plant growing where it is not wanted.

weel. An arrangement of hairs in a flower which keeps out undesirable insects.

weeping. 1. Bleeding, excessive loss of sap from wounds. 2. Having slender pendent branches.

weft. A collection of interlacing hyphae or other filaments.

Weismannism. The teaching of Weismann in connection with evolution and heredity, dealing chiefly with continuity of germ plasm and nontransmissibility of acquired characters.

Welwitschietum. An association of *Welwitschia*.

Wendungszellen. A disk-shaped group of hyaline cells (or a single cell) at the base of the oosphere in *Characeae*.

wetmeadow. Lowland covered with coarse grass or rank herbage.

wheat ear. An abnormal increase of bracts in carnations.

whirl. A whorl.

white chlorophyll. Chlorophyll which is rich in hydrogen and colorless.

white heads. The take-all disease in wheat.

white root rot. A disease in parts of Europe caused by *Dematophora necatrix*.

whorl. The arrangement of leaves or flower parts in circles or groups at nodes, a whirl.

whorl, false. A verticillaster.

whorled. With more than two leaves at a node in a circle around it, arranged in whorls.

wicker hairs. Trap hairs, weel.

Wiesner's law. Leaves are usually placed so as to receive the maximum illumination from a source of light.

wildering. Wilding.

wilding. A cultivated plant that has run wild or reproduced itself spontaneously.

wilt disease. Any of various fungus diseases of plants marked by wilting.

wilting coefficient. The percentage of moisture present in soil when permanent wilting takes place.

wilting point. The point at which water lost through transpiration exceeds the water available for plant use, expressed pF4.

wind dispersal. The dispersal of spores, seeds, and fruits by the wind.

wind fertilization. Fertilization of plants by pollen carried by the wind.

wind pollination. The conveyance of pollen from anthers to stigmas by means of the wind, anemophily.

windflower. The *Anemone*.

window bearing. Having openings or windows.

windows. An opening when the flowers do not expand but remain united at the base and the apex of perianth, as in *Cryp-tophoranthus*.

wing. A thin filmy expansion as the lateral petal in the flower of *Leguminosae*.

wing bract. The attached subtending bract of *Tilia*.

wing petal. The lateral petal in papilionaceous flowers.

winter annual. A plant which germinates in the fall, lives over winter, and produces seeds and dies in the following season; a biennial.

winter green plants. Small plants, especially woodland plants, which retain green leaves throughout the winter.

winter killing. The killing by cold or exposure to winter weather.

winter node. The point at which a winter bud has existed.

winter rot. A disease occurring in stored potato tubers caused by *Nectria solani*.

winter spore. A resting spore, originally considered a special spore to resist severe or winter conditions.

witch's broom. A disease on the silver fir, birch, cherry, hackberry, and other trees characterized by the development of a tangle of shoots in a tuft caused by the attacks of a fungus or mites.

witches, steppe. Ball-like felted masses of plants in steppe regions which have become detached from their roots and are blown about by the wind, wind witches.

wither tip. A disease of *Pomelo* in which the young twigs wither.

withering, persistent. Withering and dying but remaining attached to the stem.

withy. Like a willow twig or a pliable wand.

woad. Isatin, the blue coloring matter of *Isatis tinctoria*.

wold. A woodland.

wolgaricus. Of the region of the Volga River.

wood. The hard part of a stem between the pith and the bark, secondary xylem, the principal strengthening and water-conducting tissue of stems and roots, xylem.

wood, autumn. The outer portion of each annual ring of growth having smaller ducts and wood cells and with much-thickened walls.

wood ball. The spheroblast.

wood cells. The chief cells found in and composing wood.

wood, cryptogamic. The centripetal portion of the xylem in the stem of *Cycadoxyleae*.

wood elements. The cells or fibers composing the xylem.

wood fiber. An elongated wood cell with a thick wall and a narrow cavity, fibrovascular tissue.

wood gum. Gum contained in the wood of dicotyledons consisting of xylan and yielding xylose on hydrolysis.

wood meadow. The park-like forests of Sweden; see PARKLAND, SAVANNAH.

wood parenchyma. Thick-walled parenchyma in the secondary xylem, xylem parenchyma.

wood parenchyma cells. The cells of lignified parenchyma in the secondary xylem of the vascular tissue.

wood parenchyma fibers. Wood parenchyma cells.

wood parenchyma strands. Vertical series of two or more wood parenchyma cells derived from a single cambial initial.

wood ray. A xylem ray, a medullary ray.

wood ray parenchyma. Parenchymatous cells in a xylem ray.

wood rot. Rot of wood caused by various fungi, such as *Stereum hirsutum*.

wood, spring. The inner portion of each annual increment (or ring) of wood consisting of larger, thinner-walled cells and ducts.

wood vessels. Elements of tracheal tissues, long tubular structures formed by cell fusion.

woodland. An area in which woody plants dominate the vegetation, a forest.

woodland climate. A climate having a warm vegetative season, continually moist subsoil, and damp and calm air especially in winter.

woody fiber. Wood tissue, the vascular bundle.

woody rings. The annulations seen in cross sections which usually denote one year's growth.

woody tissue. Xylem, tissue which is hard because of the presence of lignin in the cell walls.

woody wedges. The fibrovascular bundles in the fossil *Calamites*.

wool. Any densely felted pubescence on the surface of plants, a tomentum.

woolner tubercle. A darwinian tubercle.

working depth. The average distance reached by the general root system of a plant in the soil.

wormwood. *Artemisia*, a bitter aromatic plant now used chiefly in absinthe.

Woronin hyphae. Hyphae coiled and occurring in the place where a sporocarp subsequently develops (probably homologous with an archicarp).

wort. 1. A plant or herb (now used chiefly as a suffix). 2. Filtered mash used in fermentation. 3. A malt extract used in the culture of microorganisms.

wound. An injury caused by abrasion or incision in the cortical layers of trees or plants.

wound cambium. A layer of phellogen resulting from the tangential division of epidermal cells or from cortical cells beneath the epidermis.

wound cork. The nonconducting tissue which shuts off fungus-diseased portions of bast from the sound parts.

wound gum. A substance abundantly secreted in the vessels by the starch cells closing the wound cavities.

wound hormone. A substance produced in wounded tissues which is able to influence the subsequent development of parts of the plant.

wound parasite. A fungus which attacks the surface of a wound and so effects an entrance into the tissues of the host.

wound rot. Various forms of decay not accounted for by parasitic fungi.

wound tissue. A pad of parenchymatous cells formed by the cambium after wounding. It may give rise to groups of meristematic cells from which roots and buds form.

wound wood. Abnormal growth distinguished by its short cells and absence or scarcity of vessels.

wrapper. The volva in mushrooms.

Wuchsort. Locality, a place of growth.

Wuchstelle. Wuchsort.

Wurzelort. Station or root place.

X

X & Y chromosomes. Sex-determining chromosomes; the normal female is XX, the normal male XY.

X body. An inclusion in a plant cell which is suffering from a virus disease.

X chromosome. The chromosome conveying the factors which control sex determination.

X element. The sex chromosome.

X generation. A gametophyte.

xanth-. A prefix meaning yellow.

xanthacanthous. With yellow spines.

xanthein. Yellow coloring matter of plants, anthochlorin, xanthine.

xanthic. Some tint of yellow.

xanthine. A yellow coloring matter found in some flowers, a pure yellow substance from chlorophyll.

xanthocarpous. With yellow fruits.

xantholeucite. A leucite found in etiolated plants.

xantholeucophore. A cell bearing yellow pigments.

xantholeucous. Yellowish white.

xanthones. Yellow coloring substances in plants, flavones.

xanthoneurous. With yellow nerves or veins.

xanthophane. Chromophane, a yellow pigment.

xanthophyll. A constituent of chlorophyll, yellow in color and insoluble in water; the yellow coloring matter in yellow autumn leaves thought to be a decomposition product of chlorophyll.

xanthophyllidrine. A yellow crystalline pigment somewhat similar to xanthophyll but soluble in water.

xanthophyllins. The yellow constituents of chlorophyll, such as carotin, erythrophyll, and chrysophyll; see CHLOROPHYLLINS.

xanthophyllous. With yellow leaves.

xanthopicrine. A bitter yellow substance derived from the bark of *Zanthoxylon caribaeum*.

xanthopous. Having a yellow stem or stipe.

xanthorhamnin. A yellow crystalline glucoside which occurs in the fruits of various species of *Rhamnus*.

xanthorrhizous. With yellow roots.

xanthospermous. Having yellow seeds.

xanthotrametin. The colored resin occurring in certain fungi, as *Polyporus cinnabarinus*.

xanthoxylum. Zanthoxylum.

xenautogamy. The condition of homogamous flowers which are usually cross-pollinated but are self-pollinated under unfavorable conditions.

xenembryosperm. A parthenembryosperm with the endosperm arising from fecundation and the pollen derived from a flower of another stock.

xenia. 1. The effect of pollen or male germ cells upon the characters of the young plant as a result of pollination or fertilization. 2. The visible effect produced by pollen from another strain usually resulting in hybrids in color, form, etc.

xeniophyte. The endosperm (3n) of angiosperms constituting a third generation in addition to the sporophyte (2n) and the gametophyte (n) generations.

xenocarpy. The production of fruit resulting from xenogamy.

xenochroma. A change in the color of fruit caused by foreign pollen.

xenodoch. An anomalous succession of plants.

xenoendosperm. The parthenogenetic endosperm of an embryo which has resulted from fertilization by pollen coming from another individual.

xenogamy. Cross-fertilization, fecundation by pollen from some other plant of the same species; see GEITONOGAMY.

xenogenesis. Heterogenesis, the fancied production of an organism altogether and permanently unlike the parents.

xenomorphosis. Actinomorphosis, heteromorphosis.

xenoparasite. A specialized form of a parasitic fungus when growing on injured parts of a strange host or on injured parts of its host which previously were immune to the injury.

xenoplasma. A change in shape of fruit due to action of foreign pollen.

xenoplastic graft. A heteroplastic graft that survives and continues to develop in its new site. Most heteroplastic grafts are short-lived.

xerad. A xerophyte.

xerampeline. The dull red or purple color, as in dead grape leaves.

xerarch. A plant succession which originates in a dry habitat and becomes more mesic in its successive stages.

xeras. A dry form of a plant.

xerasium. A succession due to drainage or drought.

xeric. With scanty moisture.

xeric environment. An environment in which there is little soil moisture and conditions favor rapid transpiration.

xeriobole. A plant whose seeds are scattered by dehiscence due to dryness.

xero-. A prefix meaning dry.

xerochastic. Having fruits burst because of drying.

xerocleistogamy. Pollination in closed flowers due to dryness.

xerocline. A dry warm slope.

xerocolon. A xerophile.

xerodrymium. A xeric forest community.

xerogeophyte. A plant having its rest period during the dry season.

xerohylad. A dry forest plant.

xerohylium. A dry forest formation.

xerohylophilous. Dwelling in dry forests.

xerohylophyte. A dry forest plant.

xeromorphic. Protected against excessive loss of water by thick cuticles, coatings of hairs, and similar structures.

xeromorphosis. Changes induced by the action of increased temperature or drought, e.g., thickening of epidermis, etc.

xerophile. A xerophyte, a plant growing in a dry situation.

xerophilous. Able to withstand drought, adapted to a limited water supply, needing much heat but requiring little water, growing in arid places.

xerophobous. Shunning drought.

xerophorbium. Tundra, dunes, etc.

xerophyll. The leaf of a xerophyte.

xerophyllous. Having leaves characteristic of plants of arid situations.

xerophylophilous. Dwelling in dry forests.

xerophyte. A plant adapted to dry conditions of air and soil.

xerophytia. Dry forest formations, dry land communities.

xerophytium. A xerophytic formation.

xeroplastic. Xerophilous.

xeropoad. A heath plant.

xeropoium. A heath formation or steppe formation.

xeropoophilous. Heath-loving.

xeropoophyte. A heath plant.

xeropteridetum. An association of the bracken fern with heath plants.

xerosere. A sere community on dry sites characterized by a low water content.

xerosion. Xerosium.

xerosium. A plant succession on drained and dried-up soil.

xerostatic succession. A succession completed under constantly xeric conditions.

xerotactic succession. A succession unchanged by dry conditions.

xerothamnium. A spiny shrub community.

xerothermic. Capable of withstanding drought and heat.

xerothermic period. The postglacial period.

xerotherous. Adapted to a dry summer or a rainless period.

xerotropic. Becoming xerophytic.

xerotropism. The tendency of plants or parts of plants to alter their positions to protect themselves from dessication.

xiphioid. Sword-like, sword-shaped, xiphoid.

xiphophyllous. Having sword-shaped leaves.

xylan. Tree or wood gum, a gummy substance of the pentosan class present in woody tissue and yielding xylose on hydrolysis; a water-soluble saccharide occurring in the cell wall of some algae *Rhodophyta* and Chlorophyceae); callose.

xylase. An enzyme which acts on xylose.

xylem. The portion of a vascular bundle which consists of tracheal tissue and wood parenchyma, woody tissue, the wood of the vascular bundle. Xylem serves to conduct fluids in plants and also provides mechanical support.

xylem arch of cambium. The part of the cambium on the outside of a xylem bundle in roots.

xylem bridges. The connections surrounding phloem islands, trachea and wood fibers of a fibrovascular bundle.

xylem bundles. The bundles composed of tracheal elements (vessels or tracheids) and parenchyma.

xylem core. A solid strand of xylem occupying the middle of the stele.

xylem islands. Detached strands of xylem found in some species of *Thumbergia*.

xylem mother cell. A cambial cell which is later converted into a component of the xylem.

xylem parenchyma. Parenchymatous cells occurring in xylem apart from those present in the vascular rays; oblong cells which retain their protoplasm with thick and lignified walls, occurring in longitudinal bands.

xylem plate. A radial plate of xylem between two medullary rays.

xylem, primary. Xylem differentiated from the procambium.

xylem rays. Radial plates of xylem between two medullary rays.

xylem, secondary. Xylem formed by the cambium.

xylene. Xylol, a hydrocarbon of the benzene series.

xylic gap. A gap in the xylem tissue which sometimes occurs opposite a leaf base.

xylinous. Woody.

xylium. A saprophytic or epiphytic wood community.

xylocarp. A hard woody fruit.

xylocarpous. Having a fruit which becomes hard and woody.

xylochrome. A wood dye, chiefly tannin.

xylodium. An achene, a woody fruit.

xylogen. The forming wood in a bundle, nascent wood or xylem.

xylogenous. Growing on wood.

xyloid. Wooden or resembling wood.

xylol. Xylene.

xyloma. A sclerotioid body of varying shape which produces sporogenous tissue in its interior instead of producing spore-bearing branches, a sclerotioid body producing spores internally.

xylomyces. A fungus which grows on wood or bark.

xylon. Wood.

xylonacanthous. With woody spines.

xylonite. Cellulose manufactured into plastic masses, celluloid.

xylophagous. Eating, boring in, or destroying wood.

xylophilous. Wood-loving, growing on wood.

xylophyte. A wood plant.

xylopodium. 1. A more or less stony, hard, tuberous thickening of the roots and underground parts of shrubs in steppe regions in Brazil. 2. A fruit like a nut, lacking a cup and borne on a fleshy support, as in the cashew family.

xylose. Wood sugar, a pentose occurring in wood.

xylostroma. The felt-like mycelium of some wood-destroying fungi.

xylotomous. Able to bore or cut wood.

xylotomy. The anatomy of wood and woody tissue.

Y

Y chromosome. The sex chromosome that is present and paired with the X in one sex. It is said to contain few genes and in general does not control sex determination.

yam. The edible, tuberous root of various plants of the genus *Dioscorea*.

yeast. A simple ascomycete producing zymase and inducing the alcoholic fermentation of carbohydrates.

yeast, bottom. Sedimentary yeast giving rise to bottom fermentation.

yeast bud. An asexually formed gonidia-like structure in yeast.

yeast budding. Yeast producing buds in the characteristic asexual manner.

yeast fungus. A fungus of the *Saccharomycetales*, sometimes used synonymously with sprouting yeast.

yeast, low. Yeast forming at the bottom of a vat.

yeast spore. A spore formed in yeasts, sometimes applied to a spore budding from another spore.

yeast, upper. Barm which floats on the surface resulting in top fermentation.

yeast, wild. An undesired yeast in a fermentation which gives a bitter taste to the wort without fermentation.

Yeddo spruce. An ornamental tree of eastern Asia cultivated for its handsome foliage. It has dark green leaves which are silvery underneath.

yeddoensis. Of or pertaining to Yeddo, Japan.

yellow cells. Cells surrounding the gut in earthworms, probably excretory in function, sometimes considered symbiotic algae or *Zoochlorellae*.

yellow earth. Soils yellow in color, usually found in the tropics and warm temperate regions.

yellow snow. Snow colored yellow because of the growth of certain algae upon it.

yellows. A plant disease manifested by yellow leaves and stunted growth. There are various causes: bacteria, virus, fungi, poisons, etc.

ygapo. A Brazilian forest wholly submerged for two months of a year.

young growth. Forest growth which comes up naturally after cutting, fire, or other disturbing causes; a residual stand of second growth.

ypomnema. An inferior calyx.

yuccal. Of or pertaining to Yucca.

yunnanensis. Of the province of Yunnan, China.

Z

Z chromosome. See SEX CHROMOSOME.

zanthophyll. Xanthophyll.

zeaxanthol. Lutein, a yellow pigment, xanthophyll.

zebrinous. With zebra stripes.

zecanin. A simple protein, a glutelin.

zein. A protein allied to gluten obtained from *Zea mays*.

zelotypic. Asexual.

zenotropism. Negative geotropism.

zeorine. Resembling the genus *Zeora*, a lichen having a double margin on the apothecium.

zero, physiological. The point of adaptation to temperature.

zero points. Extremes of high and low points which plants can endure without being killed.

zerophyte. A xerophyte.

zerozygous. In a situation in which a special factor is wholly absent.

zeugite. The spore or cell of a fungus which is derived from the fusion of two nuclei, as a teleutospore; the cell or organ in which the fertilization processes are completed and the dicaryon ends.

zeuxis. Chromosomal heredity.

zeylanicus. Of Ceylon.

zibethinous. Malodorous, like the civet cat.

zimome. Zymome.

zizanioid. Like *Zizania*, a genus of tall grasses.

zoadula. A zoospore, a spore having the power of independent movement.

zoallospore. The zoospore of *Bulbochaete* and *Coleochaete*.

zoandrospore. The motile androspore or antherozoid of *Oedogonium*.

zodiophilous. Pollinated by animals, including animals in the lower groups; zoidiophilous.

zoetic. Of or pertaining to life, living, vital.

zoic. Of or pertaining to animals, animal life, and action.

zoid. A zoospore or swarm spore.

zoidiogamous. Fertilized by water-carried ciliated antherozoids or spermatozoids.

zoidiogamy. Fertilization by motile spermatozoids.

zoidiophile. A plant pollinated by animals.

zoidiophilous. Pollinated by animals.

zoidiospore. A seed or spore dispersed by animals.

zoidogamic. Fertilized by zoids.

zoidogamy. Fertilization by antherozoids.

zoidospore. A plant whose seeds are dispersed by animals.

zonal. 1. Appearing in belts or zones. 2. Banded, girdled.

zonal symmetry. Metamerism, the division into nearly like segments.

zonal view. The view of a diatom in which the zone or girdle is seen.

zonaric. Of or pertaining to the intermediate depths, as the mesoplankton.

zonate tetragonidia. The gonidia formed by transverse divisions.

zonate view. The side or girdle view of a diatom frustule.

zonation. 1. The gradual spreading outward from a center as shown in many plants. 2. The arrangement of zones.

zonation complexes. Complexes of plants more or less zonally arranged.

zone. 1. One of the great climatic belts of the earth with more or less uniform vegetation. 2. A belt of uniform vegetation due to the presence of similar edaphic factors. 3. A circular band or stripe of color.

zone lines. Dark brown or black lines found in decaying hard woods which are usually caused by fungi. Black line or black zone.

zone of vegetation. A belt of plants having well-marked characters occurring with other zones of different character.

zonociliate. Banded with cilia.

zonoid. Like a zone.

zonolimnetic. Of or pertaining to a certain zone in depth, applied to plankton.

zoobiotic. Having an animal host.

zoocarp. A zoospore.

zoocedidea. Plant galls produced by animals.

zoochlorellae. Symbiotic green algae living in various animals.

zoochore. A plant or plant part distributed by animals.

zoochorous. Distributed by animals.

zoocoenocyte. 1. A free-swimming coenocyte having cilia, as *Vaucheria*; a zoospore.

zoocyst. A sporocyst, a cyst giving rise to ciliated or amoeboid zoogonidia.

zoodomatia. Shelters formed by plants for animals which help them.

zoogamae. Groups of plants having motile reproductive elements.

zoogamete. A motile gamete.

zoogamy. Sexual reproduction in animals and plants having motile sex cells.

zoogenesis. The origin of animals.

zoogenous. On animals.

zoogloea. A mucilaginous mass of bacteria embedded in slimy material derived from the swollen cell walls.

zoogonangia. Certain cells in *Ctenocladus* which enlarge, become pear-shaped, hibernate, and later give rise to planogametes.

zoogonid. A zoogonidium, a zoospore.

zoogonidangium. The structures in algae in which zoospores form.

zoogonidium. A zoospore which develops directly into a plant.

zooidiogamus. Having a gamete which is actively motile, flagellate, ciliate, or amoeboid.

zoolapton. Organisms transported on the exterior of animals, a zoochore.

zoomorphosis. A change in plants caused by animals, such as galls, etc.

-zoon, zoon-. A suffix or a prefix meaning antherozoid.

zoopenous. On animals.

zoophagous. Consuming animals or animal products.

zoophile. A plant with seeds adapted for the dissemination by animals or pollinated by animals.

zoophobous. With protection from animals by hairs, secretions, odors, etc.

zoophyte. An animal which resembles a plant in appearance and growth.

zooplankton. Plankton which is made up of animals.

zoosperm. A spermatozoan, a zoospore, one of the spermatic particles.

zoosphere. A biciliated swarm-cell of certain algae which usually becomes an oosphere.

zoosporange. A sporangium in which zoospores are produced.

zoosporangiophore. A sporangiophore bearing or supporting zoosporangia.

zoospore. A motile asexual spore, a swarm spore.

zoosporiferous. Producing zoospores.

zoosporocyst. A sporange in the *Saprolegneaceae*.

zoothecium. A zoocytium.

zooxanthellae. Small yellow or brown one-celled algae which live symbiotically in some radiolarian protozoa and color them.

zoozygosphere. A planogamete.

zoozygospore. A motile zygospore.

zosteretum. An association of *Zostera*, widely distributed marine plants.

zygnemetum. An association of *Zygnema*, green algae.

zygo-. A prefix meaning yoke.

zygogamae. The algae excluding the *Floridae*.

zygogenic. Derived from sexual union.

zygogonium. The female conjugating cell of the *Conjugatae*.

zygolytic. Separating allelomorphic pairs of unit characters.

zygomites. Pairs of conjugated filaments.

zygomorphic. Bilaterally symmetrical, divisible into similar halves in only one plane.

zygomycete. A phycomycete producing zygospores.

zygonema. The zygotene stage meiosis having a pair of fused threads of chromatin in the zygotene phase.

zygopachynema. The transitional condition of the meiotic nucleus in which heavy pachytene threads are fusing side by side to form a zygonema.

zygophase. The diploid phase.

zygophore. A conjugating hypha in certain fungi.

zygophyte. A plant in which reproduction takes place by the union of two similar cells.

zygopleural. Bilaterally symmetrical.

zygopteridean. Similar to or related to the fossil genus *Zygopteris*; Zygopteroid.

zygosome. A body formed by the union of gamosomes in pairs forming bivalent chromosomes, a mixochromosome.

zygosperm. A zygospore, a spore resulting from conjugation.

zygosphere. A gamete, the last conjugating cells in zygophytes which have a differentiation of sex.

zygosporangium. A sporangium in which zygospores are formed.

zygospore. The thick-walled resting spore which results from the conjugation of two independent and morphologically similar cells (isogametes).

zygosporocarpic. Having a fruit body in which zygospores are produced, as in the *Endogonaceae*.

zygosporophore. A suspensor or a special branch supporting a copulating branch, as in *Mucorales*.

zygosporous. With resting spores formed by the conjugation of similar sex cells.

zygosus. Conjugation.

zygotactism. Zygotaxis.

zygotaxis. The pairing attraction of two gametes, the attraction between two zygophores resulting in conjugation, mutual attraction.

zygote. The cell resulting from the fusion of two gametes, the first cell of the new individual in sexual reproduction.

zygotene stage. The second stage in the meiotic prophase (between the leptotene and pachytene stages) in which the chromatin threads conjugate in pairs and become loops, followed by synapsis of homologous chromosomes.

zygotic meiosis. The reduction of the chromosome number taking place during the first two divisions of the nucleus which was produced by the fusion of two haploid gametes.

zygotic number. The diploid chromosome number, 2n.

zygotoid. The result of the union of two gametoids, apocytial structures as in *Mucor*.

zygotonucleus. The nucleus formed by the fusion of two gametonuclei.

zygotropism. The attraction of hyphae of opposite sexes or strains toward each other which results in their fusion.

zygozoöspore. A motile zygospore.

zymase. The enzymes of yeast plants which convert glucose into ethyl alcohol and carbon dioxide with the release of a relatively small amount of energy.

zymic. Of or pertaining to fermentation.

zymin. An enzyme or ferment.

zymogen. A substance from which an enzyme is formed.

zymogenous. Ferment-producing.

zymohydrolysis. Fermentation induced by the absorption of water.

zymologist. A student of fermentations.

zymolysis. Decomposition due to action of enzymes.

zymom. One of the substances in wheat gluten.

zymosis. Fermentation.

zythozymase. An enzyme of yeasts which may also be found in certain other fungi.

APPENDIX

Outline of the Plant Kingdom

This outline of the plant kingdom is provided to assist the student in finding the location of the larger divisions of the plant kingdom. The outline includes the more common groupings and in many instances carries the classification to the family level.

Since few Latin names are included in the dictionary, this list should guide the student in locating an unfamiliar plant group. The student can then more easily find a definitive work to which he can refer.

Improved research techniques now enable botanists to discover new relationships among plants. These discoveries frequently lead to changes in the location of plants in the taxonomic order.

SUBKINGDOM		*Thallophyta*
Division		*Schizophyta* (bacteria and viruses)
Class		*Schizomycetes*
	Order	*Eubacteriales*
		Chlamydobacteriales
		Pseudomonadales
		Actinomycetales
		Beggiatoales
		Caryophanales
		Spirochaetales
		Hyphomicrobiales
		Thiobacteriales
		Myxobacteriales
Class		*Microbiotomycetes*
	Order	*Rickettsiales*
		Virales
Division		*Myxothallophyta* (slime molds)
Class		*Myxomycetes* (true slime molds)
Subclass		*Ceratiomyxomycetidea (Exasporeae)*
	Order	*Ceratiomyxales*
Subclass		*Myxogastromycetidea (Endosporeae)*
	Order	*Liceales*
		Trichiales
		Echinosteliales

507

	Stemonitales
	Physarales
	Amaurosporales
	Lamprosporales
Subclass	*Acrasiomycetae* (cellular slime molds)
Order	*Acrasiales*
Subclass	*Labyrinthulomycetae* (aquatic cellular slime molds)
Order	*Labyrinthulales*
Division	*Eucomyphyta* (true fungi)
Class	*Phycomycetes* (algal fungi)
Subclass	*Chytridiomycetidae*
Order	*Chytridiales*
	Blastocladiales
Subclass	*Hypochytridiomycetidae*
Order	*Hypochytriales*
Subclass	*Oomycetidae*
Order	*Saprolegniales*
	Peronosporales
	Leptomitales
Subclass	*Zygomycetidae*
Order	*Mucorales*
	Entomophthorales
Class	*Ascomycetes* (cup fungi)
Subclass	*Hemiascomycetideae*
Order	*Ascoideales*
	Endomycetales
	Taphrinales
Subclass	*Euascomycetideae*
Series	*Plectomycetes*
Order	*Eurotiales*
	Plectoascales
	Exoascales
Series	*Pyrenomycetes*
Order	*Erysiphales*
	Xylariales
	Clavicepitales
	Hypocreales
	Doditheales
	Sphaeriales
	Laboulbeniales
	Pleosporales
Series	*Discomycetes*
Order	*Pezizales*
	Helvellales
	Tuberales
	Phacidiales
	Hysteriales
	Helotiales
	Gymnoascales

Class	*Basidiomycetes* (club fungi)
Subclass	*Heterobasidiomycetidae*
Order	*Ustilaginales*
	Tremellales
	Uredinales
	Auriculariales
Subclass	*Homobasidiomycetidae*
Series	*Hymenomycetes*
Order	*Polyporales*
	Agaricales
	Thelephorales
	Clavaricales
	Hydnales
Series	*Gasteromycetes*
Order	*Hymenogasterales*
	Lycoperdales
	Phallales
	Nidulariales
Class	*Fungi imperfecti*
Order	*Phomatales*
	Melanconiales
	Sphaeropsidales
	Moniliales
Class	*Lichens*
Series	*Ascolichenes*
Order	*Pyrenulales*
	Caliciales
	Hysteriales
	Lecanorales
Series	*Hymenolichenes*
SUBKINGDOM	*Algae*
Division	*Cyanophyta* (blue-green algae)
Class	*Cyanophyceae (Myxophyceae)*
Order	*Chroococcales*
	Chamaesiphonales
	Dermocarpales
	Oscillatoriales
	Hormogoniales
Division	*Pyrrophyta*
Class	*Dinophyceae* (dinoflagellates)
Order	*Dinophysidales*
	Dinotrichales
Class	*Cryptophycaeae* (cryptomonads)
Order	*Cryptomonadales*
Class	*Desmokontae*
Order	*Desmomonadales*
Division	*Chrysophyta*
Class	*Chrysophyceae* (golden algae)
Order	*Chrysosphaerales*

		Chrysotrichales
Class		*Bacillariophyceae* (diatoms)
	Order	*Centrales*
		Pennales
Division		*Xanthophyta*
Class		*Xantophyceae* (yellow-green algae, *Heterokontae*)
	Order	*Heterochloridales*
		Heterococcales
		Heterotrichales
		Heterosiphonales
Class		*Chloromonadophyceae*
	Order	*Chloromonadales*
Division		*Phaeophyta* (brown algae, seaweeds)
Class		*Phaeophyceae*
Subclass		*Isogeneratae*
	Order	*Ectocarpales*
		Sphacelariales
		Tilopteridales
		Cutleriales
		Dictyotales
Subclass		*Heterogeneratae*
	Order	*Chordariales*
		Sporochnales
		Desmarestiales
		Punctariales
		Dictyosiphonales
		Laminariales
Subclass		*Cyclosporeae*
	Order	*Fucales*
Division		*Rhodophyta* (red algae, seaweeds)
Class		*Rhodophyceae*
Subclass		*Bangiophycideae*
	Order	*Porphyridiales*
		Goniotrichales
		Bangiales
Subclass		*Florideophycidae*
	Order	*Nemalionales*
		Gelidiales
		Cryptonemiales
		Gigartinales
		Rhodymeniales
		Ceramiales
Division		*Euglenophyta*
Class		*Euglenophyceae*
	Order	*Euglenales*
Division		*Chlorophyta* (green algae)
Class		*Chlorophyceae*
	Order	*Volvocales*
		Tetrasporales

		Chlorococcales
		Ulotrichales
		Schizogoniales
		Zygnematales
		Oedogoniales
		Cladophorales
		Siphonales
		Siphonocladales
		Dasycladales
		Conjugales
		Chaetophorales
Class		*Charophyceae* (fresh water stoneworts)
	Order	*Charales*
Division		*Nematophyta* (fossil algae)
Class		*Nematophyceae*
Division		*Bryophyta*
Class		*Hepaticae* (liverworts)
	Order	*Marchantiales*
		Sphaerocarpales
		Jungermaniales
		Calobryales
		Metzgeriales
		Monocleales
Class		*Anthocerotae* (hornworts)
	Order	*Anthocerotales*
Class		*Musci* (mosses)
	Order	*Sphagnales*
		Andreales
		Tetraphidales
		Polytrichinales
		Buxbaumiales
		Bryales
SUBKINGDOM		*Tracheophyta* (plants with conducting tissue)
Division		*Pteridophyta*
Class		*Psilophyta (Psilopsida)*
	Subclass	*Psilophytae*
	Order	*Psilophytales*
		Psilotales
Class		*Lycopodophyta (Lycopsida)*
	Subclass	*Lycopodinae*
	Order	*Lycopodiales*
		Selaginellales
		Lepidodendrales
		Isoetales
		Pleuromeiales
Class		*Arthrophyta* (*Sphenopsida,* articulates)
	Order	*Hyeniales*
		Sphenophyllales
		Pseudoborniales

	Calamitales
	Equisetales
Class	*Filicinae* (ferns and fern allies)
Subclass	*Primofilices* (pre-ferns)
Order	*Coenopteridales*
	Protopteridiales
	Cladoxyales
Subclass	*Eusporangiatae*
Order	*Ophioglossales*
	Marattiales
Subclass	*Leptosporangiatae*
Order	*Eufilicales*
Family	*Osmundaceae*
	Schizaeaceae
	Gleicheniaceae
	Matoniaceae
	Polypodiaceae
	Hymenophyllaceae
	Dicksoniaceae
	Cyatheaceae
	Dennstaedtiaceae
	Parkeriaceae
Order	*Hydropteridiales*
Family	*Marsileaceae*
	Salviniaceae
SUBKINGDOM	*Phanerogamae*
Division	*Spermatophyta* (seed plants)
Class	*Gymnospermae*
Subclass	*Pteridospermophyta* (seed ferns)
Order	*Pteridospermales*
Family	*Lyginopteridaceae*
	Medullosaceae
	Peltaspermaceae
	Corystospermaceae
	Caytoniaceae
Subclass	*Cycadophyta* (cycads)
Order	*Bennettitales*
Family	*Cycadeoidiaceae*
	Williamsoniaceae
Order	*Cycadiales*
Family	*Cycadaceae*
Subclass	*Ginkgophyta*
Order	*Ginkgoales*
Family	*Ginkgoaceae*
Subclass	*Coniferophyta*
Order	*Cordaitales*
	Coniferales
Family	*Lebachiaceae*
	Pinaceae

	Cupressaceae
	Taxodiaceae
	Podocarpaceae
	Araucariaceae
	Taxaceae
	Cephalotaxaceae
Subclass	*Gnetophyta*
Order	*Ephedrales*
	Welwitschiales
	Gnetales
Class	*Angiospermae* (flowering plants)
Subclass	*Monocotyledoneae*
Order	*Pandanales*
Family	*Typhaceae*
	Pandanaceae
	Sparaganiaceae
Order	*Najadales (Helobiae)*
Family	*Zosteraceae (Potomogetonaceae)*
	Najadaceae
	Juncaginaceae
	Alismataceae
	Butomaceae
	Hydrocharitaceae
Order	*Graminales (Glumiflorae)*
Family	*Gramineae* (grasses)
	Cyperaceae (sedges)
Order	*Palmales (Principes)*
Family	*Palmaceae*
Order	*Cyclanthales (Synanthae)*
Family	*Cyclanthaceae*
Order	*Arales (Spathiflorae)*
Family	*Araceae*
	Lemnaceae
Order	*Xyridales (Farinosae, Bromeliales)*
Family	*Xyridaceae*
	Mayacaceae
	Eriocaulaceae
	Bromeliaceae
	Commelinaceae
	Pontederiaceae
	Flagellariaceae
	Restionaceae
	Centrolepidaceae
	Thurniaceae
	Rapataceae
	Cyanastraceae
	Philydraceae
Order	*Liliales (Liliflorae)*
Family	*Juncaceae*

	Liliaceae
	Stemonaceae
	Haemodoraceae
	Amaryllidaceae
	Taccaceae
	Dioscoreaceae
	Iridaceae
	Trilliaceae
	Smilacaceae
	Velloziaceae
Order	*Zingiberales (Scitaminae)*
Family	*Marantaceae*
	Cannaceae
	Zingiberaceae
	Musaceae
	Strelitziaceae
Order	*Orchidales (Microspermae)*
Family	*Burmanniaceae*
	Orchidaceae
Subclass	*Dicotyledons*
Order	*Casuarinales (Verticillatae)*
Family	*Casuarinaceae*
Order	*Piperales*
Family	*Saururaceae*
	Piperaceae
	Chloranthaceae
Order	*Hydrostachyales*
Family	*Hydrostachyaceae*
Order	*Salicales*
Family	*Salicaceae*
Order	*Garryales*
Family	*Garryaceae*
Order	*Myricales*
Family	*Myricaceae*
Order	*Balanopsidales*
Order	*Leitneriales*
Family	*Leitneriaceae*
Order	*Juglandales*
Family	*Juglandaceae*
Order	*Julianales*
Order	*Batidales*
Family	*Batidaceae*
Order	*Fagales*
Family	*Betulaceae (Corylaceae)*
	Fagaceae
Order	*Utricales*
Family	*Ulmaceae*
	Moraceae
	Cannabinaceae
	Utricaceae